77th Congress, 2d Session · House Document No. 527

Keeping Livestock Healthy

Yearbook of Agriculture

1942

UNITED STATES DEPARTMENT OF AGRICULTURE

UNITED STATES GOVERNMENT PRINTING OFFICE, 1942

II

Yearbooks
IN THIS SERIES

YEARBOOK COMMITTEE
1942

John R. Mohler, Bureau of Animal Industry, *Chairman*
F. C. Bishopp, Bureau of Entomology and Plant Quarantine
D. S. Burch, Bureau of Animal Industry
C. A. Cary, Bureau of Dairy Industry
Adolph Eichhorn, Bureau of Animal Industry
J. A. Hyslop, Bureau of Entomology and Plant Quarantine
H. E. Moskey, Food and Drug Administration
S. A. Rohwer, Bureau of Entomology and Plant Quarantine
H. W. Schoening, Bureau of Animal Industry
Benjamin Schwartz, Bureau of Animal Industry
A. E. Wight, Bureau of Animal Industry

Gove Hambidge, Office of Information, *Editor*
Marion J. Drown, Office of Information, *Assistant Editor*

FOREWORD

Keep 'Em Healthy!

IN THIS WAR the slogan "Keep 'Em Flying" has a counterpart for the livestock man—"Keep 'Em Healthy."

Few persons not engaged in the livestock business realize the number, variety, and seriousness of the diseases and parasites that attack domestic animals or the care and skill necessary to keep them healthy under the conditions of intensive production that prevail in this country. Few outside of those familiar with the situation as a whole realize the extent of the losses caused by diseases, parasites, and insect pests; in the United States they amount to well over $400,000,000 a year in spite of an enviable record in working out and applying control methods. Finally, few except those acquainted with public health problems realize how closely many animal diseases are associated with similar or identical diseases in human beings.

There is some satisfaction in knowing that the United States is widely regarded as the safest country in the world in which to conduct stock raising. We have a well-developed veterinary service, and with the protection of quarantines and other safeguards the United States is free from several animal diseases that cause great losses abroad. Yet there is much room for improvement.

One of my keenest boyhood memories is of digging holes almost daily all one summer to bury hogs that had died of cholera. We had no effective way to fight cholera in those days; we had to take the losses from the disease, and it hit hard and treacherously. Now, thanks to scientific research, we have a positive preventive for this disease and our pork production for the needs of this war is safer by a large margin.

We still need more knowledge about how to deal effectively with certain animal-disease problems; but we also need to apply more fully

v

what is already known.   Applying the results of research pays large dividends.   The benefits that livestock owners are now receiving from the eradication of cattle ticks exceeds, every year, the total cost of the eradication campaign extending over more than one-third of a century.

Anyone who keeps livestock on a small or a large scale may confidently expect to profit by applying modern disease-prevention practices in his daily farm operations.   If we were to apply known methods of prevention and control to all livestock diseases as conscientiously as we have done in combating some of them, we could produce with much greater efficiency and in time of war increase the total output of products with little increase in the numbers of breeding stock.

Keep 'Em Healthy!   Applying that slogan to both human beings and animals in the crisis that faces us today. is a patriotic service.   I hope this guidebook to animal health, the 1942 Yearbook of Agriculture, will be a contribution to that end.

CLAUDE R. WICKARD,
Secretary of Agriculture.

CONTENTS

Part 1.—Fundamentals of Disease and Insect Control

Part 4.—Diseases and Parasites of Cattle

Part 5.—Diseases and Parasites of Swine

Part 8.—Common Diseases and Parasites of Dogs and Cats

Part 9.—*Wildlife Diseases and Parasites*

At the time this book went to press, the drugs and other materials mentioned in various articles—chiefly as disinfectants, insecticides, and anthelmintics—were still available for veterinary and medical use. Under war conditions, however, it is possible that some of these materials may become scarce or unavailable. In that case, the reader should obtain professional advice from the Department of Agriculture, the State experiment station, a local veterinarian, or the county agent as to available substitutes.

Keeping Livestock Healthy
—A Summary

BY GOVE HAMBIDGE [1]

WAR brings sharply to men's minds the fact that wasting our substance means more than a loss to the individual; it is an act of sabotage against society, even though it is unconscious and unintentional. In ordinary times the farmer who loses a high percentage of his hogs because of diseases or parasitism that he could largely have prevented by careful husbandry and the application of existing knowledge is perhaps harming only himself in that he wipes out any profit he might have made. In wartime he is reducing the potential food supply of the Nation by just so much and making the remainder more costly.

The responsibility for preventing this kind of waste does not lie entirely with the individual. Discovering how to combat diseases and parasites and applying the discoveries after they are made demand the mobilization of brains and skill much as they are mobilized for war. In fact, it is war, of a sort—a never-ending war on a perpetually shifting front, against elusive and for the most part invisible enemies. During times like these the duty of the Nation to wage this war vigorously becomes especially clear because our food resources are especially vital.

But the truth is that this war must be waged all the time. Abandoning the battle against animal diseases would spell the doom of livestock production as it is practiced in the United States. An 80- to 90-percent mortality is not unusual in a serious outbreak of some of these diseases, and even the mild ones mean a crippling of production for a longer or shorter time—not to mention the danger to human health from the considerable number of diseases that we human beings share with our livestock. This country has made a notable record in fighting livestock diseases and parasites; yet with all our effort we can still chalk up a loss of hundreds of millions of dollars every year to these enemies. That loss is greater than it should be or need be; but what would it be if we gave up the field to the teeming hosts of viruses, germs, protozoa, and worms that are as eager

---

[1] Gove Hambidge is Principal Research Writer, Office of Information.

as we to have the possession and use of our livestock? Eventually
a balance would come about, to be sure, as it always does in nature;
but it would not be a balance favorable to us or to the concentrated
production on which the very existence of our industrial civilization
depends.

Every livestock man knows that keeping animals healthy is a major
part of the production job, both for himself as an individual and for
the Nation. This Yearbook, the seventh in a series dealing with
important aspects of modern agriculture, is intended to serve as a
manual or reference book of animal health. There are some diseases
and parasites—mostly of minor importance—that it omits, but it
is reasonably complete. It covers all classes of livestock—horses
and mules, dairy and beef cattle, swine, sheep and goats, poultry,
and even dogs and cats, which are so useful on many farms.

The effort has been to give both the needed practical information, and its scientific background. This is partly because a man
can do a better job in the difficult business of controlling animal
diseases if he knows the whys and wherefores and partly because
the job calls for full cooperation between farmers and scientists;
hence each should know what the other is talking about.

The reader will find no fancy writing, since the articles were
prepared by scientists who as a group dislike exaggeration, are
likely to bend over backward in being cautious, and in general are
averse to dramatizing their own work or that of their colleagues;
some of the work has been much more dramatic than anyone would
ever realize from this book. If anything, the book is packed too
full of facts, but that is perhaps a fault in the right direction, since
it is intended to be useful to students of agriculture and technical
workers as well as to farmers. If certain facts are not known—which
is often the case in both veterinary and human medicine—the authors
are very frank in saying so. There is a certain amount of repetition in the book, at least in the material on internal parasites; but
this whole field is so complex that repeating some of the information, from different angles and in relation to different animals, is
considered desirable.

A few points that stand out in connection with the book as a whole
are worth emphasizing.

(1) The number of veterinarians in this country in proportion
to the number of livestock is so small that they have to spread themselves out pretty thin. It is all the more necessary that farmers
should be well informed about livestock diseases, not to act as their
own veterinarians but to prevent disease and to make the best possible
use of available scientific services when outbreaks occur.

(2) Much disease exists that could be prevented by sheer good
management, such as following practices suggested in the articles in
this book. Why do we, who rightly pride ourselves on our agricultural achievements, continue to have this needless waste? Is it because many farmers still do not know the principles of good sanitation
and care? Or because some farmers cannot afford to put these
principles into practice? Or what? This problem is one that
deserves a great deal of attention, especially at the present time.

(3) Just as we do not yet know the cause of cancer in human beings and cannot combat it with full effectiveness until we do, so there are animal diseases that we cannot combat with full effectiveness until we have more knowledge. The avian leukosis complex, which includes fowl paralysis, is an example of this group; it accounts for about half the total annual loss due to infectious diseases in poultry. Until research discovers the cause of this disease and the way it spreads, we are shooting in the dark in our efforts to control it.

(4) Despite the heavy production losses that could be prevented by better management and more scientific knowledge, we have much to be thankful for. Some very devastating and dangerous animal diseases, such as rinderpest, surra, and mal de caderas, have been kept entirely out of the country; contagious pleuropneumonia, foot-and-mouth disease, and fowl pest have been eradicated every time they made temporary invasions; others, such as cattle tick fever, bovine tuberculosis, dourine, and glanders, have been practically conquered by the application of vigorous eradication methods; still others, for example, brucellosis of cattle (Bang's disease) and pullorum disease of poultry, are under much better control than they were, and there is good reason to believe that they can gradually be reduced to the vanishing point. This battle is not one waged by official agencies alone. In a democracy, it demands the full cooperation of producers and the public.

(5) When a deadly contagious disease is allowed to take its course, it tends to kill off the susceptible animals (or human beings, in the case of a human disease) and leave those that are resistant. But if the disease is kept away entirely, all the susceptible animals are left alive—ready to take it at any time. In other words, the more thoroughly a serious contagious disease is brought under control, the more vigilant we have to be to make sure that it never gains a foothold thereafter. Otherwise, it can do untold damage among the immense numbers of animals highly susceptible to it.

(6) Veterinary medicine has had a noble history, and it is more closely associated with human medicine than most persons realize. Many of the discoveries of human medicine are applied by the veterinarian, but the reverse is as often the case; some of the discoveries made in animal-disease research have been of inestimable value in human medicine. The lines cross at many points. To take a single example, the virus that causes sleeping sickness of horses also causes sleeping sickness of human beings, and in its action it is not unlike other viruses that produce a group of dreaded diseases of the brain and spinal cord. The more we can find out about such a disease-producing agent, the better. Or, to take another example of a different sort: The number of animals that go through our federally inspected slaughterhouses in the course of a year, if placed in a line, head to tail, would circle the earth three times at the Equator. Every one must pass at least two careful inspections, one before and one after slaughter. Why? Mainly because animals and animal products are inseparably associated with human health and disease.

SUMMARY OF THE YEARBOOK

As in other Yearbooks in this series, each of the articles is briefly summarized in this introduction so that any reader who wishes may quickly get a grasp of the subject as a whole.

PART 1

FUNDAMENTALS OF DISEASE AND INSECT CONTROL

LOSSES CAUSED BY ANIMAL DISEASES AND PARASITES

J.·R. Mohler, Wight, MacKellar, and Bishopp give a broad picture of the nature as well as the extent of the losses caused by livestock diseases and internal and external parasites in this country. Only a few selected cases can actually be covered, and there is little doubt that the total figure for losses quoted at the end of the article ($418,000,000 a year) is an underestimate rather than an overestimate.

There are four main things that can be done to keep such losses within reasonable bounds in the crowded livestock population of today: (1) Aggressive research can discover how to combat livestock enemies. (2) Vigilant regulation can prevent the spread of certain diseases and safeguard the public's food supply. (3) Extensive campaigns of eradication can reduce especially dangerous diseases to a minimum. (4) Losses could be enormously reduced if all farmers and others directly concerned with the livestock industry would adopt sound practices in their everyday operations. For example, it has been estimated that losses due to preventable injuries in the shipping of livestock amount to 11.5 million dollars a year. Great numbers of animals are unnecessarily lost every year, or fail to produce what they should, because management practices that would prevent ordinary diseases and parasites from getting a foothold are not followed on the farm.

A few diseases are considered separately in the article. The record in the case of cattle tuberculosis is excellent; the campaign of testing and slaughter has brought this disease to a very low point in less than 25 years. There is considerable avian tuberculosis in poultry, however, and most of the tuberculosis in swine is of the avian type, spread by poultry. The outlook for successfully combating brucellosis of cattle (Bang's disease) is good; this campaign was begun in 1934, and results are very promising. In the case of Johne's disease, which is incurable, a diagnostic skin test has been developed that makes it possible to eliminate diseased animals. Cattle tick fever has been reduced to negligible proportions by an extensive eradication campaign. Hog cholera is still the most destructive disease of swine, but present immunization methods prevent the devastating periodic outbreaks of the past.

Much of the loss from internal parasites is indirect, taking the form of stunted growth, ill health, reduced production, and condemned meat products; but conservative estimates indicate that these parasites rob the country of at least 125 million dollars a year. It has been amply proved both in experimental work and in farm practice that these losses can be sharply reduced by effective medication and the use of sound control measures, including good sanitation especially.

In the case of insects, much of the loss is also indirect, and part of it is due to the sheer tormenting of the animals by the more vicious insect enemies. The grubs or maggots of certain insects are serious internal parasites; lice and mites in heavy infestations do an immense amount of damage; and one of the worst aspects of the insect menace is that several dangerous diseases of animals and human beings are spread by these creatures. Not all insects can be successfully combated at present, but many can be, and the damage done by others can at least be reduced.

Causes of Disease

"Disease," says Schoening, who writes the first part of this article, dealing with bacteria and viruses, "may be defined as any abnormal condition of the tissues of the body." Such an abnormal condition may be due to injuries (wounds, contusions), bacteria, viruses, internal and external parasites, chemicals, poisons of various kinds, faulty nutrition, and inherited abnormalities. When cells are damaged by a disease agent, the body hastens to repair the injury, and the repair process sets up an inflammation, indicated in medical language by the ending "itis." Hence the names of many diseases end in itis—for example, appendicitis, an inflammation of the appendix.

Bacteria are minute living things visible only under a microscope. They are distinguished and classified by such differences as those in size, shape, the conditions under which they can grow, the kind of food they can utilize, and their effects on experimental animals. They exist everywhere in nature, and many of them perform necessary or useful functions, while others produce disease. Some can move around on their own power, others cannot. Some can go into a resting, or spore, stage during which they are especially resistant to destruction. Some—diphtheria germs, for instance—produce powerful poisons called soluble toxins. Some produce abscesses or other local inflammations that under the right conditions can set up a general poisoning of the system, or septicemia.

Viruses are too small to be seen under a microscope, and they pass through a filter fine enough to hold back bacteria. Only in recent years has it been possible to propagate some viruses artificially, by the use of living tissues; and these studies have revealed many facts and led to the development of certain immunization methods. More than 35 virus diseases of animals are now known. Some viruses attack nerve tissue primarily, as in rabies and encephalomyelitis; others, skin and membrane tissues, as in foot-and-mouth disease; and still others, several or all kinds of tissue. After a virus has weakened the body's defenses, bacteria that may not ordinarily be very harmful will often become secondary invaders, with serious results, as in hog cholera complications.

Bacteria and viruses invade the body in various ways, mainly through the respiratory, digestive, and genital tracts and the skin.

They are transmitted from animal to animal by biting insects, by the blood, excretions, and secretions of infected animals which contaminate the surroundings, and by carriers—that is, animals that harbor an infective agent without apparently getting the disease themselves or continue to harbor the agent after recovering, as in foot-and-mouth disease.

Whether an infective agent actually causes a disease in any given case depends on the resistance of the host and the virulence of the agent. Some disease organisms (anthrax bacteria in the spore stage, for instance) are very resistant to destruction and can live for a long time outside an animal's body.

Malaria, African sleeping sickness, and amoebic dysentery are examples of diseases of human beings caused by internal parasites. There is no hard-and-fast line, says Schwartz, who writes the section on parasites, between such diseases and those produced by bacteria and viruses, though the parasitic diseases are likely to develop more slowly and less noticeably. Perhaps all animals harbor some parasites, but comparatively few of the many species are of major importance to animal and human health. A peculiarity of many internal parasites is that they cannot go through their entire life cycle in a single kind of animal; part of their development must take place in a different kind of animal, called an intermediate host, and this often complicates the problem of control. The intermediate host takes in the eggs or larvae of the parasite; then the final host takes in the intermediate host or some infected part of it, or acquires the parasites by being bitten by infective intermediate hosts such as ticks and mosquitoes.

There are two broad groups of internal parasites—the protozoa (minute one-celled animals) and the helminths, or worms.

Protozoa multiply rapidly in the animal body, either by division or by a process resembling sexual reproduction, and often cause severe diseases. Some protozoa have only one host, and infection takes place through food or water contaminated by droppings—as in the case of amoebic dysentery, blackhead, and coccidiosis, the last one often a serious disease of poultry, cattle, and sheep—or through some other direct means. In other cases, the protozoa are transmitted only through agents known as vectors—the cattle tick fever organism through ticks, for instance.

The worm parasites range in length, as adults, from a small fraction of an inch to several feet. They are often equipped with spines, hooks, teeth, or suckers to attach themselves, and they can move around in the host's body. Helminths reproduce sexually by means of eggs, and in most cases the eggs or young larvae must leave the host's body and go through one or more stages of development in the open or in intermediate hosts. Infection takes place through the swallowing of contaminated feed or water, penetration of larvae through the skin, the swallowing of intermediate hosts, or the bites of insects. Practically all the tissues and organs of the body are subject to attack by various kinds of worms, including all parts of the digestive tract and abdominal cavity, the skin and muscles, the liver, pancreas, spleen, and kidneys, the heart, lungs, brain, eyes.

Severe hemorrhages, anemia, emaciation, and death are common results of heavy infections by some worm parasites.

Of the three main groups of worms, (1) the flukes require snails as intermediate hosts (flukes that attack the liver of animals are the only ones of importance in this country); (2) the tapeworms occur as adults in the intestine and as bladder worms (immature forms) in the muscles, abdominal cavity, liver, lungs, brain, eyes, and elsewhere, and they require intermediate hosts, which include mites, lice, fleas, beetles, and higher animals; and (3) the roundworms, or nematodes, occur in practically all parts of the body, often wander extensively, and are among the most injurious of parasites, causing such serious maladies as trichinosis and hookworm disease. Some nematodes require intermediate hosts, and some do not.

Modern discoveries concerning nutritional diseases have been as dramatic and important as the earlier discoveries that established infections as causes of disease, Madsen points out, and they have made it possible to guard against many dangers not understood in the past. Since Madsen takes up the nutritional diseases of livestock at length elsewhere in this volume, his discussion here is very brief and general.

Plant poisoning is also discussed at some length elsewhere in the volume. Here Couch points out certain general facts, such as: Some parts of a plant are likely to be more poisonous than other parts, and the poison may affect certain species of animals more than others. There is a great deal of variation in the symptoms and the injuries caused by poisonous plants because of the many different toxic substances involved, and sometimes these symptoms can easily be mistaken for those of other diseases. Moreover, plants that are not poisonous in themselves sometimes take up toxic substances from the soil—as in the case of selenium particularly—in sufficient quantities to be damaging or deadly to livestock.

PROTECTIVE MECHANISMS AGAINST DISEASE

The body is equipped by nature to fight against disease. Among its chief defenses are certain large cells called phagocytes, which can devour invading disease organisms. Under the stimulus of a particular invading organism, the phagocytes can also produce antibodies capable of destroying it or neutralizing its poisons (toxins). Through many years of research, medical science has learned how to immunize animals and human beings against certain diseases by either stimulating this process, producing what is called active immunity, or supplementing it, producing what is called passive immunity.

In a sense, active immunity is induced by giving the animal a mild or modified case of the disease. Some of the virus, the germs, or the toxins, usually in a weakened form, are injected into the animal. This sets its defense mechanism to work producing antibodies. Then, if the animal should be attacked by the disease at some time in the future, the antibodies are already there to fight the invasion; in other words, the animal is immune. It usually takes a week or two to produce active immunity, but it lasts a long time because the animal keeps on manufacturing antibodies.

In case a disease threatens in the immediate future or has already attacked, it may be desirable to produce passive immunity. This is done by taking immune bodies out of another animal, usually in its blood serum, and injecting them into the animal to be protected. Such borrowed immunity acts at once (it may also have a curative effect), but it does not last long because the borrowed immune bodies gradually disappear; they are not continuously produced in the animal's own body.

Sometimes both active and passive immunity are produced at the same time by injecting the disease organism or toxin plus immune bodies from another animal. This is the method called simultaneous vaccination.

Disease organisms and toxins are treated in various ways, described by Eichhorn, to make them relatively harmless to the animal getting the injection or injections. The whole process is usually extremely delicate and exact. As the author points out, however, much more is involved in effective immunization than merely using these biological products. Everything possible should be done to build up the animal's general health and vigor and to eliminate the sources of infection; and exactly the right techniques must be used in preparing, handling, and administering the biological products themselves.

Certain biological products, called diagnostic agents, have been developed for detecting the presence of a disease, even when it shows no outward signs. Two of these tests, the complement-fixation test and the agglutination test, are described by Eichhorn.

In the case of internal parasites, Sarles points out, the existence of any protective mechanism or immunity was considered to be improbable until a few years ago. Now it is known that immunity, both natural and acquired, against parasites does exist and that it is basically similar to immunity against virus and bacterial infections. Antibodies are evidently of primary importance in acquired immunity to parasites—so much so that immune serum can be used to transfer immunity to susceptible animals. Adequate methods of artificial immunization against parasites have not been developed, however, and for practical purposes it is necessary to depend on the recognized means of prevention and treatment of parasitism.

There can be no doubt, Ellis indicates, that good nutrition is essential if the animal body is to combat and counteract disease-producing organisms; but evidence that any specific nutritive factor has a direct relationship to the mechanism of immunity, in the medical sense, is still inconclusive. Vitamin A may contribute to resistance by keeping the tissues of the lining membranes from breaking down, but artificial injections of disease organisms tend to prove that the vitamin does more than this. In the case of vitamin B_1, possibly the lowered body temperature and the lack of appetite associated with a deficiency may decrease the ability of the body to produce phagocytes, or devouring cells. Other dietary factors discussed by Ellis in their relationship to certain infectious diseases include vitamin D, nicotinic acid, protein, and calcium.

THE ENDOCRINE GLANDS IN HEALTH AND DISEASE

The hormones secreted by the endocrine glands have such extraordinary effects in the animal body that to the layman they sometimes seem almost magical. As Frank points out, much research in this field is now under way, and it holds great promise for the future. He briefly describes the chief functions of the nine glands.

The pituitary gland, at the base of the brain, has two parts, or lobes. The anterior, or upper, lobe may well be called the master gland of the body. It secretes at least eleven complex hormones. Two of these, the gonadotropic hormones, act directly on the gonads (ovaries of the female and testicles of the male), and extracts are used medically (one is used in a test for pregnancy after breeding). A third hormone (the mammogenic) stimulates the development of the mammary glands of the breasts or udder; a fourth (the lactogenic) stimulates the production of milk; a fifth directly influences growth, an excess producing giants and a deficiency dwarfs; a sixth apparently has an indirect influence on calcium metabolism; a seventh controls a very vital part of the adrenal glands; an eighth influences carbohydrate metabolism; possibly a ninth influences fat and protein digestion; a tenth governs the activity of the thyroid gland; and an eleventh influences the secretion of insulin by the pancreas.

The posterior (lower) lobe of the pituitary secretes pituitrin, which stimulates the muscles of the uterus at parturition, the small blood vessels, the intestines, and, in females, the mammary glands. Pituitrin is valuable medically.

The male gonads secrete the male sex hormone, testosterone, which, among other functions, is responsible for the development of secondary sex characters. It has been made synthetically and is used in medical practice. The female gonads secrete the two female sex hormones, estrogen and progestin. The former (also produced synthetically and used in medical practice) acts directly on the female sex organs and is concerned in the sex cycle, including estrus, or heat. Progestin acts with estrogen to stimulate the production of the mammogenic hormone by the pituitary.

Four other glands are very important. The parathyroids, in the neck, produce a hormone that is responsible for maintaining the balance between calcium and phosphorus in the body. The adrenal glands (one in front of each kidney) have (1) an inner (medullary) part secreting adrenin, which acts like pituitrin and is used medically as a heart stimulant and to check hemorrhages, and (2) an outer (cortical) part secreting cortin, without which an animal cannot stay alive. The thyroid gland, in the neck, secretes thyroxin, which controls the energy output of the body and needs iodine for its formation; a deficiency of thyroxin results in goiter, cretinism, and other abnormal conditions. The pancreas gland, near the stomach, secretes digestive juices and the hormone insulin, which is necessary for the proper utilization of sugar by the body.

Little is known about the functions of two other glands—the pineal, in the central part of the brain, and the thymus, which is well developed in young animals (the so-called sweetbread of calves) but degenerates at maturity.

THE RELATION OF GENETICS TO DISEASE

Plant breeders have not only proved that disease resistance is inherited; many of their greatest triumphs have been due to the breeding of resistant varieties. Can the same thing be done with animals?

As proof that it can, McPhee cites Lambert's work with fowl typhoid. By injecting White Leghorns with fowl typhoid bacteria and using only the most resistant individuals for breeding, Lambert reduced the mortality from this disease by about 90 percent in the fifth generation. Similar, though not such extreme, results have been obtained in experiments with mouse typhoid and with pullorum disease of chickens. Recently, in California, pigs have been discovered that apparently transmit resistance to brucellosis of swine.

Theoretically, then, it should be just as possible to cut death losses from certain diseases in half by breeding as it is to double egg production by breeding. The question is whether it can be done on a practical basis. It is expensive to develop and maintain a resistant line; the animals must be deliberately inoculated to prove that they are resistant; and a single outcross to a susceptible animal means that the work has to be done all over again. But, says McPhee, the case for or against the practical use of inherited resistance has never been proved because in no single instance has an experiment been carried far enough to see whether it might have practical applications. He believes there is evidence that warrants optimism for the not too distant future.

Popularly, a vigorous animal is supposed to be resistant to disease, but McPhee cites experiments which show that the various elements making for vigor are inherited independently of disease resistance. Again theoretically, however, vigor and disease resistance might be twin goals in a breeding project.

It is well known that the virulence of a disease organism changes. Is this due to environment, or does the organism itself mutate and hybridize? We cannot find out much about it, says McPhee, until we first have animals of known genetic constitution on which to test the organism. Otherwise it is always possible that apparent changes in virulence may really be due to variations in the host animals.

At the end of his article, the author describes various abnormalities in cattle, horses, sheep, swine, and poultry, the mode of inheritance of which is known. Many of these abnormalities are lethal—that is, the animals in which they appear cannot survive—and most are recessives. When such a recessive shows up, the sire, the dam, and all their offspring should be discarded for breeding purposes.

ARTIFICIAL INSEMINATION AND DISEASE CONTROL

Artificial insemination of dairy cows is now widely practiced in the United States. This method of breeding has been used also to some extent with other domestic animals and poultry. In the main, the object is to increase the usefulness of outstanding sires, but the technique is also helpful in controlling diseases spread by sexual contact. Among these, Frank and Phillips list granular vaginitis of cattle, abortion in cows caused by an organism called *Vibrio fetus*, trichomoniasis of cows, navel ill of foals, dourine of horses, possibly brucellosis of cattle and of swine, coital exanthema of horses, and vent gleet of poultry.

From the standpoint of disease control, the essentials are (1) the selection of males known to be free from disease, and (2) absolute cleanliness and the sterilization of all instruments used in the collection and transfer of seminal fluid. The latter precaution is extremely important because instruments used on an infected female might transfer the infection to another female even if the male were completely free from disease.

DISINFECTION AND DISINFECTANTS

The first step in preventing infection, says Tilley, is cleanliness; proper cleaning removes most germs, and with clean animals in clean surroundings there will usually be no need for disinfectants unless disease breaks out.

There is no such thing as a general disinfectant; different disinfectants are effective against different germs, and even then other conditions are important also. In general, in using a disinfectant, (1) do a thorough cleaning job first, leaving as little dirt as possible, (2) allow plenty of time for the disinfectant to act, (3) use it warm or hot if possible, (4) apply it liberally and thoroughly. A spray pump is best for large areas; a whitewash brush can be used for small ones.

Simple, inexpensive disinfectants can usually be used in place of more expensive preparations. Lime and lye are two of the cheapest.

Tilley goes into the practical details necessary to use the following substances or methods, giving the chief limitations of each and indicating whether it will or will not kill certain especially resistant germs and spores of disease.

Heat.—Dry heat, in an ordinary oven, and moist heat—boiling water or steam—are both effective when properly applied.

Sulfur dioxide.—Not classed as a good germicide.

Formaldehyde.—May be used as a gas under certain conditions, or as a solution with a high disinfecting power.

Boric acid.—A cleansing agent with little power to kill germs.

Acetic acid.—More potent than boric acid. Full-strength vinegar will kill some of the less resistant disease germs.

Lime.—Widely useful. Quicklime only should be used to prepare slaked lime, milk of lime, and whitewash.

Lye.—Also very useful. May be mixed in whitewash. Is a caustic poison and should be used with caution.

Sodium carbonate (washing soda, soda crystals, soda ash).—Chiefly a cleansing agent but has some disinfecting value.

Trisodium phosphate (tribasic phosphate of soda).—About like sodium carbonate.

Sulfate of copper (blue vitriol).—Effective against algae.

Chloride of lime (bleaching powder).—A powerful disinfectant, but not very practical for various reasons, including its odor, which is readily absorbed by food products.

Hypochlorites.—Often employed to sterilize dairy equipment but useless unless the equipment is thoroughly cleaned first.

Iodine (tincture of iodine).—The standard substance for skin disinfection and treatment of surface wounds.

Alcohol (70 percent).—Effective against the less resistant disease germs.

Carbolic acid (phenol).—Has several disadvantages but can sometimes be used on a small scale.

Cresol.—Better and more powerful than carbolic acid. Especially useful in a soap solution (compound solution of cresol or saponified cresol). Also occurs mixed with coal-tar oils and soap in coal-tar emulsion disinfectants.

Soaps.—Valuable chiefly for cleanliness. Their germicidal power is limited.

How Research Aids in Disease Control

The Chief of the Bureau of Animal Industry here discusses some of the problems of research in animal disease and tells how research works and what it accomplishes.

A typical problem: A good many years ago certain swine growers called for help. What, they asked, was causing half their young pigs to die and stunting many of the survivors? Investigation showed that the swine were infested with ascarids, or roundworms. Close study of the life cycle of this parasite showed the conditions under which it could survive and spread—and those were exactly the conditions under which pigs were commonly farrowed and raised. On the basis of this study, a radical new system was worked out to prevent infestation—a sort of combination of maternity hospital and pasture parlor for swine. Farmers tried this system out for 6 years. It worked, eliminating 98 percent of the parasite infestations and filth-borne diseases. It is now widely used.

Mohler lists many fundamental discoveries and advances made by veterinary research, some of which apply to human as well as animal diseases. A few of them: Simultaneous injection of immune serum and virulent blood as a means of immunization; proof that certain diseases can be carried from one animal to another only by an intermediate insect host; discovery that hog cholera is caused by a virus, and development of methods of immunization; discovery of a remedy for hookworm in dogs that has been successfully used for millions of human beings; discovery of phenothiazine as an anthelmintic; development of a vaccine to combat encephalomyelitis (sleeping sickness) of horses—a disease that is also a menace to human beings. Research work is back of meat-inspection service, which protects the health of consumers; the improvements made in the handling of livestock and livestock products in interstate and foreign trade; and advancements in the standards of veterinary education and practice.

Research projects now being carried on under congressional authorization include studies in brucellosis of cattle, mastitis of cattle, tuberculosis, Johne's disease, nutritional deficiencies of cattle, bovine trichomoniasis of cattle, anaplasmosis of cattle, equine encephalomyelitis, rabies, swine erysipelas, swine influenza, periodic ophthalmia of horses, hog cholera, and many other diseases, including parasitic diseases in general and various diseases of poultry. Fundamental investigation of the mechanisms of infection and of methods of control for all kinds of diseases is also in progress. The Federal research work on disease subjects is done in various parts of the country, and much of it is in cooperation with the States.

Mohler shows that in the course of their work, research men sometimes risk health and even life in the service of science. The results of the work, most of which is directed toward the solution of specific disease problems that have baffled livestock owners, are made available to everyone. As a whole, it has alleviated suffering among animals, greatly reduced economic losses, helped to safeguard the livestock and food industries, and contributed to the advancement of medicine.

Origin and Spread of Important Insect Pests of Animals

Before the white man arrived in America, Stage and Hyslop point out, there had been no horses, cows, sheep, goats, or chickens on this continent for many ages. Presumably, then, the insect pests of these animals came to America along with the livestock imported by white men. Ages ago there used to be hoofed animals in America. Why did they completely disappear? Possibly the tsetse fly, not now found in this country, was responsible. A fossil tsetse fly, closely related to the insect that makes the keeping of domestic livestock impossible in extensive areas in Africa, has been found in Colorado in shale beds that go back 40 million years.

Stage and Hyslop show that insects originated the practice of "thumbing a ride" and are so expert at it that they can spread far and wide from an original center. They not only travel on their own power but drift with the wind, float on water, ride as stowaways on all sorts of conveyances (including the airplane), and in particular accompany animals and animal products everywhere. The first horn fly, an insect that does 10 million dollars' worth of damage a year, was recorded in the United States near Camden, N. J., in 1887. Ten years later it had spread throughout North America and even to Hawaii. But many insects that are serious pests abroad have not yet been introduced into the United States.

How can we prevent the introduction and spread of insects? The measures briefly discussed by these authors include quarantines, careful inspection of animals and animal products in interstate commerce, better livestock management, the introduction of natural enemies of injurious insects, and in some cases temporary removal of wild animals that may serve as hosts of certain insects.

FEDERAL AND STATE REGULATORY ACTIVITIES IN ANIMAL DISEASE CONTROL

The huge and complicated livestock industry of today, which feeds millions of people and gives a livelihood to millions of farmers, handlers, tradesmen, and others is subject to a constant menace—the menace of certain diseases that can decimate herds, wipe out profits, and endanger the health and the lives of consumers. No individual acting alone could hope to meet this menace. There are diseases that can be fought only if everyone acts together, with the Federal and State Governments, to mobilize the full aid of science and put into effect such control and preventive measures as each situation demands.

This is what is back of the Federal and State regulatory activities described by Miller, Fladness, Wight, Skidmore, and Joss, of the Bureau of Animal Industry, and Moskey, of the Food and Drug Administration. The legal basis of these regulations goes back to the act of Congress that established the Bureau of Animal Industry in 1884, an amendment in 1920, another amendment in 1926, and other acts of Congress in 1890, 1903, and 1905.

The grand strategy of the fight against animal diseases has several distinct aspects. Back of all of them is constant research in the field and the laboratory to track down the causes of disease with greater and greater accuracy and discover practical safeguards, preventives, and remedies.

(1) Federal and State quarantines. The object of any quarantine is to confine a dangerous infectious disease to the smallest possible area and hold it there until it can be stamped out. By keeping imported animals under observation in quarantine, several deadly diseases have been kept out of the United States, including rinderpest, surra, and mal de caderas of horses. Drastic Federal and State quarantines have been a factor in preventing the spread of foot-and-mouth disease. Quarantines should not be imposed unless they are absolutely necessary, and they should be lifted as soon as possible.

(2) Campaigns for control and eradication. When it seems necessary and possible to wipe out a widespread disease by attacking it State by State and county by county, a long-time campaign is put into execution. The methods used depend entirely on what is most practicable in each particular case—fundamentally, that is, on the findings of the research men—the bacteriologists, parasitologists, chemists, veterinarians. In the scabies campaign, the mites that cause the disease are eradicated; in the tick fever campaign, the ticks that carry the disease. In the dourine and the bovine tuberculosis campaigns, the infected animals have to be destroyed. In the hog cholera campaign, the animals are immunized wholesale. In the case of foot-and-mouth disease, which spreads like wildfire, swift and drastic measures are taken whenever the slightest outbreak appears, to destroy not only the affected animals but those that have been definitely exposed to infection.

(3) Public stockyards inspection. In the livestock industry today, vast numbers of animals—60 to 70 million head in a single year—are assembled at public stockyards, either for immediate slaughter or for

reshipment to widely scattered areas. These crowded yards are potential centers of infection for serious diseases. The only safeguard is to man them with skilled detectors of disease who inspect so many thousands of animals day after day that they can readily spot a beast infected with diseases having visible symptoms. Among the diseases for which these men are on the lookout are anthrax, cattle and sheep scabies, tick fever, hog cholera, shipping fever, swine erysipelas, foot-and-mouth disease. Infected and exposed animals are handled as the case demands, and frequently a disease can be traced back to its local source so that the farmer can take appropriate steps. The stockyards force also supervises the necessary disinfection of premises and equipment; and in the case of animals that are to be reshipped, these men see to it that dipping for scabies, testing for Bang's disease (brucellosis) and tuberculosis, or immunizing against hog cholera are carried out.

(4) Meat inspection. The job does not end with the stockyards inspection; every animal that is to be slaughtered in the meat-packing establishments engaged in interstate commerce gets an inspection—and for most of the 70 million head, this is the second one—before it is killed; and the carcass and all its edible parts are again inspected after slaughter by white-coated veterinarians on the packing-house floor. These two inspections, of course, are primarily to safeguard the public against dangerous or objectionable meat products, but the careful records kept by the inspectors are also of great value in work on the control of animal diseases.

(5) The 28-hour law. To prevent cruelty to animals; there is a Federal law against holding them in interstate shipment for more than 28 hours in common carriers without unloading them for feed, water, and rest for a period of 5 hours. This measure has a direct relation to the health of animals, and hence to their susceptibility to disease.

(6) Regulation of biological products. A group of biological products—viruses, serums, toxins, etc.—are vitally important nowadays in combating animal diseases, just as similar products are vitally important against human diseases. Any of them that are worthless, contaminated, dangerous, harmful, or in fact anything other than they should be, can do untold damage. Hence, under Federal law, these products are regulated by the Department of Agriculture.

(7) Control of drug remedies. Drugs are somewhat similarly controlled through the laws that prohibit misbranding; these laws were tightened up by the Food, Drug, and Cosmetic Act of 1938. Insecticides are controlled under the Federal Insecticide Act. In both cases, the laws apply only to products sold outside the State in which they were manufactured.

FIGHTING DISEASE WITH KNOWLEDGE

There are about 8,000 veterinarians in private practice in the United States to serve the needs of some 5 million livestock owners with 200 million head of cattle, horses, swine, sheep, and goats. About 4,000 more veterinarians are engaged for the most part in various public services.

These figures, says Burch, show the necessity for keeping the public accurately and adequately informed about animal diseases. The veterinarians alone, because of their limited numbers, could not possibly do all that needs to be done. Livestock owners should be familiar with the characteristics of diseases, their dangers, and the value of sound methods in dealing with them; and this is especially true of the most serious infectious diseases and those transmissible to human beings. Veterinary practitioners, scientists, and students in training need information to keep up to date with the constant developments in this field. In short, public understanding is one of the most effective of all weapons in combating disease, whether human or animal.

Burch briefly outlines the information services and material of the Department of Agriculture in this field. Publications, extension agencies, motion pictures, lantern slides, film strips, posters, exhibits, demonstrations, public addresses, and radio broadcasts are all used. The publications include a good many intended for laymen, technical papers for veterinarians and research workers, and official reports for public officers and others. The radio performs a unique service in its ability to reach large numbers of people speedily, as in warning the public of an outbreak of foot-and-mouth disease; in dealing with such a malady even an hour saved may be important. Much worthwhile educational work is also done through the personal contacts of veterinarians with farmers in the course of testing for such diseases as brucellosis and tuberculosis.

PART 2

IMPORTANT DISEASES COMMON TO SEVERAL SPECIES

TUBERCULOSIS

Practically every species of animal is subject to tuberculosis, and the disease usually results in a slow wasting of body tissues. It is incurable; it can be arrested in human beings by hospitalization and complete rest, but with animals this method is neither effective nor practical.

Wight, Lash, O'Rear, and Crawford make clear that there are three kinds of tuberculosis germs—the human, the bovine, and the avian (bird) types. Cattle are readily susceptible to the bovine type, but much less so to avian or human tuberculosis. Horses and mules are very resistant to all three, and so are sheep and goats. Swine are susceptible to all three, but nine-tenths of the cases are due to the avian type. Dogs are more susceptible to the human than to the bovine type, but the reverse is true of cats. Chickens are susceptible only to the avian type. Human beings are susceptible to the human type, slightly to the bovine, and hardly at all to the avian; but children, especially infants, are very much more susceptible to the bovine type than are adults. These facts have a direct bearing on control of the disease.

Tuberculosis takes several forms. Human beings get tuberculosis of the skin (lupus), of the lymph nodes (scrofula), of the bones and joints, of the linings of the brain (tuberculous meningitis), of the lungs. Animals get mostly tuberculosis of the lungs, though in poultry the liver and spleen are chiefly affected. In cows, the udder becomes infected in chronic cases.

Infection is spread through sputum, droppings, the milk of infected cows. The germs are taken in through the mouth, in feed or water, or are breathed in through the nose. After entrance they are attacked by certain blood cells but, owing to their waxy coating, resist destruction. They are then walled in by the defending body cells, forming small lumps called tubercles. A tubercle may remain for life, ready to become active at any time.

In general, the symptoms of tuberculosis are gradual loss of weight and condition and a chronic cough, but an infected animal may appear to be in prime condition. The test for the disease depends on the fact that after infection an animal develops a sensitiveness, or allergy, to the germs or their products. A filtered, concentrated preparation (tuberculin) is made from the germs and injected into the skin; in 24 to 72 hours there will be a reddened swelling if the animal is infected. Other tests can also be used, notably the X-ray in the case of human beings.

Tuberculosis of cattle is on its way out in the United States. In 1917, when a thorough Nation-wide Federal-State campaign of eradication began, 1 animal in 20 had the disease; today the number is less than 1 in 200. Meanwhile, human mortality from tuberculosis has dropped from 150 per 100,000 in 1918 to well under 50 per 100,000. The cattle campaign has been based on testing all animals, slaughtering the reactors (with indemnity payments), and educating cattle owners and the public. Some 232,000,000 tests and retests have been made; 3,800,000 animals have been sacrificed.

In the Central and West Central States tuberculosis of poultry is now a serious menace; the disease has been found on 75 percent of the farms in some counties. This is due mainly to keeping old birds, which become spreaders. Producers can remedy the situation by (1) raising the new flock on clean ground, (2) disposing of the old birds at the end of the laying season or at 18 months of age, (3) practicing thorough sanitation, (4) testing all birds kept over 18 months and disposing of the reactors immediately.

Losses from tuberculosis among swine have been reduced by the bovine campaign, but there is still considerable condemnation of carcasses and parts under Federal meat inspection. The remedy: (1) Dispose of tuberculous swine, cattle, and poultry, (2) practice sanitation, (3) rotate feed lots at least once a year.

ANTHRAX

The bacillus that causes anthrax, one of the most vicious of all the organisms that attack animals or human beings, seems to be indigenous to the soil in certain areas, and it can survive for years in a spore stage, resisting all destructive agents. Cattle grazing the vegetation closely after a drought or on land that has been flooded pick up the germ directly from the soil. It is also excreted in the droppings of diseased animals, to contaminate feed and water. It can be spread by dogs, coyotes, buzzards, and other flesh eaters, flies and other insects, and all kinds of infected animal products. Grazing animals are especially subject to the disease, but practically all animals as well as human beings are susceptible. In "anthrax districts" there is a more or less definite "anthrax season" when the disease tends to break out.

When the germ gets into the blood, it sets up a rapid and violent poisoning of the system. In the most acute form of the disease, an animal may suddenly die as though from an apoplectic stroke, without any previous sign of illness. In less acute forms, there are depression, stupor, spasms, and staggering before death. Blood commonly discharges from the natural openings of the body, and there may be swellings in various places. The carcass decomposes quickly and soon becomes bloated.

In the United States, human beings get the disease mostly from handling diseased or dead animals on the farm or hides, hair, and wool in factories. The skin, the lungs, or both may become infected, and the resultant blood poisoning may be rapidly fatal.

Suspected or actual cases of anthrax in livestock call for definite procedures, which Stein describes in considerable detail.

In a suspected case, never open the carcass of a dead animal yourself; call a veterinarian at once. There are post mortem findings that can be used in diagnosis, but more often a definite diagnosis can be made only by a laboratory examination of a blood sample.

When the presence of the disease is proved, all carcasses and contaminated material should be completely burned or deeply buried, preferably on the spot; everything used in handling a carcass should be burned or thoroughly disinfected; the entire herd should be examined for symptoms; all sick animals should be isolated and immediately treated with large doses of antianthrax serum; all healthy animals should be vaccinated; pastures should be changed immediately if possible; and the premises should be placed under a rigid quarantine. In the case of a dairy, no milk should be distributed until the place has had a clean bill of health from the proper officials.

Anthrax is one of the diseases that can now be largely prevented by vaccination. In areas where annual vaccination is necessary, it should be carried out well in advance of the anthrax season. There are now at least nine immunizing agents—serums, bacterins, and vaccines—available. Each has a definite field of usefulness as well as definite limitations, and the choice in a given case depends on the judgment of the local veterinarian or State livestock sanitary officials. Much new information, Stein points out, has been obtained about several of these immunizing agents from recent experiments of the Bureau of Animal Industry.

FOOT-AND-MOUTH DISEASE

Foot-and-mouth disease is one of the animal maladies that is dreaded like certain devastating human plagues. In this country, drastic measures are taken by the Federal Government to see that it does not gain a foothold; as a safeguard against introducing it, even the research work on the disease is not carried on in the United States but has been done abroad. There were six outbreaks between 1902 and 1929, each of which was stamped out by the prompt slaughter of every affected and exposed animal. No outbreak of this foreign disease has occurred since 1929.

Practically all cloven-footed animals, especially cattle, hogs, sheep, and goats, are subject to the disease, which is caused by a virus. The outstanding symptom is the formation of vesicles, or blisters, on the mucous membranes of the mouth (and the snout in the case of hogs), on the skin between and around the claws of the hoof, and on the teats and udder. The vesicles soon break but leave raw surfaces. The mortality of adult animals is not ordinarily high except in a malignant form of the disease that affects the heart, but the usefulness or productivity of the animal is likely to be greatly damaged.

To show how the disease spreads and the extreme danger from all kinds of infected material, Mohler and Traum go into considerable detail regarding the results of research on this aspect of the subject. In brief: The virus is quite resistant to destruction and is not readily killed by ordinary chemical disinfectants. During the fever stage of the disease, the saliva, urine, milk, and probably other secretions and excretions of a sick animal are infectious. The virus can be spread mechanically by animals and human beings. Infected milk, meat, and animal byproducts can spread the virus; so can infected biological products, such as smallpox vaccine and hog cholera virus and serum; so can the cattle fever tick.

Because of the need for drastic measures to suppress foot-and-mouth disease, accurate diagnosis is extremely important, and Mohler and Traum describe in detail the methods used. One of the principal points is to avoid confusing it with vesicular stomatitis or with vesicular exanthema of swine, both of which cause inflammatory changes in the mucous membranes of the mouth and the skin of the feet in cloven-footed animals. The final determination is made by inoculating swine, cattle, guinea pigs, and horses with material from the sick animal. If all except the horse develop symptoms, a diagnosis of foot-and-mouth disease can be made with certainty.

A major discovery in connection with foot-and-mouth disease was the fact that a solution of the cheap and common chemical, sodium hydroxide (lye), destroys the virus quickly.

It is vitally important to notify State or Federal authorities, preferably by telephone or telegraph, the moment the presence of the disease is suspected. If the existence of the disease is then confirmed by careful diagnosis, the premises are immediately put under strict quarantine, slaughter and burial of infected and exposed animals are carried out, everything is thoroughly cleaned and disinfected, and as a final test, susceptible cattle and hogs are allowed to feed and roam over the premises to see whether they contract the disease. Owners are paid indemnities based on the appraised value of all animals slaughtered in eradication campaigns.

PARASITES AND INSECTS AFFECTING LIVESTOCK

In this article Schwartz and Bishopp give a broad picture of the parasites and insects that attack livestock.

In general, Schwartz points out, each species of animal has its own particular kind of coccidia, the minute one-celled organisms that cause coccidiosis. In the animal, these organisms produce resistant forms called oöcysts by a process resembling sexual reproduction. Thousands of oöcysts reach the ground in the droppings of the animal and are in turn swallowed with contaminated feed or water. In the intestine, each oöcyst releases 8 sausage-shaped sporozoites, and each sporozoite can attack and destroy a cell in the intestinal membrane. During this destructive process, the sporozoites divide into new infecting bodies. Thus the membrane is rapidly stripped of many cells, the finer blood vessels are exposed and ruptured, and hemorrhage results. Bloody diarrhea is a characteristic symptom of coccidiosis.

Of the worm parasites, the threadworms, or trichostrongyles— some of which are popularly called "bankrupt worms" because they are said to lead stockmen into bankruptcy—occur in the stomach or intestines. The eggs reach the ground in the droppings, hatch, and finally develop into infective larvae, which can migrate upward on vegetation when it is covered with a film of moisture. An animal may swallow dozens of these larvae with a mouthful of forage. In the alimentary tract the larvae penetrate the mucous membrane, undergo further development, and return to the surface of the membrane to live as adults. Some are bloodsuckers. Infected animals can be severely injured, suffering from anemia, malnutrition, and digestive disturbances evidenced by diarrhea and constipation. The net result is unthriftiness, sometimes so marked that it leads to wasting and death.

Hookworms are primarily parasites of the small intestine. The eggs reach the ground in droppings, hatch, and develop into infective larvae. These larvae may be swallowed, reaching the small intestine and developing like trichostrongyles, or they may penetrate through the skin of the host. In the latter case they enter the blood vessels and are carried to the heart and thence to the lungs, where they rupture the finer blood vessels, get into the air spaces, and migrate upward to the back of the mouth—to be swallowed and finally reach the small intestine. Here the worm attaches itself to the lining, lacerates the finer blood vessels with its teeth or cutting plates, sucks blood, and moves on to another spot to repeat the process. The many small wounds produce hemorrhages, and the net result for the host is anemia, dropsical swelling, weakness, and digestive disturbances.

Nodular worms are much like hookworms. Eggs are discharged in the droppings, and infestation occurs through the swallowing of infective larvae, which penetrate the intestinal lining. Here each larva is quickly surrounded by cells mobilized by the protective mechanisms of the host's body, and a lump, or nodule, is built up that may eventually be filled with pus or cheesy material. The worm finally leaves the nodule—though sometimes it is trapped and dies there—to live, as an adult, on the lining of the surfect of the intestine.

Ascarid infestations result from the swallowing of infective eggs rather than larvae. In the intestine the eggs hatch into embryo worms. The immature worms penetrate the intestinal wall, get into the blood stream, and are carried to the liver and thence to the lungs. Eventually, like hookworms, they are swallowed, reach the intestine again, and develop into adults. In their wanderings the larvae injure the liver and the lungs; in the latter, they cause many small hemorrhages, and pneumonia may result. The adult worms, which are large, damage the intestinal lining and sometimes become tangled together in a solid mass that produces serious intestinal obstruction. Various other injuries can result from ascarid infestations, and stunting, marked unthriftiness, or even death may be the final outcome.

Lungworm eggs hatch in the lungs, and the larvae are coughed up and swallowed, to reach the ground with the droppings. Here some species develop to an infective stage and are taken up by the host in feed or water. Other species must first go through a period of development in the bodies of earthworms or snails before they become infective to higher animals. In either case, the worms apparently reach the lungs by way of the lymph vessels and the arteries, passing through the heart en route. In heavy infestations, the lungs may be seriously damaged.

Liver fluke eggs reach the ground in the droppings and hatch into larvae called miracidia, which can swim around in water. The miracidium penetrates the body of a snail and produces several more generations of larvae, the final one being a free-swimming creature called a cercaria, which leaves the snail and ultimately surrounds itself with a protective membrane, becoming a cyst. The cysts, floating on water or attached to vegetation, are swallowed by the higher animals. In the intestine, the cercaria escapes from the cyst, migrates in the body cavity, enters the liver and finally the bile ducts, and there develops to maturity. Liver flukes are bloodsuckers and may cause extensive hemorrhages, besides injuring delicate membranes and obstructing the flow of bile. Anemia, dropsy, liver rot, secondary infections by bacteria, weakness, emaciation, diarrhea, constipation, and death are common results.

No system of management yet devised, Schwartz points out, will completely control parasites. They can be reduced, however, by such practices as rotation of pastures, drainage of wet land, fencing, sanitation, provision of clean water and feed, and, in the case of liver flukes, destruction of snails. This author strongly advises against spreading manure on pastures to which the same or any other susceptible species of animal will have access during the same season. Medication for the removal of worms from livestock is a necessary part of animal husbandry in many cases. It should be based on a sound diagnosis of the parasites present and must be done with full knowledge of the properties of worm medicines, which are more or less toxic to the host animals.

The characteristics and habits of insects and their ways of injuring livestock are so diverse, says Bishopp, that it is not possible to make an accurate grouping of different types. He divides them roughly, however, into five groups.

Mites live exclusively on the body of the host animal and suck its blood. Scabs and various skin affections are among the results of these attacks. Dipping and applications of insecticides are used to control the pests.

Ticks breed on animals but pass part of their lives away from the host. They weaken the animal by withdrawing blood and also transmit various diseases. Control methods include dipping, the application of insecticides to the host animals and the breeding places of the ticks, and the removal of animals from infested areas.

Flies, gnats, and mosquitoes are extremely varied in their habits, their breeding places, and the types of injury they cause. They may suck large quantities of blood, torment animals, and transmit dangerous diseases. In many cases the larva of the insect lives as an internal parasite in the host. Each species of fly requires different control measures.

Lice breed on the host animal, lower its vitality, and reduce the quantity and quality of its products. Control measures consist of dipping, spraying, and dusting.

Fleas breed in debris and dirt. They suck blood, irritate and weaken the animal, and in one instance transmit a tapeworm of dogs. They are controlled by cleaning up and treating infested premises and applying insecticides to the host.

Bishopp stresses the fact that though we human beings are not responsible for the existence or the deplorable habits of insects, we are frequently responsible for the enormous numbers of them in certain areas; and those great numbers, in turn, are responsible for much of the damage done. Unsanitary buildings and barnyards, manure piles and old strawstacks, neglected pigpens and chicken houses, stagnant water, injuries to animals caused by careless handling, and lack of vigor due to undernourishment or other causes—all these are conditions that favor the breeding of insects or predispose animals to their attacks. The first step in controlling insects, then, is to eliminate such conditions. Other steps depend on the life history and habits of each species.

Bacterial Infections and Parasites Common to Man and Animals

Livestock diseases are a public health problem because many of them affect human beings as well as animals. This article considers only those caused by bacteria and parasites. Fungus diseases common to animals and man may be illustrated by lumpy jaw and virus diseases by sleeping sickness (encephalomyelitis of horses, encephalitis of human beings).

Stiles briefly discusses the bacterial infections. In the case of diseases covered elsewhere in this book, further details will be found in the separate articles.

Brucellosis affects cattle, swine, goats, and, according to recent evidence, horses. It causes undulant fever in human beings, who can acquire the infection from unpasteurized milk or by careless handling of diseased animals and their products. Bovine tuberculosis can be passed on to human beings, children being the most susceptible. Usually it is acquired by drinking raw milk. Hence both the Bang's disease (brucellosis) and the tuberculosis eradication campaigns are important public health measures as well as being of benefit to farmers.

Septic sore throat in human beings is often traceable to the consumption of raw milk from cows harboring *Streptococcus epidemicus*. The common mastitis organisms in cows (*Streptococcus agalactiae*) have not been shown to be capable of setting up a disease process in man. Milk, of course, can easily be contaminated after it leaves the cow.

Tularemia affects many wild animals, including rabbits, and is passed on to human beings by contact with diseased animals, by the eating of undercooked infected meats, and by the bites of ticks, deer flies, and other arthropods. The wearing of heavy rubber gloves will protect persons who dress rabbits and other game.

Anthrax affects many species of animals, including domestic livestock, and is readily passed on to human beings. Efficient methods of sterilizing hides, wool, and hair should prevent infection from these sources. Persons who handle carcasses of animals that have died of anthrax must use the utmost precautions.

Swine erysipelas can affect turkeys, ducks, pigeons, and sheep; possibly it is now becoming more widespread among domestic animals. It causes erysipeloid in human beings, the organism usually entering through broken skin. True human erysipelas is an entirely different disease, not caused by the swine organism.

Glanders, a disease of equines that can affect human beings, has been practically wiped out in the United States.

Bubonic plague (black death), a disease of wild rodents, is carried to human beings through the bites of fleas that infest rats, three species of which harbor the plague organism. Small areas of infection among rodents have been found in 11 Western States. Serious epidemics have occurred elsewhere in the world within recent years.

Food poisoning of various types may result from eating products contaminated with *Salmonella* bacteria and staphylococci, which infect animals.

Botulism is caused by three types of botulinus organisms which produce deadly toxins in perishable foods. The poison of each type can be neutralized by its own antitoxin. Botulinus spores are extremely resistant to destruction even by boiling, and they can infect many kinds of food products.

The parasitic infections are discussed by Lucker, who comments that man probably acquired most, if not all, of his parasites from his long association with animals.

Among the external parasites, the fleas of dogs and cats infest man, as does the sticktight flea of chickens, which can carry endemic typhus fever virus. A rat flea transmits bubonic plague to human beings. The red mite of poultry can parasitize man. Several kinds of ticks are transmissible from animals to man, and some carry the organisms of such diseases as Rocky Mountain spotted fever, tularemia, and sporadic relapsing fever.

It is suspected that wild and domestic animals act as reservoirs for certain protozoan diseases of human beings, notably African sleeping sickness.

Perhaps the most important worm parasite transmissible from animals to man is the nematode that causes trichinosis. It usually is acquired from infected pork that has not been thoroughly cooked. The beef tapeworm and the pork tapeworm are also acquired by human beings from raw or undercooked meat. If eggs of the pork tapeworm are swallowed, bladder worms may lodge in the heart, brain, or eye. Several species of worm parasites that normally infest animals can develop to maturity in the human body.

The common liver fluke of sheep and cattle has been reported as an accidental parasite of human beings in this country, and a liver fluke of dogs and cats not uncommonly infests human beings in Europe. In the Philippines certain flukes of dogs and cats are associated with a form of heart disease in man. Two tapeworms of dogs and cats are transmissible to man. A number of species of hairworms of sheep and goats, certain eye worms of dogs and sheep, the threadworm of swine, the giant kidney worm of dogs and mink, and the common thorn-headed worm of pigs have been reported occasionally in human beings.

The larvae of the hydatid tapeworm of dogs and other carnivores can produce huge hydatid cysts in the liver, lungs, or brain of human beings, and the larvae of several other worm parasites of animals are capable of developing in the human body. The larvae of blood flukes of birds sometimes invade the skin of bathers in the lakes of Michigan, Wisconsin, Minnesota, and elsewhere, producing a temporary inflammation called swimmer's itch. A skin disease reported in the South and called creeping eruption is caused by the larvae of a hookworm of dogs and cats.

THE SCREWWORM AND BLOWFLY PROBLEM

When an animal is cut or wounded accidentally or by such operations as marking, branding, shearing, castrating, dehorning, or docking, it is ripe for attack by the primary screwworm fly. Cushing and Parman describe how this fly lays 50 to 300 eggs in an open wound and repeats the operation every 4 days until perhaps 3,000 eggs have been laid. Maggots hatch from the eggs in 11 hours and burrow into the living flesh, feeding on it for 4 to 7 days; then they drop off, to become pupae and eventually adult flies. Eighty-five percent of all livestock losses in the Southwest are reported to be caused by this insect, and in the past it has made livestock production impossible in some areas. Very likely the modern plague of these flies was brought on originally through the mad scramble to brand cattle with hot irons, which, together with indiscriminate surgical operations and the introduction of barbed-wire fencing, helped to create ideal conditions for propagating the insects in immense numbers.

Some five other flies of the blowfly group also engender maggots that infest living flesh, but all of them more commonly breed in dead flesh. The blowflies extend much farther north than the primary screwworm, reaching, in fact, as far as Alaska.

There are practical ways to reduce this menace materially.

(1) Avoid injuring animals as much as possible, and time all ranch operations that necessarily produce wounds so that the operations are carried out in the seasons when the screwworm fly is least abundant and least active. Cushing and Parman chart the periods when these operations should be performed.

(2) Whenever a wound occurs on an animal, whether infested or not infested with fly maggots, it should be treated immediately with a mixture of diphenylamine, benzol, turkey-red oil, and lampblack. On the average, this treatment need be repeated only twice each week, but occasionally more frequent applications are necessary. This remedy is effective in killing screwworms. It also protects wounds against infestation.

(3) To combat blowflies, destroy all carcasses and waste meat products. Use fly traps and poisoned bait (with due precautions). When the hair of sheep and goats is infested with blowfly maggots, shear it from the affected areas and apply the screwworm remedy.

Nutritional Diseases of Farm Animals

This general article covers several important groups of farm animals. Other articles later in the book give more details on the nutritional diseases of cattle, hogs, poultry, and dogs and cats.

In general, Madsen points out, modern livestock production is intensive and often involves such artificial practices as stall feeding or lot feeding and close confinement. Under these conditions animals are deprived of their own natural choice of feedstuffs, and whether or not they are properly nourished depends entirely on the judgment of the producer. Failure to provide proper rations can lead to serious nutritional diseases that reduce production and profits. To prevent or cure these diseases requires specific knowledge. A considerable body of knowledge about animal nutrition has been developed by research during the last 30 years or so.

Ordinarily the essential minerals can be supplied by careful choice of common feedstuffs. When supplements are really needed, only the specific minerals that are deficient should be supplied and they should be given in carefully measured quantities. An excess is not only wasteful but may actually do harm.

Among the mineral deficiency diseases Madsen discusses rickets first, giving a careful description of the symptoms in young animals. The long bones, ribs, spinal column, pelvis, and teeth may all be affected, but by the time symptoms become evident in these structures, the disease is already well advanced; it should be and often can be diagnosed at an earlier stage. Other diseases similar in some respects to rickets occur in adult animals and may seriously interfere with production and general health. Certain rather common bone abnormalities of horses may also belong in this class. The whole group of diseases is caused by an insufficient supply of calcium, phosphorus, or vitamin D, or an unbalance between the two minerals. Heavy grain feeding at the expense of other dietary factors, a phosphorus-deficient soil, or drought are examples of conditions that can cause a serious shortage of one of the necessary minerals. Madsen discusses the feedstuffs and supplements that can be used to prevent or cure these conditions.

Magnesium is extremely important in the animal body but is unlikely to be deficient in ordinary farm rations. Common salt, however, can easily be lacking in sufficient quantities in the rations of grazing animals unless they have a supply available at all times.

A number of minerals are vitally essential in very small quantities. Lack of iodine means that the thyroid gland will not form enough of the hormone called thyroxin, a regulator of great importance in the body; the result is the disease known as common goiter. In certain areas carefully regulated iodine feeding is necessary. Manganese is essential, but except in chickens and pigs the symptoms of deficiency in farm animals have not been well established. Iron, copper, and cobalt are all necessary in blood formation, and deficiencies of one or another of these elements can readily occur under certain conditions—as on mineral-deficient soils—and cause very serious diseases and death. The essential mineral, sulfur, must be supplied to animals in sulfur-containing proteins.

The poisonous minerals discussed by Madsen are selenium and fluorine. The former, which causes so-called alkali disease, occurs in certain sections in the Great Plains and Rocky Mountain areas; the latter is chiefly dangerous as an impurity in rock phosphates sometimes fed to cattle in mineral mixtures, though it also occasionally occurs in drinking water.

Modern research on vitamins has cleared up many mysterious diseases previously attributed to vague infections or other causes.

Vitamin A deficiency can affect animals of all ages, but young animals are particularly susceptible. Abortion, the birth of weak or blind young, pneumonia, night blindness, convulsions, muscular incoordination, and diarrhea are some of the results of a severe shortage of this vitamin in livestock. The preventive or remedy is to supply enough of the vitamin (or of carotene, the substance from which the animal makes vitamin A) in the feed. Madsen gives the minimum amounts required by various animals and discusses the sources in feedstuffs.

Most of the seven B vitamins listed by Madsen can be synthesized by bacteria in the paunch of cattle, and the evidence on the dietary requirements of these animals is incomplete. Deficiencies in swine, however, produce typical disease symptoms; but in practice most of the cases are borderline, evidenced by such signs as slow growth, digestive disturbances, unthriftiness, and lameness.

Vitamin C is now receiving attention in connection with reproductive failures in farm animals. Vitamin D is associated with calcium and phosphorus metabolism, already discussed. Vitamin E is considered at some length by Madsen because of recent findings that it is associated with other vital functions besides reproduction.

Urinary calculi (sand, grit, gravel) are known to be due to dietary factors, but what these factors are has not been definitely determined. A deficiency of vitamin A is thought to favor the condition, but the evidence with farm animals is not clear-cut, and at present the recommendations for treatment, if it is undertaken, are rather general.

Madsen briefly discusses the serious effects of overfeeding lambs, cattle, horses, and breeding animals in general, and also of underfeeding as distinct from deficiencies of specific minerals or vitamins.

PLANTS POISONOUS TO LIVESTOCK

Over 40 plants poisonous to livestock are listed by Huffman and Couch in a concise table that includes the common and scientific names of the plants, the locations where they are commonly found, the parts of the plants that usually cause poisoning, the animals most commonly poisoned, the conditions under which poisoning usually occurs, the minimum quantity required, and the characteristic effects on the animal.

In discussing the poison-plant problem in general these authors point out that it is now more acute in the western range area than in the East, because in the latter so much of the native vegetation has been plowed up. Treatment of poisoned animals is seldom effective, and prevention must be relied on to reduce the livestock losses from plant poisoning, which are sometimes very heavy.

The authors suggest several preventive measures, based mainly on the fact that most poisonous plants are not generally so palatable as nonpoisonous species, and animals eat the former mostly when there is nothing else available or when they are exceptionally hungry. (1) Avoid overgrazing, and in particular reduce the rate of stocking on drought-stricken ranges and pastures. (2) Be particularly careful about turning hungry animals onto the range after they have been shipped or driven long distances without feed. (3) Be careful not to harvest poisonous plants with hay, or their seeds with grain. (4) Eradicate poisonous plants on pastures and ranges if it is practicable. At least eradicate them along trails and around watering places, where they are most likely to be eaten. (5) Where poisonous plants start growth earlier in the spring than good forage plants, do not turn animals out to graze too early. (6) Where plants are present that injure one kind of livestock more than another, permit only the animals that are least injured to graze the area. (7) The few poisonous plants that are really palatable to livestock should be eradicated, or the areas where they grow should be fenced off.

The bulk of the article is devoted to rather detailed discussions of many poisonous plants. In this brief summary it is not possible even to list all of them. They are grouped in the article according to the type of poisonous substance they contain. Much valuable information, the authors point out, has been developed by research in this field in recent years, but there is still a good deal that is not known.

Alkaloids.—(To this group belong such well-known poisons as caffeine, morphine, nicotine, strychnine.) Plants containing alkaloids include certain larkspurs, which cause heavy losses among livestock every year, and certain lupines (bluebonnets).

Cyanogen (hydrocyanic, or prussic, acid).—Some plants are able to develop this poison under certain circumstances—among them wild chokecherry, sorghum, Sudan grass, Johnson grass, wild flax, arrowgrass, and wild lima beans. Hydrocyanic acid acts quickly, but the victim can sometimes be saved if a veterinarian is called in time. The sorghums (including Sudan grass and Johnson grass) are normally good feed and develop the poison in sufficient amounts to be harmful only when growth has been interrupted.

Saponins.—These irritant poisons, which cause vomiting, are found in bitter rubberweed, pingue, corncockle seeds, bullnettle, and bittersweet (*Solanum dulcamara*).

Resinoids.—Several resinoids that act as severe poisons are found in various plants. Poisonous milkweeds contain toxins in this group; the whorled milkweed has caused heavy losses among sheep and another milkweed, *Asclepias labriformis*, is even more toxic. Some of the rhododendrons and azaleas contain a poisonous resinoid; so does waterhemlock, reputed to be the most toxic plant in the United States.

Oxalic acid.—The most important plant that contains sufficient oxalic acid to be poisonous to livestock is greasewood.

Tremetol.—This oily alcohol, which causes so-called trembles in livestock and milk sickness in human beings—a disease that baffled physicians for 150 years—has been found in white snakeroot and rayless goldenrod (jimmyweed).

Unknown and miscellaneous poisons.—To this group belong certain locoweeds, which have caused heavier livestock losses than any other poisonous plants in this country, and also copperweed, paper flower, littleleaf horsebrush and spineless horsebrush (the principal causes of so-called range bighead of sheep), and bracken.

PART 3

COMMON DISEASES OF HORSES AND MULES

EQUINE ENCEPHALOMYELITIS

This brain disease of horses has received a great deal of attention from research workers during the past few years for three reasons: (1) The virus is capable of causing an encephalitis, or inflammation of the brain, known as sleeping sickness, in human beings; there were over 2,000 cases of encephalitis in five Western States in 1941. (2) Since 1930 the equine disease has gradually spread eastward until it now practically blankets the entire country. (3) During this period nearly a million horses and mules have been attacked by the disease.

Here are some of the facts about encephalomyelitis (which means literally inflammation of the brain and spinal cord) discussed by Giltner and Shahan:

It is now known that there are two types of virus, an eastern and a western, that produce the disease. The eastern type causes death in about 9 out of 10 cases, the western type usually in only 1 out of 4 or 5 cases.

The symptoms in a horse or mule include fever, sleepiness, stupor, grinding of the teeth, uncoordinated and wobbly movements, and difficulty in chewing and swallowing. Body functions become more or less paralyzed and ultimately the animal collapses, lying in a stupor or delirium, and dies. In some cases, however, the disease stops with the early fever stage, and it might be thought that the animal was suffering only from some other mild illness. Both types of attack confer considerable immunity.

The disease occurs in epizootics (the animal equivalent of epidemics) during the warm months, is essentially confined to pastured animals, and is most common where there is water or marshy land. Every indication points to the fact that it is spread by bloodsucking insects. Experiments have proved that several species of mosquitoes and the Rocky Mountain spotted fever tick can transmit the virus, and it has been found in the field in one species of mosquito and in the assassin bug. It has also been proved that over 20 species of birds, as well as cattle, swine, sheep, goats, dogs, cats, guinea pigs, rabbits, monkeys, rats, mice, gophers, hedgehogs, and woodchucks can be infected; and since 1938 the virus has been definitely found in cases of brain disease in human beings. In fact, so far as is known, no other virus is capable of infecting so many different species of animals.

Diagnosis of the disease is based on clinical symptoms, post mortem examination, and sometimes inoculation of laboratory animals or a neutralization test with serum. Control measures, which should be carried out by a qualified veterinarian, include: (1) Vaccination before the epizootic season with a vaccine prepared from artificially infected chick-embryo tissue treated with formaldehyde to destroy its ability to produce the disease. (An antiserum may be used, but the vaccine is usually preferable.) (2) Control of bloodsucking insects by all practicable means; in particular, protection of affected animals against these insects. (3) Extermination of rats, mice, and other vermin and exclusion of pigeons and stray animals from the premises. (4) Prompt and thorough disposal of animals dead of the disease, and thorough disinfection of their quarters.

Medicinal or other treatments may be used by the veterinarian to relieve certain symptoms in a sick animal. The caretaker's job is to follow instructions and do everything possible to keep the animal comfortable.

Various other diseases, some of which affect the brain, may be confused with encephalomyelitis, including moldy corn poisoning, plant poisoning, tick paralysis, anthrax, shipping fever, swamp fever, rabies, heat stroke, brain tumors and abscesses, mechanical injuries, botulism, azoturia, and an acute, highly fatal malady called toxic hepatogenous icterus which seems to follow encephalomyelitis in some areas.

EQUINE INFECTIOUS ANEMIA

As Stein points out, infectious anemia of horses, mules, and asses—also known as swamp fever, malarial fever, and by other names—has become a problem of world-wide concern. In the past 10 years outbreaks have occurred in 17 States in this country.

Caused by a virus, the disease may be either acute and rapidly fatal or, more commonly, chronic and characterized by intermittent attacks of fever (each lasting several days), loss of weight, progressive weakness, marked depression, and dropsical swellings. During and immediately after the fever there is a reduction in the number of red corpuscles in the blood, and post mortem examination frequently shows internal hemorrhages and damage to the spleen, liver, kidneys, and heart. In most areas the disease is confined to low-lying, swampy, or wooded sections, but in the Mississippi Delta it is widespread, principally in the chronic form, sapping the strength of large numbers of mules and making them incapable of work when they are most needed.

How infectious anemia spreads is not definitely known, in spite of considerable experimenting. Biting insects may play an important part; so may feed and water contaminated by the virus-laden excretions of infected animals; so may long-continued, intimate contact of infected with normal animals. It is definitely known that after recovering from an attack, animals can carry the disease in a latent form for many years, serving as unrecognized sources of infection for other animals. Diagnosis is difficult, since the symptoms can easily be confused with those of various other diseases and of parasitic infestations. The only positive means of diagnosis is to inoculate a well horse with material from the suspected case. Nor is there any medicinal treatment that will bring about a cure or any method of preventing the disease by vaccination. Control depends primarily on the identification of carriers. Stein suggests the following steps as having practical value:

(1) Destroy any animal proved to have infectious anemia and dispose of the carcass by deep burial or cremation. (This is not practicable, of course, in regions like the Mississippi Delta, where the disease is widespread in a chronic form.)

(2) Where infected animals are to be kept and worked, separate them from healthy animals and carry out all practicable steps to prevent transmission of the disease to the latter.

(3) Do not breed infected mares, since they can transmit the disease to their offspring.

(4) Plow and fence off badly contaminated pastures or other areas and exclude horses and mules from them for at least 6 months.

(5) Provide good sanitation, control intestinal parasites and flies, supply pure, fresh drinking water, and never permit animals to drink from stagnant pools.

PERIODIC OPHTHALMIA OF HORSES

According to some estimates, 10 percent of the horses and mules in the United States are afflicted with periodic ophthalmia, with the figure running as high as 30 percent in some areas. Known for 2,000 years and the subject of considerable scientific research, the disease is still a mystery from the standpoint of cause, method of spread, cure, and prevention. Primarily a disease of the eyes, it is characterized by sudden recurring attacks of inflammation, which may affect only one eye or both and may extend over a period of several years. Symptoms include swollen, tender lids, a watery discharge from the eyes, some rise in body temperature, and cloudiness of the fluid within the eye and usually of the cornea. In this disease there are usually many successive attacks, all of which are acute. Blindness is the usual termination, but it may occur very early—for example, during the first attack. Diagnosis of the disease is not easy.

Mott and Seibold discuss the world distribution of periodic ophthalmia in some detail; a peculiarity is that it apparently seldom occurs in high altitudes. They also discuss several theories that have been advanced as to the cause of the malady. Little that is definite can be said, though the disease appears to be infectious, and possibly susceptibility to it may be inherited. Recently the Bureau of Animal Industry made a careful study of the microscopic changes in the eye that result from periodic ophthalmia, and these are described in detail by the authors.

In the absence of more definite knowledge, the best practical advice that can be given is (1) to obtain veterinary services promptly if an attack occurs, so that the animal's sight may be prolonged; (2) to keep healthy horses and mules isolated from any possible contact with animals affected by the disease; (3) not to breed animals that have the disease.

GLANDERS

An ancient disease of horses, mules, and asses, glanders can do an immense amount of damage, especially where these animals are concentrated in large numbers; over 58,000 had it in the French Army alone during the last war, and many of them had to be slaughtered. Occasionally other animals and human beings get the disease. Fortunately, glanders has now been practically eradicated in the United States, but as Cole points out, vigilance in excluding it from the country is all the more necessary for that reason.

The disease, which may be either acute or chronic, is caused by the germ *Bacillus mallei*. The outstanding symptom is the formation of nodules and ulcers in the nasal cavity and respiratory passages, almost always in the lungs, which are seriously affected, and sometimes in and under the skin. (The skin form of the disease is called farcy.) Few animals ever recover.

A serum test, an animal inoculation test, or a mallein test—made by putting a few drops of culture into the eye—can be used for accurate diagnosis; the last is the one most commonly employed because of its simplicity and reliability. Since there is no cure for the disease and no known way of conferring immunity, positive reactors should be destroyed, all exposed animals should be promptly tested, and premises and equipment should be adequately disinfected. Many States require prompt reporting of suspected cases and pay indemnities for animals destroyed under official supervision.

DOURINE

Dourine is essentially an equine syphilis caused by one of the microscopic parasites called trypanosomes and transmitted by sexual contact. As Cole points out, the first symptoms, which appear on the sex organs, may be entirely unnoticed. Secondary symptoms, appearing some time later, consist of wheals, like hives, on various parts of the body. Months or even years after the disease first strikes, it may give rise to marked disturbances of the central nervous system which often end in paralysis and death. A mortality rate of 50 percent is not uncommon. There is no known cure.

Since 1912, when a serum test made it possible to diagnose cases positively, great progress has been made in eradicating the disease in this country, and it now exists only in restricted areas in three States. Serum samples, which must be prepared by an expert, are tested by the Bureau of Animal Industry. All animals with a positive test are destroyed, and the owners are indemnified.

MISCELLANEOUS DISEASES OF EQUINES

Mott, Shahan, Giltner, and Frank deal with a considerable number of diseases of the horse, mule, and ass, for the most part not discussed elsewhere in this book.

Influenza (also called shipping fever and by other names).—Probably this is the most contagious and widely distributed disease of equines. The death rate is not especially high, but losses due to the incapacitating of work animals are serious. The disease is caused by a virus and is sometimes complicated by bacterial invasions; overwork, undue exposure, and poor hygiene are predisposing factors. Typical symptoms include fever, weakness, depression, rapid breathing, a harsh cough, watery discharges from eyes and nose, inflamed conjunctiva (pinkeye). Pneumonia, paralysis, or other serious complications may ensue. Preventive measures include quarantine of incoming animals, injections of bacterins for animals going to market (there are no specific vaccines or serums as yet, however), isolation of sick animals, disinfection of premises and equipment. Treatment consists mainly in rest and good nursing, with such medication as a veterinarian may recommend.

Distemper (*strangles*).—Probably caused by a streptococcus germ, distemper presents early symptoms somewhat like those described for influenza. In most cases there is a hot, painful swelling of the submaxillary glands (under the jaw); abscesses may form in other glands and tissues, and pneumonia and septicemia may be complications. Predisposing factors are like those for influenza. Affected animals should be isolated and carefully nursed, and premises and equipment should be disinfected. Various treatments may be prescribed by the veterinarian, including the placing of a tube in the windpipe to prevent suffocation. Preventive measures may include the use of a bacterin and the quarantining of newly purchased animals.

Purpura hemorrhagica (*petechial fever*) is not contagious and the cause is unknown, but it seldom occurs except after severe septic infection. Hemorrhages, edema (watery swellings), a rapid pulse, and jaundice are among the usual symptoms. Serious complications are common. Veterinary treatment is directed toward alleviating symptoms.

Wounds and wound infections, which occur very commonly among horses, can cause serious trouble. The germs of tetanus, or lockjaw, are widely distributed; so are streptococci, staphlyococci, and other organisms. Whether an infection remains localized or spreads throughout the body depends on the animal's resistance at the time and the number and character of the germs. Much of the damage from this cause is preventable by following out the management practices suggested in this article to keep animals from acquiring wounds in the first place, and by giving injuries prompt and proper care when they do occur. The article outlines first-aid treatment for wounds, describes the steps taken by the veterinarian, and in particular includes an account of the symptoms, prevention, and treatment of tetanus.

Breeding troubles frequently result from carelessness and ignorance in the handling of animals. Good diet, housing, and sanitation and proper exercise are the major preventives, but specific procedures should also be carried out in connection with breeding. These authors briefly describe the anatomy and physiology of the genital organs, and point out the need for keeping records of the heat period of mares, which varies among individuals from 12 to 30 hours. Since the egg is released near the end of the heat period, and the male sperm remains alive only 12 to 48 hours (varying among individuals), accurate timing of breeding operations is essential.

Good breeding hygiene demands a rather elaborate program that includes veterinary examination of the mare at intervals between heat periods to determine whether there is infection or any abnormal condition of the ovaries or uterus and laboratory examination of the semen of the stallion. The actual breeding operation, which may be by normal mating or artificial insemination, demands extreme hygienic precautions to eliminate any possibility of infection. Pregnancy can be determined by manual examination or by the injection of blood serum from the mare into laboratory animals.

Abortion is due to various causes, including the effects of certain drugs (some worm medicines, for instance), poisons, certain illnesses, injuries, and infections. Streptococci are said to cause 25 percent of all abortions in mares. Contagious equine abortion, caused by a specific *Salmonella* organism, may be largely controlled by the elimination of reacting animals as breeders and the vaccination of pregnant mares. There are indications that many abortions of unknown cause are due to a specific virus.

Difficult labor, the authors point out, may result in the death of both foal and dam and calls for prompt veterinary attention. Retained placenta (afterbirth) may also have very serious consequences.

Diseases of newborn foals are due chiefly to infection, though parasitism, poor nutrition, and poor housing are also important factors. One or more of several different micro-organisms may be involved, acquired for the most part through the uterus of the dam or the umbilicus of the foal after birth. The fact that these infections are so often fatal before any treatment (even if one is available) can be effective throws special emphasis on the need for adequate breeding hygiene, carried out by veterinarians rather than laymen, and for proper disinfection of the umbilical stump of the newborn foal. Drugs, serums, bacterins, and blood transfusions, however, are useful in some cases.

Lameness, of course, is particularly important in the case of equines. It should seldom occur if animals are given good care, are free from hereditary defects or seriously inferior conformation, and are properly trained and properly harnessed. Immediate attention should be given to the slightest lameness, the animal should be rested, and an accurate diagnosis should be made. The treatments used in addition to rest depend on the nature and extent of the trouble.

There are many causes and forms of lameness, of which the following are some of the more common: (1) Sprains are a stretching, laceration, or actual rupture of tissues due to strains that may occur in a great many ways. A sprain may result in serious injury to a joint, ultimate invasion by bacteria, and such abnormalities as "bowed tendons," "bucked shins," "water knee." (2) Arthritis is an inflammation of a joint caused by injury and sometimes complicated by bacterial infection. (3) A luxation, or dislocation, is the displacement of a bone from its normal position—most frequently, the patella, in the stifle joint. It requires prompt treatment by special manipulation. (4) Injury to the nerves may cause lameness, paralysis, and in some cases the muscular wasting known as sweeny. (5) Inflammation of the blood vessels or the formation of blood clots (thrombosis) caused by parasites or by injury may lead to lameness. (6) Fractures, or broken bones, may result from severe injury or strain. In very few cases and only under ideal conditions can they be treated successfully. (7) Stringhalt, or springhalt, which takes the form of spasmodic contractions of the muscles of the hind leg, is sometimes treated by the severing of nerves or tendons. The cause is unknown.

Bone diseases are probably the most common cause of lay-offs of draft horses and mules. They are due to faulty feeding (especially a lack of mineral balance in the diet) and to hereditary defects, with strains, injuries, and improper shoeing as contributing factors. The diseases discussed in this article are bone spavin, an enlargement of the hock bones; ringbone, an enlargement of the bones immediately below the fetlock; sidebones, a hardening of certain important cartilages on each side of the foot; splints, an abnormal growth of bone between the cannon bone and the small splint bones; navicular disease, an inflammation involving a joint within the forefoot; and the nutritional diseases, rickets and bighead, associated with calcium, phosphorus, and vitamin D metabolism. In some cases, the authors point out, specially designed shoes and appropriate trimming of the hoofs can compensate for bone deformities enough to make an animal serviceable. The whole problem of bone diseases emphasizes the need for good nutrition and a thorough understanding of conformation.

Foot ailments.—After describing the structure of the foot in some detail, the authors discuss a number of foot ailments and their causes and treatment. Chief causes of foot troubles are faulty conformation and improper care of the feet, including stabling on too dry floors or in wet and filth. The following specific ailments are dealt with but cannot be more than mentioned in this brief summary: (1) Brittle hoof is an abnormally dry, hard state of the horn, often treated by special trimming and a suitable ointment. (2) In spongy hoof the horn is abnormally soft, and shoeing must be done with great care. (3) In crooked foot, one side wall is higher than the other. Special shoes are sometimes used to compensate for the unevenness. (4) A contracted foot is sometimes benefited by special shoes or by leaving the animal unshod. (5) Sand cracks, or splits in the hoof, call for expert treatment of various kinds, depending on the location and extent of the cracks. (6) Corns, due to changes in the tissue as a result of bruising, may be dry, moist, or suppurating. Treatment is not always satisfactory. (7) Thrush is a diseased condition of the tissues caused by infection and nearly always produces lameness. It requires antiseptic treatment. (8) Canker, a diseased condition that may cause the growth of a fungoid mass instead of normal horn, usually calls for surgery and other special treatments. (9) Grease heel, an inflammation of the skin of the pastern and fetlock, calls for antiseptic treatment and sometimes surgery. (10) Quittor is a discharge of pus in the region of the coronary band caused by infection. Most cases require a radical surgical operation.

Skin diseases are often due directly or indirectly to faulty nutrition, unsanitary surroundings, and lack of regular grooming. Accurate diagnosis is the first step in successful treatment, but it may be difficult and require laboratory examinations. If a communicable skin disease is suspected, the animal should at once be isolated pending a diagnosis. Prescription and application of medicinal agents should be left to a veterinarian.

In addition to discussing briefly such conditions as excessive sweating, failure to sweat, so-called sweating of blood, and dandruff, the authors go into more detail regarding the following diseases: (1) Eczema, an eruption with more or less severe itching; (2) acne, an inflammation of the hair follicles and sebaceous glands caused by pus-forming bacteria; (3) urticaria, or hives, which may be due to any one of several causes, including a reaction to certain substances in feeds; (4) light sensitization, manifested in white-skinned and white-spotted animals and apparently induced by the eating of certain plants; (5) ringworm, a contagious disease caused by microscopic molds; (6) lymphangitis, an inflammation of the lymph vessels, which produces symptoms resembling those of glanders and is of three types—sporadic (essentially dietary in origin), ulcerative (due to bacterial infection), and mycotic (due to fungus infection).

Abnormalities of the teeth.—Alveolar periostitis, an inflammation of the tissue (periosteum) that attaches the tooth to the socket (alveolus) in the jawbone, caused by food particles and infective materials that gain entrance to the alveolus, calls for prompt extraction of the affected tooth. Uneven teeth, which may lead to serious injury to the mouth and to malnutrition, may be remedied by appropriate cutting or filing.

Fistula of the withers and poll evil.—These maladies are essentially the same except that they affect the withers and the poll, respectively. They involve a deep-seated, chronic inflammation of structures associated with the spine, possibly due originally to injuries caused by blows or pressure. A threadlike worm has been recovered from the tissues in many cases. It is now thought that the germ responsible for brucellosis of cattle may be associated with the disease. Control measures include avoidance of injury from such causes as low feed racks and ill-adjusted collars, sometimes internal medication, careful surgery where necessary, the elimination of brucellosis in cattle and swine.

Diseases connected with management.—The authors list the following troubles as due directly to mismanagement: (1) Azoturia (black water, Monday morning disease) is characterized by a sudden stiffening and paralysis of the muscles, profuse sweating, and very dark urine. It usually appears in working animals kept on full feed during a period of rest. Treatment, if the animal is to be saved, demands immediate rest on the spot where the attack occurs and the prompt services of a veterinarian. (2) Heaves (broken wind, asthma) is a chronic respiratory disease characterized by difficult breathing and a dry cough. The condition is associated with the feeding of damaged roughage. Proper feeding will control mild cases, but little can be done once the lungs are extensively involved. (3) Colic is a symptom of any one of about a dozen disorders of the stomach and intestines, caused most frequently by faulty feeding, overwork, exposure, and other preventable factors. Treatment is variable and should be prescribed by a veterinarian. (4) Founder (laminitis) is a serious ailment of the feet, chiefly caused by gross overeating, with extreme pain and fever as the principal symptoms. Treatment requires the services of a veterinarian. In advanced cases little can be done except suitable shoeing. (5) Collar and saddle sores result from failure to harden the animal gradually to work, lack of regular grooming, ill-fitting harness. (6) Poisoning usually results from the consumption of such substances as arsenical and lead preparations, commonly used in farm operations. Symptoms and treatment are described by the authors.

INTERNAL PARASITES OF HORSES AND MULES

Horses, mules, and donkeys "provide shelter and subsistence"—as Foster puts it—for about 150 different internal parasites, which are of two kinds, the protozoa, or minute one-celled animals, and the worms, or helminths. Practically speaking, it can be said that no horse or mule is ever entirely free of internal parasites of some kind. Some of these parasites are confined to certain geographic regions; others are found everywhere. Many are highly specialized in the parts of the body they attack; some do a good deal of wandering in the body, often following certain regular routes. Thus practically every organ of the body has its parasites. The importance of these enemies is not generally recognized, partly because the damage they do is seldom in the nature of a specific or spectacular disease; rather it is a general sapping of the animal's vitality and efficiency.

In general, the protozoa are of two types, those that live in the blood and those that live in the intestines, and the former are the ones that cause serious diseases, though fortunately they are limited in distribution. Only one of these diseases, dourine (discussed elsewhere in this volume), occurs in the United States. Other dangerous protozoan diseases not occurring in the United States are surra, carried by horseflies; nagana (African sleeping sickness), carried by the tsetse fly; mal de caderas, probably carried by horseflies and stableflies; murrina, carried by vampire bats; and piroplasmosis, carried by ticks.

About 50 species of ciliated protozoa—those equipped with hairlike organs for moving around—live in the intestines, but there is no evidence that they cause disease; in fact, some of them may be useful. There are also several other protozoa, about which little is known, in various parts of the body.

The worm parasites are much more important economically than the protozoa, but the harm they do is insidious, general, and often hard to diagnose.

The strongyles are perhaps the most important single group of worms; there are about 40 species all told, of two different types, large and small, but only about 15 species are really significant. An infestation of 30 to 50 thousand strongyles in an animal is considered moderate; when the number goes over 50 thousand, relatively severe symptoms are likely to result, including lack of appetite, anemia, and progressive emaciation. The strongyles live in various parts of the large bowel. The females lay eggs, which pass out with the manure and develop into infective larvae. Animals swallow these larvae while grazing. The bloodsucking worms cause anemia, internal hemorrhages, colic, and stoppage of blood vessels, which may result in intermittent lameness.

At least eight other kinds of worm parasites besides the strongyles are harmful to horses and mules. (1) Flukes sometimes attack the liver, blood vessels, and alimentary tract, but they are not normal parasites of equines. (2) Three species of tapeworms are important economically—a large one that causes intestinal catarrh; a smaller one that commonly causes an intestinal obstruction, which may be fatal; and a dwarf tapeworm, less damaging than the other two. (3) Four species of stomach worms cause a serious inflammation of the stomach called verminous gastritis. Three of these worms are transmitted by stableflies and horseflies. The larvae of some of the stomach worms also cause the skin disease known as summer sores, or bursati. Infestation with the small stomach worm is considered to be the most common forerunner of a sudden loss of condition in horses. (4) The ascarids, or large roundworms, are particularly dangerous to foals and young animals. The larvae migrate through the liver and lungs, often causing extensive damage, and eventually reach the small intestine, which may become completely obstructed.

(5) The small, slender worms called *Strongyloides* infect the small intestine of nursing foals and are probably partly responsible for cases of scours. (6) Pinworms live in the large intestine, and the females crawl out of the anal opening and rupture, leaving deposits of eggs and causing intense irritation, evidenced by tail rubbing. (7) Lungworms, which reach the lungs after extensive migrations in the body, cause a chronic cough and bronchitis in heavy infestations. (8) Two species of threadworms (filariae), probably transmitted by insects, infest horses. One, seldom serious, causes an inflammation and discharge of fluid into the body cavity. The other attacks a ligament in the neck and probably plays an important part in the development of poll evil, or fistulous withers.

Foster discusses various remedies used in the treatment of some of the protozoan diseases, including antimony and arsenic compounds injected into the veins.

Among the anthelmintics, or worm medicines, carbon disulfide is commonly used for roundworms. The remedies for strongyles include oil of chenopodium, carbon tetrachloride, normal butylidene chloride, and normal butyl chloride. Each of these drugs has certain serious effects on the animal, and all should be administered only with expert knowledge and care. The new anthelmintic, phenothiazine, developed by the Bureau of Animal Industry, is free of most of the drawbacks of the other drugs and can be administered in any one of several different ways. Occasionally, however, phenothiazine produces intoxication which may lead to death.

As for prevention—the author emphasizes the need for cleanliness and good sanitation around stables and barns, and for maintaining good pastures, not overstocked. The best way to combat parasites is to pay attention to these details and give the animals periodic medication.

MANGE OF EQUINES

Mange, scabies, scab, or itch in equines is caused, as in other animals, by three species of mites, the sarcoptic, psoroptic, and chorioptic, described by Imes. Usually the disease is transmitted by direct contact, but it may be carried in other ways, since both the mites and the eggs can live for a time off the host animals; hence when mange appears, the premises and equipment should be cleaned and disinfected, and all the horses should be treated.

Itching and the formation of blisterlike vesicles and of scabs are characteristic signs of mange, but a definite diagnosis must be based on finding the mites. Sarcoptic mites penetrate the upper layer of skin and make burrows in which mating and egg-laying take place. Psoroptic and chorioptic mites live on the surface of the skin, the latter being confined mainly to the lower parts of the legs and to the tail.

Treatment for mange consists in dipping the animals in a vat containing, usually, either a lime-sulfur or a nicotine solution. For the psoroptic and chorioptic types, two dippings are made 10 to 12 days apart, since the first does not kill the eggs and it is necessary to wait until the next generation of mites hatches. For sarcoptic mites four or more dippings, 6 or 7 days apart, may be required. The mites, buried in their tunnels, are hard to reach, and old chronic cases may be practically incurable. When there are only a few horses to be treated, the solution may be applied with a spray pump instead of in the form of a dip.

Horse Bots and Their Control

Horse botflies specialize in attacking animals of the horse family, though occasionally a young larva, or bot, burrows into the skin of a human being. Three of the four species of these flies are common in the United States. As Bishopp and Schwartz make clear, each has its own fiendishly ingenious way of getting its larvae inside the bodies of horses.

The nose botfly hovers about the head of a horse and suddenly darts in to attach its eggs, one at a time, to hairs on the lips. When the eggs hatch, the young bots burrow for a month or so in the mucous membrane lining the mouth. They then pass to the stomach and intestines, where they remain 8 to 11 months, perforating the lining membranes and causing considerable damage in addition to paving the way for germ infections. Finally, grown to full size, they pass to the rectum and thence leave the animal. On or in the ground, the larvae become pupae and then develop into flies.

The throat botfly attaches its eggs to hairs not on the lips but under the jaw. The young larvae crawl into the mouth and establish themselves in pockets in the gums, between the molars. Then they too pass to the stomach and intestines.

The common horse botfly attaches its eggs to hairs on the horse's body and legs, usually on the inner side of the knee. These eggs will not hatch until the horse bites and rubs the infested spot. Then, stimulated by the warmth and rubbing, the larvae burst the eggs open, stick to the horse's lips, burrow into the mucous membranes of the lips and tongue, and ultimately pass to the stomach and intestines.

The attacks of nose and throat botflies, especially the former, are maddening to horses, and they do everything they can to escape the creatures.

The adult flies cannot eat, and the females are simply egg-laying machines; hence they cannot be attracted to traps or poisoned bait. Nor is there any practical way of killing the eggs. Three methods of control are used, however.

(1) As a protection against the attacks of the nose botfly, fasten a broad band, 4 to 6 inches wide, beneath the lips, attaching the ends to the bit rings. A piece of burlap hung under the jaw will similarly keep off the throat botfly. Unfortunately these simple devices cannot be used readily while the animals are grazing. (2) After heavy freezes have killed all common botflies, rub the infested parts of the horse's legs with a swab or sponge soaked with warm water (105° to 110° F.). This causes many of the eggs to hatch, and the exposed larvae soon die. (3) To destroy the bots in the stomach, use carbon disulfide as a worm medicine, preferably a single dose administered in gelatin capsules or by a stomach tube (1.5 fluid drams, or 6 cubic

centimeters, for each 250 pounds of body weight—6 drams for a 1,000-pound horse). A veterinarian should do the dosing, and it should be done early in the winter—December or January, depending on the locality. Cooperative community campaigns in which all the horses in an area are rounded up and treated at one time by the local veterinarians have proved to be very successful.

SOME INSECT PESTS OF HORSES AND MULES

In this article Bishopp gives much information in little space on a number of insects that for the most part are not discussed elsewhere in this volume.

Mosquitoes and sand flies (*punkies*).—Often very annoying to animals. Mosquitoes can carry encephalomyelitis, or sleeping sickness. Control measures include screening, use of pyrethrum sprays, eliminating stagnant water, using oil on pools, pasturing livestock on high ground, using smudges.

Houseflies.—Annoy animals; transmit some parasites and diseases. Control measures include proper disposal and handling of manure and vegetable refuse, screening, use of fly traps and pyrethrum sprays.

Horseflies and deer flies.—Bloodsucking; bites are painful; carry some very serious diseases. Control, which is difficult, involves eliminating breeding places (swamps, marshes, etc.) Darkened sheds and smudges give some protection.

Buffalo gnats (*blackflies*).—Severe outbreaks greatly affect the condition of animals; may be fatal. The gnats breed in running water, and control is difficult. Bishopp discusses special handling of streams, use of poison in streams, pasturing on high ground, use of repellants, inoculation with gnat extract.

Fleas.—Discussed elsewhere in this volume.

Lice.—Three kinds are found on equines. Control is by application of suitable insecticides, especially by dipping.

Ticks.—Several kinds attack equines. Treatment with a pine tar-cottonseed oil mixture is used for those that attack the ears; arsenical dips, or washing or dusting with rotenone mixtures, are advised for those that attack the body.

PART 4

COMMON DISEASES OF CATTLE

BRUCELLOSIS OF CATTLE

Abortion, sterility, and diminished milk and meat production are among the train of evils that follow infection of cattle with the *Brucella abortus* germ, the cause of brucellosis, or Bang's disease. The losses due to this disease have been estimated very conservatively at $30,000,000 a year. It is introduced into healthy herds primarily by the addition of infected cows or infected pregnant heifers. The germ also causes undulant fever in human beings, but this danger can be greatly reduced by pasteurizing milk and by taking precautions in handling infected animals. Brucellosis cannot readily be diagnosed by the symptoms alone, but a blood-agglutination test, properly carried out, is a dependable means of diagnosis.

Lash and O'Rear point out that livestock owners spend large sums of money every year for remedies for abortion caused by bovine brucellosis, and they mention careful experiments conducted by the Department of Agriculture with two of those remedies, which proved that they were absolutely worthless.

In 1934 a brucellosis control and eradication project was begun in connection with the cattle-reduction program necessitated by the drought of that year. It was then estimated that 10 percent of the cattle in the United States were infected with the disease—twice the percentage that were infected with tuberculosis in 1917, when the tuberculosis eradication program began. The brucellosis program called for testing all dairy and breeding cattle over 6 months of age. At first begun with scattered herds, it was subsequently changed to an area basis in many States. Cattle owners are partially reimbursed for the slaughter of animals that react positively to the test. Retests are applied at frequent intervals, and owners are carefully instructed as to the sanitary measures necessary to eliminate the disease. Many counties have now been certified as practically free of bovine brucellosis. Cattle owners participating in the program have reported excellent results in increased calf crops, reduced sterility, higher milk production, lower costs, and improved sales of breeding stock.

Meanwhile extensive field trials of calfhood vaccination against brucellosis were going on, and these were so successful that since December 1940 almost all the States have adopted a vaccination program as part of the general control project. In this program, vaccinated animals gradually replace positive reactors.

Another method used effectively to supplement test-and-slaughter or vaccination is sanitary control. In herds where this method is adopted, animals about to calve or abort are placed in an isolated maternity barn, shed, or stall, and special sanitary precautions are observed in handling them.

General preventive meaures in the fight against bovine brucellosis include such practices as adding only tested or accredited stock to the herd, segregation and testing of each animal added, testing of animals that have been sent to fairs or shows, diversion of drainage from infected premises, proper pasteurization of milk used for feeding, and precautions against introducing infection on clothing.

JOHNE'S DISEASE

A gradual wasting away and an intermittent, increasingly severe diarrhea are the chief visible symptoms of Johne's disease, or paratuberculosis, which affects cattle chiefly but also sheep, goats, deer, and horses. As Simms, Mohler, and Johnson point out, symptoms take a long time, months or even years, to develop, and sometimes an animal can have a severe case yet show no apparent symptoms. The disease is incurable and fatal. It is caused by a bacillus very much like the tuberculosis organism and spreads by direct contact or through contaminated surroundings. There is reason to believe that it is much more prevalent in the United States than has been realized, and it may also be increasing; a recent test of some 5,000 cattle in the Southeast showed positive reactions in 1 out of every 10. A positive johnin test (much like the tuberculin test) is considered to indicate the disease, though not all animals with the disease react positively to the test.

When Johne's disease appears in a herd, the owner faces at least a 2-year fight to get rid of it, and unless he gets rid of it, it is likely to ruin the herd. A program of control, as outlined by these authors, includes frequent, regular testing, removal of all reactors, thorough disinfection measures, and strict sanitary precautions. In several States, indemnities can be paid for the slaughter of cattle with Johne's disease on the same basis as for the slaughter of tuberculous cattle. Since human beings are not subject to the disease, and it does not damage edible parts of the carcass, the meat is suitable for human consumption, subject, of course, to inspection.

There are uncertainties and difficulties about this insidious disease that make it impossible to say as yet that its conquest is clearly in sight. For that, additional facts need to be uncovered by research.

BOVINE MASTITIS

It is not unusual to find infectious mastitis in half the cows in many dairy herds. The total annual loss that results from reduced production, poor quality milk, and seriously diseased cows is enormous. There are two forms of mastitis—chronic and acute. The disease usually occurs in the chronic form and is difficult to detect. The acute form, which is a flare-up of the chronic form in most cases, is easily recognized by redness and swelling of the affected quarter, reduced milk flow, and marked changes in the appearance of the secretion. In advanced cases of chronic mastitis, the quarter becomes hardened and milk production is greatly reduced. The disease is caused by bacteria, which are spread on the hands of milkers or in the cups of milking machines.

The best method of controlling the spread of mastitis is to segregate the infected animals and use sanitary measures. Detection of diseased cows and supervision of the control program should be entrusted to the veterinarian. When the infected animals have been separated from the healthy ones, the producer can detect mastitis in its early stages in the latter group by the regular use of the strip cup and the bromthymol-blue test.

In the control program, healthy cows are milked before the infected ones at every milking. Strict sanitary procedures, outlined by Miller, are additional safeguards to prevent spreading of infection. A grain ration high in protein should be avoided. Everything possible should be done to protect the udders from injury.

BLACKLEG

Blackleg, one of the really deadly diseases of cattle, affects mostly young animals 6 to 18 months of age. The organism that causes it enters the body through small wounds in the skin or the mucous membranes of the mouth and quickly causes extreme symptoms, including rapidly swelling tumors, high fever, great depression, and violent convulsions. Death usually occurs within 36 hours, and the carcass rapidly becomes bloated by gas.

There is no cure for blackleg, but Mohler points out that five kinds of vaccine have been developed, any one of which will make animals immune for 12 to 18 months, the period depending on the vaccine used. There is also an antiblackleg serum for treating calves already affected, but it cannot be relied upon to stop the progress of the disease.

When an animal has died of blackleg, the carcass should at once be completely burned or deeply buried and covered with quicklime. Any place where the animal has lain should be disinfected with a strong disinfectant. Since the organism is very resistant to destruction and may linger in pastures for a long time, annual vaccination is the only way to conquer the disease.

SHIPPING FEVER, OR HEMORRHAGIC SEPTICEMIA

Hemorrhagic septicemia, as the name implies, is a poisoning of the blood (often quickly fatal), accompanied by internal hemorrhages. It has been considered that a specific germ, *Pasteurella boviseptica*, causes the disease, but some authorities now believe that, as in the case of swine influenza, it is the result of the combined action of a germ and a virus. In the main it attacks young cattle, especially those in poor condition that have been exposed to severe shipping conditions—lack of rest and proper shelter, irregular feeding and watering, etc.—during bad weather. The symptoms, described by Stein, are often severe and a fatal pneumonia is a rather common complication. Since the disease is infectious, the carcasses of animals that have died of it should be safely disposed of and the premises should be thoroughly disinfected.

Primary emphasis in preventing hemorrhagic septicemia must be placed on proper shipping of animals, including ample provision for feed, water, and rest to conserve their vitality, and the following of simple precautions with animals that have just been received after shipment. In many instances, if the injections are administered at the proper time, good results follow injection with a bacterin or aggressin, which produces a lengthy immunity, or of an antiserum, which quickly produces a brief immunity and has some curative value. The use of these products, as well as the treatment and diagnosis of the disease, should be left to a competent veterinarian. Diagnosis is often difficult because various other diseases have similar symptoms, and laboratory tests may be necessary.

MILK FEVER

Among the serious maladies of dairy cows, says Giltner, milk fever is the most common; moreover, it affects the high-producing cow rather than the poor one, and usually strikes during the best part of her life. The disease commonly occurs soon after calving, the first symptom being a general depression, followed by nervousness and spasms, then collapse, and finally loss of consciousness. Untreated animals are likely to die very soon.

At first thought to be due to infection of the udder, the disease is now considered to be caused, or at any rate it is always accompanied, by a marked shortage of calcium in the blood, together with an unbalanced condition of other minerals. Treatment, which is highly successful unless there are complications with other diseases, consists in injecting calcium gluconate into the veins, or, with extreme sanitary precautions, inflating the udder with filtered air. An animal in a state of collapse should be kept from lying on its side as there is grave danger that regurgitated material will get into the lungs and cause pneumonia.

No positive methods of preventing milk fever are known, and those that might be helpful are accompanied by certain other dangers. A special ration before and at the time of calving is a wise precaution.

Miscellaneous Diseases of Cattle

In this article, Knudson and Creech give a concise account of a number of cattle diseases, with particular attention to symptoms and possible measures for prevention and control.

White scours (infectious diarrhea, or acute dysentery).—A contagious and infectious disease of young and newborn calves, caused by micro-organisms, particularly colon bacilli, which enter the digestive tract by way of the navel cord at birth or the mouth later on. Chief symptom, a profuse light-colored diarrhea with a characteristic odor; also weakness, lassitude, and other signs of a general disturbance. Severe attacks may be fatal. Diagnosis is often difficult, since diarrhea may be due to various other causes. Medicines are of little use after symptoms appear; inoculation with hyperimmune calf-scour serum soon after birth, before any infection takes place, will help prevent heavy losses. The chief aim should be to prevent infection of the newborn calf. Knudson describes the sanitary measures that should be taken before, at the time of, and immediately after birth, including suitable disinfection and strict cleanliness. He also outlines a plan for the care and proper feeding of the very young calf from the time it takes its first feeding of colostrum milk, and tells what to do if the disease appears.

Acetonemia (ketosis, or chronic milk fever).—This disease of dairy cattle, particularly of heavy milkers, is discussed in the article on Nutritional Diseases of Cattle.

Pseudorabies (mad itch, infectious bulbar paralysis, or Aujeszky's disease).—An infectious disease of cattle, not very common in the United States, caused by a virus which attacks the central nervous system (brain). Often rapidly fatal. Common symptoms, intense itching, drooling at the mouth, high temperature, weakness, paralysis. The disease affects hogs and is rather common among rats; both may be carriers, and rats especially are suspected, though the actual mode of transmission is not definitely known. There is no known treatment. If the disease appears, the diseased animals should be isolated and their quarters thoroughly disinfected; hogs should not be permitted to run with the cattle; rats should be exterminated.

Papilloma, or common warts.—Several kinds of tumors affect cattle, but as Creech points out, most of them are rare. The most common are warts, cancer of the eye, and internal tumors affecting the lymph glands. Common warts of cattle are infectious or catching, and it has been proved that they are caused by a virus, which probably gains entrance through injuries in the skin. They may be large or small, appear almost anywhere on the body, and spread to other areas. The chief damage is to hides, which are reduced in value. Creech describes treatment by tying off; clipping; surgery; the use of glacial acetic acid, silver nitrate, and iodine; and internal medication. A wart vaccine is now being used experimentally, with promising results. Prevention consists in removing warty cattle and taking suitable sanitary precautions.

Epithelioma (carcinoma, or cancer eye).—A malignant tumor, or cancer, affecting the eye or related tissues, but eventually spreading elsewhere in the body, with fatal results. Cause unknown; irritation and overexposure to strong sunlight may be contributing factors. There is no known cure after the disease has had a good start. Complete surgery of the cancerous tissue and the eyeball by a veterinarian usually gives satisfactory results if performed early enough. Otherwise, the animal should be sold for slaughter, subject to inspection.

Lymphocytoma (lymphatic leukemia, or pseudoleukemia).—A cancerous, incurable, always fatal disease affecting the lymph glands primarily and showing various manifestations. The first noticeable symptom is usually an enlargement of the superficial lymph glands—submaxillary gland (throat), prescapular gland (shoulder), precrural gland (flank), supramammary gland (above the udder). Laboratory examinations may be necessary to distinguish the disease from tuberculosis and actinomycosis.

Actinomycosis and actinobacillosis.—Chronic infectious diseases, the first caused by a fungus, the second by a bacillus, but both having similar symptoms. Actinomycosis causes enlargement of the bones of the head, particularly the lower jawbone (lumpy jaw), which become spongy and filled with pus. Actinobacillosis produces tumorous swelling and frequently ulceration of the soft tissues of the mouth and throat, often including the tongue (wooden tongue) and the lymph glands. Various internal organs may be affected. The mode of infection is not definitely known, but it is believed that the organisms gain entrance through injuries to the mucous membranes. Actinomycosis cannot be treated satisfactorily; affected animals should be fattened for slaughter. Actinobacillosis can be treated with suitable drugs, and by surgery. There are special Federal meat-inspection regulations covering the disposal of carcasses of animals affected with these diseases, to which human beings are also susceptible.

Nasal granuloma (snoring disease).—A disease long known in India but only recently (1933) discovered in the United States, and apparently confined to Louisiana. Chief symptoms, a thickening of the nasal mucus membrane, usually only the first 3 inches; many small nodules on the membrane; discharge of mucus, pus, and sometimes blood from the nose; difficult breathing, accompanied by a snoring sound. The cause of the disease in this country has not been definitely determined; in India there are two forms, one caused by a parasitic worm, the other by a spore-bearing organism. Experimental treatments have so far not been successful.

Goiter.—This disease is discussed elsewhere in this volume, under nutritional diseases. It is chiefly important in cattle as a disease of newborn animals due to iodine deficiency in the dam.

Specific ophthalmia (infectious conjunctivitis, infectious keratitis, or pinkeye).—Pinkeye usually begins as an inflammation of the conjunctiva (conjunctivitis), but may later involve the cornea (keratitis) and eventually destroy the sight. In addition to local redness, swelling, watering, and discharge of pus, symptoms usually include some fever, loss of appetite, decreased milk secretion, and other signs of general disturbance of the system. The disease is believed to be infectious, with irritation or injury of the eye tissues as a predisposing factor. Several organisms have been found to be associated with the condition, but it has not been proved that any one of them is the specific cause. Healthy animals should be separated from those affected by the disease, and the latter should be kept in dark stables or sheds, specially fed, and dosed with Epsom salts. It is important to consult a veterinarian in cases of pinkeye to avoid serious results. Creech describes treatment with cocaine, silver nitrate, boric acid, mercurochrome, and mixed keratitis bacterins.

Calf diphtheria.—An acute, infectious, often fatal disease of suckling calves caused by a widespread organism (*Actinomyces necrophorus*) which gains entrance through wounds in the mucous membrane of the mouth. Sometimes as many as 70 percent of the calves in a herd may be affected. The symptoms include extensive ulceration of the mouth caused by destruction of tissues, slobbering, a discharge from the nostrils, sometimes wheezing and coughing, depression, weakness, and emaciation. Prevention consists in prompt isolation of sick animals and thorough cleansing and disinfection of quarters. Treatment, which is useful only in the early stages or in mild outbreaks, consists in removing dead tissue, painting ulcerated surfaces with appropriate medicinal agents, washing the mouth frequently with warm water, and good nursing.

Pneumonia.—An inflammation of the lungs caused by specific infections, parasitism (rarely in cattle), such conditions as chilling from exposure, or foreign material getting into the lungs; often a secondary condition in some other disease. The symptoms may include dullness, lack of appetite, high temperature, disturbed respiration, wheezing or gurgling sounds in the lungs, diarrhea, a discharge from the nostrils. Either death or recovery may be rapid, or the disease may persist for several weeks. Treatment consists in good nursing, the use of tonics and stimulants, sometimes the application of counterirritants such as mustard plasters. There are no specific sera or vaccines such as are used for pneumonia in human beings, but large injections of blood from normal cattle are reported to be beneficial. Experiments with sulfonamide drugs have not progressed far enough to give definite recommendations. As Osteen points out, pneumonia demands treatment by a trained veterinarian.

Choke.—Cattle do not chew thoroughly, and food or foreign objects may lodge in the throat or lower down in the gullet, causing such symptoms as retching, coughing, and eventually, bloating. If the object is in the neck, it may be possible to force it upwards by gentle manipulation with the hands. If it is in the chest region, it can sometimes be gently pushed downward to the rumen by the use of an oiled stomach tube fitted with a probang, or slender wooden rod, at the end. If neither can be done, a veterinarian may have to operate. In any case, rough treatment should be carefully avoided. Before removing the object, it may be necessary to relieve the pressure of gas by puncturing the abdomen with a trocar.

CATTLE COCCIDIOSIS

Coccidia, says Boughton, are minute parasites related to those that cause malaria. They multiply in the intestinal tract for a time, then change into oöcysts—a resistant form—which are discharged in the feces and are picked up by cattle from contaminated surroundings. Practically all cattle become infected, not only once but repeatedly. Whether the infection is dangerous depends on the number of organisms taken in; small numbers may produce only mild symptoms or none at all. Cattle frequently recover spontaneously from attacks, and many animals are carriers, constantly spreading infection though apparently not harmed themselves. Very young calves are especially susceptible to serious coccidiosis.

Among the symptoms of an acute attack are bloody diarrhea, anemia, weakness, and emaciation. Death may occur in a week or two; if it does not, the animal is likely to recover. Secondary complications, especially pneumonia, are common. There is no known medicine that will effect a cure, though the symptoms can be alleviated.

Boughton discusses in some detail the control methods that can be expected to prevent serious cases of coccidiosis. They include such measures as daily removal of manure and contaminated bedding, careful sanitary precautions, and isolation of young calves in individual box stalls if possible—if not, segregation of all calves in four age groups. Protection of young calves is the most important point; later, the animals can usually withstand ordinary infections.

CATTLE TICK FEVER

A minute parasite called a piroplasm is responsible for cattle tick fever. The discovery that this parasite is carried by the cattle tick opened the way for a long series of discoveries regarding the means by which certain other diseases are transmitted—including such human maladies as malaria, yellow fever, Rocky Mountain spotted fever, and typhus.

MacKellar tells how it also opened the way for a finish fight against this deadly disease of cattle, which used to be responsible for losses of 40 million dollars a year, not counting the indirect cost of burdensome restrictions and quarantines applied to the South.

In 1906 a campaign was begun to eradicate the tick—in itself a very damaging pest, quite aside from its role in spreading the fever. The method most commonly used in this campaign, which has been going on ever since, is to dip all the cattle in tick areas at regular intervals, usually every 2 weeks, during the tick season.

Gradually the ticks have been wiped out, until today the only places quarantined are a small area in Florida, where deer continue to harbor the ticks, and another in Texas, where infestation filters in across the Mexican border. Losses from the disease are almost entirely eliminated, and the removal of restrictions against former tick areas has been of immense benefit to the South.

The cost of the whole campaign to the Federal Government, the States, and the counties has been little more than the former losses amounted to in a single year.

Anaplasmosis: A Disease of Cattle

Anaplasmosis is known to exist in 23 of our own States and in many foreign countries. Characterized by marked anemia and depression, among other symptoms, this disease, caused by a minute parasite that invades the red blood cells, is fatal in 25 to 60 percent of the cases. Considerable research work, discussed by Stiles, has been done in recent years on the mode of transmission. It has been proved that the disease can be spread by the use of unclean instruments in such operations as dehorning, castration, and the giving of injections, as well as by at least 18 species of ticks, 7 species of horseflies, and several species of mosquitoes.

No preventive or cure has been discovered, but research is being carried on in this field. In some foreign countries, young animals are immunized by inoculation with the blood of a carrier, but these animals themselves become carriers, as does every animal that has recovered from the disease; hence the method is not used in the United States.

Because of the danger of spreading the disease through carriers, any animal that recovers should be fattened and sold for slaughter. Sick animals should be kept in the shade and given plenty of clean water, a little appetizing green feed, protection against insects, and good nursing. Medicinal and other treatment by a veterinarian may include various procedures discussed by Stiles.

Cattle Scab and Its Control

Four kinds of mites cause the contagious skin disease of cattle known as scab, mange, or itch. (1) Common scab, caused by the psoroptic mite, which lives on the surface of the skin, was once a widespread menace in this country but is now rare as a result of a vigorous campaign of quarantine and eradication. (2) Barn itch, caused by the sarcoptic mite, was once rare, but as Snyder points out, it has increased in the last few years and is now a very troublesome problem. Dairymen and breeders of purebred cattle can suffer heavy losses if the disease gets a foothold. The mites burrow into the skin instead of living on the surface and hence are more difficult to detect and combat than psoroptic mites. (3) Chorioptic scab, caused by the chorioptic mite, is much like common scab but spreads slowly and is usually confined to the tail or legs. (4) Follicular mange, caused by the demodectic mite, produces nodules or lumps on the skin that seriously damage the hides as leather. There is no practical remedy for this type of mange in cattle, but infected animals should be isolated.

The other three types of mange can all be controlled by dipping the animals in an officially approved solution of lime-sulfur or nicotine. For common scab and chorioptic scab, there should be two dippings 10 to 12 days apart. For sarcoptic scab there should be four dippings at intervals of 6 to 10 days, and just prior to the first one all affected areas on the body should be well scrubbed and soaked with the dipping solution. (One dipping of crude petroleum will kill this mite and apparently also the eggs, but it is injurious to the animals in some cases.) In addition to dipping, all stables, enclosures, and equipment that have been in contact with mangy cattle should be thoroughly cleaned and disinfected before being used for clean or dipped cattle.

Tapeworm and Roundworm Parasites of Cattle

The more important tapeworm and roundworm parasites of cattle take a heavy toll every year from the beef and dairy industries in the form of deaths from gross parasitism, lowered vitality, poor growth and production, and the condemnation of meat and livers in packing plants. In discussing these parasites, Porter refers the reader to the article on sheep and goat parasites for further details, since the information in the latter field is more extensive and much of it applies to cattle.

Three groups of tapeworms are discussed. (1) Those that live as adults in the intestines probably do less damage in cattle than in sheep, though calves may be sufficiently parasitized to be weak and unthrifty and hence should be excluded from pastures known to be a source of infection. (2) Two tapeworms that infest dogs and other canines pass through an intermediate stage in cattle—the hydatid, and the thin-necked bladder worm. To prevent infection, dogs on the place should be kept free of worms, and stray dogs and wild canines should be kept off. (3) A tapeworm of human beings occurs in the larval, or bladder worm, form in the muscles of cattle, causing what is known as beef measles—oval white vesicles about the size of a pea. Proper sanitation prevents passing the infestation from human beings to cattle, and thorough cooking of infected beef prevents passing it from cattle to human beings. Measly beef is condemned in federally inspected packing plants.

The roundworms included in the article are in five groups. (1) Those infesting the lungs occur much more frequently in calves than in mature cattle. Heavy infestations cause progressive weakness and can prove fatal if the lungs are extensively involved, especially when a secondary bacterial invasion occurs. Infested animals should be removed from pasture to clean, sanitary quarters and given liberal quantities of feed. (2) Three species of stomach worms infest cattle, producing such symptoms as gastritis, loss of flesh, general weakness, anemia, and in some cases diarrhea and bottle jaw. Calves and yearlings are in general more seriously affected than adult animals. (3) The small worms known as cooperids infest the small intestine chiefly and can cause extensive intestinal inflammation in calves, with diarrhea, emaciation, and anemia as symptoms in severe cases. (4) The blood-sucking cattle hookworm, a prevalent parasite of young animals, also causes emaciation, diarrhea, and anemia. The infective larvae, which can penetrate the skin as well as being swallowed, normally parasitize the small intestine. (5) The nodular worm occurs in the large intestine and cecum, the attacks of the larvae producing nodules that are subject to bacterial invasion. Anemia, scouring, and emaciation are among the symptoms in severe cases.

All the roundworms discussed are acquired largely from pasturage contaminated by droppings. Preventive measures include drainage of low, wet areas (or excluding calves and yearlings from such areas), conservative stocking of pastures, rotation as often as possible, keeping calves away from older stock and from contaminated pastures and quarters, good sanitation and good feeding, and isolation of infected animals for special treatment.

Medicinal treatment for cattle is much like that for sheep and in fact it is based largely on investigations with sheep. Worm medicines should be given only after competent veterinary diagnosis and advice, since their use is attended with danger to some of the animals. Porter discusses the use of some of the common anthelmintics for parasites in the stomach and intestines.

Bovine Genital Trichomoniasis

Trichomonas foetus is a one-celled, microscopic, wriggling organism with three threadlike whips at the front end. When it infects the uterus of a cow, the result may be failure to conceive, abortion, or death and disintegration of the fetus, though sometimes normal birth takes place. The disease is spread by infected bulls during service; but since it has been reported in virgin heifers, it may perhaps also be spread by close contact with infected cows. It was first reported in this country in 1932.

A tentative diagnosis can be made from the breeding history of the herd and of individual animals, and a definite diagnosis by direct microscopic examination of material from the sex organs of the cow or bull, or by culturing the material.

There is no specific treatment for the disease. Cows that abort should be given a period of sexual rest. Generally no other treatment is required provided the abortion is complete. When the abortion is incomplete, that is, when part of the fetal membranes is retained, and infection develops in the uterus, the case should be treated like any other form of uterine infection. Cows that fail to conceive should be allowed to pass two or three normal estrual periods without being bred. Cows that develop pyometra (pus in the uterus) should be treated by a veterinarian.

The use of infected bulls should be restricted to cows that have been exposed to the disease.

For prevention of the disease, Dikmans makes the following recommendations: (1) Investigate breeding records before adding any animal to the herd, or bringing any animal in or sending any animal away for breeding. (2) Consult a veterinarian at once if breeding troubles occur; stop breeding operations temporarily if the trouble is due to trichomoniasis, and determine which animals have been exposed to infection. (3) Restrict the use of infected or suspected bulls that have had or have been exposed to the disease. (4) Provide a new bull for heifers coming to breeding age and cows that have not been exposed.

CATTLE GRUBS, OR HEEL FLIES

The heel fly, warble fly, or gadfly attaches its eggs neatly to separate hairs, mostly just above the hoofs of cattle. The fly itself does not sting or bite; it is unable to feed itself and lives only about a week. Its mere presence, however, terrorizes cattle much as some human beings are terrorized by snakes; during the heel fly season the animals lose flesh or fail to gain, and milk production falls off. The eggs of the fly hatch in a few days, and the grubs immediately burrow deep into the tissues, where they wander around, feeding and growing for about 9 months. Finally they reach the back, and here each larva makes a hole in the skin and becomes enclosed in a pocket, or cyst, remaining about 5 weeks and molting twice. Then it crawls out, drops to the ground, and becomes a pupa. In 6 to 10 weeks the adult fly emerges. A female can lay as many as 300 eggs.

There are two species of heel flies, one confined to the North, the other common throughout the country. The fly season begins very early in the spring in the South and gradually spreads northward, terminating about the first of August at the northern limits of the flies' range. The damage done by the flies, as summarized by Laake, Bishopp, and Wells, includes loss of production through nervous disturbance, the loss entailed in grub-infested meat, which has to be trimmed and discarded, injury to sausage-casing material, and very extensive damage to hides. At the minimum, the losses due to heel flies are estimated at 50 million dollars a year.

Much research has been done on methods of control. So far the best method seems to be to kill the grubs while they are in the backs of cattle. This may be done by applying derris or cube powder (5 percent rotenone) mixed with wettable sulfur. The material may be dusted on and rubbed in by hand, or mixed with water and rubbed in with a stiff brush, or sprayed on with a power sprayer. The last method is the most economical and the quickest for large numbers of animals, which are treated as they pass through a chute. The grubs may also be squeezed out of the backs of the animals by hand and extracted with forceps, a method that is slow but reputedly very effective in some cases.

THE STABLEFLY

The big, vicious stablefly, which jabs painfully through the skin to suck its daily meal of blood, is a menace for three reasons, Bishopp and Laake point out—it worries and in large numbers can actually kill horses and cattle, it is an unbearable annoyance to human beings, and it can carry infantile paralysis as well as such livestock diseases as hog cholera, anthrax, and swamp fever. This last is the more serious because the stablefly can travel long distances; marked flies have been found to go as far as 52 miles.

The eggs are laid in moist, fermenting organic matter such as plant refuse or manure, in which the maggots live and grow; one female in a laboratory cage laid as many as 600 eggs. The most important single step in preventing infestations, then, is to eliminate such breeding places. For example, bale straw immediately without letting it get wet; scatter stack butts, grass clippings, vegetable trimmings, and peanut litter immediately and manure at least twice a week instead of letting it pile up; spray windrows of beach grass with a mixture of creosote oil and fuel oil.

Where breeding cannot be entirely prevented, fly traps fitted in barn windows will catch some of the flies. Oil sprays containing rotenone or pyrethrum are even better. If the spray used on an animal contains as much as 10 percent of either of these extracts, it will give protection for a day or more.

THE HORN FLY

Bruce estimates that in a herd of 500 head of cattle, with the common infestation of about 4,000 horn flies per animal (sometimes it runs much higher) the amount of blood extracted by the flies totals some 312 quarts in a year. In addition, these small, black, stabbing flies torment the animals, prevent them from eating properly, and cause sores that may become infested with screwworms. The fly stays on the animal day and night, always resting with its head downward. It lays its eggs in droppings. Warm, damp, cloudy weather is especially favorable for the development of the insect.

The pest is harmful enough to warrant serious efforts to control it. In small pastures, the maggots may be killed by systematically scattering all droppings. Pyrethrum sprays can be used to kill the flies on the animals. A special fly trap, which Bruce describes, is also effective. It is a large boxlike affair through which the animal is forced to pass on its way to water or feed. An arrangement of curtains and weighted strips brushes the flies off its body, and the insects are caught in trapping elements as they try to get away. Some interesting tests have also been made in feeding cattle substances that would make the droppings poisonous to the fly maggots without harming the animals, but this work is still in the experimental stage.

Cattle Lice

Cattle in the United States are preyed on by the red louse, which bites, living on bits of skin and hair; two long-nosed blue lice, which suck blood; and the bloodsucking short-nosed ox louse. Infestation is worst during winter and spring, when the animals may sometimes be literally covered with lice, and least in the hot weather of summer. The chief damage, Babcock and Cushing point out, is unthriftiness and lowered vitality; occasionally an animal succumbs to a severe attack.

Dipping in an insecticide is the best remedy, and the best insecticide for this purpose consists of 100 pounds of wettable sulfur (325 mesh) plus 10 pounds of cube or derris containing not less than 5 percent of rotenone, to each 1,000 gallons of water. The animals are driven through the dipping vat, the head of each animal being ducked at least once. Usually the first dipping is done in the early fall, followed by a second 12 to 14 days later, and a third 17 to 21 days after the first dipping. If the third dipping must be omitted, two 17 to 21 days apart will give good control. Animals should not be hot when dipped, and in cold weather they should be dipped early enough in the day to dry off before evening.

Coal-tar-creosote dips mixed in soft water are also effective. Arsenical dips are widely used but do not control the bull-nosed ox louse.

For a few animals only, the sulfur-rotenone mixture can be sprayed on with a bucket pump and rubbed into the skin by hand; or a dry mixture of 1 pound of the derris or cubs with 9 pounds of sulfur (325 mesh, wettable or nonwettable) may be dusted on and rubbed in. The dry powder should always be used in cold weather, especially in winter in the North. Second and third treatments should be given as in dipping.

Cattle Injuries Caused by Ingesting Foreign Objects

Giltner and Patton give photographs of an extraordinary collection of objects that have been recovered at various times from the stomachs of cattle.

One of the fairly common results of swallowing a sharp object such as a nail or a piece of wire is that it eventually works its way forward to the heart sac, where it sets up an inflammation known as traumatic pericarditis that seriously affects the animal's general health and in the long run usually ends fatally. The symptoms of the condition and the post mortem findings are described by the authors.

Treatment is of little use, though in a few cases a radical surgical operation can be performed. Traumatic pericarditis and other injuries caused by ingesting foreign objects can be prevented, however, by keeping the premises free at all times of things that cattle might swallow—baling and barbed wire, for instance, staples, nails, scraps of metal. In many cases losses due to this cause have been eliminated by systematic clean-up and pick-up efforts.

PAINT POISONING IN CATTLE

Cattle are more sensitive to lead poisoning than any other domestic animal, says Giltner, and most cases are due to their licking and swallowing lead paint. The danger exists on every farm; sometimes many animals in a herd are affected. Among the common early symptoms are slobbering, choking, colic, loss of appetite, reduced milk flow, and constipation. The most striking symptoms, however—trembling, fits, apparent attacks of mania and blindness, and deep coma—are caused by the effects of lead on the brain. Death occurs quickly in severe cases.

A few drugs are used by veterinarians to treat lead poisoning, but in most instances little can be done except to relieve the symptoms. The important thing is to prevent poisoning by seeing that the animals never have access to lead in any form. In particular, keep them away from freshly painted objects of any kind, see that paint cans are properly disposed of, and use nonpoisonous paints for objects from which cattle cannot be kept away, such as stalls and stanchions. In other words, always treat lead paint as a poison so far as cattle are concerned.

NUTRITIONAL DISEASES OF CATTLE

In this review Madsen includes mineral deficiencies, vitamin deficiencies, and certain miscellaneous disorders related to nutrition.

Calcium deficiency is rare in cattle, especially when they have roughage of good quality, but phosphorus deficiency is likely to occur when feed is restricted owing to drought, overgrazing, or other causes, or when feeds low in phosphorus make up a large part of the ration. The first apparent symptom is usually a depraved appetite; the animal chews bones and eats all kinds of material—some of it toxic—in an effort to get phosphorus. Later symptoms include loss of appetite, emaciation, weak bones, stiff joints, decreased productivity, and reproductive failure. There are three ways to prevent or cure calcium or phosphorus deficiency—furnish feeds (listed by Madsen) that are good sources of these minerals, use mineral supplements, or increase the mineral content and yield of forage by fertilizing the soil. The author quotes figures on experiments with the feeding of a mineral mixture which show that this method can be a rapid and efficient means of increasing beef production on phosphorus-deficient range.

Recently an acute, sometimes fatal disease of high-producing dairy cows, common in the intermountain areas of the United States, has been found to be associated with a marked drop in the phosphorus content of the blood. Characterized by anemia and other blood abnormalities, general weakness, blood-tinged urine, and other symptoms, it can apparently be prevented by liberal feeding of grain during the lactation period and regular use of a phosphorus-rich mineral supplement. Injections of dibasic sodium phosphate and drenches of this material or of bonemeal have been used successfully in treating the disease.

Calves fed rations low in magnesium develop acute symptoms characterized by temporary blindness and convulsions, as well as injuries to the blood vessels and heart. The trouble is not likely to occur unless the animals are fed too long on milk without supplementary feeds.

Grass tetany, a highly fatal disease of cattle recently turned out to good pasture, is characterized by a low blood content of magnesium and calcium, severe muscular spasms, violent cramps, and paralysis. Treatment, if it can be given in time, consists in injecting calcium and magnesium chloride into the veins. Prevention consists in improving winter rations and regulating pasture feeding early in the season.

It is extremely important that cattle have an ample supply of salt. When the ration of dairy cattle is deficient in sodium chloride, there is a decline in condition and in milk yield and a loss of appetite, along with other symptoms.

Iodine deficiency is largely a sectional problem. When the dam is deficient in this element, her calf may be still-born or be weak at birth and die within a few days, or it may be affected with a "big neck" (goiter) but appear normal otherwise.

"Salt sick" disease in Florida and "Grand Traverse" or "lake-shore" disease in Michigan have caused considerable losses among cattle in certain areas. A deficiency of cobalt or copper (and possibly iron and other minerals in some cases) is associated with these conditions, which may be identical and due primarily to anemia. In Michigan, cases have responded well to cobalt supplements in the ration; in Florida, a mineral mixture containing iron, copper, and cobalt is recommended.

The selenium and fluorine problems are discussed in the article on Nutritional Diseases of Farm Animals.

So far as is now known, vitamin A and vitamin D are the only vitamins that must be supplied in the feed of cattle. A deficiency of vitamin A is by far the more likely of the two to occur, and since it can be responsible for extensive losses, Madsen devotes considerable attention to it. Night blindness is one of the first symptoms that can be detected in adult animals, but, as the author points out, an animal may be getting enough vitamin A (or carotene) to prevent night blindness or other common symptoms and yet not nearly enough for normal reproduction and the birth of healthy calves. Calves severely deficient at birth are likely to have such symptoms as total blindness and convulsions and to survive only a short time. A watery swelling (anasarca) of the legs and forequarters characteristic of vitamin A deficiency has recently been observed in large numbers of fat cattle from the Corn Belt. The vitamin A problem should be in the forefront of the producer's planning of cattle rations, especially since animals may be critically low in this factor and yet appear to be in good condition.

Although many of the vitamins of the B complex are synthesized in the rumen of cattle, there is some evidence that the supply may not be sufficient to meet their needs under all circumstances—for example, in cases of infectious disease or intestinal parasitism. This point needs further research. Somewhat the same situation holds with vitamin C; recent work indicates that injections of this vitamin can in some cases markedly improve the breeding efficiency of both bulls and cows.

Evidence on the value of vitamin E in treating noninfectious barrenness in cattle in the United States is meager and conflicting.

Miscellaneous nutritional diseases discussed by Madsen include urinary calculi, bloat, and ketosis. In the case of urinary calculi, many factors are suspected; those that are nutritional in nature include vitamin A deficiency and a lack of balance between calcium, phosphorus, and magnesium intake. Bloat, a sporadic disease that often results in heavy losses, may be due, among other causes, to overeating or eating spoiled foods; Madsen discusses what is known about preventing and treating it, but points out that the problem needs further study. Ketosis, a disorder characterized by a high content of certain chemicals (ketone bodies) in the blood, urine, and milk, and a marked decline in milk flow, is an important problem in the dairy industry. Feeding corn sugar or molasses, increasing the grain allowance, and improving the quality of the hay fed or putting the animals on good pasture will be beneficial in treating and preventing this condition.

PART 5

DISEASES OF SWINE

Hog Cholera

To picture what hog cholera has done to the swine population during the great outbreaks of the past, imagine that some virulent disease were to wipe out 13 million or more people in the United States in a single year. As McBryde points out, up to 1914, when hog cholera began to be controlled, it cost swine growers an average of at least 20 million dollars every year.

The disease is highly infectious and contagious, appears suddenly, and usually runs an acute course, ending in death. The chief clinical symptoms are loss of appetite, fever, and great weakness; a post mortem examination generally shows striking changes in the lymph glands and other characteristic tissue injuries. In the North, severe outbreaks are largely confined to the late summer and fall, but they may occur at any season in the South.

The disease is spread by the secretions and excretions of infected animals; carcasses are also a menace and should be promptly rendered, burned, or buried deeply and covered with quicklime. Studies indicate that houseflies and stableflies may be important factors in disseminating hog cholera widely and rapidly. Since infection may be spread even during the incubation period, before visible symptoms appear, McBryde advises that all new hogs brought to the farm should be segregated and kept under observation for a period of 2 weeks. He also strongly emphasizes good sanitation and proper feeding as preventive measures.

There is no known drug that will cure or prevent the disease. The first big forward step in combating it was the discovery that it is caused by a virus, not by a bacillus, as was formerly thought to be the case. Following this discovery, the Bureau of Animal Industry succeeded in developing a preventive serum early in the 1900's. Prepared from the blood of hyperimmunized—that is, highly immunized—hogs, this serum gives an immunity lasting several weeks. If a small amount of virus or virulent blood is injected at the same time as the serum, however, the animal develops its own antibodies capable of fighting the virus, and the immunity thus produced usually lasts throughout its lifetime.

Simultaneous inoculation is now the method generally used in immunizing swine herds. The one great disadvantage is that for 2 or 3 weeks after vaccination the animal may suffer a set-back, its general resistance may be lowered, and it may fall a prey to such complications as infection by other disease germs or by intestinal parasites. In spite of such "breaks," immunization has been a tremendous boon to producers; many now make it a regular practice to have each year's pig crop vaccinated while the animals are small. The serum is produced commercially, and all that is made in establishments doing an interstate business is produced under strict supervision by the Bureau of Animal Industry.

In an effort to overcome the drawback mentioned, research workers recently discovered that if a certain aniline dye, crystal violet, is added to the virus and the mixture is incubated, the virus is so weakened that it produces no bad effects and yet creates an immunity which apparently lasts up to marketing age at least. This method is now being extensively tested. Since there is a lag of 2 or 3 weeks after vaccination before active immunity is produced by the crystal-violet vaccine, it probably cannot entirely supplant the older method, but it promises to be both cheaper and safer in many instances.

SWINE ERYSIPELAS

Schoening, Grey, and Osteen point out that swine erysipelas in its acute form appears suddenly and can run quickly through a herd, killing many of the hogs and making the rest unprofitable for market. Some of the typical symptoms in an acute outbreak are a scaly eczema, dryness, and red discoloration of the skin, patches of which may slough off; loss of pieces of the ears and tail; enlarged and evidently painful joints; swellings on the legs, ears, snout, and elsewhere; reluctance to move unless forcibly roused; and a high temperature. The disease may also take a low-grade, chronic form, characterized perhaps by a stubborn eczema or by swollen joints; or apparently healthy animals may harbor the organism in the tonsils, the intestines, or elsewhere.

Sheep, cattle, horses, dogs, turkeys, chickens, and ducks are all susceptible to swine erysipelas, as are human beings; handlers of livestock and livestock products are frequently infected. Fish-handler's disease, so-called, is due to the swine erysipelas organism, which has been found on the skin of many salt-water fish. Recent studies show that a large percentage of cases of swine arthritis—which has become widespread in recent years—may be due to erysipelas; at any rate the organism was recovered from more than three-fourths of 572 enlarged joints collected in 16 States.

The organism that causes swine erysipelas is a bacillus, long known to produce serious outbreaks of the disease in Europe but not definitely found in this country until about 20 years ago. The bacillus can live for a long time and apparently even propagate in certain soils, though it is rather easily destroyed by heat and by disinfectants. In acute cases, it is found in the blood and excretions of sick animals, so that their surroundings become contaminated, but exactly how the disease passes from animal to animal is not yet known. Because of certain difficulties in diagnosis, much attention has been given recently to the development of a serum test, and one is now available that, within limits, has proved to be of value when properly handled.

Control measures at present are somewhat uncertain. Chronic cases should be removed from the herd. Pens can readily be cleaned and disinfected, but this gives no assurance that the organism will not continue to exist somewhere in the soil and cause an outbreak later on. There is an anti-swine-erysipelas serum which will produce an immunity lasting 2 or 3 weeks, but it is effective only when given very early in the acute stage of the disease. In Europe the disease is combated much as hog cholera is in this country, by the use of a hyperimmune serum and a live culture given simultaneously, but the fear has been that the general use of this method in the United States might actually spread the disease in cases of mistaken diagnosis. A carefully planned large-scale experiment with this method is now being carried on, however, in certain sections where the disease is especially serious.

It is very important, in actual or suspected outbreaks of swine erysipelas, to get in touch with State and local veterinary services.

ENTERITIS OF SWINE

The term "enteritis" means an inflammation of the intestines, and there are many kinds of enteritis of swine, says Dale.

Necrotic enteritis, sometimes called paratyphoid and other names, is an infectious disease caused by a micro-organism known as *Salmonella choleraesuis*. The symptoms of the disease, often fatal, include a rise in temperature, diminished appetite, diarrhea, emaciation, weakness, and prostration. In the beginning stages, the malady is frequently mistaken for hog cholera, with very serious results; for hog cholera virus-serum inoculations may be given, and the virus and the *Salmonella* together make a deadly combination. Whenever necrotic enteritis could possibly be present in a herd, extreme precautions must be observed in hog cholera immunization.

There is no satisfactory cure for necrotic enteritis, but rigid sanitary measures such as those recommended for the control of roundworms will go a long way toward preventing it. When a vitamin deficiency is a complicating factor, as sometimes happens, the ration must be corrected.

Swine dysentery, also called black or bloody scours, and by other names, is another serious enteritis, responsible for much mortality among hogs. Acute and infectious, its outstanding symptom is a profuse bloody diarrhea. This disease, too, is especially deadly in combination with hog cholera and demands extra precautions in cholera immunization. No specific cause has been determined, but, in general, infected animals are found to have been directly or indirectly in contact with sales barns or public stockyards; and the disease frequently occurs in hogs following cattle. There is no satisfactory cure. Preventive measures must include a broad program of sanitation, separation of sick and healthy pigs, quarantine of newly purchased animals, and other measures. Both necrotic enteritis and dysentery call for the services of a veterinarian.

Young pigs are subject to an enteritis, called scours, which annually wipes out large numbers of them, especially during the first few days of life, and is responsible for much of the heavy loss—often 50 percent or more—that occurs on many farms. The trouble has been attributed to faulty nutrition (especially of the sows during the gestation period), poor housing, poor care, and lack of sanitation. If this is true, it would seem that farmers who neglect to follow good swine-husbandry practices are responsible for waste that affects the public as well as themselves.

Swine Influenza

Caused by the combined action of a virus and a germ, swine influenza is an acute, infectious, and highly contagious disease which, once started, spreads rapidly through a herd. Apparently improper housing and undue exposure to cold and dampness are predisposing factors. Sick animals, which should be given good care, usually recover rapidly after 5 or 6 days, but complications may retard recovery and increase the mortality from the disease. No medicinal remedy is known, and no vaccine is available for general use.

Swine influenza was first definitely described in 1919. Subsequent research on it has been closely associated with research on human influenza and has contributed a great deal to our present understanding of the human disease. For this reason, Dale describes the progress of the work in some detail. Some of the outstanding discoveries include the following:

(1) Swine influenza was successfully transmitted to healthy animals by instilling infected mucus into the nose (nasal instillation).

(2) A micro-organism, *Hemophilus influenzae suis*, was isolated from experimental cases but, when used alone, failed to produce the disease.

(3) Filtered material (virus), when used alone, produced only a mild form of the disease.

(4) Virus and the organism together produced typical swine influenza.

(5) Serum from the blood of pigs that had recovered from swine influenza neutralized the virus, or made it harmless.

(6) Serum from swine that had recovered from the virus disease alone neutralized a mixture of the virus and the organism.

(7) Intramuscular injection of the virus alone immunized pigs against true swine influenza without producing the disease.

(8) Virus from human cases produced influenza in ferrets, and when they recovered they were immune to the same strain of virus.

Serum from ferrets that had recovered neutralized the human virus. Human serum neutralized the human virus.

(9) Swine virus produced disease in ferrets. Ferrets that recovered from swine influenza were immune to human influenza, but the reverse was not true.

(10) Both the human and the swine virus produced disease in mice, which have since been used to test blood serum for antibodies.

(11) In mice, different strains of human virus acted differently in producing immunity against swine influenza. Mice immunized against swine influenza were resistant only to certain strains of the human virus.

(12) Serum from animals exposed several times instead of only once to either human or swine virus contained antibodies against both viruses.

(13) Human virus produced a mild disease in young pigs. When the virus and the swine influenza organism were mixed, the disease was more severe, but it was not quite the same as true swine influenza. (The human virus has not yet actually been isolated from swine in the field.)

(14) Lungworms were found to harbor the swine influenza virus and may act as reservoirs to carry it over from season to season. The infected worms did not produce the disease in swine except in late fall, winter, and spring.

(15) A mixture of swine virus and the hemorrhagic septicemia organism instilled intranasally into swine produced a disease like swine influenza.

MISCELLANEOUS DISEASES OF SWINE

Creech discusses more than a dozen different diseases or injuries of swine that for the most part are not covered elsewhere in this volume.

Swine pox is caused by two types of virus, and the disease is spread by lice. It seldom attacks pigs over 6 months old. Poxlike eruptions on the skin, starting as small reddened areas and developing into characteristic blisters, are the chief symptom; in acute cases there may also be dullness, weakness, loss of appetite, chills, and fever. There is no known cure for the disease, which may be disastrous to sucklings, especially if there are complications with other diseases. Sick pigs should be isolated and well cared for, and the hog houses and equipment should be thoroughly cleaned and disinfected. The best preventive is to eradicate lice according to the directions given in the article on that subject.

Infectious arthritis (*joint ill, or navel ill*) is a usually fatal disease of newly farrowed pigs due to infection of the navel at the time of birth by one or more of several different germs. The infection eventually spreads to the joints, causing arthritis. Symptoms usually include marked weakness and rapid emaciation. Since there is no known cure, prevention is extremely important. It consists for the most part in proper handling at the time of birth, disinfection of the navel, and, above all, the provision of strictly sanitary farrowing quarters.

Necrotic rhinitis (*bull nose, or sniffles*) is an infectious disease caused by a tissue-destroying micro-organism, usually picked up from filthy surroundings and gaining entrance through injuries around the mouth or nose. (A similar or identical disease of suckling pigs is called necrotic stomatitis, or infectious sore mouth.) Sneezing, swelling of the face and nose, and eventually extensive destruction of tissues are characteristic symptoms. In advanced cases the animals should be destroyed, but in the early stages the removal of puslike material and treatment with tincture of iodine may be effective. Good sanitation is the best preventive.

Goiter (*hairless pigs*) is discussed in the article on nutritional diseases of swine. It is due to iodine deficiency and can be prevented by supplying iodine to the pregnant sow.

Paralysis of the hindquarters (*posterior paralysis*) is evidenced first by a wobbly or unsteady gait and finally by complete inability to stand on the hind feet and dragging of the hindquarters. The condition may be due to any one of several causes, including vitamin and mineral deficiencies and infectious diseases and parasites. In other words, the paralysis is a symptom, and the cause is often very hard to discover: hence treatment is usually unsatisfactory. Perhaps the best preventive is a good diet.

Pneumonia, the result of irritation of the lung tissues, may also be due to several causes—dust and other foreign materials, disease germs, internal parasites. It is a very common accompaniment of other diseases. Chills, fever, and difficult breathing are common symptoms. One of the most important points about pneumonia in swine is to make sure whether or not it is accompanied by some other and perhaps more serious disease. Sick animals should be well cared for and specially fed. The best general preventive is good sanitation and care. In particular, hogs should not be allowed to become chilled in severe weather.

Mastitis (*mammitis, or garget*) is an inflammation of the udder caused by infection with various micro-organisms, which may enter through injured tissues. A general disturbance of the system may follow the original condition. Treatment in acute cases consists of hot and cold applications, a purgative, cleansing of wounds or sores, surgery of abscesses. Tumors caused by the ray fungus, by tuberculosis germs, or by botryomyces require surgery by a veterinarian.

Skin diseases discussed by Creech include: (1) Erythema. This is a diffuse reddening and itching which sometimes accompanies serious diseases and is sometimes due to external irritation. Proper sanitation, good feeding, and eradication of lice are the general preventives. (2) Urticaria (nettle rash). Equivalent to hives in human beings, this condition may be due to digestive disturbances or external irritation and filthy surroundings. (3) Eczema. This eruptive skin inflammation may be caused by improper feeding, an insanitary environment. and irritation by lice; or it may accompany more serious diseases. Prevention, of course, is related to these causes. (4) Sunburn. This affects light-colored hogs and can be prevented by supplying shade. (5) Freezing, or frostbite. Pigs farrowed in winter in the North and improperly housed may have their ears and tails frozen. Hogs in transit may also suffer frostbite.

In most of these cases of skin inflammation or injury, there are simple remedies, described by Creech, which will give relief.

Swine plague, or hemorrhagic septicemia, is an infectious disease caused by an organism known as *Pasteurella suiseptica.* In the United States it usually occurs as a complication with other diseases, particularly hog cholera, and chiefly affects the lungs, giving rise to pneumonia. Common symptoms include a high temperature, spasmodic cough, discharge of mucus, or mucus mixed with pus, from mouth and nose, loss of appetite, constipation, bloody diarrhea, and prostration. Death usually follows. Diagnosis is difficult, and a veterinarian should be consulted because of the danger of complications. There is no cure. Preventive serums, aggressins, and bacterins may be used, but the best preventive is good sanitation and care.

BRUCELLOSIS (INFECTIOUS ABORTION) OF SWINE

Recent surveys show that so far brucellosis in swine is much more limited in extent than brucellosis in cattle, but the disease is extremely important from a public health standpoint because (1) *Brucella suis,* the organism in hogs (discovered in 1914), causes a more severe type of undulant fever in human beings than does the Bang's disease organism of cattle; (2) half of the cases of human infection are due to the organism found in hogs; (3) human infection frequently occurs in swine-raising localities and in packing plants. Eichhorn concludes that definite, systematic measures to control or eradicate brucellosis of swine are amply justified.

The disease, which may cause sterility in boars as well as abortion in sows, is usually introduced into a herd of swine through the purchase of an infected animal. It spreads through contaminated feed and water and the eating of aborted fetuses and fetal membranes. Diagnosis is made by isolating the *Brucella* organism from infected animals, and also by a blood test, which, however, is not so reliable with swine as it is with cattle. Since there is no known cure for the disease, control measures are confined to prevention. Animals that react to the blood test should be eliminated, and subsequently the herd should be tested frequently until there is no positive or suspicious reaction. The sanitary measures recommended in the article on brucellosis of cattle should also be applied.

MANGE OF SWINE

Common mange of hogs, which is widespread in the United States, stunts the growth of young animals, delays fattening, and causes some deaths, the total penalty probably being about $2 an animal in infected herds. In addition, mangy hogs are usually docked 50 cents to $1.50 a hundredweight at the market. The aggregate losses due to common mange are very great every year. They are also unnecessary, since the disease can easily be eradicated; but as Imes points out, the methods used by many producers are not adequate.

The symptoms of common mange include itching, inflammation and swelling of the skin, the formation of vesicles that break and discharge serum, and eventually a thickening and folding of the skin. Final diagnosis must be based on actually finding the mites, which live in burrows in the skin.

Control measures include good sanitation and careful feeding, cleaning up infected premises and disinfecting them with a coal-tar-creosote preparation, and treating the whole herd if any of the animals become mangy. (Incidentally, the sarcoptic or common mange mite is transmissible to human beings; hence after handling mangy hogs, the operator should bathe and change clothing.) Treatment consists in dipping the hogs in unprocessed crude oil, processed oils—of which crankcase drainings are probably the cheapest—or lime-sulfur dip. Imes describes the methods of applying the dips in considerable detail. If a commercial or home-made dipping vat is not used, oil may be floated on top of the water in a properly constructed hog wallow.

In addition to sarcoptic mange, hogs are subject to demodectic mange, caused by a different mite. This disease spreads much more slowly in the herd than common mange, and it cannot be cured except at an unjustifiable expense. Hence any animal found to be affected by demodectic mange should be promptly disposed of or killed, the premises should be disinfected, and the rest of the herd should be dipped as a precautionary measure.

Hog Lice

The female hog louse lays her eggs on hog bristles, chiefly back of the ears and around the shoulders, neck, and flanks. She also travels along a bristle to get to another hog in contact with her original host. The hog louse is large—about a quarter of an inch long—and it makes a fresh puncture in the skin every time it feeds. The punctures often become raw spots that serve as centers of infection by other parasites, and constant irritation by lice puts the hogs off feed and makes them lose condition. For both financial and humanitarian reasons, then, these insects should be controlled.

The methods of control, described by Babcock and Cushing, are easy and inexpensive. (1) Use crude petroleum—either natural or processed crude oil—in a dipping vat or a simple concrete hog wallow, such as is used for mange. If a heavy processed oil is used, dilute it with not over 20 percent of distillate oil. (2) If there are too few hogs to justify a dip or vat, apply the crude oil by hand with a brush, mop, or cloth. (3) Or apply kerosene emulsion by hand (not in a vat or wallow). To make the emulsion, dissolve ½ pound of soap in 1 gallon of warm water. Add 2 gallons of kerosene, mixing thoroughly to form an emulsion. Dilute this with 11 gallons of soft water. In all hand applications, distribute the insecticide evenly over the head and body, paying special attention to the armpits and the inside of the ears.

Keep freshly oiled hogs quiet and in the shade for at least 48 hours. Do not expose them to direct sunlight or allow them to become chilled or force them to move rapidly.

Internal Parasites of Swine

As in the case of all livestock, internal parasites are a constant drain on the vitality of swine and hence a menace to full production as well as to the profits of the producer. In addition to causing death and general unthriftiness, Spindler points out, they are responsible for a rather extensive condemnation of parts of carcasses in packing houses. There are two methods of combating them—treatment with worm medicines, and the use of carefully worked out management practices to prevent infection. In the case of swine (not necessarily of other animals), the second is by far the more important and effective. Like a military campaign, it must be based on a knowledge of the activities and the weak points of the enemy, hence the importance of scientific studies of the life histories of parasites.

Spindler first discusses the three great groups of worm parasites—tapeworms, flukes, and roundworms.

The tapeworms occur in swine only in the larval, not the adult stages. These larvae resemble swollen bladders; hence they are called bladder worms. Three kinds are important. (1) The pork bladder worm, which invades the muscles and may occur in nerve tissues of swine, is the larva of a tapeworm that infects human beings. The latter excrete the worm eggs, which are then picked up by swine. Only a very small percentage of pigs are infected in the United States. (2) The hydatid is the larva of a tapeworm that infests dogs and wolves. These animals pass the eggs, which are then picked up by swine. The chief point of attack in swine is the liver; other internal organs may also be involved. Human beings can also be infected by these worms in the larval stage. (3) The thin-necked bladder worm is the larva of a tapeworm of dogs. It attacks the liver and abdominal organs of swine and may be fatal to young pigs.

The lung flukes and the liver flukes are more important as enemies of other animals than of swine.

Roundworms are the largest and most important group of worms infesting swine. Spindler discusses 10 different kinds.

(1) The gullet worm, which attacks the gullet and tongue, lives part of its life in certain dung beetles and cockroaches, which pick up the eggs from manure. Swine, in turn, eat the infected insects. Human beings can also be infected with these or similar worms. (2) Two species of thick stomach worms are very important parasites of swine. They live part of their lives in dung beetles, and under certain conditions one of them can also be transmitted to swine through birds, snakes, and other reptiles. The red stomach worm does not live in an intermediate host but infests the soil directly from contaminated swine droppings. (3) Intestinal threadworms also are picked up directly from contaminated soil. The larvae penetrate the skin or are swallowed, get into the blood stream, reach the lungs and then the throat, are swallowed again, and finally pass to the small intestine. In a larval stage, these worms can penetrate the skin of human beings. (4) Four species of nodular worms, the commonest worm parasites of swine in some sections of the United States, attack the blind gut and large intestine, where they produce lumps, or nodules, in which the young

worms live for a time. The infective larvae are picked up directly from soil contaminated by droppings. (5) Whipworms inhabit the blind gut and large intestine, and the eggs are picked up directly from soil infected by droppings. (6) Lungworms are widespread parasites of swine, do great damage to young pigs, and may help to spread swine influenza. They live part of their lives in various species of earthworms, which pick up the eggs from swine droppings. Then pigs eat the earthworms. (7) The kidney worm causes heavy losses in the South and may now be spreading northward. These worms become embedded in the kidneys and ureters, sometimes after considerable migrating in the body, and immense numbers of eggs are passed in the urine of infected swine. The larvae are picked up by the pigs from contaminated soil, and under certain conditions they can also penetrate the skin. The growth of infested animals is often markedly stunted. (8) The hookworm, which infests the small intestine and may cause hemorrhages, is picked up in a larval stage from contaminated soil.

(9) Thorn-headed worms, which may reach a length of 12 inches or more, attach themselves to the wall of the small intestine by means of spines on the head. Eggs are passed in the droppings of swine and picked up by white grubs (insect larvae), which in turn are eaten by swine. (10) Ascarids, or large intestinal roundworms, are very common and widespread swine parasites. They wander extensively in the body but tend to become localized as adults in the small intestine. A full-grown female may contain more than 25 million eggs, which are passed in huge numbers in the droppings of infected swine; the eggs are sticky enough to adhere wherever they fall. Even light infections can stunt animals; heavy infections can kill them.

So much for the worm parasites. Spindler also discusses four kinds of protozoa that are parasites of swine, though less is known about them than about the worms. Of these, (1) the amoebae parasitize the intestine and are said to cause dysentery and other disorders, just as similar protozoa do in human beings. (2) The balantidia probably have the same effect. (3) Coccidia invade the intestinal lining and produce an extensive destruction of tissues. (4) The *Sarcocystis* is common in garbage-fed hogs, invading the muscles and producing cysts which may appear as white specks.

Spindler points out that only three kinds of swine parasites can really be effectively removed by worm medicines—ascarids, nodular worms, and stomach worms; but it is worth while to treat swine for these worms. The treatment should be carried out by a veterinarian. The drugs chiefly used are chenopodium, santonin, hexylresorcinol, phenothiazine, and carbon disulfide. Removal of worms, of course, is no insurance against reinfection.

Two plans for swine management to avoid infection by parasites are discussed in considerable detail. The object of both is to break the life cycle of the parasites at its weakest point, the stage outside the host animal, and to build up the resistance of the animals by good nutrition.

The McLean County system of sanitation was first tried out extensively in McLean County, Ill., about 20 years ago. Essentially, it consists of the following procedures, each of which is the result of careful experimenting and should be carefully followed:

(1) Before the sows farrow, clean the farrowing pens thoroughly and scrub them with scalding water and lye. Then close them until farrowing time and allow no one to enter. Shut off any outside pens with dirt floors so they cannot be used by the pigs. (2) Clean the sows with soap and water just before they are placed in the farrowing pens. After farrowing do not allow the sows or pigs out of the pens. Keep the pens clean and sanitary. (3) Haul—do not drive—the pigs to a clean pasture. A stoneboat and crates may be used. (4) Keep the young pigs in a clean pasture until they are at least 4 months old. This should not be a permanent pasture but one that has been cultivated and sown to a forage crop. In the pasture provide an individual shelter house for each sow and her litter. Allow no other hogs to get into the pasture and do not let the pigs out.

Careful records of the results of following this system show that it affords about 98 percent protection against parasitic and associated diseases, reduces the loss of pigs to about 24 percent instead of the 50 percent usual under a nonsanitary system, and permits the marketing of pigs as much as 7 weeks earlier.

The second system was devised to meet the special needs of producers in the Southeast, where kidney worms are a major hazard, and it is based on a close study of the habits of this parasite. It involves the following steps:

(1) Shortly before farrowing, put the sows in a specially prepared pasture, plowed and seeded after it was last used by hogs. (2) In sowing, leave a bare strip at least 5 feet wide on three sides of the pasture and 30 feet wide on the fourth side. On this wide bare strip place the farrowing or shelter houses, water barrel, creep for pigs, and feeding pen for sows. (3) Keep the bare strip on all four sides free of all trash, litter, and vegetation, cultivating it from time to time if necessary. (4) Place the creep for pigs and the feeding pen for sows some distance apart on the wide bare area and arrange the sow feeding pen so that the pigs cannot have access to it. (5) Arrange the water barrel so that it cannot overflow and wet the soil. (6) Place the farrowing houses—one for each sow—on the wide bare area some distance apart, about 6 feet from the fence and facing it. Allow no trash or litter to accumulate around them.

Spindler shows the part played by each of these steps in kidney worm control. Analysis shows that the system results in the raising of more pigs, better and more economical gains, a saving of 3 weeks or more in time of marketing, larger dressing percentages, and the passing, by inspectors, of nearly all livers and kidneys for food in contrast with the condemnation of about 92 percent of the livers and 100 percent of the kidneys in hogs raised without any attempt to prevent infection by parasites.

Under both these systems good feeding is essential in addition to the sanitary practices outlined.

TRICHINOSIS

Trichinosis is a serious disease of human beings acquired by eating raw or partially cooked pork infested with trichinae. The minute immature forms of these roundworms are carried by the lymph and the blood stream from the intestines to all parts of the body, finally settling down chiefly in the muscles, where they become enclosed in small, hard cysts. About 5 percent of the human cases are fatal. The symptoms are so easily confused with those of other diseases that mistaken diagnoses have been common, and supposed cases of typhoid, undulant fever, influenza, nephritis, tuberculous meningitis, gastroenteritis, colitis, rheumatic endocarditis, syphilis, and tuberculosis have turned out to be trichinosis. Recent investigations have shown that there is a high percentage of infection in the urban population of the United States—from 14 to 27 percent in unselected post mortem examinations; but only a small proportion of these are severe enough to produce any symptoms of trichinosis.

The disease is obviously important from a public health standpoint, and that is the angle from which Schwartz considers it. He tells how trichinae were first discovered in human muscles when an English medical student in 1835 came on small gritty particles that dulled his scalpel while he was dissecting; how an American scientist in 1846 found trichinae in pork he was eating; and how three German scientists in 1860 discovered that a woman who had supposedly died of typhoid had really died of trichinosis acquired from uncooked sausage. These were three of the steps that gradually disclosed the nature of the disease. During the investigations that followed it was found that a considerable number of animals, including rats and mice, harbor the parasite; cases of human trichinosis have been traced to the eating of the improperly cooked meat of bears and other animals.

As a safeguard against trichinosis, some countries require that samples of pork be examined microscopically for trichinae at the packing plant. Schwartz shows that this method is very uncertain of results as well as being expensive; sometimes infected pork has to be examined 20 or 30 times before the trichinae are discovered, and one study made over a long period of years showed that about a third of more than 6,000 cases of human trichinosis resulted from eating pork that had been inspected microscopically and passed as trichina-free.

To determine what percentage of hogs in the United States are infected, a much more accurate test has been developed. This consists in digesting the diaphragms of hogs in artificial gastric juice in an incubator and counting the number of trichinae remaining in the digestive juice. By this method, tests were made with large numbers of hogs, beginning in 1933. Of the farm-raised hogs, less than 1 percent were found to be infected, and about two-thirds of these contained the parasites in very small numbers. Of the garbage-fed hogs (which presumably had access to scraps of fresh pork) well over 6 percent were found to be infected, and in two-thirds of these the infections were more or less extensive. But among hogs fed cooked garbage, about one-half of 1 percent were found to be infected, and these only slightly.

Schwartz's conclusions:

There is no known practical method of inspecting hogs for trichinae.

Under Federal meat-inspection requirements, all pork in meat products intended to be used without cooking, or the products themselves, must be so treated by heating, special refrigeration, or special processing that any trichinae they might contain are killed. Only about 60 percent of the hogs consumed in this country are slaughtered in federally inspected plants.

All fresh pork and ordinary cured pork not specially prepared in this way under the eyes of trained inspectors should be thoroughly cooked. Proper cooking makes the pork absolutely safe.

In the case of garbage-fed hogs, garbage—or at least all pork scraps in it—should be sterilized by heat before being fed. This might be accomplished by voluntary action or through State and municipal laws.

To safeguard hogs on the farm from getting trichinosis, the farmer should not feed offal or any scraps containing raw pork, should not throw dead rats and mice into hogpens, and should burn or bury deeply in quicklime the carcasses of hogs and other animals that have died.

Salt Tolerance and Salt Poisoning of Swine

The amount of salt required by hogs is known to be small as compared with the amounts required by other livestock, but evidence regarding the amounts that are actually poisonous to the animals has been somewhat conflicting. Ellis undertakes to review the scattered work that has been done in this field and gives the hitherto unpublished results of recent experiments at the Beltsville Research Center, Beltsville, Md. In the Beltsville work some of the pigs received relatively enormous quantities of salt—in one case, as much as 20 percent of the ration for a period of 4 weeks—yet there was only one instance, an animal fed salt at a level of 8 percent of the ration, in which there were apparent signs of severe poisoning, beginning on the eighty-sixth day of the experiment. Nor did pigs starved for salt for a preliminary period suffer any ill effects when they were later given free access to salt.

There is very little danger, Ellis concludes, that the use of the animal protein supplements and mineral mixtures ordinarily fed in this country will lead to salt hunger. On the other hand, it does not seem likely, from the evidence he presents, that even relatively large amounts of sodium chloride, per se, will poison hogs. The danger seems to lie in giving pigs waste salt products such as old pickling brine or salt contaminated with other substances; these other substances in the brine or dry mixture may be severely poisonous.

Nutritional Diseases of Swine

As Madsen points out, nutritional diseases of swine can make economical production impossible and cause considerable mortality. Controlling these diseases is one of the first essentials of successful swine husbandry.

The protein concentrates ordinarily fed to hogs are good sources of phosphorus but not of calcium, which may be deficient in the ration. When the animals are confined indoors and fed largely on grains, without good sun-cured roughage and with no access to sunlight, they may also be short of vitamin D. The result is likely to be rickets, a bone disease that weakens the young pigs and possibly makes them susceptible to other diseases. Sunlight and high-grade sun-cured legume hay are the best sources of vitamin D, but in the North in winter it may be advisable also to use some such source as fish oil. Several feeds, listed by Madsen, are good sources of calcium. The author suggests four different mineral mixtures that may be used as supplements with different kinds of rations.

An abundant supply of calcium is especially necessary for breeding animals. When brood sows are deficient in calcium, farrowing is difficult, the milk supply is low, and the few pigs that survive at weaning time are likely to be weak and unthrifty. Though a phosphorus deficiency is not very common in swine, it may occur when they are grazed on pasture or cultivated root crops, with little or no grain or suitable supplements.

One of the chief causes of unthriftiness and death among young swine, especially those farrowed in late fall, winter, or early spring and kept confined without access to soil or vegetation, is nutritional anemia, resulting from a lack of iron and copper. Young pigs need a regular supply of these minerals beginning shortly after birth. It may be furnished in various ways, including drenching the pigs or swabbing the udder of the sow with a mineral solution.

Iodine deficiency is discussed in Nutritional Diseases of Farm Animals.

A lameness like that of rickets but apparently due to a manganese deficiency has occurred in pigs fed certain rations. Wheat and oats are usually higher in this mineral than is corn.

Like other animals, swine are subject to fluorine poisoning, and they are apparently even more susceptible to selenium poisoning than are horses and cattle.

Vitamin A deficiency occurs most commonly in swine fed in the dry lot without sufficient feeds that are good sources of this vitamin. The serious results of such a deficiency include irregularity in breeding behavior, abortion, the birth of dead or weak pigs, and failure in lactation. It is extremely important to feed sows and young growing swine rations that will enable them to store up reserves of vitamin A. Madsen discusses the feeds that are especially good sources.

Among the various B vitamins, a deficiency of thiamin has been produced only experimentally; though the requirement for reproduction and lactation is high, the vitamin is not likely to be deficient on a ration including plenty of whole cereal grains or pasture and well-cured legume forage. A deficiency of riboflavin, resulting in severe symptoms, has also been produced experimentally; skim milk, buttermilk, and whey are high in this vitamin, and yellow corn is a fair source. Nicotinic acid deficiency, according to recent experimental work, may be a factor in susceptibility to necrotic enteritis, which causes widespread losses among swine; further investigations are needed on this point. A deficiency of pyridoxine (vitamin B_6) has produced epileptic fits and a certain type of anemia in swine, according to recent experiments, but the vitamin is not likely to be lacking in ordinary swine rations. Pantothenic acid deficiency has been found to produce a degeneration of the sheath of the nerve fibers in young swine, resulting in muscular incoordination. A similar disorder that occurs in swine under farm conditions is of considerable economic importance, and experiments indicate that pantothenic acid deficiency is perhaps the chief cause. Dry heat treatment of swine feeds apparently destroys the vitamin, and in addition many common feeds apparently contain insufficient amounts.

Madsen discusses a highly fatal disease of newborn pigs apparently due to a marked lowering of blood sugar, which in turn is probably caused by failure to get enough food during the first few days after birth. Affected pigs can usually be saved in the early stages by injections of glucose and hand feeding. Suggested preventive measures include liberal feeding of sows and gilts throughout pregnancy and close watching of newborn pigs to make sure they get enough food and do not become chilled.

PART 6

DISEASES OF SHEEP AND GOATS

FOOT ROT OF SHEEP

Foot rot is sometimes a major disease of sheep (and occasionally of goats), especially where crowded corrals or pastures are used. It is caused by infection of the hoofs, though authorities do not yet agree on the specific organism involved; several different micro-organisms have been found to be associated with the disease. Starting with lameness, redness, swelling, and intense pain around the hoofs, the symptoms may progress until even the bones and joints become involved. Sometimes animals seem to recover spontaneously, but the infection remains.

The treatment described by Shahan is effective but should be carried out by a veterinarian. It consists in (1) segregating all animals showing symptoms; (2) carefully trimming the hoofs and cutting away all dead tissue; (3) disinfecting the feet with a suitable antiseptic, usually copper sulfate (bluestone), which must be handled with caution. For a few sheep, a bucket may be used for dipping the feet; large numbers are usually driven through a shallow trough containing the antiseptic. The nature and strength of the antiseptic and the length of time the sheep should stand in it depend on the severity of the disease.

Prevention, of course, is better than cure. Shahan advises such measures as (1) quarantining newly purchased sheep for at least a month; (2) perhaps selling all infected sheep for slaughter under inspection instead of treating them; (3) thoroughly cleaning and disinfecting barns, sheds, corrals, etc., used by infected sheep; (4) taking special precautions after handling infected sheep; (5) draining muddy corrals and wet pastures if possible; (6) removing healthy sheep to fresh ground and keeping them off infected pastures for 1 to 4 months, depending on the location and season.

Sore Mouth of Sheep and Goats

A highly contagious disease caused by a virus, sore mouth usually attacks animals less than a year old, producing raw sores, chiefly around the mouth. Occasionally older animals are infected, and the sores may appear elsewhere, notably on the udders of nursing dams. Subsequent bacterial infection may occur, with a high mortality, or the sores may become infested with screwworms. The chief damage from uncomplicated sore mouth comes from serious interference with feeding, which causes loss of weight and failure to grow. The disease is also known as contagious ecthyma.

Within recent years an effective vaccine has been developed. Applied much like smallpox vaccine, it confers immunity for several months to 2 years or longer. In range areas where the disease is known to prevail, vaccination may be done at the time of marking; in the case of feed-lot sheep, it should be done at least 10 days before the animals are shipped. As Shahan points out, it should be left to the veterinarian to decide whether vaccination should be used in any given case, or whether isolation of affected animals and disinfection of the premises are sufficient. Medicinal aid is seldom required and is rarely practical; the chief aim, after a case occurs, should be to prevent bacterial and screwworm infections.

Miscellaneous Diseases of Sheep and Goats

Shahan discusses some 36 or more diseases and injuries that affect sheep and goats, for the most part those not discussed elsewhere in the Yearbook. They can be little more than mentioned in this brief summary. Many of them are largely preventable by good management, especially sanitation.

Diseases of the digestive organs: (1) Bloat, an accumulation of gas in the stomach or intestines, resulting from the consumption of damaged or unsuitable feeds, is dangerous in an acute form and must then be treated practically by first-aid methods. (2) Constipation resulting from impaction of foodstuffs can be relieved by drugs, water, laxatives, and manipulation. (3) Diarrhea may be due to any one of many different causes, discussed under other diseases. (4) Enterotoxemia, or intestinal poisoning, probably the most frequent cause of losses of lambs in western feed lots, results from the overeating of concentrates or lush forage. Prevention is a matter of good management; treatment is seldom successful.

Diseases of the respiratory system: (5) Hemorrhagic septicemia, or shipping fever, attacks sheep and goats as well as cattle. It is discussed briefly by Shahan and at length elsewhere in this volume. (6) Nasal catarrh, or snuffles, is common in sheep but seldom serious unless it is a symptom of some severe disease, in which case control and treatment depend on the cause.

Diseases of the nervous system: (7) Listerellosis, or circling disease, is a severe, incurable, usually fatal inflammation of the brain caused by infection with *Listerella* organisms. (8) Rabies, discussed elsewhere in this volume, is brought to sheep and goats, as to other

animals, by the bites of rabid dogs. (9) Meningitis, an inflammation
of the lining membranes (meninges) of the central nervous system,
may be produced in sheep by infection with any one of several
micro-organisms, including *Staphylococci* and *Streptococci*. Treatment is almost never practical. (10) Paralysis is usually an accompaniment of one of the infections of the central nervous system, but
it may sometimes be due to the bites of certain ticks or to injuries
to the spine.

Diseases of the skin: (11) Purulent dermatitis is due to invasion
of the skin by pus-forming micro-organisms that enter through injuries or wounds. In severe cases, general poisoning of the system
may result. (12) Ringworm, caused by various fungi, is relatively
rare in sheep. (13) Sheep pox, which is similar to but not identical
with smallpox in man, has not become established in the United
States. (14) Actinobacillosis, an infectious disease caused by micro-
organisms that enter through small punctures or cuts, is discussed
at length elsewhere in the Yearbook under Miscellaneous Diseases of
Cattle.

Diseases connected with reproduction: (15) Abortion in sheep is
rarely due to *Brucella* organisms, but it may be caused by any one of
several other infections as well as by damaged feeds, injury, undernourishment, and various diseases. Goats may contract brucellosis
or other infections causing abortion. (16) Pregnancy toxemia includes pregnancy disease of sheep and also milk fever. Both are
discussed elsewhere in the Yearbook, the latter under the diseases of
cattle. (17) Metritis is an inflammation of the uterus due to any
one of various infections. It is associated with abortion or with
difficult birth and may spread like wildfire, often causing death or
loss of fertility. The preventive is to control abortion and use strict
sanitary procedures during lambing. (18) Mastitis, or inflammation
of the udder, may be due to any one of several types of infection.
It may be fatal or lead to partial or complete loss of ability to nurse
young. Prevention demands strict sanitary measures, particularly
in goat dairies. (19) Prolapsis is a misplacement or eversion of the
vagina or uterus, due to severe strain or rough handling during
lambing. It is fatal if treatment, which consists largely of careful
manipulation, is delayed until general intoxication sets in from
stoppage of body functions. (20) Venereal infection of the male
or female genital organs in sheep is primarily due to a virus. Antiseptic treatment is generally beneficial if begun early. Control demands thorough sanitary measures. (21) Orchitis, or inflammation
of the testicles, caused by injury, excessive service, or infection, may
be fatal or lead to impotence. Treatment and control depend on the
cause; where a definite infection has been identified, bacterins or
other biological products may be useful.

Diseases of the eye: (22) Wool blindness, caused by wool growing
close to the eyes, may be prevented by breeding sheep without this
characteristic and by suitable trimming. (23) Entropion, an inversion of the eyelid over the eyeball, is treated by surgery. It may be
hereditary and hence avoidable by controlled breeding. (24) Foreign

bodies may become imbedded in the eye tissues. They should be removed and suitable treatment should be given. (25) Infectious keratitis, or pink eye, which sometimes spreads rapidly in a flock, causes acute inflammation and may end in blindness. It demands isolation and careful treatment of affected animals.

Other infectious diseases: (26) Arthritis, or inflammation of the joints, probably most common in lambs and rare in goats, is usually caused by infection of the navel stump at birth, or of wounds caused by castration, docking, shearing, or ear-marking. Pus-forming organisms or the swine erysipelas organism are usually involved. Acute cases may be rapidly fatal; others may become chronic. Prevention depends on the use of proper sanitary measures and disinfection. (27) Black disease (infectious necrotic hepatitis) is an acute malady of mature sheep due to infection of the liver by a specific germ which accompanies infestation by liver flukes. Affected animals sometimes die overnight without any sign of illness, and recovery is rare. Prevention depends on the control of flukes. (28) Caseous lymphadenitis is a widespread chronic disease chiefly affecting the lymph glands; it is caused by a bacillus that may enter the body in various ways. There is no practical treatment. Prevention depends partly on good sanitation. (29) Paratyphoid dysentery, caused by infection with a *Salmonella* organism, is comparatively rare in sheep and can probably be largely prevented by proper care of animals during shipment. (30) Lamb dysentery, or white scours, is a disease of very young animals that may kill 20 to 40 percent of the lamb crop in severe outbreaks. It is essentially filth-borne and is attributed to any one of several micro-organisms. Medicinal treatment is usually useless. Prevention depends on strict sanitation and good management. (31) Johne's disease, or paratuberculosis, is discussed under Diseases of Cattle, and requires the same kind of control meaures when it occurs in sheep as when it occurs in cattle. (32) Necrobacillosis is caused by a tissue-killing organism that enters through wounds or very commonly through the lesions produced by other diseases. As a secondary invader, it may greatly complicate the primary malady. Treatment is often unsatisfactory. Strict sanitation is the best preventive. (33) Wound infections, as the author points out, cause enormous losses that could be largely prevented by proper care and disinfection during various operations and in lambing. Many micro-organisms can infect wounds, and some, such as those that cause malignant edema, lockjaw, and blackleg, are very deadly.

Miscellaneous noninfectious diseases: (34) Goiter, a nutritional disease caused by lack of iodine, is briefly discussed here and in more detail elsewhere in the Yearbook. (35) Urinary calculi (sand, gravel) are mineral aggregations in the kidneys, ureters, bladder, or urethra. Unless the condition is relieved, it causes death, but treatment is generally not practicable. (36) Stiff lambs (white muscle disease) is a peculiar degeneration of the muscles, usually affecting winter or early spring lambs. The cause is unknown, and there is no successful treatment, but the trouble can be prevented to some extent by good feeding and management.

INTERNAL PARASITES OF SHEEP AND GOATS

Dikmans and Shorb deal in considerable detail with some 40 internal parasites of sheep and goats, classified as protozoa (minute, one-celled animals), flukes, tapeworms, and roundworms. These parasites attack many parts of the body, including the esophagus, rumen, abomasum, small intestine, cecum, colon, trachea, bronchi, carotid and mesenteric arteries, tear ducts, liver, bile ducts, mesentery, brain and spinal cord, lungs, and voluntary muscles. In general they are a greater menace in the farm areas than in the range areas, partly because of greater crowding in the former, partly because of climatic conditions.

Of the four main groups mentioned, flukes, tapeworms, and some protozoa spend part of their lives in an intermediate host. Most roundworms, on the other hand, do not; they live on the ground during the stages when they are not in the principal host. Only at a certain stage of their development on the ground can roundworm larvae infect sheep and goats.

The symptoms of parasitic infection are usually complicated because more than one species of parasite is present at the same time. In a few experiments it has been possible to bring about "pure" infections with one parasite only, and these have thrown considerable light on symptoms. In general the typical symptoms of worm infestation include unthriftiness, loss of weight, diarrhea, anemia, potbelly, and bottle jaw.

Two types of protozoa are discussed by these authors. (1) Coccidia attack the wall of the small intestine. In a resting, or spore, state (oöcysts) they are discharged in the droppings. Probably almost all lambs become infested; light infestations seem to do little harm, but severe ones result in marked symptoms and may be fatal. There is evidence that heavy infestations can be built up in feed lots if feed is handled in such a way that the lambs can continually recontaminate it. Lowered resistance from various causes, as well as heavy infestations, may have much to do with the severity of the symptoms of coccidiosis. (2) A protozoan (*Globidium gilruthi*) for which there is no common name occurs in the fourth stomach and small intestine of sheep, causing severe symptoms only when the infestation is heavy.

Two kinds of flukes occur in the liver and two in the rumen, or paunch. Eggs of flukes pass out in the droppings and hatch in water. The embryonic flukes then enter snails and develop to a larval stage. Leaving the snails, the larvae, now enclosed in a cyst, attach themselves to vegetation and are swallowed by grazing animals.

The common liver fluke, which infests the liver, bile duct, and gall bladder, is one of the worst parasitic enemies of sheep, severe infestations sometimes causing death in a few days. Common symptoms include loss of condition, anemic-looking mucous membranes, stiff gait, swellings under the jaw, potbelly. The liver may be greatly damaged. The large American liver fluke, another species, is primarily a parasite of deer, but when it attacks sheep it causes severe symptoms. The rumen flukes, which infest the paunch, have life histories like that of the common liver fluke, but under natural conditions they apparently do not parasitize sheep in the United States.

Several species of tapeworms infest sheep, some as mature worms, some as larvae, a stage in which they are called bladder worms.

Two common adult tapeworms (moniezias) that infest the small intestine pass part of their lives in the bodies of beetle mites, which take up the eggs contained in sheep droppings. Experiments indicate that these tapeworms in themselves do not have such serious effects on lambs as they are usually believed to have. The effects are serious, however, when other parasites are present at the same time.

The adult fringed tapeworm infests the small intestine, bile duct, gall bladder, and sometimes the pancreatic duct. Nothing is known about its life history and little about its effects on sheep.

A bladder worm does not look like an adult tapeworm but like a sac into which the head of the worm is inserted. The sacs may be very large, sometimes several inches long. The adult tapeworms infest dogs and related animals, which void the eggs. Sheep pick up the eggs from contaminated ground.

In sheep the thin-necked bladder worm starts in the liver but eventually attaches itself to certain abdominal membranes; severe infestations make an animal very sick and may be fatal. Another bladder worm, which primarily infests the heart, diaphragm, and various muscles, causes a condition known as sheep measles, which is usually not serious but makes infested meat subject to condemnation in meat-packing plants. The gid bladder worm, sometimes larger than a hen's egg, infests the brain and less often the spinal cord, causing severe nervous disturbances, brain fever, and death. Another bladder worm, the hydatid, usually attacks the liver and lungs but may be found almost anywhere in the body, including the heart and brain. The symptoms depend on the location and size of the parasites.

Except where liver flukes are prevalent, Dikmans and Shorb point out, the roundworms are the most serious parasites of sheep and goats. There are many kinds, infesting different parts of the body.

The most serious of the roundworms in its effects (and therefore the most serious of all sheep parasites) is the twisted stomach worm, which infests the abomasum, or fourth stomach. The eggs of this worm pass out with the droppings, and the infective larvae, which are quite resistant to unfavorable climatic conditions except drought, are taken up by sheep with contaminated feed and water. Symptoms in severe cases include great weakness, anemia, and bottle jaw; sudden death sometimes occurs following a heavy infestation acquired in a short period of time.

A number of smaller worms, called small trichostrongyles, infest the abomasum and small intestine. The larvae of some of these worms are able to survive long periods of drought and resume their development on pastures as soon as moisture becomes available. Essentially, they cause a slow, protracted disease of young animals, characterized by unthriftiness, diarrhea, and anemia. Death may result from a severe infestation.

The sheep hookworm enters the body by way of the mouth but can also penetrate the skin. It extracts blood from the animal and also secretes a substance that destroys red corpuscles and prevents coagulation, so that prolonged internal hemorrhages may occur at the points where the worms have been attached. Anemia, dropsical swellings, and unthriftiness are common effects of hookworm infestation.

The thread-necked strongyles, which also infest the small intestine, are apparently not of great importance as disease producers except when the infestations are very large.

A number of roundworms infest the cecum, or blind gut, and the colon. The whipworm apparently causes no marked visible symptoms in sheep. The nodular worm, on the other hand, produces nodules, or lumps, throughout the length of the intestine, making them unfit for sausage casings and surgical-suture material, and can cause severe clinical symptoms. The large-mouthed bowel worm, which infests the colon, may produce diarrhea, slow growth, and cause weakness and emaciation, but usually these symptoms gradually disappear.

Two roundworms—the thread lungworm and the hair lungworm—infest the respiratory tract. They lay their eggs in the lungs. The larvae develop, are coughed up and swallowed, and pass out with the droppings. The larvae of the thread lungworm develop to an infective stage on the ground, are swallowed by grazing sheep, bore through the small intestine, and reach the lungs by way of the lymph stream. The irritation caused by these worms produces a cough, and heavy infestations may result in suffocation, bronchitis, pneumonia, and death. The larvae of the hair lungworm penetrate into and develop in certain species of snails. Infested sheep do not show the marked symptoms that result from infection by the thread lungworm.

Certain small roundworms parasitize the eyes of ruminants, and one has been reported in sheep, causing abnormal sensitiveness to light, profuse watering of the eyes, and perhaps more severe symptoms. A careful examination of the eye will reveal the worms, and they can be removed mechanically.

Roundworms also occur in the circulatory system. The adults produce no known symptoms, but their larvae, or immature stages, are reported to cause an inflammation of the skin.

Medication and preventive measures are both important in controlling the parasites of sheep and goats, these authors point out.

There is no specific medicinal treatment for coccidiosis. Affected animals should be isolated, soiled feed or other material should be burned or otherwise disposed of, and the premises should be cleaned and disinfected. Feed should be so handled as not to become constantly contaminated.

The medicine commonly used to rid sheep of adult flukes is carbon tetrachloride. Occasionally it is toxic, and it should be used with the precautions outlined by the authors. Fluke infestations can be effectively reduced by wiping out the snail host of the parasite and thereby breaking its life cycle. This involves adequate drainage, where practicable, to dry up wet ground, or the treatment of streams, lakes, and swamps in snail-infested areas with copper sulfate.

Roundworms are attacked by medication with any one of several drugs: Phenothiazine, copper sulfate, tetrachlorethylene, or a combination of copper sulfate and nicotine solution. Dikmans and Shorb list the worms for which each of the drugs seems to be effective, and also those for which there is at present no really effective medicinal treatment. (The latter include the lungworms, the gullet worms, and the fringed tapeworm.)

The authors recommend that sheep be treated during the winter to prevent pasture contamination in the spring. Other recommendations include frequent rotation of pasture, avoidance of low-lying, wet pastures, and maintaining a good nutritional state. To prevent bladder worm infection, all infected sheep carcasses and parts should be properly disposed of, stray dogs should be eliminated, and dogs on the place should be periodically examined and wormed when necessary.

The last part of the article is devoted to a discussion of the sheep nasal fly, the grub of which is an internal parasite infesting the nasal passages and frontal sinuses. Bacterial infection follows, resulting in the condition known as snotty nose. Repellents placed in the nasal passages are of little or no value in keeping away infestations of the grub. The authors describe several treatments, including injections, that have been reported to give satisfactory results in clearing up infections.

SHEEP SCAB AND ITS CONTROL

Fifty years ago, sheep scab was the worst problem our sheepmen faced; many ranchers would not raise sheep because of the prevalence of scab, and England prohibited the importation of live sheep from the United States. Ninety percent of the flocks in some States were infected. Today, thanks to rigid inspection, quarantine, and required dipping, most of the range States in which sheep are important are entirely free of the disease. It is still a serious problem among farm flocks in areas where auction markets and truck transportation have made eradication difficult, but this problem too is being gradually solved by Federal and State cooperation. Miller advises that every flock owner report the appearance of sheep scab immediately to the nearest veterinarian, State livestock official, or Bureau of Animal Industry representative and that the dipping be done under veterinary or other expert supervision. Only lime-sulfur or nicotine solutions are allowed for official dipping, and the dip must be of a specified strength.

Four kinds of mange mites cause sheep scab. The psoroptic mite, living on the surface of the skin, causes common scab, which covers extensive areas over the body, including the withers, back, sides, and rump. The sarcoptic mites, which are not common in the United States, burrow into the skin, usually attacking the head and face where there is little or no wool. The chorioptic mites live on the surface and usually attack the legs. The demodectic mites live in the hair follicles and glands of the skin, producing pimples or nodules. Miller describes the symptoms of the different kinds of scab, but a definite diagnosis should be based on finding the mites.

Of the four kinds of scab, demodectic is incurable; affected animals can be removed from the flock and treated by carefully opening and disinfecting each nodule, or the animals can be destroyed. Sarcoptic (head) scab is difficult to eradicate but can be cured by soaking the affected parts with warm lime-and-sulfur dip every 5 or 6 days for a month or 6 weeks. Chorioptic (foot) and psoroptic (common) scab are cured by dipping, but during very cold weather a wading tank instead of a dipping vat may be used for foot scab.

Miller goes into considerable detail regarding the method of dipping in lime-and-sulfur or nicotine solution. In particular, there are various precautions that must be carefully observed if the job is to be done satisfactorily and danger or injury to the sheep is to be avoided.

SHEEP TICKS

Sheep ticks—which are not true ticks but wingless flies—are widespread in the United States and attack both sheep and Angora goats, puncturing the skin to suck blood, causing damage to fleeces, and injuring the health of lambs and kids. The ticks do not lay eggs but give birth to larvae enclosed in a membrane that soon becomes a hard puparium and is attached to the wool fibers by a gluelike substance. Ticks spread rapidly in a flock, especially when the sheep are crowded together during cold weather.

Two general types of dips are used to control the parasites. With the first type, consisting of a solution of nicotine, or coal-tar creosote, or cresol, the sheep must be dipped twice; the second dipping is made 24 to 28 days after the first to catch the new crop of ticks hatching out from the pupae not killed by the first dipping. The other type of dip (fused bentonite-sulfur-cube, or arsenic-sulfur-rotenone, or derris, or cube) remains active in the fleece long enough to kill the new ticks emerging from the pupae, so that a second dipping is unnecessary. In their article, Imes and Babcock give general directions for using both types of dips.

Since the pupae can remain alive off the sheep for about 60 days during warm weather, it is important to clean and disinfect quarters that have been occupied by ticky sheep and to keep clean sheep out of infested pastures for about 2 months.

GOAT LICE

Lice are the worst external parasites of goats in this country; yet the widespread damage they do every year is unnecessary because they can be easily eradicated. All told, five species of lice infest goats, of which two are bloodsuckers and three have mouth parts fitted only for chewing. All reproduce by means of eggs, which are attached to the hair fibers. Heavily infested animals lose weight and become unthrifty, and in the case of Angora goats both the quality and the quantity of mohair are greatly reduced. The lice spread rapidly in a herd.

The only certain method of eradication is to dip the entire herd, using a solution of wettable sulfur (preferably mixed with cube or derris powder) or an arsenical or coal-tar-creosote dip. For a small number of animals, a large washtub or a small galvanized iron tank will suffice; for a large number it is necessary to have a regular dipping vat. The best time to dip Angora goats is a month to 6 weeks after they are sheared, provided this is before the arrival of cold weather; other breeds may be dipped at any time when the weather is favorable. The authors give general directions for dipping, including the precautions that should be observed.

If a heavy infestation makes treatment of a few animals necessary during the winter, they may be hand-dusted, or sprayed with a combination of sulfur and derris or cube. Although this will not eradicate the lice, it will greatly lessen their numbers.

PREGNANCY DISEASE OF SHEEP

"The death of one or more ewes just before lambing time is sufficient to justify suspicion of pregnancy disease," says Shahan. The first signs of the disease, which strikes for the most part during the last month of pregnancy, usually include grinding of the teeth, dullness, weakness, frequent urination, trembling when exercised; the final stage is complete collapse, followed by death in 90 percent of the cases. Affected ewes are almost invariably those carrying more than one fetus, and they are usually animals between 3 and 6 years of age.

The specific cause of pregnancy disease is not known, but it is attributed to disturbances in metabolism; and this is supported by the fact that the disease is accompanied by an increase in certain complex acids (ketones) in the blood and urine and a decrease in blood sugar. (Laboratory analysis may detect these changes even before visible symptoms appear.) Prevention consists in (1) giving the ewes a good ration during the strain of pregnancy, with its greatly increased demands on the body, and (2) seeing to it that they get regular, moderate exercise during this period. Shahan gives suggestions for the kind of ration that should be used to avoid both undernourishment and overfeeding.

LUNGER DISEASE OF SHEEP

Lunger disease, found mostly among range sheep in the Northwest, is chronic progressive pneumonia, incurable at present and generally considered to be fatal in all cases. The symptoms include labored and rapid breathing, pumping (flank breathing), dilated nostrils, sometimes coughing and a nasal discharge, and finally great weakness and emaciation before death. Investigators in the United States and in South Africa, where a similar disease occurs, have attributed it to various micro-organisms, but the cause has not been definitely determined as yet. Possibly certain environmental conditions make the animals especially susceptible. In the absence of any known method of prevention or treatment, Creech advises separating affected sheep from the healthy ones as a precaution and, if possible, moving the flock to a new environment.

PART 7

DISEASES OF POULTRY

Pullorum Disease

The poison-forming germ, *Salmonella pullorum*, primarily attacks the ovaries in hens and may produce no visible symptoms or signs except reduced productivity of the hen and hatchability of its eggs. In chicks, however, it produces a devastating disease, formerly called bacillary white diarrhea, which may practically exterminate an entire brood within three weeks after hatching. The germ is transmitted through the egg and also in excreta and on bits of contaminated material, such as fluff, floating in the air. The disease is extremely contagious and infectious. Unfortunately, many of the infected chicks do not die but grow up and in their turn produce infected eggs, perpetuating and spreading the malady. Thus pullorum disease has become exceptionally widespread and has been responsible for enormous losses to poultrymen. It is one of the major problems of the hatchery industry, since a few infected eggs in one of the giant modern incubators are a source of danger to the whole hatch.

There is no medicinal cure or preventive for pullorum disease, and control depends fundamentally on locating and eliminating all carrier hens. Agglutination tests have been developed that make this possible. Three methods are commonly used, all involving expert skill and laboratory facilities. Bunyea describes them with a degree of detail that gives the layman an insight into the kind of procedures involved in making tests for various diseases.

(1) The long method, or tube test, involves taking samples of blood from fowl and sending them in test tubes packed in ice to a laboratory, where the blood serum is mixed with a specially prepared suspension of bacteria, known as an antigen, derived from cultures of the pullorum germ. In a positive reaction, the bacteria are clumped together and settle to the bottom of the tube, leaving the fluid clear. This method is relatively costly, and the other two have been developed in recent years to reduce the expense of testing and bring it within reach of more poultrymen. (2) In the rapid serum test the serum from the blood of the fowl is mixed with a concentrated antigen on a glass plate over an illuminated dark background. In a positive test the bacteria are clumped together and separate in the form of particles or masses that are easily visible, with clear surrounding fluid, whereas in a negative reaction the smear remains uniformly cloudy. (3) The stained-antigen, rapid whole-blood test, the most recently developed method, does not require the collection of serum, and it can be carried out on the farm. A single drop of blood is mixed with a single drop of antigen, which has been stained with crystal violet, on a white glass plate. In a positive test, the stained bacteria clump together and are easily seen as violet-colored particles.

With these tests as a weapon and the seriousness of the disease as a motive, a National Poultry Improvement Plan was inaugurated in 1935 to make a concerted drive against the scourge on a countrywide scale. The plan is administered by State officials cooperating with the Federal Bureau of Animal Industry. By 1940–41, 44 States were participating and nearly 9 million birds had been tested. Under the plan, flocks are certified in three classes, U. S. Pullorum-Tested, U. S. Pullorum-Passed, and U. S. Pullorum-Clean.

Reports from all over the country indicate that as a result of this plan, the hatchability of eggs is improving and the mortality among chicks decreasing.

Meanwhile pullorum disease has become increasingly important as a menace to the turkey industry. Turkey poults seem to be very susceptible and suffer a high mortality. The tests used for chickens do not give as clear-cut results with turkeys, and more work is being done on this problem. The best preventive is to have turkey hatching and brooding done entirely separate from these operations with chickens.

FOWL PARALYSIS AND OTHER FORMS OF THE AVIAN LEUKOSIS COMPLEX

Of the $100,000,000 toll taken by poultry diseases every year in the United States alone, about half is due to a disease, or a group of diseases, concerning which science knows comparatively little. The manifestation of this disease complex most familiar to poultrymen is probably fowl paralysis, also called range paralysis, in which the nerves are affected so that the bird is partly or completely paralyzed. But there are many other manifestations described in this article by Brandly, Waters, and Hall. One type affects the eye, causing loss of color in the iris, bulging of the eyeball, changes in the size and shape of the pupil, and sometimes partial or total blindness. Another, the visceral type, affects the internal organs—liver, lungs, heart, spleen, ovary, testicles, kidneys, intestines—causing loss of flesh, weakness, and nonproductiveness. In still another type, the long bones become thickened and enlarged. In the blood type, there are alterations in the blood, the circulation, and sometimes the bone marrow (source of red blood cells) which may quickly endanger the life of the bird. A dozen or more lengthy scientific names have been applied to these various manifestations, all of which have features that are similar and also are suggestive of certain diseases of other animals and human beings.

Fowl paralysis first appeared in this country about 1920, and in the twenty-odd years since, there has been a good deal of scattered investigation of the avian leukosis complex. Quite recently, in 1938, a Regional Poultry Research Laboratory was established by the United States Department of Agriculture at East Lansing, Mich., and here major attention is being given to this disease group. The work of the laboratory is done in cooperation with 25 States in the North Central and Northeastern States.

What is the cause of the disease complex, and how is it spread? No one yet knows. Apparently poor nutrition, an unfavorable environment, and parasitic infestation are not causes, though any of them may well predispose birds to attack. Nor have any specific bacteria been found to cause the disease. Most authorities consider that a virus or viruslike agent is responsible. Various types of the disease can be transmitted by inoculating young birds with material prepared from the blood or organs of diseased birds, but how it is transmitted under ordinary conditions has not been discovered. There are indications that it is passed on through the egg and also by contact. Resistance increases rather rapidly with age, and apparently there are inherited differences in susceptibility. All in all, pending further knowledge, the best practical advice that can be given to poultrymen for combating this malady is to use strict sanitary measures in the whole process of raising poultry and to follow careful breeding procedures, mating only birds from blood lines that have a record of good health and high viability, and closing flocks to outside breeding.

The authors of this article review much of the scientific work that has been done to date on the avian leukosis complex and then describe in some detail the coordinated investigations being carried on at the regional laboratory. In these investigations, genetics and pathology are receiving major attention at first. Because of the lack of knowledge about the cause of the disease and how it spreads, the physical arrangements at the laboratory involve extraordinary precautions to prevent unintentional transmission of the disease from one group of birds to another.

In the genetic work an effort is being made to form families inherently resistant and families inherently susceptible to the avian leukosis complex, the latter to be used in pathological studies and also in determining the mode of inheritance of resistance and the influence of the environment. Ten different White Leghorn strains are being used. The pathology program includes studies on methods of diagnosis, means of detecting carriers, means of transmission, nature and tissue distribution of the causative agent, embryo and chick susceptibility, and the mechanism of acquired immunity. Several strains of the avian leukosis complex are being used in inoculation experiments. Other aspects of the problem that will need to be studied include management, nutritional, and physiological factors.

RESPIRATORY DISEASES OF CHICKENS AND TURKEYS

Hall discusses a group of diseases that cause heavy losses in flocks throughout the country, especially in winter, when replacement is costly.

Infectious laryngotracheitis, a virus disease, comes on suddenly and in an acute form may be fatal in less than a week; a less virulent attack may last 3 weeks. Mortality may be as high as 70 percent, and the disease also causes a marked drop in egg production. The outstanding symptoms are gasping and coughing, caused by the collection of mucus, pus, and blood in the respiratory passages. Diagnosis is not easy because of possible confusion with other respiratory diseases; a laboratory diagnostic test may be necessary. A bird that recovers naturally from the disease becomes a carrier for life, and these carriers are the principal spreaders of the virus. Strict sanitation and vaccination are the best preventives. The vaccine is applied to the mucous membrane of the cloaca by scarifying with a stiff bristle brush. Immunity lasts for the life of the bird. Hall says that vaccination should not be practiced if the disease does not exist in the neighborhood and there is little or no chance that the flock will be exposed to it.

Infectious bronchitis, probably also caused by a virus, is primarily a disease of young chicks. Mortality ranges from 10 to 90 percent. As in laryngotracheitis, diagnosis is difficult, and laboratory tests may be necessary. Vaccination is not practicable because the virus in the vaccine reaches the lungs before immunity is established. The best preventives are careful inspection of purchased chicks, good management of brooder houses, thorough disinfection after an outbreak of the disease.

Infectious fowl coryza (coryza is the medical term for a cold) is an acute inflammatory contagious disease primarily affecting the upper air passages, sinuses, and eye membranes. It occurs in two types, a very rapid one, caused by a germ, and a slower one, of which the cause is not definitely known. (Fowl cholera can also cause a coryza.) The first symptom is a watery discharge from the nasal passages and often the eyes; later symptoms may be severe. A bacteriological examination and laboratory tests may be necessary for a definite diagnosis. Just how the disease spreads is not known. Preventives include careful attention to housing conditions and nutrition; in California, where "colds" occur annually among pullets, disposal or segregation of old stock before pullets are brought in is recommended. Recently it has been found that sulfathiazole is effective in the treatment of the germ-produced, acute type of coryza.

Noninfectious coryzas may also be caused by a vitamin A deficiency (nutritional roup) and by mechanical irritation. The former is cured by adding supplements rich in vitamin A to the diet.

Sinusitis in turkeys, also called roup and swellhead, is a coryza characterized by swelling of the sinuses in front of the eyes. It may be infectious (cause unknown) or nutritional. The infectious type may be treated successfully by injections of argyrol or silver nitrate according to procedures described by Hall. The nutritional type may be prevented by furnishing an adequate amount of vitamin A in the diet.

Fowl Pox (Diphtheria)

It used to be thought, says Bunyea, that fowl pox and avian diphtheria were two separate diseases. Now it is known that they are different manifestations of a single disease, caused by a virus. In the pox form, characterized by the formation of blisters and later scabs on the skin—usually the unfeathered parts—the disease is generally mild. The diphtheritic form, in which cheesy patches appear on the mucous membrances of the mouth, air passages, and eyes, interfering with breathing and eating, may be fatal. Recovery from the disease confers a prolonged immunity. The virus enters the body through scratches or wounds in the skin or mucous membranes, and dried material from diseased birds remains infectious for a long time.

There are two types or strains of the virus. One produces the symptoms in pigeons; the other affects all other fowl. Pigeons are relatively resistant to the fowl type, and other fowl to the pigeon type.

Poultry can be successfully vaccinated against fowl pox with vaccines prepared from either type of virus. The usual procedure is to apply the vaccine with a stiff bristle brush to feather follicles on a prepared area of skin, or to stab it into the skin with needles; if pigeon pox vaccine is used for chickens, 12 to 20 feather follicles are inoculated instead of only a few, as when fowl pox vaccine is used. The vaccine, which was formerly prepared from pox scabs, is now prepared from virus propagated on developing chick embryos. Vaccination of healthy birds after an outbreak occurs is worth while only if the disease is in a mild form and if the vaccinating is done early in the outbreak.

There is no known cure for fowl pox, and if an outbreak is severe or has been prolonged, it is best to slaughter affected birds. If they are exceptionally valuable, they may be kept under quarantine to await possible recovery. In any event, as soon as the disease appears, the affected and the healthy birds should be separated, and strict sanitary measures, including disinfection of quarters from which diseased birds are removed, should be put into effect. Poultry keepers should be on their guard against introduction of the disease into pox-free flocks or areas.

PSITTACOSIS

The striking new development disclosed by Meyer is that a case of psittacosis (so-called parrot fever) in a human being has apparently been traced to chickens and 10 other cases have been traced to pigeons.

Psittacosis was first discovered as a disease of birds of the parrot family and occasionally of other cage birds such as canaries and finches. The fact that it causes a peculiar type of pneumonia in human beings, reputed to be fatal in 20 percent of the cases, has been known for a long time; but human psittacosis was a medical curiosity until over 750 cases occurred in 1929–30, and 600 more were recorded in subsequent years. As a result, embargoes on imported birds and other restrictive measures were put into effect in the United States. Some States maintain a permanent quarantine against birds of the parrot family. In an effort to stamp out the disease, California has instituted a system, described by Meyer, requiring testing of parrakeets in commercial aviaries and certification of the aviary.

Psittacosis is caused by a virus and is highly infective; it can be spread, for instance, by particles of dust floating in the air. It can now be diagnosed by a blood test and also by an inoculation test with mice, which are very susceptible. These methods have been extremely useful in detecting carriers—apparently healthy birds that harbor and disseminate the virus.

A few years ago it was proved by experiment that chickens are susceptible to the disease. Subsequently, a fatal case of human psittacosis was traced to a sick pigeon; then 9 other cases were traced to pigeons; and finally tests made in pigeon flocks in 5 States showed a surprisingly high percentage of positive reactions. The most recent discovery, already noted, was the isolation of the virus from 2 chickens on a poultry farm in the course of an investigation of a human case of the disease. It has also been isolated from 25 individual pigeons.

How widespread is the infection among birds on farms? How do they acquire it? What is the risk to human beings? These, as Meyer points out, are among the pressing questions posed by the new discoveries.

MISCELLANEOUS DISEASES OF POULTRY

Bunyea covers a number of diseases, most of which are not discussed elsewhere in the section devoted to poultry.

Paratyphoid infection, caused by organisms of the *Salmonella* group, occurs mainly in young birds, may be either acute or chronic, and has various symptoms. It is difficult to control; sanitation in hatching and rearing the young is of first importance. Both infected duck eggs and the flesh of infected squabs may cause food poisoning in human beings, but possible danger from this source is eliminated if these products are thoroughly cooked.

Fowl typhoid, like fowl cholera, is caused by bacteria that live in the blood stream. No remedy or vaccine is available; sanitary measures are important in preventing the disease. The blood test for pullorum disease also detects typhoid carriers. Fowl typhoid is declining among chickens, increasing among turkeys.

Fowl cholera, characterized by intestinal disturbances, depression, and mortality, may be either acute or chronic. Fortunately the bacteria are easily destroyed by sanitary measures. A rapid whole-blood test for the diagnosis of fowl cholera carriers is a recent development. Although not yet widely used, it is a possible aid in detecting the birds that are harboring the infection.

Mycosis includes three types of disease due to different fungi. (1) Thrush is due to the presence of fungi in the digestive tract. It produces a discharge from the mouth, loss of appetite, weakness, emaciation, and diarrhea, and is frequently fatal. Thorough sanitation is the best preventive, but Bunyea also describes a simple medicinal treatment. (2) Aspergillosis is caused by fungi in the air passages. It produces gasping, unthriftiness, and emaciation and may easily be confused with other respiratory diseases. In young chicks it is rapidly fatal. Strict sanitation is the only known preventive. Sick birds should be segregated or destroyed. (3) Favus (white comb, avian mycotic dermatitis) is caused by a fungus that attacks the skin. Growths or crusts appear on the unfeathered head parts; elsewhere feathers break off. The disease is said to infect human beings. Treatment with petroleum jelly and formalin, as described by Bunyea, is reported to be very effective.

Infectious avian encephalomyelitis (epidemic tremor), an inflammation of the central nervous system, is spread by direct contact and may be passed on through the egg. A large percentage of a flock may be affected. Although spontaneous recoveries occur, it is recommended that infected birds be quickly fattened and marketed to eliminate carriers.

Avian tuberculosis is discussed in the general article on tuberculosis in this volume. A few additional points are given by Bunyea.

Poisoning of poultry may be due to various causes. (1) Botulism (limber-neck) is caused by eating feed or other products contaminated with the botulinus organism and its toxins. The condition is likely to be rapidly fatal. Exposed birds may be drenched with Epsom salts and given antitoxin injections. (2) Common sources of chemical poisoning of poultry include rat poisons, vegetation sprayed with arsenicals, fish brine, ice-cream salt, spent fireworks, poisoned grasshoppers and grasshopper bait, and certain worm medicines. (3) Even small numbers of the insects known as rose chafers will poison young chickens.

Lameness may also be due to any one of various causes. (1) Wire cloth with a large mesh may catch the feet or legs of chicks. (2) Toes and feet may be frozen in cold weather if the birds are not kept in properly arranged houses. (3) Bumblefoot, a swelling characterized by an accumulation of cheesy material, is probably due to infection of wounds. It causes great suffering and should be treated by minor surgery, disinfection, and bandaging. (4) Sod disease is an inflammation of the skin accompanied by small swellings filled with fluid. It may affect the feet and the eyelids and is often fatal. The cause is unknown, but birds should be excluded from unplowed prairie land. (5) Nutritional deficiencies, discussed elsewhere in this volume, may cause lameness. (6) Fowl paralysis, also discussed elsewhere, is manifested in lameness. Avian tuberculosis, paratyphoid infection, and fowl cholera may all cause lameness. Infection with one of the staphylococcus organisms is responsible for a lameness in the feet, legs, or wings that often ends in death. (7) Scaly leg, discussed in the article on poultry mites, is a condition caused by a parasitic itch mite.

"It is normal for a fowl to be in good condition if it is given a chance," says Bunyea. He discusses some of the practices that give the birds such a chance, among them: (1) Proper location of the poultry house. (2) Clean, comfortable, well-ventilated houses; abundant, nourishing feed; clean water. (3) Proper management of brooder houses. (4) Frequent moving of houses or shelters for growing birds on the range to keep the birds off polluted ground. (5) Cleaned, disinfected, dry laying houses ready for the birds when they come off the range. (6) Separate houses for pullets and old hens and for birds of different species. (7) Mesh wire, or preferably fly screening, on doors and windows. (8) Exclusion of all visitors from the poultry houses; provision of clean overshoes for those admitted; disinfection of the soles of footwear when entering the poultry house if certain diseases are prevalent in the area. (9) Quarantining of newly purchased birds or those that have returned from contests or shows. (10) Prompt action in cases of infectious diseases, including destruction or segregation of sick birds and disinfection of premises.

INTERNAL PARASITES OF POULTRY

Chickens are kept on 85 percent of the farms of the United States, which makes it all the more striking that almost a fifth of the birds are lost every year because of disease. The annual financial loss has been estimated at 180 million dollars, a good deal of it waste because it is preventable.

Wehr and Christensen describe the practices necessary to reduce the part of this loss that is due to internal parasites. These practices depend chiefly on three simple facts: (1) Most, though not all, poultry parasites are eliminated in the droppings of the birds. (2) In the crowded poultry communities of today, the surroundings quickly become contaminated. (3) Birds pick up parasites from these contaminated surroundings—feed, water, soil, and infected intermediate hosts such as snails and slugs.

The great preventive, then, is to have clean surroundings. This means, for example, carefully selecting the site for the poultry house; using a type of house that can easily be kept clean; not crowding the birds in runs or yards that cannot be kept clean—instead, either using a series of runs that can be rotated, or confining the birds entirely within the house except perhaps for a "porch" with a wire floor or a small fenced yard covered with cinders or other porous material; disposing of manure promptly and storing it properly; keeping different types of poultry, such as turkeys and chickens, or turkeys and pigeons, entirely separate, since a disease that is mild for one type may be disastrous for another; and being careful not to spread infection on shoes or clothing. Following these general principles of good hygiene and at the same time feeding the birds well will go a long way toward preventing trouble with parasites.

If an outbreak of parasitism occurs, the healthy birds and the diseased birds should be promptly separated and kept separate, and a strict sanitation program should be carried out. If no local veterinarian is available to make a diagnosis and advise on treatment, the State agricultural experiment station should be consulted as to the advisability of sending birds to the laboratory for diagnosis.

There is little in the way of medicinal treatment for most poultry parasites, the authors point out, through anthelmintics, or worm medicines, are effective for the gapeworm, the large roundworm, and the cecum worm; and trichomoniasis of the lower digestive tract of turkeys can be successfully treated by heat therapy—enclosing the birds for certain periods of time in a box heated to a certain temperature.

After discussing these practical control measures, the authors deal in considerable detail with the principal poultry parasites.

With the exception of coccidiosis, discussed elsewhere in this volume, the diseases produced by protozoa are important mainly in turkeys.

A severe catarrhal inflammation of the intestines of turkeys, caused by a protozoan called *Hexamita meleagridis*, is becoming increasingly important in the United States. The mortality in acute outbreaks runs from 20 to 90 percent, and most birds that recover from an acute attack remain stunted. Adult turkeys are the primary source of infection.

Histomoniasis, or so-called blackhead (the head does not always turn dark), is an acute, highly fatal disease caused by infection with *Histomonas meleagridis.* Until methods of preventing it, based on sanitation, were found, this disease made turkey raising impossible in many parts of the country. Chickens, which are not seriously affected by histomoniasis, become carriers; so do the few turkeys that recover.

A malarialike disease of young turkey poults and ducklings is caused by organisms of the genus *Leucocytozoon,* which attack the blood cells. The disease strikes suddenly in young birds and runs a brief, acute course, with a mortality up to 50 percent in turkeys and 100 percent in ducklings. The causative organisms are transmitted by blackflies.

Two species of trichomonads cause intestinal disturbances in young turkeys, one attacking the crop and gullet, the other the cecum and liver. Occasionally, though not usually, the mortality from trichomoniasis of the upper digestive tract is high. The disease in the lower digestive tract may be confused with histomoniasis and often takes an insidious, slow course, ending in death.

A considerable number of worm parasites, of the general types that attack other animals, are found in poultry.

At least three species of flukes, or trematodes, parasitize poultry, but none are of great economic importance. One occurs in the skin of domestic and wild birds, producing hard, cystlike structures, usually in the region of the vent. Another, found in muskrats and water birds, may be responsible for an inflammation of the proventriculus, or true stomach, in chickens. A third is located in the reproductive organs and can greatly reduce or completely stop egg production in laying hens, as well as causing extreme emaciation and anemia. Snails and dragonflies are the intermediate hosts of this fluke.

Several species of tapeworms (cestodes) inhabit the small intestines of fowl; all pass through certain stages of development, when they are known as bladder worms, in intermediate hosts, including houseflies, snails, slugs, ants, earthworms, beetles, grasshoppers, and sandhoppers. Fowl become infected by swallowing the intermediate hosts.

Roundworms, or nematodes, which parasitize almost every organ in the body of birds, include three groups—those that are transmitted directly, those that are transmitted through intermediate hosts such as various insects, and those that are transmitted in both ways. Among the nematodes are the crop worms, the stomach worms, the gizzard worms, the large intestinal roundworms, the small intestinal roundworms, the eye worm, and gapeworms, which infest the windpipe and cause the condition known as gapes. The nematodes cause more or less severe illness, and sometimes death, depending on the severity of the infestation. In the case of *Ascaridia galli,* one of the large intestinal roundworms, it has been shown that foods high in vitamin A and in the B vitamins increase resistance and that a lack of the vitamin B complex definitely favors parasitism.

COCCIDIOSIS OF THE CHICKEN

Coccidiosis occurs in all domesticated fowl and in cattle, sheep, goats, pigs, and dogs, but, as Christensen and Allen point out, it probably causes heavier economic losses among chickens than among all the rest combined.

The life history of the common coccidia of poultry goes like this: (1) The egglike, resistant oöcysts are discharged in the birds' droppings. (2) Each oöcyst divides into four elongated bodies, and each of these into two sporozoites. (3) An oöcyst thus divided (sporulated) is swallowed by a chicken. (4) The eight sporozoites are released in the intestinal canal and penetrate cells in the membrane tissue. (5) After growth, each divides into many merozoites, which parasitize other cells. (6) Again growth and division occur. (7) Finally, some of the merozoites develop into males and females and mate. (8) The fertilized females secrete a resistant shell, becoming oöcysts, and are discharged in the droppings.

Coccidia may become localized in the cecum, causing an acute, often highly fatal disease, mostly of chicks 3 to 5 weeks old, characterized by severe cecal hemorrhage; or they may become localized mainly in the small intestine, causing a serious, prolonged disease of older birds characterized by extreme emaciation. The first disease is caused by *Eimeria tenella*, the second by any one of at least six species of coccidia, of which *Eimeria necatrix* produces the most severe symptoms.

In addition to the deaths caused by coccidiosis, many of the birds that recover are permanently unthrifty, as well as being carriers of the infection.

Control of the disease consists in strict isolation of young birds from adult fowl and in extremely careful sanitation, including such measures as thorough, regular, frequent cleaning of brooder houses with soap and hot water; daily cleaning of chick cages; frequent cleaning of feeding and watering equipment; occasional transfer of movable brooder houses to new ground; careful locating of permanent brooder houses and provision of sloping concrete runs; the same kind of cleaning of laying houses as of brooder houses; provision of clean ground for each group of pullets.

In case of an outbreak, medication does little good, but losses can be minimized by meticulous attention to every detail of good feeding and care.

POULTRY LICE AND THEIR CONTROL

All the lice that attack poultry, says Bishopp, are of the biting and chewing rather than the bloodsucking type. They cause heavy indirect losses, probably chiefly among farm and backyard flocks. The specialized poultry keeper usually does not permit them to get a foothold, and there is no reason why they should not be controlled even in the smallest flock.

All lice live continuously on the host and soon die if removed, but different kinds attack different parts of the body.

The head louse is usually found on the top and back of the head and beneath the bill. Among lice, it is the chief pest of young chickens and turkeys, sometimes causing death before the birds are a month old. The body louse of chickens stays on the skin, usually where the body is not densely feathered, and is the most important of the lice attacking adult birds. The shaft louse rests on the shafts of the feathers and apparently feeds only on feathers. Four other fairly common chicken lice are the wing louse, the fluff louse, the large chicken louse, and the brown chicken louse.

Turkeys are subject to the attacks of the slender turkey louse and the large turkey louse, as well as of chicken lice. Geese and ducks are seldom noticeably affected by lice, but there are six species that attack pigeons, sometimes damaging the feathers of show birds and perhaps adversely affecting the speed and endurance of carriers.

In general it is best to delouse the poultry flock in the fall so that they will be free of these pests through the following spring. Treatment with sodium fluoride is very effective and practical. Each bird may be thoroughly dusted (most expensive method); or the insecticide may be applied in small pinches to several designated parts of the body; or the birds may be dipped in a solution containing 1 tablespoonful of sodium fluoride to each gallon of water (least expensive method). Sodium fluoride irritates the air passages when breathed in and is a poison when taken internally, and Bishopp outlines the necessary precautions in handling it. Sodium fluosilicate may also be used as a dip. Other treatments, not so effective, are the use of fine sulfur as a dust and the painting of roosts with nicotine sulfate.

Poultry Mites

A large percentage of poultry of all kinds, according to Bishopp, are constantly infested with mites which lower the vitality of the birds, reduce their egg production, and in some cases actually cause death.

The common chicken mite is what Bishopp calls a night raider, generally hiding in cracks and crevices during the day. It attacks all parts of the body and feeds by sucking blood, and it will attack other animals and human beings as well as poultry. Heavily infested setting hens have been known to die on the nest. To get rid of these mites, remove all boards, boxes, and trash that might serve as hiding places; burn the litter and nesting material; spray the poultry house thoroughly with one of the carbolineums, crude petroleum, or creosote oil. One treatment is usually enough.

The feather mite, which remains constantly on the birds, requires a different treatment. Each bird should be dipped in a sulfur bath (2 ounces of fine sulfur and 1 ounce of soap to a gallon of water) on a warm, sunny day or in a heated building; or the birds may be thoroughly dusted with sulfur; or nicotine sulfate may be applied to the perches. The house should also be disinfected as for the common chicken mite.

The scaly-leg mite attacks the shanks and feet, and sometimes the comb, wattles, and neck. The legs of infested birds may be dipped in crude petroleum. Painting the roosts and nests with a carbolineum also helps to control this mite.

The depluming mite burrows in the skin near the base of the feathers. It may be completely eliminated by dipping each bird in the sulfur bath already described.

Chiggers, the young of the small red harvest mite, attack chickens as well as other animals and human beings. They inject an irritating poison into the skin, to which they attach themselves (they do not burrow in as is commonly supposed). Severe infestations can have a very serious effect on young chickens and turkeys; hence in chigger areas it is best to hatch early or keep the chicks from late hatches out of grass and weeds. Dusting the birds and the ranges with sulfur is helpful.

THE FOWL TICK

The fowl tick, or blue bug, is a serious handicap to poultry raising in the Southwest, Bishopp points out, and it now also occurs in Florida. Its attacks weaken the birds and cause a tick paralysis; egg production is reduced, and not infrequently the birds die.

The tick, a flat, oval, leathery-skinned creature, resists many insecticides and can live for more than 3 years without food. It feeds exclusively on blood, preferring birds but also occasionally attacking domestic animals and human beings. Active at night, when the birds are on the roosts, it hides by day in cracks and crevices and is often shipped around the country concealed in poultry crates and other objects. In heavy infestations it may spread from poultry houses to barns and other buildings.

The tick can be controlled by thorough spraying of the building with one of the carbolineums; crude petroleum and creosote oil are less satisfactory. A second application 20 or 30 days after the first may be necessary, and sometimes even a third. Bishopp gives directions for the spraying job. He also tells briefly how to construct roosts and nests to make control of the tick comparatively easy.

The fowl tick can be prevented from getting a foothold by such measures as proper choosing of a site and proper construction of a poultry house, buying chicks from tick-free hatcheries, thoroughly spraying used crates, and isolating, for a period of 10 days, any fowl brought to the place.

BEDBUGS AS PESTS OF POULTRY

Bedbugs are common pests of poultry as well as of human beings and domestic animals; in fact, as Back and Bishopp point out, they can easily be carried from poultry houses, where they hide in cracks and holes, to human dwellings. Wooden poultry crates are often heavily infested. The bugs feed mostly at night or in subdued light, take about two days to digest a full meal, and can go without food for as long as 2 months. When they are abundant, they suck so much blood that chickens do not fatten and setting hens may die, and the effects are especially disastrous in the case of squabs. The Mexican chicken bug (coruco, adobe bug), an important pest of poultry in the Southwest, is very much like the bedbug.

Keeping these insects under control requires vigilance and persistent effort. Hiding places should be eliminated as far as possible by simple construction, the removal of stray boards and trash, and, where it is practicable, the filling of cracks. Fumigants, such as burning sulfur, are effective in killing the bugs if the poultry house is tight enough (but few are). Thorough spraying with creosote oil or a carbolineum is satisfactory, and so are kerosene and pyrethrum-kerosene fly sprays. In feeding establishments, it is well to spray crates once a month. In pigeon lofts, spraying the nests if not properly done may have a bad effect on eggs and squabs; treating the lofts with live steam has been effective under some circumstances.

The Pigeon Fly

A little smaller than a housefly and very active, the pigeon fly is a parasite only of pigeons and their close relatives. Bishopp describes how the insect crawls rapidly about among the feathers and sucks blood from both adult birds and squabs. In addition to causing irritation and loss of blood, it carries the pigeon malaria organism. It also bites human beings.

The fly lays neither eggs nor larvae, but pupae already formed, from which adult flies emerge, usually in about a month or less. These egg-shaped pupae tend to drop to the bottom of the nest boxes. The simplest way to control the pest, then, is to clean the nests and floors thoroughly every 25 days. The trash should be burned, or stored in a screened manure pit or bin equipped with a fly trap, or promptly spread and plowed under. Thorough soaking with a high-grade pyrethrum-kerosene spray will also kill the pupae.

Adult flies on squabs can be killed by applying two or three pinches of pyrethrum, derris, or cube powder. Kerosene extract of pyrethrum kills the flies on adult birds or squabs, and also in handling and killing rooms. When used on the birds, it should be applied with great care.

Once a loft has been freed of pigeon flies, Bishopp emphasizes, it should be kept free.

Nutritional Diseases of Poultry

Before discussing a considerable number of nutritional diseases of poultry, Titus points out that knowledge in this field is in a state of active change.

Vitamin A.—Perhaps the primary function of vitamin A is the nourishment and repair of the epithelial structures (skin and internal membranes), which are the body's first line of defense against infection. It is also necessary for the normal functioning of the eye. In severe cases of deficiency, practically every organ of the body is affected. There are degenerative changes in the nerves, and the eyes are inflamed. A partial deficiency in the diet of chickens, especially after dry weather has damaged green forage, is more common than is ordinarily supposed. Titus gives the amounts of vitamin A needed by chicks, turkey poults, chickens kept for egg production, and breeding stock, and also the amounts contained in the richer sources of this vitamin used in feeding.

Vitamin B_1.—According to present evidence, vitamin B_1 is necessary for the proper metabolism of carbohydrates; in its absence, pyruvic acid, an intermediate product of this metabolism, accumulates and has a toxic effect on the nervous system. A deficiency does not occur in ordinary poultry production but can be produced experimentally. Typical symptoms of the experimentally produced disease in chickens are a decrease in appetite, a loss of weight, general paralysis, and a peculiar raising and drawing back of the head. There is no evidence of an actual degeneration of the nerves such as was attributed to vitamin B_1 deficiency by earlier workers.

Vitamin B_6.—Little is known about the requirements of poultry for this vitamin or the symptoms of a deficiency, which in fact does not occur under ordinary conditions.

Vitamin D.—This vitamin is required for the normal metabolism of calcium and phosphorus in the chicken. A deficiency in the diet of growing chickens produces the abnormal condition of the bones known as rickets; in the adult chicken it causes a thinning of the eggshells and, in severe cases, a decrease in egg production and hatchability. Various other conditions can cause abnormal bone development (rickets or osteoporosis), but vitamin D deficiency is the most common cause in poultry. As Titus points out, it was impossible to raise poultry in strict confinement, without access to sunshine, before the importance of vitamin D in their nutrition was discovered. Now some vitamin D is commonly included in the diet whether the birds have access to sunshine or not. The usual sources are cod-liver oil, sardine oil, certain other fish oils, and D-activated animal sterol. Titus gives the amounts of the vitamin required, as well as the amounts contained in various commonly used sources.

Vitamin E.—Crazy chick disease (nutritional encephalomalacia), which is usually characterized by extensive tissue changes in the brain, has been produced in chicks, ducklings, and poults by feeding a diet high in fat but very low in vitamin E. It occasionally occurs in commercial flocks, perhaps through destruction or inactivation of vitamin E in feed kept too long. Titus recommends feeding mixtures while they are fresh, and avoiding excessive quantities of cod-liver oil or other fats and oils in the diet. The disease can be checked in a flock, and some cases can be cured, by feeding 1 percent of the oil extracted from corn, soybeans, peanuts, wheat germ, or cottonseed. Another condition produced experimentally by vitamin E deficiency is nutritional myopathy, a disease involving the skeletal muscles in ducklings and the muscles of the gizzard in poults.

Vitamin G.—This vitamin plays a basic role in cell processes, and available evidence indicates that the growing chick requires it for the normal functioning and maintenance of the nervous system. A partial deficiency in chicks results in a condition known as curled toe paralysis as well as other symptoms, including marked adverse effects on growth; in turkey poults, a skin inflammation occurs. Since relatively few feedstuffs contain enough vitamin G to meet minimum needs during the first few weeks of life, it should be provided by careful selection of feeds. Titus gives requirements and the amounts contained in various rich sources.

Vitamin K.—Apparently, vitamin K is needed for the formation of prothrombin, which in turn is necessary for the normal clotting of blood. Hemorrhages occur in very young chicks fed an experimental diet deficient in the vitamin. No deficiency is likely to occur under ordinary conditions.

Pantothenic acid.—Observations indicate that this vitamin or vitaminlike factor is necessary for the maintenance of a normal spinal cord in the growing chick. A deficient diet fed experimentally produces, among other symptoms, a characteristic skin condition around the corners of the mouth and on the soles of the feet. Possibly some skin conditions seen in poultry flocks are due to a deficiency of pantothenic acid, such as might occur with certain diets. Titus gives the requirements tentatively set and the amounts in some of the rich sources. He also describes a condition called egg-white injury which closely resembles pantothenic acid deficiency but appears to be due to a deficiency of biotin (vitamin H).

Manganese and choline.—It is now known that manganese and choline (a substance found in most animal and plant tissues) somehow have a combined action in the development of a normal skeleton. Choline is seldom deficient in poultry diets; manganese, however, can easily be deficient unless the birds have access to the natural source, the soil. A deficiency of manganese (or choline, or both) in the diet of chicks, poults, and ducklings produces perosis, also called hock disease and slipped tendon, characterized, among other symptoms, by enlarged joints and bending of the shank and drumstick bones. In mature birds, eggshells tend to become thin; in severe cases egg production is reduced, embryonic mortality is high, and the embryos are abnormal in development. Titus gives directions for including enough manganese sulfate in the diet, mixed with salt, to serve as insurance against perosis.

Iron and copper.—Anemia rarely if ever occurs among chickens under ordinary conditions. It has been produced experimentally by feeding a diet extremely deficient in iron or copper or both, as well as by a deficiency of some unknown nutritional factor. Anemic embryos are sometimes encountered, and there is evidence that lack of sunshine, or of cod-liver oil in the diet, reduces the transfer of iron and copper to the eggs.

Iodine.—Goiter has been produced experimentally in chickens by feeding a diet low in iodine, and it has been reported to occur in Montana and Minnesota. It is probably more common in certain parts of the country than is generally realized. Titus suggests that the use of iodized salt for poultry may be a worth-while insurance, at least in areas where goiter occurs in other farm animals.

Gizzard erosion.—A weakening of the gizzard lining occurs commonly in chicks and is of several distinct types, apparently due to different causes. It seems to have no ill effects but probably indicates a somewhat unsatisfactory diet if it continues after the chicks are 4 weeks old. Titus lists several substances reported to be of value in clearing up the condition.

Feather picking and cannibalism.—Cannibalism in a flock is more serious than feather picking and nearly always leads to heavy losses.

Experiments indicate that diets very low in crude fiber content are a likely cause. The use of ruby lights in place of ordinary lights and the feeding of a diet containing 20 percent of barley or oats or 30 percent of bran and middlings are reported to be useful preventives. Titus gives directions for the use of salt to cure birds of these practices, and for trimming back the beaks if the salt cure fails to produce results.

Fluorine and selenium poisoning.—Fluorine poisoning depresses the rate of growth and egg production but does not occur in chickens unless the drinking water contains a certain percentage of fluorine, or unless rock phosphate or phosphatic limestone that contains fluorine is included in the diet. Selenium poisoning has several serious effects. As Titus points out, selenium has been found in the soils and vegetation in at least 11 States and probably occurs in others.

Diseases of unknown origin.—Titus describes several conditions, encountered for the most part in experimental work, that apparently have dietary causes, not yet definitely determined—an enteritis, or inflammation of the intestines, a paralysis, an arthritis and an associated leg deformity, a dermatosis, and fatty degeneration of the liver.

Titus concludes his article with a brief discussion of the influence of nutritional deficiences on growth and reproduction.

PART 8

COMMON DISEASES OF DOGS AND CATS

RABIES AND ITS CONTROL

Rabies can be controlled and even eradicated, but in the United States, which has so successfully combated other animal diseases, it is allowed to be widely prevalent.

The disease is caused by a virus, which attacks the brain and spinal cord, with fatal results. In this country it is spread chiefly by the bites of mad dogs; the virus exists in the animal's saliva and infects the wound. It has been estimated that about 15 percent of the human beings bitten by mad dogs contract the disease unless they receive treatment, which consists of a series of vaccine injections. Among domestic animals, about 35 percent of those bitten become infected. These are general figures only and have been estimated over a period of years. The incidence of the disease may be higher or lower in specific outbreaks.

In most cases, symptoms of the disease develop within 2 weeks to 3 months after infection. When a human being is bitten by a dog that might possibly be rabid, it is important to confine the animal under the observation of a veterinarian until the disease, if it is present, has a chance to develop and run its course. Death occurs within a few days after symptoms appear, and the dog's brain can then be examined for specific evidence of rabies. The treatment given to exposed human beings depends to a large extent on this evidence.

The symptoms of rabies in dogs follow two general patterns, the furious and the dumb forms, and both are described by Schoening in some detail. He also describes the symptoms in cats and in cattle.

Many wild animals are subject to the disease; in 1940 there was a serious outbreak among foxes in several Southern States, centering in Georgia, during which at least 90 head of livestock contracted rabies from fox bites, and 17 human beings were given treatment. Schoening gives figures showing all the reported cases of rabies in each State during 1938 and 1939, including human beings, dogs, and all other animals, and briefly discusses the situation in other countries, showing that several have been free of this disease for the past 10 years.

The Pasteur treatment and its modifications are used after exposure to the disease. About 20 years ago a one-shot vaccine was developed to be used for dogs as a preventive before exposure. Although this vaccination has definite value, it cannot be relied on as the sole method of controlling the disease, because there are dogs to which it does not give sure protection against a severe exposure. Moreover, the stray dog always plays an important part in the spread of the disease.

Adequate control or eradication of rabies demands the simultaneous use of several measures under uniform regulations applied by all States. Schoening quotes the 1939 and 1940 reports of the Committee on Rabies of the United States Live Stock Sanitary Association as embodying a suitable program for this country. In brief the regulations recommended are:

(1) License all dogs annually.

(2) Require that the dog wear the license attached to its collar at all times when on public property.

(3) Destroy or impound all unlicensed dogs. Local conditions should determine whether impounded dogs can be safely returned to their owners or sold.

(4) Provide a sufficient full-time personnel to control stray and unlicensed dogs.

(5) Determine adequately whether any suspected dog is rabid. If it is, destroy all dogs that have been bitten or exposed, or quarantine them for 6 months on the owners' premises, or give them vaccination treatments and quarantine them for 2 months. In addition, place a 60-day quarantine on the entire area over which the rabid dog may have strayed, allowing no dog on public property during this period unless it is held on a leash not over 6 feet long in the hands of a competent person.

(6) Make ample funds available in each community for carrying out the regulations.

(7) Have the veterinary profession represented in the personnel concerned with the control of the disease and provide for adequate publicity in case of outbreaks and quarantines.

(8) Encourage or advocate preventive vaccination on a voluntary basis when it seems advisable, but do not give vaccinated dogs special privileges.

DISTEMPER OF DOGS

Distemper, "the scourge of dogdom," is quite similar to influenza in human beings and, like the latter, is caused primarily by a virus, followed by a secondary bacterial invasion. For the most part it attacks young dogs from 2 months to a year old, producing a catarrhal inflammation of all the mucous membranes of the body, frequently accompanied by nervous symptoms caused by disturbances of the brain and spinal cord. The disease is highly contagious and often fatal; affected animals should be promptly isolated, and the premises should be thoroughly disinfected.

Stein emphasizes that diagnosis and the prescription of treatment should be in the hands of a competent veterinarian. There is no cure, but injections of an antiserum administered early enough can lessen the severity of an attack. Otherwise, treatment consists in careful nursing and feeding.

Two basic methods of immunization are effective in preventing the disease, one involving the use of a vaccine and a living virus, the other the use of an antiserum and a living virus. Some investigators believe that puppies vaccinated under 4 to 6 months of age do not become completely immune; hence they should not be vaccinated until after this age. In case of imminent exposure, however, puppies 6 to 8 weeks old can be protected by a vaccine or antiserum and then immunized later.

FELINE ENTERITIS

Considered to be the most serious disease of cats and frequently occurring in severe outbreaks, feline enteritis is especially disastrous to young animals, among which the mortality rate is often higher than 80 percent. The virus that causes the disease is spread by direct or indirect contact and by fleas. Stein describes the disease as sudden in its appearance and rapid and violent in its course, producing a high fever, an acute inflammation of the intestinal tract, a marked decrease in the number of white blood cells, great depression, and rapid loss of flesh. Sometimes kittens die before any apparent symptoms develop. Parasitic infestation, undernourishment, and other devitalizing factors lower the resistance of animals.

Reports indicate that certain biological products—vaccines, antisera, and bacterins—are of value in combating feline enteritis, some being used as preventives and others to furnish temporary immunity or, in the early stages of the disease, to reduce the violence of its course. The administration of these products, or of drugs, should be undertaken only by a veterinarian. Affected cats should be immediately isolated, kept in warm dry quarters, and fed broth, milk, and raw eggs if they will take nourishment. It is important to disinfect the quarters thoroughly and to eliminate fleas.

MISCELLANEOUS DISEASES OF DOGS AND CATS

In a condensed account of a great many diseases and other conditions of dogs and cats, Stein gives general information and suggestions rather than details because of space limitations. This brief summary can do little more than list the topics he covers. As the author points out, even an elementary knowledge will help pet owners to keep their animals in good condition. For definite diagnosis and treatment it is necessary in most cases to consult a veterinarian specializing in the diseases of pets.

Abnormal growths or swellings encountered in pets include abscesses, cysts, tumors (malignant and nonmalignant), mumps, goiter, enlargements of the lymph glands caused by Hodgkins disease, and rupture (hernia).

Anal gland infection, followed by clogging of the glands, is especially likely to occur in old dogs.

Ascites (dropsy) is usually the result of diseases of the heart, liver, or kidneys.

Ailments of aged dogs include a considerable number of afflictions, some of which may require persistent treatment as well as good care and feeding.

Diseases of the digestive system are common in dogs and cats and are usually due to improper feeding. Various treatments are required according to the nature of the disturbance.

Depraved appetite (pica) may be due to nutritional deficiencies, parasites, or simply habit.

Foreign bodies sometimes lodge in the digestive tract and are likely to require veterinary attention. Regular grooming of cats will prevent their swallowing enough hair to form hair balls in the intestine.

Intestinal obstruction, caused by indigestible material, is likely to require irrigation and other special treatment.

Gastroenteritis, or intestinal inflammation, is a common ailment, especially of dogs, and is due to any one of a number of causes, including faulty feeding.

Hemorrhagic gastroenteritis, an inflammation accompanied by internal hemorrhage, is especially serious and demands veterinary attention.

Ear diseases include external and internal canker and a sensitive swelling called haemotoma, caused by an injury that ruptures small blood vessels.

Eclampsia, a nervous malady of nursing bitches, characterized by convulsions, is usually treated with injections of calcium gluconate.

Eye diseases include conjunctivitis, keratitis, ulcers on the cornea, cataract, glaucoma, and two types of eyelid affections known as entropion and ectropion.

Fits, characterized by convulsions and nervous spasms, are symptoms of some underlying disorder that may have any one of a number of causes. The cause must be determined to prevent further attacks.

Icterus (jaundice) may be a symptom of a liver disease or a stomach disorder, or it may be caused by a specific infection, considered to be identical with that responsible for Weil's disease in human beings.

Metritis and pyometra are diseases of the uterus due to various causes; severe cases require surgery.

Posterior paralysis, or paralysis of the hindquarters, is due to any one of a considerable number of causes.

Urinary calculi, or stones in the kidney, bladder, or urethra, usually require surgical treatment.

Respiratory affections to which pet animals are subject include colds, laryngitis, bronchitis, pleurisy, and pneumonia.

Warts (papilloma) may be hard or soft, and certain types are considered to be contagious.

Poisoning demands immediate veterinary attention as well as first aid. The author deals with poisoning by arsenic. phosphorus. lead, strychnin, carbolic acid, carbon monoxide, snake bites, and decayed food.

Car sickness, not uncommon in nervous dogs. may be forestalled to some extent by certain simple precautions.

First aid is often required for pet animals; Stein tells what to do for some of the common injuries.

Spaying and castration of dogs and cats are briefly discussed by the author, with recommendations as· to the best ages at which to have the operations performed.

INTERNAL PARASITES OF DOGS AND CATS

Price and Harwood discuss preventive measures and medicinal treatment at the end of their article, but in this brief summary prevention and treatment will be considered with the discussion of the parasites. As these authors point out, preventive measures are often not feasible on the farm, where dogs and cats usually run free. Medicinal treatment, they emphasize, should always be based on accurate diagnosis, which usually requires expert knowledge. They argue against the periodical dosing of pet animals regardless of the presence of parasites; worm medicines are toxic and should be used only when necessary. They also stress the importance of good nutrition as a factor in building general resistance to internal parasites.

Protozoa.—Minute one-celled organisms, of which two types cause important diseases in this country. (1) Piroplasmosis: A *Piroplasma*, transmitted by the bite of ticks, attacks the red blood cells of dogs, causing an acute or chronic disease with symptoms that in some ways resemble those of distemper. Prevention: Control of ticks. Medicinal treatment: Injections of acaprin or other drugs. (2) Coccidiosis: Caused by coccidia invading the intestinal tract, and transmitted by oöcysts (egglike forms) passed in the feces and contaminating the ground. Diarrhea is the chief symptom in heavy infections. Prevention: Sanitation and prompt disposal of feces. Medicinal treatment: None available.

Flukes.—The most important is the salmon-poisoning fluke, associated with a serious disease of dogs in the Pacific Northwest. This fluke passes part of its life cycle in a snail. another part in a salmonoid fish. Dogs acquire the parasite by eating the infected fish. Apparently a virus accompanies the fluke infestation in the intestines. causing a disease that resembles distemper and is fatal in 50 to 90 percent of the untreated cases. Prevention: Keep raw fish away from dogs and cats. Treatment: Sulfanilamide (first used for this purpose in 1938).

Tapeworms.—(1) Several kinds of armed tapeworms (equipped with suckers and hooks) infest dogs, one kind infests cats, and at least two kinds infest both. The larvae (bladder worms) of these parasites develop in other mammals, including rodents, rabbits, hares, sheep, goats, cattle, swine. and in at least one case. human beings; one armed tapeworm, however. usually passes its larval stages in certain fleas and

lice. Mild infestations in dogs and cats apparently do no harm;
heavy ones may result in such symptoms as digestive disturbances and
general restlessness. Prevention: Control fleas and lice; do not permit dogs and cats to feed on the infected flesh of intermediate hosts.
Treatment: Dosing, under proper conditions, with arecoline hydrobromide. (2) One unarmed tapeworm infests dogs in the Great Lakes
region; another occurs in cats and sometimes dogs in New York and
Louisiana. The parasites require two intermediate hosts, first a small
crustacean, second a fish or an amphibian, reptile, or mammal. The
symptoms of infestation are usually not marked in the case of dogs,
but cats may be severely affected. Prevention: Keep dogs and cats
from eating the infected flesh of the second intermediate host. Treatment: Dosing, under proper conditions, with oleoresin of male fern.

Roundworms (nematodes) are the most injurious parasites of dogs
and cats. (1) Hookworms, of which one is widespread, one occurs in
the South, and one in the North, are the most injurious of the roundworms. The eggs of hookworms pass out in the feces of the animal,
and the infective larvae are taken up in contaminated feed or water
or penetrate the skin. Dogs may be infected even before birth.
Marked anemia from the bloodsucking activities of the parasite in the
intestines, and from internal hemorrhage, is the principal result. Prevention: Sanitation and prompt disposal of feces; sterilization of contaminated soil in runs with strong salt brine. Treatment: Dosing,
under suitable conditions, with tetrachlorethylene or normal butyl
chloride. (2) Large intestinal roundworms (ascarids): One species
infests dogs, one cats, and one both dogs and cats. The eggs pass out
with the feces, develop to an infective stage, and are swallowed with
contaminated feed or water. The larvae migrate extensively in the
body, affecting the liver, lungs, and intestines, and causing unthriftiness, intestinal disturbances, obstruction of the intestines, sometimes
pneumonia, and other injuries. They are especially injurious to young
animals. Prevention: Sanitation and prompt disposal of feces.
Treatment: As for hookworms.

(3) The dog whipworm infests the cecum, or blind gut, and is probably injurious, though the symptoms of infestation are vague. Infection is acquired as in the case of ascarids. Prevention: As for
ascarids. Treatment: Dosing, under suitable conditions, with normal
butyl chloride. (4) The heart worm infests dogs and occasionally cats,
usually occurring in the heart and the pulmonary artery. It is most
abundant in the South and along the Atlantic coast as far north as
New York. Active larvae are discharged directly into the blood
stream, from which they are picked up by mosquitoes and possibly by
fleas. Symptoms include gasping, coughing, collapse, and nervous
disturbances. Prevention: Keep dogs free of fleas and confine them
at night in mosquito-proof kennels. Treatment: Injections of antimony compounds (dangerous to dogs—should be given only by a
veterinarian).

(5) The esophageal worm of dogs, found in tumors in the esophagus
and stomach, passes part of its life in the body of a beetle. In dogs it
can produce such serious consequences as pleurisy, peritonitis, suffocation, rupture of blood vessels. (6) Lungworms are relatively rare in

dogs and cats but may be important in some areas. Coughing, wheezing, general unthriftiness, and emaciation are among the symptoms of infestation. (7) The kidney worm is not a common parasite of dogs in the United States. It occurs in the abdominal cavity and sometimes the kidney and may cause serious injury. (8) An eye worm that infests other animals has also been reported in dogs and cats in California. It lives under the eyelid and in the tear ducts, sometimes causing serious injury and blindness.

In general, less is known about the life histories of the esophageal worms, lungworms, kidney worms, and eye worms than about the other worm parasites of dogs and cats, and the authors give no specific recommendations for control or treatment.

The authors describe a new treatment, consisting of hydrogen peroxide administered as an enema, that is reported to be effective for all types of worms that infest the intestinal tract. It should be used with caution.

Mange of Dogs

Dogs are attacked by three kinds of mites, each of which causes a different kind of mange, described by Price and Bishopp. (1) Sarcoptic mange, or scabies, caused by a tiny mite the female of which burrows into the skin, is characterized at first by red points, then by small blisters, and finally by scabs and crusts, baldness, and a peculiar odor. Itching is intense, the whole body may eventually be involved, body functions are upset, and the disease may be fatal if untreated. It can also be transmitted to human beings. (2) Ear mange is caused by a larger mite that lives deep in the ear canal, where it punctures the skin. Bacterial invasions may follow, producing inflammation of the inner ear and even of the brain. (3) Demodectic or red mange, the most common of the three, is caused by a wormlike mite that lives in the hair follicles and sebaceous glands. The disease is characterized by gradually spreading bald patches, a coppery color of the skin, pustules (pimples), and invasions by pus-forming bacteria, which produce poisons that may eventually cause death.

Mange of dogs should be diagnosed and treated by a veterinarian. Ear mange is the easiest to cure, and various remedies containing phenol, carbon tetrachloride, or rotenone are used. Sulfur in various forms or rotenone in ointments or washes is used for sarcoptic mange. Red mange is the hardest to cure; rotenone used in various ways is a promising remedy, and a combination of carbolic aid, sulfur, oil of tar, kerosene, and linseed oil is sometimes employed. A good diet, comfortable quarters, and adequate disinfection of the premises should accompany any treatment for mange.

Ticks Affecting Dogs

Bishopp and Smith describe eight different species of ticks that attack dogs, but most people know them all as "dog ticks" or "wood ticks." Practically all of them also bite human beings. Several carry Rocky Mountain spotted fever and tularemia, or rabbit fever.

All have somewhat similar habits and life histories and must feed on blood to reproduce.

The American dog tick, the most widely distributed and abundant, is found particularly along the Atlantic and Gulf coasts, in the Mississippi Valley, and along the Pacific coast south of Oregon. It carries Rocky Mountain spotted fever and tularemia, though these diseases do not occur everywhere and only one tick in several hundred is actually infected. An engorged female deposits 3,000 to 6,000 eggs in a mass on the ground, and the seed ticks and nymphs feed on meadow mice and other rodents. The adults feed on dogs, other large animals, and human beings. Larvae and nymphs can live a year without feeding and adults over 2 years.

The best way to control these and other ticks is to immerse or wash the dog regularly twice a week in a derris dip (1 ounce of mild soap and 2 ounces of derris or cube powder to each gallon of warm water). The liquid will keep for 2 or 3 weeks in a tank in a dark place, but if no dipping tank is available the dog can be washed thoroughly in a tub. The authors describe the procedure in detail. In lieu of a dip, derris, or cube powder may be applied as a dust. Ticks can also be removed individually with tweezers and dropped in turpentine or kerosene, care being taken to prevent infection. Destruction of rodents, keeping vegetation closely cut or grazed, burning over, and spraying vegetation with nicotine sulfate are all useful control measures under certain circumstances.

Other ticks described are the Rocky Mountain spotted fever tick (Rocky Mountain region), the Pacific coast tick (California and southern Oregon), the black-legged tick (Eastern and Southern States), the California black-legged tick (Pacific coast), the Gulf coast tick (Gulf and southern Atlantic coasts), and the lone star tick (Eastern States as far west as Texas). For each of these, certain of the control measures recommended for the American dog tick are applicable.

Two other ticks require different treatment. The spinose ear tick, which gets deep into the dog's ear, can be killed with a few drops of derris or cube powder mixed in medicinal mineral oil and dropped into the ear; or a mixture of pine tar and cottonseed oils may be used. The brown dog tick, which occurs all over the United States, can live entirely indoors in heated buildings, needs no other animal except the dog on which to complete its life cycle, and is especially difficult to eradicate. The derris dip should be used at 3-day intervals. Wooden kennels should be sprayed with undiluted creosote oil and metal kennels with triple-strength creosote dip (or a blowtorch may be used along cracks). In dwelling houses, pyrethrum-kerosene sprays and powder may be employed to combat infestations.

FLEAS

Human fleas, dog fleas, cat fleas, and the sticktight fleas of poultry. all attack dogs and cats, and the human flea can also breed on hogs. The cat flea, dog flea, and human flea serve as intermediate hosts for the dog tapeworm, which can infect human beings. All three of these flea species can—although they usually do not—carry bubonic plague.

Fleas are also apparently associated with summer eczema of dogs. To this list of evils must be added the torment caused by fleas and the fact that, uncontrolled, they can completely overrun houses and farm buildings. Why put up with them, asks Bishopp, when they can easily be suppressed?

For dogs and cats, scatter a small amount of derris, cube, or fresh pyrethrum powder next to the skin along the neck and back; or wash the animal in water containing derris or cube powder and soap. Repeat the treatment every 10 days or 2 weeks. For hogs, sprinkle the back lightly with crude petroleum or strained crankcase oil. For poultry, destroy the fleas on the premises.

Flea eggs are deposited on the host but soon drop off and hatch out tiny maggotlike larvae, which become pupae about the size of a wheat kernel and finally adult fleas. To kill fleas and larvae on the premises, use a creosote-oil spray. In infested buildings, such as homes, where creosote oil would be damaging, scatter flaked naphthalene liberally—about 5 pounds to a room—and close up and vacate the building for at least 48 hours. Close cutting of grass will usually kill fleas in lawns, or the grass can be sprayed with nicotine sulfate.

Running Fits (Fright Disease)

The symptoms of running fits, also known as fright disease, barking fits, furious fits, and canine hysteria, are rather accurately indicated by the names given to this nervous disease; for no apparent reason the dog suddenly starts running and barking, then hides in a dark place, or may have spasms and convulsions. Attacks recur and the condition may last for years. Many persons have mistakenly confused it with rabies. No cause is definitely known, though the disease has been attributed to infection, heredity, inbreeding, circulatory disturbances, deficiency of vitamin A or vitamin B_1, indigestion, intestinal poisoning, parasites, estrum, and various irritations and excitements.

Among measures for treatment and prevention suggested by Stein are a good diet, high in fresh meat, milk, and eggs; good regulation of the bowels; correction of any parasitic infestation; occasional use of small amounts of cod-liver oil, calcium lactate, and yeast for dogs that are kept confined. During an attack the dog should be left unmolested in a dark room, and afterwards it should be kept as quiet as possible. If treatment, such as intestinal irrigation or the administration of nerve sedatives, is necessary, it should be undertaken only by a veterinarian.

Nonparasitic Skin Diseases of Dogs and Cats

When a dog or a cat develops some skin disease, most people are inclined to call it either mange or eczema. As a matter of fact, it might be any one of a number of other skin maladies, some of which are common, others uncommon; and expert diagnosis, including a microscopic examination or even a culture test, may be necessary to determine the exact trouble, and hence the treatment. Moreover, of the 11 nonparasitic diseases discussed by Stein in this article, only 2, ringworm and favus, have absolutely specific causes—in these two cases, fungi. The other nine conditions—alopecia (falling hair), dandruff, dermatitis (inflammation of the skin), eczema, impetigo, seborrhea, acne, lip ulceration of cats, and urticaria (hives)—may all be due to various causes. In other words, the name of the disease does not identify any particular cause, but simply designates a group of symptoms.

These symptoms are described in the article, which discusses the known or possible causes in each case and the treatments that may be used. Prevention, of course, depends on avoiding or eliminating the causes of a given condition.

Nutritional Diseases of Dogs and Cats

Much more is known about the nutrition of dogs, Earle points out, than about that of cats, but it is assumed that both suffer from the same nutritional diseases. In practice, such diseases are usually due to two or more deficiencies occurring at the same time rather than to one, as in the laboratory. A well-balanced diet of natural foodstuffs is the best preventive and the best cure, though it may be advisable to use pure vitamins for emergency treatment. The author gives the quantitative vitamin requirements wherever possible and suggests common food sources from which the vitamins and minerals are obtained. The following nutritional diseases are discussed in some detail:

Rickets in young dogs and cats, as in other animals and human beings, is due to a deficiency of calcium, phosphorus, or vitamin D, or to an unbalance between the two minerals. The condition can be detected much earlier by X-ray than by clinical symptoms.

Eclampsia, a malady of female dogs and cats at the time of parturition, is apparently due to a deficiency of calcium and a vitamin D disturbance.

Scurvy, or a condition like it, occasionally occurs in dogs and can be relieved by the administration of vitamin C. Dogs are supposed to manufacture their own vitamin C, but there may sometimes be a failure in normal functioning of the animal organism.

Nutritional anemia is commonly associated with a deficiency of iron or copper, or a prolonged shortage of proteins necessary for the formation of red blood cells. The necessary iron can easily be supplied by meat, especially liver. Apparently a deficiency of vitamin B_6 can cause a certain type of anemia, associated with blacktongue.

Vitamin A deficiency is often not diagnosed until it is so advanced that the animal may fail to recover even under treatment; xerophthalmia, a serious eye disease, is an advanced symptom. Conditions due to a partial deficiency are particularly hard to diagnose. Not much work has been done with night blindness in dogs, but Earle suggests that it might be studied as an early symptom of a deficiency of this vitamin.

Thiamin (B_1) deficiency produces a disease in dogs that closely parallels beri-beri in human beings. Marked loss of appetite is an early symptom of a deficiency of this vitamin in dogs; others include nervousness and fatigue. There is some evidence that thiamin deficiency may be a factor in fright disease.

Riboflavin (B₂) deficiency results in a redness and dry scaliness of the skin, with severe symptoms such as a staggering gait and collapse in acute stages.

Blacktongue, a disease that apparently parallels pellagra in human beings, can be cured and prevented by a diet containing adequate amounts of nicotinic acid and other B vitamins.

Other vitamin B deficiencies. For normal health, dogs require pantothenic acid and biotin (the so-called anti-gray-hair factor) as well as the other B vitamins mentioned.

PART 9

WILDLIFE DISEASES AND PARASITES

Diseases of Farm-Raised Game Birds

Shillinger discusses some of the more common diseases and parasites that, in the aggregate, often cause heavy losses among game birds raised on farms for restocking purposes.   Control measures are suggested wherever possible.   The discussion is purposely brief because so many of the same diseases and parasites affect domestic poultry; the reader should therefore refer to the poultry articles for further details.   As the author points out, transmission of diseases from domestic to wild birds is favored when the two use the same range or when domesticated hens incubate game-bird eggs or brood the young.

The author deals with the following diseases and parasites:

Pullorum disease is only occasionally observed in pheasants and quail.

Tuberculosis is often transmitted from domestic to game birds.

Ulcerative enteritis is the most destructive disease of quail and grouse on game farms. Unchecked outbreaks may kill 70 to 100 percent of the birds.

Salmonella infection produces a disease of obscure character among quail.

Blackhead is especially destructive to wild turkeys but also affects quail and ruffed grouse.

Coccidiosis is as destructive to young game birds as to young chickens.

Trichomoniasis causes severe losses among quail and wild turkeys.

Aspergillosis is a fungus disease that may cause losses as high as 90 percent in affected broods of quail.

Thrush is another fungus disease that affects quail and wild turkeys.

Worm parasites of several kinds attack various internal organs, as in the case of domestic fowl.

Nutritional diseases—especially vitamin A and vitamin D deficiencies—are responsible for diseases among farm-raised game birds; and cannibalism (corrected by feeding extra salt) also occurs.

DISEASES OF FUR ANIMALS

Shillinger covers some of the more important diseases of silver foxes and minks; the latter, as he notes, are particularly subject to infection because they are so often kept in crowded quarters. For further information on some of these diseases the reader should refer to the articles on dogs and cats in this book.

Paratyphoid, which occurs fairly frequently in severe outbreaks among silver foxes, can be checked by the use of a vaccine, preferably prepared from material on the farm where the disease occurs.

Infectious enteritis, caused by a *Salmonella* organism, produces severe inflammation of the intestinal tract. Careful hygiene is necessary to prevent the spread of infection. A specially prepared buttermilk is sometimes given to sick animals.

Distemper is so easily spread that the utmost hygienic precautions must be taken when a case occurs. The antiserum used for dogs gives temporary protection to foxes. Experiments are being made to develop a vaccine that will produce more lasting immunity.

Anthrax among minks has been traced to the feeding of meat from infected domestic animals. Since it entails heavy losses and is very dangerous to human beings, extreme care should be taken to prevent its introduction from this source.

The internal parasites that infest fur animals include hookworms, ascarids, and lungworms. The use of wire-mesh flooring to reduce infection from droppings is a wise precaution. Anthelmintics, discussed by the author, are used for hookworms and ascarids.

Fleas, which may damage pelts, can be controlled by the use of sulfur, pyrethrum, or derris, preferably used as a dust rather than a dip. Body mange seldom affects fur animals; when a few are affected, it may be better to destroy rather than treat them. Ear mange, which is common among silver foxes, can be treated with various preparations suggested by the author.

Food poisoning, chiefly botulism, sometimes occurs on fur farms, especially among minks. It is due to inadequate refrigeration or unsanitary handling of feed.

Chastek paralysis, a disease of silver foxes fed liberally on certain kinds of fresh fish, is apparently due to a factor that destroys vitamin B_1. This factor itself can be destroyed by adequate cooking of the fish. Administration of vitamin B_1 cures the disease.

DISEASES OF WILDLIFE AND THEIR RELATIONSHIP
TO DOMESTIC LIVESTOCK

The fact that many diseases and parasites affect both domestic animals and wildlife poses a threefold problem—how to prevent their spread from domestic to wild animals, and also in the reverse direction; and how to control them in wild animals. Shillinger's discussion of these maladies is brief, to avoid repetition of details given in the articles on livestock; but some of the important facts he brings out will be new to readers not intimately acquainted with wildlife problems. The diseases and parasites included are the following:

Brucellosis is rather common among big-game ruminants. Brucellosis-free herds of buffalo and elk are being built up by vaccination.

Hemorrhagic septicemia is responsible for extensive losses among deer and buffaloes. An effective bacterin has been produced for the latter.

Tuberculosis has frequently been diagnosed in deer, foxes, wild ducks, and wild pheasants.

Necrobacillosis is a rather common cause of losses, especially among the larger wild ruminants fed in concentrated herds by attendants.

Malignant edema is a fatal disease of deer.

Tularemia affects not only rabbits but many other animals and has been responsible for heavy losses among dense populations in the wild.

Foot-and-mouth disease, in one outbreak in this country, affected deer as well as cattle.

The virus of encephalomyelitis, a disease of equines (and human beings), has been found in wild pheasants and semiwild pigeons.

Virus tumors, of both fatal and nonfatal types, occur in rabbits.

Leucocytozoan disease is caused by a protozoan organism that infects wild as well as domestic ducks and is especially dangerous to young ducklings.

A malarial organism has recently been found in the blood of sharp-tailed grouse, and its possible relationship to losses in other wild and domestic birds is now being studied.

Anaplasmosis has been found to be infectious for Columbian black-tailed deer, which may serve as reservoirs of the blood parasite.

Whether mange mites are transmissible from wild to domestic animals and vice versa is not definitely known.

Screwworms have caused rather heavy losses among deer.

Worm parasites of several kinds are parasitic in wild animals, causing damage similar to that in livestock.

Pollution of water by sewage, oil, and industrial waste has caused considerable destruction of aquatic mammals and birds.

Botulism has been responsible for many deaths among waterfowl and shore birds around stagnant pools.

At the time this book went to press, the drugs and other materials mentioned in various articles—chiefly as disinfectants, insecticides, and anthelmintics—were still available for veterinary and medical use. Under war conditions, however, it is possible that some of these materials may become scarce or unavailable. In that case, the reader should obtain professional advice from the Department of Agriculture, the State experiment station, a local veterinarian, or the county agent as to available substitutes.

108

Losses Caused by Animal Diseases and Parasites

BY JOHN R. MOHLER, A. E. WIGHT,
W. M. MAC KELLAR, AND F. C. BISHOPP [1]

GERMS AND WORMS and other low forms of life pick close to half a billion dollars a year from the pockets of our livestock producers, often so expertly that the producer does not even realize his loss. Here are enemies that must be fought with our very best strategy, based on research.

THE TRADITIONS of the oldest civilized nations show that they early recognized the importance of diseases among their animals and the danger these diseases meant to human health. Today, with a dense livestock population in many parts of the world, modern transportation facilities, and the daily concentration of large numbers of farm animals at hundreds of market centers, the opportunities for animals to become infected with diseases and parasites are greatly increased in comparison with those of the past. The prevention or control of these diseases and the protection of the public from exposure to those that are communicable to man have become complicated and costly.

The far-reaching economic consequences of animal diseases, parasites, and insects are frequently not understood or are overlooked. Most of us think little of the death of a chicken; yet the aggregate monetary loss from poultry diseases, involving mortality and nonproductivity among adult fowls as well as the death of young and growing birds, is incredibly high in the course of a year. Moreover, in many cases of disease, the losses are much more extensive than

[1] John R. Mohler is Chief, Bureau of Animal Industry; A. E. Wight is Chief, Tuberculosis Eradication Division; W. M. MacKellar is Chief, Division of Tick Eradication and Special Diseases, Bureau of Animal Industry; and F. C. Bishopp is Assistant Chief, Bureau of Entomology and Plant Quarantine.

the direct loss due to the death of the affected animal or the depreciation in its value. Some diseases, such as cattle tick fever, have even restricted the whole agricultural program in the infected districts.

Some of the cost of disease prevention is chargeable to diseases that do not even exist in the United States but which in self-protection this country has to guard against by maintaining an effective quarantine service at ports of entry. The communicability to man of a number of animal diseases is well known, and this danger adds to the economic losses. The need for and the cost of meat and milk inspection are in large part due to the necessity of guarding the consumer against animal diseases that may be transmitted by these food products. Quarantines within our own country, which either prevent or restrict the movement of animals from a specified area, are important and necessary control measures, but generally they adversely affect the value of the healthy as well as the diseased animals within the quarantined area; and sometimes, as in an area quarantined on account of cattle tick infestation, even the land values may depreciate. For protection against other diseases, such as hog cholera, anthrax, and encephalomyelitis, enormous numbers of healthy animals have to be immunized each year. In addition to the monetary losses from contagious and infectious diseases, there are those resulting from sporadic diseases, poisonous plants, wounds, and injuries, which, taken together, amount to a very large sum. In fact, it has been estimated that the loss solely from shipping injuries to food-producing animals due to abuse, carelessness, or other preventable causes amounts to at least 11.5 million dollars annually.

The intangible or indirect nature of much of the loss due to animal diseases makes it impossible to calculate the exact amount in dollars and cents. However, it has been estimated to be nearly one-half of a billion dollars annually. In the never-ending fight to reduce this drain on the livestock industry, hundreds of scientific workers are constantly employed, both publicly and privately. Large sums are expended each year by the States and the Federal Government for the prevention, control, and eradication of diseases now present in the United States and to guard against the introduction of new diseases and pests from abroad.

The following examples of a few of the more important diseases and pests will serve to show the extent of some of these losses.

TUBERCULOSIS

The existence of tuberculosis among farm animals causes serious losses, partly because the disease is communicable between different classes of livestock. Swine, for example, readily contract the avian type of tuberculosis when exposed to poultry infected with the disease, and the susceptibility of human beings to tuberculosis of the bovine type has an important bearing on public health problems.

Much progress has been made in the control and eradication of tuberculosis in livestock during the last 24 years, as evidenced by the great reduction in the percentage of cattle that react to the tuberculin test and by the reduction in the number of carcasses and parts of carcasses condemned for this disease at slaughtering establishments operating under Federal inspection. During the fiscal year 1941 approximately 12,229,500 tuberculin tests were applied to cattle by veterinarians under the direction of the officials conducting cooperative tuberculosis-eradication work. The percentage of cattle that reacted to these tests was 0.3, the lowest average degree of infection found in any year since the work was undertaken in 1917. The percentage that year was approximately 5, while the annual financial loss from bovine tuberculosis alone was conservatively estimated at 25 million dollars. Also during 1917 slightly more than 2 percent of all the cattle slaughtered in establishments operating under Federal supervision were retained for further inspection because some evidence of tuberculosis was shown on post-mortem examination. About 195,500 cattle carcasses were retained, of which about 41,000 were condemned as unfit for human food. On the other hand, during the fiscal year ended June 30, 1941, the percentage of cattle retained, exclusive of known reactors to the tuberculin test, was 0.07. About 8,000 cattle carcasses were retained, of which 1,584 were condemned as unfit for human food.

During the fiscal year 1917, evidence of tuberculosis was reported in approximately 10 percent of all the hogs slaughtered under Federal supervision, and about 168,000 carcasses, or 0.41 percent of the number slaughtered, were condemned as unfit for food or passed for sterilization. The percentage of retentions increased gradually up to 1924, when it was 15.2, an increase of about 50 percent during that period of 7 years. Since 1924 the percentage of retentions has gradually diminished; during the fiscal year 1941 it was 8.2, and the number of carcasses condemned and sterilized was 31,200, or 0.06 percent of the number slaughtered. Much of the tuberculosis now being reported in swine is of the avian type.

The cooperative tuberculosis-eradication work among livestock has consisted largely in the tuberculin testing of cattle and the removal of reactors to the test. Through the combined efforts of all State, Federal, and county livestock officials, breeders, dairymen, and others, it was possible to apply about 241,950,000 tuberculin tests to cattle in this country from 1917 to June 30, 1941; about 3,809,000 reactors were disclosed and disposed of for slaughter. All the counties in all the States had qualified as modified accredited tuberculosis-free areas on November 1, 1940, indicating that the disease was present in less than one-half of 1 percent of the cattle population.

The losses caused by tuberculosis in poultry are considerable each year, especially in 11 of the North Central States, owing to mortality, decreased egg production, and general unthriftiness.

OTHER DISEASES

Brucellosis exists among cattle to some extent in all parts of the United States, but it is much more prevalent in some localities than in others.

Considerable research work on the control of this disease had been accomplished in this country before 1934, and in some States quite a large number of herds of cattle had been freed of it. In 1934 a cooperative eradication plan was put into effect. At that time it was estimated that approximately 10 percent of the dairy and breeding cattle over 6 months of age in this country would react to the blood-agglutination test used to diagnose the disease, and many writers estimated that the annual loss due to the disease from reduction in the calf crop, nonbreeding, and reduction in milk production was in the neighborhood of 50 million dollars. Many breeders of purebred cattle, who had spent a lifetime building up herds with animals of irreplaceable blood lines, were forced out of business by the presence of a virulent type of the disease.

Since 1934 the incidence of infection with brucellosis has been considerably reduced. A large number of herds have passed three tests showing no infection within a period of a year and have qualified as accredited brucellosis-free herds. Also, a considerable number of counties have qualified as modified accredited areas, indicating that in county-wide testing of all the dairy and breeding cattle over 6 months of age, not more than 1 percent of the cattle or 5 percent of the herds were found to be infected. In many of these counties the degree of infection is less than 1 percent.

Johne's disease, which affects ruminants principally, was identified in this country probably 35 or 40 years ago. The causative agent, a bacillus, is expelled through body excretions and can be easily spread from farm to farm in many ways, the most important of which, no doubt, is by the introduction of infected cattle into clean herds.

It is difficult to estimate the monetary losses due to Johne's disease, as it probably exists unreported in many localities. On the basis of information from various reliable sources, however, it is believed that the financial losses are approximately half a million dollars a year. The disease has not been reported in human beings, although medical authorities have reported a chronic dysentery with symptoms similar to those found in cattle affected with Johne's disease. No satisfactory treatment for the disease is known at present.

Cattle tick fever was once the most serious obstacle faced by the cattle owners of the South. During the last half of the nineteenth century cattle died from it by the thousands, and at the beginning of this century it was estimated to be taking an annual toll of 40 million dollars from the South. All attempts at medicinal treatment had proved ineffective in controlling these losses. Following the discovery that the cattle tick was the only natural carrier of the disease, however, it became evident that without the tick the disease would be of little importance and would probably die out. On this theory efforts to eradicate the cattle tick were undertaken in 1906 and have continued uninterruptedly up to the present time, with the result that the area quarantined for cattle tick fever has been reduced to about 1 percent of its original size and the disease is no longer considered a serious menace in the United States.

Probably no other infectious animal disease is so widespread as hog cholera, and few parts of the world where swine are grown are free from its ravages. Since the first report of its appearance in

Ohio in 1833, it has spread to every State in the Union. During certain years, notably 1887, 1897, 1913, and 1926, the disease seemed to flare up in a virulent form and was unusually widespread in the United States, with estimated monetary losses amounting to 65 million dollars for a single year. In recent years the extensive immunization of swine with anti-hog-cholera serum and virus has held losses to a lower level, but notwithstanding these extensive prophylactic measures hog cholera continues to be the most serious and destructive disease of swine. It is estimated that directly and indirectly the disease is still responsible for an average annual loss of about 12.5 million dollars to the swine growers of the country.

PARASITES AND OTHER PESTS

The losses from the depredations of parasites affect not only the producers of livestock but also the meat industry and some other industries that utilize certain animal products for commercial purposes. The greatest losses, however, are sustained by livestock producers in the form of unthriftiness in stock, debility usually associated with digestive and respiratory disturbances, stunting, and death of young stock and poultry. The unhealthiness in particular is a serious drain on the resources of livestock producers, since it involves the expenditure of rather large sums of money for medication to alleviate symptoms of sickness as well as waste of feed in unsuccessful attempts to promote growth and fattening of parasitized animals.

It is difficult to estimate the death losses from parasites because there is no machinery for collecting information of this sort. That such losses are considerable, however, is evident from the fact that parasitism in livestock and poultry is widespread in this country; that severe death losses, sometimes as great as 10 percent, occur quite frequently among all classes of stock and poultry; that the losses have been reduced sharply in special cases by resorting to control measures and effective medication; that it is the common experience of sheep producers that lambs cannot be raised successfully on the farm without resorting to periodic drenching or other treatment with medicinal preparations and without making provision for rotation or other methods of parasite control; and that successful swine husbandry involves a special system of management designed to hold in check infections with roundworms, lungworms, kidney worms, and the other parasites that are responsible for most of the unthriftiness and stunting so common in pigs in many parts of this country.

The losses due to unthriftiness and stunting are even more difficult to estimate than the actual death losses. It is known, however, from information published by various investigators, that the waste of feed in raising and fattening parasitized stock must be enormous. For instance, it has been determined that whereas an average of 3.1 pounds of feed produced a gain of 1 pound in 7 weeks in chicks protected from parasites, 4.5 pounds of feed was required to produce this gain in weight in parasitized birds. In extensive studies conducted some years ago on 150 farms in the Middle West on which effective parasite control for swine was practiced, it was found that pigs with which these special precautions were taken were ready for market 7 weeks younger than the average age at which pigs in that area were usually marketed, and that at 4 months of age the pigs so protected weighed 28 pounds more than pigs that had become parasitized. In a recent study by parasitologists of the Bureau of Animal Industry it was determined that sheep that acquired even a moderate infection with nodular worms on a pasture over a period of several months weighed on an average 10 pounds less than comparable sheep on a similar pasture free from nodular worm larvae.

The losses sustained by the meat industry have been ascertained much more extensively and accurately than those occurring on the farm. In large sections of the South where pigs are commonly affected with kidney worms the average loss per pig due to condemnation of the liver, kidneys, and kidney fat and trimming of loins to remove worms and lesions is nearly 40 cents a head. Several years ago it was estimated that the losses due to the condemnation of sheep intestines (used for casings and in the preparation of surgical suture material) because of pathological conditions produced by nodular worms amounted to about $200,000 in one State. The annual loss on beef and sheep livers condemned under meat inspection because of parasitic infestations of various kinds may be conservatively estimated at half a million dollars a year.

In spite of the general paucity of information on which to base accurate figures, it may be estimated conservatively that the total losses from parasites of all kinds, including the cost of drugs to keep these pests in check and the labor and equipment involved in special systems of management for controlling them, are about 125 million dollars a year. Of this large total, it is estimated that the diseases due to protozoan parasites, of which coccidiosis is of greatest economic importance, exact an annual toll from the resources of farmers, stockmen, and poultrymen of about 10 million dollars, half of which is chargeable to poultry coccidiosis. Furthermore, the combined losses from liver flukes in cattle, sheep, and goats and from tapeworms in all classes of stock and poultry are estimated at 5 million dollars a year. The large bulk of the remaining loss (about 110 million dollars) is chargeable to nematodes, or roundworms.

Insects, mites, and ticks are responsible for tremendous losses among livestock of all kinds. Many of these pests act as disease transmitters, most of them carrying diseases accidentally. Some serve as intermediate hosts of disease organisms, that is, the organisms must pass through an essential cycle of development in the body of the insect. Insects damage livestock directly by causing loss of blood or destruction of tissue, and they irritate and worry the animals by their presence or their bites. The resulting losses take the form of increased mortality, lowered general condition, slower growth, increased feed consumption, lowered work output, and reduced quantity and quality of such products as milk, wool, and hides.

The constant and persistent attacks of such pests as horn flies, stableflies, and horseflies, and, to some extent, mosquitoes produce nervous reactions that often cause grazing animals to stop feeding and seek such shelter as may be found in streams and shady places.

Under such circumstances it is impossible for them to put on flesh, and consequently it is difficult to bring them to a marketable condition. In dairy animals there is a direct loss due to lowered milk flow. Death is sometimes caused by concentrated attacks of particularly vicious species. The buffalo gnat is notorious in some of the Southern States for its destruction of animals, especially mules.

Mosquitoes cause heavier losses among livestock than is generally realized. For the most part the losses are more or less intangible and incapable of being appraised in terms of dollars and cents; they are due chiefly to interference with the normal development and well-being of the animals. Along the Gulf coast cattle are frequently driven from their feeding grounds in the marshes into the open water by mosquito attacks. Deaths of cattle from the concentrated attack of the large mosquito (*Psorophora columbiae*) are a matter of record.

The common housefly annoys all classes of livestock by crawling about on them and feeding on the secretions of the eyes and body openings. It also is capable of transmitting certain diseases of livestock, such as mastitis. What is more important, this fly may contaminate milk and other dairy products with the germs of such human diseases as typhoid, dysentery, tuberculosis, and cholera.

The most extensive losses to the livestock industry caused by insects are those due to the attacks of species that penetrate the living tissues of the animal and derive their entire sustenance during their period of growth from the body of their host. Some of these, such as the cattle grub, or heel fly, the horse bot, and the head bot of sheep, spend the greater part of the year within the body of the host animal. All three of these insects occasionally attack man and penetrate the body or head tissues. They cause much suffering and make medical attention necessary.

The damage wrought by screwworms and blowflies on livestock is spectacular, and the losses are all too apparent. The primary screwworm will attack any animal on which there is an injury, however slight. Thousands of cases of screwworm injury occur each year in the South and especially the Southwest. The cost of treatment, added to the value of animals killed by screwworms each year, constitutes a very heavy loss, which has been estimated to be at least 5 million dollars annually in the United States.

Lice of various species attack practically all the domestic animals and cause varying degrees of loss. Goat lice retard the development of young goats, lower the quality of mohair, reduce the amount of the clip, and frequently cause death. Chicken lice reduce egg production to a marked degree and lower the vitality of the fowls. Mites, fowl ticks, and sticktight fleas supplement the attacks of lice on chickens, and the combined result is a heavy loss to the poultry industry. The loss caused by the attacks of lice on cattle, horses, and hogs is less tangible but no less real. At the least a heavy infestation means decreased vitality.

Mites producing scabies or mange are the source of varying degrees of loss. In sheep, infestations of scab mites result in the loss of large quantities of wool by shedding, and heavy infestations may so weaken the animals that they may die. Mange mites produce an unhealthy condition in other animals which in extreme cases may destroy their usefulness. The expense of enforcing quarantines against scab and mange is by no means a small item. Fortunately losses in this country from these mites have been greatly reduced in recent years by dipping operations.

Certain insects and allied classes of arthropods, such as ticks, transmit diseases to animals and are thus chargeable with the losses caused by these diseases. Outstanding in this group is the cattle tick, which transmits tick, or splenetic, fever of cattle. Anthrax is transmitted from animal to animal by biting flies and may be transmitted to man in the same way. Anaplasmosis is likewise transmitted by ticks and certain insects, and equine encephalomyelitis has been shown to be transmitted by mosquitoes. Buffalo gnats transmit the leucocytozoan disease of wild and tame ducks and a similar disease of turkeys. In Michigan some severe losses of ducks have occurred, and apparently heavy losses among young turkeys result from this malady.

Various parasitic worms of animals pass an essential stage of their existence in the bodies of insects. Without the insects as intermediate hosts they would never reach the stage where they can become animal parasites.

Finally, insects that destroy forage are responsible for considerable loss of livestock feed. The devastation of ranges by grasshoppers within the last few years has cut rather deeply into the profits from stock raising in the affected regions.

A TABULATION OF LOSSES

A conservative estimate of annual losses from the more important diseases, parasites, and pests of livestock and poultry, as of January 1, 1942, is included in the following tabulation:

Internal parasites	$125, 000, 000
External parasites of poultry	85, 000, 000
Cattle grubs	65, 000, 000
Poultry diseases (except tuberculosis and those caused by parasites)	40, 000, 000
Brucellosis of cattle (Bang's disease)	30, 000, 000
Mastitis	19, 000, 000
Hog cholera	12, 500, 000
Tuberculosis (cattle, swine, and poultry)	10, 500, 000
Swine abortion	10, 000, 000
Stablefly and horn fly	10, 000, 000
Screwworms	5, 000, 000
Cattle and sheep scabies	1, 000, 000
Encephalomyelitis	1, 000, 000
Swine erysipelas	1, 000, 000
Anthrax	750, 000
Johne's disease	500, 000
Hemorrhagic septicemia	500, 000
Goat lice	500, 000
Cattle tick fever	400, 000
Rabies	250, 000
Anaplasmosis	100, 000
Total	$418, 000, 000

Causes of Disease

BY H. W. SCHOENING, BENJAMIN SCHWARTZ,
WARD T. HUFFMAN, AND LOUIS L. MADSEN [1]

THIS ARTICLE gives basic information about bacteria, viruses, and internal parasites—what they are, what they do to the body, and how they do it—and includes brief discussions of nutritional deficiencies and plant poisons as two other important causes of disease in livestock.

THE ANIMAL BODY is composed of an intricate, coordinated collection of cells of various types, bound together by connecting tissues. The outer layer of all the tissues together is the common covering, the skin. The cells that make up the various tissues have specific functions to perform, and a certain interdependence of all the tissues and functions is necessary for the maintenance of health. Any agent that is inimical to the life and functions of the cells and tissues may be considered a disease-producing agent, and disease may be defined as any abnormal condition of the tissues of the body.

Among disease-producing agents may be mentioned germs, viruses, parasites (internal and external), chemicals, poisons of various kinds, faulty nutrition, and injuries.

In a broad sense, a disease process can be considered as an inflammation. The suffix "itis" means "inflammation of," and when attached to the root of the name of an anatomical part, it means an inflammation of that part; examples are appendicitis, an inflammation of the appendix; tonsillitis, an inflammation of the tonsils; and peritonitis, an inflammation of the peritoneum, the abdominal lining membrane. Whatever the factor that causes disease may be and

[1] H. W. Schoening, Chief, Pathological Division, Bureau of Animal Industry, prepared the introductory statement and the section on Bacterial and Virus Infections; Benjamin Schwartz, Chief, Zoological Division, Bureau of Animal Industry, prepared the material on Animal Parasites; Ward T. Huffman, in Charge of Stock Poisoning Caused by Plants, Pathological Division, Bureau of Animal Industry, at Salt Lake City, Utah, wrote Poisonous Plants as Causes of Disease; and Louis L. Madsen, Nutritionist, Animal Nutrition Division, Bureau of Animal Industry, contributed the section on Nutritional Deficiencies as Causes of Disease.

wherever it may be located in the body, its activities result in an inflammation of the part affected. Any injury results in the destruction of tissues and cells, and the inflammatory reaction that follows is an effort on the part of the body to repair the injury. The effort is manifested by an increased circulation to the part affected and the seepage of serum and other blood elements into the tissues for the purpose of removing the damaged tissue. The ability of the body to repair the damage caused by the disease-producing agent determines. whether or not the affected part will recover, or return to its normal state.

In this article, infection with bacteria, viruses, and parasites, poisoning by plants, and nutritional deficiencies will be considered as factors in the production of disease.

BACTERIAL AND VIRUS INFECTIONS

Infections that cause disease are the result of invasion of the tissues by micro-organisms (bacteria) or viruses. These agents gain entrance to the animal body in various ways through the respiratory, digestive, and genital tracts and the skin, and they then multiply and attack the tissues, producing a disease condition. This is not readily accomplished, however, for the body forces make strenuous efforts to repel the invaders. The mechanism of infection and resistance is quite complex. The two factors primarily concerned are the disease-producing agent and the animal itself (the host). For an infecting agent to invade the tissues of a host successfully, it must have sufficient virulence (ability to overcome the body defenses) to establish itself within the host's body, and then it must be able either to multiply actively, producing a disease process, or to survive in a quiescent state (the carrier stage) until conditions are right for multiplication or it escapes from the host and becomes infectious to other susceptible animals. The host, on the other hand, is protected, within limits, by the barrier known as immunity or resistance. Generally speaking, resistance is relative, and varies considerably among individual animals. In some it may be quite strong; in others, weak or entirely lacking.

The infective agent is greatly influenced by its surroundings, either within or outside the animal host. Its invading ability is determined to a large extent by the environment. It is well known that certain species of animals are highly resistant to certain types of infection; the resistance of cattle to glanders, a disease of horses, may be cited as an example. In the species susceptible to a specific infection, however, there will also be found a wide variation in susceptibility and resistance among individuals. Resistance (immunity) to a disease process may be built up in certain animals to an appreciable extent by natural contact with limited amounts of infection in the field that do not produce a frank expression of the disease, and also by artificial procedures such as vaccination. It should be noted, however, that there is a wide variation in the immunity response of individual animals to the same vaccination procedure. It is not possible to say at present just what makes one animal more resistant to infection than another; it may be that a number of factors, either singly or in combination, are involved.

The success achieved in breeding plants resistant to certain diseases is well known. That heredity plays a part in some, at least, of the disease processes in animals is also known. Experimental work on cancer of mice has shown the part heredity can play in this disease, and evidence has been found in studies of bursati, or summer sores, in horses that the primary causative factor is a genetic one.

Other factors to be considered are nutrition, the influence of the glands of internal secretion, and even management practices. Recent experiments have shown that the diet of pregnant mice and actively growing young mice has a considerable influence on the resistance of these animals to invasion by a virus affecting the nervous system. Hereditary, physiological, nutritional, and management factors may all play an important part in the development of disease.

BACTERIA AS DISEASE-PRODUCING AGENTS

Bacteria, or germs, are microscopic organisms of various sizes and shapes. They are found everywhere in nature. Though some of them are capable of producing disease, many more are not only harmless but are of actual benefit through their activity in changing the composition of substances—for example, those that create the fermentation processes used in the manufacture of vinegar and the ripening of cheese. Bacteria capable of producing disease are known as pathogens, or pathogenic bacteria; those that do not produce disease are known as saprophytes, or nonpathogens.

During the last 50 years tremendous advances have been made in the science of bacteriology, and large numbers of micro-organisms have been identified as either causing specific diseases or being associated with a disease process. A system of classification has been developed whereby these microscopic organisms are identified and placed in various groups. In this article, the term "bacteria" is used in its broad sense to include all the various classes of micro-organisms that cause disease.

Bacteria are of various sizes and shapes and have distinguishing features by which they can be identified. It has been possible to grow them on artificial media in test tubes, and through various laboratory techniques it is possible to study pure strains of the organisms. The ability of various bacteria to utilize certain food substances is a further aid in differentiation. Some bacteria grow only in the presence of oxygen, others only in the complete absence of oxygen, and a third group with or without oxygen.

Some bacteria are actively motile; their physical make-up enables them to move about swiftly in the proper media. Others do not have this power of locomotion and are spoken of as nonmotile.

Some bacteria are capable under certain circumstances of forming spores. As spores, they are in a resting stage during which they are highly resistant to adverse influences, such as heat and the action of disinfectants, and may remain alive for years.

Some bacteria are able to produce powerful poisons, known as soluble toxins, in the medium in which they grow. Other bacteria carry toxins within their bodies which are liberated and exert their action when the bacteria are broken up. These, which are known as endotoxins, are not as powerful as the soluble toxins. Diseases such as tetanus (lockjaw) and diphtheria are caused by bacteria that produce powerful soluble toxins.

Further studies of pathogenic bacteria can be made through their disease-producing action on laboratory animals, such as rabbits, guinea pigs, and mice, when they are introduced into these animals by injection, feeding, or through contact exposure.

Certain diseases are produced by specific bacteria. The bacteria that cause diseases are of various types and classes, and the diseases they produce and their methods of spread are also quite varied.

Certain types of bacteria produce localized inflammatory changes in tissues, such as abscesses. Depending on the virulence of the organism and the resistance of the animal, these abscesses may remain localized, or the infection may enter the blood stream and cause a serious general disturbance and sometimes death from septicemia.

THE FILTRABLE VIRUSES

In addition to diseases produced by bacteria, there are others caused by filtrable viruses. A virus may be defined as an infectious agent capable of passing through filters that retain bacteria. The viruses are ultramicroscopic, that is, they cannot be seen under the highest powered microscope. Among the animal diseases caused by viruses are foot-and-mouth disease, hog cholera, rabies, equine encephalomyelitis, fowl pox, and laryngotracheitis of poultry. Smallpox, measles, influenza, and mumps are examples of virus diseases of man. To date, more than 35 virus diseases of animals have been identified and studied.

The virus diseases have come into special prominence in the past few years, and as a result of a vast amount of experimental work in various countries of the world, knowledge concerning them has increased considerably. Exact information on the nature of viruses is not available. They have been considered to be living entities, although recent work indicates that some of them may not be living but that they may be able to produce a substance that acts as a catalytic agent and causes cell injury. This work has been principally in the field of plant viruses, and no evidence has yet been produced to indicate that animal viruses are not living agents. Although for many years bacteria have been grown on artificial media and this process has provided an excellent opportunity to increase our knowledge concerning these organisms and the part they play in the production of disease, it has not been possible until recently to cultivate the viruses in artificial media. It is necessary that media for viruses contain living cells. The use of tissue cultures has made it possible for certain viruses to be carried indefinitely through regular transfers.

In addition to growing the viruses on tissue culture, it has also been possible to propagate many of them in growing chick embryos by methods developed through studies begun in 1931. Through certain technical procedures, an opening is made in the eggshell, and suitable material containing the virus is inoculated in the membranes surrounding the embryo. The virus multiplies in the living cells and produces pathological changes in the membranes or the embryo or both.

Through these recently developed methods of propagating viruses, it has been possible to obtain much information on their physical and chemical properties, and this has resulted in the development of immunization methods for the control of many virus diseases. Not all the disease-producing viruses have been grown on artificial media, however. Just why it has been possible to grow some and not others is not yet known, and much research work is still needed to obtain additional information on this subject.

The viruses that cause diseases of animals may be classified for the purposes of study and discussion according to the tissues they invade. Thus, the virus diseases are sometimes spoken of as neurotropic, epitheliotropic, and viscerotropic, which means that they attack principally neuron, or nerve, tissue (nerves, brain, spinal cord, etc.), epithelial tissue (skin and membranes), or visceral tissue (many or all internal tissues).

Some diseases produced by viruses are confined principally to certain tissues, but others, though affecting a certain type of tissue primarily, may also involve other tissues. The division indicated is, therefore, quite arbitrary but is used as a basis for discussion.

Secondary Bacterial Invaders

Certain of the virus diseases are often complicated by the action of so-called secondary bacterial invaders. These are bacteria that may be normally present in the animal without harm or may be responsible for a low-grade infection that is of no serious consequence but becomes active and capable of invading the tissues to produce severe disease complications following a virus infection. A vicious circle may be established by the virus and the secondary bacterial infection, the action of one increasing the virulence of the other, with disastrous effects. This often occurs in distemper of dogs and horses, swine influenza, hog cholera, and other virus diseases.

How Diseases Are Transmitted

Once established in a susceptible animal, as already noted, the infectious agent attacks certain tissues, multiplies, and sets up a disease process. Quantities of the causative agent are eliminated in various ways by the infected animal through its secretions and excretions so that its surroundings become contaminated. Susceptible animals coming in contact with the contagion thus have an opportunity to become infected. The ability of the infection to survive outside an animal body until it is able to gain entrance to a new host determines to a large extent its disease-spreading ability.

Biting insects, such as flies and mosquitoes, and other pests, such as ticks, are capable of transmitting and do transmit specific infections from infected to healthy animals under proper conditions.

In diseases such as tuberculosis the contagious matter is eliminated with the secretions and excretions of the animal. The surroundings become contaminated, and susceptible animals coming in contact with material that is still active can readily become infected. On the other hand, exposure to sunlight, dryness, or similar conditions over a suitable period of time has an adverse effect on the viability of the organism and its ability to invade susceptible animals.

Certain bacteria can live for indefinite periods outside the animal body and still retain a high degree of virulence. An outstanding example of this is the anthrax organism. In the final stages of the disease in an animal, the blood stream and all the tissues contain large quantities of the organisms in what is known as a vegetative stage. When these vegetative forms become exposed to the air through the opening of the carcass or the escape of blood from the natural openings of the body, they develop into spores. In this stage the organisms are extremely difficult to kill. They can withstand high and low temperatures and have been known to retain their infective capacity for years. It can therefore be seen that once soil becomes infected with anthrax spores it may remain dangerous for susceptible animals for long periods of time.

Another disease-producing organism that is quite resistant to adverse influences is the germ causing swine erysipelas. While this organism does not go into a spore stage, it can live in certain soils for long periods, and the suggestion has even been made that active multiplication may take place in suitable types of soil. Here again the infected animal contaminates its surroundings through its discharges.

Although the virus diseases have certain things in common, their mode of transmission may vary considerably, depending on the nature of the disease and the extent to which the virus has multiplied within the body of the affected animal. Infection takes place when the virus in a proper state is introduced into a susceptible animal.

Rabies and equine encephalomyelitis may be mentioned as examples of the neurotropic virus diseases of animals.

Rabies is caused by a filtrable virus which is found in the saliva of an animal affected with the disease and is transmitted under natural conditions through the bite of a rabid animal, usually a dog. The disease results in degenerative changes in the brain which cause affected animals to become aggressive and attack or bite any available object. After the virus is deposited in the tissues, usually through the injury made by the bite, it is considered that it moves from the site of deposit by way of the nerves, eventually reaching the central nervous system—the brain and spinal cord. The symptoms of the disease, which terminates fatally, then develop.

Equine encephalomyelitis, sometimes known as sleeping sickness or blind staggers of horses, is another virus disease that attacks principally the brain and spinal cord, although experimentally it has also been found capable of propagating in other tissues, including those of the skin. Early in the infection the virus of equine encephalomyelitis is found for a short time in the blood stream. It then disappears from the blood and is found only in the brain and spinal cord. Nervous symptoms of the disease are noted early. It has been shown experimentally that this disease can be transmitted by the bites of a number of different species of mosquitoes and other insects. The virus of the western type has been isolated from mosquitoes (*Culex tarsalis*) found in nature and also from the assassin bug (*Triatoma sanguisuga*). The disease is therefore considered to be spread chiefly through biting insects.

Foot-and-mouth disease is an example of an epitheliotropic virus. Although not now present in the United States, it has been one of the chief animal scourges for many years in other parts of the world. In addition to being one of the most important, if not the most important, of the animal diseases, it has particular interest in this discussion because it was the first animal disease shown to be caused by a filtrable virus. This was accomplished in 1898 through the research work of two German investigators, Loeffler and Frosch.

The vesicles, which contain the infective agent, break, and the virus is thus disseminated in the litter and on the ground where susceptible animals coming in contact with it easily pick up the infection. In the early stages of the disease the blood itself is infectious, and it has been shown that at that time the milk, the saliva, the urine, and also the feces may contain the virus. Because of the large quantities of the virus eliminated by affected animals and its highly infectious nature, a wide dissemination of the disease within a comparatively short time is possible.

Carriers of Disease and Reservoirs of Viruses

In addition to the transmission of disease from a sick animal to a normal one, either by direct contact or through contamination of the surroundings with the disease-producing agent, disease may be transmitted by another means, namely, by the carrier animal.

A carrier animal is one that carries an infective agent within its body without showing appreciable evidence of illness. The infective agent may be eliminated from time to time and act as a source of infection to other animals; or the carrier animal itself through some adverse condition may develop a frank attack of the disease; or the infection may be carried from a carrier to a normal animal through the bite of an insect.

It has been believed for many years that certain animals that have recovered from infection with the virus of foot-and-mouth disease may retain active virus within their bodies over a period of months and even years, eliminating it from time to time in sufficient quantities to produce the disease in susceptible animals. The virus might be enclosed in the growing hoof as the result of infection of the coronary band, escaping when the growth of the hoof reaches a certain stage; or it might rest in some part of the body in an inactive state and later be eliminated in the secretions or excretions of the animal.

In infectious anemia of horses—so-called swamp fever—a carrier stage is seen in which an apparently normal animal carries the infective agent in its blood stream for many years, perhaps during the rest of its life. It appears from the available evidence that this disease is transmitted principally by biting insects.

When animals or birds of a wide variety of species are susceptible to a common infection, an individual of one of the species may be a carrier or reservoir of the disease from which infection may be spread to other susceptible species through insect bites. For example, a large number of avian species have been found experimentally to be susceptible to equine encephalomyelitis, and the pigeon and ring-necked pheasant have been found to be affected with this disease in nature. Other laboratory tests indicate that other birds and mammals may harbor the infection. It is considered quite probable that birds may act as reservoirs of the virus to a greater extent than horses and other mammals and that infection may be carried from infected birds to a variety of susceptible species by mosquitoes and other biting insects.

ANIMAL PARASITES

As used in this book, the term "parasites" refers to low forms of animal life that live on or in other animals larger than themselves. An animal that harbors parasites is known as a host. Some parasites require only one host for the completion of their life cycles, whereas others require more than one. In the former case the life cycle is direct; in the latter, it is indirect. The host in which a parasite develops to maturity is known as the final, or definitive, host; that in which only the parasite's larval (immature) stages develop is called the intermediate host. As a rule, hosts are more or less seriously affected by their parasites, the injury suffered depending on the kinds and, usually, the numbers of parasites harbored.

When parasites invade a host in numbers sufficient to produce injury to health, they set up an infection, which is designated as a parasitic infection to differentiate it from infections produced by bacteria or viruses. There is no absolute dividing line, however, between infections caused by parasites and those caused by other living agents. Bacteria multiply within the host, as do many parasites also. Most of the larger parasites that do not increase in number within the host increase greatly in size. In both instances there is multiplication of foreign cells within the host.

Parasites have played an important role in the history of civilization, because they cause many of the ills to which human beings and animals are subject. Certain parts of the world are unsuited for civilization largely because of the prevalence in those regions of parasitic diseases that injure and destroy human life and domestic animals. Many areas that were formerly unsuitable for civilized living, however, have been made safe, in whole or in part, by the vigorous application of sanitary measures designed to keep parasitic diseases in check or to eradicate them.

Malaria, one of the most deadly diseases of mankind, African sleeping sickness, and amoebic dysentery are examples of devastating human parasitic diseases caused by micro-organisms known as protozoa. Diseases more or less closely related to them occur also in domestic animals and poultry. Hookworm disease, at one time an important factor in the physical and mental retardation of a considerable portion of the population of the southern part of the United States, and still a public health problem of considerable importance in the tropical and subtropical belts of the globe, including parts of this country, is an outstanding example of a dangerous worm infection. Hookworms and related bloodsucking parasites occur in all kinds of domestic animals, producing injuries essentially similar to those observed in infected human beings. In short, parasites are capable of adversely affecting the health of animals as well as of man and of producing debilitating diseases that may result in death.

If all the parasites to which man and domestic animals are subject were equally injurious, the human and livestock populations would have been decimated long ago. Of the hundreds of species of parasitic organisms that find a haven on or in the bodies of human beings, animals, and birds, some are far more injurious than others, and many inflict more or less injury without actually producing a distinct disease. Unlike the diseases caused by bacteria and viruses, which appear suddenly with almost explosive violence and are accompanied by prostration and high fever, many of those produced by parasites tend to be chronic and are not accompanied by fever. Parasitic infections of many types are characterized by stunted growth, emaciation, general unthriftiness, digestive disturbances, and gradual wasting. Even when such infections are only moderate, deaths may occur here and there; but as a rule there is nothing comparable to the wholesale mortality that takes place in outbreaks of infectious diseases such as anthrax or hog cholera. Because of their insidious nature, however, some parasitic infections may take a rather severe toll from the resources of farmers and stockmen before the presence of the offending organisms in a herd is even suspected. The stealthy march of parasitism, in contrast to the open approach of infectious diseases, sometimes makes the former the deadlier of the two.

Hundreds of different kinds of parasites affect human beings, livestock, and poultry. Thousands of others occur in various wild animals, birds, fishes, and other forms of animal life. Many of the parasites of domestic animals and poultry occur also in wild animals and birds. In some cases parasites of one kind of domestic animal are transmissible to other kinds of domestic animals. Certain parasites of animals are transmissible to man, and vice versa. In view of the diversity of parasitic organisms and their range in host relationships, it is essential to classify parasites on the basis of their natural relationships and, for the sake of convenience, also with reference to their adaptability to various hosts.

Under the designation of parasites are included a number of animal groups, some of which are only remotely related to one another. In fact parasitism is so widespread in the animal kingdom that very few of the major groups of animals are altogether free from forms that lead a parasitic existence. Fortunately, however, from the standpoint of human and animal health only three groups need be taken into consideration: (1) Protozoa, or unicellular animals, (2) worms, or helminths, and (3) insects, ticks, and related forms, known as arthropods, many of which act as intermediate hosts and vectors for infective parasites.

PROTOZOA

Protozoa, or protozoans, are the simplest forms of animal life, the entire body of one of these organisms consisting of a single cell. The protozoans are thus differentiated from all other animals, which are designated as metazoans (many-celled animals). Protozoans were first discovered during the latter part of the seventeenth century by Leeuwenhoek in Holland, who constructed the simple microscopes that he used in their discovery. This man of genius, known as the inventor of the microscope and the discoverer of micro-organisms, investigated, among other things, stagnant water and the intestinal contents of various animals. He even made studies on himself, thereby discovering human parasitic protozoans.

Since Leeuwenhoek's day an ever-growing army of investigators has studied protozoan organisms, some of which are free-living and occur in fresh, brackish, and salt water, in soil, and in a variety of other locations. Other protozoans are not free-living but parasitic in various parts of the bodies of animals of all kinds, including human beings. With the exception of a few that are within the limits of unaided vision, the vast majority of protozoans can be seen only through the microscope. Certain protozoans, particularly among those that are parasitic, are so small that they must be studied with the highest magnification available.

Some groups of parasitic protozoans resemble more or less closely related free-living forms, whereas others contain only parasitic species. The latter (sporozoans) have become so greatly modified by the parasitic mode of life that they have no organs of locomotion. Some protozoans (amoebae) move by a flowing of the entire body substance, others (flagellates) by means of one or more whiplike lashes known as flagella, and some (ciliates) by small vibratile processes, called cilia, located all over the body. Protozoans of all four groups occur in man and animals, and some of them produce serious and fatal diseases.

Many protozoans multiply by simple division, the entire body dividing into two parts, each a more or less exact duplicate of the other. The two individuals that result from simple division become separated, and each leads an independent existence. The process of division is repeated many times, until eventually a host that originally acquired only a few of the organisms may be teeming with them. In other protozoans multiple division takes place, the body dividing in succession into a number of similar parts, each of which finally grows into a form like the parent organism. Since each of these organisms is capable sooner or later of repeating the process of multiple division, they can overwhelm the host in a comparatively short time. Parasitic amoebae and flagellates that live in man, domestic animals, and poultry multiply by simple division, as do also

ci   es parasitic in man and animals.   Some of the sporozoans, how-
ev   , including malarial organisms, coccidia, and other forms, increase
in   mber by multiple division.   In addition to simple and multiple
divi   on, some protozoans exhibit more complicated reproductive
phenomena that resemble sexual processes in higher animals.

The rapid multiplication of protozoans produces a severe invasion
of the host.   If the parasites live in the lumen, or cavity, of the digestive tract without penetrating the tissues proper, the host can
usually cope successfully even with huge numbers, but if they penetrate the lining of the digestive tract, invade the blood, or are carried
to various organs and tissues, serious consequences are likely to
follow.

As already noted, some parasitic protozoans—including amoebae
and some flagellates, ciliates, and some sporozoans—have but one host,
infection resulting from the ingestion of food or water contaminated
with the organisms eliminated with the droppings of infected animals.

In some such manner human beings acquire amoebae, which produce
the disease known as amoebic dysentery, and various flagellates and
ciliates that are responsible for digestive disturbances.   Among the
protozoan diseases of animals acquired in a similar manner are blackhead of chickens and turkeys, trichomoniasis of turkeys, and coccidiosis.   Coccidiosis, often a serious disease of poultry, cattle, and sheep,
is caused by coccidia, acquired as a result of swallowing feed or
water that has become contaminated with the infective stages of the
organisms.

There are various modifications of the general method of direct
transmission just described.   For instance, a breeding disease of cattle,
known as bovine genital trichomoniasis, caused by flagellates known
as trichomonads, is transmitted during copulation.   Blackhead of
turkeys and chickens may be transmitted not only by the birds' swallowing contaminated food or water but also through the ingestion of
the eggs of poultry cecal worms (roundworm parasites of the ceca
of chickens and turkeys) in which the infective organisms apparently
become lodged.

As in the case of other parasites, certain protozoans are transmitted
from host to host only through vectors.   The vector-borne protozoan
diseases are among the most serious and are very difficult to control.
Malaria is transmitted by certain species of mosquitoes, which acquire the infection from the blood of an infected human being, and
tick fever is transmitted by cattle ticks.   Anaplasmosis, a protozoan
disease of cattle related to tick fever, is also transmitted by ticks and
by certain bloodsucking flies.   Certain diseases of horses and other
livestock in tropical countries are caused by trypanosomes, which are
transmitted by insect vectors.

WORM PARASITES

The worms parasitic in human beings, livestock, and poultry are
visible to the naked eye in the adult stage, when their length
ranges from a fraction of an inch to several feet.   They are rather
complex in structure, containing an alimentary canal (except tape-

worms and thorny heads), excretory and nervous systems, highly complex reproductive systems, and other organs. The surface of the body has a hard covering which protects the softer internal parts. Spines, hooks, teeth, and suckers are among the armatures of worms, these structures serving various purposes and enabling the parasites to attach themselves to the organs and tissues of the host. Worm parasites in the immature stages wander more or less extensively in the course of their invasion of a host, and some do so even as adults. They are provided with specialized contractile tissue or muscles for locomotion.

Parasitic worms multiply by a sexual process. Single individuals of some of these parasites contain both male and female reproductive systems; such forms are said to be bisexual, or hermaphroditic. In others, called unisexual, the males and females are separate individuals. In both cases the parasites develop from eggs.

Save for a few conspicuous exceptions, the eggs or the larvae that hatch from the eggs must leave the host animal in which they originate to undergo further development on the ground or elsewhere in the open or in intermediate hosts. Depending on the kinds of parasites concerned, susceptible hosts acquire worms by (1) swallowing infective eggs or larvae with feed or water, (2) the penetration of infective larvae through the skin, (3) swallowing intermediate hosts, as previously noted, and (4) being bitten by skin-piercing insects harboring infective larvae. Slight or moderate infections in a host animal are increased in intensity by the entrance of additional infective organisms.

Worms occur in a variety of locations in the bodies of human beings and animals, the entire digestive tract, from the mouth to the large bowel, being one of the principal habitats of these pests. They also occur under the skin; in the muscles; in the abdominal cavity, liver, pancreas, spleen and kidneys; in the chest cavity, heart, and lungs; in connective tissue; in the brain and other parts of the central nervous system; in the eyes and other organs of sense; and in other locations. In fact, hardly an organ, tissue, or cavity in the human or animal body is absolutely resistant to invasion by worm parasites.

When worms get into the vital organs such as the liver, lungs, brain, or heart, they interfere with the proper functioning of these organs and do damage in other ways. The invasion of vital organs frequently results in more or less serious damage, the severity of the injuries and the resultant disability of the host being proportional, as a rule, to the number of invaders. It should not be assumed, however, that worms elsewhere in the body are comparatively harmless. On the contrary, some of the severest losses of sheep and cattle are due to stomach worms and related parasites living in the alimentary canal; they commonly attack the lining of the canal and often pierce the finer blood vessels of the stomach or intestinal wall, producing hemorrhage and injuring the host in other ways. The net result of such parasitism is anemia, emaciation, and death when the infection is heavy.

Although the worm parasites have much in common, they naturally fall into four distinct groups: (1) Flukes, or trematodes, (2) tapeworms, or cestodes, (3) roundworms, or nematodes, and (4) thorny heads, or acanthocephalids. These groups have more or less distinct habits and modes of transmission and will be considered separately.

Flukes

Flukes (fig. 1), or trematodes, are soft, more or less flattened, usually leaflike parasitic worms. Some forms are more or less cylindrical,

FIGURE 1.—Liver flukes of sheep, *Fasciola hepatica.*

others are conical, and a few are elongated. These worms generally range in length from a fraction of an inch up to about an inch or so, the largest known fluke attaining a length of 4 inches. Flukes are covered wth minute spines and possess adhesive organs, in the form of muscular, cup-shaped suckers, that serve for attachment of the parasite to the tissues of the host. With the exception of one group, a l flukes are bisexual.

The flukes that are of importance to human and animal health require snails as intermediate hosts. The mode of transmission is briefly as follows: The eggs of the parasites, eliminated as a rule with the host's droppings, hatch under favorable conditions of temperature and moisture. The larva penetrates into the body of a snail, within which it is considerably transformed in structure and where it produces one or more generations of very small flukes. The stage that escapes from the snail is known as a cercaria, a single egg ultimately giving rise to many cercariae. The cercariae secrete a protective covering around themselves after they have lodged on vegetation, on the surface of water, or elsewhere. Grazing animals, such as cattle, sheep, swine, horses, and others, swallow the encysted cercariae with forage or water. The cercariae of some flukes penetrate the skin of the definitive host and thus bore into its body; others require a second intermediate host. The cercariae of lung flukes of swine penetrate into crayfishes, and hogs become infected by swallowing the parasitized crayfishes.

Flukes are known to produce serious diseases in man and animals in various parts of the world, but fortunately some of the most harmful do not occur in this country. The only flukes that are definitely known to be important in the United States are the liver flukes that commonly parasitize cattle, sheep, and goats and may also occur from time to time in horses, swine, and other animals. These flukes produce injury as a result of their migrations in the body and in other ways. The activities of the flukes produce extensive destruction of the liver tissue, and more or less extensive hemorrhage may result from the rupture of blood vessels.

Tapeworms

Like the flukes, all tapeworms are strictly parasitic. Tapeworms of economic importance occur as adults in the intestine and as bladder worms in various locations outside the alimentary canal, including the muscles, abdominal cavity, liver, lungs, brain, eye, and other organs and tissues. On casual inspection there appears to be little resemblance between a bladder worm and an adult tapeworm. The fact is, however, that bladder worms are the larval stages of intestinal tapeworms. The head of the bladder worm resembles that of the adult tapeworm in practically all respects. Bladder worms vary considerably in size, some being only about half an inch or less in diameter, whereas others are much larger. The so-called hydatids that parasitize man as well as cattle, sheep, swine, and other animals may attain the size of a child's head.

Adult tapeworms range in length from a fraction of an inch to several feet. They are elongated, flattened worms, each individual consisting of a head, an unsegmented neck, and a chain of segments. The head is provided with four suckers or similar organs of attachment and in many cases with hooks also. The neck is more or less constricted, and the segments behind the neck vary considerably in shape in different species. Those immediately below the neck are the immature segments, and the mature ones, each containing both male and female reproductive organs, are farther down in the chain. The segments toward the end of the chain are known as the ripe, or gravid, segments, and each contains hundreds of eggs. The gravid segments of some tapeworms become detached either singly or in groups and pass out of the body with the excreta; in others detachment does not take place, the tapeworm eggs being liberated into the host's intestine and excreted. In either case the eggs serve as the starting point for new infections, the intermediate host swallowing them in contaminated feed or water.

Various animals serve as intermediate hosts. The tapeworms affecting cattle, sheep, and goats develop in small free-living mites that live on grass; those affecting chickens develop in various beetles and other insects and in other invertebrates; some of those affecting dogs develop in rabbits, some in sheep, cattle, goats, and swine, and some in lice and fleas. Of the tapeworms affecting man, one species develops in swine, another in cattle (fig. 2), and one in certain freshwater fishes. The definitive host becomes infected as a result of swallowing the intermediate host in whole or in part.

Since worm parasites that live in cavities of the body have less opportunity for doing serious damage than those that occur in or have intimate contact with tissues, it is obvious that bladder worms, which as a rule occur in tissues, produce more injury than the corresponding adult tapeworms. Furthermore, bladder worms occurring in the liver, lungs, brain, eyes, and other organs produce more injury than those that occur in the abdominal cavity attached to the mesenteries. Bladder worms that get into the brain are particularly dangerous, a disease of sheep known as gid being caused by the presence in the brain of a bladder worm an inch or so in diameter. Man sometimes harbors the bladder worm or the pork tapeworm, these cystic worms in man showing a predilection for the brain and eye. Hydatids, already mentioned, occur in man as well as in animals, becoming localized principally in the liver and lungs. Because of their size and location, they produce serious disturbances. Infection in man requires surgical intervention. Though adult tapeworms in the intestine produce more or less injury to the intestinal lining, irritate its nerve endings, and rob the host of food, they are not so important as disease producers, in spite of their relatively large size, as adult flukes and roundworms.

Roundworms

Roundworms, or nematodes, constitute a group of rather slender cylindrical worms, more or less attenuated at both ends. Some nematodes are free-living, some parasitize plants, and others are parasitic in man and animals. The last-named group shows a wide range in size, the smallest ones being but a fraction of an inch long and as thin as a fine silk thread. The large ones attain a length of about a foot and are as thick as or thicker than an ordinary lead pencil. The kidney worm of dogs, which occurs in the abdominal cavity as well as in the kidneys, is the largest known nematode and may attain a length of about 3½ feet and a width of about half an inch.

FIGURE 2.—The human tapeworm, *Taenia saginata*, the larval stage of which occurs in cattle.

Nematodes occur in a variety of locations in and outside of the alimentary canal, some of them wandering extensively as larvae and as adults, thereby getting into situations from which, sometimes, they cannot extricate themselves and in which they ultimately die. Their presence in strange locations produces injury by pressure on tissues and in other ways. All organs and tissues of the human body previously mentioned as habitats of parasites, and others as well, are subject to attack by nematodes.

As a rule, parasitic nematodes occur as male and female worms. Usually the eggs are expelled by the female worm into the alimentary canal or cavities that communicate with it and reach the outside with the excreta. The eggs of nematodes that live in the urinary system are discharged with the urine. The eggs of species that require intermediate hosts are usually infective when they reach the outside, whereas those of species that have a direct life history undergo development before they can infect new hosts. The infective, unhatched eggs of the large intestinal roundworms, or ascarids, of pigs and those of some other forms are swallowed by the host and hatch within it. The eggs of the sheep stomach worm and related parasites hatch on the ground, where the larvae undergo considerable development before they become infective. In the indirect mode of infection the egg is swallowed in some instances by the intermediate host, which, in turn, is swallowed by the final host, which thus becomes infected. For example, hogs acquire longworms by eating earthworms that harbor them in the infective stage, the earthworms having acquired the lungworm larvae by swallowing lungworm eggs with swine manure. In other indirect modes of transmission, the eggs hatch within the nematode, and the larvae get into the host's blood, transmission to another host being effected through skin-piercing insects, particularly flies and mosquitoes, which act as intermediate hosts. Heart worms of dogs and related filarid nematodes of man and animals are transmitted in this manner. Other methods of transmission also occur and are discussed in the various articles dealing with specific nematode infections.

Nematodes are among the most injurious parasites of man, domestic animals, and poultry. They cause trichinosis, a disease of the muscles of man and swine; hookworm disease in man and animals, characterized by anemia, stunting, and emaciation; stomach worm disease in cattle, sheep, and goats and strongylidosis in horses, which are characterized by similar symptoms; heart worm disease in dogs and a more or less related disease known as filariasis in man and animals; verminous bronchitis and pneumonia in all food animals; nodular disease in sheep; gapeworm disease in chickens and turkeys; and many other serious conditions. The anemia characteristic of some of these diseases is produced by the bloodsucking activities of the parasites and leads to malnutrition and wasting; the invasion of the lungs by lungworms and wandering larvae of other nematodes produces the bronchitis and pneumonia characteristic of other diseases; the lodgement of worms in the heart and principal blood vessels produces profound disturbances in circulation and respiration; the invasion of the muscles produces severe pain; and other activities of nematodes produce either acute disease or a gradual undermining of the host's vitality.

Thorny Heads

Thorny heads, or acanthocephalids, constitute a group of elongated cylindrical worms related to the nematodes but differing from them in a number of ways, especially in the presence of an alimentary canal. The name "thorny heads" is derived from the peculiar anatomical structure characteristic of these worms, namely, a retractile proboscis, or snout, armed with hooks. The sexes are separate, and the life history is indirect. Only one species, the thorny head of swine, is of importance to the livestock industry.

INTERMEDIATE HOSTS AND VECTORS

As already stated, some parasites are transmitted from one host animal to another directly, without the intervention of intermediate hosts. Intermediate hosts play an essential role in the transmission of others, however. When more than one intermediate host is involved, the one which the parasite invades first is called the first intermediate host and the next the second intermediate host. In this article the term "intermediate host" is restricted to animals that harbor the larval stages of worm parasites. Hosts that transmit the minute unicellular organisms known as protozoa are referred to as vectors (carriers). Knowledge of intermediate hosts and vectors is as important as knowledge of the parasites they harbor. Control of parasites that require intermediate hosts or vectors frequently requires as much or more attention to the latter as to the parasites themselves. Without mosquitoes, for example, there would be no malaria. Tick or splenetic fever, which at one time was widespread in cattle in the South, has almost completely disappeared as a result of a systematic campaign of tick eradication.

Common intermediate hosts and vectors of parasites are ticks, flies, mosquitoes, beetles, snails, slugs, and other small invertebrate animals that are usually common in farm lots, barnyards, and pastures. Larger animals also may serve as intermediate hosts. In fact, almost any animal, including domestic animals and human beings, may serve as an intermediate host of parasites.

Ticks and biting insects, particularly flies and mosquitoes, are especially adapted to serve as intermediate hosts or vectors of parasites that occur in the blood. Malaria in man, tick fever and anaplasmosis in cattle, heart worm infection in dogs, and other parasitic diseases are transmitted by bloodsucking insects and related forms. Dung beetles, snails, slugs, earthworms, and other small creatures that feed on animal manure serve as intermediate hosts for specific parasites. These hosts ingest, or swallow, parasite eggs and larvae present in manure, and the definitive host becomes infected by eating the parasitized intermediate host. In other cases parasites are acquired by animals and human beings by eating the flesh and other tissues of parasitized animals. For instance, dogs acquire certain tapeworms by eating rabbits that harbor bladder worms, the immature stages of these pests. Man acquires certain tapeworms by eating raw or rare beef or pork infected with bladder worms, and he acquires trichinosis by eating raw or rare trichina-infected pork.

POISONOUS PLANTS AS CAUSES OF DISEASE

Poisonous plants occupy an important place among the causes of animal diseases. Owing to their wide distribution and relative abundance, such plants have been responsible for heavy livestock losses in many sections of the country. The action of poisonous plants on animals varies greatly. It is dependent not only on the character and amount of toxic substance present, but also on the animals involved, since the same plant may be much more toxic to certain species of animals than to others. Often there is considerable variation in toxicity in the different parts of a plant and at different stages of its growth, and there may be some difference in the toxicity of the same species of plants growing in different localities and environments.

Poisoning may result from a single feeding or from repeated feedings scattered over a period of days or weeks. Many poisonous plants can be eaten daily in relatively small amounts over a long period of time with no apparent injury, whereas others eaten in the same way may produce a cumulative effect, the animals eventually developing acute symptoms of poisoning some time after they have stopped eating the plant.

Chemical analyses of plants proved to be poisonous have resulted in many cases in the isolation of the specific principles responsible for the trouble. Since there are many different toxic substances in poisonous plants, the diseases resulting from their consumption show a wide variation in the symptoms observed and the tissue changes that may occur. Certain species of plants may produce their primary effects on specific tissues or organs of the body, such as the nervous system, digestive tract, liver, or kidneys, causing manifestations that may easily be mistaken for diseases originating from other causes.

The duration of the diseases caused by poisonous plants varies from the acute, rapidly fatal condition produced by highly toxic substances to chronic cases resulting from the cumulative action of some of the slower acting poisons.

In addition to those poisonous plants in which the toxic principles are normal constituents and more or less uniform in all plants of the same species, other plants, ordinarily considered nontoxic, when grown on certain soils may become poisonous owing to the presence in the soil of the very poisonous element selenium. The presence of selenium in the soil, combined with the ability of certain plants, which may include native species as well as some cultivated ones, to assimilate this element in sufficient quantities to render them toxic to animals, has created an unusual disease problem which in some areas has resulted in considerable livestock loss.

NUTRITIONAL DEFICIENCIES AS CAUSES OF DISEASE

As dramatic as the researches of Pasteur, Lister, Koch, and the others who firmly established the germ theory of disease has been the discovery that errors in diet can cause specific diseases and other debilitating conditions in animals and man no less extreme than those due to germs and other organisms. In fact, it is now recognized that certain animal diseases may be caused by the combined effects of nutritional deficiencies or excesses and of infection. In some instances the dietary deficiency precedes the invasion of the body by organisms, while in others an infectious disease, once established in a well-nourished animal, may lead to nutritional complications if the functions of digestion and assimilation of food or the excretion of waste products are disturbed.

It is now recognized that the maintenance of life and health in animals depends on the orderly coordination of numerous chemical and physical reactions within the body cells and fluids. Some of these reactions are concerned with the transformation of food into heat to maintain body temperature and energy for body activities, and others with the synthesis of building materials to be used in growth, in repair or replacement of essential constituents of body tissues and fluids, or in such functions as reproduction. Some components of food appear to act merely as catalysts, starting or helping along these complex reactions. These substances are probably used up in the process and apparently do not remain as definite structural elements.

Whenever a vital function or series of vital reactions is interrupted owing to continued failure of the diet to supply sufficient quantities of essential nutrients or to the inability of the body to utilize these nutrients because of a dietary imbalance, the so-called nutritional diseases develop. Toxic manifestations can also result from the feeding of an excess of some nutrients. The symptoms of these diseases depend on the particular functions of the body that are affected. Some nutritional deficiencies inhibit the growth of animals; in others growth continues, but faulty development occurs. Detection of the early symptoms of nutritional diseases and an understanding of the pathological and biochemical changes involved are proving to be of great value in diagnosing diseases of nutritional origin and thereby making it possible to work out means for their control.

The recognition of the essential nature of such dietary factors as certain minerals, vitamins, and amino acids, along with protein in general, carbohydrates, fats, and water, has led to the conception of a complete or balanced diet. Such a diet, however, must vary with the food requirements of animals according to species, age, rate of growth, sex, and amount of physical work as well as with such functions as reproduction and lactation. Recent developments that have led to outstanding advances in the field of animal nutrition have included the isolation and synthesis of practically all of the known vitamins, recognition of the need for several minerals in very small amounts, the demonstration of the essential nature of several amino acids, and a better understanding of how to preserve nutritive values in harvested crops. It is now evident that many diseases which were formerly believed to be caused by some obscure infection or some toxic principle in the feed are really due to a deficiency of essential nutritive factors.

At the time this book went to press, the drugs and other materials mentioned in various articles—chiefly as disinfectants, insecticides, and anthelmintics—were still available for veterinary and medical use. Under war conditions, however, it is possible that some of these materials may become scarce or unavailable. In that case, the reader should obtain professional advice from the Department of Agriculture, the State experiment station, a local veterinarian, or the county agent as to available substitutes.

Protective Mechanisms Against Disease

BY ADOLPH EICHHORN, MERRITT P. SARLES, AND N. R. ELLIS [1]

PROBABLY the most brilliant achievement of modern medical science has been the gradual disclosure of nature's methods of producing immunity against disease, and the use of these methods to protect human beings and animals by artificial immunization. Not only livestock producers but everyone should understand the fundamentals of this process.

BACTERIAL AND VIRUS DISEASES

IN THE PREVENTION and treatment of diseases of animals a knowledge of the principles of immunity is highly desirable, especially when biological products, such as vaccines, bacterins, toxoids, and immune serum, are to be used.

In its true sense immunity denotes complete resistance to a disease, but since all individuals of a species can seldom be made resistant enough to withstand severe exposure, the term is now used chiefly in a relative sense; that is, it does not necessarily mean absolute resistance, but signifies that the natural resistance, if any, of an individual has been increased to a certain degree, which may be slight or marked, usually the latter. Susceptibility is the opposite of resistance, denoting that an animal of a certain species or the large majority of animals in a given species may contract a disease readily if exposed to it.

[1] Adolph Eichhorn is Director of the Animal Disease Station ; Merritt P. Sarles is Assistant Parasitologist, Zoological Division ; and N. R. Ellis is Senior Chemist, Animal Nutrition Division, Bureau of Animal Industry. Dr. Eichhorn prepared portions of the text relating to bacterial and virus diseases ; Dr. Sarles contributed the section on parasitic diseases ; and Mr. Ellis prepared the section on nutrition and disease resistance.

NATURAL AND ACQUIRED IMMUNITY

Immunity may be natural or acquired. Natural immunity to a specific disease is inherited, and the degree of immunity varies considerably in different individuals. Just as no two animals are exactly alike in physical appearance and mental attributes, no two are exactly alike in susceptibility or resistance to disease. When a herd of swine has been exposed to hog cholera, for example, a few animals commonly die within 48 to 72 hours after the first symptoms develop; others—probably the majority—are sick for 4 to 10 days before dying; some recover after being slightly sick, and some after being very sick; and a few may show no indication of illness. The last group would be considered naturally immune.

Again, horses and cattle may be exposed directly to hog cholera, but they never contract this disease. Such natural resistance is known as species immunity, meaning that all or most individuals of a species of animals are resistant or immune to a specific disease.

Other factors operate in resistance to a disease, chief of which are the severity of exposure and the virulence of the germs or virus causing the disease. It can be readily understood, therefore, that resistance is a complex problem and that natural immunity may be broken down in many instances by severe exposure.

For an understanding of acquired immunity it is necessary first to be familiar with certain physiological processes.

The inroads of bacteria, parasites, and other foreign substances into the body of a susceptible animal stimulate three remarkable, complex, and somewhat related protective reactions: Inflammation, immunization, and repair. By means of these processes the body attempts to localize, neutralize, and ultimately destroy the foreign organisms or substances; to produce chemical substances—antibodies—antagonistic to or protective against the foreign materials; and to repair and compensate for injuries sustained.

Two types of physiological elements, namely, cells and antibodies, are chiefly concerned in these processes. Of primary importance, since they produce the antibodies, are the living, microscopic cells of which all tissues are composed, and especially those of the blood and connective tissues, including the specialized larger phagocytic, or devouring, cells called macrophages. Macrophages are present in all the connective or supporting tissues of the body and are concentrated in great numbers in the liver, spleen, and lymph nodes. The cells of this protective system are of great importance against infection, since they not only take up and devour foreign organisms and substances but also appear to be the main elements concerned in the production of antibodies.

Thus an animal's body may be considered a battleground in which the invading forces seek to overcome the defenses. The aim of the livestock owner and his ally, the veterinarian, is to aid animals in acquiring sufficient immunity to resist the invading organisms.

Active and Passive Immunity

Acquired resistance can be increased by one or a combination of several means. If the animal produces its own antibodies, the resultant immunity is called active immunity. If the resistance of an animal is increased by the injection of antibodies produced by another animal, the immunity is known as passive.

Animals acquire an active immunity to certain diseases when they have survived a natural or modified course of the disease produced either by infection with the particular germs or by inoculation with their specific vaccines, bacterins, or toxins. In these cases, the animal produces its own immunity, either because it had the disease naturally or because it sustained a less severe form of infection produced intentionally by artificial means. Intentional active immunization is commonly called vaccination, although the latter term, to be exact, signifies that a vaccine has been used to produce the protection.

Passive immunity is produced in an animal by the introduction of immunizing substances obtained from an actively immune animal. Such immunity is usually conferred by the injection of blood serum from immunized animals; such serum carries with it the substances by which the protection is conferred. The immunizing substances (antibodies) of an actively immunized animal are known also as immune bodies. In relation to infectious diseases, they comprise two classes. Those acting on bacteria are antibacterial, as, for instance, anti-white-scours serum and antianthrax serum, whereas those acting on .toxins are called antitoxin, as, for instance, tetanus antitoxin.

Active immunity develops only after 1 or 2 weeks, whereas passive immunity is established immediately after the injection. Passive immunity does not protect animals for a long period; it usually disappears within 3 to 6 weeks. This is due to the fact that as soon as the injected immune bodies are eliminated from the animal organism, the immunity is ended. In active immunity, however, the stimulation of the infection on the body cells causes the prolonged development of immune bodies, and thus a more lasting immunity is produced.

It can be seen from this brief description that active immunity has a great advantage over passive immunity, and the tendency is to produce active immunity whenever possible. On the other hand, there are times when it becomes necessary to employ means by which the spread of a disease can be immediately checked, and in such instances passive immunity has the advantage, since it affords immediate protection against infection; in some instances it also exerts a curative action. Frequently, both methods are used in a combined inoculation by which the animal is given immediate and also lasting protection against an infectious disease. This form of immunization is known as the simultaneous method, a familiar example of which is virus-serum inoculation against hog cholera.

Scientists the world over have expended much effort in attempts to discover and perfect effective and at the same time practical means of immunizing animals against the more destructive of the infectious diseases. Large sums have been appropriated for the advancement of these researches, both from governmental sources and by private gifts and endowments. The goal sought is the discovery of some means by which immunity may be conveyed to a large number of animals at the least expense. After successful vaccination, the animal is sufficiently protected to withstand exposure that would have proved deadly before vaccination was performed. The same principle is used in protecting man from many diseases; for example, smallpox and diphtheria.

It appears natural, then, that the best and surest results from immunization should be expected in those diseases in which the specific cause has been definitely established and for which means of effective protection are known. This is the case in actual practice.

VACCINATION

In localities where a disease appears year after year it is advisable to vaccinate susceptible animals while they are healthy; that is, before exposure. It is not advisable to delay the immunization until the disease actually makes its appearance. Such a practice may prove costly because of the time required before actual protection is established and also because some of the animals may already have become infected though not yet showing symptoms.

The object of vaccination, as already noted, is to induce in the animal a reaction, sometimes a mild form of the disease, which stimulates the body to develop antibodies against the infective agent. It is very important that the vaccination be undertaken when the animal is in a healthy condition, as any devitalization will adversely affect the immunization. It is well known that the presence of the infection is not the sole cause of a diseased condition. In most cases the combined effects of various contributing factors are necessary. Immediately after the invasion of the infective agent, the protective mechanism of the body is set in motion, and the disease results only if the attack is stronger than the defense; that is, if the animal is not capable of producing sufficient antibodies.

Influences that tend to weaken the normal functioning of the body include overwork, exposure to cold, lack of proper feed, and shipment of animals over long distances, especially in stormy weather. Chronic infections also may lower resistance. In particular, a disease condition or a parasitic infestation may predispose an animal to infection, because while it is still fighting one disease it is called upon to combat a new invader. The failure under such circumstances explains the frequent occurrence of two diseases simultaneously, or of one following immediately after another. A disease devitalizes the body and prepares it for an attack by either latent or invading germs of a secondary infection. This situation is often observed in hog cholera, equine influenza, canine distemper, and other maladies. The formation of antibodies is influenced also by the age of the animal; neither very young nor old animals respond to vaccination so well as those between these extremes.

Susceptibility to disease is also influenced to some extent by breeding practices, such as inbreeding, as well as by selection for high productivity or performance. (See the article The Relation of Genetics to Disease, p. 167.) Feeding, discussed later, also plays an important part.

To increase the chances of success in vaccination, therefore, it is advisable to eliminate all debilitating influences before the immunization is carried out. In vaccinating against hog cholera or canine distemper, for instance, the animals should be freed of parasites if any are present and should be protected from exposure to cold and dampness. Any vitamin or mineral deficiency in the diet should also be corrected. It is a mistake to depend solely on vaccination; every effort should be made to eliminate all adverse conditions that might interfere with its success.

PREPARATIONS USED IN PRODUCING IMMUNITY

For the production of immunity to various kinds of infection, veterinary research has developed numerous biological products. The preparation and distribution of these biologics in pure and potent form contribute greatly to the safety of modern livestock production. Probably the most familiar class of biologics is the vaccines.

A vaccine is an attenuated, weakened, or even apparently dead virus of the disease, specially prepared so that it will perform its function with the least possible danger to the animal. The reduction of virulence is accomplished by subjecting the virus to heat, desiccation (drying), or other unfavorable influences strong enough to weaken but not to destroy it. Examples are anthrax vaccine and blackleg vaccine. In some instances an organism modified in virulence is used for immunizing purposes, as, for instance, in bovine brucellosis (Bang's disease); or, again, an unattenuated virus may be used when it has passed through certain species of animals, a procedure that increases its virulence for that particular species but reduces it for other species. For instance, suspensions of a brain emulsion of fixed rabies virus passed through rabbits are used for immunizing other species of animals against rabies. In the use of viruses for immunizing purposes, the general opinion formerly was that immunization with "killed" virus had not been successful. Recently, however, very dependable immunity has been produced with such virus, as illustrated by successful immunization against equine encephalomyelitis with chick-embryo vaccine, in the preparation of which the virus is killed (fig. 1). The vaccine has proved highly effective not only in experimental tests but also in extensive field use.

Bacterins, another class of biologics, are standardized suspensions of killed pathogenic bacteria and their products in physiological salt solution [2] or in oil. Immunization with bacterins against certain diseases, such as hemorrhagic septicemia, blackleg, and other infections, is now an established procedure. Bacterins are standardized to a definite number of dead organisms per cubic centimeter.

---

[2] This term signifies approximately the same dilution of salt (sodium chloride) that is found in body fluids, usually 0.85 percent.

This procedure involves either the counting of stained organisms in a special counting chamber or the use of a photoelectric apparatus which determines the density of a suspension by measuring the quantity of light refracted or absorbed in passing through the suspension. The latter method has greatly simplified the standardization of such suspensions.

Another biological product used in combating disease is immune blood serum (or immune serum), so-called because of its content of

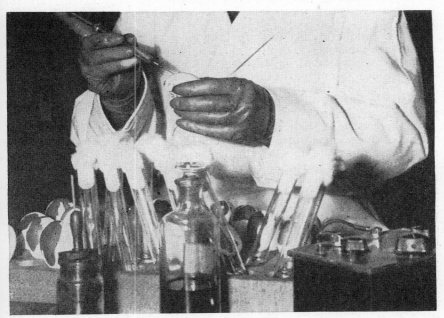

FIGURE 1.—A step in the production of chick-embryo vaccine, used for protecting horses against equine encephalomyelitis. The use of chick embryos as a culture medium is one of the newer developments in the preparation of veterinary biologics.

immunizing bodies. When injected into the body, such serum, by reason of the protective nature of the antibodies, does one of two things. It either exerts an inhibitory (stopping) action against the virulent virus or acts as an antitoxin, neutralizing the poisonous products (toxins) of the disease-producing organisms.

For the preparation of immune serum, horses are generally used, principally because their size makes possible the drawing of large volumes of blood. In treating a horse for the production of antitoxin, small quantities of the respective toxin are first injected; for the production of antibacterial serum, suspensions of the bacteria of the specific disease are injected. Periodical tests are made of the potency of the serum, to determine among other things its ability to protect other animals. When a suitable potency is obtained, a quantity of blood is drawn from the jugular vein into sterile containers.

After standing 24 hours, the separated serum is siphoned off, properly preserved, filtered if necessary, and put into final containers.

Immune serum is assimilated most rapidly if administered intravenously (into the veins), especially if therapeutic (healing or curative) action is desired. For prophylactic (preventive) purposes, the injection is made either intramuscularly (into the muscles) or subcutaneously (under the skin).

Toxoids (anatoxins), consisting of detoxified disease-producing toxins, are gaining in importance and are used very extensively for immunization purposes; examples are diphtheria toxoid and tetanus toxoid.

Other products employed for the protection of animals against disease are sensitized vaccines, sensitized bacterins, germ-free extracts, natural and artificial aggressins, and bacterial filtrates. Although the methods of preparation and characteristics of these biologics vary somewhat, the principle of action is essentially the same. It consists in the production of protective substances against corresponding infections.

In the course of their studies bacteriologists propagate bacteria on various kinds of culture media and sometimes produce different strains, comparable to the various strains of plants and animals (fig. 2). For the purpose of immunization, vaccines or bacterins are sometimes prepared from a single strain of an organism, constituting what is called a monovalent vaccine or bacterin. When prepared from two or more strains, the product is known as polyvalent. A polyvalent vaccine or bacterin is not the same as a "mixed" vaccine, or "mixed" bacterin, which is a mixture of different kinds of bacteria.

At times an autogenous (self-generated) vaccine is employed—that is, one prepared for an organism isolated from an animal affected with a disease and used for the protection of the same animal or similar animals in the locality. An autogenous vaccine has the advantage of containing the particular strain of organism that caused the infection.

Although one injection of the vaccine or bacterin induces the production of antibodies, naturally repeated injections produce a higher degree of resistance, which often is hastened by successively larger doses. The correct quantities are established through experimentation.

BIOLOGICAL PRODUCTS AS DIAGNOSTIC AGENTS

A highly useful specialized class of biological products is that comprising diagnostic agents. As the name signifies, these are used not for preventing or curing a disease, but rather for indicating its presence. The diagnostic agent tuberculin, used in detecting tuberculosis in cattle, swine, and poultry, is a familiar example.

There are three principal methods of tuberculin testing—the intradermic, subcutaneous, and ophthalmic, of which the first is the method now principally used. It consists in the injection of tuberculin into the dermis, the true skin. If the animal is tuberculous, a characteristic swelling later occurs at the site of injection. Expert knowledge of the technique of the test is necessary for its proper use and for interpretation of the results.

The accuracy, as diagnostic agents, of tuberculin and of mallein (used to detect glanders in horses) is so great that veterinary officials destroy reacting animals even though they appear healthy. The animals are slaughtered with absolute confidence that in the great

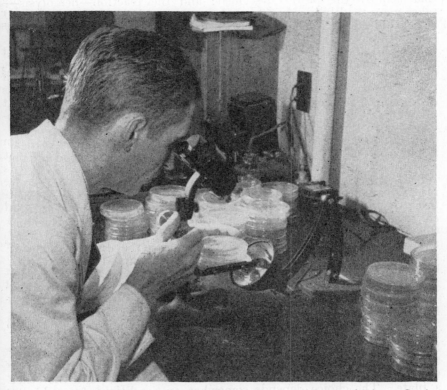

FIGURE 2.—Examining cultures of *Brucella* organisms at the Animal Disease Station of the Bureau of Animal Industry. Most of the experimental work leading to successful vaccination against brucellosis by means of a selected strain of the organism was conducted here.

majority of instances the post mortem examination will justify the diagnosis, made solely on the findings of the biological test.

Ability to detect latent cases and to verify clinical ones is a valuable aid in eradication measures. Early diagnosis of such diseases also obviates the necessity of long periods of quarantine. For combating dourine in horses the complement-fixation method of diagnosis has given excellent results. This is also the laboratory test used for the diagnosis of glanders; the mallein test—comparable in principle to the tuberculin test—is used chiefly in testing for glanders on farms

The complement-fixation method (*12*) [3] is based on the phenomenon of hemolysis, or the dissolution of red blood cells. When the cells dissolve, the hemoglobin in them is set free in the surrounding fluid. Research has shown that when the red blood cells of an animal are introduced into another animal of a different species, the latter's blood acquires the ability to dissolve the blood cells of the first animal. The dissolving action is due to the development of antibodies that acquire the power described; and the reaction—hemolysis—takes place readily in laboratory equipment, such as a glass container. The acquired so-called hemolytic property of the blood depends on two substances, one of which, the hemolysin, has been found to resist heating to about 56°–58° C., whereas the other, the complement, is rendered inactive by this degree of heating. When the complement is "fixed" by union with a specific substance in the serum of the animal under test (the substance resulting from the presence of the disease), the red corpuscles are not dissolved but settle to the bottom of the test tube. This represents a positive reaction, indicating disease. In the case of a healthy animal, no fixation of complement occurs; consequently hemolysis takes place, and the test is read as negative. The Wassermann test for syphilis, widely used in human medicine, is a complement-fixation test.

Still other diagnostic tests that have been extensively applied in recent years are the agglutination test for the detection of brucellosis in cattle (*7*) and the rapid whole-blood test for pullorum disease in chickens (*5*). In testing for brucellosis, use is made of the production by the body of specific antibodies, previously mentioned, that are believed to assist the animal in resisting the disease. One of these substances, existing in the body of an animal infected with brucellosis, is known as agglutinin. It is present in the blood serum in a quantity that depends on the extent and activity of the infection. When serum from an infected animal is brought into contact with a preparation of *Brucella* organisms, called antigen, the organisms gather together in clumps and are technically described as agglutinated. This principle is the basis of the agglutination test, which has been found to compare favorably in accuracy with the tuberculin test for tuberculosis. There are two methods of making the agglutination test, one of which involves the use of a tube and the other a plate. The choice depends somewhat on conditions favorable to the use of each. In general they are equally efficient.

In the control of pullorum disease in poultry, which for many years caused extensive losses, the principle of agglutination is likewise employed. The form of test principally used is the rapid whole-blood test, the basis of which is a stained antigen. The discovery through research that a chemical stain added to antigen makes the reaction more easily seen has greatly facilitated the detection of pullorum disease in poultry. With modern equipment for holding and testing the birds, the rate of handling them is very rapid, usually less than 2 minutes each.

Diagnostics are prepared and used in various ways, and the reac-

[3] Italic numbers in parentheses refer to Literature Cited, p. 153.

tions of animals to them are likewise widely different, requiring specialized training for their proper application and for correct interpretation of the results.

BIOLOGICAL PRODUCTS NOT TO BE USED AS SOLE RELIANCE

The remarkable results often obtained with biological products in combating disease have unfortunately led to a tendency to rely on them solely. A much better course is to give due consideration to the various factors associated with the condition concerned and utilize all measures that will contribute to the desired result. Thus, in treating a case of fistulous withers, it is not enough merely to inject a polyvalent vaccine and then wait for the animal to get well. Supportive treatment, including the possible aid of surgery, should also be considered.

Further, in attempting to control a disease, it is not sufficient to limit activities to vaccination of the exposed and susceptible animals; it is equally essential to inaugurate the necessary sanitary measures, and if possible the source of infection should be looked for and eliminated.

Animals suffering from infectious diseases may be thought of as living factories that produce and distribute vast numbers of disease germs. Thus they are more or less directly a menace to others, and the healthy animals should be segregated from the sick. This is best accomplished by removing the healthy animals immediately to a disease-free environment. In some cases destruction of the infected animals is the wisest course. Thorough disinfection (see Disinfection and Disinfectants, p. 179) and efforts to minimize the danger of exposure to possible subsequent infection should also be a part of the disease-control plan.

As already indicated, the passive form of immunity, conferred on animals as an immediate protective measure, is of short duration, lasting at times not more than a month. Therefore, when the danger of infection is still believed to exist, steps must be taken to guard against losses when the temporary immunity expires. In such instances the passive immunization should be followed with the active form, which renders the animal safe for a much longer time.

IMPORTANCE OF PROPER ADMINISTRATION AND CARE OF BIOLOGICS

The technique of administration must be given careful attention if best results are to be obtained. The animal to be treated should be properly prepared; the site of inoculation should be carefully cleansed and disinfected; and all instruments and utensils coming in contact with the product to be administered should be thoroughly sterilized. Bacterial suspensions should be shaken vigorously to insure an even mixture, and great care should be taken to see that the dose administered is accurate. When dealing with such products as anthrax vaccine and hog cholera virus, it is important that the empty containers and unused portions of such products be disposed of properly. If they should be carelessly thrown aside, there is a possibility that they might be a factor in causing future outbreaks of the disease. It is always essential that the products intended for use in vaccinating should be pure, potent, and used with proper skill. In accordance with the provisions of the Virus-Serum-Toxin Act, a Federal statute, most biological products for the prevention and cure of infections in animals are prepared under license of the United States Department of Agriculture. The products should preferably be administered by a trained veterinarian.

Most biological products are sensitive to light and heat, and directions for their proper storage should be strictly followed to prevent deterioration. Practitioners have no ready means of recognizing changes that may have taken place in a product. If its previous handling or storage has been faulty, a biologic may have become inert. This phase of biological treatment is especially important in connection with highly infectious diseases. When an inert vaccine is used in such cases, both the veterinarian and the stock owner are often unable to explain the subsequent appearance of the disease. Unfortunately, such cases are rather numerous, and from the writer's personal experience in testing vaccines from various sources he can state that the failure to keep the vaccines under proper conditions is responsible for many such disappointing results. The importance of using dependable biologics and having them properly stored and competently administered can scarcely be overemphasized.

Although many different products are prepared for the prevention and treatment of disease, some stand out prominently over others in their specific action and rank among the triumphs of modern medicine. Diphtheria antitoxin, tetanus antitoxin, rabies vaccine, anthrax vaccine, blackleg aggressin, and calf scours serum have given results absolutely unattainable by any other means. Yet it must be remembered that a biological remedy is not specific in the sense that it will always prevent or cure. Neither do the diagnostic agents always detect disease. To the trained mind, these limitations are not unexpected; they exist because the ever-varying individual factor is involved.

Each year of research and experience extends the usefulness of biologic therapeutics. Increasing knowledge also continues to emphasize these basic points: (1) Biologic remedies should be used early, in full dosage; (2) they must be potent at the time of use; (3) antisepsis must be thorough; and (4) supplementary treatment that tends to ameliorate symptoms or conserve vital powers is a valuable adjunct to the use of biologics.

PROTECTIVE MECHANISMS AGAINST PARASITES

Until a few years ago it was considered improbable that there is any protective mechanism or immunity against animal parasites. The few reactions observed in parasitic infections were believed to be fundamentally different from those in other types of infection. It is now well established, however, that many animals do manifest both natural and acquired protective mechanisms against parasites and that these are basically similar to those observed in virus and bacterial infections. The occurrence of immunity and its effectiveness varies greatly in different host animals and against different parasites.[4]

Natural and acquired immunity is now generally considered to play an important part in reducing the damage done by parasites. Since it does not afford complete protection, however, and adequate methods of artificial immunization are lacking, it would seem safest and wisest for the livestock producer not to depend on it for prevention of parasitic losses. Instead it would seem highly advisable for him to attempt to prevent and remove parasitic infection wherever possible through sanitation and treatment and to foster the good health of his animals in all possible ways. He would thus not only greatly lessen the necessity for protective reactions but would insure their having the highest effectiveness when mobilized to combat the comparatively small amount of parasitic infection which he may be unable otherwise to control.

The great importance of protective mechanisms in the control of parasitic disease can perhaps be best illustrated by outlining what usually happens under natural conditions when susceptible animals are placed in contact with parasitized ones. The new arrivals will, in general, be protected against the parasites of other unrelated kinds of animals by what is known as natural immunity. For example, hogs will not become infected, even though exposed to infection, with the parasites of horses, and vice versa. Older stock not previously exposed to infection may also be protected by what is known as age immunity. This form of natural immunity is of widespread occurrence. It is especially marked in dogs and cats against hookworms and in chickens against gapeworms. Some of the animals will also be innately more immune than others because of the possession of an inherited individual, species, or breed immunity. For example, Rhode Island Red and Plymouth Rock chickens have been found to be more resistant to certain experimental infections than Leghorns, Buff Orpingtons, and Minorcas (1), and in mixed flocks of sheep Cheviots were found more tolerant of parasitism than Leicesters (6).

Susceptible animals introduced into an infected environment may be expected to acquire infection and suffer from parasitic injury. As a result their natural mechanisms of defense are stimulated to repair the damage and to counteract the presence of the parasites. Multiplication of the parasites in the blood or tissues or their increase through continual exposure to new infection forces the animals to react more vigorously to the increasing number of parasites. If the number of parasites increases more rapidly than the activity of the protective reactions, the animals suffer and perhaps die from the effects of severe parasitism. If the number of parasites is small or increases slowly, the defense forces of the animals have time to become mobilized and may produce an acquired immunity.

---

[4] Readers interested in a more extensive or more technical discussion of immunity to parasites than that given here are referred to the extensive literature reviewed in citations *6, 14, 19, 21.*

This type of immunity has been shown to develop in many different kinds of animals and with many parasitic infections under both experimental and natural conditions. Especially interesting studies have been made of acquired immunity in cattle against cattle tick fever (*16*) ; in birds, against malaria (*20*) ; in sheep, against stomach worms (*18*) ; and in laboratory animals, against ticks.

The maintenance of a high level of general health is regarded as important in promoting immunity to parasitism. Such factors as the presence of bacterial disease, multiple parasitic infection, hemorrhage, and the extra demands of breeding, gestation, and lactation have all been cited as detrimental. Inadequate and deficient diets have also been shown to lessen immunity. For example, it has been shown that both natural and acquired immunity to hookworm infection breaks down when immune dogs are fed a generally deficient diet (*8*) ; that chickens on diets deficient in vitamins A, B, and D become more susceptible to infection with the common intestinal roundworm (*2, 3, 4*) ; and that whereas a diet deficient in vitamin A increases susceptibility to infestation with lice, a diet containing an abundance of this vitamin will prevent or cure such infestation (*15*).

When the parasites and the injuries they cause are localized in one particular part of the body, blood cells and circulating antibodies are mobilized at that point by the process of inflammation. Although this process occurs in all animals during the course of the primary infection, it is much more rapid and more marked in an immune animal. The harmful products of the parasites are precipitated, neutralized, and destroyed by the cells and fluid of the inflammatory exudate (material discharged), such as pus. The larger, many-celled parasites may also ingest the exudate and be subjected to its action internally as well as externally. Evidence of such action may be seen in the formation of precipitates in the intestine and on the outside of parasites immobilized in the tissues of immune animals.

After the parasites have become inactive and their development has been checked, they are gradually hemmed in by densely packed cells, which form nodules or cysts that become fibrous by the gradual formation of scar tissue around them. The parasite is imprisoned until it dies and is either gradually dissolved by the surrounding macrophages or persists as a calcified, or hardened, remnant. Meanwhile, the tissues injured by the parasite are being repaired by the replacement of destroyed cells and by scar-tissue formation.

The general mechanism of immunity outlined in this brief description is probably of wide occurrence since it has been observed with such diverse parasites as fly maggots, tapeworm larvae, and the larvae of roundworms. The basic phenomenon involved—interference with the normal feeding and development of the parasite by a protective substance in the animal—is probably also operative in immunity against parasites which are essentially outside the tissues. This has been demonstrated in the case of ticks and intestinal worms. Antibodies are evidently of primary importance in these cases of acquired immunity to metazoan parasites, since it has been shown that the immunity can be transferred to a normal animal by the injection of immune serum.

NUTRITION AND DISEASE RESISTANCE

Generally speaking, poor nutrition tends to break down the natural barriers of the animal organism against the ravages of the infecting agents of disease. The whole question of how this is accomplished is an exceedingly complex one. Infections vary widely in their nature, they involve various parts of the body, the many structures are affected differently, and their proper nutrition or repair calls for different food elements. Determining the specific functions of the food constituents has challenged the skill of many investigators. In recent years the vitamins have received major attention, but the various essential mineral elements, the proteins, and the energy intake have also been the subject of research, especially with a view to correcting deficiencies.

Much of the experimental work on the relation of nutrition to resistance has been done on laboratory animals such as the rat, guinea pig, and pigeon. Relatively little attention has been given to farm animals. Because of species differences in the need for several vitamin factors, generalizations from the results with laboratory animals are not necessarily applicable to cattle, sheep, swine, and horses.

The need of the higher animals for vitamin A and the early work which showed a close association of bacterial infection with xerophthalmia, a serious nutritional disease due to lack of vitamin A, have naturally focused attention on this factor. Vitamin A has been properly termed the "anti-infective factor." It has been suggested that the underlying cause for the increased susceptibility of vitamin-A-deficient animals resides in the changes produced in the epithelial tissues (those of the skin and lining membranes) through the substitution of keratinized, or horny, tissue for normal tissue. This change occurs in the respiratory, alimentary, and genitourinary tracts, the eye, and the glands of the throat and ear. If this is the case, the change in epithelial tissues brought about by lack of vitamin A increases the susceptibility to invasion by disease-producing organisms, but there is not necessarily a decrease of immunity in the strictly medical sense. Certain experiments in which the disease organisms were artificially injected into the animal have demonstrated that the decrease in resistance is due to more than the mere break-down of epithelial tissue. Animals that received an adequate supply of vitamin A in their food were much less susceptible to the disease produced by the injection of the infecting agent than were the deficient animals.

All farm animals require vitamin A, and a number of reports are available on experimental work on the association of the deficiency and disease resistance. There is considerable evidence that the incidence of white scours in calves is associated with vitamin A; thus Stewart and McCallum (*17*) found that a lowered vitamin A content in the colostrum of the cow was associated with an increased number of deaths among calves infected with *Bacillus coli*. It does not necessarily follow that all cases of white scours will respond to vitamin A therapy. Some persons have suspected that increased resistance to tuberculosis was associated with adequate vitamin A intake, but a limited amount of work with pigs has not brought out such a relationship.. Cattle maintained on a vitamin-A-deficient diet have appeared to be more susceptible to infections and have shown a relatively high mortality rate as compared with animals fed on adequate rations.

The evidence on the influence of vitamin D on infection is conflicting. Experimental findings with laboratory animals fed on diets that produced rickets have indicated a decreased resistance to certain micro-organisms and no change in resistance to other organisms.

It has been established that the needs of herbivores for the factors of the vitamin B complex are or can be met for the most part through synthesis of the vitamin factors by micro-organisms residing in the alimentary tract. Swine and poultry, however, depend upon the diet for these factors. Experimental work on vitamin B_1 deficiency has shown that animals so affected are generally less resistant to infection and succumb more readily to the ravages of disease than normal animals. It is believed that the lowered body temperature and possibly the loss of appetite resulting from a prolonged intake of the vitamin-B_1-deficient diet is largely responsible. The pronounced fall in body temperature that may occur is well illustrated in studies on pigs (*22*), in which a drop of as much as 8° F. was recorded. From the standpoint of loss of appetite, a decrease in the power of the blood to promote the formation of phagocytes (devouring cells), which occurs in starvation, as established by the work of Gellhorn and Dunn (*9*), may well account for the decreased resistance.

Evidence is accumulating that necrotic enteritis in swine, a disease produced by *Salmonella suipestifer* and possibly other related organisms, can be alleviated by the use of nicotinic acid. The fact that liver and certain other natural feedstuffs are more effective than nicotinic acid in effecting cures or in preventing the disease suggests that other factors besides nicotinic acid are involved. The mode of action is not understood, but there appears to be an increase in the building of scar tissue over the lesions of dead tissue in the intestine.

The quality and quantity of protein in the diet are thought to bear a close relation to the resistance of human beings to certain infective diseases. The unusual food habits of certain primitive tribes or of groups of people on restricted diets in wartime have been cited to show that a decreased protein intake was associated with an increase in the occurrence and severity of infectious diseases such as tuberculosis. Lowered protein intake apparently reduced the resistance to certain infections in dogs and in suckling pigs. On the other hand McCay and others (*11*) have reported that moderate restriction in the food intake of rats, sufficient to retard their growth and development but prolonging their span of life, lessened their susceptibility to lung disease at approximately 1 year of age, when normal rats suffered severely. Well-founded evidence is available to show that lowered incidence of middle-ear and lung disorders is found among retarded animals.

A lowered intake of protein and calcium by sheep kept on poor pasture has been suspected of contributing to a decrease, below the normal levels, in the amounts of the normal lysins (substances capable of dissolving bacteria) of *Bacillus coli* and *B. suipestifer*, and of the agglutinins (substances capable of causing the clumping of bacteria) of *Brucella abortus* and *B. paratyphosus.*

On the other hand, studies on the relation of diet to infectious abortion by Hart, Hadley, and Humphrey (*10*) showed that a good ration well fortified with protein, fat, calcium, phosphorus, and iodine did not increase resistance to inoculation with *Brucella abortus* over that shown by heifers fed a so-called poor ration. The authors observed that vitamin A was an important cause of failure in reproduction. Where the restriction is so severe that it approaches starvation conditions, there seems to be little doubt that the resistance of the body to infection is decreased. The Colorado Agricultural Experiment Station (*13*) has found that sheep deprived of feed for short periods are subject to paratyphoid dysentery. It appears that the organism *Salmonella aertrycke* is a normal resident of the intestinal tract and develops added virulence under certain conditions, among which deprivation of feed is one.

The general belief is that both the normal antibodies of the serum and the power to form antibodies are not affected by dietary deficiencies. Even this premise may be contradicted, however, as evidence accumulates on the corrective and stimulative action of food factors in the formation of antibodies.

The examples presented on the relationship of nutrition and disease resistance in farm animals are intended to show, on the one hand, the nature of the relationship and, on the other, the scarcity of conclusive data. In spite of the latter, there can be little doubt that nutritive well-being in general is essential for the animal body to combat and counteract the action of disease-producing organisms. The fact that a certain nutritive essential does not appear to bear a direct relation to resistance to a particular infectious disease should not be taken as proof of a lack of relationship.

LITERATURE CITED

(1) ACKERT, J. E., EISENBRANDT, L. L., WILMOTH, J. H., and others.
    1935. COMPARATIVE RESISTANCE OF FIVE BREEDS OF CHICKENS TO THE NEMATODE ASCARIDIA LINEATA (SCHNEIDER). Jour. Agr. Res. 50: 607–624, illus.

(2) ——— MCILVAINE, MARIAN FISHER, and CRAWFORD, NAOMI ZIMMERMAN.
    1931. RESISTANCE OF CHICKENS TO PARASITISM AFFECTED BY VITAMIN A. Amer. Jour. Hyg. 13: 320–336.

(3) ——— and NOLF, L. O.
    1931. RESISTANCE OF CHICKENS TO PARASITISM AFFECTED BY VITAMIN B. Amer. Jour. Hyg. 13: 337–344, illus.

(4) ——— and SPINDLER, LLOYD A.
    1929. VITAMIN D AND RESISTANCE OF CHICKENS TO PARASITISM. Amer. Jour. Hyg. 9: 292–307.

(5) BUNYEA, HUBERT.
    1939. USE OF THE RAPID WHOLE-BLOOD TEST FOR PULLORUM DISEASE. U. S. Dept. Agr. Misc. Pub. 349, 18 pp., illus.

(6) CAMERON, THOMAS, W. M.
    1935. IMMUNITY AGAINST ANIMAL PARASITES. 12th Internatl. Vet. Cong. (1934) Proc. 3: 44–65.

(7) EICHHORN, A., and CRAWFORD, A. B.
    1941. BRUCELLOSIS OF CATTLE (BANG'S DISEASE, INFECTIOUS ABORTION). U. S. Dept. Agr. Farmers' Bul. 1871, 21 pp., illus.

(8) FOSTER, A. O., and CORT, W. W.
   1935.   FURTHER STUDIES ON THE EFFECT OF A GENERALLY DEFICIENT DIET
           UPON THE RESISTANCE OF DOGS TO HOOKWORM INFESTATION.   Amer.
           Jour. Hyg. 21: 302–318, illus.
(9) GELLHORN, ERNST, and DUNN, J. O.
   1937.   UNDERNUTRITION, STARVATION AND PHAGOCYTOSIS.   Jour. Nutr. 14:
           145–153, illus.
(10) HART, E. B., HADLEY, F. B., and HUMPHREY, G. C.
   1932.   THE RELATION OF NUTRITION TO CONTAGIOUS CATTLE ABORTION.   Wis.
           Expt. Sta. Res. Bul. 112, 45 pp., illus.
(11) McCAY, C. W., ELLIS, G. H., BARNES, LeROY L., and others.
   1939.   CHEMICAL AND PATHOLOGICAL CHANGES IN AGING AND AFTER RE-
           TARDED GROWTH.   Jour. Nutr. 18: 15–25, illus.
(12) MOHLER, JOHN R., and EICHHORN, ADOLPH.
   1911.   THE DIAGNOSIS OF GLANDERS BY COMPLEMENT FIXATION.   U. S. Bur.
           Anim. Indus. Bul. 136, 31 pp., illus.
(13) NEWSOM, I. E., and THORP, FRANK, JR.
   1938.   LAMB DISEASES IN COLORADO FEEDLOTS.   Colo. Expt. Sta. Bul. 448,
           42 pp., illus.
(14) SANDGROUND, J. H.
   1929.   A CONSIDERATION OF THE RELATION OF HOST-SPECIFICITY OF HEL-
           MINTHS AND OTHER METAZOAN PARASITES TO THE PHENOMENA OF
           AGE RESISTANCE AND ACQUIRED IMMUNITY.   Parasitology 21:
           [227]–255.
(15) SEARLS, ED. M., and SNYDER, FRED M.
   1939.   A STUDY OF THE RELATION OF VITAMIN A TO LOUSE RESISTANCE IN
           RATS.   Jour. Parasitol. 25: 425–430.
(16) SMITH, THEOBALD, and KILBOURNE, F. L.
   1893.   INVESTIGATIONS INTO THE NATURE, CAUSATION, AND PREVENTION OF
           TEXAS OR SOUTHERN CATTLE FEVER.   U. S. Bur. Anim. Indus.
           Bul. 1, 301 pp., illus.
(17) STEWART, JAMES, and McCALLUM, JENNIE WHITELAW.
   1938.   "WHITE SCOUR" IN CALVES AND RELATED INFECTIONS.   I. THE SIGNIFI-
           CANCE OF THE VITAMIN A CONTENT OF THE COLOSTRUM AS A PRE-
           DISPOSING FACTOR IN THE CAUSATION OF SUCH CONDITIONS.   Jour.
           Compar. Path. and Ther. 51: 290–295.
(18) STOLL, NORMAN R.
   1929.   STUDIES WITH THE STRONGYLOID NEMATODE, HAEMONCHUS CON-
           TORTUS.   I. ACQUIRED RESISTANCE OF HOSTS UNDER NATURAL REIN-
           FECTION CONDITIONS OUT-OF-DOORS.   Amer. Jour. Hyg. 10:
           384–418, illus.
(19) TALIAFERRO, WILLIAM H.
   1929.   THE IMMUNOLOGY OF PARASITIC INFECTIONS.   414 pp., illus. New
           York and London.
(20) ———
   1931.   THE MECHANISM OF ACQUIRED IMMUNITY IN AVIAN MALARIA.   South.
           Med. Jour. 24: 409–415, illus.
(21) ———
   1940.   THE MECHANISM OF ACQUIRED IMMUNITY IN INFECTIONS WITH
           PARASITIC WORMS.   Physiol. Revs. 20: 469–492.
(22) VAN ETTEN, CECIL, ELLIS, N. R., and MADSEN, L. L.
   1940.   STUDIES ON THE THIAMIN REQUIREMENT OF YOUNG SWINE.   Jour.
           Nutr. 20: 607–625, illus.

The Endocrine Glands in Health and Disease

BY A. H. FRANK [1]

SOME of the most extraordinary discoveries of modern medicine are those concerned with the endocrine glands and the hormones they secrete. These glands act as a complicated, delicate set of controls over many vital bodily processes. Some of the hormones have remarkable results, both experimentally and in medical practice, and the future will undoubtedly see further developments.

IN A NORMAL BODY the endocrine glands with their secretions function as a very delicately balanced mechanism. An excessive or deficient secretion of one or more of these glands may lead to an abnormal or diseased condition. Many such conditions are now recognized, several of which, such as diabetes, goiter, cretinism, and sexual impotency, may be successfully treated. This is true of man more than of animals. Some secretions are also being studied with the expectation of increasing certain desirable bodily functions beyond what is considered normal.

All animals have endocrine glands. There are nine of them: The pituitary gland, which is located at the base of the brain; the pineal body, also in the brain; the thyroid, parathyroid, and thymus glands, located in the neck; the adrenal glands, in the abdominal cavity near each kidney; the pancreas, also in the abdominal cavity; and the testicles in the male and ovaries in the female. Because the secretions of these glands are emptied directly into blood vessels within themselves, instead of passing through excretory ducts as in ordinary glands, they are also known as ductless glands or glands of internal secretion.

[1] A. H. Frank is Associate Veterinarian, Animal Disease Station, Beltsville, Md., Bureau of Animal Industry.

Each of the endocrine glands secretes one or more substances called endocrines, or hormones. The secretions are usually in very minute quantities and are normally formed as needed through nervous impulse or the direct action of one endocrine upon a gland secreting another endocrine. In particular, the hormones control sexual growth and the various stages of reproduction.[2]

The functions of some of the endocrine glands have been recognized for years, but only recently have the particular stimulating substances been recovered from them in pure chemical form. The Bible refers to castrated men (eunuchs), and the changes in physical make-up and behavior following castration are commonly known; in animal husbandry it is common practice to castrate young bulls, rams, boars, and roosters to improve the tenderness and tastiness of the meat. But the extraction from the testicles of the hormone responsible for male physical characteristics was first made in chemical form in 1935.[3] The action of this substance is proved by the fact that continued treatment of castrated animals and men with it results in the return of male characteristics and conformation.

As will be noted in the following description of the various endocrine glands and their functions, the actions and interactions of the various hormones are very complex. Though much has been learned about the nature of the endocrines during the last 15 years, only a beginning has been made in the discovery and application of remedies involving them. This is due in part to the difficulty of obtaining many of these substances in pure form in sufficient quantities for extended experimentation, since the endocrines are not stored in the glands but are formed as needed and released immediately. Since the various hormones are fortunately identical in all animal species, these substances can be obtained from animals killed in abattoirs.

In view of its past accomplishments and the vast amount of work being done at present, endocrinology holds promise of great achievements in the future, especially in the purification and possible synthetic preparation of hormones and their application in medical treatment.

THE PITUITARY GLAND

The pituitary gland is unquestionably the master gland of the body. It consists of two parts, a larger anterior lobe and a smaller posterior lobe. It is located at the base of the brain in a bony cavity and is surrounded by a rich supply of blood vessels.

In the cow it is about 1 inch in diameter and in the rat about $\frac{1}{16}$ of an inch. Its secretions are protein in nature and are so complex that chemists have not been able to analyze them. The anterior lobe is the master part. Eleven or more secretions have been attributed to it alone.

---

[2] ALLEN, EDGAR, ed. SEX AND INTERNAL SECRETIONS; A SURVEY OF RECENT RESEARCH. 1346 pp., illus. Baltimore. 1939.
[3] BUTENANDT, ADOLF, and HANISCH, GÜNTER. ÜBER TESTOSTERON. UMWANDLUNG DES DEHYDRO-ANDROSTERONS IN ANDROSTENDIOL AND TESTOSTERON; EIN WEG ZUR DARSTELLUNG DES TESTOSTERONS AUS CHOLESTERIN. Hoppe-Seylers Ztschr. f. Physiol. Chem. 237: 89–97. illus. 1935.

SECRETIONS FROM THE ANTERIOR LOBE

Gonadotropic Hormones

The development of such sex characteristics as body conformation and voice, and in the female the estrus cycle, which includes the ripening of the ovum, or egg, in the ovary and its passage into the uterus, or womb, is directly or indirectly the result of stimulation by hormones secreted by the anterior lobe of the pituitary gland. Two of these are the gonadotropic hormones, so-called because they act on the gonads (ovaries in the female and testicles in the male). They are known as the follicle-stimulating principle, or prolan A, and the luteinizing principle, or prolan B.

The ovary contains thousands of minute eggs, and during the first half of each estrus cycle one or more of these is developed through the action of the follicle-stimulating hormone. A covering is formed around the egg, and the whole is called a follicle. As the follicle grows in size its expansion is in the direction of the periphery, or outside of the ovary. Its growth is characterized by an increase in the quantity of fluid, and when mature it has the appearance of a large blister protruding from the surface of the ovary. After ripening, one of two things may happen to the follicle:

(1) Normally, the follicle is ruptured by the action of the other gonadotropic hormone, the luteinizing principle, and the ovum is set free to advance into the uterus. After the escape of the ovum from the follicle, the latter becomes filled with yellowish cells and is thereafter known as the corpus luteum, or yellow body. The luteinizing hormone derives its name from the corpus luteum, which it stimulates directly.

(2) Abnormally, the follicle may fail to rupture, developing into a cyst. The cyst may remain stationary or increase in size. Other follicles generally develop similarly, and their walls become thickened. The follicular fluid (containing estrogenic hormone, described later) in these cysts may change the normal reproductive cycle to frequent or constant heat. Cystic ovaries, if treated early, may be benefited by the gonadotropic hormones; but chronic cases do not respond satisfactorily to such treatment, and the cysts may have to be broken down mechanically. Sometimes the cysts reform and must again be ruptured. Ovariectomy, or removal of the ovary, is recommended in persistent cases.

An excess of luteinizing hormone may act on an immature follicle to stimulate the production of a corpus luteum before rupture occurs, thus preventing the subsequent release of the egg.

In males the luteinizing principle stimulates the cells in the testicle to secrete the male sex hormone. The luteinizing hormone is predominant in the urine of pregnant women from about the eighth day after missing the last menstrual period to parturition. A test for its presence makes possible the early detection of pregnancy.

After ovulation in the female, if fertilization occurs, the corpus luteum remains active until pregnancy is ended, but if not, it gradually disappears. No further heat periods occur until the corpus luteum has become inactive. In cattle its disappearance is sometimes sluggish and it must be expelled by pressure of the hand on the ovary before the cow can again come in heat. The luteinizing hormone activates the corpus luteum, and the latter in turn secretes hormones that act directly on the uterus and indirectly on the mammary glands, as described later.

In addition to initiating ovogenesis (ripening of the germ cells in the ovaries of females) and maintaining this ovarian germ-cell activity, the follicle-stimulating principle, prolan A, initiates spermatogenesis (ripening of the germ cells, or spermatozoa, of the testicles) in young males and maintains this activity in mature males. It is used in man and animals to overcome some types of sterility.

When extracts containing this follicle-stimulating hormone are injected into sexually immature animals, precocious sexual maturity is produced. Ovaries of infantile female rats may be increased in weight 10 to 20 times in 96 hours. Young children who suffer from a tumor involving the pituitary, which causes an excessive secretion of this hormone, may reach sexual maturity at 5 years of age or younger.

Between the 42d and 120th days of pregnancy, the blood of pregnant mares is rich in this principle, and a physiological test of their blood serum for the presence of this hormone may be used to determine whether pregnancy exists.

Various preparations rich in gonadotropic principles have been used to overcome sexual sluggishness, especially inactive gonads, in mature animals. Ewes may be brought into estrus with serum from pregnant mares or with pituitary extracts and bred during their nonbreeding season. Some types of sterility in women and animals can be successfully treated with this extract. Overdosage may result in the ripening of abnormally large numbers of eggs. This is undesirable, as there is not enough space in the female reproductive tract for a large number of fetuses to develop, and abortion or mummification of a number of them may follow.

Mammogenic Hormone

The gonadotropic hormones indirectly stimulate the pituitary to secrete other hormones. As already noted, their action upon the ovary stimulates the growth of the follicle and the corpus luteum, and these in turn secrete the two female sex hormones. One action of the female sex hormones is the direct stimulation of the pituitary to secrete the mammogenic principle. The mammogenic principle directly stimulates the growth and development of the mammary gland, in which milk is secreted and stored. The hormone is secreted during each estrus cycle and produces some growth of the mammary gland; but following conception it is secreted continuously and stimulates the complete development of the mammary gland for that gestation period. If an unlimited supply of this hormone were available, it might be possible to grow large udders on all cows.

Lactogenic Hormone

At parturition, or delivery of young, there is a rapid reduction in the secretion of the sex hormones. This may furnish the stimulus which activates the pituitary to secrete the lactogenic, or milk-stimulating, principle.

The lactogenic hormone initiates milk secretion in the completely developed mammary gland. Both males and females of most species of mammals may be brought to full lactation by injections of this hormone when their mammary glands have been experimentally developed. The stimulus for continued milk secretion is maintained by this hormone. Injections into cows in declining lactation resulted in a pronounced increase in milk and butterfat,[4] but this added stimulus is only of short duration.

Growth Hormone

Experimental evidence and observations of certain disease conditions indicate that the pituitary directly influences the growth of animals. By injecting pituitary extracts that contain the active growth principle into growing mice, it is possible to double the normal mature size of the animals.

Pathological conditions of the pituitary, such as tumorous growths, may result in an excessive secretion of the growth hormone. When this occurs in immature animals they grow abnormally large. If it occurs before maturity in man, gigantism (abnormal tallness, 8 feet or over) may be the result. In adults, it produces the condition known as acromegaly, a chronic disease characterized by enlargement of the bones and soft parts of the hands, feet, and face. Retardation of pituitary activity or the destruction of the gland by X-ray checks these conditions, and the injection of sufficient pituitary extract will maintain normal life.

It is fairly evident that the secretion of the growth hormone in normal individuals is controlled through heredity. Inherited characters are transmitted through genes in the female egg and the male sperm cell. The gene responsible for growth of the cells of the pituitary that secrete this hormone may be absent, as has been shown in a colony of dwarf mice. The dwarfism was shown to be due to a single recessive character, dependent upon a single gene. Through microscopic study of the pituitary tissues of these mice in comparison with those of normal mice, it was found that certain cells of the pituitary were absent in the dwarfs. When pituitaries from normal mice were transplanted into these dwarfs they made normal growth. Growth also occurred when the growth hormone extract was injected into the dwarfs.[5] This condition can occur in both man and animals Cases of human pituitary infantilism or dwarfism occur frequently where the pituitary has been destroyed by disease processes. The injection of pituitary extracts containing the growth principle in proper amounts restores normal growth in these individuals.

The importance of careful selection of individual animals for breeding purposes is clearly seen, since the quantity of growth hor-

[4] FOLLEY, S. J., and YOUNG, F. G. THE EFFECT OF CONTINUED TREATMENT WITH ANTERIOR PITUITARY EXTRACTS ON MILK VOLUME AND MILK-FAT PRODUCTION IN THE LACTATING COW. Biochem. Jour. 33 : 193–197, illus. 1939.
[5] SMITH, PHILIP E., and McDOWELL, E. C. AN HEREDITARY ANTERIOR-PITUITARY DEFICIENCY IN THE MOUSE. Anat. Rec. 46 : 249–257, illus. 1930.

mone secreted by an immature animal evidently determines the rate and extent of its growth. In the future it may be possible to run a quantitative test for the growth hormone and eliminate undesirable animals at birth.

Other Anterior-Lobe Hormones

There is evidence that the anterior lobe of the pituitary gland may secrete an active principle (parathyrotropic hormone) that influences the activity of the parathyroids in calcium metabolism.

The outer, or cortical, portion of the adrenal glands (to be described later), which is essential to the maintenance of life, is under the influence of the adrenotropic hormone of the pituitary gland. In animals with the pituitary removed, the cortical portion of the adrenal glands becomes inactive.

Carbohydrate metabolism is known to be influenced by a hormone secreted by the pituitary. Following injections of active pituitary extracts the blood sugar increases considerably, while removal of the pituitary causes the blood sugar to fall 50 percent below normal. Some forms of obesity (those in which people weigh 600 pounds or more) are attributed to glandular dysfunctions or upsets, especially dysfunctions of the anterior pituitary.

There are indications that the digestion and assimilation of fats and proteins may be influenced by anterior-pituitary hormones.

An anterior-pituitary principle (the thyrotropic hormone) activates the thyroid gland to secrete the thyroid hormone, thyroxine, described later. In men and animals with the pituitary removed the thyroid becomes inactive.

The secretion of insulin by the pancreas is influenced by the pituitary. In most animals and in man, the disease diabetes mellitus, with its characteristic symptoms of an increased excretion of urine of high sugar content, can be artificially produced by removal of the pancreas. If the pituitary is also removed, the sugar level approaches normal; but if pituitary extract is injected into an animal without the pancreas or pituitary the original condition of excess sugar is again produced. The addition of pituitary extract to insulin has improved the general well-being of some diabetic people.

SECRETIONS FROM THE POSTERIOR LOBE

Pituitrin Hormone

The posterior lobe of the pituitary secretes the hormone pituitrin. Pituitrin may be split into two active principles, both of which act to contract the smooth muscles of the body. One, oxytocin, stimulates the uterus to contraction. Its action is variable, and it is effective in some mammals only near the end of pregnancy. It is used in difficult labor cases to initiate or to increase the power of uterine contractions. If too much is given, the contractions may be too severe and persistent.

The other principle, vasopressin, activates the muscular tissue of the capillaries and arterioles, or small blood vessels, and thus induces a rise in blood pressure. It increases peristalsis, the wavelike motion of the intestines, by contracting the intestinal muscles. In the dairy cow, it is responsible for the letting down of the milk. Manipulation of the udder and teats at the beginning of milking stimulates the release of this hormone. By contracting the muscles of the udder, it forces the milk into the larger milk channels and cisterns, where it can be readily removed. Its stimulus is short-lived, so a fast milker can obtain more milk than a slow one.

The kidneys are influenced directly by the posterior lobe through its stimulation of the filtering mechanism. Removal or destruction of the posterior pituitary leads to the disease diabetes insipidus, a chronic condition marked by great thirst and passage of large amounts of urine with no excess of sugar.

THE TESTICLE

The testicle has two major functions: (1) Production of spermatozoa, which is seasonal in the majority of animals but continuous in man, monkey, and most of the domestic animals; and (2) the secretion of the male sex hormone, testosterone. In most species, with the exception of birds, the testicles are located in the scrotum, which is outside of the body cavity proper. As previously stated, their activities are under the direct influence of the pituitary.

TESTOSTERONE HORMONE

The testicles begin to secrete testosterone actively at the time of puberty, or sexual maturity. This hormone induces the development of secondary sex characters and stimulates the accessory male sex glands, the prostate, seminal vesicles, and Cowper's gland. Small or infantile genitalia of immature and mature men may be grown to normal size or larger by the injection of this hormone, and in some cases fertility is restored in sterile males by the simultaneous injection of prolan A.

Sexual desire may be enhanced in subnormal and castrated males by the injection of this hormone. Its continuous injection into castrates enables them to perform the copulatory act successfully and restores the characteristic secondary sex characters in long-standing cases. It also tends to correct the castration atrophy (drying up) of the adrenal glands and restores them to normal condition.

Testosterone has been chemically analyzed and synthesized, so that it is available in pure form. It has been used successfully in correcting cryptorchidism (failure of the testicle to descend into the scrotum) in boys and young men; testicles not descending during such treatment are generally retained by mechanical impediments. It is antagonistic to the female sex hormone, estrogen, which induces heat and female characteristics in the female. The injection of testosterone will prevent heat, and prolonged injections produce male characteristics in normal females.

OVARIES

The ovaries, two in number, are the reproductive glands of the female. They are located in the abdominal cavity, one on each side, and are connected to the uterus, or womb, by a tube which serves as a passage channel for the eggs, or ova. Their functions are three-fold: (1) Production of the egg; (2) production of the follicle, which secretes the female sex hormone, estrogen; and (3) production of the corpus luteum, which secretes the other female sex hormone, progestin. In normal females ovarian activity, which is under the influence of the anterior pituitary, is exhibited in rhythmic cycles, subject to interruption by pregnancy.

ESTROGEN HORMONE

The fluid within the ovarian follicles of normal females and the blood, urine, and amniotic fluid (contained in the sac that surrounds the embryo) of pregnant mammals are rich sources of estrogen. Small traces have also been detected from other sources. Estrogen has been analyzed chemically and prepared synthetically.

In the nonpregnant female estrogen is secreted by the developing follicle, previously described, during half of the estrus cycle (the changes that take place from the beginning of one heat period to the beginning of the next). Ripening of the follicle and the height of estrogen production is characterized by the onset of heat in the female. It also induces a new growth of the epithelium, or lining cells, of the uterus and vagina. A deficiency of estrogen is manifest in some animals. A large percentage of mares are known to pass through estrus cycles without showing signs of heat, although ovulation (releasing of the egg) occurs at the normal time, as proved by mares becoming pregnant following artificial insemination. Estrogen induces the development of the secondary sex characters of the female, about the most noticeable of which are the character-istic plumage of birds and a certain refinement of stature and features in some mammals. During the cycle, as already indicated, it stimu-lates the pituitary to secrete mammogen to a limited extent.

In most animals the egg or eggs are expelled from the ovary dur-ing or immediately following estrus. Primates (man and monkey) do not outwardly express estrus, but their reproductive tracts pass through similar cyclic changes. Estrus may be induced by the in-jection of estrogen in both normal females that do not come into heat and those with their ovaries removed. It acts directly upon the vagina and uterus, inducing a new epithelial growth similar to that of the normal cycle.

Because of its action on the epithelium, estrogen is used to treat gonorrhea in young girls, and it should be beneficial in diseases that affect the epithelium of the vagina and the uterus of animals. Large injections immediately following conception (fertilization of the egg) will terminate pregnancy. The presence of this hormone during preg-nancy inhibits the pituitary from secreting the follicle-stimulating principle.

PROGESTIN HORMONE

Immediately following rupture of the follicle, the corpus luteum begins to grow into the follicular cavity under the stimulus of the luteinizing hormone (prolan B) of the pituitary. It immediately begins to secrete progestin, which stimulates an increase in blood supply and further development of the epithelium of the uterus in preparation for implantation or embedding of the egg, if fertilized. Small amounts of estrogen are also secreted, which act with the progestin to further stimulate the pituitary to secrete mammogen. When the male sperm cell unites with the ovum, the latter becomes attached to the wall of the uterus. This implantation of the fertilized egg furnishes a stimulus to the pituitary to secrete prolan B and maintain the corpus luteum for the duration of pregnancy. With advancement of pregnancy, an increase of estrogen, together with the progestin, stimulates the maximum secretion of mammogen, and the mammary gland is completely developed.

In sterile cycles the corpus luteum is short-lived, and the stimulus from estrogen and progestin soon ceases. This is followed by menstruation in primates, while there is no outward sign in other mammals. A new cycle begins with the growth of a new follicle.

Abortions and resorptions (absorption of the embryo) that occur during early pregnancy may be due to a deficiency of progestin. The corpus luteum may be slow to develop and thus fail to prepare the uterus for implantation.

THE PARATHYROID GLANDS

The parathyroids are ductless glands that in large animals are about as large as a grain of wheat. They are two to four in number and are located one or two under each lobe of the thyroid gland.

Parathormone is produced by the parathyroids and maintains the equilibrium between the insoluble calcium and phosphorus compounds in the skeleton and the soluble compounds of these essential minerals in the blood. Extracts are used in treating cases of reduced secretion of the hormone (hypoparathyroidism).

THE ADRENAL GLANDS

The two adrenal glands are located in the abdominal cavity, one in front of each kidney. They are ductless and consist of two parts, the medullary (inner) and cortical (outer) portions.

The hormone adrenin is secreted by the medullary part of the adrenal glands. Its action is similar to that of pituitrin. It is used extensively in cases of shock as an indirect heart stimulant and to check hemorrhages by contracting the muscles of the small blood vessels.

The hormone cortin, which is essential to the maintenance of life, is contained in the cortical portion of the gland. Extracts of this portion have been used to maintain life in animals after the glands are removed. This hormone is similar to testosterone in its chemical make-up and its antagonistic reaction to estrogen. When tumorous growths of the adrenal glands in young girls cause an excessive secretion, this antagonism to estrogen is demonstrated by the production of male characteristics, such as growth of beard on the face coarseness of voice, cessation of menstruation, and decreased modesty. The condition is alleviated when the tumor is removed.

Addison's disease, which is characterized by bronzelike pigmentation of the skin, severe prostration, progressive anemia, low blood pressure, diarrhea, and digestive disturbances, is due to a decreased secretion or functioning of the cortical portion of the adrenal gland. The disease can be corrected in most cases by injections of cortin.

THE THYROID

The thyroid is a ductless gland resembling a tiny shield in shape. It is located in front and on both sides of the windpipe. The familiar enlargement in the neck called goiter is an enlargement of this gland.

The thyroid, as stated previously, is stimulated by the pituitary to secrete the hormone thyroxin, which controls the energy output, or metabolism, of the body. Chemical analysis shows that thyroxin contains large amounts of iodine. An increased production of thyroxin gives the individual an excessive amount of energy. The metabolic rate may be doubled by injection of thyroxin. Its injection into rams has been found to activate their sexual functioning and enhance the production of fertile semen during the nonbreeding season, summer. Practical use of the method would materially increase the possibility of getting early lamb crops by rendering the rams fertile at an earlier date than their normal breeding season. In hibernating animals the thyroid diminishes in size and practically ceases activity during hibernation. The injection of thyroxin interrupts the hibernal sleep. An overactive gland may be corrected in part by surgical removal of a portion of the tissue.

A decreased secretion of thyroxin makes the individual sluggish. The metabolic rate may be decreased at least half by removal of the gland. Animals born without the thyroid or those in which it becomes inactivated during infancy fail to develop normally in mental, physical, and sexual activity. In children this is known as cretinism. A similar condition in adults is known as myxedema, a disease characterized by the decreased function of the thyroid gland and marked by dropsylike swelling, especially of the face and hands, and a general slowing-down or sluggishness. In this condition the gland may become quite small. All cases of cretinism and myxedema are benefited and most cases may be cured by the continuous administration of thyroxin. Feeding the dried gland provides a satisfactory supplement for the normal gland. In some cases of cretinism the addition of the growth principle from the pituitary may prove beneficial.

A deficiency of iodine in the diet may result in a decreased functioning of the thyroid gland. This is discussed in the articles on nutritional diseases in this volume.

THE PANCREAS

The pancreas is located in a loop of the small intestine adjacent to the stomach. It has a twofold function. It secretes digestive juices, which enter directly into the intestine, and the hormone insulin, which enters the blood stream. Insulin is secreted by small islets of cells scattered throughout the connective tissue of the pancreas.

When the secretion of insulin falls below the normal level or ceases, diabetes mellitus is produced. The carbohydrate metabolism is badly upset, and the patient is unable to utilize sugars, large amounts of which appear in the blood and are eliminated in the urine, which is decidedly increased in volume. Insulin for the treatment of the disease is now available in both crystalline form and water solution.

An oversecretion or an injection of insulin into normal animals results in a decrease of sugar in the blood and if continued will lead to coma. An increase in the blood-sugar concentration appears to be a stimulus for insulin secretion.

THE PINEAL GLAND

The pineal is a ductless gland located in the central part of the brain. Injection of pineal extracts and implants of the gland have no effect on growth and development of normal animals. There is some indication, however, that daily administration of 1 cubic centimeter of pineal extracts to successive generations of rats has resulted in an increase in the frequency of breeding and a retardation in the rate of growth of the offspring.

THE THYMUS GLAND

The thymus is an irregular glandular mass extending from the thyroid gland to the thorax or chest; it is very prominent and well-developed in young animals, especially calves, in which it is called sweetbread. It becomes degenerate at the time of maturity. Experiments performed to establish the action of the thymus on growth and sexual development have led to conflicting results. The majority of workers have found it to be negligible. There is some indication that the offspring of successive generations all of which have received injections of thymus extracts may grow to maturity at a faster rate but do not exceed normal size.

ANTIHORMONES

Certain experimental evidence indicates that the hormones may be held in check or inactivated by antihormone principles. For instance, after long-continued injection of prolan B into an animal, the blood serum is found to contain antibodies to this hormone, and the injection of blood from this animal into a normal female will prevent ovulation and the growth of the corpus luteum.

This should be a warning that the wholesale, repeated injection o
animals with hormones may aggravate rather than alleviate certai
troubles. To apply any hormone treatment successfully, it is firs
essential to determine the cause of the condition that needs to b
corrected and then choose the appropriate treatment. The diagnosi
of any hormonal difficulty may be complicated by an unbalanced con
dition among various hormones as well as by the presence of antibodies

The Relation of Genetics to Disease

BY HUGH C. MC PHEE [1]

THE BREEDING of disease-resistant varieties of plants is one of the major triumphs of modern genetics. Could disease losses in livestock be reduced in much the same way that production is increased by breeding methods? Here is a cautious yet optimistic viewpoint on a question of great interest to agriculture.

THAT THERE IS an inherited resistance or susceptibility to diseases is by no means a new concept, but experimental evidence to substantiate the idea is relatively new. In the case of animal diseases, however, practically all the attention has been centered on the disease organisms themselves, the tissue changes brought about by their presence in the host, and therapeutic measures for control. Such studies have been remarkably fruitful in medical science, including veterinary medicine; the extensive use of vaccination as a means of avoiding disease is an example of the importance of the results. Nevertheless, during recent years there has been a growing interest in the natural resistance to disease shown by some individual animals. Interest has been stimulated primarily by advances in genetic knowledge, particularly in relation to physiological characteristics, and by the marked progress made by plant breeders in controlling plant diseases through the development of resistant strains.

The science of genetics seeks to explain the variations in characteristics shown by individuals connected by a common line of ancestry. If disease is defined as any abnormal condition of the body tissues, then inheritance may have a four-way relationship to it. There may be (1) specific inherited resistance to certain infectious diseases, (2) a connection between inherited vigor and resistance, (3) inherent variations in the disease organism itself, giving rise

[1] Hugh C. McPhee is Chief, Animal Husbandry Division, Bureau of Animal Industry.

to strains differing in virulence, and (4) various specific abnormalities, many of them lethal. Many such abnormalities have been shown by experimental evidence to be inherited; in fact, there is much more information on this point than on the other three.

INHERITED RESISTANCE TO DISEASE

Specific inherited resistance to an infectious disease is perhaps best illustrated by Lambert's [2] experiments with White Leghorn chickens, the object of which was to determine whether continued selection for resistance to fowl typhoid would lower the death loss in the flock. The foundation stock consisted of 220 birds, all of which were given a massive dose of virulent fowl typhoid bacteria. Of this group 47.7 percent died. Among the survivors those showing the least severe clinical symptoms of fowl typhoid were saved as breeders to furnish the first selected generation of chicks. All chicks in this and the four succeeding generations, when 7 days old, were given injections intraperitoneally (into the abdominal lining) of a standard dose of the disease organism. The death losses resulting from these injections for five consecutive generations were 39.8, 29.3, 15.4, 15.0, and 9.4 percent. At the same time the losses in unselected control stock were 89.6, 93.2, 86.2, 86.4, and 85.0 percent. This remarkable difference was brought about by simple selection. It is also of interest that most of the mortality occurred sooner after inoculation in the control lot than in the selected group, indicating an even higher resistance in the latter than the figures for losses show. Following the five generations of selection, matings were made between males selected for resistance and unselected females, and also between selected females and unselected males. The results showed that the male as well as the female transmits resistance and that a passive transfer of immunity through the eggs probably is not involved. The death loss among the chicks from the resistant male × unselected female cross was 63.5 percent, while in the reciprocal group (unselected male × resistant female) it was 50.7 percent. These figures are intermediate between those for the selected and the control stocks.

A few other investigators have reported somewhat similar results for other diseases. Schott [3] was able in 6 years of selective breeding to reduce mortality from mouse typhoid from 82 to 24 percent. Roberts [4] developed a strain of chickens which showed only 35 percent mortality from pullorum injection, as compared with 73 percent in an unselected group. A recent case reported from the California Experiment Station concerns the discovery of some pigs that seem to be immune to repeated injections of the *Brucella* organism and to transmit the resistance to their offspring. Only a preliminary report has been made, and more breeding results are needed

[2] LAMBERT, W. V. NATURAL RESISTANCE TO DISEASE IN THE CHICKEN. Jour. Immunol. 23 : 229–260, illus. 1932.
[3] SCHOTT, RALPH. THE INHERITANCE OF RESISTANCE TO SALMONELLA AERTRYCKE IN VARIOUS STRAINS OF MICE. Genetics 17 : [203]–229, illus. 1932.
[4] ROBERTS, E. INHERITANCE OF RESISTANCE TO DISEASE IN ANIMALS. Internatl. Cong. Genetics Proc. 6 (2) : 169–170. 1932.

before it will be known whether or not this is a case of a genetic factor giving practically complete resistance to a specific disease. It is to be hoped that the resistance of these pigs to *Brucella* will prove to be hereditary and that this finding can be used to advantage in combating brucellosis in swine. There have been reports in the past, however, of pigs immune to another disease, hog cholera, but no resistant strain has yet arisen from such animals, and it is entirely possible that such resistance may be due to acquired immunity or to some other factor that confused the genetic picture.

The cases cited show clearly that selective breeding can result in a marked decrease in death losses from certain diseases. If, for example, a loss of 85 to 90 birds out of every 100 can be cut down to 10, it would seem to be a matter of considerable economic importance. Why, then, has a system of selective breeding never been adopted in practice? The answer is probably to be found in the fact that resistance so secured is difficult and expensive to maintain. As Lambert's results show, a single outcross, bringing in other genetic factors, eliminates a large part of the resistance; then the process of selection, including tests with the disease organism, has to be repeated all over again in order to bring the stock back to a reasonably high degree of resistance. All this takes time and money. Unless the livestock industry can use such a system economically, it cannot be expected to find widespread application.

Theoretically, it would seem just as possible, through the application of genetic principles, to cut death losses from disease in half as it is to double egg production by breeding. The fact is, however, that in no single investigation of the possibility of breeding resistance to disease has the work been carried far enough to show how it might be given really practical application.

The plant breeder can hand the farmer seed from resistant plants, and the resulting plants will remain resistant in succeeding generations because their genetic purity is held relatively constant by self-fertilization, which is a natural process for many crop plants, including some of the grains. This the animal breeder cannot do. What can be done with animals is to approximate genetic stabilization through a less intense system of inbreeding than is possible with plants, but one sufficiently intense to fix any heredity for disease resistance that may now exist in a diluted form in animal populations. The problems of distributing resistant stocks to farmers and maintaining resistance afterward are bridges that must be crossed at a later time. The first step is for the experimenter to locate resistance and build up strains that breed reasonably true for this characteristic.

It can be said that such work has been begun only in a very minor way. The method of breeding used by most livestock breeders does not lead quickly to the formation of lines sufficiently inbred to mean much as far as the fixation of heredity for resistance to disease is concerned. Moreover, any selection that is practiced probably would be carried out in the absence of disease, because it is not to the advantage of the breeder to have disease in his herd. Thus any closely bred line developed under such conditions would not show significant resistance to any disease except by pure chance. But it is very easy for the experimenter using modern medical and veterinary methods to infect animals with definite doses of disease organisms or agents and identify individuals possessing resistance The fact that such procedure may work successfully is well illustrated by the recent report, mentioned earlier, by Cameron, Hughes and Gregory, of the California station, on genetic resistance of swine to brucellosis. Apparently these workers have located an inbred strain in which some individuals possess resistance to this disease Resistant × resistant matings have produced pigs showing either a complete immunity or a very high resistance. If this resistance persists through following generations, this inbred line will be the first brucellosis-resistant line of pigs to be developed and may furnish the starting point for controlling the disease by breeding methods

VIGOR VERSUS RESISTANCE

The belief is fairly widespread that a vigorous individual is more resistant to infectious diseases than one less vigorous. It would be logical then to assume that inherited vigor would mean inherited resistance to disease. Whether this is true depends to a large extent on the definition of vigor.

The vigor of a family or line of animals is not inherited as a single unit but as a complex of several units which are largely independent of each other. This was shown by Wright[5] with guinea pigs. Long-continued inbreeding brought about a fixation of genetic factors affecting growth, body size, fertility, the occurrence of certain abnormalities, and resistance to tuberculosis. The differences in the closely inbred lines followed a pattern of independent assortment and fixation of heredity for these characteristics; resistance to tuberculosis, for example, did not show a tendency to be associated with any particular element of vigor. Possessing heredity for the elements of vigor is therefore no guaranty of heredity for disease resistance. Moreover, resistance to one disease does not necessarily have anything to do with resistance to another disease. A possibility coming out of the evidence on the lack of a relationship between resistance and inherited vigor is that heredity for vigor might be combined by suitable breeding methods with that for disease resistance; in other words, there is no reason why breeding cannot be used to raise the general levels of vigor and of resistance to disease at the same time.

CHANGES IN VIRULENCE OF DISEASE ORGANISMS

It is a matter of common knowledge that pathogenic organisms vary considerably in virulence, but not much is known about the causes of such variations. They may be due to the effects of a changing environment, or to some inherent change in the organism itself, or to both. The one thing certain is that there are changes

---

[5] WRIGHT, SEWALL, and LEWIS, P. A. FACTORS IN THE RESISTANCE OF GUINEA PIGS TO TUBERCULOSIS, WITH ESPECIAL REGARD TO INBREEDING AND HEREDITY. Amer. Nat. 55 : 20–50 illus. 1921.

The fact that such changes occur introduces another complexity into the relation of genetics to disease. If the agent itself can mutate and hybridize, there is almost no end to the possible interactions between the host and the organism. What is interpreted to be an increased resistance might well result from a lower virulence, and vice versa. During the last 10 or 15 years there have been many reports on variability in pathogenic bacteria, but it is still not known whether genetics is playing a decisive role in bringing about such changes. Until new evidence is produced, speculation should be held to a minimum. The very important matter of a varying virulence should not, however, be overlooked; but nothing much can be done about it, nor can the facts be discovered, until the animals on which it is tested are stabilized genetically so that the results can be attributed to variations in the organism rather than in the host. Here is a relatively virgin field that is a challenge to research workers.

HEREDITARY DEFECTS IN FARM ANIMALS

Numerous physical variations that occur among animals should be mentioned here because of their relation to disease. Many of them can be classed as defects, and a high proportion are lethal—that is, they kill the animals inheriting them. In many cases the mode of inheritance of the defects has been worked out by actual breeding experiments.

No attempt will be made here to cite all the references to the scientific literature on the subject. Eaton [6] has published a summary report which includes about 150 literature citations, and the reader is referred to his paper for original sources of information.

CATTLE

Achondroplasia. Two types of achondroplasia have been reported, one of which seems to be a dominant and the other a recessive. The dominant form is the cause of the bulldog calves which occur in the Dexter breed and some African cattle. The affected calves have very short legs, a large rupture, and a much shortened bulldoglike head. The thyroid gland and kidneys are also markedly affected. Such fetuses are usually aborted during the fourth month of pregnancy. The recessive form, which occurs in Telemark and Holstein cattle, also results in a very short head, deformed jaws, and sometimes a cleft palate. Death occurs a few days after birth.

Acroteriasis congenita. Characterized by either the absence of all limbs or their development only to elbows and hocks, atrophy of the upper jaw, almost complete absence of the lower jaw, and a cleft palate. The affected calves either are still-born or die shortly after birth. Genetically the defect is a single-factor recessive.

Ankylosis. An ossification, or stiffening, of the joint of the lower jaw, which is shortened. It is reported to occur in Norwegian

---

[6] EATON, O. N. A SUMMARY OF LETHAL CHARACTERS IN ANIMALS AND MAN. Jour. Hered. 28: 320–326. 1937.

Lyngdal cattle. What is probably a related form in which there is ossification of all joints and a cleft palate occurs in some German cattle. Both are recessive.

Congenital dropsy.—Probably a single factor which results in an accumulation of water in the subcutaneous tissues (those immediately under the skin) and in the body cavities. Affected individual fetuses are frequently dropped 1 or 2 months prematurely.

Congenital icthyosis.—A recessive factor that causes scaly and cracked skin. This factor may have some relation to the epitheliogenesis imperfecta (imperfect formation of skin) reported in Holstein-Friesian and Jersey cattle. Affected individuals have large hairless patches over the body and defective skin on the legs and the mucous membranes of the mouth and nostrils. The animals are born at term but die from septicemia (a general poisoning of the blood) soon afterward.

Hypotrichosis congenita.—A single-factor recessive which prevents hair development except on muzzle, eyelids, ears, pasterns, and top of tail. Affected calves die very soon after birth. It is reported to occur in Swedish Holsteins.

Impacted molars.—The premolars are impacted in the jaw, and the lower jaw, or mandible, is shortened. Affected calves are born at term but usually die during the first week. The defect is reported to occur among Milking Shorthorn cattle.

Muscle contracture.—A single-factor recessive causing a bending backward of the head, stiff neck, and rigid joints. It is reported to occur among Norwegian and Holstein cattle. A related form in Red Danish cattle makes the hind legs lame so the calf cannot stand. Such calves are born alive but soon die.

Short spine.—A single-factor recessive which occurs in Norwegian mountain cattle. The axial skeleton is much shortened, and the ribs and vertebrae are fused. Affected calves are usually still-born.

Some other lethal defects, such as mummification of fetuses and short limbs, have been reported, but there is some question as to whether they may not be only a phase of the action of one of the other factors already mentioned.

HORSES

Atresia coli.—A single-factor recessive which results in death 3 or 4 days after birth. The ascending colon is greatly restricted or has a blind ending. Often the affected individual has a brain tumor.

Abnormal sex ratio.—A sex-linked recessive factor which kills about one-half of the male colts before birth.

Stiff forelegs.—Characterized by failure to stand and early death, probably due to hereditary factors. Matings between animals known to carry the defect produced 8 crippled to 18 normal foals.

SHEEP

"Amputated."—The absence of hoofs on all four feet. It has been reported to occur in Holland, but the mode of inheritance is unknown.

Earlessness and cleft palate.—A single-factor recessive which causes cleft palate, earlessness, short lower jaw, and tripartite claws. It has been reported to occur in Norwegian sheep.

Lethal gray.—A recessive factor reported in Turkana sheep in Rumania and in Karakul sheep in Russia. Homozygous gray lambs die.

Muscle contracture.—A recessive factor which makes leg joints stiff and neck crooked. Lambs are still-born. It is reported to occur in Welsh mountain sheep.

Paralysis.—A recessive factor which paralyzes the hind legs and causes death of the affected lamb a few days after birth.

Skeletal defects.—A single-factor recessive, reported to occur among sheep in Iceland, which produces a short body, large skull, short upper jaw, rigid fetlocks, and absence of wool from brisket to anus. The lambs are born alive but soon die.

Swine

Atresia ani.—Partial or complete closure of the anus of pigs. Affected animals die soon after birth. It has been reported in Europe and observed in the United States.

"Catlin mark."—A single-factor recessive which causes an opening between the parietal (side) and frontal bones of the head. Death occurs within an hour after birth.

Cleft palate.—A recessive factor which gives various degrees of abnormal palate. Pigs die soon after birth owing to inability to nurse.

Fetal mortality.—A factor, probably recessive, which seems to be associated with inability to utilize certain vitamins and salts, causing death of fetuses.

Hypotrichosis.—The hereditary form of hairlessness in swine, which is not lethal as it is in cattle. The most common type of hairlessness in swine is due to an iodine deficiency and usually results in still-born pigs. The administration of iodine to the sow will prevent the occurrence of this type but has no effect on the hereditary form of hairlessness.

Muscle contracture.—A single-factor recessive which causes stiff front legs. Affected individuals are either still-born or die soon after birth.

Paralysis.—A single-factor recessive which produces complete paralysis of the hind legs.

Poultry

Abnormal upper mandible.—A recessive factor which reduces the maxillae (jawbones) and nasal bones and bends the beak to one side. Such chicks rarely hatch.

Chondrodystrophy.—Fetal deformation of bones and joints. Inheritance of this defect is complex and probably involves three recessive factors.

Congenital loco.—A single-factor recessive which results in bending back the head and in inability to stand. Over three-fourths of the affected individuals die within a month after hatching.

Creeper.—A dominant factor which in homozygous condition causes death on the fourth day of incubation.

Dwarf.—A single-factor recessive which causes death when in homozygous combination.

Recessive white.—A recessive factor which may be sex-linked. The homozygous whites die.

Short legs.—A factor reported to occur in Dark Cornish fowl which when homozygous causes death near the end of the incubation period.

Sticky embryo.—A recessive factor which causes the presence in the egg of sticky liquids that prevent chicks from hatching.

Crested.—An inherited factor which causes extreme cerebral hernia in ducks. Affected individuals die when nearly ready to hatch.

There are some other conditions such as malposition of embryos and embryonic abnormalities of several types, which cause death before hatching, for which the inheritance has not yet been determined.

CONCLUSIONS

The preceding list of lethal defects includes those that have been studied sufficiently to determine that they are due to genetic factors. New cases are continually being brought to light as more attention is given to genetic investigations in livestock. For instance, a case of what appears to be inherited hemophilia (delayed clotting of blood) was observed in swine in 1940. This defect is due to a single autosomal recessive factor and thus differs from hemophilia in man, which is sex-linked in its inheritance.

There are some types of defects in small animals, such as guinea pigs and mice, which are known to have a hereditary basis, but which have not been studied in farm animals. An illustration is the well-known case of otocephaly in the guinea pig, which produces cyclopean monsters, with only one eye. The same kind of defect has been observed in cattle, sheep, swine, cats, dogs, and man. While its inheritance is very complex, enough is known to say that herd or flock sires producing it should be discarded.

Fortunately, the number of hereditary lethals occurring among breeds of livestock in the United States is not very great, nor do they appear very often in most stocks. Nevertheless, they are a big factor in some strains, and because most of them are recessive they can be spread far and wide without showing their presence. When lines of ancestry containing such a defect are brought together it may be expected that some of the offspring will show the character. When this occurs it is important to remember that both the sire and the dam carry the recessive genetic factor, and they and all their offspring should be eliminated from the breeding herd if it is desired to get rid of the trouble.

Artificial Insemination and Disease Control

BY A. H. FRANK AND RALPH W. PHILLIPS [1]

SEVERAL livestock diseases are spread either partly or exclusively by contact during breeding. For these, the authors point out, artificial insemination offers an excellent method of control.

THE TECHNIQUE of artificial insemination is not new, but only in recent years has it been used on a large scale. Considerable use has been made of it in the Union of Soviet Socialist Republics and other countries. In the United States there is wide interest in the subject; much research is under way, new techniques are being developed, old ones are being improved, and it seems probable that the use of artificial insemination will continue to increase. The most extensive development in the use of artificial insemination in this country has been with dairy cattle; large numbers of cows are now bred to bulls maintained at central points. In March 1941 the number of cows recorded in cooperative artificial-breeding associations for dairy cattle was 70,751, and 237 bulls were being used.[2] The technique has also been used, less extensively, with beef cattle, horses, sheep, goats, swine, poultry, and fur-bearing animals.

The basic reason for developing artificial insemination has been to increase the usefulness of outstanding sires. There are other advantages of the technique over natural breeding, however, one being that it aids in controlling certain diseases. Many diseases that attack the reproductive organs and glands of animals may be spread by sexual intercourse, and some are transmitted only in this way. Artificial insemination can be used to prevent the spread of a disease from one female to another through the male. If improperly practiced,

---

[1] A. H. Frank is Associate Veterinarian and Ralph W. Phillips is Senior Animal Husbandman, Bureau of Animal Industry.
[2] U. S. BUREAU OF DAIRY INDUSTRY. COOPERATIVE DAIRY-CATTLE BREEDING ASSOCIATION. Dairy Herd-Improvement Assoc. Letter 17 (3), 29 pp. 1941. [Proposed.]

however, it may be the means of spreading diseases. Most cooperatives obtain the services of a veterinarian for this work, which requires not only a knowledge of the symptoms of diseases but recognition of the necessity for cleanliness, sanitation, and the proper disinfection of utensils before and after use.

Usually in collecting semen from the male, a rubber artificial vagina is used into which the penis is directed when he mounts the female. The semen is collected in a small tube attached to the opposite end of the artificial vagina. There are other methods of collection, but in most cases this is the best for use with mammals. In inseminating the female, a lighted speculum is inserted into the vagina. This illuminates the cervix, into which the semen is injected by means of a long tube attached to a syringe. The technique of collection and insemination in poultry differs from that in mammals because of anatomical differences in the genital tracts. Techniques for both mammals and poultry are described in detail by Lambert and McKenzie.[3]

Semen samples collected from the male in the artificial vagina are subject to contamination with germs or bacteria, just as is milk drawn from the udder. Bacteria in semen may come either from the reproductive organs of the male or from the apparatus used for collection. When the males are healthy, the bacteria are generally harmless to females, but occasionally there may be pus-producing organisms that, if present in excessively large numbers, may temporarily affect the female organs. By such measures as the provision of sanitary surroundings, regular grooming, and the use of sterile apparatus for collecting, the bacteria in semen from healthy males can be kept down to a very low number, and under such circumstances most types of bacteria do not materially affect fertilizing and keeping qualities.

The male may communicate diseases to the female either mechanically, by carrying the infective organisms from one female to another during mating, or as a result of infection in the reproductive organs. When the disease is communicated mechanically, the infecting organisms are found in the sheath and on the outer surface of the penis. Such cases are especially dangerous, because to all outward appearances the males are healthy and would not be suspected of carrying infection. When the genital organs of the male are actually infected, the organisms are transmitted in the semen, not mechanically. In chronic infections, noticeable swellings may be visible, or the health of the animal may be impaired, and usually his breeding efficiency is greatly reduced or lost. In the early stages of a disease, however, though no impairment of health may be noticeable, the disease-producing organisms may be transferred in the semen to the female.

In most cases of reproductive disorders males contract the disease through sexual contact with infected females; hence the importance of sanitary precautions to prevent the mechanical transfer of infection from one female to another by the instruments, even when the male is absolutely free of disease. It is essential that all instruments be thoroughly cleaned and disinfected after their use on each indi-

[3] LAMBERT, W. V., and McKENZIE, FRED F. ARTIFICIAL INSEMINATION IN LIVESTOCK BREEDING. U. S. Dept. Agr. Cir. 567, 68 pp., illus. 1940.

vidual. Chemical disinfectants are generally used for this purpose and may be recommended for all equipment that does not come in direct contact with the semen. As sperm is quickly killed on coming in contact with disinfectants, other means of sterilizing equipment for handling semen must be used. Boiling and sterilization by live steam are the most desirable methods of preparing the applicators and syringes, and sufficient sterile equipment should be provided for each day's work. If only one applicator is available, it should be sterilized before it is used again.

DISEASES THAT MAY BE CONTROLLED THROUGH ARTIFICIAL INSEMINATION

If only males known to be free from disease are selected for semen collection, artificial insemination can play an important part in controlling diseases spread through sexual contact. Among the diseases in this group are granular vaginitis, a disease caused by the organism *Vibrio fetus*, trichomoniasis, navel ill, dourine, brucellosis, coital exanthema, and vent gleet of poultry.

Granular vaginitis is usually a chronic infection of cattle in which the lining of the vagina is attacked by the disease-producing agent. This results in inflammation and the formation of small pustules, which develop a granular appearance. The discharge from an affected cow contains the virus. The external genitals of a bull serving such a cow become contaminated, and he may transmit the disease to other cows in mating.

Vibrio fetus is a micro-organism found at times in the uterus and fetal membranes of pregnant cows and ewes and in the stomach of the fetus. It often causes abortion. It is believed that males may spread the disease during sexual intercourse.

Trichomoniasis is an infection of the genital tract of cows caused by a microparasite. In the female the parasite lodges first in the vagina, where it sets up an irritation and causes a discharge. It may later invade the uterus and cause sterility or abortion during the early stages of pregnancy. It is a true venereal disease transmitted by the male to the female, or vice versa, during mating.

The common condition known as navel ill occurring in foals is produced by a number of different germs. In one type of the disease the sire, in breeding, may transmit the germ to the mare, and the germ then becomes localized in the mare's genital tract. The foal may become infected in the uterus of the dam before birth or outside the uterus at the time of birth.

Dourine, a disease of horses, is similar in many respects to syphilis of man. Stallions become infected from sexual contact with infected mares and spread the disease to other mares. Dourine has been eradicated from most portions of the United States and by the spring of 1942 existed in only a few isolated localities.

Brucellosis of cattle, or Bang's disease, is a disease of the genital organs in both the cow and the bull. It is caused by a germ that is found in vast numbers in the discharge from the uterus of an infected dam following abortion. The bull may become infected in serving an infected cow shortly after she has aborted. In some instances it is possible that the bull, harboring the germs in his seminal fluid, may transmit the disease directly or indirectly to the cow, but the disease is usually spread in other ways.

In brucellosis of swine, which is similar to the disease in cattle, the germ often becomes localized in the testicles of the boar and is discharged in the seminal fluid. It is possible that sows may become infected in breeding and that boars may become infected when serving infected sows.

Coital exanthema of horses is a venereal disease affecting the external genitalia of mares and stallions. It is transmitted from one sex to the other at breeding time.

In poultry, vent gleet and possibly several other diseases may be spread by the male to the female during sexual intercourse.

Other diseases, such as tuberculosis, may affect the genital organs of male and female animals, but there is no proof of their transmission from one to the other in mating.

The extent to which many diseases are spread through contact during breeding is yet to be determined, but artificial insemination can play a very important part in controlling the diseases which may be spread in this manner. If only healthy sires are used, if sanitary precautions are followed, and if the procedure is entrusted to the care of a qualified and careful practitioner, artificial insemination will break the link in the transmission of genital diseases.

Disinfection
and Disinfectants

BY F. W. TILLEY [1]

WHEN disease breaks out among farm animals, it is often necessary to do a thorough clean-up and disinfecting job to get rid of the infection. Here is practical information about the principal kinds of disinfectants, the advantages and drawbacks of each, and how to use them.

DISINFECTION is the destruction of the disease germs in or on infected material, and a disinfectant is a substance or agent that destroys disease germs. As they are usually employed, the words "disinfectant" and "germicide" are synonymous. An antiseptic is a substance that prevents the growth of germs without necessarily destroying them.

There are two opposing forces in infection—the disease germ and the defensive force of the animal body. The ability of germs to invade depends primarily on the number present and their vigor. The healthy animal body is able to resist invasion by considerable numbers of germs, especially if the germs have lost most of their original vigor. On the other hand, an animal in poor condition is generally more susceptible to infection.

The essential sources of disease germs are the bodies of diseased animals. After leaving such animals, the germs die or tend to lose their vigor. Their survival outside the animal body is favored by the presence of manure and other waste matter—the substances to which we give the general name "dirt."

The importance of cleanliness in the care of animals cannot be emphasized too much. Proper cleaning removes most of the germs along with the dirt that protects them, and the remaining germs are usually so weakened or so few in number that they are harmless under ordinary conditions.

[1] F. W. Tilley is Senior Bacteriologist, Pathological Division, Bureau of Animal Industry.

77434°—51——13

179

If in addition to having clean surroundings the animals themselve:
are kept clean, well-fed, and in good condition, there is ordinarily n
need for the use of disinfectants. If disease breaks out, however, i
will be necessary to make use of disinfectants as well as of the usua
cleaning agents. Since the sick animal is the original source o\
infection it should be kept away from healthy animals, and since
the number and vigor of disease germs are greatest near their source
in the sick animal the best place to use disinfectants is in its immediat\
vicinity. The materials to be disinfected include manure, urine, an
other body discharges and bedding or other material soiled by such
discharges. If infected material is scattered, it becomes necessary to
apply disinfectants very extensively and thoroughly in order to b\
sure of reaching all of it.

In some instances—for example, in scabies—disease is caused by
insectlike parasites which are very small but not microscopic in size
In combating such diseases the destruction of the causative organism
is usually accomplished through total immersion of the infected anima\
in a solution that is poisonous to the parasite but not dangerous to
the animal. Such a process is called dipping, and the substance used
for preparing the solution, or the solution itself, is called a dip. I\
cattle tick fever, formerly known as Texas fever, the causative organism is microscopic in size, but the disease is combated by destroying
the tick that carries the micro-organism; hence in this case also dip:
are employed. A few chemicals or compounded mixtures may be
useful for both dipping and disinfection, but there is no necessary
relationship between dips and disinfectants because insects and ordinary disease germs are so different that a substance fatal to one may
not be harmful to the other. Dips are therefore usually considered
in a class by themselves, apart from disinfectants.

Disinfectants differ from one another in many of their properties,
including their ability to kill micro-organisms, and germs also differ
widely in their susceptibility to the various disinfectants. No single
disinfectant is efficient against the germs of all diseases, nor is any disinfectant equally effective against the same germ under all conditions.
for the activity of every disinfectant is influenced by such factor:
as the time of exposure to the disinfectant, temperature, chemical
reaction and concentration, and the kind and amount of organic matter
that may be present. Strictly speaking, there is no such thing as a
"general disinfectant." So far as possible a disinfectant should be
selected for its efficiency against the germs of a particular disease
and its suitability for use in the place where it is to be applied.

GENERAL RULES FOR USING DISINFECTANTS

No matter what disinfectant may be chosen, however, there are certain general principles to be considered in using it. In the first place,
since very few disinfectants act instantaneously even under the most
favorable circumstances, it is always necessary to allow them ample
time. In the second place, temperature has a great effect on the
activity of disinfectants. Cold decreases and heat increases activity,
so disinfecting solutions should, if possible, be used warm, or even

ot. Furthermore, under practical conditions there is always more
or less dirt present, especially manure and other organic materials.
Most disinfectants penetrate slowly and poorly, especially when organic matter is present. Solutions usually penetrate better than
emulsions, while gaseous disinfectants cannot be depended on to
penetrate to any depth. If manure or other similar material is to be
disinfected, it must be broken up and thoroughly mixed with the
disinfecting solution so that the latter is distributed through the
mass.

Since organic matter serves to protect disease germs and otherwise
interferes with the activity of disinfectants, disinfection should always be preceded by thorough cleaning. All manure, bedding, and
rubbish in stables or barnyards should be removed to a place inaccessible to livestock and burned, if possible, or thoroughly mixed with
disinfectant. Then after the area has been cleaned with hot water
and soap or washing soda, the disinfecting solution should be applied
liberally and thoroughly. If only a small surface is to be disinfected,
the solution may be applied with a whitewash brush. In all cases,
however, the best method of application is by means of a spray pump.

PRINCIPAL DISINFECTING AGENTS AND SUBSTANCES

Although no attempt will be made here to enumerate all the agents
or substances that may be used to kill disease germs, some of the most
useful physical agents and chemical substances will be discussed briefly.
Among the physical agencies are sunlight and heat. Direct sunlight
is an active germicide, but its intensity is so variable and its disinfecting power so superficial that it cannot be considered a reliable disinfecting agent. Heat may be applied in various ways. The chemical
substances include acids, alkalies, compounds of various metals,
chlorine and iodine and their compounds, and the general group
that includes alcohol, carbolic acid, and substances chemically related
to them. Some of these, such as sulfur dioxide and formaldehyde,
are used as gases. The rest are used in solutions, usually in water.

Various substances or compounds are recommended or used as
disinfectants on account of their odor. There is no connection between
odor and disinfecting value, and disinfectants should be chosen only
on account of their known disinfecting value.

Although none of the disinfecting agents or substances described
in this article is universally useful, some of the simplest and least
expensive can usually be employed in place of expensive proprietary
preparations. When they can be used, such simple processes as burning, baking, boiling, or steaming will usually be more effective than
any chemical disinfectant. Except for disinfection against the germs
of tuberculosis, lime and lye, which are cheap and readily available,
will be found quite generally satisfactory.

HEAT IN VARIOUS FORMS

Burning is a most useful way of applying heat wherever circumstances permit. For example, if the place to be disinfected contains

a great deal of rubbish and articles of little value, burning will ofte
be cheaper and easier than disinfection. Burning is also the mos
satisfactory method of disinfecting and disposing of small amoun
of infected body discharges.

Dry heat is not so satisfactory as moist heat, since it lacks penetrat
ing power and scorches fabrics, but it may occasionally be preferrec
The ordinary household oven may be used for the purpose, and i
should be heated sufficiently to brown cotton slightly (to about 320
F.). Objects to be disinfected should remain in the oven at this ten
perature for at least 1 hour. Moist heat is most often employed a
boiling water or steam. Exposure to boiling water will destroy a
ordinary disease germs, although it sometimes fails to kill the spore
of such diseases as anthrax (splenic fever) or tetanus (lockjaw,
Many disease germs are killed by moist heat at temperatures muc
below the boiling point of water as, for example, in the pasteurizatio
of milk, and most of the ordinary disease germs are killed by boilin
water in a very few moments. Boiling water may be used for th
disinfection of fabrics of many kinds and of articles or implement
made of materials that are not injured by boiling. In disinfectin
objects made of iron or steel the addition of 1 percent of carbonate c
soda to the water will prevent rusting. Although, as stated abov
most of the ordinary disease germs are killed by boiling water ver
quickly, it is advisable in practice to allow at least 10 minutes' exposu
so that every particle of the material to be disinfected may be heate
to the required temperature.

Steam under pressure is perhaps the most effective of all disinfect
ing agents, but under farm conditions steam would usually be em
ployed at atmospheric pressure as "streaming" steam. This has th
same basic disinfecting power as boiling water, since streaming stean
and boiling water have the same temperature—100° C. (212° F.). I
practice, however, such steam requires a longer time to bring all c
the material to be disinfected to the required temperature, and it i
advisable, therefore, to allow an exposure of half an hour to a
hour. Steam is useful for the disinfection of many kinds of materia
but it shrinks woolen fabrics and ruins leather, fur, skins of all kind
rubber shoes, oilcloth, and articles containing glue or varnish. Dis
infection with streaming steam does not require any apparatus excep
a boiler to supply the necessary steam and a hose or tube to carry i
Feed bags or other articles of similar material may be disinfected b
being hung in any sort of small compartment and treated with stean
Such a structure need not be tight, for the steam escaping throug
the cracks serves to produce a circulation that aids penetration o
the heat.

SULFUR DIOXIDE

Sulfur dioxide is the gas liberated by burning sulfur. Althoug
commonly used in the past, it is little used at present because it is to
destructive to fabrics, colors, and metals. It is not a very good germi
cide and is more useful for the destruction of insects and vermi
than for disinfection.

FORMALDEHYDE GAS AND SOLUTION

Formaldehyde is practically the only gas suitable for general application because it does not injure fabrics, colors, or metals. The gas is used rather than the solution (formalin) where the value of materials, such as hay or fodder, would be lessened by wetting. Under farm conditions, however, its use is often impracticable. Since the gas escapes readily through any openings, compartments to be disinfected must be tightly closed and all openings sealed during the period of disinfection. Formaldehyde gas is not effective at temperatures much below 65° F., and it is desirable that the air be moist.

In disinfecting small compartments, formaldehyde solution (formalin) may be sprayed into the compartment and allowed to evaporate. At least 10 ounces of the solution should be used for every 1,000 cubic feet of space. For rooms and large compartments the usual method of liberating the gas is by the action of potassium permanganate on formalin. Since some of the formalin is used up in the chemical reaction with the permanganate, it is necessary to use 20 ounces of formalin and 16⅔ ounces of potassium permanganate for the disinfection of 1,000 cubic feet of space. The permanganate is placed in a wide-bottomed bucket or basin and the formalin poured over it. Since the reaction between the two substances liberates considerable heat, it is advisable to place the container on bricks or some other suitable material in order to prevent injury to the floor. As the action of formaldehyde gas is quite superficial, objects or materials to be disinfected should be spread out so as to offer the greatest possible surface to the action of the formaldehyde. After the formaldehyde gas has been liberated, the room or compartment should be kept tightly closed for at least 8 hours before it is opened and aired.

Formaldehyde solution is often used for disinfecting objects that are not injured by wetting. Its disinfecting power is great and not much affected by organic matter, but since it acts rather slowly ample time must be allowed. Formalin does not injure metals except after prolonged action, and it does not injure ordinary fabrics. It is not suitable for disinfecting furs because it tends to harden skins and make them brittle. It is usually employed in a 10-percent solution in water.

BORIC AND ACETIC ACIDS

Boric acid is a very feeble germicide, although it is often used in solution as an application for the eyes and other sensitive parts of the body. Acetic acid is a more effective germicide, and the amount usually found in full-strength vinegar (usually about 5 percent) is sufficient to kill some of the less resistant disease germs. It is a stronger acid than boric and too irritating for application to the eyes or other sensitive parts of the body. Vinegar is sometimes used in the treatment of local infections or of skin diseases.

LIME AND LYE

Lime is a very cheap and useful disinfectant. It is usually employed in the form of "milk of lime." Only quicklime should be used, since

air-slaked lime is practically useless. The quicklime is first slaked
by adding 1 pint of water to 2 pounds of quicklime. Milk of lime
is obtained by adding 4 parts of water to 1 of the slaked lime and mixing thoroughly. Whitewash may be prepared by adding water to
milk of lime until a mixture of suitable density is obtained.

The following formulas for special whitewashes (from Farmers'
Bulletin 1452, Painting on the Farm) may be found useful:

Whitewash No. 1 (for sheds, etc.).—Carefully slake half a bushel (38 pounds)
of good quicklime; strain the paste, while still thick, through wire fly screen and
add it to a solution made by dissolving 15 pounds of common salt in 7½ gallons
of water, mixing thoroughly. Thin with more water.

Whitewash No. 2 (for sheds, etc.).—Carefully slake half a bushel (38 pounds)
of good quicklime; strain the paste, while still thick, through wire fly screen and
add about 4 gallons of hot water. While stirring vigorously pour into the lime
mixture a solution made by first dissolving 12 pounds of salt and 6 ounces of alum
in about 4 gallons of hot water and then adding 1 quart of molasses. Thin with
water.

Whitewashing will help to make fences, pens, and outbuildings
sanitary, besides improving their appearance. Milk of lime is well
suited for use around dairy barns because it lacks odor. It is not
effective, however, against the spores of germs that cause anthrax and
lockjaw or against the germs of tuberculosis.

Ordinary lye usually contains about 94 percent of a chemical known
as sodium hydroxide, which is a very effective disinfectant. It is
effective against the viruses of foot-and-mouth disease and hog cholera
and the germs of fowl cholera and bacillary white diarrhea of young
chicks. In strong solutions it is effective against the spores of anthrax
but not against the germs of tuberculosis. It is usually employed as
a 2-percent solution in water, but for disinfection against anthrax it
is necessary to use a 5-percent solution. A 2-percent solution may be
prepared by adding 1 pound of lye to 5½ gallons of water. In cases
where lime is not objectionable, the addition of 2½ pounds of water-
slaked (not air-slaked) lime to the 5½ gallons of lye solution to form
a whitewash will increase the effectiveness of the solution by preventing the transformation of the sodium hydroxide into a carbonate.

A whitewash made in this way should not be applied to materials
that are injured by lye. **Concentrated lye is a caustic poison. Care
should be taken to avoid getting any of it into the eyes or breathing
in any of the fine dust that may arise while handling the dry material. Solutions should be so disposed of as to prevent injury to
livestock.** Solutions of lye are injurious to painted or varnished surfaces and to woolen or silk fabrics if allowed to remain in contact with
them for a considerable period of time. Since they do not injure bare
wood, earthenware, enamelware, or any of the common metals except
aluminum, they may be kept in containers made of these materials.
Since exposure to the air soon converts sodium hydroxide to the relatively inactive sodium carbonate, containers should be kept tightly
covered.

Various Chemical Compounds

Sodium carbonate and trisodium phosphate are used chiefly as
cleansing agents, but they also have appreciable disinfecting value.

If they are to be used in solution for disinfecting purposes at ordinary temperatures it is advisable to add 0.5 percent of sodium hydroxide, but if the solutions are to be used hot this will not be necessary. Sodium carbonate is obtainable in the form of washing soda, soda crystals, and also as soda ash. Washing soda should be used in 6-percent and soda ash in 2-percent solution. Trisodium phosphate can be obtained as tribasic phosphate of soda, which should be used in a 2.5-percent solution.

The various inorganic compounds of mercury, especially the bichloride (corrosive sublimate), are known to be powerful disinfectants. They are not suitable for farm use, however, on account of the danger to the farm family and to livestock as well as their relatively high cost. From time to time various compounds of copper, arsenic, or zinc have been recommended as germicides, but they all have relatively little germicidal value. Sulfate of copper (blue vitriol), however, is extremely effective against algae, and since algae often cause unpleasant odors or tastes in drinking water, copper sulfate is sometimes added to water to check or destroy their growth.

Chlorine gas as a disinfectant is almost exclusively used for the treatment of water supplies or sewage. Some of its compounds, however, are widely used for disinfection on the farm. Chlorinated lime is commonly known also as chloride of lime, or bleaching powder. Although it is a powerful disinfectant its potency is greatly reduced by contact with organic matter, so that when it is employed for disinfecting manure or body discharges it must be used in considerable quantities. Since it is often of uncertain strength, is injurious to metals, and has an odor that is readily taken up by milk, it is not a very practical disinfectant, especially for use around dairy barns. It is usually employed in a water solution containing about 6 ounces to the gallon, or 1 pound to 3 gallons.

Besides chlorinated lime certain other chlorine compounds are in more or less general use. The hypochlorites, usually sold in solution and under various proprietary names, have been used quite extensively to disinfect dairy equipment such as milk cans and bottles. In the concentrations usually employed they are effective when applied to clean surfaces, but their efficiency, like that of chlorinated lime, is largely reduced by organic matter. They will not sterilize dirty equipment, and their application to surfaces that are not thoroughly clean is entirely useless. Chlorinated lime and the hypochlorites are not effective against the germs of tuberculosis.

IODINE

Iodine in solution is extensively used for skin disinfection, and it remains the standard for this purpose although there are many proprietary preparations containing organic compounds of mercury or silver that are widely advertised. Tincture of iodine is the solution most generally employed. Although complete sterilization of the skin by any disinfectant is almost impossible, the application of tincture of iodine for treatment of superficial wounds or for preparing the site for an operation does serve to reduce the number of disease germs to a minimum. Since dirt interferes with the germicidal efficiency of iodine, the skin should be cleaned as well as possible before the solution is applied.

ALCOHOL

Grain alcohol has been used more or less as a disinfectant, and laboratory tests have shown that it is effective against the less resistant disease germs, such as those that cause typhoid fever. Absolute alcohol or solutions containing less than 50 percent of alcohol have comparatively little germicidal value. The most effective solutions are those containing about 70 percent of alcohol—the amount usually contained in "rubbing" alcohol.

CARBOLIC ACID AND CRESOL

The term "carbolic acid" has been rather loosely employed to designate a variety of substances that are chemically related but differ in their disinfecting properties. Although so-called carbolic acid has been widely used as a farm disinfectant, there is little to be said in its favor. It is generally uncertain in composition, and it has no advantages over other disinfectants that are readily available. The true carbolic acid (phenol) is not well suited for disinfection on a large scale because it is expensive and not as powerful as other disinfectants that cost less. It may be found useful, however, for disinfection on a small scale. Carbolic acid is not effective against the virus of hog cholera or the spores of anthrax, but it is very effective against most of the ordinary disease germs. It is most often used in a 5-percent solution in water. Carbolic acid and other similar disinfectants are not suitable for use in refrigerators or compartments where food is stored or in dairy barns, because food products tend to take up these substances from the air and acquire a disagreeable taste and odor.

Commercial cresol is known under various names such as tricresol, cresylic acid, and liquid carbolic acid. It consists of a mixture of closely related chemical compounds, all of which are superior to pure carbolic acid in disinfecting value. Cresol is not readily soluble in water and is therefore most generally used in mixtures with soap. It may, however, be used in a water solution in the same way as pure carbolic acid. Since it is more powerful than the latter, a 2-percent solution of cresol may be considered the equivalent of a 5-percent solution of carbolic acid. Unlike carbolic acid, cresol is effective against the virus of hog cholera.

A soap solution of cresol, known as the compound solution of cresol, is described in the United States Pharmacopoeia (U. S. P. XI, Liquor Cresolis Saponatus) and may be obtained at drug stores. A substitute for the compound solution of cresol, known as saponified cresol (also called cresylic disinfectant), is sold by companies dealing in disinfectants. Saponified cresol is cheaper than the compound solution and is just as good a disinfectant. It is extensively used for disinfection under the supervision of the Bureau of Animal Industry. Saponified cresol is usually employed in a water solution, 4 ounces to a gallon of water. Solutions of cresol should not be used in or near compartments where food is kept, on account of the odor. Soap solutions of cresol do not mix well with hard water.

Besides disinfectants containing cresol in soap solution there are many proprietary disinfectants that contain cresol along with coal-tar oils and soap in mixtures that form milky emulsions in water. The disinfecting power of these products varies. Since there is no trustworthy method of determining their relative values by chemical analysis, they are compared by laboratory tests on typhoid fever germs. They are tested along with carbolic acid (phenol), and their values in comparison with it are expressed in the form of a "phenol coefficient." Since these coal-tar-emulsion disinfectants vary so much in disinfecting value, it is advisable to use only those that have a guaranteed phenol coefficient. However, since phenol coefficients are determined under laboratory conditions that are likely to differ from conditions in practical disinfection, the coefficient often does not accurately indicate the relative values of disinfectants in actual use. Thus it is safer to use these disinfectants, especially in the presence of organic matter, in concentrations twice as great as would be indicated by the phenol coefficient.

In the disinfection of dairy barns and similar places in the campaign for eradication of tuberculosis the cresol disinfectants have been found objectionable on account of their odor. Under such conditions a disinfectant called sodium orthophenylphenate is extensively used because it is free from objectionable odor.

SOAPS

Soaps have some germicidal power, especially when used with hot water, but this power is rather limited. Cleaning with soap and hot water kills some of the less resistant disease germs but the effect is largely mechanical through the removal of dirt and infective material. Of the soaps commercially available those prepared exclusively from coconut oil, such as so-called salt-water soap, usually have the greater disinfecting value. Medicated soaps, in general, have little disinfecting power and cannot be relied upon to destroy resistant organisms.

How Research Aids In Disease Control

BY JOHN R. MOHLER [1]

WHAT are the problems of research in animal disease? How does research tackle these problems? What does it accomplish? How is it organized? These are the questions considered by the Chief of the Bureau of Animal Industry.

IN THE United States Department of Agriculture and cooperating agricultural institutions, groups of skilled scientific workers have been assembled to whom not only agricultural interests but a number of others as well look for the solution of many perplexing problems (1).[2] These problems run the gamut of human experience, but most of the questions, now as in the past, are concerned with improving man's security from the dangers that beset him and his means of livelihood. Adequate food, clothing, and shelter are still the basic needs. In their attainment, domestic animals have long been utilized.

DEVELOPMENT OF VETERINARY SCIENCE

Man early learned to guard his domestic animals from wild beasts, but he has had much greater difficulty in dealing with enemies of microscopic size that cause diseases. That the contagious nature of several animal diseases was recognized as early as the first century is clearly indicated in the writings of Columella, whose observations on animal and human health caused him to urge the segregation of the sick as a means of preventing the spread of infection.

Early in the Christian Era, Vegetius, another Roman writer, urged a revival of interest in what was then known as veterinary art, in order to curb losses from outbreaks of animal plagues. Much later,

---

[1] John R. Mohler is Chief of the Bureau of Animal Industry.
[2] Italic numbers in parentheses refer to Literature Cited, p. 202.

about the time of Galileo, modern science, and with it the methods known today as those of scientific research, began to develop. Facilities for research in disease were meager, however, until the development of the microscope by the Dutch naturalist, Leeuwenhoek, in the seventeenth century. Since then, and particularly since the discoveries of Pasteur, veterinary science has been marked by a succession of discoveries that have greatly reduced hazards to animal life. Throughout the world diligent scientific workers have traced scores of animal diseases to their sources, revealing as causes specific viruses, bacteria, parasites, toxins, and nutritive deficiencies.

During the period from 1860 to 1885 the names of foreign scientists, including Pasteur, Koch, Lister, and Davaine, dominated veterinary literature. But soon after the establishment of the United States Bureau of Animal Industry by Congress in 1884, Salmon and Smith (7, *p. 4*), of the United States, laid the foundation of bacterin therapy—the use of bacterial extracts for disease prevention—and since then veterinary science in this country has commanded world-wide respect and recognition.

Scientific research is inherently altruistic. It has no local, regional, or national boundaries and knows no barriers of race or creed. Any professional lines of separation or demarcation are purely artificial, for research deals essentially with the collection of facts and the operation of natural laws that embrace all science. Veterinary research is based primarily on a group of fundamental sciences—biology, pathology, and parasitology—but it includes many others, such as chemistry, serology, and immunology. Statistical analyses of data have also been used with increasing frequency in recent years. Although great discoveries are occasionally accidental, the vast majority are the result of planning, patience, and critical evaluation of experimental findings.

It is regrettable that technical terminology has tended to act as a barrier to a better public understanding of research studies and services. There is, however, nothing inherently formidable about scientific terms. Like mechanical terms such as "carburetor" and "differential," many of them gradually become a part of common speech. One purpose of this article is to remove the aura of magic and mystery that often surrounds research and to show its intensely practical nature and its value to agriculture and industry.

A TYPICAL RESEARCH PROBLEM AND ITS SOLUTION

A brief account of the development of a typical research project will serve to illustrate the definite manner in which science contributes to livestock health.

A certain stunted condition and rather high death losses among young pigs were reported by large numbers of swine growers in the Middle West some years ago. When cases were investigated by a field veterinarian, they were usually described by the owners about as follows: "My sows farrowed good litters of healthy pigs. They were doing fine until several weeks old. Then they stopped growing and began coughing, 'thumping,' and dying."

Post mortem examination of pigs from such farms revealed the presence of ascarid (roundworm) larvae in the windpipe and lungs. Observation of the surroundings showed that where these troubles occurred the pigs were housed and fed on lots where hogs had been kept continuously for many years. Associated with such conditions were cases of intestinal inflammation, sore mouth, and lungworm infestation.

The next step taken by the investigators was an intensive study of the life cycle of the swine ascarid, a history that proved to be highly involved. One key to the problem had been provided by F. H. Stewart, a medical officer of the British Army stationed in Hong Kong, who had studied the ascarid of man and found that it followed a circuitous route in the human body. The swine ascarid also was soon found to follow a devious route through the pig, including visits to most of the vital organs and a brief stay in the windpipe and lungs. The last explained the coughing and the thumping noises in the chest.

The study also involved the determination of conditions that would limit the development of ascarid eggs, their resistance to chemicals, heat, and cold, and their longevity under various circumstances. A thorough examination of all scientific literature having a direct or indirect bearing on the problem was also made. All these lines of research were directed by B. H. Ransom, at that time chief of the Bureau's Zoological Division.

Investigators assigned to the problem found live embryos in ascarid eggs that had been buried as long as 375 days in soil in northern Illinois, where winters are severe and summers hot. Infected soil would thus remain dangerous for long periods. From all available data bearing on the problem, Ransom concluded that the key to the health and normal development of newly farrowed pigs was to protect them from infection with worm eggs. "It would seem," he stated, "that the chief source of infection in the case of young pigs is the dirt-soiled skin of the sow." He therefore advised the thorough cleaning of farrowing quarters with lye solution and the brushing of all loose litter and mud from the sides of sows before they farrowed. He proposed that the sows' udders especially should be washed with soap and water and that the sows be placed in clean farrowing pens several days before the litters were expected.

Besides specifying clean conditions at the birth of the pigs, his plan provided also for keeping the young pigs on clean pasture, to which the sows and litters would be hauled, not driven, so as to prevent any contact with the soil.

After being placed on the clean pasture, the young pigs, of course, would sooner or later be exposed to the danger of swallowing some roundworm eggs passed by the sow, but the chances of infection, at any rate of heavy infestation, from this source, when the eggs were scattered over a large, clean pasture, were considered to be relatively small by Ransom and his associates.

This general plan, based on research findings, was revolutionary in swine production. It proposed to change long-established practices in hog raising. It took pigs from their usual dusty lots or muddy wallows and put them in a pasture "parlor." At first swine growers were inclined to be skeptical of the new method. They awaited practical tests with interest. The system had its first trial under farm conditions in the fall of 1919 in McLean County, Ill. (8). This county was chosen because of the large previous losses there and assurances of cooperation from members of the local farm bureau. The first year 17 farmers agreed to cooperate in the project; later others joined until the total number of cooperators was 34.

Records of the results were kept for a period of 6 years. During that time 6,204 sows farrowed 47,536 pigs, of which 39,855 were placed on pasture. When losses from all causes were included, 76 percent of all the pigs farrowed were marketed and 24 percent were lost. Records showed that the losses were from stillbirths, accidents in farrowing and on pasture, hog cholera, worms, and all other diseases. Under ordinary farm conditions with pigs in old hog lots, about 50 percent of the pigs farrowed are normally marketed. Thus, under the sanitation system, 6 pigs were marketed to 2 lost, whereas under ordinary conditions 4 would have been marketed and 4 lost. On this basis, under the sanitation system the farmer can raise more pigs with the same number of sows, or he can raise as many but better pigs with fewer sows. In either case he can get a larger return for the feed consumed.

Further study of the experimental data showed that the system was much more effective in attaining the purpose for which it was intended than the foregoing results indicate. A system designed to control parasites should not be expected to protect pigs from hog cholera, stillbirth, and miscellaneous accidents. When such losses were excluded and the sanitation system was judged solely for its ability to control parasites and related filth-borne diseases, the records showed it to be nearly 98 percent effective. As was to be expected, some cooperators followed the various steps in the system more faithfully than others. Those whose cooperation was only fair obtained about 94 percent efficiency in preventing parasites and filth-borne diseases, whereas those following the system to the letter attained almost 99 percent.

The foregoing example illustrates the manner in which research is conducted and applied. Notwithstanding the seemingly revolutionary nature of the practice of taking sows out of old hog lots and washing them, the system has been widely adopted by hog raisers in all parts of the country, and they have obtained results substantially the same as those recorded in the field trials described. (See fig. 1.) A modified form of the swine-sanitation system to combat kidney worms of swine in the South has likewise proved highly effective (9).

RECENT ADVANCES IN VETERINARY SCIENCE THROUGH RESEARCH

Much of the Department's scientific work has been developed in this way, to meet pressing needs, to throw up defenses quickly

against pests, and to solve economic problems; yet at the same time
it has added to knowledge of basic laws and principles. In the veterinary field the more notable discoveries and their application may
be summarized as follows:

The principle that injection of sterilized cultures or dead bacteria
confers immunity to subsequent inoculation with virulent material.

Simultaneous injection of immune serum and virulent blood as a
means of immunization.

Proof that certain diseases can be carried from one animal to
another only by an intermediate insect host.

Discovery of the nature of cattle tick fever, leading to a successful
method of eradicating cattle ticks.

Development of a method of testing the strength of dips in vats.

FIGURE 1.—A practical result of veterinary research—a uniformly healthy and well-
grown lot of pigs raised free of parasites in accordance with sanitary methods.

Discovery that hog cholera is caused by a filtrable virus, and the
development of a product that produces lasting immunity.

Development of crystal-violet vaccine against hog cholera.

Discovery and perfection of a practical, rapid method of tattooing
hogs, which has been especially useful in determining the original
ownership of hogs shipped to market.

Perfection of a serological method—that is, one based on the reaction
of blood serum in a laboratory test—of diagnosing the disease dourine.

Success in destroying trichinae in pork by refrigeration.

Development of a Federal meat-inspection service, based on scientific principles, that has won world-wide recognition.

Discovery of a new and effective remedy for hookworms in dogs
that has also been used successfully on millions of human beings
infected with hookworms.

Development of methods of preventing losses from roundworms
and kidney worms of swine.

Improvement in methods of making tuberculin, used in tuberculosis eradication.

Discovery of a rapid, stained-antigen test, highly useful in the detection and eradication of pullorum disease in poultry.

Development of numerous effective dips and disinfectants.

Discovery of phenothiazine as an effective anthelmintic, or worm medicine.

Successful use of barium antimonyl tartrate to remove gapeworms from chickens.

Improvement in the diagnosis and treatment of bovine mastitis.

Investigation of brucellosis (Bang's disease), leading to successful calfhood vaccination.

Development of a vaccine to combat encephalomyelitis.

Improvement in methods of handling livestock and livestock products in interstate and foreign trade.

Advancement in standards of veterinary education and of private practice, including hospitalization and the use of biological products, anesthetics, and the X-ray.

Coincident with the advances in veterinary science just mentioned, research workers have made extensive contributions to modern knowledge of livestock breeding, feeding, management, housing, and sanitation.

RESEARCH IN RELATION TO REGULATORY MEASURES

A very close relation exists between research findings and regulatory measures designed for the protection of animals and the wholesomeness of their products. Scientific knowledge enables veterinary officials, for instance, to determine the feasibility of regulatory measures for accomplishing a specified purpose. The practical eradication of bovine tuberculosis from the United States is based on knowledge concerning the cause and spread of the disease and the dependability of the tuberculin test as a means of diagnosis (10). Systems of meat and milk inspection have their foundation in the bedrock of scientific knowledge. The selection and use of the proper dips and disinfectants for combating animal diseases depend on thoroughgoing tests of various chemicals.

Since successful law enforcement is based to a considerable degree on the testimony of expert witnesses, in branches of public service that operate under the direction of regulatory officials there is need for experts qualified in various fields of science.

VETERINARY RESEARCH HELPS PROTECT HUMAN HEALTH

As previously pointed out, research in veterinary science has had numerous applications in human medicine. The constant operation of the Federal meat-inspection service (4) in approximately 700 establishments throughout the United States is a further means of protecting human health. In the course of their work, inspectors have to be on the watch for no less than 50 diseases and conditions for which condemnations of animal carcasses are made. Of these,

6 have been found to be transmissible to man through fresh meat—tuberculosis, anthrax, glanders, trichinosis, brucellosis (in man usually called undulant fever), and a tapeworm infestation known scientifically as cysticercosis. Knowledge provided by research concerning these and other diseases has established means by which man may protect himself from infections that might otherwise be dangerous or even fatal.

A useful aid to human health, developed within the last half century, is the preparation of extracts from the glands of animals slaughtered in inspected packing establishments. Medical science has shown that deficiencies in the glands of human beings may be corrected by the skillful use of preparations from those of healthy animals. Since many of the glands are small—for example, the pituitary, parathyroid, and suprarenal—several thousand of them are sometimes necessary to make as much as a pound of finished extract. Large-scale slaughtering operations, combined with thorough veterinary inspection, are accordingly necessary as a basis for this branch of the pharmaceutical industry. A high degree of technical skill based on extensive research is, of course, necessary in the preparation and standardization of the hundred or more glandular extracts that are made commercially for medical use.

Occasionally the relationship between animal and human health is highly involved, and the means by which the offending organism gains entrance to a vulnerable part of the body may even seem fantastic. One of the tapeworms, *Diphyllobothrium latum*, has a life cycle which involves temporary residence in a carnivore, such as a dog or cat, then in a crustacean, next in a fresh-water fish, and finally in a human being, in whose intestine the tapeworm may grow to a length of 25 feet or more. Each stage of the tapeworm's development must be in the host specified in the order given. Any break in the cycle destroys the parasite. Man's-simplest positive protection against this tapeworm, then, is to cook fish thoroughly.

In the case of anthrax (*3*), a disease affecting cattle and some other species, research has disclosed the danger to livestock owners who fail to curb their natural tendency to open a carcass. The anthrax organism is extremely virulent, frequently having fatal effects. The body fluids of an animal dead of anthrax teem with the bacilli, and a post-mortem examination with the bare hands invites fatal infection. In its literature the Department of Agriculture is emphatic in warning against this danger. Research has also disclosed the danger to man from other animal diseases, among which rabies, or hydrophobia, is especially serious (*5*). Fortunately the Pasteur treatment prevents death from hydrophobia.

In conducting their investigations, research workers often undergo exposure to organisms that are either known to be dangerous to human life or are proved to be so as the studies develop. Many workers have suffered impaired health, and some have died as martyrs of public service. Zealous, public-spirited scientists have at times also used themselves as subjects of tests for which laboratory animals were deemed unsuitable.

RESULTS OF RESEARCH AVAILABLE TO ALL

In keeping with the basic policy of the United States Department of Agriculture to gather and disseminate useful information, the results of research are promptly made available to scientific organizations and to the public.

Although scientific knowledge is utilized in some of its aspects chiefly by professional workers, it is equally available to interested laymen and others concerned. This broad policy is desirable because the further advancement of science depends on public interest and understanding, because the diffusion of knowledge is a fundamental principle of a democracy, and because it enables producers who are not themselves scientists to use scientific principles in their work—in fact they must use them to be successful under modern conditions.

In the research field, as in industry, many discoveries constitute improvements or refinements in methods. For instance, tuberculin, employed in the test for the presence of tuberculosis, has been known and used for many years, but the present type of tuberculin is a greatly improved product as compared with that first made and used by its originator, Koch. The present improved, or so-called new, tuberculin is grown on a synthetic medium of controlled composition and is about 10 percent more efficient than the former type.

COOPERATION OF RESEARCH WORKERS WITH LIVESTOCK OWNERS

The research worker in veterinary science is far from being a recluse, as he is so often pictured. More often he carries on his work in cooperation with other technically trained associates and tests the practical application of his findings to a considerable extent with farmers on their own farms. This was the procedure used in the development of the swine-sanitation system, described earlier in this article.

Another example was the conduct of research on hog cholera that led to the preventive-serum treatment. During the period 1897–1907 three Department investigators, Marion Dorset, C. N. McBryde, and W. B. Niles (fig. 2), conducted a series of experiments on hog cholera in southwestern Iowa, near Sidney (2). The disease had been causing serious losses there, and samples of disease-producing blood from natural outbreaks were thus readily obtainable. After many technical studies these workers finally developed a serum that gave promising results on a small laboratory scale. They then sought and obtained the cooperation of swine owners in making tests under practical farm conditions.

Figure 3, a photograph of one of the early cooperators, **J. K. Peterson**, is of historical interest.

Before the discovery of this method of immunization, entire herds of hogs often fell victim to cholera about the time they were ready for market. Today the inexpensive, practical serum treatment is a positive protection against such losses. The process is made available to all persons by a public-service patent, and still further protection is provided through Federal legislation for assuring serum

Figure 2.—The discoverers of anti-hog-cholera serum. Left to right, W. B. Niles, Marion Dorset, and C. N. McBryde. This picture was taken at the scene of their first experiments, near Sidney, Iowa.

of satisfactory purity and potency. Since the original discovery, continued research has resulted in improvement of serum by clarifying, concentrating, and pasteurizing processes.

In dealing with other disease problems, also, research workers have maintained close association with practical farmers, veterinarians, and others concerned in the use of preventive or control measures. The development and testing of the vaccine used in calfhood vaccination for the prevention of brucellosis (*6*) involved field trials on more than 260 herds in 24 States before the Bureau of Animal Industry considered the vaccine sufficiently perfected for general use.

Simplicity in the treatment of disease is naturally desired by most livestock owners, and research is directed to that end. Yet the nature

FIGURE 3.—J. K. Peterson, a farmer-cooperator, whose herd of hogs was one of the first to be immunized with anti-hog-cholera serum.

of animal maladies is such that the best method of prevention or control varies greatly in different diseases. In one case it may be a vaccine, in another a serum, in still another a chemical dip, and in dealing with internal parasites it may be an anthelmintic. In controlling tuberculosis, brucellosis, and pullorum disease the usual procedure is to apply a diagnostic test and dispose of the animals that prove by a positive reaction to have the disease.

Various complexities may enter disease situations so that the goal of simplicity cannot be attained. One of the newer means of disease control, which has been successful in treating trichomoniasis of the lower digestive tract of turkeys—a disease easily confused with blackhead—is the artificial elevation of temperature, so-called fever therapy. Exposure of birds in a cabinet (fig. 4) where the temperature is about 104° F. and the relative humidity about 65 percent results in an internal temperature in the body 2° to 6° above normal, which in turkeys is 106.5° F. Several of these heat treatments, lasting from 1 to 2 hours each, have resulted in early improvement and a large percentage of cures.

With all the skill and ingenuity of research workers in solving disease problems, the fact remains that, in most cases, simple cleanliness, combined with care to exclude infection from the premises, is the best and cheapest insurance of livestock health. For the greatest success with this method, however, buildings and equipment should be designed and constructed so that sanitary standards can be effectively maintained. Figure 5 illustrates an insanitary environment in which an entire flock of poultry was lost from the inroads of bronchitis. In general, sanitation may be considered the first line of defense, with veterinary science and services backing it up.

CONGRESSIONAL CONTROL OVER FEDERAL RESEARCH

As a control over the kind, amount, and cost of research conducted by the Department of Agriculture, congressional committees for many years have weighed the merits of various projects proposed by research leaders. After full consideration of the available facts and prospective benefits in each case, Congress authorizes only those projects that are deemed to be in the best public interest. Thus the people of the United States, under the authority vested in their congressional representatives, have a controlling hand over the services that research workers seek to render.

From time to time special legislative acts have authorized the establishment and support of regional and other experiment stations. The Bankhead-Jones law, for instance, in 1935 provided for basic research of specified kinds in the Department of Agriculture and in the State experiment stations and land-grant colleges. This law directed the Secretary of Agriculture to conduct research for improving the quality of agricultural commodities, to discover uses for farm products and byproducts, and to study the conservation, development, and use of land.

Animal diseases being studied by the Bureau of Animal Industry under current projects, following authorization by Congress, include the following:

Brucellosis of cattle.
Mastitis of cattle.
Tuberculosis.
Paratuberculosis (Johne's disease).
Nutritional deficiencies of cattle.
Bovine trichomoniasis.
Calf scours.
Anaplasmosis of cattle.
Equine encephalomyelitis and forage poisoning.
Rabies.
Swine erysipelas.
Swine influenza.
Miscellaneous diseases, including blackleg, paratyphoid infection of swine, foot rot, and alkali disease.

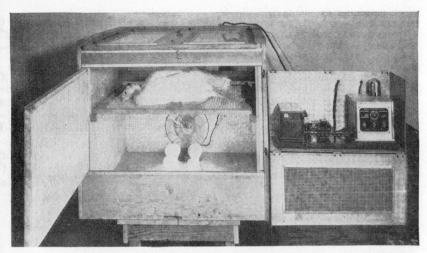

FIGURE 4.—Treating trichomoniasis in a turkey by fever therapy. The temperature of the cabinet is carefully controlled thermostatically.

FIGURE 5.—The removal from the autoclave of the sterilized flasks of culture medium upon which the antigen cultures are grown for the production of pullorum antigen.

Stock poisoning by plants.

Poultry diseases, including laryngotracheitis, fowl paralysis, tuberculosis, pullorum disease, and fowl pox.

Methods of producing immunization against hog cholera.

Periodic ophthalmia of equines.

Parasitic diseases of animals, including parasites of livestock, dogs, cats, and wild animals.

Mechanisms of infection in contagious, infectious, and parasitic diseases of domestic animals and poultry and methods of control.

To cope with many of the foregoing diseases on their home grounds, so to speak, the United States Bureau of Animal Industry maintains field stations in various parts of the country. The principal ones devoted to veterinary studies are:

The Animal Disease Station, Beltsville, Md., the staff of which collaborates on specific problems with field cooperators in 7 States.

The Regional Poultry Research Laboratory, East Lansing, Mich., the staff of which cooperates with workers of 25 State experiment stations.

The Field Station, Ames, Iowa.

The Regional Animal Disease Research Laboratory, Auburn, Ala., the staff of which cooperates with workers of 13 Southern States.

Additional resources for the study of disease problems, usually of a regional nature, are provided by the assignment of trained men to work with State and local authorities and also to conduct laboratory studies of disease in connection with Federal meat inspection. Work of these types is conducted in Colorado, Georgia, Illinois, Kansas, Nebraska, New Mexico, Texas, and Utah. The studies frequently involve cooperation with additional States having related problems.

RESEARCH AS A HUMANE INFLUENCE

Besides providing accurate information of a positive, useful nature, veterinary research has also shown the fallacy of many old beliefs. To a large degree science has caused the discontinuance of ineffective and often cruel treatments. It has shown that alleged diseases, such as "hollow horn," were purely imaginary; the hollow condition of cows' horns is entirely normal, and the old, cruel practice of drilling a hole in a horn and pouring in turpentine has largely disappeared. Research has been and will continue to be a powerful influence in alleviating animal suffering, partly by discouraging futile, barbarous methods of treatment, but principally by removing the causes of maladies. In conquering sheep scab, caused by a mite that burrows into the flesh, science has saved millions of sheep from the torments of these parasites.

LIMITATIONS OF PROPRIETARY DRUGS

As a result of claims of manufacturers of proprietary products, livestock owners have spent large amounts of money for drugs. No drug remedy known to science will prevent or cure certain diseases, including hog cholera, infectious abortion of cattle, and blackhead of turkeys. (By drugs, of course, are not meant biological products, such as vaccines and bacterins, used to prevent or cure diseases.)

Some manufacturers have claimed to have drugs or chemicals that will combat those maladies successfully; others claim for their drugs the ability to increase the milk yields of cattle and egg yields of fowls. Some claims have led credulous farmers to believe that the remedies will do things which no medicines will or can do. Dependable figures on the money spent annually for proprietary remedies are lacking, but conservative estimates indicate that it considerably exceeds 10 million dollars. Some dairymen with meager incomes have spent as much as $10 a pound for worthless abortion remedies. A survey by the Federal Food and Drug Administration embracing the field of veterinary preparations disclosed more than 1,000 misbranded or worthless antiseptics, stock powders, liniments, salves, and similar products. Broadly speaking, the investment in such questionable articles would have yielded vastly better results in improved health of livestock if the money had been expended to improve sanitation and for capable veterinary services.

VETERINARY EDUCATION

Fundamental training is, of course, necessary for the successful practice of veterinary medicine. It is likewise necessary for research work and related duties, including regulatory and administrative activities.

The chief sources of such training are the veterinary colleges maintained in conjunction with State universities and agricultural colleges. At the close of the fiscal year 1941 there were 10 of these veterinary institutions in the United States with equipment, faculties, and curricula affording 4 years or more of intensive study. As a means of safeguarding the quality of veterinary service; all the States and the District of Columbia have laws that regulate the practice of veterinary medicine. This form of supervision consists principally in licensing only properly trained and otherwise qualified and competent persons.

RESEARCH AS A PUBLIC SERVICE

A summary of the manner in which research aids in disease control and renders a broad public service properly includes the following observations:

In contrast to the fragmentary and inaccurate knowledge of a century ago concerning animal diseases, modern veterinary science provides dependable protection to the health of livestock.

Research is a fact-finding process that determines the soundness of previous beliefs or new hypotheses.

Research is altruistic, leading usually to the prompt announcement of results for use by any person anywhere.

As conducted in the United States, veterinary research is sponsored largely by the United States Department of Agriculture, agricultural experiment stations, and cooperating institutions.

For the most part, veterinary research is directed toward the solution of specific disease problems that have baffled livestock owners and on which they desire assistance. Research planned and conducted by trained specialists is the best known means of solving such problems.

More dependable knowledge concerning the nature and control of animal diseases has been assembled in the last 100 years than in all previous time.

Research is the foundation for the successful administration of animal quarantines, inspection services, and other beneficial regulations.

The results of research have alleviated suffering among the lower animals and greatly reduced the economic losses formerly caused by diseases, parasites, and related causes.

The net result of all types of veterinary service has been to surround the production of livestock and related food industries with increasingly effective safeguards. Discoveries in the course of such research have had many beneficial applications in other fields, including the advancement of human medicine.

LITERATURE CITED

(1) CHEW, ARTHUR P.
    1933. SCIENCE SERVING AGRICULTURE. U. S. Dept. Agr. Spec. Pub., 42 pp., illus.
(2) DORSET, M., MCBRYDE, C. N., and NILES, W. B.
    1908. FURTHER EXPERIMENTS CONCERNING THE PRODUCTION OF IMMUNITY FROM HOG CHOLERA. U. S. Bur. Anim. Indus. Bul. 102, 96 pp.
(3) GOCHENOUR, W. S.
    1934. ANTHRAX. U. S. Dept. Agr. Farmers' Bul. 1736, 14 pp., illus.
(4) JOSS, EDWARD C.
    1939. UNITED STATES MEAT INSPECTION. U. S. Dept. Agr. Yearbook (Food and Life) 1939: 355–359, illus.
(5) MOHLER, JOHN R.
    1911. RABIES OR HYDROPHOBIA. U. S. Dept. Agr. Farmers' Bul. 449, 23 pp. (Revised 1923.)
(6) ——— WIGHT, A. E., and O'REAR, H. M.
    1941. CALFHOOD VACCINATION AS AN AID IN COOPERATIVE BANG'S DISEASE (BOVINE BRUCELLOSIS) CONTROL. Amer. Vet. Med. Assoc. Jour. 98: 1–9, illus.
(7) POWELL, FRED WILBUR.
    1927. THE BUREAU OF ANIMAL INDUSTRY. ITS HISTORY, ACTIVITIES AND ORGANIZATION. Inst. Govt. Res., Serv. Monog. U. S. Govt., No. 47, 121 pp. Baltimore.
(8) RAFFENSPERGER, H. B., and CONNELLY, J. W.
    1927. THE SWINE SANITATION SYSTEM AS DEVELOPED BY THE BUREAU OF ANIMAL INDUSTRY IN M'LEAN COUNTY, ILL. U. S. Dept. Agr. Tech. Bul. 44, 20 pp.
(9) SCHWARTZ, BENJAMIN.
    1934. CONTROLLING KIDNEY WORMS IN SWINE IN THE SOUTHERN STATES. U. S. Dept. Agr. Leaflet 108, 6 pp., illus.
(10) WIGHT, ALEXANDER E.
    1933. TUBERCULOSIS IN LIVE STOCK. DETECTION, CONTROL, AND ERADICATION. U. S. Farmers' Bul. 1069, 18 pp., illus.

Origin and Spread of Important Insect Pests of Animals

BY H. H. STAGE AND J. A. HYSLOP [1]

A GOOD MANY AGES AGO, insects originated the idea of thumbing a ride from one part of the country or one part of the world to another. Any conveyance suits them—an animal, a bale of hay, a ship, automobile, or airplane, or just the winds that scud over land and sea. Here is a small part of the story of the world's craftiest and most dangerous stowaways.

As FAR BACK as the days of Pliny in the first century, and probably long before, horses, cows, sheep, goats, dogs, and chickens were known to be infested with fleas, bots, and lice. Until the white man arrived in America not one of these animals had been present on this continent for a long time, with the possible exception of the dog. It is natural to assume therefore that all of the specific parasites that take so large an annual toll of our domestic animals were brought to the Western Hemisphere along with their hosts.

In the geological past, long before even the most remote historical periods, the American Continent was well supplied with ungulates, or hoofed animals. A great many species of wild horses were well established over much of the country, and elephants and camels were then indigenous. The hoofed animals disappeared during the early Quaternary geological period, estimated at a million years ago. The stony records of paleontology disclose a remarkable and interesting coincidence. In the Oligocene period some 40 million

---

[1] H. H. Stage is Senior Entomologist, Division of Insects Affecting Man and Animals, and J. A. Hyslop is Principal Entomologist, Division of Insect Pest Survey and Information, Bureau of Entomology and Plant Quarantine.

years ago, great shale beds were laid down in the vicinity of Florissant, Colo. These beds are particularly rich in insect fossils and have been very well explored. Among the fossilized insects is none other than a tsetse fly (fig. 1), closely related to the fly that has practically prohibited the establishment of domestic animals in extensive areas of Africa. It is not impossible that this fly was the cause of the absolute extinction of the North American hoofed animals that might have carried the pests and parasites now found on domestic animals throughout the world. Because of the long lapse of time, however, between the early Quaternary period and the discovery of North America, none of the lice, fleas, ticks, bots, and mites that now infest our domestic animals could have been on this continent when the early settlers arrived. Some of our domestic-animal pests do attack wild animals, but in most instances this is probably an adaptation of the pests to a different host. In a few instances, also, the natural enemies of wild animals have turned their attention to our domestic livestock.

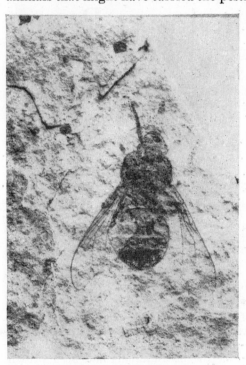

FIGURE 1.—A fossil tsetse fly.

In the early days many of the pests of plants were prevented from reaching this continent by the long period of overseas travel required and the lack of suitable food and habitat in transit. The pests of domestic animals, on the other hand, found a ship's hold full of their natural host animals an excellent place in which to live and reproduce; in fact, ships' holds often became unbearably infested with vermin.

Early breeders in North America were constantly seeking new sources of breeding stock. Not satisfied with the domestic cattle of Europe, they went farther and brought in the humped cattle (or zebu) from southeastern Asia, the Arabian horse, the peculiar varieties of poultry developed in India and China, the remarkable fur-bearing sheep of southwestern Asia, the Siamese cat, and the Pekingese dog. And all these introduced animals brought with them their peculiar pests and parasites.

DAMAGE DONE BY VARIOUS INSECT PESTS

The insect pests of livestock are extremely important from an economic standpoint. It has been estimated that the damage to livestock amounts to $168,900,000 annually, and this does not include the loss occasioned by mosquitoes, horseflies, scab mites, and a large number of less important pests, or damage to animal products such as woolen goods and leather.

It may be illuminating to review the damage done by some of the pests already introduced into the country.

The northern cattle grub, *Hypoderma bovis*, first recorded here in 1910, is probably of European origin. It and a native species cause severe damage to hides and losses in beef and milk production amounting to over $65,000,000 annually.

Another insect, the nose botfly (*Gasterophilus haemorrhoidalis*), has been a serious pest of horses since it was first reported in this country. The early history of the occurrence of this insect in the United States seems to be somewhat clouded, but the earliest reports show that it was present in western North Dakota in 1883, in Montana in 1890, in Wyoming and Minnesota in 1910, in Nebraska in 1911, in Iowa in 1912, and in other States more recently. Just why this pest of horses did not become prominent years before these dates is difficult to tell. It seems almost certain that it was brought into this country at an early date with shipments of horses from Europe. The habits of the insect indicate that its dissemination is largely brought about by the movement of horses from place to place. The long time which the larvae spend within the host and the rather extended period during which they normally live away from the animal add to the danger of spread whenever horses are shipped or driven from infested to uninfested areas. Its failure to become established earlier may have been due to conditions surrounding the imported animals after arrival here, such as adverse climate. It is possible that climate may have a marked influence on the perpetuation of the species in any region and that it will not thrive in the more humid area east of the present area of great abundance, in North and South Dakota. Certainly it has become established in the United States only comparatively recently.

Another familiar pest is the sheep botfly (*Oestris ovis*), the injurious effects of which are well known to most ranchers. Although comparatively new in the United States, it has been known in Europe for centuries. In ancient Greece, the Delphic oracle recommended its use as a cure for epilepsy.

Horn flies are a well-known pest of cattle throughout the length and breadth of the United States. The constant annoyance caused by these flies results in decreased weight and lessened milk production, and the loss from this source has been estimated at $10,000,000 annually. The horn fly was first recorded in this country near Camden, N. J., in 1887. It is interesting to note that almost immediately preceding the appearance of this insect in New Jersey—in fact, the year before it was first observed—there was an extensive importation of Holstein cattle from Holland into that State. By the summer of 1889, the horn fly was recorded in Virginia, and it had established itself in Ohio by 1891. By 1892 it had spread northward into Canada and southwestward to eastern Texas. By 1895 it had covered practically all of the United States and Canada east of the Rocky Mountains, and 2 years later it was found in California and Oregon. Ten years from the time of its introduction, this pest had spread throughout North America and even to Hawaii.

In addition to the insects that attack our domestic animals, there is another group so closely associated with livestock that they are practically dependent on them for existence. In fact these insects rarely reproduce in noxious numbers in any substance other than the excreta of domestic animals. The most notorious is the housefly. The danger of contamination of dairy products by houseflies is now recognized in the milk laws of most States, which prohibit the sale of such products from premises where precautionary measures are not taken against the presence and breeding of houseflies. Compliance with these regulations involves huge expenditures of money and labor, but when the bacterial count in milk or cream is too high there is complete financial loss because the permit to sell is revoked.

LIVESTOCK PESTS NOT YET INTRODUCED INTO THE UNITED STATES

Though many livestock pests are quite cosmopolitan, many of the important ones known in other parts of the world have apparently not reached our shores. Among these might be mentioned the Golubatz fly (*Simulium columbaizense*), which is known to have caused the death of many thousands of wild and domesticated animals in Rumania in 1923. A botfly (*Hypoderma crossi*) seriously infests goats and occasionally attacks cattle in India. In the Union of Soviet Socialist Republics there is a fly (*Wohlfahrtia magnifica*) the larva of which injures the hoofs of animals. In the Philippines a foot maggot (*Booponus intonsus*) produces myiasis, a disease due to the presence of larvae; and in the Soviet Union a horse bot (*Rhinoestrus purpureus*), not known to occur in this country, causes considerable injury to horses. In parts of Africa, India, and the Philippines there is a screwworm' (*Chrysomyia bezziana*) which, if introduced into this country, would greatly complicate our own screwworm problem, and already extensive damage is done to livestock here by these pests. The well-known primary blowflies (*Calliphora stygia* and *C. augur*) of Australia, which breed in the soiled wool of sheep, might invade America if the right combination of circumstances was present. And last, but probably most serious of all, is the dreaded tsetse fly of Africa, which carries African sleeping sickness.

HOW INSECT PESTS SPREAD

The spread of insect pests of animals is definite and continuous. It is carried on in many different ways. For example, the tremendous swarms of adult buffalo gnats concentrating in the lower Mississippi Valley late in the spring, which have caused enormous losses of livestock, are hatched from eggs laid many hundreds of miles to the north and carried to the Mississippi lowlands on the crests of annual freshets.

It has been known that insect pests are carried great distances by the wind, but until collections were made by means of airplanes, the numbers and species that may be found at great heights were not fully comprehended. For example, a flea has been found 200 feet above the ground, mites and spiders at 1,000 feet and more, and flies and bees at an altitude of 14,000 feet—nearly 3 miles.

One of the most remarkable cases of insect spread by wind currents is that of a springtail, a primitive wingless species, collected at an altitude of 3,000 feet. Although this insect was found over southern Louisiana, the species is known only in Cuba. Many of our most serious insect pests of animals are strong fliers in their own right and do not need the aid of wind currents for a change of scenery— witness the screwworm, which overwinters in southern Texas and flies northward on its own power approximately 35 miles a week, and the deer fly, which is one of our swiftest flying insects, although it does not travel far.

There are many other ways in which insect pests of animals may spread. It is not difficult to understand how easily ticks may be carried long distances in bales of hay or imported from outside the United States in guano; and the larvae and pupae of pests such as horn-flies, stableflies, and bots are commonly included in shipments of manure.

The common practice of shipping animals of all kinds long distances to agricultural fairs for exhibition and racing purposes gives their parasites easy and direct entry into new localities. The parasites of poultry are provided a safe and swift journey from their birthplace in eastern America when their hosts are sent to the west coast of the United States or Canada to take part in important egg-laying contests.

The movement of livestock to new ranges and new feed lots, and even to market, provides easy transportation for these insect pests from one section of the country to another and even across national boundaries. Modern passenger and express-carrying airplanes provide them with still another mode of travel.

PREVENTIVE MEASURES

Some of the measures that might aid in preventing the introduction of species or retarding those already established include quarantine and rigidly enforced inspection of both animals and their products, improved ranch management, and introduction of parasites and predators that prey only upon the injurious insects. In extreme instances it might become necessary to control certain parasites by temporary removal of their wild host.

It is generally known that many insect pests are controlled or their numbers greatly reduced by the introduction of their natural predators and parasites. The introduction of parasites of the eggs of horseflies into parts of Texas has been recorded as effectively reducing the numbers of these troublesome insects. Investigations have been made in Australia regarding this phase of control, apparently with some degree of success.

Wild animals sometimes harbor parasites that pass over to domestic species, causing injury and even death. In such cases it may be necessary to control the wild host or remove it entirely until control measures have been established for the injurious insect. A good example of this is the difficulty encountered in controlling the cattle tick in southern Florida. There it was found that the native white-tail deer served as a host for the southern cattle tick, and no matter how thoroughly the domestic animals were treated the wild reservoir continued to furnish sufficient numbers of ticks to prevent complete control. Unless quarantined, animals brought to this country for zoological gardens may easily bring their parasites along with them.

One of the important measures proposed by the Bureau of Entomology and Plant Quarantine for reducing screwworm losses is an improved form of ranch management which recommends timing of the birth of young and performing castration, docking, dehorning, and other surgical operations during the seasons when the screwworm fly is least abundant and least active.

Quarantines of sufficient duration should provide for thorough treatment of animals for such external parasites as lice, fleas, mites, ticks, and tick flies, and such internal parasites as bots, wound-infesting flies, and insect-borne protozoa, bacteria, and viruses. The time element is all-important, as bots, grubs, screwworms, and hoof maggots may spend more or less extended periods within their hosts and are not readily diagnosed from external examination. Certain forms of insects may emerge as adults even after their hosts have been in quarantine for 6 or 8 months. Proper precautions would allow these species to develop and emerge from their hosts while the animals are in quarantine, so that the pests can be destroyed.

Although quarantine regulations have caused many heated arguments and much dissatisfaction and are irksome and often difficult to apply, they are nevertheless exceedingly useful in preventing the spread of parasites as well as diseases.

A rigid and well-enforced inspection of animals entering interstate trade would prevent the transportation of screwworms by common carriers. Severe infestations of this insect have been started in the Central and Northern States by the shipment of infested animals from south Texas late in the spring. The local infestation then increases in size and importance until winter puts a stop to the depredations. An enforced inspection of animals in transit should be supplemented by a thorough cleaning and treatment of the common carrier and holding pens, as scab mites, ticks, fleas, and flies could otherwise be carried to more distant points after their hosts have been unloaded.

At present the United States quarantine laws do not provide against the introduction of animal insect pests in the same thorough manner as against the importation of plant pests; they do, however, prohibit the importation of animals suffering from communicable diseases, some of which are transmitted by insects.

Regulatory Activities in Animal-Disease Control

BY A. W. MILLER, S. O. FLADNESS,
A. E. WIGHT, D. I. SKIDMORE,
E. C. JOSS, AND H. E. MOSKEY [1]

CERTAIN ANIMAL DISEASES are so devastating when they gain a foothold that merciless war must be waged against them. No individual alone could protect his animals against these disease invasions; all must band together and take combined action through government. Here is the strategy of control, in which the real weapons are the findings of science.

FEDERAL AND STATE REGULATORY ACTIVITIES have a most important bearing on animal-disease control and eradication work. In fact such activities are often the foundation upon which programs for the conduct of this work are built.

The first basic Federal legislation on this subject was the act approved May 29, 1884 (23 Stat. 31), which authorized the establishment of the Federal Bureau of Animal Industry. The purpose of this legislation was to prevent the exportation of diseased cattle and provide means for the suppression and wiping out of pleuropneumonia and other contagious diseases among domestic animals. This act contained authority for the promulgation of rules and regulations deemed necessary for the suppression of communicable diseases of livestock and also authorized the Department of Agriculture to establish quarantines.

At the time this legislation was enacted, the large export business in live cattle to Great Britain was endangered on account of the prev-

[1] A. W. Miller is Assistant Chief, Bureau of Animal Industry; S. O. Fladness is Chief, Field Inspection Division; A. E. Wight is Chief, Tuberculosis Eradication Division; D. I. Skidmore is Chief, Virus-Serum Control Division; and E. C. Joss is Chief, Meat Inspection Division. H. E. Moskey is Senior Veterinarian, Food and Drug Administration, Federal Security Agency.

alence of contagious pleuropneumonia among cattle in the United States. The first great achievement in this country in completely eliminating a dangerous animal malady was the eradication of contagious pleuropneumonia, accomplished in 1892.

An amendment to the act of 1884, approved May 31, 1920 (41 Stat. 694, 699), contained a provision with respect to the interstate movement of cattle that had reacted to the tuberculin test. Another amendment, approved June 28, 1926 (44 Stat. 774), struck out provisions in the original act of 1884 under which it had been possible to ship cattle infested with cattle fever ticks across State lines. The effect of this amendment, which made it impossible to ship tick-

FIGURE 1.—Inspection of import cattle from Mexico. Inspection is made principally to see whether any cattle ticks are present. The high, strong chute makes possible close inspection of the animals, many of which are semiwild and unaccustomed to being handled.

infested cattle between States for immediate slaughter, was to provide a much-needed stimulus to tick-eradication work, especially in some areas where it had been lagging.

The act of February 2, 1903 (32 Stat. 791), was passed to enable the Department more effectually to suppress and prevent contagious and infectious diseases of livestock. The act of March 3, 1905 (33 Stat. 1264), broadened the authority of the Secretary of Agriculture to establish and maintain quarantine districts and to permit and regulate the movement of cattle and other livestock therefrom.

The acts of August 30, 1890, and February 2, 1903, as well as provisions in various appropriation acts, gave the Secretary of Agriculture additional authority to prescribe regulations for the inspection (fig. 1) and quarantine of livestock offered for importation and for control and supervision over such imported products as hay, straw, etc., which are possible conveyers of infection. These regulations are modified from time to time as new knowledge is developed regarding conditions under which the various infections will survive for long periods and the manner in which they are disseminated.

In safeguarding livestock producers in the United States from losses due to animal diseases it is essential that every possible effort be made to prevent the introduction of foreign animal maladies, to stamp out promptly any infection that may gain a foothold, and to employ comprehensive and adequate measures in combating diseases that have been long established in this country.

If the contagion of any disease normally nonexistent in this country is introduced and threatens the livestock industry, the Secretary has authority to cooperate with the States concerned in drastic eradication measures, including the purchase and destruction of diseased or exposed animals and contaminated materials.

Among the more important regulatory features that have been of material assistance in the work of combating animal diseases are Federal and State quarantines; campaigns for disease control and eradication; the keeping of records to disclose the extent and distribution of various maladies; and public-stockyards inspection, including testing livestock before interstate shipment, cleaning and disinfecting premises and vehicles, immunization of swine against hog cholera, dipping of cattle and sheep for scabies, and the enforcement of the so-called 28-hour law. Supervision over the production of biological products and control of drug remedies are also important phases of the work.

FEDERAL AND STATE QUARANTINES

Federal and State quarantines are of very great value in campaigns for the control and eradication of animal diseases. These measures are usually put into effect through the issuance of rules and regulations based on legislation which in many instances is general but which confers on the enforcing officer ample authority to prescribe definite and detailed specifications for the work.

In combating most infectious diseases of livestock the stoppage of the movement of diseased and exposed animals is essential. This can seldom be accomplished without some kind of quarantine. The principal object for the establishment of any quarantine is to confine the infection to the smallest possible area and to hold it there until it can be stamped out through the use of appropriate eradication measures. The problem of protecting our herds and flocks has been greatly simplified by the fact that several of the most serious communicable diseases of animals have not gained a permanent foothold in this country.

Sometimes it is possible to prevent a highly infectious disease from gaining a foothold by the strict enforcement of a local quarantine. This is well demonstrated by the practice of holding animals offered for importation into the United States in quarantine at ports of entry for a period of observation. This practice in a number of instances has prevented the introduction of foreign animal maladies into this country, the most noteworthy case having been the detection of surra in a consignment of Brahman cattle on arrival in the United States. The detection of the disease in this instance and the slaughter of the affected animals made it possible to maintain the record of never having had an outbreak of surra in the herds of this country. Rinderpest has never gained entrance into the United States. Foot-and-mouth disease has been brought in six times since the Bureau of Animal Industry was organized, but in each instance complete eradication has been successfully accomplished. The United States has remained free from mal de caderas of horses and several other destructive maladies which, along with surra, are caused by a class of organisms known as trypanosomes.

When an outbreak of foot-and-mouth disease occurs it is the practice of both the Federal and the State officials concerned to impose drastic quarantine measures. These not only prohibit all movement from infected premises but in addition prohibit or greatly restrict the movement within the quarantined area of livestock and materials considered likely to serve as means for the spread of the disease. Usually the borders of a quarantine established on account of foot-and-mouth disease are identical in the quarantine orders issued by the Federal and the State authorities. In some instances the State may, as a precautionary measure, establish a modified quarantine area around the infected area from which a limited movement of animals and farm products is permitted under close supervision of the State sanitary officials.

When the disease to be combated is not especially virulent and has not become widespread, it is possible to handle outbreaks by the application of State quarantines without the imposition of a Federal quarantine. When the disease has become widespread and well established, however, local quarantines are not adequate, especially when it is necessary to regulate the movement of livestock and vehicles used in their transportation from an entire State or a number of States. In such instances a Federal quarantine is imposed, and the interested States cooperate by putting State quarantines in effect, as was done in the campaigns to eradicate sheep and cattle scabies, southern or splenetic fever tick, and foot-and-mouth disease.

To be effective and to have the support of interested agencies, especially of livestock producers, quarantine measures must vary greatly and be appropriate for the particular disease that is being combated. They may range from a complete prohibition against the movement of all animals, produce, and vehicles, and even restrictions on human beings, as in the case of an outbreak of foot-and-mouth disease, to mere physical examination and movement under proper certification or official permit, as in the case of sheep and cattle scab, in which the animals are subjected to certain prescribed treatments that have been found to be effective.

While the campaign for the eradication of tuberculosis was at its height, regulations were issued by cities, counties, and some States prohibiting the sale of any butter or other dairy products not produced from cream or milk obtained from cattle from noninfected dairy herds in the modified tuberculosis-free area. Although these were not technically quarantine measures, the results very noticeably hastened the work of eradicating bovine tuberculosis.

The cooperation of livestock producers in the enforcement of quarantine measures, both State and Federal, usually has been excellent, although in a few instances it has been necessary to employ armed guards in order to maintain an effective quarantine.

Since quarantine measures interfere in varying degrees with the operations of livestock producers, they should be imposed only when other means would be ineffective and lifted as promptly as conditions warrant. It would be impossible, however, to control and eradicate some of the contagious diseases in this country without the authority, both Federal and State, to impose quarantines.

CAMPAIGNS FOR DISEASE CONTROL AND ERADICATION

A long-term program of eradication, undertaken county by county and State by State with active cooperation between Federal and State livestock sanitary organizations, livestock producers, and others, is commonly called a campaign.

Although some of the most dangerous diseases have been successfully excluded, a number of others unfortunately had become widely disseminated and were serious deterrents to the livestock industry before there were means for dealing with them effectively. These diseases, which included hog cholera, scabies (mange), splenetic or tick fever, dourine of horses, and bovine tuberculosis, naturally engaged the attention of the Bureau of Animal Industry very soon after its organization. Through careful study and research important gaps in the knowledge of the causative agents and their characteristics and mode of transmission were gradually filled in and the foundation was thus laid for the next step, which was to devise means for combating the diseases mentioned. In this step, too, the investigators achieved notable results. Methods were developed which rendered possible the complete elimination of all the diseases except hog cholera.

The act of Congress approved May 29, 1884, which created the Bureau of Animal Industry, also provided authority for the Secretary of Agriculture to cooperate with the various States in the eradication of diseases and prescribed conditions under which such cooperation may be extended. That law has been supplemented from time to time by other statutes, including provisions in annual-appropriation acts, in regard to special problems that have arisen in dealing with particular diseases. Accordingly, as fast as practicable and effective methods have been devised and the specified conditions fulfilled in the different States concerned, cooperative eradication projects have been organized and systematic work done on as large a scale as available funds and personnel have made possible from year to year. The first of these extensive cooperative programs to be undertaken was the eradication of scabies of cattle and sheep in the great range areas of the West. This was begun in 1905. The following year witnessed the inauguration of the campaign to eradicate the ticks which transmit splenetic or tick fever, then prevalent in all the Southern States. Intensive efforts to eliminate dourine date from 1912, and the eradication of bovine tuberculosis, the most extensive and costly of all the programs to date, got under way in 1917. All these campaigns are now nearing completion

OBJECTIVES IN CAMPAIGNS COMBATING ANIMAL DISEASES

While complete eradication is the final objective in all of these campaigns, two quite different principles are involved which call for correspondingly different methods and procedures. Scabies and tick fever, for instance, are caused or transmitted by external parasites, and eradication must be accomplished by treatment of the affected animals for the destruction of the parasites. On the other hand, the presence or absence of dourine and tuberculosis is determined by diagnostic tests, and animals found to be infected are appraised and slaughtered. Owners of destroyed animals are indemnified by the Department and the cooperating State or local government, within certain limits fixed by the governing laws and regulations.

The manner in which hog cholera is dealt with in the United States represents another form of cooperative effort. The existence of that disease was general throughout the country, and widespread epizootics (equivalent to epidemics in the case of human disease) more or less regularly caused enormous losses. Early in the present century scientists of the Bureau of Animal Industry determined the cause of hog cholera and devised a practical and reliable method of rendering swine immune to the disease. Cooperative projects were set up in a majority of the States to demonstrate the application of the method and promote its general use, along with indicated sanitary measures. This project, inaugurated in 1913, aimed at control and prevention rather than eradication.

The efforts toward the control and eradication of communicable animal diseases within the different States are primarily the function of the respective State authorities. The direct authority of the Federal Government extends only to control over the interstate movement of livestock from districts where any such disease is known to prevail. Authority to enforce local quarantines and to compel the destruction or the treatment of infected or exposed animals rests entirely with the States. Consequently, the work of these Federal and State cooperative projects is done chiefly under State laws and regulations. Cooperative work as contemplated by section 3 of the act of May 29, 1884, is not undertaken in any State unless or until there are State laws and regulations which make it possible to apply established methods effectively and to protect the results achieved and unless State authorities undertake to proceed in harmony with the general policies and practices agreed upon by Federal and State livestock sanitary authorities.

It will be apparent from the foregoing that in formulating plans for dealing with communicable diseases of livestock the objective to be sought is a primary consideration.

In the case of tick fever and scabies the course to be followed is very clear. Methods of eradication have been developed which, if properly carried out, are completely effective. In the case of some diseases, however, no means of accomplishing complete eradication have been found. In others, while eradication might be possible it would be quite impracticable to attempt it, either because the cost would be prohibitive or because effective and economical methods of control are available. In still others, no such methods of control have been developed, and eradication is possible and feasible if prompt and thorough action is taken before the disease has gained too strong a foothold.

Anthrax and blackleg are examples of diseases that are not susceptible of eradication but losses from which can be largely prevented through the prophylactic treatment of susceptible animals in infected areas, along with collateral sanitary measures. An example of a disease which can be eradicated but which it is most often more feasible to control is hog cholera. In Canada, where the disease rarely appears, the occasional outbreaks that do occur are eradicated by the prompt slaughter of all swine in affected herds, followed by disinfection of the premises. In the United States, on the other hand, in view of the fact that hog cholera exists in all regions and the further fact that swine can be effectively protected against it, a policy of prevention and control was indicated and is being followed.

Foot-and-mouth disease and hog cholera, as they are dealt with in this country, furnish the most striking illustrations of the application of the policies of eradication and control. Both diseases are caused by viruses, those minute organisms that are invisible under the strongest microscope, pass through the finest filters, and can be cultivated only in living tissues—characteristics which render diseases caused by them unusually difficult to deal with. Both are eradicable if extreme measures are taken before the virus has become too widely disseminated. In other respects they are quite dissimilar. The hog cholera virus causes disease only in swine, whereas all ruminants as well as swine are susceptible to foot-and-mouth disease. Losses from hog cholera can be reduced to the vanishing point through the application of control measures of proved efficiency. On the other hand, experience in European countries where foot-and-mouth disease is always present has demonstrated that when the virus is widespread effective control of the disease is not possible. Consequently, when an outbreak of foot-and-mouth disease occurs in the United States there is no choice but to proceed with eradication, no matter how drastic the measures that must be taken.

The practical impossibility of controlling foot-and-mouth disease where it exists enzootically—that is, where there are always a few cases in the animal population—may be ascribed to a combination of factors. Probably first among these is the fact that it is the most infectious disease of animals known and spreads with extreme rapidity. Another factor is the existence of several types of the virus and the fact that immunity resulting from infection by one type does not protect animals exposed to other types. Still another factor is the failure thus far to develop an immunizing product at once

effective against all types of the virus and practicable for use on a
large scale, without which no adequate control over the disease when
it exists extensively can be hoped for. This situation pointedly illustrates the need, in the United States, for adhering to the policy
of complete eradication of any outbreaks that may occur.

PUBLIC-STOCKYARDS INSPECTION

The closing decade of the nineteenth century and the first of the
twentieth witnessed a tremendous growth of public markets in the
United States and the development of a considerable number of additional stockyards for the receipt of livestock from all parts of the
country. Some of these were for disposition for immediate
slaughter; others were for reshipment after sale to widely scattered
country points for feeding, stocking, or breeding purposes. Realiz-
ing that the intermingling of the tremendous numbers of animals
involved might cause these market places to become centers of infection from which serious animal maladies would be spread to
ranches and farms throughout the country, the Department set up
an inspection service which has proved to be an important factor in
the campaign to control and eradicate animal diseases. This service
is separate and distinct from ante mortem inspection at slaughtering
establishments where Federal meat inspection is maintained. Although often adjacent to meat-packing establishments, public stockyards are separately managed.

Livestock-inspection service is maintained at 48 stockyards in 46
cities. Veterinarians who, through years of experience, have become
skilled in the detection of animals affected with disease or other abnormal conditions are constantly on duty examining the animals
that pass through these stockyards each day. These veterinarians are assisted by laymen skilled in such work as the inspection
of livestock, supervising the dipping of cattle and sheep for scabies,
and cleaning and disinfecting premises, cars, and trucks used in the
handling of diseased animals.

So far as possible all livestock that arrive at these market centers
during daylight hours are inspected at the time of unloading, while
animals that are unloaded and yarded during the night are inspected
early in the morning before the trading commences.

Among the principal diseases for which inspections are made are
anthrax, scabies of cattle and sheep, tick or splenetic fever, hog
cholera, hemorrhagic septicemia (shipping fever), and erysipelas of
swine. If signs of these or any other communicable disease are detected, all infected and exposed animals are promptly segregated and
treated or otherwise handled in accordance with Department regulations. The inspectors are constantly on the watch for animals showing any symptoms suspicious of foot-and-mouth disease.

The livestock sanitary official of the State in which a diseased shipment originates is notified, as well as the Department field office in
that territory. In this way centers of infection are located, and the
spread of the disease to other herds and premises is frequently prevented by the prompt application of appropriate sanitary control

measures. Instances are not uncommon in which the detection of disease in a shipment at a public stockyard is the owner's first inkling of the existence of infection on his premises.

Not only are incoming shipments of livestock inspected, but a reinspection is made of outgoing shipments, both to detect disease and also to determine whether there has been compliance with certain requirements, such as the tests for tuberculosis and Bang's disease, dipping for scabies, and immunization against hog cholera. The very large scale on which this livestock-inspection service is conducted is indicated by the fact that each year there pass through these public markets for slaughter or other purposes between 60 and 70 million head of livestock, the figures for the fiscal year 1940 being 18,135,667 cattle, 21,832,485 sheep, and 29,540,954 swine. As an indication of the importance of this service, the detection at one market during the calendar year 1940 of more than 160 consignments of sheep affected with scabies may be cited.

Testing Livestock Before Interstate Shipment

Interstate shipments of livestock for immediate slaughter may be made to public stockyards under regulations that are less restrictive than if the animals are to be forwarded direct from some country point in one State to a country point in another State for feeding, stocking, or breeding purposes. If, however, it is found after arrival that some of the animals would sell to better advantage for the latter purposes than for slaughter, they then must meet the same test requirements that would have been applicable if they had been shipped direct for such purposes.

Department employees at public stockyards supervise the application of the tests for tuberculosis and Bang's disease and see that those animals which do not pass a satisfactory test are removed from the consignments to which they belong and are slaughtered or otherwise properly disposed of, as may be prescribed in existing regulations. The bulk of all the cattle that react to the tests for tuberculosis and Bang's disease in the present cooperative Federal and State campaign are sent to these public markets for slaughter. The employees at the markets exercise the utmost vigilance to see that the identity of these reactors, estimated at 180,000 in 1940, is maintained during their passage through the yards and that they are sold and finally disposed of for immediate slaughter.

Cleaning and Disinfection

Whenever disease is found in a shipment of livestock to these public markets, immediate steps are taken to see that the pens occupied by the animals at the market, the car or other vehicle in which they have been transported (fig. 2), and the yards through which they have been handled at the point of origin—and en route if they have been unloaded for feed, water, and rest—are properly cleaned and disinfected.

IMMUNIZATION AND DIPPING

Another activity over which the Department exercises supervision at public stockyards is the immunization of swine against hog cholera. Included in receipts at many of the large markets, especially at certain times of the year, are a considerable number of pigs which are not in first-class slaughter condition. Under the regulations in effect it is possible to sort out such animals from the consignments in which they are received and sell them for shipment to country

FIGURE 2.—A Government veterinarian supervising the cleaning and disinfection of a stock car that had carried tuberculous cattle. The airtight container at the right contains the disinfecting solution and is provided with a pressure gage and valve to admit compressed air, brought to the spot by underground pipes. The air pressure, controlled by a valve, forces the disinfectant through the hose, which is fitted with a nozzle for spraying the inside of the car.

points for further feeding, provided they are properly treated against hog cholera.

Such swine may be moved interstate from public stockyards for any purpose only to States the laws, rules, and regulations of which provide for the segregation and quarantine of imported hogs for a period of not less than 3 weeks. In order to be eligible for such shipment certain inspection and certification requirements must be met. The swine must be inspected by a Bureau inspector at the yards. If they are found free from symptoms of cholera or other contagious, infectious, or communicable diseases and in a thrifty condition, they must be treated by a competent veterinarian under

Bureau supervision, provided that the temperature of each animal is taken before treatment and that only those with a temperature of less than 104° F. shall be permitted interstate movement. If the Bureau inspector finds any hogs affected with cholera, the entire lot to which they belong must be treated by a competent veterinarian under Bureau supervision in a portion of the yards set aside for that purpose. At the expiration of not less than 30 days, if no signs of disease are observed on examination of the hogs, they may be released for shipment. All immunized swine must be disinfected by dipping in or spraying with a permitted solution, must be accompanied by a certificate issued by a Bureau inspector, and must be transported in cleaned and disinfected cars or other vehicles.

These swine in many instances originate in localities where feed supplies are short, often because of drought conditions, and they are usually sold at stockyards to purchasers who in most instances are located in sections which at the time have surplus feed. The immunization of these animals, therefore, is of value not only to the producer, who is afforded an outlet for his unfinished animals, but also to the purchaser, who needs additional animals to consume the feed he has available.

Consignments of sheep and cattle received at public stockyards in which scabies infection is found or which have been exposed to the disease, if not sold for immediate slaughter, are dipped in accordance with applicable regulations under Department supervision. Included in the receipts of sheep at these stockyards are many animals not in a fit condition for slaughter. These are sorted out of their consignments and sold for feeding or breeding purposes. Many of them are dipped as a precautionary measure to comply with the requirements of the States to which they are destined or at the request of the purchasers, even though there is no actual knowledge that they have been exposed to scabies. This dipping also is conducted under Department supervision.

MEAT INSPECTION AS AN AID IN ANIMAL-DISEASE-CONTROL ACTIVITIES

An important service of the Bureau of Animal Industry is the administration of the Federal meat-inspection laws. The purpose of the inspection is to protect consumers of meat and meat food products, so far as the Federal Government has legislated, against bad meats and against insanitary conditions and deceptive and fraudulent practices during the preparation of meat products for the channels of commerce.

Some 70,000,000 or more cattle, sheep, swine, and goats are submitted each year to this inspection. These animals, if lined up closely in single file, would encircle the world at the Equator more than 2½ times; yet, as they daily flow into federally inspected establishments each animal is inspected twice before its transformation into meat is completed.

Inspection procedure is as follows:

First, the animals are scrutinized and if necessary examined more closely in the pens of the establishment in order that those that are sick or for some other reason are unfit for human food purposes may be sorted out and destroyed or otherwise properly disposed of. Although a very large percentage of these animals have passed through public stockyards and have been inspected there, these establishments are not a part of the yards and this ante mortem inspection is distinct from the public-stockyards inspection.

Second, as the animals passed on the ante mortem inspection are slaughtered and dressed in the establishment, each carcass with its parts, including the internal organs, is inspected for signs of disease or other conditions which render the meat unsafe or objectionable as food.

Third, hams, bacon, lard, sausage, canned meats, and other food products of the meat and organs are marked "U. S. Inspected and Passed" after post mortem inspection.

The ante mortem and post mortem inspections form the main stem of the Federal system of inspection, and to conduct this part of the service more than 800 veterinarians are regularly employed, along with a somewhat smaller number of trained lay inspectors as assistants.

Through a system of daily reports by the veterinarians who make the ante mortem and post mortem inspections, a record is available of the affected animals and carcasses examined and disposed of. These records have value other than as mere statistics. For example, when a veterinarian engaged in meat inspection finds an animal or a shipment of animals affected with a communicable disease of importance to livestock sanitary officials and when he can ascertain the origin of the diseased animal or animals, he reports the circumstances directly to the State or Federal sanitary officials having jurisdiction in the region from which the infected livestock came. By means of eartags, earmarks, brands, tattoo marks, or even descriptions of animals, the center of infection is often located, with quick and beneficial results to the livestock owners in the vicinity. The veterinary meat-inspection records are also useful to research scientists and others in ascertaining the location and spread of animal diseases in various regions of the country.

THE ACT TO PREVENT CRUELTY TO ANIMALS IN TRANSIT

The act to prevent cruelty to animals in transit—the so-called 28-hour law—although not designed primarily for the control of animal diseases, does have such a direct influence on the health of livestock that it merits a discussion in this article. This measure has general application throughout the United States, but most of the work in connection with its enforcement is performed at public stockyards.

Department employees at such yards examine waybills, interview shippers, and in other ways endeavor to discover alleged violations of this law. Any cases that appear suspicious are thoroughly investigated, and if sufficient evidence to warrant prosecution is found, the violation is reported to the Department, which sends it through the Office of its Solicitor to the Department of Justice for prosecution.

This act prohibits railroads or other common carriers from confining cattle, sheep, swine, or other animals shipped across State lines for longer than 28 hours without unloading into properly equipped pens (fig. 3) for feed, water, and rest for a period of 5 hours, unless prevented by storm or other accidental or unavoidable causes which could not be anticipated or avoided by the exercise of due diligence and foresight. The law contains a provision that on

FIGURE 3.—Cattle on their way to market leaving railway rest pens to be reloaded in cars. Before the enactment of the 28-hour law, livestock were often confined in cars for long periods without water, feed, or rest. Such conditions sapped the vitality of the animals, many of them arriving at their destination exhausted or sick, or even crippled. Deaths in transit were also much more frequent than under present improved conditions.

written request of the shipper the time of confinement may be extended to 36 hours. The provisions of this law, which was enacted in 1906 before motor transportation had come into general use, have been held not to apply to animals moved interstate in trucks. An effort is being made to have the law amended to cover this new development in livestock transportation.

For a number of years following the enactment of this measure a great deal of difficulty was experienced in enforcing it. Opposition was encountered from both the railroads and the shippers of livestock. However, as it was gradually realized that livestock would reach market in better condition if the law were observed, violations dropped off. Today the Department has the hearty cooperation of practically all the railroads in the United States, and violations are relatively few.

Enforcement·of the act has resulted in the provision by railroads of more adequate facilities at feed, water, and rest stations and the expediting of the movement of livestock to avoid penalties for infractions of the law. On a number of occasions efforts have been made to amend the law so that the time of confinement could be extended to 40 hours. In the opinion of the Department such a provision would be an unwise one and detrimental to the interests of the shipper, especially as the vitality of animals that are deprived of feed, water, and rest for long periods is lowered and they thus become more likely to develop diseases such as hemorrhagic septicemia.

REGULATION OF BIOLOGICAL PRODUCTS

The virus-serum-toxin law of March 1913 authorizes the Secretary of Agriculture to make and promulgate such rules and regulations as may be necessary to prevent the preparation, sale, barter, exchange, or interstate shipment of worthless, contaminated, dangerous, or harmful viruses, serums, toxins, or analogous products for use in the treatment of domestic animals. Under this authority Bureau of Animal Industry Order 276 and its amendments have been issued. The main purpose of these regulations is to insure that there will be available for the treatment of livestock such serums, vaccines, diagnostic agents, and like biological products as will assist in effectively preventing, controlling, or eradicating diseases that threaten the health of the farmer's domestic animals and indirectly his livelihood.

Biological products that are contaminated or not properly prepared or used may fail to prevent or control an outbreak of disease or may even be the means of spreading disease, endangering not only the animals on the farm on which they are used but perhaps other herds in the community. Biological products produced under licenses issued by the Secretary and in accordance with his regulations carry reasonable assurance that if they are properly applied and their use is restricted as indicated by the trade label they will be effective as an aid in preventing the specific disease named on the label and will not be harmful to the farmer's animals on which they are used or endanger those of other owners.

During the last year a sufficient quantity of anti-hog-cholera serum was produced by licensed establishments under Department regulations to treat more than 33,000,000 shoats. It is not difficult to imagine what would have happened had any considerable part of this serum been worthless or impotent or contaminated with the causative agent of a dangerous communicable disease of animals. Biological products that do not meet requirements are withheld from the market and destroyed under the supervision of Bureau inspectors.

From time to time the regulations have been amended or supplemented with orders designed to improve the quality of biological products marketed by licensed establishments. Whenever new tests are developed, licensed producers are required to subject their products to these tests and to market none that are found unsatisfactory.

Likewise, when new production procedures are developed, they are applied to products to improve their quality.

A considerable part of the supervision exercised over establishments producing biological products under license involves the proper labeling of each product. The purpose of the regulations relating to labeling is to prevent misbranding by insuring as far as possible that the products are properly identified by name and descriptive matter, that adequate directions are given for the proper use of each product, and that no statement, design, or device that may deceive the purchaser or that is false and misleading in any particular is used.

DRUG REMEDIES AND THEIR CONTROL

Naturally desiring healthy livestock but lacking knowledge of diseases and the limitations of drugs in preventing and treating diseases, many farmers have been led to spend much money for remedies of no value whatever. Though there are no exact figures on the subject, it has been estimated that farmers spend many millions of dollars each year on livestock and poultry remedies, in spite of the fact that the value of drug medication in the prevention and treatment of infectious diseases caused by bacterial agents and filtrable viruses is extremely limited. In addition to involving a monetary loss, the use of worthless remedies gives farmers a false sense of security.

Scientists all over the world have spent much time seeking to discover chemicals or drugs that when administered internally would destroy the causative agents of infectious or communicable diseases of livestock without being toxic to the tissues or organs of the body. Up to the present time veterinary authorities know of no chemicals or drugs that have been scientifically established as being effective in the prevention or treatment of any of the specific diseases of animals caused by bacteria or filtrable viruses. Valuable discoveries have been made by scientists in the treatment of certain specific bacterial infections in man with the sulfanilamide compounds, but unfortunately, this group of drugs has not fulfilled the expectation of veterinarians in the treatment of bacterial diseases of livestock, including poultry.

This is not to say that all drugs are worthless in the treatment of animals. Many have physiological or therapeutic effects that have been more or less well established scientifically. These drugs are not used or prescribed with the idea that they will remove or destroy the bacterial or virus infection or prevent the disease from spreading to other animals. They are useful for their known effects on the tissues or organs of the body, and their use may be highly desirable in the treatment of sick animals. For example, powdered nux vomica and gentian are the basic drugs in many livestock tonics. A combination of drugs of this character when prescribed in therapeutically significant amounts is scientifically recognized to have a stimulating effect on appetite and tone, but it will not be effective in removing the cause of any disease condition. Likewise the drug digitalis is valuable for its specific action on the heart, but its use will not correct any abnormal condition of the heart.

The combination of iron and copper is frequently prescribed for its effect in increasing the hemoglobin content of the blood. This treatment is especially useful in cases of anemia associated with a deficiency of iron and copper in the diet, but it is not effective in the removal of other causes of anemia. Supplementing the ration with certain minerals and vitamins in which the feed is known to be deficient has been recognized by scientists to be effective in correcting abnormal conditions associated with particular mineral or vitamin deficiencies. A good example of the real value of certain minerals is the treatment of the disease of cattle known as milk fever, which is associated with a calcium deficiency. This condition responds almost immediately to injections of sterile calcium compounds into the veins or under the skin. On the other hand, unscrupulous manufacturers of mineral mixtures and vitamin preparations have attempted, by advertising, to create the unwarranted and misleading impression that products of this nature are of value in the control of infectious diseases and worm infestation.

In recent years internal parasites of animals have received considerable attention from veterinary investigators in this country as well as elsewhere. A number of specific drug treatments have been discovered, particularly by the United States Bureau of Animal Industry. A notable example is the new drug phenothiazine. No known drug or combination of drugs, however, will remove all species of worms from all species of animals. As a rule, these drugs are specific in their effects in each species of animal for each species of worm.

Laymen commonly believe that because a drug is effective for certain types of worms in one animal it will be equally effective for similar types of worms in other animals. This is a mistaken idea. The drug arecoline hydrobromide, for example, is effective in the removal of the common species of tapeworms from dogs, but it has not been found to be effective in the removal of the common species of tapeworms infesting chickens. Another example is the drug nicotine, or powdered tobacco containing nicotine, which has proved to be effective for the removal of large roundworms from poultry but has not been found to be of any value in removing large roundworms from hogs, dogs, or horses.

Livestock and poultry raisers have been more or less familiar with the activities of the Food and Drug Administration in the enforcement of the Food and Drugs Act of 1906. In the past 15 years, the Administration has issued approximately 500 Notices of Judgment concerning misbranded livestock remedies on which seizure and prosecution cases were terminated by the Federal courts. During this time, thousands of samples have been collected and analyzed. Many of these were simple inexpensive drugs disguised in different ways. Others contained many drugs in minute amounts. One preparation consisted of cornstarch with just enough potassium permanganate to make a pink solution in water. It was represented as a treatment for Bang's disease and sold for $5 to $12 a package.

The article had no value whatever in the treatment of any disease. This case, like many similar cases, was referred by the Food and Drug Administration to the Department of Justice for criminal prosecution. While in most of the Food and Drug cases the defendant enters a plea of guilty, the case referred to was contested by the defendant and tried before a jury, which found him guilty of misbranding his product.

Such activities of the Food and Drug Administration have resulted in the disappearance from interstate channels of misbranded drug remedies represented to be effective for the prevention and treatment of Bang's disease, mastitis or garget, sterility or breeding troubles, hog cholera, swine fever, hog influenza, "necro" (necrotic enteritis), mixed infections, influenza of horses, horse distemper, strangles, sleeping sickness of horses, fowl cholera, chickenpox, coccidiosis, roup, bronchitis, fowl paralysis, pullorum disease, blackhead of turkeys, distemper, running fits, and blacktongue of dogs, and the prevention of intestinal worms.

RECENT FOOD AND DRUG LEGISLATION

On June 25, 1938, Congress enacted the new Federal Food, Drug, and Cosmetic Act designed to replace the act of 1906 and to provide for more effective control. The Food and Drug Administration, which is charged with the enforcement of this act, was transferred on June 30, 1940, from the Department of Agriculture to the Federal Security Agency.

Farmers should know that the Federal Food, Drug, and Cosmetic Act gives the Food and Drug Administration no authority to regulate veterinary remedies sold within the State in which they are manufactured and no control over advertising matter distributed separately from the product. The recently enacted Wheeler-Lea Act, which is enforced by the Federal Trade Commission, does give that Commission authority to regulate advertising of foods, drugs, and cosmetics for man or animals; and the Post Office Department has authority to prevent fraudulent use of the mails in the sale of livestock and poultry remedies.

The Food, Drug, and Cosmetic Act of 1938 contains several new provisions which should be of interest to the purchasing public.

The term "device" under the new act is defined to mean "instruments, apparatus, and contrivances, including their components, parts, and accessories, intended (1) for use in the diagnosis, cure, mitigation, treatment, or prevention of disease in man or other animals; (2) to affect the structure or any function of the body of man or other animals."

For example, owners of dogs have been led to believe that certain chemically treated, copper-lined collars when worn by dogs will prevent or cure mange. For cattle wooden plugs or metal tubes intended to be inserted into the wombs of cows have been represented as a means of correcting breeding troubles. Such devices are not only of no value but may even be injurious.

Before any new drug can legitimately be shipped in interstate commerce, the manufacturer is required under the act to file an application with the Administrator of the Federal Security Agency, giving a full report of investigations that have been made to show whether or not the drug is safe for use. Interstate shipments of drugs dangerous to the health of livestock and poultry when used in the dosage or with the frequency or duration prescribed, recommended, or suggested in the labeling thereof are prohibited. The act requires the labeling of drugs and devices to bear warnings against probable misuse which may be dangerous to health; it also requires special precautionary labeling for drugs that are liable to deterioration. The act also prohibits interstate traffic in drugs that have been prepared or handled under insanitary conditions whereby they may have been contaminated with filth or that may have rendered the contents injurious to health. Drug remedies when shipped in interstate commerce must bear in a conspicuous manner on the main or principal display panel of the label the common or usual name of each active ingredient, including quantities or proportions of certain specified drugs. The label also must bear an accurate statement of the quantity of the contents in terms of weight, measure, or numerical count and the name and address of the manufacturer, packer, or distributor. By one of the most important provisions of the act a drug is deemed misbranded if its labeling is false or misleading in any particular. Since livestock and poultry feeds also are subject to the Federal Food, Drug, and Cosmetic Act, the Food and Drug Administration actively cooperates with the State feed officials in the removal of adulterated or misbranded feeds from the channels of interstate commerce.

Drugs represented as useful for the treatment and control of insects infesting animals, as well as disinfectants for contaminated premises or objects, are subject to the Federal Insecticide Act of 1910. These types of products when shipped in interstate commerce are under constant surveillance to see that they will do all that is claimed for them in the labeling material. Like the Food, Drug, and Cosmetic Act, the Insecticide Act gives the Federal Government no authority to regulate such products when sold within the State in which they are manufactured or over advertising material distributed separately from the product. The Insecticide Act was formerly enforced by the Food and Drug Administration, but since June 30, 1940, it has been enforced by the Agricultural Marketing Service of the Department of Agriculture.

Fighting Disease With Knowledge

BY D. S. BURCH [1]

"THE MOST SUCCESSFUL livestock owners appear to have prospered in large measure because they have built up effective barriers against disease, utilized veterinary services, and otherwise sought to reduce losses from the inroads of diseases and pests." Knowledge, the author holds, is the first step toward this kind of success, and supplying knowledge is one of the basic functions of public agencies concerned with disease control.

FACTUAL INFORMATION concerning animal diseases is of paramount value in dealing with them intelligently and effectively. Veterinary science has already provided such information concerning most animal maladies and is steadily adding to the reservoirs of useful scientific knowledge. Because science is altruistic, it has made its findings available to all people throughout the world, largely in the form of published literature.

VETERINARY EDUCATION AND SERVICE

To provide for the application of scientific knowledge through professional services, veterinary colleges have utilized published information in training students to engage in private practice or to serve the public in inspection work, research, or other technical capacities. In the school year 1941–42, 10 colleges in the United States and 2 in Canada offered degrees in veterinary medicine on

[1] D. S. Burch is Agricultural Editor and Assistant to the Chief of the Bureau of Animal Industry, in charge of publications and related information work.

completion of a 4-year course. In recent years enrollment in these 12 colleges has ranged from about 2,100 to 2,400 students, and their graduates have numbered 400 to 500 annually. All the other countries in the world have a total of 13 veterinary colleges and schools. Most veterinarians in the United States are graduates of the North American institutions. In all States the practice of veterinary medicine is regulated by laws with which veterinarians must comply before they may legally pursue their profession. In most States applicants must pass examinations or licensing tests in order to engage in veterinary practice.

According to census data and supplemental estimates, the United States has approximately 12,000 veterinarians, of whom about two-thirds are in private practice. The remainder are engaged in Federal, State, county, and municipal inspection activities or research, teaching, or commercial work. In relation to the number of veterinarians it is noteworthy that there are approximately 5 million livestock producers in the United States and that the number of cattle, horses, swine, sheep, and goats is normally about 200 million. On the basis of 8,000 practicing veterinarians, there is thus, in round numbers, only 1 veterinarian to every 625 livestock owners, and to every 25,000 animals. Nor do these comparisons include the veterinary needs of the extensive poultry industry or of thousands of pet animals, notably dogs and cats, for which hundreds of well-equipped veterinary hospitals are maintained.

DIFFUSION OF KNOWLEDGE
A BASIC PUBLIC POLICY

From the foregoing data it is clear that the services of research workers and practicing veterinarians must be greatly extended if current knowledge concerning livestock health is to be most beneficially applied. Moreover, the knowledge is constantly increasing. In dealing with this condition, the Bureau of Animal Industry and other agencies of the United States Department of Agriculture have long fostered the policy of sponsoring not only veterinary education and research, but also the distribution of useful knowledge in those fields to all interested persons.

To obtain wide and prompt diffusion of information, the Bureau utilizes at least 10 main channels, comprising publications, extension agencies, motion pictures, lantern slides, film strips, posters, exhibits, public demonstrations and addresses, and radio broadcasts. Veterinarians and other specialists of the Bureau have prepared approximately 100 publications dealing with animal diseases and parasites, including those of poultry. Periodic revision keeps the information up to date. Other Department agencies and State experiment stations, having similar information policies, likewise have issued numerous publications and other material.

In contrast to the specific personal services rendered by veterinarians, the information distributed through publications and other such means is usually of a more general character. It is intended chiefly to familiarize livestock owners and others with the characteristics of diseases, their dangers, the importance of prevention, and the value of sound, tested methods in dealing with them. It emphasizes the need and value of qualified veterinary services as compared with methods that are wasteful, ineffective, and sometimes cruel. One result of information services has been a greater familiarity on the part of the general public—consumers as well as producers—with animal diseases transmissible to human beings. Rabies, tuberculosis, anthrax, and trichinosis are typical examples of such diseases. Constructive legislation for the protection of both man and animals has resulted from this greater knowledge.

TYPES OF INFORMATIONAL MATERIAL

In general, the most convenient sources of information on veterinary and livestock subjects are Federal and State publications. Most of them are supplied on request, either free or at nominal cost. They may also be consulted in libraries, in the offices of county agents, and in veterinary institutions. Publications on animal diseases or related subjects are of three general types: (1) So-called popular publications intended for laymen, (2) technical papers intended for veterinarians and research workers, and (3) official reports and similar publications dealing with such matters as the status of animal diseases, the progress of eradication work, and losses caused by disease; this last type of publication is commonly distributed only to public officials and practicing veterinarians, but it is available also to other interested persons.

Exhibits, lantern slides, film strips, and posters acquaint the public with pertinent facts concerning animal diseases and veterinary services. Pictorial presentation is especially suitable for showing typical symptoms of diseases. A collection of 12 veterinary posters, known as the Livestock Health Series, issued by the Bureau of Animal Industry, has met with favor among both professional workers and livestock owners.

On frequent occasions veterinarians and officials engaged in extension work have cooperated in arranging for demonstrations to familiarize livestock owners with the characteristics of diseases in combating which community cooperation is desirable. Commonly the extension worker arranges for the meeting and explains the purpose and value of the service to be rendered. The veterinarian then conducts the demonstration and supplies technical information.

In conducting tick-eradication work in the South, much of the preliminary information was conveyed by motion pictures shown by means of a portable projector (fig. 1). Pictures shown in this way proved to be highly effective also in combating tuberculosis, hog cholera, and several other diseases. A widely distributed talking motion picture, Livestock and Mankind, produced by the Department of Agriculture, is essentially an illustrated lecture by John R. Mohler, Chief of the Bureau of Animal Industry. It deals in large measure with the development and uses of scientific knowledge concerning livestock. Motion pictures commonly serve two useful purposes—

they help to draw a crowd as well as furnishing information in an interesting and often dramatic manner.

In recent years radio has been a useful informational ally of veterinary science. The speed of radio transmission makes it especially valuable when dealing with outbreaks of dangerous animal maladies. The radio was used successfully in warning livestock owners of the presence of foot-and-mouth disease in the United States during the outbreaks of 1924, 1925, and 1929. In dealing with such a highly

FIGURE 1.—Preparing to show a motion picture on cattle-tick eradication, projected by portable equipment. This method has proved to be highly effective in furthering public understanding of Department disease-eradication projects and obtaining the necessary cooperation.

infectious malady, a saving of even an hour's time is important. A broadcast notification may prevent the marketing of diseased animals or their distribution on large range pastures where they could expose other animals to infection.

In the radio field, the Farm Credit Administration has distributed four transcriptions of talks on veterinary subjects presented in human-interest style. Prepared on disk records, the talks, averaging about 15 minutes each, deal with hog cholera, cattle ticks, foot-and-mouth disease, and Federal meat inspection. Several hundred radio stations have either already used the transcriptions or applied for them. In recent years also, officers in charge of arrangements at meetings of veterinary medical associations have arranged for the broadcasting of important addresses.

Another type of information concerning animal diseases is contained in a series of handbooks relating to agriculture sponsored by

Federal and State officials. These publications contain the names and addresses of officials and agencies prepared to render services along various lines; many States, for example, maintain laboratories where specimens of diseased tissues and small animals may be examined as a basis for diagnosis and remedial measures. As an aid in acquainting livestock owners with effective dips and disinfectants, the Bureau of Animal Industry issues lists of such products as have been approved for official use, giving the names of the various commercial brands and specifying the diseases or parasites against which each product is effective.

As a guide to persons contemplating buying or selling transactions that will involve interstate shipments of livestock, the Bureau of Animal Industry has prepared a compilation entitled "State Sanitary Requirements Governing the Admission of Livestock." This publication, printed in convenient handbook form, contains digests of State laws on this subject and gives the requirements of each State with respect to necessary certificates, tests, inspections, and dippings applicable to various species of domestic animals, including dogs and poultry.

Diseases common to horses and cattle are discussed also in two Congressional documents entitled "Diseases of the Horse" and "Diseases of Cattle," which may be obtained from United States Senators and Representatives who have quotas of the books for distribution or by purchase from the Superintendent of Documents, Government Printing Office, Washington, D. C.

As a part of the cooperative Federal-State campaigns against bovine tuberculosis and brucellosis (Bang's disease), inspectors who make tests for these diseases furnish considerable information to livestock owners, both verbally and through printed matter left with them. Combating brucellosis necessitates a number of sanitary precautions to prevent reinfection, and the veterinary inspectors discuss the various requirements with each livestock owner and obtain from him a signed agreement indicating that the owner understands the procedures to be followed and will carry them out. In campaigns that involve the testing of thousands of herds, these personal contacts have far-reaching informational value.

To help bring about a broader knowledge of Federal meat inspection, the Bureau of Animal Industry, which conducts this service, has provided its inspectors with educational literature, including the text for a 10-minute talk on the subject. The same material is available to lecturers and other persons in need of authoritative information on safeguards to the meat food supply.

LARGE EXPENDITURES FOR INEFFECTIVE REMEDIES

A further service that science seeks to render is that of cautioning the public against expenditures for drugs and nostrums that are worthless in preventing or treating animal maladies. Although most manufacturers distribute dependable goods and advertise their merits truthfully, others have been found by the Food and Drug Administration of the Federal Security Agency to make exaggerated claims wholly unwarranted in the light of scientific knowledge and tests. Some of the advertising has led worried stock owners to believe that the so-called remedies would cure diseases for which there is no known cure.

Estimates of the money spent in the United States for ineffective proprietary remedies for animal diseases indicate that the amount still exceeds 10 million dollars a year. This huge expenditure is largely wasted. The spending of half or even a smaller fraction of the amount for veterinary services would be vastly more productive in accomplishing the desired results. It is highly important also to distinguish clearly between the purpose for which different biological products and chemicals are intended. Some are diagnostic, their sole value being to detect disease conditions; other have immunizing value; and still others, although not many, have curative properties. In the treatment of internal parasites, products known as anthelmintics, when properly used, are beneficial in eliminating all or most of the parasites from affected animals, but periodic use may be necessary to prevent further infestation.

Accurate diagnosis of a disease or ailment should always precede any attempt at treatment, both in order that the treatment may be intelligently applied and to save the expense of administering ineffective or needless remedies. Recently a Federal veterinarian investigated promiscuous dosing of sheep, allegedly for worm parasites, in an area in the Southwest. Inspection of the animals together with several post mortem examinations showed that the parasites for which treatment was being given did not exist in that area. The incident illustrates how time, money, and labor may be needlessly expended.

PRACTICAL VALUE OF ANIMAL-DISEASE INFORMATION

Persons about to engage in raising livestock or those who have recently undertaken it should inform themselves as promptly as possible concerning diseases, parasites, and other ailments likely to affect the species of animal concerned. This is desirable both to safeguard the stock owner's individual investment and as a protection for all livestock in the community.

Conservative estimates indicate that animal diseases and parasites cost the average livestock owner about $40 a year, partly through the death of animals (fig. 2) but even more through impaired efficiency (fig. 3), slower growth, and reduced market value. Animals that are seriously affected with disease at some time in their lives generally cost more to raise and bring less money when sold than consistently healthy stock.

The most successful livestock owners appear to have prospered in large measure because they have built up effective barriers against disease, utilized veterinary services, and otherwise sought to reduce losses from the inroads of diseases and pests. The stockmen who have paid the heaviest toll in disease losses are usually those least able to sustain such losses.

It is especially desirable that livestock owners should be informed regarding diseases that spread rapidly and are likely to endanger animals on neighboring premises. For example, any condition suspected of being foot-and-mouth disease should be reported immediately, by telephone or telegraph, to the nearest veterinarian (fig. 4). Success in keeping this disease out of the country or immediately stamping out its invasions means large savings to the live-

FIGURE 2.—Disease takes its toll. Typical appearance of a herd of swine when hog cholera strikes. Too late now for treatment; the loss will be several hundred dollars.

stock industry. Stockmen are therefore urged to familiarize themselves with the characteristics of this and other serious maladies.

In dealing with certain diseases that develop rapidly and can be prevented by immunization, such as hog cholera, prompt action is essential. When outbreaks have appeared on neighboring farms prompt application of the preventive serum treatment may be the means of saving large numbers of animals not previously immunized.

The practice of leaving dead animals unburied is especially dangerous for the reason that dogs or birds may feed on the carcasses and carry the infection far and wide. When animals are crowded together, the chances for diseases and parasites to spread are increased.

BENEFITS OF BROAD PUBLIC UNDERSTANDING

It has been shown that livestock owners in the United States have readily available (1) extensive factual material that acquaints them with the principal disease problems and methods of prevention and control, and (2) the personal services of veterinarians engaged in private practice or representing local, State, or Federal agencies.

The Bureau of Animal Industry does not concur in the belief occasionally expressed that information on animal diseases should be distributed only or primarily to veterinarians and applied by them in response to calls for their services. As a public agency, the Bureau

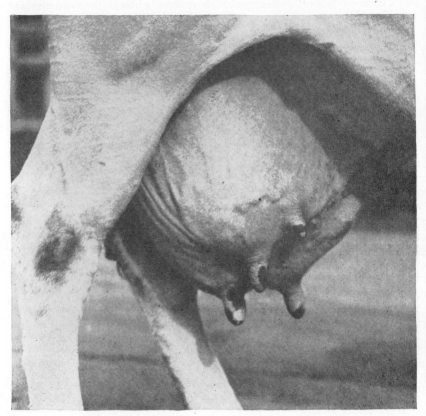

FIGURE 3.—A case of chronic mastitis. Only about half of this udder is functioning. Dead animals by no means represent all the losses caused by disease.

is prepared to furnish information to all interested persons so that the largest possible number will be adequately informed concerning the problems underlying animal health, for these problems have a bearing on public safety and public welfare. This policy is deemed constructive from a public standpoint and fair to livestock owners and veterinary practitioners. It is also in line with what is done by public agencies and by the medical profession in relation to human diseases. Official publications concerning livestock health have emphasized that the diagnosis of disease, the treatment of animals, and any necessary surgery should be performed by veterinarians who have a thorough knowledge of animal physiology and are trained to render such services. Under this system the informational work and veterinary services supplement each other in an effective manner.

The net result is to provide, on the one hand, a dependable basis for preventing diseases and, on the other, the professional selection and use

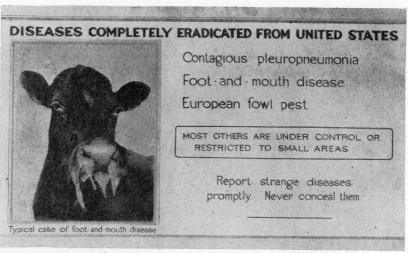

FIGURE 4.—An exhibit panel designed to acquaint livestock owners with the symptoms of foot-and-mouth disease so that they may recognize and report this foreign malady promptly should it appear in the United States.

of proper procedures for combating them when they occur. Under the policies outlined, the production of domestic animals in the United States, already a sound enterprise, is proceeding with increasing safety.

At the time this book went to press, the drugs and other materials mentioned in various articles—chiefly as disinfectants, insecticides, and anthelmintics—were still available for veterinary and medical use. Under war conditions, however, it is possible that some of these materials may become scarce or unavailable. In that case, the reader should obtain professional advice from the Department of Agriculture, the State experiment station, a local veterinarian, or the county agent as to available substitutes.

236

Tuberculosis and Its Eradication

BY A. E. WIGHT, ELMER LASH,
H. M. O'REAR, AND A. B. CRAWFORD [1]

PRACTICALLY ALL animals are subject to tuberculosis, particularly cattle, hogs, and poultry. Human beings, especially children, can get it from cow's milk. Here is a careful account of the disease in livestock, including the results of the relentless campaign of eradication that between 1917 and 1942 has reduced the number of tuberculous cattle in the United States from 1 animal in every 20 to less than 1 in 200.

TUBERCULOSIS is one of the oldest of the recognized diseases of man and animals. Examination of Egyptian mummies and of the earliest historical writings furnishes evidence that this disease undoubtedly existed at least from the time men began to live in compact social groups. The ancient Mosaic laws as written in the Talmud classed any animal carcass showing adhesions between the lungs and the pleura as unsatisfactory for edible purposes. Since pleural adhesions often accompany tuberculosis of the lungs, the possibility of transmission of the disease from animal to man may have been recognized at that time.

CAUSE—THE TUBERCLE BACILLUS

In 1882, the eminent German scientist Robert Koch, making use of improved methods of preparing culture media for growing bac-

---

[1] A. E. Wight is Chief, Elmer Lash is Assistant Chief, and H. M. O'Rear is Senior Veterinarian, Tuberculosis Eradication Division, and A. B. Crawford is Assistant Director of the Animal Disease Station, Bureau of Animal Industry.

teria and staining them so they might be seen clearly under the microscope, definitely proved that a germ could be obtained from a tubercle and grown artificially, that this germ on being inoculated into another animal would reproduce tuberculosis, and that an identical germ could be recovered from tubercles in the inoculated animal. This organism was at first called the Koch bacillus and later the tubercle bacillus. It is now known technically as *Mycobacterium tuberculosis*.

After this extremely important discovery tuberculosis received the attention of research workers throughout the world, and additional facts were disclosed in rapid succession. It was shown that practically every species of animal could be affected and that the disease in each species was very similar in character, always ending in slow wasting of the body tissues. It was at first believed that only one kind of tubercle bacillus was involved in tuberculosis in all species, but later it was shown that the kind found in man could not produce progressive disease in many animals, that the tubercle bacillus in cattle was different from the human type, and still later, that a third type existed in poultry. The three kinds of tubercle bacillus were classed as the human, bovine, and avian (bird) types.

The tubercle bacillus is a rod-shaped organism varying in size from 1½ to 4 microns long, which means that it would take 6,000 to 16,000 laid end to end to measure 1 inch. The bacillus has a waxy capsule which is not readily penetrated by the various stains used in bacteriological studies. Micro-organisms of the genus *Mycobacterium* are acid-fast, which makes them very difficult to stain, but once they are stained the dye cannot be removed by acid treatment as it can from most other germs. Thus, if the micro-organisms in a sample are stained with a red dye and then treated with acid and counterstained with a blue dye the tubercle bacilli will show red, while the other (non-acid-fast) organisms show blue.

The tubercle bacillus grows very slowly on culture media. On the first culture, it may be 1 month and sometimes 2 months before a colony growth can be seen by the unaided eye. Most other organisms show colony growth in 24 to 48 hours.

On a culture medium the three types of tubercle bacilli, human, bovine, and avian, produce colony growths different from one another. The growth of the human type appears thick and wrinkled; that of the bovine type, sparse, rough, and dry; while that of the avian type is heavy, smooth, moist, and glistening.

METHOD OF TRANSMISSION

Tubercle bacilli usually gain entrance into the body by way of the mouth in contaminated food or water, or they may be breathed into the nasal chambers and the back of the mouth and swallowed. Some scientists believe they may also be breathed directly into the lungs. A cow becomes a spreader when the tuberculous excretion from the lungs, reaching the mouth, is washed into the water trough when the cow drinks, subjecting other cattle using the trough to the most dangerous kind of exposure. When the tuberculous sputum is swallowed, the tubercle bacilli in it are passed through the intestines unaltered, and the dung is extremely infectious. Stagnant pools into which cows drop their dung thus offer means by which the disease may be perpetuated and spread, as tubercle bacilli in such pools may remain alive for a year and sometimes longer. Small streams may likewise become contaminated with tubercle bacilli. Around hayracks dung may become mixed with particles of hay. A single feeding of milk from a dam with a tuberculous udder may result in a calf's becoming tuberculous.

PARTS OF THE BODY AFFECTED

Tuberculosis exists in many forms, depending on the part of the body in which the organism lodges or becomes localized. Human beings may have lupus, or tuberculosis of the skin; scrofula, or tuberculosis of the lymph nodes; bone and joint tuberculosis; tuberculosis of the linings of the brain, or tuberculous meningitis; and so on. In animals, however, the organ most commonly affected is the lungs, and it is tuberculosis of the lungs in most species on which the spread of the disease, from man to man or animal to animal, depends. In poultry, the liver and spleen are most commonly affected, and tuberculosis is spread from the birds' droppings. In cows the udder may become infected when the disease is chronic, and tubercle bacilli in large numbers may be given off in the milk.

All organs and sections of the body have specialized glands called lymph nodes which filter out bacteria from the lymph stream and thus hinder the spread of infection to another part of the body. These lymph nodes are often the site of the first localization of tubercle bacilli. The nodes in the throat and neck have the first opportunity to become infected, next the mesenteric nodes, which drain the intestines, and next the lungs and their adjacent lymph nodes. Tubercles in other sections of the body are usually the result of the spread of infection from a primary center, or focus.

FORMATION OF TUBERCLES

When tubercle bacilli lodge in any part of the body, certain blood cells are attracted to the site and attempt to ingest them. Its waxy capsule renders the bacillus very resistant to destruction. Other blood cells congregate around the area and form a protective wall against the spread of the tubercle bacilli. Thus a tubercle, or morbid nodule, is formed. If the wall, or encapsulation, becomes dense on all sides, the tubercle remains stationary and is called an arrested lesion. Calcium salts may be deposited in the tubercle, transforming it into a gritty or calcified lesion. If the lesion is very small, it might even be absorbed. If the tubercle bacilli are not checked, the tubercle enlarges on the outside, developing into what is known as a proliferative, or spreading, lesion. Bacilli may escape from this mass and cause the formation of new tubercles, either adjacent to the old tubercle or remote from it. During the growth of a tubercle in the lungs, a terminal branch of a bronchus, or air channel, may be surrounded. The poisons secreted by the bacilli tend to soften the inner portions of the tubercle, and they may be expelled into a bronchus, thence to the trachea, and then coughed up. A tubercle thus broken down is known as an exudative type of lesion.

Tubercles vary in number and character in different individuals, according to the resistance offered. After ·localization of tubercle bacilli in the body, the resultant tubercle may completely disappear in a few weeks or months, or it may cause the fulminative type of the disease, which spreads rapidly and results in death within a few weeks or months. Usually the tubercle remains in the body as a walled-off, or encapsulated, tumor, and it may remain as such for the life of the host. At any time, however, such a tubercle may become active owing to lowered resistance and be a focus for the spread of the disease to other parts of the body.

The time elapsing between exposure to tubercle bacilli and the development of a tubercle is called the period of incubation. The length of this period is quit variable. In the first place, tubercle bacilli multiply very slowly in the animal body, and infection develops only when these germs have multiplied to a certain number in the spot where the tubercle is formed. Depending on various conditions, it may be one to several months before the disease can be detected by the tuberculin test (to be explained later). When tubercle bacilli once gain a foothold, the disease is usually very slowly progressive, and it may be months or even years before the general physical condition becomes noticeably impaired.

SYMPTOMS

Tuberculosis may be suspected when an animal shows a gradual loss of weight and condition. In cattle affected with tuberculosis of the lungs, a chronic cough develops. It is remarkable, however, that cattle that appear to be in prime condition may be grossly tuberculous and spreading the disease.

Poultry may be suspected of being tuberculous when some of the flock show lameness, thinness, especially in the breast muscles, and paleness of combs and wattles.

In swine the disease may not be suspected owing to the fact that the great majority of the animals are marketed during their first or second year of life and that the disease only rarely spreads from hog to hog. It is in older animals that the condition usually becomes apparent by a gradual loss in weight and condition or by enlargement of joints.

SUSCEPTIBILITY OF ANIMALS AND MAN

Some animals are susceptible to infection with one type only of the tubercle bacillus, others may be susceptible to two types, and still others to all three.

Cattle are the chief hosts and likewise the chief disseminators of the bovine tubercle bacillus. Only rarely do they develop lesions or visible tubercles as a result of exposure to infected poultry or a tuberculous human being.

Horses and mules are very resistant to all three types.

Chickens are susceptible only to the avian tubercle bacillus.

Sheep and goats are commonly reported in the press as being immune, or practically so, to tuberculosis, and the post mortem records of the Bureau of Animal Industry indicate that such reports are substantially correct. A few flocks of goats and, rarely, a sheep or two have been found to be infected with the bovine organism, and sheep that have been in close contact with infected poultry have in a few instances shown lesions caused by the avian organism. As a whole, however, these two species are very resistant to tuberculosis.

Swine may be infected by all three types of the tubercle bacillus. The bovine type causes the severest disease, but in the United States probably nine-tenths of the tuberculous lesions in swine are caused by the avian organism. Lesions in swine caused by the human tubercle bacillus are not of the progressive type and usually remain localized in lymph nodes of the head or intestine. The feeding habits of swine provide for ample exposure to all three types: To the bovine type in cattle-feeding lots, where the swine eat cow dung; to the avian type on farms where there are tuberculous chickens which may soil the ground or where the farmer may throw his dead chickens to the hogs; and to the human type from uncooked garbage or from the sputum of a tuberculous attendant.

Dogs may become infected with human tuberculosis, the usual source of exposure being a tuberculous owner, but they are only slightly susceptible to bovine tuberculosis.

Cats are more susceptible to the bovine tubercle bacillus than to the human type. Tuberculosis in cats is usually a result of their being fed contaminated cow's milk.

Domesticated rabbits are susceptible to both the bovine and avian types of tubercle bacilli but are very resistant to the human type. Guinea pigs, on the the other hand, are susceptible to both bovine and human tubercle bacilli, but not to avian. The rabbit and guinea pig thus are useful to the investigator in determining the type of infection in various tuberculous specimens submitted for examination.

Man is, of course, susceptible to the human type of tubercle bacillus and is slightly so to the bovine, but he is very resistant to the avian type. Human tuberculosis still continues to be one of the leading death-causing diseases, although great strides have been made by public health agencies, medical commissions, and other interested groups in preventing exposure, detecting early cases, and hospitalizing affected persons. The dangerous person is one who has an open lung lesion. A careless individual so affected may spread thousands of tubercle bacilli daily as possible sources of infection to others in expectorating and coughing openly. In coughing, hundreds of tiny droplets, which may contain tubercle bacilli, are expelled, and these may be inhaled by other persons or may fall on food to be eaten. Drinking cups and eating utensils may be sources of exposure unless properly sterilized.

Though man is much more resistant to the bovine tubercle bacillus than to the human, if exposure is sufficiently severe and often enough repeated, tuberculosis may be produced in human beings by the bovine organism in every form that is produced by the human type. This is attested by the statistics of many European countries where a relatively large proportion of cows are tuberculous.

Children, especially infants, are much less resistant to bovine tuberculosis than adults. Before 1917 vital statistics of various States showed that hundreds of children died annually of tuberculous meningitis and miliary (rapidly developing) tuberculosis contracted from cow's milk, and many others became affected with scrofula and tuberculosis of bones and joints.

Unpasteurized milk of tuberculous cows is practically the only source of the bovine type of infection in children. The bovine tuberculosis-eradication program has not only resulted in a marked decrease in tuberculosis in livestock but has also prevented hundreds of children from dying or becoming hopeless cripples as a result of this disease.

Only 35 cases of tuberculosis in man reputed to be caused by the avian type of tubercle bacillus have been reported from all over the world, so it is quite apparent either that man is very resistant to this type of infection or that sufficient exposure is lacking. The meat of poultry is not eaten raw. In some instances, eggs from tuberculous hens contain tubercle bacilli, but as a rule diseased hens lay few or no eggs. Furthermore, eggs are usually cooked, so that very few virulent tubercle bacilli are thus consumed. Poultry tuberculosis is prevalent in some sections of this country, however, and the possibility that repeated exposure might cause disease in persons handling such flocks should be a further reason why an owner should take steps to eradicate this disease from his poultry.

In résumé, it may be stated that both man and animals show more or less resistance to tuberculosis, but there are marked contrasts among species in resistance and susceptibility to the various types of tubercle bacilli, and curiously enough, exceptional individuals within a species may react differently to the various types. The degree of exposure also has a bearing on whether or not tuberculosis develops. Some individuals might withstand a moderate but not a massive or repeated exposure. The rapidity of the spread of infection within the body likewise depends upon the resistance of the individual and the degree of exposure. For instance, an adult human being might drink infected cow's milk several times without becoming infected, whereas an infant drinking the same amount of such milk would be much more likely to develop the disease. In the United States, where the incidence of tuberculous infection in cattle is now less than 0.5 percent and pasteurization of milk is extensively practiced, there is practically no recently acquired tuberculosis in human beings resulting from the drinking of cow's milk. In marked contrast, in one European country, where fully 25 percent of the cattle are tuberculous and pasteurization is not extensively practiced, it has been estimated that over 5 percent of all deaths in man from tuberculosis of the lungs and 25 percent of the deaths from nonpulmonary forms are due to bovine tuberculosis.

DIAGNOSIS

In many infectious diseases the body becomes sensitized, or allergic, to the infecting germ and its products. This phenomenon is very marked in tuberculosis. Tubercle bacilli may be grown in a broth medium and the broth filtered from the tubercle bacilli and concentrated, making a product called tuberculin. If tuberculin is injected into an animal having tuberculosis, a reaction to the substance takes place. The injection of tuberculin subcutaneously, or under the skin, is followed within a few hours by a rise in temperature, or fever, which gradually subsides. Injection made intradermically, or into the skin, causes a reddened swelling at the site of injection 24 to 72 hours later. If tuberculin is dropped on the eye (applied ophthalmically) a milky discharge from the eye appears within a few hours. The degree of infection has no relation to the extent of the reaction, for a lesion of tuberculosis so small that it can hardly be seen with the naked eye may develop a sensitization to tuberculin as marked as that caused by a lesion a hundred times larger. All three tests are almost equal in efficiency, but the intradermic test is preferred for cattle testing and is the only one used for human beings. Diagnosis may be made also by animal inoculation or culture of diseased processes or exudates, and in man by X-ray photographs.

PREVENTION AND CONTROL EFFORTS

In 1917 about 1 cow in every 20 in the United States, on an average, had tuberculosis. In 1940 the official tests showed that less than 1 in every 200 cows was affected. This decrease in infection is due chiefly to the slaughtering of infected animals, but some credit, especially for the prevention of the spread of the disease to other herds, is due to the education of stockmen regarding additions to their herds. Cattle should be admitted to a herd only if they react negatively to the tuberculin test, and they should preferably be obtained from a herd certified to be free from tuberculosis.

Some farmers buy separated milk from creameries for feeding hogs or calves. This is an undesirable practice unless the milk is pasteurized (heated to 145° F. for 30 minutes) or heated for a few minutes at the boiling point and then cooled before being fed.

Small, slow-flowing streams which pass through or drain an infected farm present a hazard to livestock having access to such a stream lower down. Such a stream should be fenced off.

Community pastures are also a hazard unless it is known that all cattle grazing on the pasture have been tuberculin-tested and found to be negative to the test.

The shipment of cattle by rail, especially if they are loaded or unloaded in public stockyards, and to or from fairs or sales, may result in exposure to tuberculosis. Such cattle should be tested with tuberculin 3 months after being returned to the home premises.

There is no cure for tuberculosis. In man, the disease may be arrested by hospitalization and complete rest, but in domestic animals a comparable procedure is not effective, nor would it be practical if it were effective owing to the cost involved in comparison with the value of an individual animal. Since practically all tuberculosis in domestic animals may be traced to cattle and poultry, freeing all livestock from this disease is a matter of eradicating tuberculosis from cattle and poultry.

Since 1917 the Bureau of Animal Industry has had in operation a Federal-State program for the eradication of bovine tuberculosis based on the test-and-slaughter plan with payment of indemnity for animals destroyed. The details of this campaign are explained later in this article. All States are now in the modified accredited status, that is, there is infection in less than 0.5 percent of the cattle in any State. With continued follow-up testing the disease should gradually approach the vanishing point (fig. 1). When tuberculous

FIGURE 1.—A tuberculosis-free accredited herd. Periodic tuberculin tests either determine that the herd is still free from the disease or detect any tuberculous animals before they become seriously affected and spread the disease.

cattle are removed as a result of a positive tuberculin test, the infected premises should be carefully cleaned and disinfected. The removal of manure is especially important. Direct sunlight kills the tubercle bacillus within a few minutes, but when the germs are covered with manure or soil they many remain alive for weeks or months.

Owing to the low cost of individual birds and the immense amount of labor involved in establishing a Federal program of eradication for poultry based on the test-and-slaughter plan, control work on avian tuberculosis has been chiefly educational. The county agricultural agent frequently participates. The subject of tuberculosis in poultry is being treated separately in this article, including a résumé of what the Federal Government has been able to accomplish in its control.

THE BOVINE TUBERCULOSIS ERADICATION CAMPAIGN

The campaign to eradicate bovine tuberculosis in the United States was inaugurated in May 1917. The principal course of action was the testing with tuberculin of all the dairy and breeding cattle of this country. On November 1, 1940, about 23½ years after the inauguration of the program, the last two remaining nonaccredited counties were officially declared to be in a modified accredited status. As a result, all of the 3,071 counties in the United States, and the Territories of Puerto Rico and the Virgin Islands, are now rated as modified accredited areas, signifying that bovine tuberculosis among the cattle in such areas has been reduced to less than 0.5 percent.

This accomplishment required approximately 232 million tuberculin tests and retests and the slaughter of about 3.8 million tuberculous animals discovered by these tests.

Although the disease was not evenly distributed throughout the country, it was found to be present to some extent in all States, with the greatest incidence in areas furnishing milk to the larger cities, particularly in the northern half of the country. During the testing by areas the disease was detected in 40

FIGURE 2.—Portion of cattle carcass showing numerous tuberculous lesions (indicated by arrows). Such carcasses are condemned and destroyed under Federal meat inspection.

to 80 percent of the cattle in some of the badly infected areas, and in a few exceptional instances the incidence of tuberculosis approached 100 percent of all the cattle in the area.

The effectiveness of bovine tuberculosis eradication is further reflected in the records of the Meat Inspection Division of the Bureau of Animal Industry, which reveal that, in 1917, of all the cattle slaughtered on regular kill in establishments maintaining Federal inspection, 49,214 carcasses, or 0.53 percent, were condemned or sterilized on account of tuberculosis (fig. 2). In 1940 this number was reduced to the condemnation and sterilization of 1,998 cattle, or 0.02 percent.

Incidentally, in 1918 there was a human tuberculosis mortality rate of 150 per 100,000 population. At present the human mortality from this insidious disease is considerably below 50 per 100,000 population. The eradication of bovine tuberculosis must be recognized as a factor contributing to this improved condition.

Since tuberculosis among cattle is now at a low point, all cattle must be regarded as highly susceptible to the disease, and for this reason, further protection of the livestock industry depends largely on maintaining adequate control until the disease has been completely eradicated. An inadequately protected, highly susceptible cattle population would afford ample opportunity for a rapid spread of the disease should it again gain a foothold.

The slaughtering establishments operating under State and Federal supervision furnish those in charge of tuberculosis eradication work with reports of cases where tuberculosis has been found in cattle and swine on the regular kill, and these reports have been of much assistance in locating centers of infection.

TUBERCULOSIS IN POULTRY

The poultry industry is facing a serious menace in the Central and North Central States because of the many flocks in that area that are extensively affected with tuberculosis. In some counties this disease exists on more than 75 percent of the farms and is causing great losses annually.

Tuberculosis in poultry was first recognized in this country about the beginning of the present century, but it was not known to be so widely distributed until about 1920, when veterinarians assigned to eradicating tuberculosis in cattle found many diseased flocks on the farms they visited in their routine work of testing cattle. This discovery resulted in a survey to determine the extent of the disease in various parts of the United States, and it was found to exist to an alarming degree in the Corn Belt, as shown in figure 3, while in the Eastern States and on the west coast, where poultry raising is practiced on a large scale, little tuberculosis was found.

A further study disclosed that the average farm flock was often heavily infected, whereas the large commercial flocks were comparatively free from the disease, even in the Central and North Central States. The investigations were continued to ascertain the reason for this, and it was found that on most of the farms where tuberculous chickens were discovered it was the practice to keep a large number of the hens until they were 2, 3, or 4 years of age, and in some instances much older, whereas in the commercial flocks few, if any, hens were kept for egg or meat production after they were 18 months old. It was also determined that hen hatching was practiced on many farms, while the commercial flocks were incubator-hatched.

Congress has made funds available with which to employ suitable personnel to assist farmers in freeing their flocks of tuberculosis, and

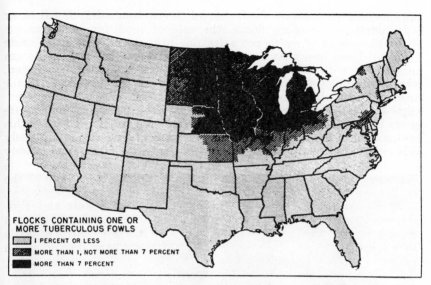

FLOCKS CONTAINING ONE OR
MORE TUBERCULOUS FOWLS
☐ I PERCENT OR LESS
▨ MORE THAN I, NOT MORE THAN 7 PERCENT
■ MORE THAN 7 PERCENT

FIGURE 3.—Approximate extent of avian tuberculosis in the United States on January 1, 1941.

progress is now being made in reducing the number of diseased flocks.

The disease is spread from flock to flock largely by the exchange of infected fowls. There is little danger of spreading it through the exchange of eggs.

The disease organism is taken into the body in feed and water. It may affect any part of the fowl, but in almost all that are extensively affected—and these are the source of the continued spread of the disease—the liver, spleen, and intestinal walls are involved, with the result that millions of the tubercle bacilli are present in the excretions. As flocks of chickens usually range over a comparatively small area, the yards and runways become polluted, especially near the poultry house.

No medicinal remedy is effective. In the management of a flock such as is maintained on the average midwestern farm for meat and egg production, it is advisable to follow a plan of raising a new flock on clean grounds and disposing of the old birds at the end of the laying season or when they are about 18 months of age. Since tuberculosis is only slowly progressive, a large majority will not have become spreaders if disposed of when they are 1 to 1½ years old. The disease may thus be materially reduced and even eradicated in a few years by this method of control. Since the tubercle bacillus may remain alive and virulent in a moist and dark protected place for as long as 2 years, sanitation plays a very important part in control and eradication. The poultry house should be thoroughly cleaned and disinfected and, if practical, moved to a new location. Where this is not possible, the runways should be used only 1 year, then plowed up and planted to some crop before being used again for chickens. A well-designed poultry house with

suitable equipment serves a valuable purpose in combating this disease.
In purebred breeding flocks, the sale of hens for slaughter at
about 18 months of age is not a feasible practice. However, in such
flocks all birds over that age that are kept should be subjected to an
annual test with avian tuberculin if the flock is located in an area
where tuberculosis is prevalent. This is done by injecting a small
drop of tuberculin into one wattle with a small needle and syringe
(fig. 4, *A*). The inoculated wattle becomes thickened within 48
hours if the bird is tuberculous (fig. 4, *B*). All reacting birds should
be disposed of immediately and the proper sanitary measures applied.
Where infected poultry have the run of the entire farm, avian tuber-

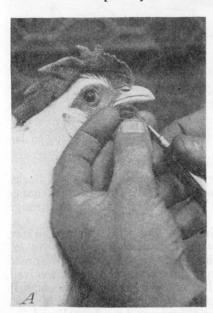 

FIGURE 4.—Detection of avian tuberculosis by the tuberculin test. *A*, Injecting
the tuberculin into the right wattle. *B*, The swelling of the wattle indicates the
presence of the disease. If the bird is healthy no swelling occurs.

culosis may be spread to other animals, especially swine, and this
results in considerable loss to the owner through condemnations in
the packing house. Many hatcheries offer a higher price for incubator
eggs from flocks free from tuberculosis, which is an added incentive
for disposing of reacting birds.

TUBERCULOSIS IN SWINE

The losses due to tuberculosis in swine have been reduced by the
cooperative campaign to eradicate tuberculosis in cattle. However,
considerable losses are still caused by the condemnation of swine
carcasses and parts affected with the avian type of the tubercle
bacillus.

Numerous reports are received from field stations on the extensive losses of swine due to infection acquired from poultry. The following case is typical: A large percentage of a lot of swine slaughtered in a midwestern establishment under Federal supervision were found to be affected with tuberculosis. The swine were traced to the farm on which they were raised, but tuberculin tests of all the cattle on the farm were negative, indicating that the cattle were not affected with tuberculosis. A tuberculin test was also applied to all the breeding swine on the farm, and all were classed as negative to the test. Seventy-five head of poultry were then injected with tuberculin, and 32 reactors were revealed. The owner was surprised to find that his poultry were so heavily infected and asked to have one of the birds killed so that he might learn more about the disease. The post mortem examination of the fowl revealed an extensive case of tuberculosis. The owner cleaned and disinfected his place and restocked with pullets raised on clean ground.

Tuberculosis in swine is not spread from animal to animal unless the udder of the sow is infected, which is seldom the case. The control and eradication of the disease in swine therefore depend on eradicating tuberculosis in the cattle and poultry on the premises. Sanitation should be practiced, and feed lots should be rotated at least once each year. In purebred breeding herds tuberculin tests with avian and mammalian tuberculins may be used to determine which animals are diseased and the reactors to such tests should be slaughtered under veterinary supervision.

Anthrax

BY C. D. STEIN [1]

THE SUDDENNESS with which anthrax strikes, the heavy toll it takes, the long life of the infection in the soil, and the many ways by which the disease may be spread make the problem of control a common cause of all livestock owners, says the author of this article. Others besides livestock owners are concerned, for anthrax is a deadly disease of man as well as of animals.

ANTHRAX, sometimes referred to as charbon or splenic fever, is an acute infectious febrile disease of livestock and man caused by a specific micro-organism which is known as the anthrax bacillus (*Bacillus anthracis*). In its most common form the disease usually presents a picture of acute blood poisoning (septicemia) and is characterized principally by its rapid onset and rapidly fatal course. From both an economic and a public-health standpoint, it is a dreaded disease against which every means of suppression needs to be exercised. The suddenness with which it strikes, the heavy toll it takes, the long life of the infection in the soil, and the many ways by which the disease may be spread make the problem of control a common cause to which every livestock owner should contribute. To this end, all persons concerned are in duty bound to put into effect every known measure of combating the disease and to cooperate to the fullest extent with the local veterinarian and livestock sanitary officials, who are charged with the responsibility of controlling diseases of livestock.

Anthrax is recognized as one of the oldest and most destructive diseases of animals recorded in history. Before the disease was known to be of an infectious nature and proper measures were taken to control it, the malady took a heavy toll among human beings and caused great losses of livestock in many countries.

Anthrax was the first of all infectious diseases of both man and the lower animals in which the causative agent was definitely demonstrated

---

[1] C. D. Stein is Veterinarian, Pathological Division, Bureau of Animal Industry.

as a specific micro-organism by Koch in 1876 (*2*),[2] and it constituted
the principal subject for study by the early investigators who laid the
ground work for the modern science of bacteriology. It was likewise
one of the first infectious diseases against which a bacterial vaccine
was found to be an effective and practical means of prophylaxis (by
Pasteur in 1881 (*4*)).
Practically all animals are susceptible in some degree to anthrax,
but herbivorous animals are the most susceptible. Cattle, horses, sheep,
goats, and the wild herbivores are most commonly affected. Omnivora (man and swine) possess a greater natural resistance to the
disease. Under certain conditions, carnivora (dogs, cats, and wild
animals of prey), birds, and frogs and toads may become infected.
Mice, guinea pigs, and rabbits, which are commonly used in the
laboratory diagnosis of anthrax, are very susceptible, while rats
are less so.

CAUSE OF THE DISEASE

The anthrax germ, *Bacillus anthracis*, which is the specific cause
of anthrax, possesses certain properties that make it one of the most
unique pathogenic micro-organisms encountered in nature. In certain areas, especially those subject to periodic flooding, in low-lying
marshy land, or in soils that are rich in decomposed vegetable or
animal remains, the germ is indigenous to the soil and survives
therein for long periods.
In their active (vegetative) state the anthrax organisms are microscopic in size and cylindrical or rodlike in form, with square ends
(fig. 1, *A*). The bacilli possess a high degree of virulence, and when
they gain access to the animal body they multiply rapidly, invading
the blood stream and producing a rapidly fatal blood infection, or
septicemia.
When exposed to conditions unfavorable to their existence and
growth, the anthrax bacilli form spores—that is, they change from
an active to a dormant, or resting, state. Live, growing anthrax
bacilli that pass from the bodies of sick animals onto the ground
usually form spores. These spores, which develop within the body
of the anthrax bacillus, are extremely small, oval-shaped objects similar to seeds, remarkable for their viability and very resistant to heat,
cold, chemical disinfectants, and prolonged drying (fig. 1, *B*). Numerous instances are on record to show that spores retain their
viability in the soil, in water, on hides, and in storage for many
years. The bacilli themselves, however, show very little resistance
to heat and drying.
Umeno and Nobata (*7*) reported experimental evidence to indicate
that dried anthrax spores can still germinate after being stored for
more than 40 years. Anthrax spores are likewise resistant to very
high temperatures and will withstand boiling for several minutes.
Murray (*3*) reported evidence, based on extensive and well-controlled
experiments, indicating that a temperature of 135° C. (275° F.) for
5 to 10 minutes was necessary to kill dry anthrax spores in the absence

---

[2] Italic numbers in parentheses refer to Literature Cited, p. 262.

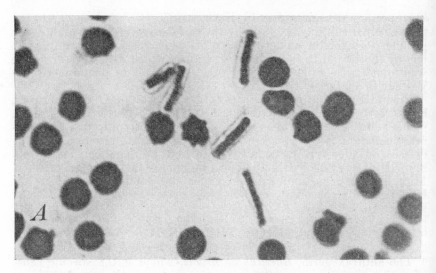

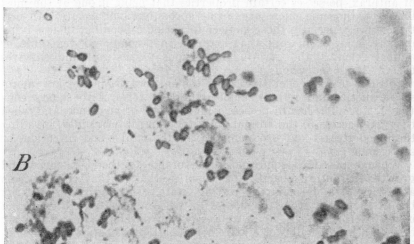

FIGURE 1.—*A*, Photomicrograph of blood from a sheep that died of anthrax, showing rod-shaped anthrax bacilli in their active state. The halolike effect around each bacillus is the capsule. The more or less round objects are red blood cells. (× about 1,000.) *B*, Photomicrograph of an anthrax culture showing the resistant oval-shaped anthrax spores. Note the resemblance to minute seeds. (× about 1,000.)

of moisture, whereas under moist conditions spores suspended in normal (0.8 percent) saline solution were killed in 5 to 10 minutes at a temperature of 100° or 105° C. (212° or 221° F.).

HOW ANTHRAX IS SPREAD

Since anthrax is essentially a soil-borne malady, it is more or less confined to areas commonly designated as "anthrax districts," where the disease is apt to occur from year to year. In such districts it constitutes a perennial problem, making its appearance during a more or less definite period of the year, known as anthrax season, usually the late summer and early fall. Certain well-defined areas in the United States, such as southeastern South Dakota, northeastern Nebraska, a belt along the Texas Gulf coast, and the delta region of the lower Mississippi, including parts of Arkansas, Mississippi, and Louisiana, are recognized anthrax districts where widespread outbreaks have occurred from time to time during the anthrax season. In such areas the disease can be kept in check by appropriate preventive measures. Isolated cases or outbreaks, however, occur at other seasons of the year in many other sections of the United States.

Most outbreaks in livestock occur when animals are on pasture, and it has been observed that they frequently follow hot, dry summers with scant growth of herbage, which necessitates grazing close to the soil. During these dry seasons, swamps, ponds, marshes, and bottom lands dry out and become available for pasture. In close grazing, roots, in many instances with infected soil clinging to them, are consumed by the animals along with the vegetation. Periods of rainy weather followed by extremely hot days also appear to favor the occurrence of the disease. Heavy losses from anthrax often follow in the wake of floods and periodic inundations of low-lying land.

During some years losses from the disease in anthrax districts may be comparatively light and the cases may be more or less sporadic in their occurrence. In other years the disease assumes a very virulent form, appearing simultaneously at a number of places, spreading rapidly to new areas, causing heavy losses of livestock, and assuming the proportions of a major outbreak, or epizootic. The cause of these fluctuations is not known.

The spread of anthrax may be brought about by contamination of the soil, drinking water, and pasture and hay plants with the excreta and discharges of diseased animals. Dogs, coyotes, and other carnivora, as well as the carrion-eating animals and birds, particularly buzzards, are potential spreaders of anthrax from one area to another. Flying insects and blood-sucking flies must be considered as potential carriers. Animals sick of anthrax become easy prey to myriads of flies and other insects. Virulent anthrax organisms have frequently been found in or on the bodies of flies collected while feeding on carcasses of animals dead from anthrax (fig. 2).

Streams contaminated with surface drainage from anthrax soil may carry the infection to distant points, especially during floods and overflows. Anthrax may spread from one country to another through the interchange of infected objects closely associated with animal life, including hides, hair, wool, bonemeal, fertilizer, forage, and other materials.

The Government endeavors to prevent the further introduction of this disease into the United States through the administration by the Bureau of Animal Industry of regulations governing the sanitary handling and control of animal products, animal byproducts, and hay and straw of foreign origin.

FIGURE 2.—A cow dead of anthrax.   Note the great number of flies on the carcass.
Virulent anthrax germs were found on flies taken from this and a partly incinerated
carcass on the same ranch.

FORMS AND SYMPTOMS OF ANTHRAX

The symptoms of anthrax vary according to the species of animals
affected and the acuteness of the attack.   The average period of incubation (that is, the period of time elapsing between exposure to
infection and the appearance of the first symptoms) under natural
conditions is not definitely known, but it is believed from experimental evidence to vary from 24 hours to 5 days or much longer.
Rose, who had the opportunity to observe and study the incubation
period of anthrax in cattle under natural conditions, reported in
1940 (5) that cattle died in 4 to 6 days following the first exposure.

The disease may occur in a peracute, acute, subacute, or chronic
form.

The peracute, or apoplectic, form, sometimes called the fulminant
type, is characterized by a sudden death as from a stroke.   The onset
of the disease is so sudden and the course so rapid that few if any
clinical symptoms are observed.   The usual picture associated with
this form is one of cerebral apoplexy—sudden staggering, collapse,
a few convulsive movements, and death.   A blood-stained discharge
from the mouth, nose, and anus may also be observed.   Victims are
frequently found dead without showing any previous evidence of
illness.   This form is most common in cattle and sheep, occurring
at the beginning of an outbreak.   The sudden death of cattle, sheep,
and horses in known anthrax territory should always be regarded
with suspicion.

The acute form usually terminates in death in a day or two, while
the subacute form may lead to death in 3 to 5 days or longer or to
complete recovery after several days.   In these forms of the disease
there is an early stage of excitement which is soon followed by de-

pression, stupor, spasms, evidence of respiratory or cardiac distress, staggering, and death. During the course of the disease the body temperature may reach 107° F., pregnant animals may abort, rumination ceases, and in milking cows the milk secretion is materially lessened. Bloody discharges from the natural body openings are common, and soft swellings that pit on pressure may develop in different parts of the body. Just before death the temperature falls below normal, respiration becomes extremely labored, and the mucous membranes become cyanotic (dark blue in color).

Chronic anthrax occurs mostly in swine, affecting the mesenteric and submaxillary lymph glands, and is usually recognized only on post mortem examination. Malignant carbuncle and anthrax edema occur in the skin and mucous membranes.

Symptoms in Different Animals

Anthrax infection in horses and mules, as in cattle and sheep, is most often acquired through infected food. In these animals the first indication of the disease may be severe colicky symptoms accompanied by high temperature, chills, loss of appetite, extreme depression, muscular weakness, and the passage of blood-stained feces. Hot, painful, and rapidly progressing swellings frequently develop over the body, especially about the neck, lower abdomen, and external genitalia. Anthrax in the horse may be confused with colic, septicemia, acute swamp fever, purpura hemorrhagica, and other conditions.

In sheep and goats, anthrax occurs most often in the peracute form. In these animals, symptoms of unsteady gait, trembling, restlessness, difficult breathing, blood discharged from the natural body openings, and convulsions may be observed preceding death. Anthrax in sheep may be mistaken for blackleg and malignant edema.

Swine are more resistant to anthrax than any other domesticated farm animal. When infection in hogs follows feeding on an anthrax-infected carcass, some of the animals may be found dead without having shown any previous signs of illness. Others of the group may show symptoms of illness with rapidly progressing swellings about the throat which in some cases cause death by suffocation. A relatively large percentage of the group may become visibly sick for a few days, with or without moderate swellings about the throat, and recover. When hogs develop anthrax from sources other than feeding on anthrax-infected carcasses, the same effects are observed, except that sudden death without visible symptoms is rare.

Anthrax in dogs, cats, and other carnivora usually occurs as a result of eating meat from anthrax-infected carcasses. Dogs are affected chiefly with pharyngeal anthrax or anthrax of the tongue, in which swelling may occur about the head and the throat. Anthrax of the intestines also occurs in dogs, manifested as a severe gastroenteritis. While all dogs are more or less resistant to the disease, older dogs seem to be the least susceptible.

Under natural conditions poultry are not susceptible to anthrax, and other types of birds, reptiles, and fish likewise are not susceptible under ordinary conditions. Although insects may transmit the disease in a purely mechanical manner, they appear to be immune themselves.

ANTHRAX IN MAN

Anthrax may occur in man as a result of direct contact with diseased animals or their discharges or with carcasses of animals dead of the disease, or it may result from the handling of hides, fur, hair, and other animal byproducts. In the former case it is referred to as agricultural anthrax and in the latter as industrial anthrax.

In man, anthrax usually occurs as a primary localized infection of the skin in the form of a carbuncle—at first hot and painful, later cold and painless—or as an infection of the lungs, which is known as wool-sorters' disease. In countries where the flesh of animals dead of disease is eaten, an abdominal form of anthrax has been reported. Skin infections result from the handling of carcasses of animals dead of anthrax or the hides, hair, or wool from such carcasses. Originating as localized infections in the form of small pimples, the lesions develop rapidly and may terminate in a fatal septicemia or blood poisoning. Prompt medical attention is most important whenever anthrax infection is suspected. The pulmonary form of the disease results from the inhalation of anthrax spores in factories where hair and wool are processed. This form of anthrax runs a very rapid course and terminates fatally. Anthrax is occasionally transmitted to man by spore-infected shaving brushes, by wearing apparel such as furs and leather goods, or by other animal byproducts not properly sterilized.

Smyth (6) reported that in the 20-year period 1919–38 a total of 1,683 cases of anthrax occurred in human beings in the United States and there were 353 deaths. From 1934 to 1938, 375 human cases and 61 fatalities occurred. During the 20-year period mentioned there was scarcely a year in which anthrax in human beings was not reported by the States reporting most of the cases of human anthrax. These were Pennsylvania, New York, Massachusetts, and New Jersey (mostly tannery and wool anthrax), and Texas, California, Louisiana, and Mississippi (mostly agricultural anthrax).

WHAT TO DO IN SUSPECTED CASES

When an animal dies within an anthrax district or on or near premises where the disease has appeared previously, it is very important to know definitely whether the death was due to anthrax. Lack of such information has often been responsible for heavy losses of livestock and at times the loss of human lives.

If anthrax is suspected, the stockman should consult a veterinarian at once rather than open a carcass for the purpose of making a definite diagnosis. The seriousness of such a mistake can hardly be overestimated because of the greatly increased danger of spreading the disease when the body is opened and discharges from it escape. Post mortem examination in suspected cases of anthrax should be made only by a qualified veterinarian who is prepared to take all necessary precautions against infecting himself and the premises. If local veterinary service is not available, the State livestock sanitary officials should be consulted.

POST MORTEM FINDINGS

Post mortem examination of animals dead of anthrax usually reveals anatomical changes associated with septicemia. In the very rapidly fatal peracute cases the alterations in the blood and tissues are usually slight, but in acute and subacute cases of longer standing the anatomical changes are marked.

Carcasses of animals dead of anthrax decompose rapidly and soon become greatly bloated. The natural post mortem stiffening of the muscles is incomplete. Dark blood escapes as a rule from the natural openings, and the visible mucous membranes are dark blue in color and frequently show hemorrhages. The blood is considerably darker than normal, does not clot readily, and is frequently spoken of as being tarry. Hemorrhages beneath the skin are common. Clear or somewhat blood-tinged gelatinous exudates are found between the muscles and beneath the skin, especially in the areas where the swellings were seen before death.

With rare exceptions the spleen shows characteristic changes, which are of considerable assistance in making a diagnosis of anthrax. This organ is greatly enlarged, and the splenic pulp is dark red to blackish in color and soft or even semifluid in consistency; it may have the appearance of blackberry jam. The liver, kidneys, and lymph glands are usually congested and enlarged and show areas of hemorrhage.

In hogs the outstanding anatomical changes are confined principally to the region of the throat, where there is a marked gelatinous and hemorrhagic condition of the connective tissues and lymphatic glands. The tonsils are enlarged and frequently are covered with a dark, discolored, false membrane. Swelling of the structures forming the glottis is also observed. Although the spleen in affected hogs is frequently normal in size and color, enlarged, dark, and soft spleens may be found in cases where the disease has become generalized.

Local lesions of long standing are sometimes found in the throat region of slaughtered hogs that had shown no visible signs of anthrax during their life and were apparently healthy prior to slaughter. In these cases the disease is confined to the pharynx and the adjacent tissues, including the lymphatic glands of that region. Localization of anthrax in the mesenteric glands has also been observed. In this chronic localized type of anthrax the lymph glands of the head, especially the submaxillary glands, may be either slightly or greatly enlarged, hard, and fibrous. The cut surface presents a mottled appearance, produced by brick-red areas, patches, or streaks having a dull-gray, parboiled appearance, and necrotic foci which may be dry and cheesy. One or both tonsils may show areas of degeneration and necrosis ranging in size from that of a pinhead to that of a silver dollar.

DIAGNOSIS AND LABORATORY EXAMINATION

Especially in noninfected anthrax territory, the diagnosis of anthrax from clinical symptoms and anatomical findings may at times be difficult because of the similarity of these symptoms and findings to other disease conditions. A definite diagnosis of anthrax in such instances can be made only by laboratory examination.

In peracute anthrax, death is so sudden and the clinical symptoms are so meager that a definite diagnosis is impossible without the aid of laboratory examination. Cerebral hemorrhage, sunstroke, lead poisoning, or some acutely fatal digestive disturbance may be confused with peracute anthrax, especially if it occurs in the so-called anthrax districts.

Any previous occurrence of anthrax on the premises is sufficient reason for considering anthrax as a possible cause of any deaths among livestock that cannot be clearly attributed to other causes. In a large number of such instances a tentative diagnosis of anthrax can be substantiated by laboratory examination. When such an examination is desired, suitable specimens should be collected by a qualified veterinarian. **In case professional services are not available and the samples are to be collected by someone else, the greatest care should be taken by the operator to avoid infecting himself. Heavy rubber gloves should be worn to prevent the infectious material from coming in contact with the hands.**

The few drops of blood that are required may be collected from a small cut made over the jugular vein or at the base of the ear immediately before the carcass is buried or cremated. The bloody nasal discharge is also suitable for this purpose. The blood may be absorbed by small pieces of blotting paper, chalk, or sterile cotton swabs, which should be allowed to dry and then placed in a sealed container. The container should be enclosed in an unbreakable outside receptacle, such as a metal mailing tube, for shipment to the laboratory for examination.

WHAT TO DO IN ACTUAL CASES OF ANTHRAX

The effective control of anthrax requires the combined action of livestock sanitary officials, local veterinarians, and owners of livestock. When the disease appears or is suspected in a herd, it is advisable to obtain the assistance of a veterinarian or State livestock official as soon as possible, so that proper measures may be promptly taken to suppress the outbreak and prevent its spread.

When a diagnosis of anthrax has been made, the following measures are generally recognized as the most effective means of control:

(1) The prompt and proper disposal either by complete burning or by deep burial of animals dead of the disease, together with all the manure, bedding, blood-stained soil, and other contaminated material.

(2) A careful examination of the herd for animals showing early symptoms of the disease, the prompt isolation of sick animals, and immediate treatment with large doses of antianthrax serum.

(3) Vaccination of the apparently well animals in the herd as soon as possible, for prevention, in accordance with methods recommended by the State livestock sanitary officials and other experienced veterinarians.

(4) Immediate change of pastures if practicable. This precaution in itself has in many instances helped to reduce losses. If the outbreak occurs during the fly season, it is best to move the herd at night so that most of the infection-carrying flies will be left behind.

(5) A strict quarantine of premises rigidly enforced, so as to prohibit the movement of livestock or other commodities of a contraband nature from or into the infected area.

In the control of anthrax, prompt and effective disposal of carcasses is of the greatest importance. This can be accomplished either by complete cremation or by deep burial under a layer of quicklime covered with at least 6 feet of earth. Carcasses should not be buried in low swampy land or adjacent to streams where overflow might inundate the grave, or on a hillside where there is a possibility of subsurface drainage reaching the surface at lower places nearby. The area above and around the grave should be saturated with oil and burned over.

In disposing of a dead animal, the following method is recommended: Immediately after finding the animal, cover it with kerosene or crude oil to keep flies, dogs, buzzards, crows, and vermin from the carcass until it is disposed of. If conditions permit, cremate or bury the carcass where it is found. If moving to a more suitable site is necessary, take the greatest care to prevent any discharges or hair from contaminating the soil over which the carcass is moved. Consequently, never permit a carcass to be dragged. A stone boat or sled may be used as a means of conveyance. Thoroughly disinfect or burn any equipment used in moving anthrax-infected carcasses. Avoid actual contact with the germ-laden body. This can be done through the use of properly applied ropes and poles, which may then be burned.

When anthrax is prevalent, it is advisable for the owner to keep all his own dogs tied up and in every possible way to prevent stray dogs from coming on the premises.

When anthrax occurs in stabled animals, prompt and thorough disinfection of the quarters should follow the removal of the dead animals. Where sick animals are being treated, every precaution should be taken to prevent spread of the infection through contaminated excreta. Since there is always a possibility of rats or mice transferring contamination to the hayloft or feed storerooms, special efforts should be made in anthrax districts to get rid of these pests.

When an outbreak of anthrax occurs in a dairy herd, the dairy should be placed under strict quarantine, and all milk should be withheld from distribution until the public-health officials and State livestock sanitary officials consider circumstances satisfactory for issuing a clean bill of health. Precautions should be taken to prevent the contamination of milking cans, mechanical milkers, buckets, and other dairy equipment by direct or indirect contact with diseased animals and their excreta. Although there appears to be little likelihood of direct transmission of anthrax through the milk of infected cows, a few instances on record indicate that anthrax bacilli may be excreted in the milk of an infected animal. Horrocks (*1*) in 1908 reported evidence indicating that virulent anthrax bacilli may be excreted in the milk of animals dying from anthrax but that this occurs only a few hours before death. Weidlich (*8*) in 1934 reported the finding of anthrax organisms in the milk secretion of a cow following infection with anthrax. How soon milk from dairies quarantined for anthrax can safely be distributed depends to a large extent on the nature of the outbreak. In mild outbreaks accompanied by no unusual conditions, this problem has been handled with safety and satisfaction to all concerned by requiring that a period of at least 3 weeks elapse following the appearance of the last case before any milk can be distributed. As an added precaution and to pick out animals showing early symptoms of the disease, temperatures of all the cows should be taken just before milking. This procedure should be followed for 2 to 3 weeks or until all danger of infection appears to have been eliminated.

Lye is one of the most effective of the disinfectants. To disinfect premises against anthrax, a 5-percent solution is recommended. (See the article Disinfection and Disinfectants, p. 179.) All places to be disinfected should be thoroughly soaked with the disinfectant, which should be allowed to remain on for at least a day and should then be thoroughly washed off with clean water before the livestock are returned.

Manure from a stable where deaths from anthrax have occurred should be burned or deeply buried or, if neither is practicable, disinfected with very liberal applications of a 5-percent solution of lye. It is questionable, however, whether any reasonably heavy applications of lye solution would completely disinfect large quantities of manure.

Thorough inspection of premises where outbreaks of anthrax have occurred may disclose pools or marshlands that are potential sources of infection. Such places, as well as parts of pasture lands known to be heavily infected, should be fenced off insofar as practicable.

ANTHRAX VACCINATION

Anthrax is one of the few more serious diseases of livestock that can largely be controlled by preventive vaccination. Where vaccination is necessarily an annual procedure, it should be performed well in advance of the anthrax season or at least before anthrax makes its appearance. There is a possibility that vaccination may be followed by an initial state of lowered resistance preceding the establishment of immunity, and exposure to anthrax during this period of increased susceptibility may prove costly. In fact, field observers have frequently witnessed the rapid development of cases of anthrax within several days after vaccination when it was performed after the disease had started. This, it was believed, could have been avoided had the vaccinating been done before the outbreak occurred.

It should be borne in mind, however, that vaccination is not 100 percent effective regardless of the method of vaccination or the vaccine that is used. It is not uncommon for anthrax to develop in an occasional animal that has been vaccinated with an anthrax biologic that apparently affords protection to the rest of the herd. When it is understood that anthrax vaccination is not 100 percent effective, an occasional loss from anthrax in a vaccinated herd does not constitute grounds for questioning the value of the biologic that was used, nor does it justify hasty revaccination of the herd.

IMMUNIZING AGENTS AND THEIR USE

For the vaccination of animals against anthrax, there are at present a number of recognized immunizing agents available in the United States. These are: Antianthrax serum, anthrax bacterin, antianthrax serum and anthrax-spore vaccine, single-injection anthrax-spore vaccine (in liquid or pill form), double- or triple-injection anthrax-spore vaccine (in liquid or pill form), anthrax-spore vaccine (intradermic), anthrax-spore vaccine in saponin solution or in alum solution. The first two of these are sterile anthrax products, and the others are living-spore anthrax products.

The selection of the anthrax biologic to be used on a given lot of animals should be left to the local veterinarian or State livestock sanitary officials, who because of their experience and knowledge of the local conditions are in a position to know which products are best suited to the needs of the herd. Each of the immunizing agents mentioned has a particular field of usefulness and also definite limitations.

Antianthrax serum produces increased resistance to anthrax as soon as it is absorbed, and the resistance is in direct proportion to the quantity of serum that is given. It is of value both as a preventive and as a therapeutic agent. The immunity which it confers, however, is of relatively short duration. As a preventive, therefore, antianthrax serum should be used when immediate protection is the principal objective, even though the immunity is only temporary. When serum alone has been given to the apparently healthy animals in an infected herd, it should be followed 10 days later by vaccination with a biologic that will produce a more enduring immunity.

Anthrax bacterin differs from antianthrax serum in that it stimulates the treated animal to produce immune bodies (active immunity), whereas the serum treatment is merely a mechanical transference of already produced immune bodies to the treated animal (passive immunity). Naturally the protection afforded by bacterin would not become established as early as that established with serum, but it would be of longer duration. This product, being sterile, is in itself incapable of producing disease in the treated animal and is, therefore, safer than the living-spore anthrax vaccines.

All anthrax-spore vaccines are composed of living anthrax spores and are prepared in either liquid or solid form (pellets). These products may be used alone or in combination with antianthrax serum. The spores in these vaccines are so weakened that under ordinary conditions they will not produce the disease in livestock if the vaccines are administered according to directions. However, a small proportion of animals are unusually susceptible and may react severely to vaccination with these spore vaccines, and occasionally one may die as a direct result of the vaccination (from vaccination anthrax). For this reason, it is ordinarily inadvisable to use living-spore anthrax vaccines on premises where the disease has not existed previously or where there is reason to believe that previous infections have died out. When these living-spore vaccines are used to control anthrax, the greatest care should be taken to prevent contamination of the surroundings with the vaccine.

Experience has shown that the living-spore vaccines produce a higher degree of immunity than do the sterile anthrax vaccines, and as a rule vaccination with any of the living-spore vaccines used either alone or in combination with serum is followed by an active immunity which lasts sufficiently long to carry the animal through the usual anthrax season. In some years, however, anthrax makes its appearance in a highly virulent form, and in these years the artificial immunity which can be produced by vaccination does not always protect against infection.

To overcome or prevent these post-vaccination outbreaks that sometimes occur in virulent form following use of anthrax immunizing agents of ordinary strength, stronger spore vaccines known as Nos. 3 and 4 have been prepared. Their use is not without danger and requires considerable discretion.

Much new information on the relative values and limitations of six of the available anthrax immunizing agents was obtained by the Bureau of Animal Industry through recent experimental tests on sheep. This knowledge emphasizes the fact that immunization against anthrax is not merely a simple mechanical operation but a highly technical procedure that should be undertaken only by experts who are thoroughly qualified in this field. Information on these comparative tests may be obtained from the Bureau.

Favorable results following the use of intradermic spore vaccine have been reported by investigators and veterinary practitioners, both in Europe and the United States. Reports from the field indicate that in recent years the intradermic method of vaccination (with anthrax-spore vaccine) is gradually growing in favor, particularly in badly infected anthrax districts, and that the results obtained from its use have been highly satisfactory. During 1939 and 1940 more than 6,000 head of cattle on 5 Indian reservations located in known anthrax districts were vaccinated by the intradermic method under direct supervision of Bureau of Animal Industry veterinarians, with excellent results.

In this method of vaccination the spore vaccine is injected directly into the skin (intracutaneously) and not under the skin (subcutaneously), the usual method used in other forms of vaccination. This method also has the advantage of requiring only one injection.

LITERATURE CITED

(1) HORROCKS, W. H.
    1908. ON THE EXCRETION OF ANTHRAX BACILLI IN MILK. Roy. Army Med.
        Corps Jour. 11: 46, 48.
(2) KOCH [ROBERT].
    1877. UNTERSUCHUNGEN ÜBER BACTERIEN. V. DIE AETIOLOGIE DER MILZBRAND-
        KRANKHEIT, BEGRUNDET AUF DIE ENTWICKLUNGSGESCHICHTE DES
        BACILLUS ANTHRACIS. Beitr. z. Biol. der Pflanz. 2: [277]-310,
        illus.
(3) MURRAY, T. J.
    1931. THERMAL DEATH POINT. II. SPORES OF BACILLUS ANTHRACIS. Jour.
        Infect. Dis. 48: 457-467.
(4) PASTEUR, [LOUIS], CHAMBERLAND, and ROUX.
    1881. COMPTE RENDU SOMMAIRE DES EXPERIENCES FAITES A POUILLY-LE-FORT,
        PRES MELUM, SUR LA VACCINATION CHARBONNEUSE. [Paris] Acad.
        des Sci. Compt. Rend. 92: 1378-1383.
(5) ROSE, A. L.
    1940. THE PERIOD OF INCUBATION OF ANTHRAX IN CATTLE. Austral. Vet.
        Jour. 16: 214-215.
(6) SMYTH, HENRY FIELD.
    1939. A TWENTY-YEAR SURVEY OF ANTHRAX IN THE UNITED STATES. Amer.
        Pub. Health Assoc., Indus. Hyg. Sect., Sixth Rpt. Com. Anthrax,
        [16] pp.
(7) UMENO, S., and NOBATA, R.
    1938. ON THE VIABILITY OF ANTHRAX SPORES. Jap. Soc. Vet. Sci. Jour.
        17: 220-223. [In Japanese. English abstract, p. 87.]
(8) WEIDLICH, NORBERT.
    1934. DAUERBESIE DE LUNG DES EUTERS MIT MILZBRANDBAZILLEN BEI EINER
        KUH. Wien Tierärztl. Monatsschr. 21: [289]-292.

Foot-and-Mouth Disease

BY J. R. MOHLER AND JACOB TRAUM [1]

THE BLISTERS and fever that are the signs of foot-and-mouth disease should be as dreaded as the symptoms of smallpox among human beings. Unfortunately, there is no practical vaccination or cure for the animal malady, which spreads like wildfire and must be fought as quickly and effectively lest it become a conflagration. Every livestock man should know the facts about foot-and-mouth disease.

In the United States and a few other countries where foot-and-mouth disease is not constantly present (endemic), it is feared as a very serious livestock malady. In this country especially, extreme precautions are taken to prevent its introduction, and rigid measures are used to eradicate it in the event of outbreaks. These procedures are accepted as necessary by the officials entrusted with the control and eradication of infectious diseases of animals, and they receive the full support of most livestock owners and the public in general. As a result the United States has enjoyed long intervals of freedom from this malady, and several of the outbreaks have been limited to only a few herds.

Foot-and-mouth disease is sometimes referred to also as hoof-and-mouth disease and as aphthous fever. Of the three names, "foot-and-mouth disease" is preferred as being the most accurate, and it is the name commonly used in the United States. Hoof-and-mouth disease is less accurate because the infection attacks the soft tissues of the foot rather than the horny wall.

Practically all cloven-footed animals, especially cattle, hogs, sheep, and goats, are susceptible to foot-and-mouth disease. Deer were affected in California in 1924 and 1925, and other cloven-footed animals have been found in other countries to be affected at times.

---

[1] J. R. Mohler is Chief of the Bureau of Animal Industry, and Jacob Traum is Professor of Veterinary Science at the University of California.

· CHARACTER OF THE DISEASE

Foot-and-mouth disease is characterized by the formation of vesicles or blisters on the mucous membranes covering the tongue, lips, cheeks, palate, or other tissues of the mouth, on the skin between and above the claws of the feet, and on the teats and udder. In cattle, any one or several of these locations may be involved. In hogs, lesions frequently occur also on and above the snout. In rare cases the muzzles of cattle are affected. In sheep, goats, and deer, the feet are the most common site of the vesicle formation. As a rule, the vesicles rupture within 24 hours, leaving a raw, eroded, red surface (fig. 1). Mouth lesions cause salivation, especially in cattle. In none of these lesions is there the pustule formation which is always so characteristic a part of the disease process in pox diseases.

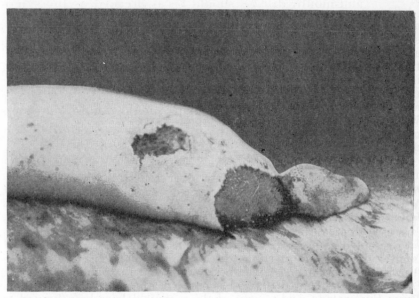

FIGURE 1.—Tongue of a cow affected with foot-and-mouth disease, showing well-defined ruptured vesicles.

The lesions of foot-and-mouth disease heal rather rapidly, but in some instances those on the feet may give rise to serious secondary bacterial infections. Before and for a short time after the appearance of lesions there is a striking rise in temperature. During the attack, the animals lose considerable flesh. In cows there is a severe reduction in the milk flow.

The symptoms vary in extent from one or two small vesicles in one of the locations mentioned to extensive involvement of several organs. In some cattle more than half the covering of the tongue may be lifted, and the claws of all four feet may be lost.

The deterioration of the animals may cause far greater loss than the actual mortality, which is estimated in ordinary outbreaks to be approximately 5 percent. There is, however, a malignant form of the disease which may be accompanied by heart lesions. In such outbreaks as many as 50 percent of the affected animals succumb or are so seriously injured that they have to be slaughtered, even in countries where eradication by this method is not practiced.

CAUSATIVE AGENT

The infective agent in foot-and-mouth disease is a filtrable virus. Viruses can pass through filters that hold back the smallest bacteria, and they cannot be seen with the most powerful microscope. The size of the foot-and-mouth disease virus has been estimated to be between 8 and 12 millimicrons, which places it among the most minute of these ultramicroscopic infective agents.

The virus is present in the fluid and the coverings of the vesicles and can also be found in the blood in the initial febrile (feverish) stage of the disease. Saliva, milk, urine, and other secretions may also contain the virus. It is not definitely known whether these fluids contain the virus at their sources, in the salivary glands, mammary glands, etc., or are infected later by becoming mixed with vesicular fluid or coverings. For practical control measures the important consideration is that the virus may be present in these secretions, which should be considered as infectious. The fluid and coverings of the vesicles in the animal usually lose their infectivity within 4 to 6 days after the lesions appear.

The conditions under which the materials harboring the virus are found outside the animal body determine its viability, or ability to remain alive, and its infectivity. Under certain circumstances, the virus perishes within a very short time. When kept at an incubator temperature corresponding to the body temperature, 37° C. (98.5° F.), it has not produced disease after 24 to 48 hours, but at room temperatures of 18° to 20° C. (65° to 68° F.) it has been kept alive for 10 weeks. In the ice box, at temperatures between 4° and 7° C. (39.2° and 44.6° F.), it has been kept alive for many months, especially when contained in a properly buffered 50-percent glycerin solution. When rapidly dried, particularly at temperatures below the freezing point and under vacuum, it remains active for several years; in fact, this is an effective method of maintaining the virus for experimental use. Likewise, ordinary refrigeration does not destroy the virus but preserves its infectivity. It is important to note, however, that owing to the great infectiousness of foot-and-mouth disease, experiments with it are not conducted within the United States. Experimental work by the United States Department of Agriculture has been done in foreign countries by arrangement with their veterinary and other public officials.

In one experiment the investigators placed small pieces of coverings from unruptured tongue vesicles of cows in a sack containing hay. After 30 days these tissues were still capable of inducing experimental foot-and-mouth disease in guinea pigs, but after 50 days they no longer had this effect. In soil the virus remained active for at least 25 days—the longest period over which it was tested in this manner. That the virus does not always die rapidly after leaving an animal is suggested by the fact that foot-and-mouth disease has appeared on premises where restocking had not taken place until 30 to 60 days after the slaughter of infected herds. Definite evidence is available to show that in one instance in the United States the virus persisted in the field for 345 days.

It is of the utmost significance in the control of outbreaks, therefore, to regard the virus as resistant to destruction. Furthermore, it is possible that a portion of the covering of a freshly ruptured vesicle may become detached, and if such a fragment finds suitable conditions outside the animal the virus in it may be active for a considerable time.

Ordinary chemical disinfectants, such as phenol, bichloride of mercury, formalin, and others, used in the generally recommended concentrations, do not destroy this virus rapidly as was for a long time assumed. In 1925, however, the American Foot-and-Mouth Disease Commission, a group of three scientists, working abroad, proved that sodium hydroxide in a 1- to 2-percent solution destroys the virus within 1 minute. This agent, conveniently and cheaply available in the form of lye, has now been adopted by the United States and many European Governments for use whenever disinfection is needed in combating foot-and-mouth disease.

METHODS OF SPREAD

The commonest agent in the spread of foot-and-mouth disease is, of course, the infected animal itself. As already stated, the virus is contained in the fluid and the coverings of the vesicles, as well as in the blood during the febrile stage of the disease. At this time the saliva, urine, milk, and probably other secretions and excretions are also infectious.

The active virus leaving the infected animal contaminates its surroundings and can be carried mechanically by living beings—people, horses, and dogs, for example—or on litter, feed, stable, utensils, and other objects. When contaminated material comes in contact with susceptible animals, the latter can readily become infected. Under conditions favoring the persistence of the virus outside the animal body the danger of spreading infection is considerable. In view of experimental evidence, it is probable that infected animals spread the virus most actively in the early stages of the disease, and they may do so even before any lesions are observable.

On the other hand, the fact that the virus loses its activity in a relatively short time within the body suggests that animals in the later stages of the disease play little part in its spread. In spite of this, investigators and livestock sanitary officials, with only a few exceptions, believe that virus carriers exist, and that such animals may harbor the virus for a long time after recovery. The percentage of carriers, however, is believed to be small. The field evidence presented to support this view is very strong, and numerous instances are reported in which the disease occurred in clean herds shortly after the addition to the herd of animals that had previously had foot-and-mouth disease, other sources of infection having been eliminated. As long as 8 months, and indeed in several instances more than a year after recovery, animals have been held responsible for causing outbreaks of the disease.

Milk, meat, and the raw byproducts of slaughter of infected animals may also be instrumental in distributing the virus. Milk may contain it and, when fed to susceptible animals, may bring about infection. While evidence has been presented to indicate that the infectiousness of milk is lost in souring and also in the fermentation that occurs in the production of cheese, data on the survival of the virus in milk under various conditions are limited in the main to work reported many years ago. This is a subject that should again be investigated experimentally with present-day methods.

The meat or other parts of animals slaughtered in the febrile stage of the disease may be infectious, and feeding such uncooked products to susceptible animals obviously may result in infection.

The British Foot-and-Mouth Disease Research Committee found that when the carcasses of experimentally inoculated guinea pigs were bled out and kept at temperatures of 2° to 7° C. (slightly above freezing), the blood remaining in tissues around the throat was virulent after 21 days, while the bone marrow contained active virus for periods of 21 to 87 days. Muscular tissue in one carcass remained infectious for 7 days and kidney tissue in another for 54 days. In unbled guinea pig carcasses kept at cold room temperatures, the blood was infectious for 35 to 46 days; bone marrow was found to contain active virus for periods up to 96 days.

In experiments with hogs slaughtered during the febrile stage of the disease, active virus was found after 42 days in the bone marrow of carcasses whether they had been kept at chilling temperature or treated by dry or wet salt processes. In cattle and hog carcasses kept at freezing temperature, active virus was found in the bone marrow for 76 days. No evidence was found through feeding or inoculation experiments to show that the muscular tissue contained virus. These results indicate the dangerous part that carcasses or parts of carcasses of animals slaughtered in the period of blood infectivity may play in the spreading of infection.

The examples mentioned explain how meat scraps, bone, and other parts from infected animals, when included in garbage or in butcher shop or slaughterhouse scraps, can be a source of infection in hogs. In fact, several foot-and-mouth disease outbreaks in the United States were traced to hogs which had been fed household, restaurant, institutional, or other garbage that could have contained meat from countries where the disease is endemic.

That biological products in the manufacture of which animals susceptible to foot-and-mouth disease are used can disseminate the disease has been proved in two instances in the United States. In 1908, smallpox vaccine from Japan, which was later proved by Mohler and Rosenau to be contaminated with foot-and-mouth disease virus, was found to be responsible for an outbreak. In 1914, hog cholera virus and serum prepared from hogs infected with foot-and-mouth disease were responsible for the extension of an outbreak.

Human beings are next in importance to infected animals and animal products as agents responsible for the spread of the disease. It is generally believed that human beings convey the virus mechanically, on the clothing or person. The susceptibility of man to infection with foot-and-mouth disease has been seriously questioned, and in fact denied, because actual attempts at direct inoculation produced negative results. Numerous cases of foot-and-mouth disease in man are recorded in the literature, but few of these have been proved, by the inoculation of susceptible animals, to have been actual cases of the disease. Thus in many of these reported cases the validity of the diagnosis can be reasonably questioned. Field observations in the United States during outbreaks also have borne out the supposition that man is resistant to the disease. It may be stated, therefore, that man is rather resistant and rarely contracts the disease.

Transmission by intermediate hosts has received some attention. The senior author of this article demonstrated that the cattle fever tick (*Boophilus annulatus*) taken from an infected cow in the febrile stage of foot-and-mouth disease was capable of transmitting the malady to healthy cattle. The seed ticks, or progeny, of these infected ticks failed to produce the disease.

The spread of foot-and-mouth disease by means of animals usually not considered readily susceptible has received attention in recent years. Experimental evidence indicates that rats, mice, and rabbits are probably not directly involved in the spread of the disease otherwise than by mechanical means.

The American Foot-and-Mouth Disease Commission was unable to infect horses artificially with foot-and-mouth disease virus. In the light of similar failure by French and German investigators, as well as field observations in the United States and other countries, it is believed that the horse plays little part in the spread of the virus except as a mechanical carrier.

DIAGNOSIS

The policy in the United States of slaughtering animals to eradicate the disease when it appears makes the establishment of a definite diagnosis more important than it is in countries where the disease is endemic. Failure to recognize the disease when it exists might permit the extensive spread of the malady, perhaps to such a point that even radical methods would not eliminate it or would do so only at very great cost. On the other hand, to make an incorrect diagnosis of foot-and-mouth disease would mean unnecessarily imposing severe and costly quarantines and restrictions, locally, nationally, and internationally, in addition to needless slaughter of animals. In the United States, therefore, extreme caution is used in making a diagnosis.

Only two other diseases cause inflammatory changes in the mucous membranes of the mouth or the skin of the feet or both in cattle, swine, sheep, goats, and other cloven-footed animals sufficiently similar to those of foot-and-mouth disease to give the experienced observer difficulty in establishing a diagnosis. These are the virus diseases vesicular stomatitis and vesicular exanthema of swine.

DIFFERENTIATION FROM VESICULAR STOMATITIS

In making a diagnosis in the field differentiating between vesicular stomatitis and foot-and-mouth disease, certain general features of the two must be borne in mind. Vesicular stomatitis, as its name indicates, is characterized by the formation of vesicles on the mucous membranes of the mouth (stomatitis means literally "inflammation of the mouth"). Although it mainly affects horses, there have at times been extensive outbreaks in cattle, though the lesions are, as a rule, not so severe as those observed in foot-and-mouth disease. Vesicular stomatitis generally does not spread so rapidly, and it seldom produces foot lesions. Teat and udder lesions are very infrequently observed. These, however, are only differences of degree, because lesions do sometimes occur on the teats and feet of cattle affected with vesicular stomatitis, and in the severe form mouth lesions may be at least as pronounced as in mild cases of foot-and-mouth disease.

Experimentally swine are readily infected by vesicular stomatitis virus, and the disease thus produced is at least as severe as foot-and-mouth disease, from which it is indistinguishable. But no proved outbreak of vesicular stomatitis in hogs has yet been reported.

DIFFERENTIATION FROM VESICULAR EXANTHEMA OF SWINE

In a paper on methods of handling foot-and-mouth disease in the United States, presented by the junior author of this article at the Twelfth International Veterinary Congress in August 1934, attention was called to a disease which appeared in garbage-fed swine in the southern part of California in 1933 and which was clinically indistinguishable from natural and experimental foot-and-mouth disease as well as from experimental vesicular stomatitis of swine. In its behavior in test animals, however, it differed sufficiently from both vesicular stomatitis and foot-and-mouth disease to warrant the use of a new term to identify it. The name "vesicular exanthema of swine" was proposed by Traum and adopted generally.

In vesicular exanthema of swine, as in foot-and-mouth disease and in experimental vesicular stomatitis, vesicles of varying size may appear on the snout, nose, lips, gums, or tongue, or on the feet between the digits, around the coronary band, on the ball of the foot, or on the dewclaws. Lesions on the udder and especially the teats have been observed in a large proportion of nursing sows. These eruptions are usually preceded and accompanied by a rise in temperature and rupture and heal as do those of foot-and-mouth disease and of vesicular stomatitis. In some outbreaks there may be a predominance of snout lesions, while in others foot lesions may be more numerous. Occasionally the hogs in some pens will have vesicles back of the rim of the snout, while nearly all the hogs in other pens on the same ranch show the infection on the front part of the snout. Often an animal will show lesions in more than one location.

As a rule the general systemic disturbance is not so severe as that seen in cases of foot-and-mouth disease. At feeding times most of the affected hogs come up to the feeding platform and eat their food.

But since there are probably also mild cases of foot-and-mouth disease in which swine feed more or less regularly, this observation cannot be safely used to differentiate between the two diseases. Various degrees of lameness result from the foot lesions.

Sometimes vesicular exanthema of swine does not spread extensively; it may affect only a small number of hogs in a pen and spread very slowly to other pens. Again, practically every hog in a pen will show lesions, and the disease will spread rapidly to other groups.

Thus far inoculation with vesicular exanthema virus has produced no lesions in cattle, though probably several hundred have been so inoculated. Horses are mildly susceptible. They have been used to differentiate foot-and-mouth disease from vesicular stomatitis, and they also play an important, though sometimes confusing, part in the diagnosis of vesicular exanthema of swine. Although lesions are induced in most horses inoculated with the virus of the latter disease, they are always mild. So far no natural cases of vesicular exanthema of swine have ever been observed in the horse, although such cases may have occurred and the immunity thus set up would perhaps explain some failures to transfer the disease experimentally from swine to horses. If this is the case, it would be very desirable to obtain horses for the tests from other ranches or localities.

Several hundred guinea pigs have been inoculated with the virus of vesicular exanthema of swine, but thus far only a few nontransferable takes have been observed.

FINAL DETERMINATION

In making a diagnosis the facts just discussed are used to determine which of the three diseases an infected animal has. The procedure is to inoculate swine, cattle, guinea pigs, and horses with material obtained from the sick animal. The diagnosis of foot-and-mouth disease is clear and can be made unhesitatingly if typical vesicles, preceded by a rise in temperature, develop in all these animals except the horses. When all the injected animals including the horses develop vesicular lesions, the disease would be diagnosed as vesicular stomatitis. When lesions are produced in swine, less frequently and to a milder degree in horses, and not at all in cattle or guinea pigs, the condition is typical of vesicular exanthema of swine.[2]

LIMITATIONS OF MEDICINAL AND IMMUNIZING TREATMENTS

No specific medicinal treatment for foot-and-mouth disease has thus far been found. The use of any medicine in the hope of curing affected animals is not advisable under conditions prevailing in the United States, where the disease has occurred infrequently and the

---

[2] The European hedgehog has been found by British workers to be highly susceptible to foot-and-mouth disease virus, whereas the virus of vesicular exanthema of swine failed to infect this animal in a trial reported by the senior author.

first object is to stamp it out as quickly as possible by the slaughter method described later. Even though animals might recover, with or without treatment, it would be impossible, while they were being held for recovery, to prevent the spread of the infection to others. Where this method has been tried in certain foreign countries it was found that the disease spread faster than it could be cured. Moreover, animals that have passed through the disease may become a source of further infection as carriers for weeks and months after they have apparently recovered.

For many years attempts have been made to develop an immunizing agent against foot-and-mouth disease that would be effective without producing the disease. Waldmann and his associates, making use of procedures and developments due to the experimentation of other workers, especially that of Schmidt, have recently obtained promising results with a vaccine made by concentrating the virus and treating it with formalin.

The immunity produced by any vaccine or serum thus far developed, however, is of very short duration.

CONTROL AND ERADICATION MEASURES

Two methods are now in general use in the control and eradication of foot-and-mouth disease: (1) The stamping-out, or slaughter method, which has been used in the United States and England and at various times in other countries; and (2) the quarantine procedure, which is used in most European countries. Which one of these methods is adopted depends upon prevailing conditions. The slaughter method is no doubt economically more practicable in the United States than in some other countries. Many European countries, however, have laws and regulations providing for the slaughter of animals affected with foot-and-mouth disease. These regulations can be put into effect whenever those in control believe that this will prevent the extension of the disease.

The United States has no reason to change its method of dealing with foot-and-mouth disease. This country eradicated the disease not only in the relatively small outbreaks that occurred in 1902, 1908, 1924–25 (in Texas), and 1929, in which only a few thousand head of livestock were involved, but also in the more severe and extensive outbreaks of 1914–15 and 1924–25 (in California).

In 1914–15 the disease occurred in 22 States and the District of Columbia and severely affected the Union Stockyards of Chicago, probably the largest stockyards in the world. In the States involved in this outbreak there has been no recurrence since the eradication of the last infection in May 1916, more than 25 years ago. During the outbreak, 77,240 cattle, 85,092 swine, 9,767 sheep, and 123 goats were slaughtered as infected or exposed.

In the 1924–25 outbreak in California, 58,791 cattle, 21,195 swine, 28,382 sheep, and 1,391 goats were slaughtered. These included many cattle and sheep grazing on the range. Although the infection spread to the deer in the Stanislaus National Forest, necessitating the destruction of 22,214 deer, of which 2,279 showed lesions of foot-and-mouth disease, it was possible to prevent the spread of the disease to other States and to eradicate it from California. A later minor occurrence of foot-and-mouth disease in California in 1929 was in no way associated with the 1924 outbreak.

The effectiveness of the slaughter method depends upon three principal procedures:

(1) The slaughter and proper disposal of animals remove at once the greatest source of active virus and avoid the possibility of having carriers remain alive. The slaughter and burial are carried out as rapidly after diagnosis as possible. Frequently disposal has been accomplished within 18 hours after the report of infection.

(2) The thorough cleaning and disinfection of the premises and of materials possibly contaminated with virus remove and destroy the greater portion of whatever virus may remain active after proper burial or burning of slaughtered carcasses.

(3) Test animals, including cattle and hogs, are allowed to feed and graze where they will come in contact with all parts of premises and objects which might have been contaminated with foot-and-mouth virus. Hogs are especially desirable in these tests on account of their rooting habits. If any virus has escaped the cleaning and disinfecting processes, the test animals should reveal it by contracting the disease.

COOPERATION OF LIVESTOCK OWNERS AND THE PUBLIC

In the foregoing discussion information concerning foot-and-mouth disease has been presented rather fully so that livestock owners and the public may be adequately informed. Additional information is available in Farmers' Bulletin 666, Foot-and-Mouth Disease, and in supplementary publications. A documentary sound motion picture portraying laboratory and field scenes is likewise available, as a loan, for projection before interested groups.

Public understanding and cooperation are essential for the prompt suppression of possible future outbreaks of this highly infectious and very serious malady. All persons should report immediately to State and Federal veterinary officials, preferably by telephone or telegraph, any case suspected of being foot-and-mouth disease. Promptness is especially desirable when there is a possibility of the animals' being moved from their home ranges, pastures, or premises. Meanwhile efforts should be made to close completely all channels by which infection may escape from the area involved. No movement of livestock or commodities from the premises should be permitted. Dogs, cats, poultry, and other roving animals should be closely confined.

Although strict quarantine of infected premises, and those nearby, is necessary for the prompt eradication of foot-and-mouth disease (fig. 2), the Federal Bureau of Animal Industry seeks to prevent unreasonable quarantines and embargoes not based on experience or scientific knowledge of the disease. Quarantines and regulations for which there is no adequate basis cause unnecessary losses to both agricultural and commercial interests.

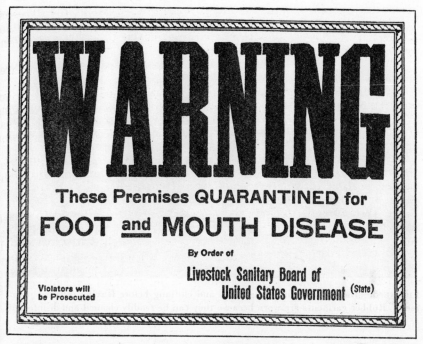

FIGURE 2.—Quarantine notice of the kind displayed on infected premises.

Since Federal and State inspectors engaged in eradication work must necessarily perform many arduous duties, the public is earnestly requested to give such workers full cooperation. Owners who witness the condemnation and destruction of their animals must consider that the sacrifice of relatively small numbers of affected and exposed livestock is for the protection of the Nation's vast herds and flocks. During an outbreak, owners often insist that veterinary authorities experiment with a wide variety of proposed drug remedies and argue that officials are ignoring possible carriers of the infection, such as flies, bumblebees, baby chicks, etc. This is an inopportune time for such contentions, which may interfere with and retard the necessary work.

Veterinary officials keep constantly in touch with new scientific and practical developments in the prevention and control of this disease. For instance, in the last outbreak in the United States in 1929, a 1½-percent solution of sodium hydroxide was extensively used as a disinfectant (fig. 3). As previously noted, the effectiveness of this simple common chemical had been established a few years before by the Department of Agriculture Foot-and-Mouth Disease Commission. Also, in the 1929 outbreak, the use of heavy chicken-wire fencing, often 7 feet high, to enclose infected premises proved highly effective (fig. 4) in restricting the movement of dogs, cats, poultry, and even persons. In some instances such fencing was used in the case of exposed herds and thus prevented the spread of the disease even before it was clinically recognized.

FIGURE 3.—Inspectors disinfecting boots and clothing before leaving infected premises. Rubber garments are worn because they can be readily cleaned and disinfected.

FIGURE 4.—High woven-wire fence around infected premises. A guard system is likewise maintained.

As a means of offsetting losses to livestock owners from the condemnation of animals during an outbreak, the State and Federal Governments have paid indemnities based on the full appraised value of animals slaughtered. To allay excitement and groundless rumors, which frequently accompany the appearance of foot-and-mouth disease, the Department of Agriculture disseminates dependable information concerning outbreaks promptly through the press and by radio broadcast.

Briefly, conditions that favor the prompt eradication of foot-and-mouth disease are: (1) Early discovery of the infection, (2) a cooperative attitude on the part of livestock owners and local agencies, (3) dependance on time-tried measures having a scientific basis, and (4) faith in the ability of the eradication forces to conquer the disease again as they have done before.

Parasites and Insects Affecting Livestock

BY BENJAMIN SCHWARTZ AND F. C. BISHOPP [1]

HERE is a general survey of the more important types of internal parasites and insects that attack livestock, telling what they are and how they affect animals and outlining the methods commonly used to control them.

PARASITES that attack livestock and poultry may live on the skin or in its layers (external parasites) or in the digestive tract, the liver, the lungs, the kidneys, and elsewhere in the body (internal parasites). With few exceptions, the external parasites are insects or forms related to insects. Most of the internal parasites are either microscopic organisms known as protozoa or belong to a group of larger parasites known collectively as worms.

Although the direct injuries produced by external parasites are confined for the most part to the skin, some of them have a profound effect on the general health. In addition to causing serious annoyance, some of the bloodsucking insects and related forms such as ticks introduce the germs of diseases.

Internal parasites seriously injure the parts of the body in which they become localized, their presence in large numbers frequently resulting in stunting, unthriftiness, wasting, and death.

In this article the more important external and internal parasites that are common to different kinds of domestic animals and poultry are discussed.

INTERNAL PARASITES AND THE DISEASES THEY CAUSE

The parasites affecting the various domestic animals are more or less related. Those that affect horses and mules in the United States,

[1] Benjamin Schwartz, who prepared the section on parasites, is Chief of the Zoological Division, Bureau of Animal Industry, and F. C. Bishopp, who prepared the material on insects, is Assistant Chief of the Bureau of Entomology and Plant Quarantine.

however, with only a few exceptions, are not closely related to those affecting cattle, sheep, and goats. Since the domestic ruminants are closely related to one another, it is not surprising that they harbor the same or closely related species of parasites, which produce similar diseases. Parasitic diseases more or less like those occurring in domestic ruminants are known to affect swine also. The domestic ruminants and swine are therefore more often common hosts of certain groups of parasites and associated diseases than are domestic ruminants and horses, or horses and swine, or all of these animals together. The parasites and parasitic diseases of dogs and cats discussed in this article, though related to some of those affecting farm animals, are not transmissible to them.

The parasitic diseases of domestic birds, with the exception of coccidiosis, which affects poultry as well as food animals and pet animals, are caused by organisms most of which are not closely related to those that cause disease in livestock, and they are not discussed in this article.

The severity of the parasitic diseases depends in general on the number of parasites present in the affected host animal. As a rule the presence of relatively small numbers of parasites produces no noticeable symptoms or only slight ones; moderate numbers produce symptoms that are more or less pronounced; and large numbers usually cause severe symptoms. It must be borne in mind, however, that light or moderate symptoms may later become pronounced or even severe. Such an increase in the severity of symptoms in parasitic infections is an outward expression of increasing damage sustained by the host, resulting as a rule from an increase in the number of causative organisms present. In coccidiosis this increase results partly from the multiplication of coccidia within the host and partly from the intake of additional infective organisms from the outside. In the other diseases discussed, the increase in the number of offending organisms results solely from the continued intake of infection.

COCCIDIOSIS

Coccidiosis, a disease affecting cattle, sheep, goats, swine, pet stock, and poultry, is caused by protozoan organisms known as coccidia, which live in the cells of the intestinal lining. The infective microorganisms gain entrance into an animal by being swallowed with feed or water that is contaminated with the droppings of animals already infected.

Coccidia are unusual among the parasites affecting domestic animals and poultry in that each of their various species is strictly specific to one species of animal, except as noted below. Coccidia of chickens and other poultry do not appear to be transmissible from one species of bird to another, and bird coccidia are not known to be transmissible to livestock, or vice versa. Each class of livestock, with the possible exception of sheep and goats, harbors its own species of coccidia. Coccidia of sheep are identical with those in goats, as far as can be judged from the structure of the organisms occurring in these two hosts, but conclusive proof of cross transmission from sheep to goats, or the reverse, is still lacking.

The life history of coccidia, beginning with the infective organism outside the host, is as follows:

An infected animal or bird may eliminate thousands of oöcysts (coccidia organisms in the resistant stage) daily with its droppings. Under favorable conditions of temperature and in the presence of moisture, each normal oöcyst develops until, in a few days, through successive division, it contains eight sausage-shaped infective bodies known as sporozoites. Susceptible animals grazing on pastures contaminated with the droppings of infected hosts or animals and birds swallowing feed or water so contaminated ingest the oöcysts. In the host's intestine, the outer membrane of the oöcyst, acted on by the digestive juices, ruptures or softens, and the sporozoites within, activated by the warmth and other conditions in the intestine, escape into the lumen (cavity) of the gut. Each sporozoite is able to attack an epithelial, or membrane, cell, penetrate it, grow at its expense, and ultimately destroy it. Before the cell has been destroyed, however, the parasite has divided into a number of new infecting bodies, which escape from the parasitized host cell when it disintegrates. Each of the new infective bodies repeats the process of cell penetration, growth, multiple division, and cell destruction. As a result, the intestinal lining becomes rapidly denuded of many of its cells, and the finer blood vessels are exposed and ruptured, producing hemorrhage into the intestinal lumen.

Sooner or later, a more complicated method of reproduction takes place, resembling in many respects the fertilization of the egg by the sperm in higher animals. The coccidial cell that has become fertilized secretes a membrane around itself and is eliminated from the intestine with the droppings. In this last stage it is known as an oöcyst. The oöcyst lives and develops in the open, as previously noted, and serves to propagate coccidiosis from host to host.

A severe infection with coccidia produces diarrhea and the liquid feces may become mixed with blood. Bloody diarrhea is characteristic of coccidiosis of poultry and cattle and occurs in other affected animals. Hosts that recover from coccidiosis continue discharging oöcysts for a long time. Livestock and pets, except in very severe infections, usually make a recovery, and chickens also recover, though less often. Susceptible young animals and birds occupying quarters with those that are or were affected are thus exposed to infection.

DISEASES CAUSED BY NEMATODES IN THE ALIMENTARY CANAL

Of the worm parasites affecting the alimentary canal, the following, all nematodes, are among the most injurious to farm animals: (1) Stomach and intestinal threadworms, known collectively as trichostrongyles; (2) hookworms; (3) nodular worms; and (4) large roundworms, or ascarids. Under certain conditions each of these kinds of worms is capable of injuring the wall of the alimentary canal and producing more or less serious injuries elsewhere in the body, making the affected host animal definitely sick. Hookworms and ascarids also affect dogs and cats, producing diseases similar to those caused by related parasites in livestock.

Threadworms as a Cause of Gastroenteritis

Threadworms, or trichostrongyles, which occur in different classes of domestic animals, are especially abundant in cattle, sheep, goats, and related wild ruminants. In domestic ruminants the different parasites concerned become localized in the fourth stomach or in the small intestine; some species become localized in both places.

The threadworms are from about a fifth of an inch to an inch long and very slender. Some species, the common stomach worms (*Haemonchus contortus*), for instance, live in the stomach. Others, like the bankrupt worm (*Trichostrongylus* species), which gets its common name from the saying that stockmen whose animals are heavily parasitized are headed for bankruptcy, occur mostly in the intestine, though one species becomes localized in the stomach. A few, particularly those belonging to the genus *Nematodirus*, occur only in the intestine. The activities of these worms cause an inflammation of the stomach and intestinal wall known as gastroenteritis.

The common stomach worm occurs in all domestic ruminants, as do several other species of threadworms. Certain other species, however, occur only in cattle. Some occur only in sheep and goats.

Swine harbor in the stomach a trichostrongyle known as *Hyostrongylus rubidus*, and one of the trichostrongyles of ruminants, *Trichostrongylus axei*, occurs also in the stomach of equines.

The cycle of infection of host animals with trichostrongyles is as follows.

Microscopic eggs are discharged by the female worms into the lumen of the host's alimentary canal and are eliminated from the body with the droppings. During warm weather the eggs in the droppings develop and hatch in a few days. The larvae feed on the manure and are transformed into the infective stage in about a week, meanwhile passing through two successive molts. Cold weather retards the development of eggs and first-stage larvae and may even kill them, but infective larvae are resistant to cold and some other hazards. The infective larvae migrate upward on grass and other vegetation after rain, fog, or dew, when a film of moisture on the plants provides favorable conditions for them. Cattle, sheep, and goats grazing on pastures at such times may swallow dozens of larvae with almost every mouthful of forage.

Once in the host's alimentary canal, the larvae are localized in the stomach or intestine, depending on the species. Usually they penetrate the mucosa (mucous membrane), where they undergo at least part of their development, finally returning to its surface, on which, in most cases, they live as adults. After the mating of the sexually mature worms, the females begin to discharge eggs, which, as already noted, are eliminated with the droppings.

Trichostrongyles in the digestive tract of ruminants are capable of producing severe injuries. Some injuries are brought about by the penetration of the larvae into the mucous lining of the stomach or intestine, which destroys its integrity. Some of the worms suck blood and thus produce minute lacerations of the stomach or intestinal wall, from which blood oozes and may continue to ooze for a time after the worms have completed their meal. It is possible also that as a result of their life processes the parasites liberate toxic substances that are absorbed by the host. When the worms are abundant, the parasitized host becomes anemic, shows evidence of malnutrition even though adequate feed is available, suffers from digestive disturbances of various kinds, as evidenced by diarrhea or in some cases constipation, and is adversely affected in other ways.

The sum total of the injuries produced results in a condition designated by stockmen as unthriftiness. Marked unthriftiness leads to wasting and death. Losses among calves, lambs, and kids all over the United States, particularly in farm flocks and herds rather than on the open range, are due to a considerable extent to the effects of trichostrongyle infection, as is also much of the unthriftiness among cattle, sheep, and goats.

Trichostrongyles in swine and horses are known to produce local injury to the stomach wall. The precise effect of these nematodes on the health of their hosts has not been adequately investigated.

Hookworm Disease

Hookworm disease, characterized principally by anemia, is produced by a group of nematodes that occur in the small intestine of domestic ruminants, swine, dogs, and cats. Hookworms of the smallest species are somewhat longer than most trichostrongyles, and all are much stouter. Hookworms are included among the strongyles, which are related to the trichostrongyles but differ from them in a number of ways. The principal difference is that a strongyle has a relatively large cup-shaped mouth, which is missing in the trichostrongyles. The mouth of the hookworm is provided with teeth, cutting plates, or both. The hookworm attaches itself to the intestinal wall, sucks a piece of the intestinal-wall lining into its cup-shaped mouth, and lacerates the finer blood vessels with the teeth or cutting plates, thus obtaining blood.

The available evidence indicates that hookworms of cattle, sheep, and swine are specific to their respective hosts and are not transmissible from one kind of animal to another. The hookworms of sheep and goats belong to the same species and can presumably be transmitted from one of these animals to the other. Hookworms of dogs and cats also are specifically identical and are transmissible from one to the other but not to domestic ruminants or swine.

Hookworms are acquired by susceptible hosts either through the swallowing of the larvae that hatch on the ground and develop in a week or so to the infective stage or through the penetration of the infective larvae through the host's skin. When the larvae are swallowed, they reach their preferred location in the host's intestine and develop to maturity as do the trichostrongyles. When hookworm larvae have penetrated the skin, they enter the blood vessels and are carried by the blood to the heart and thence to the lungs. Here they escape from the finer blood vessels by rupturing their walls, which brings them into the air spaces of the lungs. By upward migration they reach the branches of the windpipe known as the bronchi, pass through the windpipe proper, and arrive at the back of the mouth. On being swallowed, they get into the intestine, where they develop to sexual maturity and the female worms produce eggs, which are eliminated with the host's droppings.

The penetration of the infective larvae through the skin may produce inflammation and even more serious lesions. In addition, injury to the skin in any animal is fraught with more or less danger. A broken skin opens the way for micro-organisms, some of which may be capable of doing serious harm. Although the migration of hookworm larvae through the host's lungs apparently does not produce the severe injury that follows a similar migration of ascarid larvae, hookworm larvae rupture the blood vessels in the lungs and produce more or less hemorrhage. The chief injury to the host, however, is inflicted by the adult worm in the intestine. As previously stated, the parasites attach themselves to the intestinal lining and extract blood. The wounds produced by the laceration of the intestinal mucosa continue to bleed for a time after the worms detach themselves. The parasites find a new location on the intestinal wall, attach themselves, obtain blood, and seek another spot probably many times in the course of a day. When many worms are present, the bites and subsequent hemorrhages result in numerous small bleeding wounds on the intestinal wall. Marked anemia, swellings of the pendent portions of the body, weakness, and emaciation may follow. Other aggravating symptoms are digestive disturbances, including diarrhea or constipation.

Nodular Disease

Nodular disease occurs in cattle, sheep, goats, and swine. It derives its name from the lesions produced by the immature worms, which occur in small circumscribed areas, known as nodules, raised above the surface of the intestinal lining. The adult worms occur in the lumen of the large intestine. Nodular worms bear a marked resemblance to hookworms, their size range being from about half an inch to about an inch in length by about one–fiftieth of an inch in width. Their close relation to hookworms may be judged from the fact that, like hookworms, they are strongyles and possess a more or less cup-shaped mouth, which, however, is not armed with teeth or cutting plates.

Each of the susceptible domestic animals harbors its own kind of nodular worms, which so far as is known, are not transmissible from one to another except for those of sheep and goats.

Nodular disease affects sheep primarily and may lead to serious consequences in these animals if the nodules are numerous. In the other farm animals affected, the infection is more or less mild, so far as available evidence shows. Not all the pertinent facts concerning nodular disease in farm animals have been ascertained, however, and it is possible that further investigation may reveal that many species not now suspected of being particularly injurious are able to do considerable harm.

Infection with nodular worms, like that with hookworms and the trichostrongyles, results from swallowing the infective larvae with feed or water. These larvae have passed through two successive molts since they were hatched from eggs discharged with the droppings of host animals. Under favorable conditions of temperature and moisture such as prevail during the late spring, summer, and early fall in all but the dry sections of the United States, the entire development on the ground or on a pasture, beginning with the egg and terminating with the infective larva, requires about a week.

On entering the body of its host the larva penetrates into the intestinal lining, undergoes its early development there, and returns to the lumen of the intestine to complete its growth and development to sexual maturity. After mating, the females begin to discharge eggs, thus starting the cycle all over again. Some larvae become trapped within the nodules and may remain there for months or die without getting out.

The penetration of the larvae into the intestinal mucosa produces an inflammatory reaction. Wandering cells from various parts of the body, especially from the blood, are attracted to the place of irritation. The accumulation of these cells around the larvae produces the solid swelling, or nodule, that becomes raised above the surface of the intestinal lining. At the apex of the nodule there is an opening for the escape of the larva and for the discharge of pus. Nodules of the common nodular worm of swine are of pinhead size, but other species parasitizing swine create nodules that are much larger and sometimes greatly inflamed. Occasionally such nodules become greatly enlarged and are filled with pus, which gives them the appearance of abscesses. In sheep the nodules are conspicuous, particularly after they have become filled with a cheesy mass resulting from the disintegration of various cellular elements within them. This soft mass becomes hardened, or calcified. Sheep guts containing calcified nodules are spoken of as knotty guts.

Although much still remains to be determined concerning nodular disease of domestic animals, there is no doubt concerning its seriousness in sheep. In severe cases, sheep suffer from diarrhea and from disturbance of the slow, rhythmic intestinal movements known as peristalsis, and this interferes with the digestion and absorption of food. There is also a possibility that the absorption of disintegrating products within the nodules produces more or less poisoning, which, together with other effects, results in emaciation.

Ascariasis

Ascariasis designates the injuries produced by the large intestinal roundworms, or ascarids. They are the largest known nematodes affecting livestock, the average size of the adults being that of an ordinary lead pencil. Some ascarids are even larger, reaching a length of 1 foot and sometimes more. Those that occur in dogs and cats are much smaller, their maximum length being about 5 to 6 inches. In their adult state, ascarids occur in the lumen of the small intestine. The larvae, however, migrate extensively in the body of their host before settling down in the small intestine.

Horses, cattle, and swine harbor species of ascarids peculiar to them. The pig ascarid (*Ascaris suis*) [2] is also found occasionally in sheep and goats and more rarely in cattle. The true bovine ascarid (*Ascaris vitulorum*) [3] occurs in domestic cattle, the zebu, and the Indian buffalo; so far as is known, it is rare in the United States, having been found in only a few instances in cattle in the South. The horse ascarid (*Ascaris equorum*) [4] occurs in horses, mules, and zebras. Of the ascarids that parasitize pet animals, *Toxascaris leonina* occurs in dogs and cats, *Toxocara cati* only in cats, and *Toxocara canis* only in dogs.

Hosts acquire ascarids through swallowing the microscopic infective eggs of these parasites with forage, dry feed, soil, or water. The eggs, which are discharged with the host's droppings, are relatively thick-shelled and highly resistant to various factors deleterious to most of the eggs of the other parasites previously discussed. Ascarid eggs develop on the ground slowly, even under favorable conditions, 2 to 3 weeks being required, as a rule, for development to the infective stage. An infective egg contains an immature coiled worm known as an embryo. When the worm escapes from the egg it is known as a larva.

When ascarid eggs reach the intestine of the host the shell is affected by the digestive juices and ruptures as a result of the vigorous movements of the embryos within. The immature worms or larvae thus get into the lumen of the gut and attack its lining. After penetrating the intestinal wall, the larvae get into the blood stream and are carried to the liver and thence to the lungs. There they leave the capillaries and get into the air spaces. From this point their migration is similar to that of hookworms. The ascarid larvae get to the back of the mouth and are swallowed. On reaching the intestine again after their roundabout journey through the host, they settle down and develop to maturity in about 2 months. Following the mating of the sexes the females begin to discharge eggs.

The injuries produced by ascarids include those that are inflicted by the larvae in the course of their migrations as well as those caused by the adult worms in the intestine. The larvae do some damage in the liver and much more in the lungs, where they cause pin-point hemorrhages resulting from the rupture of the capillary blood vessels. When many larvae go through the lungs at the same time, the small hemorrhages become numerous and are more or less serious. Furthermore, the passage at about the same time of many larvae through the lungs of a young animal produces irritation and disturbs respiration, as evidenced by rapid breathing and a cough, symptoms of profound injuries to the lungs. In heavy invasions of the lungs by migrating larvae, the animal develops a bronchopneumonia with more or less fever. The injuries produced by the migrating larvae are especially severe in pigs, which remain more or less stunted even after recovery.

---

[2] Commonly referred to in scientific literature as *Ascaris lumbricoides*, the species occurring in man; in this article *Ascaris suis* is used largely for convenience.
[3] Regarded by some scientists as constituting a distinct genus and designated as *Neoascaris vitulorum*.
[4] Regarded by some scientists as constituting a distinct genus and designated as *Parascaris equorum*.

The adult worms in the intestine rob the host of essential food, this being, perhaps, the slightest of the injuries inflicted. Ascarids are provided with strong lips that bear numerous minute denticles, and they can abrade and otherwise injure the intestinal lining. When they are numerous, they tend to become entangled with one another, forming a mass of coiled worms large enough to produce intestinal obstruction, which may have serious and sometimes fatal consequences. In their wanderings the adult worms sometimes enter the bile duct and reach the liver, obstructing the flow of bile and producing jaundice. The worms may get into the stomach, migrate up the gullet, and enter the windpipe, where they can cause strangulation. They may even perforate the intestines and produce inflammation of the lining of the abdominal cavity, a condition known as peritonitis. Moreover, ascarids produce intestinal disturbances, characterized by constipation or diarrhea. If one or more worms die in the intestine and because of constipation are not eliminated quickly, their disintegration within the host may result in the liberation of toxic substances. This evidently occurs in bovines that harbor the true cattle ascarid. The injuries already enumerated and others not mentioned interfere with the growth of young host animals, producing more or less permanent stunting, marked unthriftiness evidenced by emaciation, a rough coat, and even death when the worms invade vital organs.

LUNGWORM DISEASE

Lungworm disease of domestic animals, known also as verminous bronchitis, is caused by nematodes living in the lungs and known, therefore, as lungworms. These parasites belong to a group of nematodes called metastrongyles, which are related to the strongyles and trichostrongyles, previously discussed. Aside from their localization in the lungs, metastrongyles differ from the two other groups in certain fundamental anatomical characters.

Horses, cattle, sheep, swine, dogs, and cats all harbor lungworms that are not transmissible from one kind of host to another, except that those occurring in sheep are also known to parasitize goats and to occur also in certain wild ruminants.

Depending on the species of lungworm concerned, the life history is either direct or indirect. In both cases, the eggs hatch in the lungs, and the larvae are coughed up and swallowed. On reaching the outside with the host's droppings, the larvae of species having a direct life history develop into the infective stage after two molts, as do those of the strongyles and trichostrongyles. The infective larvae are taken into the host's body with forage, contaminated dry feed, or water. The common lungworms (*Dictyocaulus*) of horses, cattle, sheep, and goats are acquired in this way. In the indirect life cycle, the larvae eliminated with the droppings do not develop unless they reach suitable intermediate hosts. The larvae of swine lungworms (*Metastrongylus* and *Choerostrongylus*) develop to the infective stage in various earthworms; those of the hair lungworms of sheep and goats (*Protostrongylus* and *Muellerius*) develop in snails, as do also those of cats. The life history of the dog lung-worm (*Oslerus*) has not yet been ascertained. The larvae of the cat lungworm, a species occurring in pulmonary blood vessels, may be acquired by snails as a result of active penetration into the soft parts of these intermediate hosts.

The details of the life histories of lungworms have not been ascertained in all cases. So far as the facts are known, the course of events is briefly as follows: Regardless of whether the infection is acquired directly or through intermediate hosts, the infective larvae, on getting into the host animals, reach the lungs by way of the lymph and blood. (Lymph is a body fluid that permeates all the cells and collects in lymph vessels, in which it moves toward the heart; it differs from blood in that it has no red blood cells.) Lymph moving in its vessels finally gets into large lymph vessels, one of the principal ones being known as the thoracic duct. Through this duct the lymph and any lungworm larvae it happens to contain get into large veins that empty into the heart. From the heart the larvae get to the lungs through the pulmonary arteries. In the lungs they escape from the capillary vessels into the air spaces, from which, by active migration, they reach the bronchioles and other parts of the air system of the lungs. There, in their preferred location, lungworms develop to sexual maturity and mate, and the females discharge the eggs, thus starting the life cycle all over again.

Lungworm disease is characterized by a cough, rapid respiration, weakness, emaciation, and sometimes anemia. Diarrhea may be present also, especially in calves. Lungworms appear to produce more serious disturbances in domestic ruminants than in pigs, although young pigs may suffer severely from lungworm infection and it retards their growth. Little is known about lungworm disease in horses. In farm animals that are heavily parasitized by lungworms, solidified areas, sometimes involving almost an entire lobe, may be present in the lungs. Other lung areas may become emphysematous (permanently distended with air) and cease to function.

LIVER FLUKE DISEASE

Liver fluke disease, as it occurs in domestic ruminants in the United States and Territories, is caused by three species of trematodes, of which the common liver fluke is the most important. This fluke, known to zoologists as *Fasciola hepatica*, is about an inch long by about half an inch wide. A closely related species, the giant liver fluke (*Fasciola gigantica*), about 1 to 3 inches long by about half an inch wide, is the liver fluke of cattle in the Hawaiian Islands, where the common liver fluke does not occur. A third species, the large American liver fluke (*Fascioloides magna*), reaches a size up to 4 inches long by about 1 inch wide.

The common and giant liver flukes occur in the bile ducts and the large American liver fluke in the liver substances. All three species occur in cattle, sheep, and goats. Liver flukes occur also in wild ruminants and other animals, including horses and swine. Liver fluke disease affects principally cattle and sheep among domestic animals, sheep suffering more severe effects than cattle.

Infected hosts eliminate the microscopic fluke eggs with the droppings. The eggs develop in wet or swampy pastures after a period that varies with the species as well as with the temperature; cold weather retards development, and warm weather accelerates it. The larva that hatches from the egg is provided with cilia (hairlike processes) that enable the immature worm, known as a miracidium, to swim. Unless the miracidium finds a suitable snail host within a few hours, it dies.

Snails become infected by the penetration into their soft parts of one or more miracidia. Within the snail the miracidium undergoes a marked transformation, giving rise to several generations of larvae, those of the final generation being known as cercariae. The cercariae, of which several hundred may be produced from a single miracidium, leave the snail and swim about in water for a time. Sooner or later each cercaria secretes a protective membrane, or cyst, about itself. The encysted cercariae lodge on vegetation or float on the surface of water.

Cattle, sheep, goats, and other susceptible hosts, grazing on wet pastures infested with cercariae, swallow them with forage or water. After reaching the intestine of the final host, the cercariae escape from the cysts and bore through the intestinal wall, getting into the body cavity, where they migrate for a time. Within a few days they enter the liver by perforating its capsule. After wandering in the liver substance, the young of the common and giant liver flukes enter the bile ducts, in which they become mature in about 3 months. The large American liver flukes wander in the liver of cattle, in which they become encapsulated, or surrounded by a tough wall, before attaining maturity. In sheep, these parasites do not become encapsulated, the sheep liver apparently offering little resistance to their migrations; hence in sheep, even a small number may practically destroy the entire liver and cause death. Mature liver flukes discharge eggs which reach the intestine with the bile and are then eliminated with the droppings.

The common liver fluke has been studied more extensively, with regard to both its life cycle and the injuries it produces, than the other two flukes, and hence more is known about the disease it produces. In the discussion that follows, the facts have been ascertained by investigations on the common liver fluke and apply for the most part to it.

Liver flukes are bloodsuckers, their bloodsucking activities beginning shortly after they enter the host. The flukes possess muscular suckers with which they can attach themselves to almost any tissue, and the mouth sucker exerts enough pressure on delicate linings to rupture the fine blood vessels underneath. If many flukes pierce the liver capsule at the same time or in rapid succession, more or less extensive hemorrhage into the abdominal cavity may follow. In the bile ducts, the flukes continue to suck blood as long as they remain. Because of their spiny surface, they irritate the delicate lining of the bile ducts and when present in large numbers obstruct the flow of bile. The anemia produced by the bloodsucking activities of the worms is evidenced in the host animal by the appearance of dropsy, especially a swelling of the lower jaw called bottle jaw by stockmen.

In many parts of the world, including certain sections of the United States, liver flukes are the most serious cause of sickness and mortality among sheep. In the past, the flocks of certain countries have been drastically reduced by the ravages of the common liver fluke.

In cattle, digestive disturbances, especially constipation, are symptoms of liver fluke disease. Other evidences of illness observed in these animals are weakness and, in the advanced stages, prostration. As a rule, only calves show marked symptoms, dying in extreme cases, whereas adult cattle are rather resistant to the effects of flukes. Rather serious losses result from the condemnation of cattle livers affected with flukes under Federal and other competent meat inspection. Considering the fact that liver flukes are prevalent in some of the most important areas where beef cattle are raised, namely, the South and Southwest (particularly the Gulf coast region) and the Rocky Mountain and Pacific Coast States, it is evident that the losses resulting from condemnation of calf and cattle livers are a serious financial drain on the meat industry. The financial losses involved are borne, at least in part, by the beef producers.

CONTROL OF INTERNAL PARASITES

Reduced to the simplest terms, the most effective control of the parasites discussed in this article involves systems of management that would entirely preclude the acquisition by domestic animals and pet stock of parasite eggs and larvae from contaminated ground and pastures. Unfortunately, no system of management has yet been devised that will accomplish this. As previously emphasized, parasitized animals eliminate parasite eggs and larvae with their droppings, which are deposited on the ground and on pastures from which the animals obtain their feed. In short, host animals contaminate their own table.

Although complete control by management alone is impossible in the light of present knowledge, much can be done to reduce the intensity of parasitic infection by sanitation practices designed to cut down the intake of excessive numbers of parasite eggs and larvae by grazing animals. Among the practices that experience has shown to be effective are rotation of pastures and of stock, sanitation in animal shelters, a clean water supply, and similar measures that will tend as much as possible to cut down excessive contamination of forage, dry feed, and water with droppings of parasitized host animals.

Since the parasites of horses are in general not transmissible to ruminants, it is safe to rotate equines with ruminants. One of the stomach worms of horses, however, occurs also in ruminants, and when this worm is abundant in either ruminants or equines rotation of these two classes of livestock should be avoided. It is safe to rotate equines with swine and swine with ruminants, but one kind of ruminant should not be rotated with another, because, as has been mentioned, some of the injurious parasites of cattle, sheep, and goats are specifically identical and cross-transmissible. Where there is sufficient pasture land, it is a sound procedure to move animals from one pasture to another as often as available pastures permit, because of the excessive numbers of parasite eggs and larvae that accumulate during the late spring, summer, and early fall when the same pasture is used continuously.

Special measures designed to reduce or even destroy the snail population are necessary for the control of liver flukes. Draining wet, swampy, and boggy land and broadcasting bluestone or copper sulfate are known to destroy aquatic snails, which constitute an essential link in the life cycle of the fluke. When such measures cannot be carried out, it is advisable to fence off wet areas on pastures so that cattle, sheep, goats, and other susceptible livestock will not have access to them.

Stables, barns, and other animal shelters, as well as paddocks, yards, and corrals, should be kept as clean as possible. This necessitates the frequent removal of manure, which should not be spread on pastures to which the domestic animals will have access during the same season but should be utilized as fertilizer on fields sown to crops other than forage crops. Spreading manure on pastures disseminates gross parasitism in stock, and the practice should be discontinued in the interest of sound husbandry.

Grain fed in barns and other animal shelters should be placed in boxes well above the ground, and hay should be placed in overhead racks to prevent contamination of the feed with manure that may be teeming with eggs and larvae of parasites. Other measures, especially adequate feeding and the supplying of necessary minerals that promote the health and tend to build up the resistance of animals, tend to prevent the inroads and depredations of parasites.

Young animals of all kinds appear to be far more susceptible to the acquisition of parasites and to the effects of parasitic infections than are older animals. Special attention should be paid, therefore, to young stock, which should be kept away, as far as possible, from pastures contaminated with the droppings of older stock and from association with older animals that may harbor parasites without showing clinical symptoms.

TREATMENT FOR THE REMOVAL OF PARASITES

Drugs used for the destruction of parasites and their subsequent removal from hosts are known as parasiticides. Those used specifically for removing worms are anthelmintics. There is no medicinal treatment for coccidiosis, and since all other diseases discussed in this article are caused by worms, the treatments recommended are anthelmintics.

Anthelmintic medication must be based on sound knowledge of the parasites present in the host, the anatomy and physiology of the animals to be treated, the physiological action of the drug or drugs to be used, judgment in the selection of a specific treatment where more than one drug is available, appraisal of the condition of the subject to be treated to discover indications against any specific treatment or all possible treatments, and skill in administering drugs. Medicinal treatment for the destruction of parasites is the business of the veterinarian, just as prevention of parasitic infection by sanitation and other methods is the business of stockmen and farmers.

Treatments administered to kill and expel worms from livestock and poultry have one of the following main objectives: (1) To give parasitized animals that are obviously sick or definitely unthrifty relief from the drain of parasites; or (2) to treat flocks and herds in which parasites are present or suspected, but are not yet sufficiently numerous to cause alarming symptoms, in order to prevent the development of parasitic diseases to a point where marked unthriftiness and death will occur. The former is curative treatment; the latter is largely prophylactic (preventive) treatment. In either case, a sound diagnosis must be established to determine the kinds of parasites present.

For certain species of parasites there are specific treatments; for others there are more general treatments, effective for more than one species. The diagnosis, which must be made before treatment is undertaken, should be based on (1) microscopic examination of the host's droppings to determine the kinds of parasite eggs or larvae present, or the examination of blood smears for larvae in cases of infection involving this type of parasitism; or (2) post mortem examination of one or more animals that have died from parasitism or of one or more unthrifty animals that have been slaughtered, with particular attention to the tissues and cavities where parasites commonly occur. Either procedure involves technical knowledge and skill not possessed by most stockmen. Unthriftiness and other symptoms of parasitism are useful aids in diagnosis. Some symptoms similar to those due to parasitism may be the result of faulty feeding, or inherent in poor breeding, or caused by other conditions. When unthriftiness and the related symptoms previously enumerated are present in animals of good breeding that are being fed an adequate diet, a presumptive diagnosis of parasitism is warranted in most cases. A conclusive diagnosis should be based on post mortem findings or microscopic evidence of such parasitism in the droppings.

In general, all drugs used for killing parasites are more or less toxic; ordinarily, only a toxic agent can destroy parasites, which are living creatures, leading their normal lives within a host. Since anthelmintics may be more or less toxic to the host, the doses administered must be so standardized in relation to the weight of the host animal as to cause the maximum injury to the parasites and the minimum injury to the host.

Some anthelmintics still in use were developed many years ago. Most of those used in treating livestock, pet stock, and poultry, however, have been developed during the last 2 or 3 decades by rigorous, painstaking scientific research. Much of this research was conducted by parasitologists of the Bureau of Animal Industry. In this research dozens of drugs have, in some cases, been tested on animals and birds before a useful one was discovered.

It is not the purpose here to give specific treatments for the removal of the various internal parasites discussed. Such information is given in the various articles dealing with the specific parasites and associated diseases of farm animals, pet stock, and poultry. A few drugs more or less widely used as anthelmintics are mentioned, however, for purposes of illustration.

Carbon bisulfide is used for the removal of ascarids from horses; oil of chenopodium is used for the removal of palisade or red worms from horses and ascarids from swine, dogs, and cats. Dilute solutions of copper sulfate (bluestone), with or without nicotine sulfate, are used in the form of a drench for the removal of stomach worms from cattle, sheep, and goats. Carbon tetrachloride is used for removing liver flukes from sheep, and the same drug or tetrachlorethylene, in capsules, for the removal of stomach worms and other trichostrongyles from domestic ruminants and of ascarids and hookworms from dogs and cats. There are no known anthelmintics effective for the removal of lungworms.

The ideal anthelmintic would have no injurious action whatsoever on the host and yet would kill all or practically all the parasites harbored by the animal. Such a drug has not yet been discovered. The nearest approach to it is phenothiazine, developed by the United States Bureau of Animal Industry during the last 3 years, which appears to be the most useful anthelmintic yet discovered.

This drug, administered in proper therapeutic doses in a capsule, in a drench, or in feed, is efficacious for removing stomach worms and related trichostrongyles, as well as hookworms and nodular worms, from cattle, sheep, and goats, palisade or red worms and related strongyles from horses, and nodular worms from swine. No other known anthelmintic removes so many different kinds of parasites from the host animals mentioned as does phenothiazine.

INSECTS AFFECTING LIVESTOCK

The relationship of insects to animals is one of considerable complexity. Some insects are injurious to animals in many different ways, whereas some are actually beneficial. Some carry disease germs on their beaks, hairy bodies, and feet, or even within their bodies, and transfer them mechanically and more or less accidentally; others serve as necessary hosts of disease germs or of higher forms of life such as parasitic worms; that is, the disease-producing organism must spend some stage of its life within the insect's body. Some insects injure livestock by biting—sometimes drawing considerable quantities of blood—and by crawling and scratching. Some live within the digestive tract, causing irritation and interfering with the digestion and absorption of food. Some burrow in the tissues, which become inflamed or are actually destroyed.

Many insects are more or less specific to a host—that is, they limit their attack to one or a few kinds of livestock—whereas others attack many or all kinds.

The North American cattle tick, for example, attacks cattle, horses, mules, and sometimes sheep, but it is only to bovines that it transmits cattle tick fever, the deadly disease which gives it its principal importance. The American dog tick and the Rocky Mountain spotted fever tick attack bovines and rarely transmit any disease to them, but they do transmit a deadly disease to man. On the other hand.

the screwworm attacks practically all kinds of domestic animals and many wild animals and though it does not transmit any disease, it is injurious and may be deadly to any animal it attacks.

It is thus impossible to combine in a convenient list insects having the same characteristics, habits, and methods of injuring livestock. The principal kinds of insects affecting animals may be broadly grouped, however, as follows:

(1) *Mites.* The mites that attack livestock and poultry breed exclusively on the bodies of their hosts. Injury is caused by bloodsucking and the formation of scabs and other skin affections. Considerable damage to hides intended for leather and to the wool of sheep and mohair of goats sometimes results. Mites can be controlled by dipping infested animals in insecticidal solutions or applying insecticides by hand.

(2) *Ticks* (including, among others, the North American cattle fever tick, the Gulf coast tick, the spinose ear tick, the fowl tick, the brown dog tick, the tropical cattle fever tick, the lone star tick, the Rocky Mountain spotted fever tick, and the American dog tick). In general, ticks breed on animals but pass part of their lives in pastures or in close proximity to other places frequented by the hosts. Injury consists for the most part in the weakening of the host by the drawing of blood or in the transmission of disease. General methods of control include the application of insecticidal solutions, usually by dipping, or the application of insecticides to the breeding places; in the case of cattle ticks, also removal of host animals from the infested areas until the ticks starve to death.

(3) *Flies* (including various species of mosquitoes; cattle grubs, or heel flies; the screwworm fly; the stablefly; the horn fly; horse bots; the sheep head bot; the so-called sheep tick; the pigeon fly; horseflies; and the buffalo gnat). Flies breed in various situations. The nature of their injury to animals is extremely varied. It may consist in loss of blood and irritation due to biting (the latter sometimes resulting in violent and injurious reactions on the part of the animal), in the transmission of disease, or in the feeding of the insect larva on the vital tissues of the host. It is usually necessary to use specific control measures for each species of fly. Some species can be controlled by treatment of the breeding place or by the use of insecticidal sprays at the time the insect is making its attack on the animal. In other cases it is necessary to apply insecticidal ointments or washes to the body of the host. A fumigant introduced into the stomach of the host is used, among other things, for the control of horse bots.

(4) *Lice.* Lice breed only on the host. Injury consists in lowered vitality of the animal and reduction in the quantity and quality of animal products. Control is effected by the application of insecticides, either dry or in solution. They may be applied by dipping or with spraying or dusting apparatus.

(5) *Fleas.* Fleas breed in debris, bedding, and dirt in places frequented by their animal hosts. Their bloodsucking and irritating propensities make them especially injurious to poultry. Their attacks may cause the death of young chickens. Egg production is

interfered with seriously. Dog and cat fleas transmit the dog tapeworm to these animals. Fleas also seriously annoy human beings and carry bubonic plague and endemic typhus. They can be controlled by cleaning up and treating infested premises and by applying insecticides to the host.

CAUSES OF INSECT ABUNDANCE

A distinction should be made between the causes of insect abundance and the causes of insect attacks on animals. Conditions for which man is responsible often favor insect breeding, and as a result the insects become so abundant that they are a scourge to livestock. In other cases the breeding of large insect populations is a natural phenomenon and cannot be charged directly to man's interference with nature. Man does not directly cause insect attacks on animals. The attacks are caused by natural forces—primarily hunger or the biological urge to perpetuate the species.

Any large-scale interference with nature is likely to produce far-reaching and sometimes unforeseen consequences. In general, nature tends to maintain a working balance between insects and their animal hosts whereby both may live a normal existence and neither can exterminate the other. There is no record of extensive insect depredations on the buffalo that once ranged over a wide area in the western part of our country, but since that region has been brought directly under human management, insect attacks on livestock have become a serious problem.

Grouping and holding livestock in barns and small enclosures disturbs the balance of nature. When barns and barnyards are allowed to become insanitary there is a further disturbance. Accumulations of manure mixed with straw and uneaten feed and trampled into a mire furnish breeding places for such insect pests as stableflies, houseflies, and fleas. Neglected pigpens and runs may be expected to produce houseflies and fleas, and a dirty chicken house is an ideal place for the breeding of sticktight fleas and other pests of poultry.

Insanitary household premises may also provide insect breeding places. In some parts of the country, houses are raised above the ground, and dogs, cats, and rodents run freely underneath them, creating a condition favorable to the breeding of fleas. Anything that will hold water, such as tin cans or old automobile tires scattered about the yard, is a potential breeding place for mosquitoes.

In farm fields it is not unusual to find old neglected strawstacks. The parts that become wet breed stableflies (dog flies) by the thousands. Where peanuts are grown, the same thing occurs if the trash and litter from the crop is left in piles on the field.

On irrigated farms and ranches the faulty or careless handling of water is often responsible for veritable plagues of insects. Slight leaks in the main canals form pools of standing water in which mosquitoes breed. Holding water on the fields for an unnecessarily long period produces the same result on an even larger scale, and poor drainage is likely to cause swamp conditions conducive to the continuous breeding of both horseflies and mosquitoes.

Where livestock are subject to attack by the screwworm, certain farm and ranch practices have a great influence on the breeding of this pest in destructive numbers. Any flow of blood, however slight, on an animal predisposes it to screwworm attack. Among the practices that may be expected to contribute to an abundance of screwworms are the use of excessive amounts of barbed wire; neglect of projecting nails and jagged boards or poles in corrals, pens, and barns; performing surgical operations on animals in seasons of the year when screwworms are active; faulty regulation of breeding, resulting in the dropping of young when screwworms are abundant; carelessness in shearing, resulting in cuts in the animal's skin; and the use of dogs to catch animals, resulting in wounds that attract the screwworm fly. Wounds caused by fighting between animals, the scratching of needlegrass or pricklypear in pastures, and the attacks of other species of parasites, such as horn flies, horseflies, and ticks, also favor infestation by screwworms.

In the case of such pests as lice and mange mites, it seems apparent that poor condition, for which the owner is presumably responsible, predisposes the animal to attack. Dairymen and stockmen sometimes claim that animals in poor condition are more heavily infested with cattle grubs than fat ones, but there is no conclusive evidence that this is a fact. It seems certain, however, that the attacks of internal or external parasites in considerable numbers reduce the vitality and condition of an animal.

PREVENTION AND TREATMENT OF INSECT ATTACKS

Obviously, the first line of defense against insects should be to eliminate breeding sources, so far as possible, and to avoid conditions that predispose animals to attack. When such measures are only partly successful, direct action must be taken against the insects.

The diversity of the habits and life histories of insects makes it necessary to use many different control methods. Seldom can a method of control be set up that is applicable to more than one species. Dipping vats installed for the control of cattle ticks may be used to control cattle lice or mange mites and for dipping sheep and goats for lice and scab, but for most of the insect pests of livestock individual methods of treatment are necessary.

In determining a suitable method of control it is necessary for the investigator to know the life history of the insect in detail. Most insects undergo radical changes in form in the course of their life cycle, the usual stages being egg, larva, pupa, and adult. At each stage the insect is likely to be subject to different environmental influences, and its ability to fend for itself and ward off danger is likely to be different. One of the fundamental principles of insect control is that, to be effective and easy to apply, it must be directed at the weakest or most susceptible stage in the insect's life. In some cases this is the adult stage and in others one of the immature stages. Sometimes, however, control measures may profitably be directed against more than one stage. In the case of the housefly, for instance, it is obviously the larval stage that offers the best chance for the effective use of control measures, but since considerable numbers of larvae succeed in reaching the adult stage in spite of the measures taken to destroy them, it is advantageous also to use fly traps and sprays for the control of adult flies. Likewise, in the case of the stablefly the principal control measures are directed against the larvae, which breed in massed wet straw, seaweed, and vegetable litter of various kinds; but it is impossible to locate all the breeding places, and some adults are usually present to pester livestock, so that an effective fly spray is also distinctly useful.

The horn fly, practically a specific pest of cattle, is best controlled in the adult stage by contact sprays or by cattle fly traps, which are reasonably effective. In small pastures it is possible to destroy the larvae by hauling a brush drag over the fresh droppings to break them up and allow them to dry quickly. The breeding of houseflies is also prevented by regularly removing manure from barn lots and pens and scattering it on fields soon to be plowed.

Specific treatments adapted to each of many types of insects affecting livestock are described in other articles in this volume.

Bacterial Infections and Parasites Common to Man and Animals

BY GEORGE W. STILES AND JOHN T. LUCKER [1]

THE LIST of diseases and parasites common to man and animals given in this article is only a partial one, but it is enough to show that the control of animal diseases is more than merely an agricultural problem.

BACTERIAL INFECTIONS

MAN is indebted to the animals for food, furs, clothing, leather, fertilizer, and medicines, besides work and companionship, but on the other side of the ledger, many human diseases are traceable directly or remotely to contact with diseased animals or their byproducts.

The publicity given in recent years to research on brucellosis, psittacosis, rabies, tularemia, encephalomyelitis, and other animal maladies transmissible to man has called attention to the fact that diseased animals are potential hazards to human health. The intimate association between man and his household pets and his direct contact with other domestic animals create a public health problem of universal importance, and the necessity for a closer bond between physicians and veterinarians is becoming apparent. Many physicians are now making use of the scientific facts established by veterinary research workers in the field of animal diseases.

Lower animals may harbor four general types of diseases common to man: (1) Infections caused by animal parasites, of which trichinosis, acquired from eating raw pork, is an example; (2) virus diseases, such as encephalomyelitis, or sleeping sickness, in equines and

[1] George W. Stiles is Bacteriologist in Charge, Branch Pathological Laboratory at Denver, Colo., and John T. Lucker is Associate Zoologist, Zoological Division, Bureau of Animal Industry. Dr. Stiles prepared the section on bacterial infections and Mr. Lucker that on parasites.

man; (3) mycotic, or fungus, diseases, illustrated by actinomycosis, or lumpy jaw; (4) infections of bacterial origin. The fourth group will be considered first, and a discussion of the parasitic diseases will follow. Virus and fungus diseases are not included in this article.

UNDULANT FEVER (BRUCELLOSIS)

In the United States, brucellosis, commonly known as undulant fever, probably ranks first in importance as a bacterial disease that may be acquired by man from animals. Cattle, swine, and goats, which harbor *Brucella abortus*, *Br. suis*, and *Br. melitensis*, respectively, are the three chief sources of infection. Recently several investigators have shown that horses also may be infected with *Brucella* organisms. Huddleson (*15, p. 184*)[2] says these bacteria may be isolated from suppurative lesions (injuries producing pus) involving the withers, poll, bony tissues, tendons, joints, and breastbone of horses. Stone (*29*) shows that horses in contact with cattle may have a higher incidence of brucellosis than those kept away from cattle, and he also states that horses may transmit Bang's disease to cattle and that man may acquire undulant fever from *Brucella*-infected horses.

Since cattle are more widely distributed than other domestic animals, they are largely responsible for the spread of brucellosis in man, chiefly through his use of raw milk. On the other hand, field data and studies of epidemics indicate that swine harbor a more virulent species of the *Brucella* organism than bovines and are therefore an important source of infection in hog-raising regions. Although *Br. melitensis*, the species found in goats, is considered the most virulent of the three to man, the resulting disease of man is the least common, owing to the relatively small number of milk-producing goats in this country.

Human infection with *Brucella* is acquired by contact with infected animals as well as by consumption of raw milk and other dairy products. Handlers of livestock, veterinarians, and employees in meatpacking establishments are especially exposed by their contact with infectious material from animals having brucellosis.

In combating brucellosis the chief control measures are the elimination of animals known to be diseased, the observance of sanitary precautions in handling sick animals and their discharges, and the efficient pasteurization of all milk and dairy products intended for human use. The Federal-State cooperative program for the control of brucellosis, or Bang's disease, begun in 1934, should materially reduce the incidence of human infection caused by *Brucella abortus*.

TUBERCULOSIS

The bovine type of the tubercle bacillus is the one usually encountered in human tuberculosis arising from animal sources. The avian, or bird, type may be considered as a negligible factor in producing human infection.

---

[2] Italic numbers in parentheses refer to Literature Cited, p. 310.

A case of generalized human-type tuberculosis in a 10-year-old parrot was recently diagnosed in the Denver laboratory of the Bureau of Animal Industry. Among other lesions, a canker containing large numbers of tubercle baccili was found in the mouth of this bird. The bird's owner, who was tuberculous, had allowed the parrot to eat seeds from his mouth. Hutyra and Marek (*16, v. 1, p. 734*) found parrots to be rather susceptible to the human type of tuberculosis, and it is probable that the parrot contracted the disease from the man.

Data from the Bureau of the Census show the death rate in man from all types of tuberculosis in the United States to have declined steadily from 150 per 100,000 in 1918 to 46 per 100,000 in 1940. In European countries, where the incidence of tuberculosis in cattle is still exceedingly high, human infection with the bovine type is correspondingly greater than in this country.

Infections with the bovine type of tuberculosis are more often found in children than in adults. This type of infection is manifested largely in the glands, bones, and intestinal membranes.

Although the consumption of raw milk from diseased cows is held largely responsible for the bovine infection in man, other modes of transmission are possible. The hands are subject to dangerous contamination, and through carelessness this and other deadly diseases may be contracted or spread. Hermansson (*14*) says:

> After examining the carcasses of tuberculous cattle, the meat inspectors washed their hands in sterile water. This was centrifuged and the sediment injected into guinea pigs. Eleven of the 15 inoculations produced tuberculosis in the guinea pigs. The wash water from the hands of the meat cutters was shown to contain tubercle bacilli. The rinse water from the towels used by the meat inspectors was injected into guinea pigs, producing tuberculosis in every instance.

The destruction of millions of tuberculous cattle is only one of the many factors in lowering the human tuberculosis death rate. Preventive medicine also has made remarkable progress. Hygienic education, tuberculosis associations, the general use of pasteurization, personal cleanliness, the sanitary drinking cup, greatly increased hospitalization of tuberculous patients, modern surgical methods, tuberculin tests, earlier diagnosis due to the X-ray, improved dietary and nursing facilities, and many other factors have contributed to the decline of tuberculosis in the United States.

SEPTIC SORE THROAT

Septic sore throat in human beings is often traceable to the consumption of raw milk from cows harboring the *Streptococcus epidemicus* organism. The onset of symptoms occurs within a few days after exposure. Mastitis (garget, or caked udder) in cows may be caused by a variety of bacteria, including certain types of streptococci and staphylococci. Some scientists state that the bovine mastitis streptococcus is a cause of septic sore throat in man, but others disagree.

Concerning the relationship of streptococci recovered from man and those isolated from the lower animals, Kelser (*18*) states that according to some authorities *Streptococcus pyogenes* is common to both man and animals. Others maintain that the organism is primarily a human type. The evidence indicates that man is relatively resistant to the streptococci of animal diseases, and that lower animals are not commonly affected by streptococci of human origin, but that such infections do occur occasionally.

A case of streptococcus infection in an old parrot recently came to the attention of the Denver laboratory. From a cankerous mass in the bird's throat, large numbers of hemolytic streptococci—those which destroy red blood cells—were isolated. The elderly woman who owned the parrot and frequently kissed it was suffering from sore throat and pleurisy, contracted after the bird became ill. Both recovered after sulfanilamide treatment.

Milk or other animal products may be contaminated with streptococci of human origin and the infection transmitted to other persons. Under such circumstances the organism might be mistakenly considered to be of animal origin. As a public health measure, rigid precautions should be followed to prevent udder infection by milkers suffering with sore throat. Efficient pasteurization of all dairy products is the best safeguard against human infection.

DISEASES CAUSED BY PASTEURELLA ORGANISMS

Tularemia

The germ that causes tularemia, *Pasteurella tularensis*, has been discovered during the last 25 years by workers in the United States Public Health Service. The disease was first observed in ground squirrels. In different localities it is known as deer fly fever or rabbit fever, and it is now recognized ·in a wide variety of wildlife, including birds. Although discovered in Tulare County, Calif., the disease has been found in every part of the United States, and in foreign countries. In recent years its prevalence in this country has increased. Parker (*31*) and others have recovered tularemia organisms from flowing streams in the Rocky Mountain region. A recent Public Health Report (*32*), devoted to a discussion of the sources, symptoms, and prevention of tularemia, states that there were 2,088 cases and 139 deaths from this disease in the United States alone in 1938. In 1939, 2,200 cases were reported.

Human beings acquire infection through the bites of ticks, bloodsucking flies, lice, and bedbugs, and by contact with diseased animals, especially wild rabbits. The bacteria from infected material can penetrate even unbroken skin. Eating partly cooked flesh from sick animals occasionally causes illness. Lesions in man usually appear as minute papules and pustules at the site of infection, accompanied by enlargement of the regional lymph glands. The mortality rate is about 4 percent.

Wearing rubber gloves will protect laboratory workers, butchers, cooks, and others engaged in handling or dressing rabbits or other game from infection with tularemia. The avoidance of tick-infested areas, protection against insect bites, and thorough cooking of the meat of wild animals are also recommended.

Bubonic Plague

The black death, or bubonic plague, must be considered as one of the worst pestilences known to man. It has resulted in the death of untold millions throughout the world. Serious epidemics have occurred in recent years, and the infection still smolders in China, Japan, India, the Union of Soviet Socialist Republics, the Philippines, Africa, Argentina, Brazil, Australia, and many other lands. In the United States, small areas of infection among rodents may be found in parts of Arizona, California, Idaho, Montana, Nevada, New Mexico, Oregon, Utah, Washington, and Wyoming. Recently infection has been reported in Colorado and North Dakota. Hampton (*12*), in a Public Health Report, states that from the time of the first appearance of plague in the United States in 1900 to January 1, 1940, 499 cases and 314 deaths were recorded.

Endemically, the plague is essentially a disease of wild rodents, being harbored principally by ground squirrels and three species of rats. These rats are found in every part of the world, and most of them harbor a few fleas. The fleas on rats infected with plague bacteria (*Pasteurella pestis*) consume the germs and can transmit the disease to man by their bites. It is reported that one flea may ingest several thousand germs at a single feeding, and these multiply many times in its intestinal tract. The organism can also be transmitted through the human skin by fecal contamination from the fleas, and droplet infection is an important source of contagion in the pneumonic (lung) type. The usual type of the disease is glandular, although pneumonic, septicemic, and ambulatory forms (the last not confining the patient to bed) may occur. Glandular plague is manifested by enlarged glands (buboes) accompanied by depression, high fever, and marked prostration. The incubation period is 2 to 8 days after the bite of an infected flea. The mortality rate is high.

Control measures for bubonic plague consist largely in the destruction of rats, ground squirrels, chipmunks, prairie dogs, and other rodents harboring the organism. Modern methods of ratproofing buildings, fumigating ships from foreign ports, and systematic campaigns of rodent extermination in localities where plague infection is known to exist are the chief measures used. A lasting and efficient vaccine or serum is not yet available as a preventive treatment.

Pasteurellosis

Only a few human cases of animal pasteurellosis are mentioned in medical literature. An unusual infection in a man who had been bitten by a domestic rabbit affected with snuffles is reported by Boisvert and Fousek (*5*). The man was a 53-year-old animal caretaker employed in a research laboratory. The rabbit bit him on the right index finger. Within a few hours the finger became red, swollen, and painful, and the man was sent to the hospital for treatment. The course of the illness was irregular and was followed by recovery after about 5 weeks. The same type of organism, *Pasteurella lepiseptica*, was recovered in considerable numbers from both the abscessed finger and the nasal discharge of the sick rabbit. Persons handling rabbits with snuffles should take care to avoid infection.

GLANDERS

Glanders occurs naturally in horses, mules, and donkeys. It is caused by *Actinobacillus mallei.* Commonly called farcy, it has a world-wide distribution but is now seldom encountered in the United States in either equines or human beings. The disease is acquired by human beings through close contact with infected animals. The symptoms may be obscure, but mortality in the acute form is reported as approximately 60 percent. Control measures depend upon eradication of the malady in equines.

ANTHRAX

Historically anthrax, or splenic fever, is one of the oldest bacterial diseases of man and animals. It was studied by the early investigators who laid the foundation of modern bacteriology.

Anthrax is world-wide in its distribution. It is caused by the *Bacillus anthracis*, a very resistant, spore-forming, rod-shaped organism capable of surviving many years in soil. Various species of animals, as well as man, may be affected. Sheep, cattle, and horses are susceptible. Swine are regarded as more resistant; they often harbor the organism in their cervical (neck) glands with impunity. Infection occurs occasionally in carnivores, including minks, foxes, and other fur-bearing animals.

One type of infection in man, called malignant pustule, is usually acquired from anthrax-infected animals or their byproducts. Skinning animals that have died of anthrax and handling their hides or wool frequently results in infection. The pulmonary form, wool sorters' disease, is brought about by inhaling spore-laden dust in wool establishments.

The initial lesions in man are usually on the neck, forearm, hands, or face. Dressed furs from animals infected with anthrax may be a source of infection of the neck in women. Insufficient treatment of the bristles used in making shaving brushes largely accounted for the cheek lesions in men reported during the first World War. More efficient methods of sterilizing hides, wool, and hair should prevent infection from these sources.

The Denver laboratory of the Bureau has diagnosed anthrax in 129 cattle, 10 minks, 9 hogs, and 1 man. The man contracted infection on his hand while skinning a cow.

The complete destruction of all anthrax-infected carcasses and the sterilization of the byproducts of infected animals are essential. A better understanding of the deadly nature of the disease by livestock owners, the public in general, and wool-factory workers in particular should aid in the prevention of unnecessary human infection.

SWINE ERYSIPELAS

Erysipelas in swine and other animals is caused by a minute, non-motile, slender, rodlike organism called *Erysipelothrix rhusiopathiae,*

Beaudette and Hudson (*4*) and Madsen (*20*) report erysipelas in turkeys. Graham and others (*11*) found the disease in ducks, and it is known that pigeons are susceptible. Sheep frequently become infected with the erysipelas organism.

The disease seems to be spreading among domestic animals. During the last few years the Denver laboratory has diagnosed 529 positive cases of erysipelas in swine by the isolation of the bacterium or by the agglutination test.

The disease caused by the swine erysipelas organism in man is called erysipeloid, meaning "like erysipelas," and is characterized by skin lesions. Human erysipelas is caused by streptococci and is not to be confused with the infection from swine. Swine erysipelas is transmitted to human beings by contact with diseased animals or their byproducts, gaining entrance chiefly through broken skin. Infection has been reported among workers in button factories where raw bones are used in the manufacturing process; small splinters of bone penetrate the skin, causing infection. The disease also occurs among workers in fisheries.

Erysipeloid may be prevented by precautions in handling swine products and by antiseptic treatment of cuts and abrasions on the hands, which are more liable to infection than any other part of the body.

LISTERELLOSIS

That many bacterial diseases of animals were not known until the last few decades is demonstrated by the recent discovery of another malady affecting both man and lower animals. The English investigators Murray, Webb, and Swann (*26*) described in 1926 a disease of animals characterized by a monocytosis (an increase in one of the types of white blood cells), the causative agent of which they named *Bacterium monocytogenes*. This name was later changed to *Listerella monocytogenes*.

Merchant (*22*) states that this organism affects a variety of species, including swine, sheep, cattle, foxes, and man. It is a small, motile rod with round ends. The mode of transmission is unknown. Guinea pigs, rabbits, mice, and rats were found experimentally to be susceptible, the animals usually dying within 48 hours after exposure.

Since the disease may be confused with other febrile disorders, the isolation of the organism is essential to the establishment of a definite diagnosis.

Preliminary studies of the disease in sheep by the Pathological Division, Bureau of Animal Industry (*30, 1940*), indicate that it may have potential economic importance in the livestock industry. The early recognition of this malady in animals may prevent its becoming a serious public health problem.

FOOD POISONING

Increasing evidence indicates that various types of bacterial food poisoning may come directly or indirectly from animals or their byproducts. The three general groups of organisms causing food poisoning now recognized are *Salmonella, Staphylococcus,* and *Botulinus.*

The Salmonella Group

Various members of the *Salmonella* group of bacteria, *S. aertrycke, S. enteritidis,* and *S. suipestifer,* are sometimes associated with diseased animals and their excretions. Infected cattle, sheep, swine, and poultry are the chief sources of this type of food contamination. When these bacteria gain entrance to perishable foods that are held at warm temperatures for varying periods, they form toxins.

Hardison and Shipley (*13*), of the Tennessee Department of Public Health, describe a rare case of paratyphoid septicemia in a man due to the *Salmonella suipestifer* organism. Their investigations failed to discover the probable source of the infection. The history of the case showed alternating chills and fever, high temperature, fatigue, loss of appetite, dyspnea (labored breathing), weakness, profuse sweating, and occasional vomiting. After about a month's illness the patient died of respiratory failure. Blood-agglutination tests were negative for typhoid, paratyphoid A, undulant fever, tularemia, typhus fever, and Rocky Mountain spotted fever, but the patient's blood serum reacted positively with a standard paratyphoid B antigen and also with organisms isolated from his own blood.

Read (*28*) reports a case of endocarditis in a 49-year-old woman due to *Salmonella suipestifer* infection classified as the European strain. This is the only case of endocarditis caused by the European strain that has been reported. Positive blood cultures before and after death and the demonstration of bacilli of the type of *S. suipestifer* in sections of the affected heart tissues established this organism as the probable causative agent. Fatal infections due to *S. suipestifer* are usually associated with food poisoning.

Cases of endocarditis in man ascribable to *Salmonella suipestifer* infection are rarely observed. Forster (*10*) reports two fatal cases of bacterial endocarditis due to *S. suipestifer* of the American type. Diagnosis was established by repeated blood cultures and the finding of bacilli of the *Salmonella* type in tissue studies. The identity of the organism was confirmed by cultural methods.

The Staphylococcus Group

In recent years various strains of staphylococci have been identified as the cause of toxic symptoms in human beings who had eaten contaminated foods. A case of mild gastrointestinal disturbance recently occurred among 36 persons after a luncheon. Thirty of these ate creamed chicken and became ill, whereas the remaining 6, who did not eat the chicken or ate it sparingly, were not affected. An investigation indicated that the creamed chicken was the probable source of infection. About 200 cubic centimeters (6½ ounces) of sterile water in which the cook who boned and minced the chicken dipped her fingers was shown to contain approximately 5,000 bacteria per cubic centimeter. Most of the organisms from this wash water were *Staphylococcus aureus*, and the same type was recovered in large numbers from the chicken.

In another instance the Denver laboratory found 60 million *Staphylococcus aureus* organisms per gram in ham that had been infected before cooking and held for several days without refrigeration before being served. This ham apparently caused illness in more than 300 persons, but there were no fatalities. Symptoms developed within a few hours after eating and lasted about 1 day. Nausea, vomiting, diarrhea, prostration, and griping pains were the chief symptoms. The use of pure, wholesome food materials kept under clean conditions, handled by clean hands, and served when freshly cooked will prevent such cases of food poisoning. The Denver laboratory is finding many cases of *Staphylococcus aureus* infection in men and animals from sources other than food.

In several instances staphylococcal arthritis in turkeys has been diagnosed, and *Staphylococcus* is often recovered in cases of omphalitis, or unhealed navels in poults. In a recent case of pustular dermatitis (skin eruption) in a 6-week-old chicken, *S. aureus* was recovered in large numbers from the nodules. In handling specimens affected with this organism, care should be taken to prevent self-infection.

The Botulinus Group

At least three types of botulinus organisms, A, B, and C, produce an extremely deadly toxin in perishable foods outside the animal body. Since *Clostridium botulinum* grows only in the absence of oxygen, the canning of vegetables and other perishable products favors the growth of this organism when the spores are not completely destroyed by heating. Merely tasting the contents of a can which have been spoiled by botulinus germs may cause death. Each of the three types produces its own toxin, which is neutralized by the respective type of antitoxin. This highly resistant spore-forming germ originates in polluted soil. Several animal species normally harbor botulinus organisms in their intestines, and their excretions pollute the soil, indirectly contaminating food intended for human consumption. Kalmbach (*17*) has shown that type C botulism is the principal cause of a sickness that destroys large numbers of wild ducks annually.

The botulinus bacillus is extremely resistant. Some years ago, a pure culture of one type of this organism, recovered from home-canned string beans, was boiled for 6 hours in an open kettle at the Denver laboratory without destroying the spores. The beans had been canned during the summer in glass jars by the open-kettle method and held in a storage cellar about 9 months before being used. Several persons died from botulism after eating the beans in a salad. Nearly half of the canned vegetables stored in the same cellar were found to have swollen caps and spoiled contents at the time the family became ill with botulism. Had the beans been boiled for a few minutes after the can was opened, the toxin (though not the spores of the germs) would have been destroyed, and the beans would have been safe as food at that time. However, if the same

beans containing spores had been recanned and allowed to stand at
room temperature for another long period, a new lot of toxin would
have developed.

A wide variety of food products, such as string beans, spinach,
corn, sausage, meats, and fish, are subject to spoilage from improper
canning. This is due to the fact that these products are nonacid, and
under such conditions higher temperatures than boiling are required
to kill the micro-organisms present in any reasonable time.

PARASITES COMMON TO ANIMALS AND MAN

Man probably owes most if not all of the parasites that he may
harbor to his long and intimate association with animals. Comparatively few intestinal worms or other parasites live exclusively as
adults in or on human beings. Among the worm parasites (helminths), only seven that are more or less widespread and important
are said to be confined to human beings (8). Two of these are
acquired by man from the flesh of domestic animals used for food.
The other five are transmitted from one human being to another
directly or through the agency of invertebrate animals acting as
carriers (vectors) for the worms in their infective stages.

Included in the group of adult helminths common to animals and
man are a small number of species that are frequently found in
human beings. It is believed, however, that some of them are rarely
or never transmitted from animals to man and that, despite the
identical appearance of worms of these species from human and
animal hosts, those found in man are distinct biological strains or
varieties. Man is merely an occasional host of adult worms of many
species usually found in dogs, cats, swine, sheep, cattle, and other
animals, and he may become parasitized by the larval stages of
certain worms that occur as adults in some of these animals. Such
infestations are traceable to direct or indirect association and contact
with the normal hosts or the invertebrate carriers of the parasites.

Some of the parasites transmissible from domestic and wild animals to man act as carriers for virus and bacterial diseases, and
others directly and seriously affect his health, sometimes causing
death. Many kinds of parasites do not produce well-defined, acute
symptoms following a more or less regular course, as do bacterial
and virus infections, and the injury caused by parasites usually
depends on the number present.

By no means all the parasites transmissible from animals to man,
or even from domestic animals to man, are included in this article,
but most of the important ones and most of those reported as having
been found in human beings in the United States are mentioned
or briefly discussed.

EXTERNAL PARASITES

Man has his own characteristic insect or insectlike external parasites, but he acquires others by contact with parasitized animals or
infested surroundings.

In general, lice are very host-specific—that is, each kind of louse is confined to a certain kind of host—but fleas are less particular, and man is a frequent host of the common fleas of dogs and cats. These fleas are the intermediate hosts of a tapeworm transmissible to man. In India a rat flea has a part in the transmission of the dreaded bubonic plague. The sticktight flea that infests chickens in the southern part of the United States also attacks man. Two strains of endemic, or murine, typhus fever virus have been recovered from fleas of this species (7).

In human beings, dogs, cats, ruminants, pigs, and other mammals, mange is caused by the same species of mite, *Sarcoptes scabiei*, but the mites are sometimes difficult to transfer from one species of host to another, and they are thus regarded as different biological varieties. Another mange mite that occurs on cats can live on man temporarily. It is questionable whether the hair-follicle, or demodectic, mites that attack man and other animals belong to more than a single species, but all attempts to transmit these mites from dogs to human beings have failed. Workers in poultry houses are likely to become parasitized by the red mite, which is transmissible from chickens to man.

Several kinds of ticks are equally adaptable to almost any warm-blooded animal. Ticks are extremely important as carriers of disease, and their bites also are sometimes serious. Among the ticks that usually occur on animals but may attack man are species of *Argus* that occur on poultry; the spinose ear tick of horses and other domestic animals; species of *Ixodes* that occur on dogs; the Rocky Mountain wood tick, which occurs on a variety of mammals; and the common dog tick. Both the Rocky Mountain wood tick and the dog tick carry the virus of spotted fever and transmit the disease, which is of considerable importance to man in the United States. Bites of the Rocky Mountain wood tick are known to have caused cases of so-called tick paralysis in man in this country, and this tick also carries the organisms of tularemia and other animal diseases transmissible to man. Some of the species of *Ornithodorus* that infest pigs, cattle, and other mammals also attack man, among them some that transmit sporadic relapsing fever to human beings.

PROTOZOA

So far as is known, man does not acquire any protozoan parasites by eating the flesh of meat animals.[3] Some of the protozoans that live in domestic animals are apparently transmissible to human beings, infection following ingestion of the infectious stages passed with the feces of animals. Thus *Balantidium coli*, a ciliate (having hairlike organs for locomotion) occurring in the intestines of man and sometimes causing a type of dysentery, is also found in pigs, and these animals are thought to serve as reservoirs of infection. Though some authorities deny the probability, others have consid-

---

[3] *Sarcocystis* infections are common in the striped muscle fibers of sheep, cattle, and hogs, but human infections with *Sarcocystis* are rare and probably do not result from eating infected meat.

ered it likely that cats and rodents serve as reservoirs and disseminators of infections with *Giardia*, a flagellate (having whiplike organs for locomotion) that occurs in man's intestines and sometimes causes a recurrent diarrhea and other disturbances.

Some investigators believe it probable that pigs, rats, and especially monkeys act as reservoir hosts for *Entamoeba histolytica*, which causes amoebic dysentery and is one of man's most important intestinal protozoans. Wild and domestic animals are suspected of being reservoir hosts for certain of the trypanosomes that cause disease in man. The type of sleeping sickness caused by trypanosomes, which is widespread in Africa, is transmitted by insects and ranks as one of the most important diseases of man. Possibly in some cases the organisms are transmitted from wild animals to man. Trypanosome diseases are not definitely known to occur in man in the United States, although it is suspected (*33*) that undiagnosed cases of Chagas' disease, which is caused by trypanosomes, have occurred in the Southwest. It is definitely known that in this region reduviid bugs, the vectors, and rodents and other mammals, the reservoir hosts, harbor the species of trypanosome that causes the disease.

Perhaps the most important protozoan disease of man in this country is malaria. There is no evidence, however, that animals act as reservoir hosts for the organisms that cause human malaria.

WORM PARASITES

The roundworm, or nematode, *Trichinella spiralis*, is undoubtedly the most important worm parasite transmissible from domestic animals to man. This worm causes trichinosis (see the article on p. 787 of this volume).

Two other worm parasites that man acquires by eating infected meat, either raw or imperfectly cooked, or improperly processed meat products are the beef tapeworm and the pork tapeworm. The adults live in the small intestine of man, and the eggs or segments containing eggs pass out with the feces. Cattle or swine that swallow the eggs of the respective tapeworms become infested with the larval stages, known as bladder worms, which become localized in the muscles of these intermediate hosts. When a human being swallows the live bladderworms in meat, he becomes infected with the adult worms. Man can also serve as an intermediate host of both tapeworms, and if a person swallows their eggs as a result of insanitary conditions, he becomes infected with the bladder worm stages. The pork tapeworm is the more dangerous to man in this respect, since the bladder worms may lodge in the heart, brain, or eye and cause serious consequences. Under Federal and other competent meat inspection, infected beef and swine carcasses are condemned or are so treated as to eliminate the possibility that human beings can acquire tapeworms by eating the meat. Thorough cooking of beef and pork kills the bladder worms.

A number of species of worm parasites that normally occur in animals can reach maturity in man. In some cases the evidence for this rests on a single record or a few records, but there is no assurance that all infections are detected. Moreover, it is known that individuals differ in their resistance to invasion by parasites and that nutrition is of some importance in determining susceptibility. Again, many persons rarely or never have an opportunity to acquire parasites from farm or wild animals.

The infective stages of some of the roundworms transmissible to man develop in the host animal's feces and on the ground, whereas the infective larvae of others develop in intermediate hosts. All the flukes and tapeworms mentioned in this article require intermediate hosts.

Flukes

A species of lung fluke, *Paragonimus kellicotti*, occurs in this country in minks, hogs, dogs, cats, and other mammals. This fluke is closely related to or possibly identical with *P. ringeri* (*2*), which occurs in men and dogs in Asia and causes a very serious lung disease. *P. kellicotti* is not commonly present in man in this country, probably because the crayfish, the second intermediate host of the parasite, is not generally used here as food and when it is, it is not usually eaten raw. Though there is apparently only one record of infection with *P. kellicotti* of a person who had lived in the United States, this parasite should be regarded as potentially dangerous to man (*2*).

The common liver fluke of sheep and cattle has been reported as an accidental parasite of man in this country; aquatic snails serve as intermediate hosts for this fluke.

Heart disease in man in the Philippines has been found (*1*) to be associated in some cases with infections with certain small flukes called heterophyids. These flukes normally inhabit the lumen of the intestine of certain animals. When the young stages gain entry into other animals or man, the growing flukes invade and become buried in the intestinal mucous membrane. Some of the adult flukes die there, and the fluke eggs do not escape with the host's feces in the normal manner but instead are taken up by the circulatory system and distributed to various parts of the body. In human infections, eggs reaching the heart ultimately produce acute changes in the muscle layer, and heart failure may result. One of the flukes implicated in causing heart disease in man normally occurs in cats, although it is also found in dogs and birds (herons). In intermediate stages of development it occurs first in snails and later in fish. None of the species of flukes causing heart disease in the Philippines occur in continental United States, but it is suspected that the closely related species found in dogs and cats are potential human parasites. Fortunately the habit of eating raw fish is not widespread here.

Tapeworms

A very common tapeworm of dogs (*Dipylidium caninum*), which also occurs in cats, has fleas and lice as its intermediate hosts. Human beings, especially children, who are closely associated with dogs, occasionally become infected with this worm by accidentally swallowing fleas or lice or by putting fingers contaminated with crushed fleas into the mouth. The broad, or fish, tapeworm (*Diphyllobothrium latum*) is found in man rather frequently in many parts of the world, and in the United States it is especially prevalent in the lake regions of northern Minnesota and Michigan. Since this worm also occurs in dogs, cats, bears, and other animals, it is probably to be regarded primarily as a tapeworm of carnivores (*3*). The facts suggest that the first intermediate hosts, certain minute crustaceans (copepods of the genus *Diaptomas*), usually become infected from the droppings of these animals. Certain species of fresh-water fish are the second intermediate hosts, and man becomes infected by eating the raw or imperfectly cooked flesh of the fish.

Roundworms

Among the roundworms that have a direct life cycle (one without an intermediate host) and that occur in man as accidental parasites are a number of species of small hairworms (*Trichostrongylus*). Sheep, goats, and camels are the normal hosts of these species. The human whipworm, which is a common parasite in parts of the South, has been considered identical with the whipworm found in swine, but there is disagreement on this point, and experimental evidence that cross transmission from swine to man can occur is apparently lacking. One of the most persistent questions in helminthology relates to the cross-transmissibility from pigs to man of the common large intestinal roundworm, or ascarid, *Ascaris lumbricoides*. Ascarids from man and from swine are said to be structurally identical, and are usually considered to be of the same species. It has been found possible to infect pigs with ascarids of human origin, and it is also known that if infective eggs of swine ascarids are swallowed by man, the larvae that hatch from them reach the lungs and cause respiratory disturbances related in severity to the number of eggs swallowed. But experimental evidence that the swine ascarid can become established in the intestines of man is lacking, and the tendency is to regard the worms from the two hosts as biological varieties of a single species. A rather closely related ascarid (*Toxocara*) that normally occurs in dogs and cats has been reported as a human parasite.

Among the roundworms that occur in animals and also occasionally in human beings and are known or believed to require intermediate hosts are certain of the eye worms (*Thelazia* species). In the United States one human case of infestation with a species of eye worm (*T. californiensis*), which normally occurs in the conjunctival sac of the eye and the tear ducts of dogs and sheep, has been reported (*19*). The life cycle of this worm is not known, but it is practically certain that the parasite has an insect intermediate host.

A fairly common parasite of sheep, cattle, and swine in this country is the threadworm, *Gongylonema pulchrum*. This worm lives in burrows in the mucous membranes of the esophagus, tongue, and cheeks, and is more interesting than harmful. A few cases of human infection have been reported, including about five in the United States. The worms reported from man have been given various names, but they are probably identical with *G. pulchrum*. Also reported from man on a few occasions is the giant kidney worm of dogs and minks.

The guinea worm has not been reported in man in the United States, but specimens regarded as belonging to this species have been found in several of our mammals, and it is possible that the worm is a potential human parasite in this country (*9*). The final hosts become infected by drinking water containing the tiny crustaceans that serve as intermediate hosts for the parasite.

Thorn-Headed Worms

Thorn-headed worms (*Acanthocephala*) apparently have not been reported from man in the United States, but elsewhere both a species that is common in rats and the common thorn-headed worm of pigs have been reported from human beings on a few occasions. Cockroaches are the intermediate hosts of the former species, and the infectious stages of the latter occur in June bugs and related beetles. Experimental transmission of thorn-headed worms to man was reported as early as 1888.

Larvae of Worm Parasites in Man

The larval stages of certain parasites that live as adults in mammals and reptiles and require intermediate hosts can develop in man. Animals are the usual or normal intermediate hosts for these parasites; the larvae that develop in a human being are unable to complete their life cycle, but they are likely to damage the health of the infected person. Man's skin can be invaded by the larvae of at least one nematode that has a direct life history and lives in common household pets.

One of the most dangerous to man of all parasites is the hydatid tapeworm. The minute adults live in the intestines of dogs and allied carnivores. Ingestion of the eggs of this worm by man or by herbivorous mammals results in the development of relatively huge hydatid cysts, principally in the liver and lungs but also in the brain. Hydatid disease is treated surgically, but when malignant tumorlike cysts have developed, they can seldom be successfully removed, and usually cause death. The disease is comparatively rare in natives of the United States and Canada who remain in these countries (*21*).

Man is an occasional host of the larvae of certain wormlike parasites called pentastomids. Among these are the tongue worm, a parasite of the nasal passages of dogs, and two allied species that occur as adults in the respiratory system of snakes. In man and other intermediate hosts the larvae (nymphs) develop in the viscera.

The larvae of certain species of tapeworms of the genus *Diphyllobothrium* occur in man, causing a condition known as sparganum infection. In the United States, bobcats harbor an adult tapeworm of this genus (*D.* (*Spirometra*) *mansonoides*), which also develops in house cats and dogs (*23*). The early larval stages develop in species of *Cyclops*—minute fresh-water crustaceans—and in nature the later larval stages, or spargana, develop in snakes and field mice, though they are also experimentally infective to other animals, including monkeys, in which they reestablish themselves in the muscles. Monkeys are also susceptible to infection by mouth with the early larval stage (*24*). Human infection has been demonstrated experimentally (*25*) by implantation of spargana, and it is considered probable that it can occur naturally. One case of *Sparganum proliferum* infestation has been reported from this country; the adult of this tapeworm is unknown.

A skin inflammation called swimmer's itch, prevalent among bathers in lakes in Michigan, Wisconsin, Minnesota, and other parts of the United States, is due to invasion of the skin by the larvae (cercariae) of blood flukes, some species of which are probably parasitic in water birds (*6*). The larvae escape into the water from the snail intermediate hosts of the parasites in summer and are able to penetrate the skin of swimmers and bathers coming in contact with them. They set up a rather severe but temporary inflammation. The larvae are not known to undergo further migration and development in man, but a monkey experimentally exposed to larvae of one species, which develops into an adult in muskrats and related hosts, was found to harbor migrating worms in its lungs a few days after exposure (*27*).

A number of cases of another skin disease, known as creeping eruption, have been reported from the southern part of the United States. This dermatitis is due to invasion of the skin by infective larvae of a hookworm (*Ancylostoma braziliense*) of dogs and cats. Adult worms are found in human beings in tropical countries, but in the United States the skin condition caused by the wandering larvae is of far greater clinical importance. Apparently the larvae, which in their normal hosts leave the skin in a short time to become localized in the intestine, are trapped in the human skin because of the resistance of the human host. Infection occurs by contact with the feces of infested dogs and cats or surroundings contaminated by the feces.

LITERATURE CITED

(1) Africa, Candido M., Garcia, Eusebio Y., and Leon, Walfrido de.
    1935. INTESTINAL HETEROPHYIDIASIS WITH CARDIAC INVOLVEMENT: A CONTRIBUTION TO THE ETIOLOGY OF HEART FAILURES. Philippine Jour. Pub. Health 2: 1–35, illus.
(2) Ameel, Donald J.
    1934. PARAGONIMUS, ITS LIFE HISTORY AND DISTRIBUTION IN NORTH AMERICA AND ITS TAXONOMY (TREMATODA: TROGLOREMATIDAE). Amer. Jour. Hyg. 19: 279–317, illus.
(3) Baer, Jean G.
    1940. THE ORIGIN OF HUMAN TAPEWORMS. Jour. Parasitol. 26: 127–134.
(4) Beaudette, F. R., and Hudson, C. B.
    1936. AN OUTBREAK OF ACUTE SWINE ERYSIPELAS INFECTION IN TURKEYS. Amer. Vet. Med. Assoc. Jour. 88: 475–487.
(5) Boisvert, Paul L., and Fousek, Mildred D.
    1941. HUMAN INFECTION WITH PASTEURELLA LEPISEPTICA FOLLOWING A RABBIT BITE. Amer. Med. Assoc. Jour. 116: 1902–1903.

(6) BRACKETT, STERLING.
   1940. STUDIES ON SCHISTOSOME DERMATITIS. VIII, NOTES ON THE BIOLOGY
        OF THE SNAIL HOSTS OF SCHISTOSOME CERCARIAE IN WISCONSIN
        AND EPIDEMIOLOGICAL EVIDENCE FOR THE LIFE CYCLES OF SOME AVIAN
        SCHISTOSOMES. Amer. Jour. Hyg. Sect. D, 32: 85–104.
(7) BRIGHAM, GEORGE D.
   1941. TWO STRAINS OF ENDEMIC TYPHUS FEVER VIRUS ISOLATED FROM
        NATURALLY INFECTED CHICKEN FLEAS (ECHIDNOPHAGA GALLINACEA).
        U. S. Pub. Health Serv., Pub. Health Rpts 56: 1803–1804.
(8) CAMERON, THOMAS W. M.
   1927. THE HELMINTH PARASITES OF ANIMALS AND HUMAN DISEASE. Roy.
        Soc. Med. Proc. (Sect. Compar. Med.) 20: [547]–556.
(9) CHITWOOD, B. G.
   1933. DOES THE GUINEA-WORM OCCUR IN NORTH AMERICA? Amer Med.
        Assoc. Jour. 100: 802–804.
(10) FORSTER, DONALD E.
   1939. FATAL BACTERIAL ENDOCARDITIS DUE TO SALMONELLA SUIPESTIFER.
        Amer. Jour. Med. Sci. 197: 234–240, illus.
(11) GRAHAM, ROBERT, LEVINE, NORMAN D., and HESTER, H. R.
   1939. ERYSIPELOTHRIX RHUSIOPATHIAE ASSOCIATED WITH A FATAL DISEASE
        IN DUCKS. Amer. Vet. Med. Assoc. Jour. 95: 211–216, illus.
(12) HAMPTON, BROCK C.
   1940. PLAGUE IN THE UNITED STATES. U. S. Public Health Serv., Pub.
        Health Rpts. 55: 1143–1158, illus.
(13) HARDISON, A. E., and SHIPLEY, A. B.
   1941. PARATYPHOID SEPTICEMIA IN MAN DUE TO SALMONELLA SUIPESTIFER.
        Amer. Med. Assoc. Jour. 116: 829–830.
(14) HERMANSSON, K. A.
   1939. IS THERE ANY RISK FOR A MEAT INSPECTOR OF BEING INFECTED DURING
        HIS WORK AT PUBLIC SLAUGHTER-HOUSES OR AT CONTROL-SLAUGHTER-
        HOUSES? Skand. Vet. Tidskr. 29 (9) : 926–933. [Abstract in
        Biol. Abs. 14: 1205. 1940.]
(15) HUDDLESON, I. FOREST.
   1939. BRUCELLOSIS IN MAN AND ANIMALS. 339 pp., illus. .New York and
        London.
(16) HUTYRA, FRANZ, and MAREK, JOSEF.
   1926. SPECIAL PATHOLOGY AND THERAPEUTICS OF THE DISEASES OF DOMESTIC
        ANIMALS. 3d Amer. ed., John R. Mohler and Adolph Eichorn
        editors, 3 v., illus. Chicago.
(17) KALMBACH, E. R.
   1934. WESTERN DUCK SICKNESS—A FORM OF BOTULISM. U. S. Dept. Agr.
        Tech. Bul. 411, 82 pp., illus.
(18) KELSER, RAYMOND A.
   1933. MANUAL OF VETERINARY BACTERIOLOGY. Ed. 2, 552 pp. illus. Balti-
        more.
(19) KOFOID, CHARLES A., and WILLIAMS, OWEN L.
   1935. THE NEMATODE THELAZIA CALIFORNIENSIS AS A PARASITE OF THE EYE
        OF MAN IN CALIFORNIA. Arch. Ophthal. 13: [176]–180, illus.
(20) MADSEN, D. E.
   1937. AN ERYSIPELAS OUTBREAK IN TURKEYS. Amer. Vet. Med. Assoc. Jour.
        91: 206–208.
(21) MAGATH, THOMAS B.
   1937. HYDATID (ECHINOCOCCUS) DISEASE IN CANADA AND THE UNITED STATES.
        Amer. Jour. Hyg. 25: 107–134, illus.
(22) MERCHANT, I. A.
   1940. VETERINARY BACTERIOLOGY. 628 pp., illus. Ames, Iowa.
(23) MUELLER, JUSTUS F.
   1938. THE LIFE HISTORY OF DIPHYLLOBOTHRIUM MANSONOIDES MUELLER,
        1935, AND SOME CONSIDERATIONS WITH REGARD TO SPARGANOSIS IN
        THE UNITED STATES. Amer. Jour. Trop. Med. 18: 41–66, illus.
(24) ———
   1938. STUDIES ON SPARGANUM MANSONOIDES AND SPARGANUM PROLIFERUM.
        Amer. Jour. Trop. Med. 18: 303–328, illus.

(25) MUELLER, JUSTUS F. and COULSTON, FREDERICK.
    1941. EXPERIMENTAL HUMAN INFECTION WITH THE SPARGANUM LARVA OF
        SPIROMETRA MANSONOIDES (MUELLER, 1935). Amer. Jour. Trop.
        Med. 21: 399–425, illus.
(26) MURRAY, E. G. D., WEBB, R. A., and SWANN, M. B. R.
    1926. A DISEASE OF RABBITS CHARACTERIZED BY A LARGE MONONUCLEAR LEU-
        COCYTOSIS, CAUSED BY A HITHERTO UNDESCRIBED BACILLUS BAC-
        TERIUM MONOCYTOGENES (N. SP.). Jour. Path. and Bact. 29:
        407–439, illus.
(27) PENNER, LAWRENCE R.
    1941. THE POSSIBILITY OF SYSTEMIC INFECTION WITH DERMATITIS-PRODUC-
        ING SCHISTOSOMES. Science 93: 327–328.
(28) READ, C. THOMAS.
    1939. ENDOCARDITIS CAUSED BY SALMONELLA SUIPESTIFER. Jour. Infect.
        Dis. 65: [263]–266.
(29) STONE, W. S.
    1938. BRUCELLOSIS IN HORSES. Cornell Vet. 28: 91–98.
(30) UNITED STATES BUREAU OF ANIMAL INDUSTRY.
    1939–41. REPORT OF THE CHIEF OF THE BUREAU OF ANIMAL INDUSTRY, 1939,
        82 pp.; 1940, 90 pp.; 1941, 92 pp.
(31) UNITED STATES PUBLIC HEALTH SERVICE.
    1940. TULARAEMIA INFECTION FOUND IN STREAMS. Pub. Health Repts. 55:
        227.
(32) ———
    1940. TULARAEMIA (RABBIT FEVER). Pub. Health Rpts. 55, pp. 667–670.
(33) WOOD, SHERWIN F.
    1941. NEW LOCALITIES FOR TRYPANOSOMA CRUZI CHAGAS IN SOUTHWESTERN
        UNITED STATES. Amer. Jour. Hyg., Sect. C, 34 (1): 1–13, illus.

The Screwworm and Blowfly Problem

BY E. C. CUSHING AND D. C. PARMAN [1]

AMONG ALL the insect pests that there are on this earth, those that raise their maggots in the living flesh of animals are pecularly loathsome. Screwworms and blowflies have the doubtful honor of belonging to this group. Here is an account of their ways, the damage they do, and the steps that can be taken to outmaneuver them in their deadly business.

As ENEMIES OF LIVESTOCK, screwworms and blowflies are in the forefront of many insect parasites. The primary screwworm is a native of the Americas, and few if any of the related species have been introduced into the United States from foreign lands. They have adapted themselves to conditions ranging from those of the hot dry sands of the desert to those of the frigid Arctic wastes. Fortunately, only a relatively small number of these flies are of great economic importance. Some are actually beneficial as parasites on other noxious insects and as scavengers.

The screwworm and blowfly problem in the United States today involves chiefly four groups or genera of flies, including about six species. All these different flies have one habit in common—they breed in animal flesh. One, however, the primary screwworm (scientific name, *Cochliomyia americana*), can breed only in the tissues of living warm-blooded animals, and it must depend upon finding a wounded or diseased part of the host's body in which its young can begin development. The other species of flies [2] commonly

---

[1] E. C. Cushing is Senior Entomologist and D. C. Parman is Associate Entomologist, Division of Insects Affecting Man and Animals, Bureau of Entomology and Plant Quarantine.

[2] The secondary screwworm fly (*Cochliomyia macellaria*); the black blowfly, fleeceworm fly, or wool-maggot fly (*Phormia regina*); green-bottle flies (*Lucilla* spp.); and gray flesh flies (*Sarcophaga* spp.).

313

breed in carcasses but sometimes infest wounds or unhealthy tissues of live animals. They also contaminate and infest cooked and fresh meat of all kinds and for this reason are a problem of major importance around such places as slaughtering pens, packing houses, and farm homes.

THE PRIMARY SCREWWORM FLY

The primary screwworm fly is limited in its normal range to the Southern and Southwestern States, including Arizona and the southern half of California. Occasionally, under exceptionally favorable weather conditions or through the shipping of infested animals from farther south, destructive outbreaks of the pest have occurred in Iowa, Illinois, and Indiana.

In the areas where it normally occurs, this fly is undoubtedly the greatest enemy of all the insect species with which the livestock owner must contend. In the Southwest, where it inflicts the most injury, ranchmen report that 85 percent of their usual annual losses of livestock are caused by this parasite. Under the present system of livestock production in the screwworm-infested regions, man-made wounds occasioned by marking, branding, shearing, castrating, dehorning, and docking afford ample and fertile breeding grounds for screwworms, as do injuries resulting from such plants as cacti and needlegrass, from fighting, from diseased tissues, and from the attacks of blood-sucking insects. Newborn animals are particularly susceptible to infestation of the navel cord.

The primary screwworm fly is bluish green in color and has three dark stripes on its back. The space between and below the eyes is a reddish or orange color. It is often mistaken for one of the two common carcass-breeding species of blowflies which have almost identical color markings, although as seen in nature it is more robust and has a darker color. Only rarely is it observed on dead animals, but it is frequently seen feeding and laying eggs in the wounds of live animals.

The fly generally seeks the edges or a dry portion of the wound on which to deposit its eggs. From 50 to 300 eggs are laid at one time, fastened tightly to the tissue surface in compact shinglelike masses. A single female is capable of laying 3,000 eggs, which are deposited in masses of about 300 at 4-day intervals.

Hatching of the eggs occurs in 11 hours, and the young whitish worms immediately burrow into the flesh, where they feed and grow for a period of 4 to 7 days. During the larval, or maggot, stage the worms shed their skins twice. When the worms have reached their full growth they assume a pinkish color, leave the wound, and drop to the ground, where they dig beneath the surface and undergo a change to the hard-skinned, dark-brown, motionless pupa. It is during the pupal stage that the transformation from the maggot to the adult fly takes place. After the pupa has been in the soil from 7 to 60 days the fly emerges from it, works its way to the surface, and crawls up on some nearby bush, weed, or other object to allow its wings to unfold and its outer body coverings to harden. When it first comes from the pupa, the fly is a grayish color without distinct markings, but as its body hardens it assumes its characteristic coloration. Under favorable conditions about 5 days are required before the newly emerged female fly becomes sexually mature and ready to lay eggs. During warm weather the life cycle is usually completed in 21 days, but under cold, unfavorable conditions the cycle takes as many as 80 days.

The injury this parasite does to animals is inflicted by the worms or maggots. The debilitating effect and the destruction of tissue kill the infested animal in a few days. The screwworm destroys untold numbers of domestic and wild animals from South Carolina to California, and this loss, together with the amount of labor required to prevent and treat infestations, costs North American livestock owners many millions of dollars annually.

BLOWFLIES

The blowflies of economic importance, the primary screwworm excepted, find their principal breeding ground in carrion. With the exception of the group known as gray flesh flies, which deposit tiny living maggots instead of eggs, the blowflies have a life history similar to that of the related screwworm fly, although each stage of the cycle is generally completed in about half the time.

In general the more harmful carrion-breeding species of flies are widespread over the continent, but various factors determine their relative numbers in different localities. They are most injurious in the Pacific Northwest and in the areas inhabited by the screwworm fly. Because of their prolific breeding habits they occur in large numbers, and when weather conditions are favorable, they cause their greatest damage by grossly infesting wounds and the soiled hair or fleece of animals. Some of the species, especially the black blowfly, or wool-maggot fly, produce injuries similar to those caused by screwworms. Sheep are especially susceptible to the attacks of blowflies, as their wool frequently becomes soiled or moistened by rain and accumulations of feces and urine. The maggots spread extensively over the body, feeding on the skin surface, exciting severe irritation, causing the production of a serous exudate, and destroying the ability of the skin to function. Infested animals rapidly become fevered and debilitated, and although they may recover, they may remain in an unthrifty condition for a long period.

All the important species of blowflies except the flesh flies, which are grayish and have three dark stripes on their backs, have a more or less metallic luster. The coloration varies from almost black in the case of the wool-maggot fly to a light green in some of the greenbottle species. One of the carrion-breeding species greatly resembles the primary screwworm fly and for a number of years was thought to be the principal cause of wound infestations by fly maggots.

ORIGIN OF THE PROBLEM

During the known history of the screwworm and blowfly, there is no evidence that the flies have spread from their present normal range to new areas, although they have occasionally temporarily invaded sections of the country where they are not usually found. The appearance of the screwworm in the Southeastern States in 1934 may prove to be an exception. While the information is meager, it seems certain that .the early colonists of the South and Southwest encountered cases of screwworm and blowfly infestations in buffalo, coyotes, and other wild animals native to America. Spanish explorers brought horses to the region, and later cattle, hogs, sheep, and goats were introduced.

With the increase of the population in the East, the wild herds of cattle became of high value as a source of food, and a mad scramble for the ownership of these animals began. Since the land was free and the animals roamed at will, the only way ownership could be designated was by permanently marking individual animals. Thus was introduced one of the principal causes of screwworm infestation—the fire brand. Later, barbed-wire fencing was another important factor contributing to the increasing depredations of screwworms through causing injuries to animals.

The increasing demand for more and better meat led in rapid succession to indiscriminate practices of knife castration, earmarking, docking, uncontrolled breeding, and overstocking of ranges, all of which enlarged the opportunity for screwworms to multiply. With the greatly increased number of animals on a given area, diseases and famine began to appear in the herds, and the screwworm and blowfly problem was accentuated.

By the early part of the twentieth century the problem had become so acute that the raising of cattle in certain parts of the Southwest was practically impossible. Ranchmen began to realize that if they were to continue to produce livestock profitably, something must be done to control these flies.

CONTROL OF SCREWWORMS AND BLOWFLIES

Many factors determine whether screwworms and blowflies can become economic pests in any area. Farmers and ranchers must learn to use the factors that tend to destroy these enemies and to avoid or nullify those that favor their propagation.

Climate and weather are the dominant factors governing the relative abundance of screwworms and blowflies in an area. Weather conditions during certain seasons of the year favor the propagation of these pests, while the opposite is true at other seasons. The screwworm fly cannot survive the year around in localities where the average temperature is 50° F. or lower for a continuous period of approximately 80 days. In the United States the fly is limited in its normal range to sections with 45 inches or less of rainfall annually. Unlike many of its relatives, the screwworm fly does not have a true hibernating or dormant stage in its life cycle.

The blowflies in general have adapted themselves to broader. climatic extremes. Some species are able to withstand the rigors of the Arctic and occur in areas as far separated as Texas and Alaska.

Other survive in the hot, dry desert regions. Certain ones are able to pass through periods of a year or more in a dormant state.

Although neither the screwworm fly nor the blowflies apparently have definite migratory tendencies, some of them often drift as far as 1,200 to 1,500 miles each year from winter survival areas to reinfest regions in which they were previously exterminated by weather conditions. The screwworm fly is known to spread in this way at the rate of as much as 35 miles a week.

Topography plays an important role in determining the establishment and building up of fly populations. In no case have the largest populations been found on open, wind-swept plains or in the high mountain regions. Some species find conditions most favorable for propagation on highly developed, intensively cultivated, and thickly settled agricultural lands; while others, particularly the primary screwworm fly and some of the species of blowflies most destructive to livestock, breed in the greatest numbers on sparsely settled grazing land covered with a heavy low growth of brush and timber.

Both the screwworm fly and the blowflies have natural enemies that destroy them in large numbers. For example, there are at least 17 species of small wasplike insects in the United States that lay their eggs on or in the maggots of blowflies. These eggs develop into small worms inside the fly larvae, which are eventually killed by the parasites. Other species of these parasites attack and destroy the pupae of blowflies. Predatory ants and beetles prey on the larvae and pupae of blowflies and screwworms for food. No methods, however, have been found to increase greatly the degree of control effected by these beneficial insects.

The wound-producing operations customary in connection with livestock raising in areas where the primary screwworm fly usually occurs are among the major factors that permit this pest to continue its depredations and survive from year to year; although many stockmen have learned to use the utmost care in preventing serewworm infestations following such operations.

In a study of the predisposing causes of screwworm infestations in domestic animals on several hundred thousand acres of ranch land in southwest Texas during the period 1929 to 1933, Laake [3] shows that of 20,962 cases the causes of which were known, branding, castrating, dehorning, docking, marking, and shearing were responsible for about 31 percent.

Losses from screwworms and blowflies may be avoided by preventing the propagation or breeding of the pests—the first and most important step—and by decreasing the susceptibility of animals to infestation. Under most conditions of livestock raising the two methods must go hand in hand.

THE CONTROL OF SCREWWORMS

As previously stated, the primary screwworm fly must have living warm-blooded animals in which to breed. In the regions where it

[3] LAAKE, E. W. ECONOMIC STUDIES OF SCREWWORM FLIES, COCHLIOMYIA SPECIES (DIPTERA, CALLIPHORINAE), WITH SPECIAL REFERENCE TO THE PREVENTION OF MYIASIS OF DOMESTIC ANIMALS. Iowa State Col. Jour. Sci. 10 : 345–359, illus. 1936.

occurs it produces 90 percent or more of all the fly-maggot infestations of wounds in wild and domestic animals.

The best time to begin control of the screwworm fly is during the winter. Then climatic conditions have forced it to occupy relatively small areas and even in these areas make it extremely difficult for the fly to live and breed. It must produce at least one generation during a 4-month period, or it is exterminated. The fly is inactive when air temperatures are 55° F. or lower. Continuous average temperatures of 50° or lower for approximately 3 months will eradicate the fly from any area. The flies do not hide in places like caves or animal burrows to seek protection from the cold, and hard frosts kill many of the adults. During the winter season few wounds in wild and domestic animals are available for the fly to attack. Probably not more than 3 flies emerge in the spring for every 100 pupae subjected to winter conditions, and these 3 are able to survive only because they

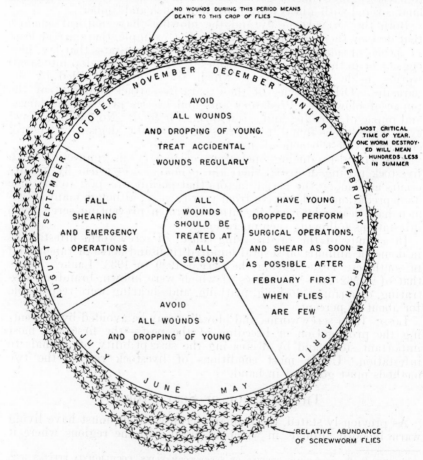

FIGURE 1.—Seasonal abundance of the screwworm fly and its relation to recommended ranch management for control in southern Texas. (See zone 1, fig. 2.)

find animals with wounds in which they may produce a midwinter generation within a 4-month period. The pupae in the soil must transform into flies within 60 days or they die; only a few survive that do not produce flies within 40 days. It is evident therefore that any screwworms allowed to mature in wounds during the winter are responsible for all the trouble which develops the following spring and summer. From 3 flies emerging in the spring, 500 may result by the following May and June.

In figure 1 is shown the seasonal abundance of the screwworm fly in one of the principal parts of the overwintering area in Texas, where careful studies are being made by the United States Department of Agriculture on the control of this pest. The sharp increase

FIGURE 2.—Zones and dates recommended for screwworm prevention in Texas. In zone 1, perform surgical operations between February 1 and April 30, and between August 1 and September 30, and avoid wounds October 1 to January 31 and May 1 to July 31. In zone 2, perform operations between December 1 and April 30, and avoid all wounds except those incidental to fall shearing May 1 to November 30. In zone 3, perform operations October 1 to April 30, and avoid wounds except in connection with fall shearing May 1 to September 30. In zone 4, October 1 to May 31 is the time for surgical operations, and wounds should be avoided between June 1 and September 30. The normal winter screwworm survival area is dotted.

in the abundance of flies during the warm periods that usually occur in the latter part of December or early in January is almost entirely responsible for producing the midwinter generation. Wounds in animals at that time become infested and this allows the insects to survive until warm weather.

The screwworm fly can be controlled by diligent care to prevent infestations of livestock during the cold months in the areas where it overwinters and by not allowing any screwworms to develop in wounds in the early spring. If ranch operations that necessarily produce wounds are timed to occur in the seasons when the flies are least abundant and least active, the animals are less exposed to attack. In figure 2 recommendations are given for ranch practices in Texas and some adjoining States, which, if followed, will minimize screwworm losses.

Treatment of Wounded and Infested Animals

Under present range conditions and with present ranch practices it is inevitable that many animals will be wounded and infested. It is folly, however, to allow any of these animals to go untreated.

First, it is highly desirable that a "hospital" pasture be provided where the injured livestock can be kept and examined easily and frequently until they are healed. Such pastures should be equipped with suitable corrals and chutes for handling animals. Some owners find it advisable to build screened, flyproof structures in which to house wounded or infested animals.

Many medicines and nostrums have been used by ranchmen for protecting wounded animals against screwworm attack and for killing the worms in infested animals. These remedies have included everything from such materials as dried horse manure, common salt, boiling water, and strong caustics, to complex chemical substances. After many years of careful experimentation and testing, the Department of Agriculture has found that benzol is the best material for killing larvae in wounds, and diphenylamine, a powdered chemical, is best for protecting wounds against infestation.

The use of these substances separately, however, has certain disadvantages, particularly the slow killing action of benzol in large bloody wounds, the fact that the maximum protection period of the diphenylamine is only 3 days, and the necessity of having to apply two remedies in treating infested animals.

Recent research by entomologists of the Department of Agriculture has developed a method of combining these excellent materials into a single remedy whereby their inferior qualities have been mostly removed and their insecticidal value increased. This new remedy is known as Formula MS 62 and is made by mixing diphenylamine and benzol with turkey-red oil and lampblack in the following proportions:

Parts by weight

Diphenylamine (technical grade) _____ 3. 5
Benzol (90 percent commercial) _____ 3. 5
Turkey-red oil (sulfonated castor oil, pH 10 or neutral) _ 1. 0
Lampblack (Germantown) _____ 2. 0

The resulting mixture has the consistency of thin paint. It kills screwworms or other fly maggots infesting a wound quickly and gives protection against reinfestation for several days. The remedy is best applied with a small paint brush to infested or uninfested wounds. Two applications each week until the injured tissues have healed are usually sufficient to protect wounds against infestation. In many cases one treatment will give complete protection.

The use of pincer-type emasculators whenever possible, the dehorning of animals when young and during the proper season, the eradication of plants that cause injuries, the breeding of animals so that the young are born during the seasons of least fly activity, and the avoidance of anything else that might produce wounds will aid greatly in screwworm control.

CONTROLLING BLOWFLIES

Since blowflies breed principally in dead animals, the first step in the elimination of these pests is the destruction of carcasses or waste meat products. Carcasses are most easily disposed of by burning, and the proper method of accomplishing this is described in Farmers' Bulletin 857.[4] The method consists essentially in digging a small trench near the carcass, placing a quantity of wood in the trench, and rolling the dead animal over the wood, which is then ignited. Care should be taken to avoid starting a range fire and to see that every part of the carcass is destroyed. As some of the larvae infesting the carcass may have matured and burrowed into the ground, it is usually advisable, except in the case of animals that have died within 48 hours, to scatter the hot coals of the fire over an area within a radius of 3 yards of the place where the carcass lay.

Traps and poisoned baits are useful supplemental control measures for all the carrion-breeding species of blowflies. The trap that has proved the most practical for general use is the Government all-metal cone-type trap described on pages 6, 7, and 8 of Farmers' Bulletin 734.[5] Around food-preparation plants, canneries, and such places, where the odors from meat-baited traps may be objectionable and where the source of flies cannot be controlled, some of the better commercially made electrified screens are efficient in reducing trouble from blowflies.

Poisoned baits, consisting of meat or the carcasses of small animals placed in shallow water containing one-half ounce of nicotine sulfate to the gallon in suitable containers exposed to the flies, will kill large numbers of them. The dead flies accumulate on the surface of the bait, and it is necessary to remove them occasionally to obtain the best results. Care should be taken to prevent chickens, hogs, and other animals from having access to the bait.

When the hair of goats, sheep, or other animals becomes infested with blowfly maggots, it should be sheared well around the affected

---

[4] BISHOPP, F. C., MITCHELL, J. D., and PARMAN, D. C. SCREW-WORMS AND OTHER MAGGOTS AFFECTING ANIMALS. U. S. Dept. Agr. Farmers' Bul. 857, 20 pp., illus. 1917.
[5] BISHOPP, F. C. FLYTRAPS AND THEIR OPERATION. U. S. Dept. Agr. Farmers' Bul. 734, 13 pp., illus. 1916.

area, and the worms should be killed by applying a small but sufficient amount of the same remedy recommended for the treatment of screwworm cases. The crutch of a sheep is a favorable site for infestations of blowfly larvae, especially in the spring, when scouring soils the wool on this part of the body. Shearing the wool from this part, the practice called tagging or crutching, will largely prevent infestations of this kind.

Wounds infested with the maggots of blowflies should be treated, and the animals should receive the same attention as in the case of screwworm infestations.

At the time this book went to press, the drugs and other materials mentioned in various articles—chiefly as disinfectants, insecticides, and anthelmintics—were still available for veterinary and medical use. Under war conditions, however, it is possible that some of these materials may become scarce or unavailable. In that case, the reader should obtain professional advice from the Department of Agriculture, the State experiment station, a local veterinarian, or the county agent as to available substitutes.

Nutritional Diseases of Farm Animals

BY LOUIS L. MADSEN [1]

AN UP-TO-DATE SURVEY of the whole field of nutritional deficiencies and the diseases they produce in various classes of livestock. Further details regarding cattle, swine, poultry, and dogs and cats are given in other articles in the Yearbook.

ANIMAL PRODUCTION has kept pace with the general trend toward intensive production in modern agriculture and methods practiced for high production of animal products or rapid growth and fattening for meat have created many problems in animal nutrition. In many large dairies and other feeding establishments the animals are stall- or lot-fed throughout the year, mostly on purchased feeds, and little or no pasture is available. An unwise choice or a poor quality of feed may lead to a shortage of some dietary essentials, or other factors may cause the development of serious nutritional diseases. Overfeeding may be as disastrous as underfeeding.

Although the cause, prevention, and treatment of many nutritional diseases are now understood, such diseases continue to reduce profits in the livestock industry because the knowledge is not put into practice.

The importance of specific treatment or specific means of preventing nutritional diseases cannot be overemphasized. As in diseases due to micro-organisms, parasites, or other causes, prevention is more satisfactory than cure because the disease may result in damage to the animal body that is difficult or impossible to repair. As Russell (55)[2] points out: "The simplest and most fundamental fact that can be stated with regard to the relation of vitamins to disease is that a given vitamin will cure only the disease condition caused by a lack of that vitamin." The same principle holds for

---

[1] Louis L. Madsen is Nutritionist, Animal Nutrition Division, Bureau of Animal Industry.
[2] Italic numbers in parentheses refer to Literature Cited, p. 350.

nutritional diseases caused by an insufficiency or excess of any of the many other dietary constituents. General tonics, which are often thought of as cure-alls, should not be relied on when a condition that may be of nutritional origin develops in animals.

Methods for the prevention and control of nutritional diseases are better understood if the nature and functions of the essential factors that must be supplied in the feed are known. Knowledge of the effects of a nutritional deficiency or disease on the body is also helpful. Many laboratory methods for the detection of dietary diseases have been perfected, but recognition of the observable symptoms is one of the most useful means of diagnosis.

THE ESSENTIAL MINERALS

The mineral elements recognized as essential in the diet of farm animals are calcium, phosphorus, magnesium, sodium, chlorine, potassium, iodine, manganese, iron, copper, cobalt, and sulfur. Experiments with rats have shown that zinc is also essential to some animals. A continued deficiency or imbalance of these minerals in the diet will often lead to the development of characteristic symptoms, such as disturbances of metabolism, injury to vital tissues of the body, an abnormal composition of the blood or other body fluids, and depraved appetite.

Ordinarily the essential mineral elements can be supplied in ample quantities by careful selection of common feedstuffs. Sometimes, however, special mineral supplements are needed and should be used, but only the specific minerals that are deficient, in the quantities indicated, need be supplied. Feeding an excessive amount of minerals or a complex mineral mixture when it is not required is expensive and wasteful and may be harmful to the animals. An excess of some mineral salts in the diet interferes with the assimilation of phosphorus, and others, such as selenium and fluorine salts, are directly toxic even in very small quantities.

THE MINERAL-DEFICIENCY DISEASES

DISEASES OF CALCIUM AND PHOSPHORUS METABOLISM AND THE INTERRELATIONSHIP OF VITAMIN D

Approximately 70 percent of the ash, or mineral content, of the animal body consists of calcium and phosphorus. About 99 percent of the calcium and over 80 percent of the phosphorus are found in the bones and teeth. The soft tissues, the blood and other body fluids, and some secretions also contain these minerals. Lactating animals utilize larger quantities of these two minerals than nonlactating animals, since milk contains considerable calcium and phosphorus. Disturbances of metabolism caused by an insufficient supply of calcium or phosphorus or an unbalanced proportion of these minerals, with or without an adequate amount of vitamin D in the ration, are largely responsible for a series of related diseases—rickets, osteomalacia, osteoporosis, and osteofibrosis—involving not only the skeletal system but also other tissues and the metabolism of the body as a whole.

Rickets (*Rachitis*)

Rickets is a disease of young animals—calves, foals, pigs, lambs, kids, pups, and chicks—which is characterized by a failure of growing bone to calcify, or harden, properly.

Bones that are rapidly increasing in length, such as the long bones of the legs and the ribs, are the most likely to be visibly affected. At the epiphysis (the region near the ends of bones where growth in length takes place) cartilage continues to be produced, but normal bone is not formed. The epiphyseal region thus becomes wider than it is normally, and because it is soft from lack of ossification (bone formation) it becomes more or less curved and bulges out, causing irregular enlargements, due presumably to the weight of the animal body and the normal tension or strain of the muscles. The result is a noticeable enlargement of the joints, particularly the knees and hocks, with an abnormal straightening or curving of the pasterns which interferes with normal walking. In addition the joint surfaces (articular cartilages) may become eroded and roughened so that movement of the joint is painful. This results in a typical stilted gait, and the animal lies down often. The costo-chondrol junction (union of the rib with the breastbone cartilage) also bulges irregularly, and the result is what is known as the rachitic rosary, or beaded ribs, which, though it can be detected in the living animal, is often noticed only in the carcass. These malformed bones may cause paralysis or pain by pressing on nerves, and they are very easily fractured because of their fragility.

Bones also become softened because of partial resorption of salts from previously formed bone when there is a deficiency of the normal quantity of mineral salts to be deposited in the newly forming bone. The shafts of the leg bones may bend, presumably owing to the weight of the body and to muscle tension. The spinal column also may bend sidewise, a hump may form, or the back may sway. The bones of the head may become distorted, with a tendency towards shortening and an increase in width. Teeth that grow in during a rachitic period may be malformed.

The skeletal abnormalities described are symptoms of the advanced stage of the disease, but they may be the first ones a stockman notices or recognizes. Symptoms that often precede the more severe clinical manifestations are loss of appetite, slowing down of growth or even loss of weight, digestive disturbances, and tetany (convulsions, rigid muscles, stiff legs). A decline in blood calcium or inorganic phosphorus or both usually precedes all other clinical symptoms. Where laboratory facilities are available to make such determinations, the loss of these minerals provides an excellent means of detecting vitamin D deficiency or other abnormalities affecting calcium and phosphorus metabolism.

CAUSE, PREVENTION, AND TREATMENT

Swine and poultry that are normally fed heavily on grains may not receive an adequate supply of calcium unless a mineral supplement or a feed source of calcium is provided. The supply of phosphorus is usually ample in a heavy grain ration. Swine are sensitive to a calcium deficiency, and colts cannot tolerate a high proportion of phosphorus to calcium. Maynard (*40*) writes, "The normal calcium-phosphorus ratio has been defined as lying between 2:1 and 1:2, but adequate nutrition is possible outside of these limits." The general statement may be made that the harmful effects of vitamin D deficiency do not develop so soon when the calcium-phosphorus ratio is between 1:2 and 2:1. This explains the difficulties resulting from feeding horses a heavy ration of grains with only a small allowance of hay. Timothy hay is usually even lower in calcium than clover or alfalfa hay. Calves and lambs rarely suffer from calcium undernutrition on ordinary rations and are not so sensitive as colts to an abnormal calcium-phosphorus ratio, but they are affected if the amount of phosphorus is inadequate.

Rickets may or may not be due to a simple vitamin D deficiency. An adequate supply of vitamin D cannot compensate for a faulty proportion or inadequate amounts of calcium and phosphorus in the diet. How vitamin D acts is not entirely clear, but in cases of rickets where vitamin D deficiency is the limiting factor the results of administering it are very specific and dramatic. Almost immediately there is an increase in the retention of calcium and phosphorus in the body, probably involving both increased absorption and reduced excretion. Blood phosphorus and calcium return to normal, and new deposits of bone salts can be demonstrated within a few hours.

Direct exposure of the body to sunlight has the same effect on calcium and phosphorus metabolism as vitamin D in the ration, but the effectiveness of sunlight in curing and preventing rickets depends on the intensity of the ultraviolet part of the light and the length and regularity of exposure. Winter sunlight is normally lower in ultraviolet rays than spring or summer sunshine. Ordinary window glass filters out the ultraviolet rays of the sun and makes the light that passes through it ineffective as an antirachitic.

Successful treatment of rickets depends on supplying adequate amounts of vitamin D and adjusting the intake and the ratio of calcium and phosphorus. Providing calves, colts, and lambs with liberal amounts of sun-cured hay of good quality and allowing them daily exposure to direct sunlight are the cheapest assurances against vitamin D deficiency. For swine, also, sun-cured alfalfa or some other legume hay of good quality is a good source of vitamin D and calcium. Roughages that are artificially dried immediately after cutting and allowed little or no ultraviolet irradiation from the sun are poor sources of this vitamin.

Commercial sources of vitamin D, such as fish oils, fish-oil concentrates, irradiated ergosterol, activated animal sterols, and irradiated yeast are also available for animal feeding when extra vitamin D is needed. The various forms of vitamin D from activated ergosterol and cholesterol [3] are in general equally valuable in the nutri-

---

[3] Several different sterols and possibly some unidentified compounds function as vitamin D when activated by ultraviolet light or by chemical treatment. The two sterols generally accepted as being the most important as precursors of vitamin D are ergosterol and 7-dehydrocholesterol. Ergosterol, the chief sterol of yeast, on activation by ultraviolet light becomes calciferol. The other important sterol, 7-dehydrocholesterol, is the chief component of animal fats, fish oils, and tissues, which become antirachitic on activation. Fish oils also contain several other sterol derivatives that function as vitamin D.

tion of all farm animals except poultry, which do not utilize irradiated ergosterol or calciferol economically.

Sunshine, cod-liver oil, and other fish oils containing vitamin D are effective in preventing and curing rickets in swine *(30)*, colts, and other farm animals, but little is known about the actual vitamin D requirements of the animals. Increasing the calcium content of rations containing a large proportion of grain may also be helpful. The prevention and treatment of rickets in calves are discussed in the article on Nutritional Diseases of Cattle, page 665.

Prompt treatment of rickets is imperative. If the disease is allowed to progress until marked joint enlargement and bending of the bones has taken place, treatment is less successful. Bony malformations usually calcify and become permanent. Stiffness may largely disappear, and bowed legs may straighten considerably, but badly eroded joint cartilages are practically irreparable. Rachitic females, after successful treatment, may reproduce normally (fig. 1).

Osteomalacia, Osteoporosis, and Osteofibrosis in Relation to Phosphorus and Calcium Deficiency

Three abnormal bone conditions are characterized by rather definite alterations in the conformation of the skeleton. Several factors, among them phosphorus deficiency, calcium deficiency, an abnormal proportion of these two minerals in the ration, vitamin D deficiency, and an altered rate of secretion of certain endocrine glands such as the parathyroids, may be involved in the production of these changes. A coexisting protein and vitamin A deficiency may also be involved in some cases.

Osteomalacia is a disease of adult animals named from one of its characteristic symptoms—softening and replacement of bone with osteoid tissue, which resembles uncalcified bone. In some respects this condition is similar to rickets and has been referred to as adult rickets, but it occurs after growth in the length of the bones has largely ceased. When the condition is caused by a deficiency of phosphorus in the animal's ration, it is usually called phosphorus deficiency. The disease is common in pregnant or lactating cows, particularly on phosphorus-deficient range or during periods of drought. It is also seen in sheep, goats, swine, horses, and mules. Calcium and vitamin D deficiency may also be involved.

Osteoporosis is a similar condition resulting from faulty bone metabolism, except that the changes in the bone are those of atrophy, producing a thin porous structure and a failure of normal bone regeneration, but without the osteoid tissue seen in osteomalacia.

Osteofibrosis is characterized by enlargement and partial replacement of the bones with soft, poorly calcified fibrous tissue which may also occupy the marrow cavity. The bones of the face and jaws especially become enlarged, and the condition in horses is commonly known as bighead. Goats and swine are similarly affected. The animals are easily fatigued and may have a snuffling respiration, and they often have enlargements of the leg bones and show varying degrees of lameness.

FIGURE 1.—A cow with bowed front legs and enlarged joints, the results of advanced
rickets early in life, with her apparently normal 5-month-old calf. Rickets in a heifer
calf does not necessarily impair her ability to reproduce later in life, even though the
disease may cause some permanent deformities of the skeleton.

Lesions or tissue changes, resembling osteomalacia, osteoporosis,
and osteofibrosis may occur to some extent in animals as a secondary
condition resulting from rickets, whether caused by vitamin D deficiency or faulty calcium and phosphorus nutrition, or as the result
of some endocrine disturbance. Such conditions can be identified
by the changes they produce in the skeleton, but changes in blood
calcium and phosphorus are not always characteristic. A reduction
in total inorganic phosphorus or in total calcium may, however,
precede extensive bone malformations and other symptoms.

Phosphorus-deficient animals have a depraved appetite (fig. 2)
and fail to breed regularly, and their milk production is markedly
decreased. Growth and development are slow, and the animals become emaciated and fail to reach normal adult size.

In horses phosphorus deficiency causes a reduction in blood phosphorus and considerable rarefaction of bone before the effects are
evident in their general condition. Preliminary results from experi-

FIGURE 2.—These sheep are eating a dried sheep carcass. The supply of phosphorus and protein was low on the natural range where they had been grazing, and phosphorus-deficient animals often chew bones and other nonfood materials apparently in an effort to remedy the deficiency. (Courtesy of G. H. Hart, California Agricultural Experiment Station.

mental work in the Bureau of Animal Industry indicate that X-ray photographs of the tail bones of horses can be used to determine changes in density and structure of bone due to phosphorus deficiency.

Ringbones, splints and bone spavins, and other unsound conditions of the bones of horses are suspected of being symptoms of abnormal bone metabolism due to a deficiency or unbalance of calcium and phosphorus in the ration. Lameness, stiffness of gait, fragility of bone, and enlargement of the bones of the face and jaw may occur in horses, swine, and goats. Bony enlargements are frequently due to osteofibrosis.

Animals receiving an insufficient supply of calcium may also develop fragile bones, and fail to reproduce and lactate normally. This condition is very rare, however, and does not usually occur if good hay or pasture forage of normal calcum content is available.

CAUSE, PREVENTION, AND TREATMENT

A deficiency of phosphorus in the forage in many areas of the world is largely responsible for the losses from phosphorus deficiency in cattle, sheep, and goats. A feed shortage due to drought or other causes may also be responsible. Calcium-deficient areas, though apparently not as widespread as those deficient in phosphorus, have been reported in parts of Florida, Louisiana, Nebraska, Virginia, and West

Virginia. Workers in the Department of Agriculture [4] and in some State experiment stations are attempting to locate all the soil areas in the United States that produce mineral-deficient forages.

As noted in the discussion of rickets, heavy grain feeding may lead to calcium deficiency unless the ration contains liberal quantities of other calcium-rich feeds. Calcium deficiency is very rare in cattle and sheep. There is little experimental evidence to indicate the necessity of adding calcium-rich supplements to the ration of growing calves or lactating dairy cows when they are fed ordinary rations of hay and grain, though the evidence is still incomplete in the case of cows producing large quantities of milk.

Diseases caused by abnormal phosphorus and calcium metabolism due to errors in diet can be prevented or treated in any one of three ways: (1) By using natural feeds that contain sufficient quantities of calcium and phosphorus; (2) by increasing the calcium and phosphorus content or the yield of pasturage or hay by fertilizing the soil on which the crops are grown; and (3) by feeding a specific mineral supplement.

Feeds low in phosphorus and requiring supplementation if they make up a large proportion of the ration are beet pulp, molasses, black grama hay, kafir or corn fodder, prairie hay, sorgo hay and fodder, and legumes and grasses grown on phosphorus-deficient soils, especially during dry seasons. Feeds rich in phosphorus are wheat bran; whole cereal grains; tankage; cottonseed, linseed, peanut, and soybean meals; and hays or other herbage from phosphorus-rich soils.

Feeds rich in both calcium and phosphorus are steamed bonemeal, skim milk, and buttermilk. When they contain bone, tankage, meat scrap, and fish meal also supply considerable calcium as well as phosphorus. High-quality ground limestone (calcium carbonate) and oyster-shell are excellent sources of calcium. Phosphatic limestone, purified to remove fluorine, may also be used as a source of calcium and phosphorus. Legume hays (alfalfa, lespedeza, soybean, clover, etc.) are generally rich in calcium, and timothy hay and other grass hays, though containing less, usually furnish adequate amounts even for lactating dairy cows if the hay is of good quality and is eaten in liberal quantities.

Meigs and his coworkers (*42*), who studied the effects of feeding low-calcium rations for long periods on calcium and phosphorus metabolism in dairy cows, writes:

It appears that, when the calcium content of a ration is reduced by substituting timothy hay or straw for alfalfa, the vitamin A content is also likely to be reduced, and that the failures in reproduction, which have occurred on rations in which the roughage was timothy hay or straw, are to be attributed to a vitamin A deficiency rather than to calcium deficiency. The physiological effects of rations which are deficient in calcium, though adequate in vitamin A, are in need of further investigation.

Hart and Miller (*18*) point out the necessity of correcting protein deficiency, which may be coexistent with a low phosphorus intake.

---

[4] A survey of deficient and excess minerals in forage in the United States was made by Hartman in 1939 (*19*). Reported phosphorus-deficient areas and areas of similar parent soil materials where natural feeds under certain conditions may be low enough in phosphorus to produce phosphorus deficiency in livestock were also outlined in Technology on the Farm (*63*).

MAGNESIUM DEFICIENCY

It is unlikely that a deficiency of magnesium will occur in ordinary farm rations. The deficiency has been produced, however, by feeding calves for extended periods on milk without hay or a grain supplement, as well as by feeding purified diets low in magnesium. Symptoms, prevention, and treatment are discussed in the article on Nutritional Diseases of Cattle, page 651. Huffman and Duncan (*22, 23*) have demonstrated that magnesium improves calcium and phosphorus metabolism and calcification of bone in dairy calves, the action being described as a "vitamin D-sparing" effect. It is most evident on rations low but not entirely lacking in vitamin D.

Magnesium is needed by the body in relatively small amounts, but it is very important physiologically. About 70 percent of the magnesium in the body is in the bones, where it occurs in combination with calcium and phosphorus compounds, forming complex bone salts. The muscles contain more magnesium than calcium, but the function of magnesium in muscles is not completely understood. Magnesium is closely related to calcium metabolism, and is also known to function as a coenzyme in various reactions involving carbohydrate and phosphorus metabolism. Magnesium is also present in the blood, organs, and tissue fluids of the body.

SALT (SODIUM CHLORIDE) DEFICIENCY

Salt is one of the essential mineral compounds most likely to be lacking in the diet of herbivorous (grass-eating) animals, but fortunately it is one of the easiest and cheapest to provide as a supplement. Both sodium and chlorine, which combine in common salt, are essential in animal nutrition. Wild herbivores, such as deer and buffalo, will travel long distances and risk danger to lick salt from natural deposits. Swine and poultry also need salt. Such animals as horses, which work hard and perspire profusely, as well as lactating animals such as heavy-producing dairy cows, need more salt than usual to compensate for that lost in perspiration and in milk.

Animals deprived of salt develop a ravenous appetite for it, and if suddenly given free access to salt may consume too much, with symptoms of poisoning and even death as a result. (See the article on Salt Tolerance and Salt Poisoning of Swine, p. 803.) Other symptoms of salt deficiency are loss of appetite for ordinary foods, loss of weight, a rough coat, and a drop in milk yield. Salt deficiency is easily avoided by giving animals free access to salt regularly. It is important, however, to hand-feed small amounts to salt-hungry animals for several days before allowing them access to unlimited quantities.

Salt has several important functions in the body. It helps to maintain osmotic-pressure relationships in body cells and fluids, aids in the regulation of water metabolism, and is an essential constituent of milk, eggs, and all body cells. Sodium is the largest in quantity of the base minerals in the body cells, fluids, and alkaline digestive juices (bile and pancreatic juice), and chlorine has a part in the formation of hydrochloric acid in gastric juice.

TRACE MINERALS IN ANIMAL NUTRITION

Chemical and spectrographic analyses of tissues and fluids of animal bodies reveal that a large number of mineral elements are present in very small quantities. Some of these so-called trace minerals, including iodine, manganese, iron, copper, cobalt, and zinc, are now known to be indispensable in animal nutrition, while the essential nature of others, including silicon, nickel, boron, bromine, aluminum, strontium, vanadium, and silver, has not been established. Some may be present in the body merely because they were contained in the food; on the other hand, they may prove to be essential to certain physiological functions. A deficiency of some essential trace minerals is now known to produce typical symptoms. Small quantities of other minerals, including fluorine, selenium, arsenic, molybdenum, and lead, may be harmful to animals.

Iodine Deficiency

Approximately half of the small amount of iodine in the body is located in the thyroid gland. Iodine was the first trace element demonstrated to be essential for normal nutrition, probably because a deficiency of this mineral causes such conditions in man as goiter and cretinism. As early as 1820 the chemist Dumas and the physician Coindet in France studied the use of iodine in the treatment of goiter. Iodine therapy was hailed for a time, but it gradually fell into disrepute for several reasons. It failed to cure all types of goiter, there were some toxic results from overdosing, and the rise of Pasteur's germ theory of disease (1873–95) caused the older chemical theories to be neglected; medical men and bacteriologists were looking for a microbe as a cause of goiter.

In 1895 Baumann *(1)* discovered iodine in organic combination in the thyroid gland, and in 1915 Kendall *(28)* isolated from thyroids an iodine-containing compound in crystalline form which had the same properties as the whole gland. Later Harrington and Barger *(16)* synthesized this compound—thyroxin—in the laboratory. The essential facts concerning thyroxin are that it contains 65 percent of iodine by weight, is the principal hormone produced by the thyroid gland, has a regulating effect on body metabolism, and is also concerned in growth, development, and the reproductive processes.

SIMPLE GOITER IN FARM ANIMALS

Enlargement of the thyroid gland is a common manifestation of iodine deficiency in domestic animals. It is an advanced symptom, however, and the chief loss from iodine deficiency is from interference with reproductive processes and the birth of weak, deformed offspring which often fail to survive *(27, 65)*. The gestation period of mares receiving insufficient iodine is frequently longer than normal, and the foal is either still-born or so weak that it is unable to get up and nurse normally. Most such colts die within a few days, although some survive and make a complete recovery.

Cows may also give birth to weak, goitrous (often called big-neck) calves. Most such calves are alive at birth, although a few may be still-born; some are weak and die within a few days; others have approximately normal vigor and are not noticeably affected except for enlargement of the thyroids, which may or may not cause difficult breathing because of pressure on the trachea (windpipe). If the calf is able to take nourishment, the goiter frequently diminishes in size until it is no longer noticeable, but sometimes it remains throughout adult life. In severe cases the hair of the calf may be thinner than normal or the animal may be almost completely hairless.

Sows may give birth to weak pigs which are often more or less hairless and may be still-born or die within a few hours. Some of the pigs in a litter may be more seriously affected than others. Thyroid enlargement may be present but is often overlooked unless a dissection is made. The skin of the abnormal pigs is often thick and pulpy, especially over the shoulder and neck region, owing to a watery swelling (edema) similar to that seen in human beings suffering from hypothyroidism.

Ewes receiving insufficient iodine also give birth to weak lambs which often show thyroid enlargement (big neck—fig. 3) and may be partially woolless. The death rate among such lambs is very high.

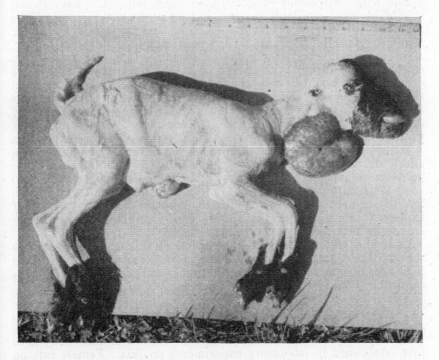

FIGURE 3.—A lamb with the skin removed to show an enlarged thyroid gland (goiter), a typical result of iodine deficiency.

Iodine deficiency in domestic animals usually results from a deficiency of this mineral in the soil and hence in the feed and water. Other factors such as diets high in calcium or fat may be antagonistic to iodine absorption. Iodine-deficient areas are known to exist in Montana, Idaho, Oregon, Washington, and parts of Utah, Wyoming, North Dakota, Minnesota, Wisconsin, and Michigan. Iodine deficiency has also been reported in certain sections of California, Nevada, Colorado, Nebraska, Iowa, and Texas (*19, 44*). The exact boundaries of the deficient areas are not known, and some sections are more deficient than others.

PREVENTION AND TREATMENT OF GOITER

The effectiveness of supplementary feeding of iodine to prevent goiter and associated symptoms due to iodine deficiency has been conclusively demonstrated for all classes of farm animals, but the exact minimum requirement of iodine has not been established. In a recent publication Welch (*66*), of Montana, confirms the finding that the control of iodine deficiency in farm animals is most easily accomplished by the use of iodized salt containing 0.02 percent of potassium iodide. Salt of this iodine content can be purchased from feed dealers, or salt containing approximately the same iodine content can be prepared by thoroughly mixing 1 ounce of powdered potassium iodide with 300 pounds of granulated stock salt. The iodized salt should be made available to sows during at least 3 months of the pregnancy period, to ewes for 3 to 4 months, and to cows and mares for 5 months or slightly more. Iodine deficiency is usually most prevalent in animals born early in the spring. If goiter appears in animals born during midsummer or fall, iodized salt in place of ordinary salt should be fed, at least to breeding animals, throughout the year. The need of feeding iodine to other than pregnant animals in iodine-deficient areas is questionable. Crampton (*7*) has recently summarized the recommendations of many investigators which have presumably been found satisfactory in the control of iodine deficiency.

Iodine compounds are expensive, however, and they have toxic effects on animals if fed in large amounts. Where extra iodine is needed, the amounts required are so small that the increase in feed costs is not appreciable. Salts of iodine readily disintegrate, with loss of iodine, if the mineral mixture is stored for long periods or exposed to sunshine and rain. Methods of stabilizing iodine in mineral feeds have recently been perfected.

Control of goiter and related conditions in animals—at one time a serious threat to the livestock industry in some areas—by feeding iodine compounds is so successful that economic losses from this condition should be very small if proper precautions are taken.

Manganese Deficiency

The essential function of manganese in the animal body was first established in laboratory experiments on rats. Female rats on low manganese rations failed to suckle their young, while male animals developed testicular atrophy. Chickens also require this mineral for normal growth of bone, normal development of embryos, and hatchability of eggs. Experiments with farm animals have been less successful in establishing symptoms of manganese deficiency, although recent work by Miller and coworkers (*43*) indicates that a lameness developing in pigs fed a ration consisting of yellow corn, tankage, soybean meal, ground alfalfa, and salt could be effectively prevented, but not cured, by adding 50 to 60 parts per million of manganese to the ration.

Iron, Copper, and Cobalt

The essential functions of iron, copper, and cobalt are in some respects interrelated, and prolonged deficiency of one or more of them causes rather characteristic symptoms. The importance of iron as a constituent of hemoglobin is widely recognized. Iron also functions in other compounds that play an important part in cellular oxidation reactions everywhere in the body. The relation of copper to iron metabolism in hemoglobin formation was discovered in 1928. Recently cobalt has been demonstrated to be indispensable in animal nutrition, functioning in an unknown way in blood formation and in the utilization of iron. A deficiency of this element may occur alone or in combination with copper or iron deficiency.

Hemoglobin formation is a continuous process throughout life, and whenever the body reserve of iron becomes depleted because of an inadequate intake of iron or copper, nutritional anemia (decrease in red blood cells and hemoglobin) develops. Such a condition is common in suckling pigs kept in indoor pens, and it may also occur in calves and lambs if they are kept on a diet of milk, exclusively, too long. Cattle, sheep, goats, and adult swine also become anemic when there is a natural deficiency of iron, copper, or cobalt in forage and grains caused by a deficiency of these minerals in the soil. In Florida this condition is known as "salt sick," and it can be successfully controlled by supplemental feeding as described later. Intestinal parasitism frequently results in anemia, and this condition may be confused with anemia due to a primary nutritional deficiency.

Cobalt feeding was known to have the effect of producing an increase in red blood cells in rats before its significance in the nutrition of farm animals was discovered. For many years a group of somewhat similar diseases of sheep and cattle have been recognized under the names "enzootic marasmus" or "coast disease" in Australia, "bush sickness" or "Morton Mains disease" in New Zealand, "nakuritis" in Kenya, "pine" or "pining" in Scotland, "salt sick" or "hill sick" in Florida, and "Grand Traverse" or "lake-shore disease" in Michigan.

The conditions named are characterized by anemia, progressive emaciation, and death. Moving the animals from the "affected" pastures of the coastal regions to pasture farther inland or feeding certain crude iron salts occasionally resulted in cures, and this led to a hypothesis that the condition was due to iron deficiency. Discouraging results frequently followed dosing with large amounts of various iron compounds, however, and it was also shown by Underwood (*61*) that the liver and spleen of sheep suffering with the disease often contained extra stores of iron. Filmer and Underwood (*12*) discovered that an iron-free extract of limonite, a curative iron compound, was just as effective in curing the condition as limonite itself. Further work by these investigators demonstrated that the active substance of the iron-free extract was cobalt (*62*) and that normal growth and health of sheep resulted from the feeding of cobalt chloride in the small amounts of 0.1 milligram of cobalt daily for sheep and 0.3 milligram daily for cattle. Dixon (*9*) obtained excellent results in the control of Morton Mains disease of lambs by providing free access to cobaltized salt lick, which was made by spraying a solution of 4 ounces of cobalt chloride on 1 ton of salt.

In coast disease of sheep in South Australia (*39*) the iron content of the liver is greatly increased above normal, and there are smaller increases in the spleen and kidneys, but the copper content of the liver is usually greatly reduced. Supplements of copper and cobalt are more effective than either alone in treating this condition.

COPPER DEFICIENCY AND COPPER POISONING

It is evident from the previous discussion of iron, copper, and cobalt that a deficiency of these minerals may occur in combination or separately. An apparently primary copper deficiency is now known to exist in Great Britain and western Australia, causing swayback, warfa, or enzootic ataxia in lambs. A similar condition has also been reported from South Africa, Sweden, and Peru. The full extent to which such a deficiency exists in the United States is not known, although sections of Florida are known to be copper-deficient, which suggests also a possible deficiency in other areas of the Coastal Plain region.

The condition called swayback usually affects lambs during the first month of life, although some lambs are unable to rise and suckle at birth or shortly afterwards. Death usually results from starvation. Degeneration of the myelin (sheath) of nerve tracts, particularly in the spinal cord, is usually found. When pregnant ewes are given access to salt licks containing 1 percent of copper as copper sulfate, the lambs are usually free from swayback (*10*), although the relation between copper and myelin metabolism is still obscure. Copper sulfate is essential in small quantities in cases of copper deficiency, but it is poisonous when fed in large amounts, and this should be remembered in all cases where copper therapy is indicated. Rietz (*54*) found that giving sheep free access to a mixture of 1 pound of copper sulfate to 30 pounds of salt while on pasture proved ineffective in controlling parasites yet caused death from copper poisoning. Losses on the range and experimental production of copper poisoning (so-called ictohemoglobinuria) in sheep by feeding copper containing commercial mineral mixtures are also reported by Boughton and Hardy (*4*), of the Texas Agricultural Experiment Station.

Sulfur

Sulfur, in the form of sulfur-containing protein or amino acids, is an essential dietary constituent for animals. Inorganic sources, such as the sulfates or flowers of sulfur, have not definitely proved to be of value when added directly to the ration or used as a constituent of mineral supplements. Prevention of sulfur deficiency therefore involves providing an adequate supply of sulfur-containing proteins.

Toxic Materials

Selenium Poisoning

In 1856 T. C. Madison, stationed at Fort Randall, Territory of Nebraska (now in Gregory County, S. D.), accurately described a new disease of army horses at that midwestern outpost. The question whether the disease was caused by the horses' eating poisonous plants or was due to contagion was not settled, however. Many reports followed in later years from ranchers, homesteaders, and veterinarians concerning losses among livestock in the north-central Great Plains area from this disease. The disease became known as alkali disease owing to a mistaken idea that it was caused by drinking alkali water, but this was finally ruled out, and attention was centered on plant poisons as the cause. In 1931 H. G. Knight, Chief of the Bureau of Chemistry and Soils of the Department of Agriculture, suggested that the disease might be due to selenium poisoning resulting from the consumption of plants that had absorbed traces of selenium from the soil. Cooperative work by the South Dakota experiment station and several bureaus of the Department of Agriculture provided evidence that this was true. A preliminary field survey report of this cooperative effort (*13*) describes the symptoms of alkali disease, which has also been called blind stagger and bob-tailed disease, as follows:

In horses, cattle, and swine, the malady manifests itself clinically by an alteration in the growth of the horn, of the hoofs, and a loss of hair from the mane and tail of horses, and switch of cattle, and the hair of swine. There are various gradations of these conditions, from mild cases in which there may be only subnormal growth or a loss of hair, to severe cases in which a break in the continuity of the growth of the walls of the hoof develops, followed eventually by a sloughing-off of the old hoofs. When this happens, the animals are more or less lame for months. In the more severe cases, the animals move about with great difficulty, and unless given careful attention may die of thirst or starvation. Many of the most severely affected animals die or are destroyed. If taken from "alkalied" areas or given food, the animals recover, but it is the belief of many that such animals are never quite as valuable as before an attack.

In swine, particularly in young pigs, in addition to lesions produced in the feet and loss of hair, death also may occur. After being badly "alkalied," many of the animals make but little, if any, gain in weight in spite of plenty of nutritious feed.

"Alkali" disease due to selenium poisoning has been reported primarily from areas in South Dakota, Montana, Wyoming, Nebraska, and Kansas, although other States in the Great Plains and Rocky Mountains have areas of seleniferous soils which produce plants of increased selenium content. Control measures for the disease are largely based on prevention. Affected animals should be transferred to areas where the disease is not prevalent and fed selenium-free grains and forage. "Alkalied" (selenium-containing) grain, hay, or grass should not be used for livestock feed or sold on the market. In the rat, diets high in casein and lactalbumin (both contained in milk) tend to protect against chronic selenium poisoning (*14*).

Fluorine Poisoning (Fluorosis)

Fluorine is widely distributed in nature in soil, rocks, water, and plants, but only in certain areas is the concentration high enough in the water or food supply to interfere with animal and human nutrition. All animals also contain traces of fluorine in their bodies, concentrated chiefly in the bones and teeth, but there is little evidence that it is an essential constituent of these structures.

Fluorine has a marked affinity for calcium, and this undoubtedly accounts for its interference with normal calcification when the intake becomes excessive. As little as 1 part per million of fluorine in the drinking water when used during the period of tooth formation will cause mottled enamel in human teeth, and severe mottling follows the continuous drinking of water containing 6 to 16 parts per million (*56*). Livestock are apparently not affected to any great extent by the low concentrations of fluorine that cause trouble in human beings. In the survey conducted by Hartman (*19*), reports were obtained that feed produced in some parts of Arkansas contained excess fluorine and that water from certain warm springs of California contained enough fluorine to cause trouble with the teeth of cattle. Mottled enamel in the teeth of cattle has also been reported in South Carolina and western Texas (*8*).

Fluorine is a cumulative poison, and long-continued consumption of relatively small quantities produces chronic fluorosis in all farm animals and poultry (*51*). By far the greatest danger from fluorine poisoning to livestock comes from the use in mineral mixtures of natural phosphatic limestone or rock phosphates, which are usually high in fluorine.

The general symptoms of chronic fluorine poisoning are abnormal teeth and bones, stiffness of joints, loss of appetite, emaciation, reduction in milk flow, diarrhea, salt hunger, kidney damage, and injury to other organs such as the liver, heart, adrenal glands, testes, and thyroid.

Prevention and treatment of fluorosis depends on eliminating any excessive fluorine intake by careful selection of feeds (particularly constituents of mineral supplements) and discontinuing the use of water with a high fluorine content. Animals suffering from marked injuries to teeth, bones, and organs due to fluorine poisoning may improve to some extent if the source of excessive fluorine is eliminated, but the damage may be permanent.

THE VITAMINS

The most important vitamins in the nutrition of cattle, sheep, goats, and horses are A and D, while in swine nutrition, in addition to these two vitamins practically all of the members of the vitamin

B complex must be considered. A general knowledge of the vitamins, including an understanding of the conditions under which deficiencies may occur and how to prevent them by the use of available feeds whenever possible, is necessary for continued success in feeding farm animals.

Vitamin A

Vitamin A is distinctive in that it is formed nowhere in nature except as a product of animal metabolism, but it is synthesized from carotenoids (alpha, beta, and gamma carotene and cryptoxanthin), which are formed only by plants. Beta carotene is the most important source of vitamin A, since it is capable of yielding two molecules of this essential substance, while the other carotenes form only one.

The carotenes are yellow to orange red in color, depending on their concentration, and are responsible for the yellow color of common varieties of carrots, corn, sweetpotatoes, etc. Carotene is also abundant in green forage of all kinds. The solution of the mystery of why both the yellow carotene and the nearly colorless vitamin A, as found in fish oils, can cure and prevent symptoms of vitamin A deficiency was one of the first triumphs of vitamin chemistry.

Farm animals of all ages may suffer from vitamin A deficiency, but young animals are particularly susceptible. The symptoms in calves are like those in older animals (*45*, *46*). Details of the symptoms in cattle and hogs are given in the articles on nutritional diseases of these animals, pages 658 and 818.

Sheep also develop night blindness from vitamin A deficiency, and pregnant ewes may abort or give birth to weak offspring which usually die shortly afterwards (*18*). Other symptoms in sheep are loss of appetite, poor condition, and weakness. Hale (*15*) reports that sows on vitamin-A-deficient rations may fail completely in reproduction or give birth to blind or eyeless pigs.

According to work by Howell, Hart, and Ittner (*21*), horses on a vitamin-A-deficient diet develop typical symptoms of night blindness, excessive lachrymation, keratinization of the cornea, difficult breathing, reproductive failure, poor appetite, scaly hoofs, and progressive weakness. Death may follow. Characteristic rarefying lesions of the joint cartilages and bones also were present in animals suffering from vitamin A deficiency, but positive evidence that the bone condition was due only to this deficiency was not obtained.

In work at the Beltsville Research Center, Beltsville, Md., microscopic examination of a urine sample obtained with a catheter from the bladder of a yearling Belgian filly on a very low carotene diet revealed a large proportion of crystalline sediment and a considerable number of large keratinized epithelial, or lining, cells. A diagnosis of vitamin A deficiency based on the abnormal cellular debris and the response of the animal to vitamin A therapy appeared to be correct (fig. 4). During the period of deficiency, there was also faulty hoof growth (fig. 5).

77434°—51——23

A lack of sufficient vitamin A or its precursor, carotene, in the diet is the chief cause of vitamin A deficiency in farm animals.

FIGURE 4.—Horses develop vitamin A deficiency if their diet is low in carotene. *A*, A yearling Belgian filly suffering from vitamin A deficiency. Note posture, rough coat, large area of scaly skin outlined in white, and poor condition. *B*, The same animal apparently normal again after vitamin A therapy.

Chronic intestinal disturbances, such as diarrhea or constipation, and insufficient secretion of bile are factors that interfere with the absorption of carotene. Liver injury may also interfere with the conversion of absorbed carotene into vitamin A, which is believed to take place largely in this organ. Charcoal added to a diet may destroy vitamin A and certain other vitamins, presumably by their removal or inactivation, and this raises the question of the advisa-

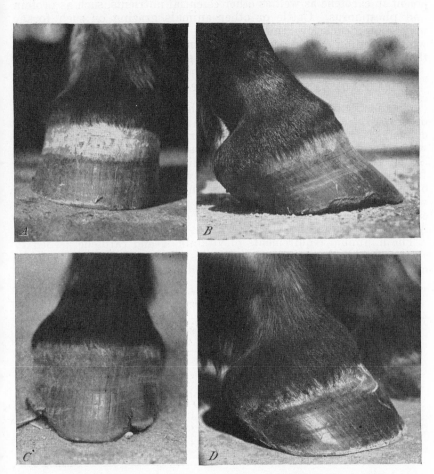

FIGURE 5.—Hoof growth is abnormal in horses during a period of vitamin A deficiency, but normal growth will probably be resumed if the deficiency is corrected. These photographs show the right front foot of the filly shown in figure 4 during the deficiency period and at two intervals during recovery. *A*, Note the band of rough, scaly hoof formed while the animal was suffering from vitamin A deficiency. *B* and *C*, Side and front views of the hoof after 5 months of vitamin A therapy. The contracted band of defective hoof is growing out and normal hoof growth is proceeding. *D*, About 11 months after the deficiency was corrected the area of defective hoof has completely grown out, and the newly formed hoof is apparently normal.

bility of using charcoal in grain or mineral mixtures. Iron salts and rancid fats in a ration also destroy vitamin A and carotene.

Carotene in hay decreases rapidly in amount under ordinary storage conditions; hence animals fed old hay may, not receive enough carotene. Moldy hay or forage that has been rained on or sunbleached during the curing process is also low in carotene content. During periods of prolonged drought, range or pasture becomes deficient in carotene as well as other essential nutrients, such as protein and phosphorus. Cattle or other animals grazing on such forage may show deficiency symptoms while on the range or go into the winter feeding period with an abnormally low storage reserve so that deficiencies develop before fresh green feed is available again.

PREVENTION AND TREATMENT OF VITAMIN A DEFICIENCY

An abundance of green grass or legume pasture in the summer and of properly cured, good-quality legume or grass hay or silage of the current season's crop in the winter or during periods of dry-lot feeding will prevent or cure this deficiency in cattle, sheep, horses, and goats. Swine also obtain considerable carotene and other essential factors from good pasture. Leafy legume hay for sows or 5 to 10 percent of high-grade alfalfa meal in the grain mixture for fattening swine will supply an abundance of carotene. Yellow corn furnishes some carotene, but it should not be depended on to meet the entire vitamin A requirement of animals.

The minimum requirements of vitamin A and carotene needed to cure night blindness in various species of animals have been determined by Hart (*17*) and are given in table 1.

TABLE 1.—*Summary of data on minimum vitamin A and carotene requirements to cure night blindness in various animals*

Animal	Daily intake per kilogram (2.2 pounds) of body weight			
	Vitamin A		Carotene	
	Micrograms	International units	Micrograms	International units
Cattle	5.1–6.4	21–27	26–33	43–55
Sheep	4.3–6.3	17–26	25–35	42–58
Swine	4.4–5.7	18–24	25–39	42–65
Horses	[1] 4.2–5.3	17–22	20–30	33–50
Rats	[2] 4.6–5.3		15–20	25–33
Rats	3.8–4.6	18–22		

[1] Data based on cod-liver oil used in cattle, sheep, swine, and horse experiments.
[2] Data based on U. S. P. reference (standardized) cod-liver oil.

Hart recommends that at least 5 to 10 times the minimum level of carotene or vitamin A should be furnished under practical conditions, since little or no storage occurs at the minimum level needed to prevent night blindness. The carotene requirements of growing calves and fattening steers and those for reproduction in adult cattle are considered in detail in the article, Nutritional Diseases of Cattle, page 662. As a practical recommendation, Meigs (*41*), from work in the Bureau of Dairy Industry at the Beltsville Research Center, Beltsville, Md., states:

The experiments so far carried out indicate that dairy cows will receive about the minimum carotene required for successful reproduction when the dry matter of their rations contains 10 p.p.m. [parts per million] of carotene. Approximately this quantity is supplied when the rations consist of equal parts of grain and hay, if the hay is U. S. No. 1 clover or U. S. No. 1 timothy.

If hays of lower grade and little or no silage or other source of carotene are fed, vitamin-A-deficient calves may be born after the cows have been on the ration for about 5 months following the pasture season. Less is known about the minimum vitamin A requirements for successful reproduction in other farm animals, but it is advisable to avoid a possible deficiency of this factor in breeding animals at all times.

Typical feeds that are deficient in carotene are cottonseed meal and hulls, linseed and soybean meals, wheat, oats, barley, white corn and corn stover, white sorghum grains, beet pulp and molasses, cereal straw, and low-grade hays. These feeds should not be fed alone or in combination with other carotene-deficient feeds over an extended period unless the ration is supplemented with carotene-rich feeds.

Feeds that are good sources of carotene are green grass or legume pasture, properly made silage, high-grade grass or legume hay of a good green color, and yellow varieties of carrots, sweetpotatoes, squash, etc. Cod-liver oil or other vitamin-A-rich fish oils and concentrates, or carotene concentrates in oil solution, may be fed animals to prevent or cure vitamin A deficiency when the regular feed source of carotene is inadequate. All oil solutions of vitamin A and carotene are relatively unstable, and if they are mixed with other feeds, it is not safe to make up more of the mixture at one time than will be used within a few weeks.

THE VITAMIN B COMPLEX

The number of recognized components of the vitamin B complex has steadily increased since 1926, when Smith and Hendrick (*57*) first demonstrated that the so-called water-soluble factor of McCollum and Davis (*31*) consisted of two fractions, one heat-stable and the other destroyed by heat. Nine so-called B vitamins are now recognized, and most of them have been synthesized in the laboratory. The vitamins of this complex that have been identified as separate entities are thiamin (B_1), riboflavin (growth factor of B-G complex), nicotinic acid (antipellagric factor of B-G complex), pyridoxine (B_6), pantothenic acid, choline, biotin, para-aminobenzoic acid, and inositol. The older method of alphabetical designation and descriptive nomenclature for these factors is rapidly being displaced by their chemical names.

Much is known concerning the essential nature and symptoms of a deficiency of these vitamins in the diet of laboratory animals, such as the rat, and of poultry. Recent studies have also shown that most of these factors are essential for the normal growth and health of swine and that a deficiency may produce typical disease symptoms. Under practical conditions, however, usually only border-line deficiencies occur which seldom manifest specific symptoms other than slow growth, digestive disturbances, unthrifty appearance, and lameness. When these symptoms appear, the possibility of a deficiency of the B vitamins should be investigated. (See the article on Nutritional Diseases of Swine, p. 820.)

A definite dietary requirement for the individual B vitamins has not been established for cattle, sheep, and goats but the existing evidence is not entirely complete. Some workers (*6, 47*) have reported good results from feeding a concentrate of B vitamins or yeast to horses on very poor rations.

Synthesis of B Vitamins by Ruminants

Bacteria growing on the contents of the rumen (paunch) of cattle and sheep have the ability to synthesize practically all of the known B vitamins, an unusual relationship that has been the subject of several recent studies. It is generally believed that vitamins thus synthesized in the rumen become available to the animal as the mass of ingesta and bacteria are digested.

Recently McElroy and Goss have made a quantitative study of the formation of riboflavin and vitamin K (*33*), vitamin B_6 (pyridoxine) (*34*), and thiamin (*35*) in the rumen of cattle and sheep fed diets low in these vitamins. It has also been demonstrated that pantothenic acid, nicotinic acid, and biotin (anti-egg-white-injury factor) are also formed in the rumen (*32*). Wegner and coworkers (*64*) made the interesting observation that when thiamin was added to the ration there was an apparent stimulation of synthesis of the other factors except nicotinic acid. Hunt and coworkers (*24*) found that riboflavin was synthesized in the rumen of steers fed yellow corn, alfalfa, and a protein supplement, although when a diet of alfalfa alone was fed, the rumen contents contained less of this material than did the hay. They point out that the synthesis of riboflavin may depend on the reaction of the rumen, since Kick and associates (*29*) had previously reported that the rumen contents of steers fed only on alfalfa were alkaline in reaction while those fed grain and a protein supplement had rumen contents that were acid in reaction.

It is impossible to say at present whether rumen synthesis of B vitamins can be depended on to furnish cattle, sheep, and goats with an adequate supply of these factors under all conditions. Work with synthetic or purified diets for herbivorous animals has led to some interesting results. Madsen and coworkers (*38*) were unable to raise young kids or lambs on purified diets low in B vitamins unless yeast or an alcoholic extract of yeast was added. Pearson and associates (*50*), however, raised lambs on a diet which was capable of producing blacktongue in dogs and pellagralike symptoms in swine. All of the lambs made good growth for 4 to 5 weeks, but then went off feed and declined in body weight, in some cases as much as 24 percent. Lambs treated with thiamin and nicotinic acid, as well as untreated lambs, subsequently recovered. These workers remark:

Whether this temporary failure reflects a period during which the animal organism was making an adjustment to the deficiency, perhaps through an increase in microörganisms in the rumen that might synthesize nicotinic acid or to some other factor, cannot be answered at present.

Johnson, Loosli, and Maynard (*26*) fed young calves on rations low in the B vitamins and were unable to demonstrate that the grass-juice factor (as yet unidentified), vitamin C, wheat-germ oil, thiamin, or riboflavin were limiting factors in the ration. However, the performance of the calves was far from normal. Most of them were 30 to 50 percent of normal in rate of growth and had frequent attacks of scours, some failed to grow during the first month of the experiment, and there was often a leveling off of appetite with periodic variations in gain and food intake after about 100 days. These findings emphasize the complexity of the dietary requirements of herbivorous animals.

Vitamin C (Ascorbic Acid)

Ascorbic acid, the vitamin that prevents and cures scurvy in human beings, monkeys, and guinea pigs, is receiving new attention in the nutrition and reproductive physiology of farm animals (*52, 53*). Further details are given in the article on Nutritional Diseases of Cattle, page 664. Ascorbic acid is rapidly destroyed in the rumen of cattle, so that treatment of the type of breeding failure which responds to vitamin C therapy can be accomplished, according to present knowledge, only by injecting the vitamin subcutaneously.

Vitamin D (Activated Ergosterol and Cholesterol)

The role of vitamin D in the nutrition of farm animals and the principal sources of the vitamin have been discussed earlier in this article in relation to its function in calcium and phosphorus metabolism and in bone formation.

Vitamin E (Alpha Tocopherol)

Twenty years ago it was demonstrated that rats fed certain purified or restricted diets often seemed to grow normally and appeared healthy but frequently failed to reproduce. The missing factor necessary for reproduction was shown to be distinct from any of the vitamins recognized at that time. Later studies have indicated that this vitamin is also concerned in growth, the metabolism of the muscular and nervous systems, and possibly the activity of certain endocrine glands, such as the pituitary and thyroid.

Vitamin E has been isolated from natural sources and synthesized.[5] In the pure synthetic form this vitamin is a light yellow, viscous, oily fluid. It is sold in sealed air-evacuated glass vials. The presence of rancid fats, the oxidation of other substances such as cod-liver oil in a feed mixture, or the presence of iron salts tend to destroy the vitamin.

---

[5] Several closely related compounds known as tocopherols have vitamin E activity, but alpha-tocopherol or 5-, 7-, 8-trimethyltocol is probably the most potent of these compounds.

Natural foods that are good sources of vitamin E are whole cereal grains, fresh or well-cured roughages, leafy vegetables, and vegetable oils, such as wheat-germ, cottonseed, corn, and soybean (*20*).

Vitamin E and Reproduction in Farm Animals

Little is known concerning the vitamin E requirements of farm animals except poultry. This is due to the widespread occurrence of the vitamin in common livestock feeds as well as to the fact that it is very expensive to prepare vitamin-E-free diets for the larger animals for experimental purposes. Wheat-germ-oil therapy for the treatment of sterility in cattle has led to conflicting results (see the article on Nutritional Diseases of Cattle, p. 666).

Attempts to determine whether farm animals require vitamin E have led to some interesting findings. Thomas and coworkers (*58*) at the Iowa Experiment Station have fed goats on a ration of chopped alfalfa hay and ground grains which had been treated with ethereal ferric chloride to destroy or inactivate vitamin E. Rats fed this ration failed to reproduce, showing that it was deficient in vitamin E, but the goats continued to reproduce normally through several generations. Ewes (*59*) given the same vitamin-E-deficient ration as the goats in preliminary breeding experiments failed to give birth to living young, while of two groups of 10 breeding ewes the group receiving weekly supplements of wheat-germ oil produced a larger lamb crop. The latter experiment was repeated with about 120 ewes, and "this time the feeding of tested wheat-germ oil appeared to be neither beneficial nor harmful to reproduction" (*60*). Similar work with dairy cattle (*5*) has been discontinued because of the technical difficulties and expense involved in preparing sufficient amounts of vitamin-E-free rations.

Madsen and coworkers produced muscular dystrophy (a paralysis; the word "dystrophy" means "faulty nutrition") in goats, sheep, guinea pigs, and rabbits by feeding purified rations (*37*, *38*). The cause of this disease is now generally accepted to be vitamin E deficiency, although specific evidence for goats and sheep is lacking. No difficulties due to muscular dystrophy were mentioned in the work by Thomas and associates previously cited.

The possible role of vitamin E deficiency in the development of a degeneration of the skeletal muscles in other animals—for example, the stiff-lamb disease, so-called white-muscle disease of calves and pigs, and paralytic myoglobinemia (azoturia, or Monday-morning sickness) of horses—is worthy of investigation. It is now plainly evident, however, that a number of species of animals other than the rat require vitamin E and that this factor has important roles in other vital functions besides reproduction.

The question whether farm animals other than poultry require vitamin E needs further study before recommendations for supplying extra sources of this factor can be made. Ordinary farm rations are usually rich in vitamin E. Good sources include wheat, bran, shorts, linseed meal, hominy feed, corn, cottonseed meal, kafir, alfalfa, white clover, and pasture grasses.

MISCELLANEOUS NUTRITIONAL DISEASES

Urinary Calculi (Urolithiasis) and Dietary Imbalance

Urinary calculi (sand, grit, or stones) formed by the precipitation of salts from the urine in the kidney or bladder are quite common, particularly in cattle, sheep, and horses. Calculi may cause no apparent discomfort to the animal, or they may result in serious symptoms or death by obstructing the flow of urine. The symptoms depend, of course, on the size, location, number, and rate of increase of the calculi and whether or not infection is present. Symptoms caused by urinary calculi are similar in the various species of animals and include frequent attempts to urinate, dribbling or stoppage of urine, pain or renal colic, restlessness in the early stages, and later walking with a characteristic straddling gait. Rupture of the bladder may follow chronic obstruction.

It is known that diet is definitely a factor in the development of calculi, but the problem is very complex and few of the factors involved have been definitely proved. Vitamin A deficiency is thought to favor calculi formation. The case is not so clear-cut for farm animals, however, as it is for laboratory animals such as the rat. Newsom (*48*) states that vitamin A is quite generally deficient in the rations in the dry lands of eastern Colorado, where calculi are so prevalent, but the disease has also been observed in cattle and sheep on good alfalfa rations.

Calculi occur in animals fed certain rations more frequently than in others. In a recent progress report from the Nebraska station [7] an experiment is described in which an attempt was made to compare Early kalo and Sooner milo with corn as a grain for fattening lambs, and to determine the advisability of adding a small amount of alfalfa hay to such rations when Atlas silage was the only roughage fed. In the experiment there were 30 lambs in each of several lots. In the group receiving Early kalo, cottonseed meal, bonemeal, and Atlas silage, and in another lot receiving Sooner milo as the grain with the other three ingredients, 42 and 58 percent of the wether lambs, respectively, developed severe cases of urinary calculi. Lambs of other lots which received one-half pound of alfalfa in addition to the rations mentioned were largely free of calculi. Lambs receiving yellow corn, alfalfa, or both, were also largely protected from calculi. The results are in agreement with findings of Newsom (*48*), who states that changing the ration of cattle or sheep to include corn and alfalfa has usually resulted in a cessation of the outbreaks of urinary calculi in fattening animals.

In work by Johnson, Palmer, and Nelson (*25*), high dietary magnesium was suspected of forming calculi in a group of 2,600 wether lambs in which 10 percent of the animals were affected, but feeding experimental rations containing as much as 1.5 percent of magnesium

---

[7] Alexander, M. A. Early Kalo vs. Sooner Milo for Fattening Lambs. Adding Alfalfa to a Silage Ration for Fattening Lambs. Soybean Pellets vs. Cottonseed Meal for Fattening Lambs. 1939–40 Feeding Season. Progress Report, Nebr. Agr. Expt. Sta. Sheep Circular 337, 6 pp. [1940.] [Processed.]

to some of these lambs did not produce calculi, although the blood magnesium of the animals was increased threefold.

Specific preventive and curative measures for severe urolithiasis have not been completely worked out. Some veterinary surgeons have become skilled in removing calculi obstructing the urethra of the male, thus giving temporary relief and making it possible for the animal to finish an approximately normal feeding period. Precautionary measures include supplying animals with plenty of drinking water, succulent feed, and an adequate amount of vitamin A; attempting to establish a normal calcium, phosphorus, and magnesium intake; and providing plenty of exercise. The fact that calculi are somewhat more prevalent in animals on full feed indicates the desirability of reducing the grain intake if cases develop. As previously pointed out, changing the ration to corn and alfalfa when possible may also prove beneficial. The value of dietary treatment when calculi are well developed is doubtful. Response may be slow at best.

OVERFEEDING

Effects of overfeeding were outlined in the Yearbook of Agriculture for 1939 (*36*), as follows:

Overfeeding of farm animals can result in heavy financial losses by causing temporary or permanent disability and even death of animals. * * * Livestock will frequently overeat if given an opportunity. The consequences may be only temporary digestive disturbances or they may be so serious as to cause death. * * * Such symptoms as diarrhea, constipation, bloat, colic, and failure to eat the usual quantities of food are danger signals, which if observed in time may be corrected. Digestive troubles from overeating may occur very suddenly, and even if the services of a veterinarian are immediately available a fatal outcome may not be prevented.

Newsom and Thorp (*49*) describe the effects of overeating in lambs and state that this condition causes more losses in the feed lots of Colorado than all other troubles combined. Lambs sick from overeating, particularly on grain, may have nervous symptoms such as head retractions, staggering gait, walking in circles and rapidly progressing weakness followed by prostration, coma, convulsions, and death within a few hours. The mortality is high, but some animals may recover. Reducing the grain intake to less than a pound daily and distributing the daily grain allotment equally in sufficient feeder space so that all lambs have an opportunity to eat may be helpful. A puzzling feature of the trouble is its sporadic occurrence and the frequent failure of attempts to produce it experimentally. Losses are usually reduced to a minimum if the lambs are started on feed slowly, with gradual increases in the grain allowance as the feeding period progresses and the appetite of the animals increases. Self-feeding of lambs with a mixture of grains and ground roughage, the proportion of grain being gradually increased, is often successful. Overeating may also occur when lambs or other animals are turned into grain or corn fields. The use of temporary fences to rotate the fields and restrict the animals to small areas that can be cleaned up in a relatively short time, thus eliminating the possibility of eating too much grain, will reduce losses.

Fattening cattle, dairy cows fed for high production, and calves also suffer from overeating. (See the article on Nutritional Diseases of Cattle, p. 669.)

Horses often overeat if given an opportunity. Various digestive disturbances known collectively as colic are frequently due to overeating or the eating of spoiled feed. Severe attacks may result in disability or even death.

Animals that are kept too fat by heavy feeding do not usually breed normally.

EFFECTS OF UNDERNUTRITION

Undernutrition results either from a deficiency of essential nutrients in the diet or from a lack of sufficient total feed to maintain body processes. Undernutrition of the first type involves the so-called nutritional diseases previously described, while that of the second type is frequently spoken of as starvation. A deficiency of a single essential factor such as phosphorus, however, often produces clinical results very similar to complete starvation. Starvation is in fact involved, because the animal voluntarily refuses to eat sufficient food and as a result multiple deficiencies develop.

The effect of undernutrition on the body depends on a number of factors, such as the nature of the deficiency; age and kind of animals and whether they are working, lactating, or pregnant; duration of the deficiency; and whether or not the available body stores of essential nutrients have been depleted. Undernutrition with respect to some factors may lead to permanent injury to the body, whereas a moderate energy or protein deficiency, for instance, may slow up growth or cause a loss of weight and yet not be particularly harmful unless continued too long. Animals can never continue to produce economically if the supply of food is insufficient or if specific nutrients are lacking. In such cases, most of the food consumed is expended in maintenance of the body, and little or none is left over for conversion into useful products or growth.

Breeding animals are also injured by undernutrition and often fail to breed regularly. Pregnant cows or ewes about to lamb die from starvation sooner than nonpregnant animals. A high death loss due to weakness of the young animals at birth or to failure of the mother to lactate normally, may also occur among calves, lambs, or colts born to mothers in poor condition. Esplin, Madsen, and Phillips (11) have reported studies on feeding ewe lambs during their first winter as compared with the usual system of grazing on the open range during the entire year. The ewe lambs that had been fed during the winter produced more wool, showed a lower death loss, and had a much higher percentage of lambs at 2 years of age than the range group.

Animals suffering from malnutrition are usually more susceptible to certain infectious diseases and parasitic infestations than well-fed animals, and for this reason, as well as because of the economic factors involved, faulty nutrition should be avoided and corrected whenever possible.

LITERATURE CITED

(1) BAUMANN, E.
    1895–96. UEBER DAS NORMALE VORKOMMEN VON JOD IN THIERKÖRPER.
    Ztschr. f. Physiol. Chem. 21: 319–330.
(2) BECHDEL, S. I., HILSTON, N. W., GUERRANT, N. B., and DUTCHER, R. A.
    1938. THE VITAMIN D REQUIREMENT OF DAIRY CALVES. Pa. Agr. Expt. Sta.
    Bul. 364, [26] pp., illus.
(3) ——— LANDSBURG, K. G., and HILL, O. J.
    1933. RICKETS IN CALVES. Pa. Agr. Expt. Sta. Tech Bul. 291, 41 pp.,
    illus.
(4) BOUGHTON, I. B., and HARDY, W. T.
    1934. CHRONIC COPPER POISONING IN SHEEP. Tex. Agr. Expt. Sta. Bul.
    499, 32 pp., illus.
(5) CANNON, C. Y., ESPE, D. L., and THOMAS, B. H.
    [1940]. RELATION OF VITAMIN E TO STERILITY IN DAIRY COWS. Iowa Agr.
    Expt. Sta. Rept. 1940 (1): 115-116.
(6) CARLSTRÖM, BIRGER, and HJÄRRE, ALBERT.
    1939. DURCH B-AVITAMINOSE VERURSACHTE MANGELKRANKHEITEN BEI MILI-
    TÄRPFERDEN. Biedermann's Zentbl. f. Agr. Chem., Abt. B, Tier-
    ernährung 11: 121–129, illus.
(7) CRAMPTON, E. W.
    1940. IODINE IN LIVESTOCK FEEDING. Feedstuffs 12 (49): 9–13, illus.
(8) DEAN H. TRENDLEY.
    1935. MOTTLED ENAMEL IN CATTLE. U. S. Pub. Health Ser., Pub. Health
    Rpts. 50: 206–210, illus.
(9) DIXON, J. K.
    1937. THE USE OF A COBALTIZED SALT LICK IN THE CONTROL OF A LAMB AIL-
    MENT AT MORTON MAINS, SOUTHLAND. New Zeal. Jour. Sci. and
    Technol. 18: 892–897, illus.
(10) DUNLOP, G., INNES, J. R. M., SHEARER, G. D., and WELLS, H. E.
    1939. "SWAYBACK" STUDIES IN NORTH DERBYSHIRE. I. THE FEEDING OF COP-
    PER TO PREGNANT EWES IN THE CONTROL OF "SWAYBACK." Jour.
    Comp. Path. and Ther. 52: [259]–265.
(11) ESPLIN, ALMA C., MADSEN, MILTON A., and PHILLIPS, RALPH W.
    1940. EFFECTS OF FEEDING EWE LAMBS DURING THEIR FIRST WINTER. Utah
    Agr. Expt. Sta. Bul. 292, 12 pp., illus.
(12) FILMER, J. F., and UNDERWOOD, E. J.
    1934. ENZOOTIC MARASMUS. TREATMENT WITH LIMONITE FRACTIONS.
    Austral. Vet. Jour. 10: 83–87.
(13) FRANKE, KURT W., RICE, T. D., JOHNSON, A. G., and SCHOENING, H. W.
    1934. REPORT ON A PRELIMINARY FIELD SURVEY OF THE SO-CALLED "ALKALI
    DISEASE" OF LIVESTOCK. U. S. Dept. Agr. Cir. 320, 10 pp., illus.
(14) GORTNER, ROSS A., JR.
    1940. CHRONIC SELENIUM POISONING OF RATS AS INFLUENCED BY DIETARY
    PROTEIN. Jour. Nutr. 19: 105–112, illus.
(15) HALE, FRED.
    1935. THE RELATION OF VITAMIN A TO ANOPHTHALMOS IN PIGS. Amer.
    Jour. Ophth. 18: 1087–1092, illus.
(16) HARRINGTON, CHARLES ROBERT, and BARGER, GEORGE.
    1927. CHEMISTRY OF THYROXINE. III. CONSTITUTION AND SYNTHESIS OF
    THYROXINE. Biochem. Jour. 21: 169–181, illus.
(17) HART, GEORGE H.
    1940. VITAMIN A DEFICIENCY AND REQUIREMENTS OF FARM MAMMALS. Nutr.
    Abs. and Rev. 10: [261]–272.
(18) ——— and MILLER, ROBERT F.
    1937. RELATIONSHIP OF CERTAIN DIETARY ESSENTIALS TO FERTILITY IN SHEEP.
    Jour. Agr. Res. 55: 47–58.
(19) HARTMAN, A. M.
    1939. DEFICIENT AND EXCESS MINERALS IN FORAGE IN THE UNITED STATES.
    U. S. Dept. Agr. Yearbook (Food and Life) 1939: 1027–1044,
    illus.

(20) HATHAWAY, I. L., and DAVIS, H. P.
   1934. THE VITAMIN E CONTENT OF CERTAIN DAIRY FEEDS. Nebr. Agr. Expt.
      Sta. Res. Bul. 73, 7 pp.
(21) HOWELL, C. E., HART, G. H., and ITTNER, N. R.
   1941. VITAMIN A DEFICIENCY IN HORSES. Amer. Jour. Vet. Res. 2: 60–74,
      illus.
(22) HUFFMAN, C. F., and DUNCAN, C. W.
   1935. VITAMIN D STUDIES IN CATTLE. II. THE VITAMIN D SPARING ACTION
      OF MAGNESIUM IN THE RATION OF DAIRY CATTLE. Jour. Dairy
      Sci. 18: 605–620, illus.
(23) ——— and DUNCAN, C. W.
   1936. MAGNESIUM CARBONATE AND MAGNESIUM OXIDE SUPPLEMENTS TO A
      WHOLE MILK RATION FOR DAIRY CALVES. (Abstract of paper)
      Jour. Dairy Sci. 19: 440–441.
(24) HUNT, CHARLES H., KICK, C. H., BURROUGHS, E. WISE, and others.
   1941. STUDIES ON RIBOFLAVIN AND THIAMIN IN THE RUMEN CONTENT OF
      CATTLE. Jour. Nutr. 21: 85–92.
(25) JOHNSON, D. W., PALMER, L. S., and NELSON, J. W.
   1940. FAILURE OF DIETARY MAGNESIUM IMBALANCE TO PRODUCE URINARY
      CALCULI IN WETHERS. Vet. Med. 35: 353–357, illus.
(26) JOHNSON, P. E., LOOSLI, J. K., and MAYNARD, L. A.
   1940. PURIFIED DIET STUDIES WITH CALVES. (Abstract) Jour. Dairy Sci.
      23: 553–554.
(27) KALKUS, J. W.
   1920. A STUDY OF GOITRE AND ASSOCIATED CONDITIONS IN DOMESTIC ANIMALS.
      Wash. Agr. Expt. Sta. Bul. 156, 48 pp., illus.
(28) KENDALL, EDWARD C.
   1915. THE ISOLATION IN CRYSTALLINE FORM OF THE COMPOUND CONTAINING
      IODINE WHICH OCCURS IN THE THYROID; ITS CHEMICAL NATURE
      AND PHYSIOLOGICAL ACTIVITY. Assoc. Amer. Physicians Trans.
      30: 420–448, illus.
(29) KICK, [C. H.], GERLAUGH, [PAUL], SCHALK, [A. F.], and SILVER, [E. A.]
   1938. DIGESTION IN CATTLE. PH OF THE INGESTA. Ohio Agr. Expt. Sta.
      Ann. Rpt. 1936–37 (Bul. 592) : 105.
(30) LOEFFEL, WM. J., THALMAN, RAY R., OLSON, F. C., and OLSON, F. A.
   1931. STUDIES OF RICKETS IN SWINE. Nebr. Agr. Expt. Sta. Res. Bul. 58,
      67 pp., illus.
(31) MCCOLLUM, E. V., and DAVIS, MARGUERITE.
   1915. THE NATURE OF THE DIETARY DEFICIENCIES OF RICE. Jour. Biol.
      Chem. 23: 181–230, illus.
(32) MCELROY, L. W., and GOSS, HAROLD.
   1939. REPORT ON FOUR MEMBERS OF THE VITAMIN B COMPLEX SYNTHESIZED IN
      THE RUMEN OF THE SHEEP. Jour. Biol. Chem. 130: 437–438.
(33) ——— and GOSS, HAROLD.
   1940. A QUANTITATIVE STUDY OF VITAMINS IN THE RUMEN CONTENTS OF
      SHEEP AND COWS FED VITAMIN-LOW DIETS. II. RIBOFLAVIN AND
      VITAMIN K. Jour. Nutr. 20: 527–540, illus.
(34) ——— and GOSS, HAROLD.
   1940. A QUANTITATIVE STUDY OF VITAMINS IN THE RUMEN CONTENTS OF
      SHEEP AND COWS FED VITAMIN-LOW DIETS. II. VITAMIN B₆ (PYRI-
      DOXINE). Jour. Nutr. 20: 541–550.
(35) ——— and GOSS, H.
   1941. A QUANTITATIVE STUDY OF VITAMINS IN THE RUMEN CONTENTS OF
      SHEEP AND COWS FED VITAMIN-LOW DIETS. III. THIAMIN. Jour.
      Nutr. 21: 163–173, illus.
(36) MADSEN, LOUIS L.
   1939. FACTORS AFFECTING MAINTENANCE NUTRITION, FEED UTILIZATION, AND
      HEALTH OF FARM ANIMALS. U. S. Dept. Agr. Yearbook (Food
      and Life) 1939: 431–449, illus.
(37) ——— MCCAY, C. M., and MAYNARD, L. A.
   1933. POSSIBLE RELATIONSHIP BETWEEN COD LIVER OIL AND MUSCULAR
      DEGENERATION OF HERBIVORA FED SYNTHETIC DIETS. Soc. Expt.
      Biol. and Med. Proc. 30: 1434–1438.

(38) ——— McCay, C. M., and Maynard, L. A.
     1935. SYNTHETIC DIETS FOR HERBIVORA, WITH SPECIAL REFERENCE TO THE
       TOXICITY OF COD-LIVER OIL. N. Y. (Cornell) Agr. Expt. Sta.
       Mem. 178, 53 pp., illus.
(39) Marston, H. R., Thomas, R. G., Murnane, D., and others.
     1938. STUDIES ON COAST DISEASE OF SHEEP IN SOUTH AUSTRALIA. Austral.
       Council Sci. & Indus. Res. Bul. 113, 91 pp., illus.
(40) Maynard, Leonard A.
     1937. ANIMAL NUTRITION. 483 pp., illus. New York and London.
(41) Meigs, Edward B.
     1939. THE FEEDING OF DAIRY COWS FOR INTENSIVE MILK PRODUCTION IN
       PRACTICE. U. S. Dept. Agr. Yearbook (Food and Life) 1939:
       566–591, illus.
(42) ——— Turner, William A., Kane, Edward A., and Shinn, Leo A.
     1935. THE EFFECTS ON CALCIUM AND PHOSPHORUS METABOLISM IN DAIRY
       COWS, OF FEEDING LOW-CALCIUM RATIONS FOR LONG PERIODS. Jour.
       Agr. Res. 51 : 1–26.
(43) Miller, R. C., Keith, T. B., McCarty, M. A., and Thorp, W. T. S.
     1940. MANGANESE AS A POSSIBLE FACTOR INFLUENCING THE OCCURRENCE OF
       LAMENESS IN PIGS. Soc. Expt. Biol. and Med. Proc. 45 : 50–51.
(44) Mitchell, H. H., and McClure, F. J.
     1937. MINERAL NUTRITION OF FARM ANIMALS. Natl. Res. Council Bul.
       99, 135 pp.
(45) Moore, L. A.
     1939. RELATIONSHIP BETWEEN CAROTENE, BLINDNESS DUE TO CONSTRICTION
       OF THE OPTIC NERVE, PAPILLARY EDEMA AND NYCTALOPIA IN CALVES.
       Jour. Nutr. 17 : 443–459, illus.
(46) ——— and Hallman, E. T.
     1936. PRODUCTION OF WHITE SPOTTED KIDNEYS IN CALVES. (Abstract) Jour.
       Dairy Sci. 19 : 434–435.
(47) Naito, K., Shimamura, T., and Kuwabara, K.
     1925. EXPERIMENTAL STUDIES ON THE EFFECTS OF POLISHED RICE FEEDING
       AND ITS VITAMIN B DEFECT IN THE HORSE. [Chosen] Govt. Inst.
       Vet. Res. Rpt. 3 : 51–53.
(48) Newsom, I. E.
     1938. URINARY CALCULI WITH SPECIAL REFERENCE TO CATTLE AND SHEEP.
       Amer. Vet. Med. Assoc. Jour. 92 : 495–502.
(49) ——— and Thorp, Frank, Jr.
     1938. LAMB DISEASES IN COLORADO FEEDLOTS. Colo. Agr. Expt. Sta. Bul.
       448, 42 pp., illus.
(50) Pearson, P. B., Schmidt, H., and Mackey, A. K.
     1939. EFFECT OF A PELLAGRA-PRODUCING DIET ON HERBIVORA. Soc. Expt.
       Biol. and Med. Proc. 40 : 423–425, illus.
(51) Peirce, A. W.
     1939. CHRONIC FLUORINE INTOXICATION IN DOMESTIC ANIMALS. Nutr. Abs.
       and Rev. 9 : 253–261.
(52) Phillips, P. H., Lardy, H. A., Boyer, P. D., and Werner, George.
     1940. "HARD TO SETTLE" COWS RESPOND TO VITAMIN C INJECTIONS. Wis.
       Agr. Expt. Sta. Ann. Rept. (Bul. 450) : 37–38, illus.
(53) ——— Lardy, H. A., Heizer, E. E., and Rupel, I. W.
     1940. SPERM STIMULATION IN THE BULL THROUGH THE SUBCUTANEOUS AD-
       MINISTRATION OF ASCORBIC ACID. Jour. Dairy Sci. 23 : 873–878.
(54) Rietz, J. H.
     1936. MASS FEEDING OF SHEEP WITH COPPER SULPHATE AND SALT TO CON-
       TROL GASTRO-INTESTINAL PARASITES. W. Va. Agr. Expt. Sta. Bul.
       271, 11 pp.
(55) Russell, Walter C.
     1939. VITAMINS IN THE NUTRITION OF ANIMALS. Amer. Vet. Med. Assoc.
       Jour. 94 : 81–89.
(56) Smith, Margaret Cammack.
     1939. MINERAL NEEDS OF MAN. IODINE AND FLUORINE. U. S. Dept. Agr.
       Yearbook (Food and Life) 1939 : 211–213.

(57) Smith, Maurice I., and Hendrick, E. G.
    1926. SOME NUTRITION EXERIMENTS WITH BREWERS' YEAST, WITH SPECIAL REFERENCE TO ITS VALUE IN SUPPLEMENTING CERTAIN DEFICIENCIES IN EXPERIMENTAL RATIONS. U. S. Pub. Health Serv., Pub. Health Rpts. 41: 201–207, illus.

(58) Thomas, Byron H., and Cannon, C. Y.
    1937. REPRODUCTION ON RATIONS FREE FROM VITAMIN E. Amer. Soc. Anim. Prod. Proc. 30: 59–63.

(59) —— Culbertson, C. C., and McNutt, S. H.
    [1939]. RELATION OF VITAMIN E TO THE REPRODUCTION OF SWINE AND SHEEP. Iowa Agr. Expt. Sta. Ann. Rpt. 1938–39 (1): 85–86.

(60) —— Culbertson, C. C., and McNutt, S. H.
    1940. RELATION OF VITAMIN E TO THE REPRODUCTION OF SWINE AND SHEEP. Iowa Agr. Expt. Sta. Rpt. 1939–40 (1): 110–111.

(61) Underwood, E. J.
    1934. ENZOOTIC MARASMUS. IRON CONTENT OF LIVER, KIDNEY, AND SPLEEN. Austral. Vet. Jour. 10: 87–92.

(62) —— and Filmer, J. F.
    1935. ENZOOTIC MARASMUS. THE DETERMINATION OF THE BIOLOGICALLY POTENT ELEMENT (COBALT) IN LIMONITE. Austral. Vet. Jour. 11: 84–92, illus.

(63) United States Department of Agriculture.
    1940. TECHNOLOGY ON THE FARM. Spec. Rpt., 224 pp., illus.

(64) Wegner, M. I., Booth, A. N., Elvehjem, C. A., and Hart, E. B.
    1940. RUMEN SYNTHESIS OF THE VITAMIN B COMPLEX. Soc. Expt. Biol. and Med. Proc. 45: 769–771.

(65) Welch, Howard.
    1928. GOITER IN FARM ANIMALS. Mont. Agr. Expt. Sta. Bul. 214, 26 pp., illus.

(66) ——
    1940. PREVENTION OF GOITER IN FARM ANIMALS. Mont. Agr. Expt. Sta. Cir. 160, 5 pp., illus.

Plants Poisonous to Livestock

BY WARD T. HUFFMAN AND JAMES F. COUCH [1]

IT IS chiefly in the grazing areas of the West that the poison-plant problem becomes serious—and there it can be very serious, especially under conditions of feed shortage and overgrazing. Here is much practical and scientific information, the fruit of many years of research.

POISONOUS PLANTS have caused extensive losses to the livestock industry in many parts of the United States since the days of the early settlements in this country, and they still constitute a major economic problem in numerous areas, especially in the western range States.

Prior to about 1894, when the Department of Agriculture began the experimental investigations that have been continued to the present time, there was very little definite information available regarding the toxic properties of most of our poisonous plants. As a result of the work of the Department and various State experiment stations a large amount of information on many toxic plants has been accumulated, and the practical application of this knowledge has enabled livestock owners to reduce losses to a considerable extent.

The list of known poisonous plants (table 1) probably contains most of those that have been responsible for heavy livestock losses in the past. The information on many of these plants is still incomplete, however, and in addition other species are proving toxic under present grazing conditions.

Changes in farming practices in the Eastern and Central States have resulted in the plowing up of much of the area that was originally forest and prairie land, and this practice has eliminated a good share of the native vegetation that formerly grew in these areas, some

[1] Ward T. Huffman is Veterinarian in Charge of Investigations of Stock Poisoning by Plants, Bureau of Animal Industry, and James F. Couch is Senior Chemist, Bureau of Agricultural Chemistry and Engineering.

354

TABLE 1.—*Essential facts about the principal poisonous plants* [1]

Common and scientific names of plant	Location	Parts of plant that usually cause poisoning	Animals most commonly poisoned	Conditions under which poisoning usually occurs, and minimum quantity required	Characteristic effects
Arrowgrass (*Triglochin maritima* L.).	Salt or alkaline marshes and wet places throughout the United States.	Leaves and stems.	Cattle and sheep.	Eating about 1 percent of animal's weight of green plants in a few minutes.	Difficult breathing, spasms, coma, illness of short duration.
Aster, Parry (*Aster parryi* A. Gray).	Dry flats of Wyoming.	do.	Sheep.	Eating 1.25 pounds of green plants in a day when animals are hungry.	Weakness, prostration, rapid weak pulse, increased urination, and cyanosis.
Azalea, western (*Rhododendron occidentale* (Torr. and Gray) Gray).	Moist places in Coast Range and Sierra Nevada Mountains of California.	Leaves.	do.	Eating a few ounces of leaves.	Salivation, vomiting, and weakness.
Baccharis (*Baccharis ramulosa* (DC.) A. Gray).	Hillsides of western Texas and southern New Mexico and Arizona.	do.	Cattle.	Scarcity of feed in fall and early winter.	Extreme prostration, severe inflammation of stomach.
Black laurel (*Leucothoe davisiae* Torr.).	Springy ground in Sierra Nevada Mountains of Calif.	do.	Sheep.	Eating 0.2 pound in a day's feeding.	Salivation, vomiting, weakness.
Bracken (*Pteridium* sp.).	Thickets, hills, and rich woods throughout the United States.	Fronds.	Horses and cattle.	Eating 5 pounds daily for about a month.	Horses: lack of control of legs, weakness. Cattle: hemorrhages in various parts of body.
Cherry, wild (*Prunus* sp.).	Hillsides, along streams, in woods throughout the United States.	Leaves.	Sheep and cattle.	Eating 1 percent of animal's weight of green plants in a few minutes.	Difficult breathing, spasms, coma, illness of short duration.
Cocklebur (*Xanthium* sp.).	In fields and waste land of the eastern half and low wet places of the western half of the United States.	First or primary leaves of seedlings.	Pigs and cattle.	Eating 0.75 percent of animal's weight of green plants in a few minutes.	**Prostration, inflamed stomach.**
Copperweed (*Oxytenia acerosa* Nutt.).	Colorado Basin in Colorado, Utah, and New Mexico to southern California.	Leaves.	Cattle and sheep.	Eating the plant in the fall when other feed is scarce.	Loss of appetite, depression, weakness, and coma.
Deathcamas (*Zygadenus* sp.).	Gravelly hills, depressions, and meadows, in western half of the United States.	Leaves and stems.	Sheep and cattle.	Eating 0.5 percent of animal's weight of green plants in a day.	Vomiting, frothing, and weakness.
Drymary, thickleaf (*Drymaria holosteoides* Benth. (*D. pachyphylla* Wooten and Standley).	Denuded areas in western Texas and southern New Mexico.	do.	Cattle.	do.	Depression, weakness, inflamed stomach and intestines.
Dutchmans-breeches (*Dicentra cucullaria* (L.) Bernh).	In woods, eastern half of United States north of Georgia.	do.	do.	Feeding on plant, particularly in spring and early summer.	Trembling, frothing at the mouth, and convulsions.
Greasewood (*Sarcobatus vermiculatus* (Hook.) Torr.).	Somewhat alkaline fields in western part of the United States.	Leaves.	Sheep.	Eating 1.5 pounds in a few minutes.	Depression, kidney lesions.

[1] **From A Pasture Handbook, U. S. Dept. Agr. Misc. Pub. 194, table 9, revised.**

TABLE 1.—*Essential facts about the principal poisonous plants*—Continued

Common and scientific names of plant	Location	Parts of plant that usually cause poisoning	Animals most commonly poisoned	Conditions under which poisoning usually occurs, and minimum quantity required	Characteristic effects
Horsebrush (*Tetradymia glabrata* Gray; *T. canascens* DC.).	Principally in Utah, Nevada, and eastern California.	Leaves and small stems.	Sheep.	Usually eaten by hungry animals while being trailed.	May cause bighead as the result of sensitization to light.
Horsetail (*Equisetum* sp.).	Wet meadows throughout United States.	Tops.	Horses.	Eating the plant in hay.	Weakness, craving for the plant, diarrhea, loss of flesh, lack of control of legs.
Larkspur (*Delphinium* spp.).	Mountains and plains throughout United States.	Leaves of young plants.	Cattle.	Eating 0.5 percent of animal's weight, especially of young plants, within a few minutes.	Weakness, trembling, constipation.
Laurel, sheep (*Kalmia angustifolia* L.).	Moist soil, hillsides, and swamps, Maine and New York to Georgia.	Leaves.	Cattle, sheep, and goats.	Eating 0.2 percent of animal's weight of green plants in a day.	Salivation, vomiting, and weakness.
Locoweed (*Astragalus* sp.; *Oxytropis* sp.).	Plains and some mountain valleys, western half of United States.	Leaves and stems.	Cattle, horses, sheep, and goats.	Feeding for several days or weeks on the plants.	Constipation, craving for the plants, rough coat, incoordination, and peculiar actions.
Lupine (*Lupinus* sp.).	Throughout United States.	Leaves of young plants, and fruit.	Sheep and cattle.	Eating 0.5 percent of animal's weight of green plants or fruit in a day.	Sheep: nervousness from some species, depression from others. Cattle: weakness and trembling.
Milkweed (*Asclepias labriformis* M. E. Jones).	Southeastern Utah.	Leaves.	Sheep and cattle.	Eaten by hungry animals, often during the fall and winter.	Weakness, shallow respiration, spasms, violent struggling.
Milkweed, broadleaf (*A. eriocarpa* Benth.; *A. latifolia* (Torr.) Raf.	*A. eriocarpa:* dry valleys in southern half of California. *A. latifolia:* dry plains of Southwest; along ditches, in abandoned fields and dry places, Colorado to Mexico and California.	...do...	Sheep.	Eating 0.1 percent of animal's weight of green plants in a day.	Depression, weakness, inflamed stomach and intestines.
Milkweed, whorled (*A. galioides* H. B. K.; *A. mexicana* Cav.).	Dry plains and foothills—*A. galioides:* Kansas to Utah and south to Texas, Arizona, and Mexico; *A. mexicana:* Southern Mexico northward to Washington, Idaho, Utah, and Arizona.	Leaves and stems.	Cattle and sheep.	Eating 0.2 percent of animal's weight of green plants in a day.	Incoordination followed by severe spasms.
Mountain-laurel (*Kalmia latifolia* L.).	Woods and hillsides.	Leaves.	Cattle, sheep, and goats.	Eating 0.4 percent of animal's weight of green plants in a day.	Salivation, vomiting, and weakness.
Nightshade, black (*Solanum nigrum* L.).	Waste ground from Maine to California.	Green fruit and leaves.	Cattle, sheep, goats, chickens, ducks and geese.	Feeding on green plant.	Thirst, diarrhea, loss of appetite, weakness, lack of coordination.
Oaks, shin and Gambel (*Quercus* spp.).	Sand hills and lower mountains of Colorado, Utah, and Southwest.	Leaves and leaf buds.	Cattle.	Feeding largely on oak for 2 weeks or more, especially in spring.	Emaciation, scabby nose, constipation, followed by diarrhea and weakness.

Oleander, common (*Nerium oleander* L.).	Fields, roadsides, edge of woods in southern part of United States.	Leaves	All animals	Eating small quantities	Stupor, trembling, convulsions, paralysis, vomiting, and diarrhea.
Paperflower, greenstem (*Psilostrophesparsiflora* (A. Gray) A. Nels.).	Northern Arizona and southern Utah.	Leaves and flowers.	Sheep	Eaten during the early spring or late fall when other feed is scarce.	Depression, weakness, emaciation.
Peganum, Harmel (*Peganum harmala* L.).	Texas and New Mexico	Fruits, leaves, and stems.	Sheep and cattle	Scarcity of desirable feed	Nervousness, incoordination, and paralysis.
Poisonbean (*Daubentonia drummondii* Rydb.).	Coastal plains of Florida and Texas.	Seeds	Cattle, sheep, and goats.	Eating small quantities of seeds.	Depression, diarrhea, and rapid pulse.
Poisonhemlock (*Conium maculatum* L.).	Widely distributed	Fruits and leaves	Sheep and cattle	Seldom eaten when other feed is available.	Nervous tremors, weakness, and respiratory paralysis.
Poisonvetch (*Astragalus* spp.)	Mountains, foothills, and valleys of Intermountain States.	Leaves and stems.	Cattle and sheep	Eating considerable quantities during a day's feeding.	Difficult breathing, nausea, and weakness.
Ragwort, or groundsel (*Senecio* spp.).	Throughout United States.	do	Cattle and horses	Feeding for several days on one of the poisonous species.	Jaundice, scabby nose, discomfort, loss of appetite, uneasiness, and loss of flesh.
Rayless goldenrod (*Applopappus heterophyllus* (A. Gray) Blake).	Fields along ditches in western Texas, New Mexico, and Arizona.	do	Cattle, sheep, and horses.	Feeding on the plant frequently for several days.	Marked weakness and trembling, especially after exercise.
Rubberweed, bitter (*Actinea odorata* (DC.) Kuntze).	Western Texas to southeastern California.	Leaves, stems, and flowers.	Sheep	Eating small quantities daily for several days.	Vomiting, weakness.
Rubberweed, Colorado (*A. richardsoni* (Hook.) Kuntze).	Gravelly hills and flats in mountains of Colorado, New Mexico, Utah, and Arizona.	Leaves and stems.	do	do	Do.
St. Johnswort (*Hypericum perforatum* L.).	Fields, waste places; and hills across northern half of the United States.	Leaves	Animals with areas of white skin and hair.	Feeding on the plant and being in bright sunlight.	Sore, scabby areas on white skin, itching, rapid respiration.
Snakeroot, white (*Eupatorium rugosum* Houtt.).	Rich woods and ravines in eastern half of the United States.	Leaves and stems.	Cattle and sheep	Feeding on the plant for several days.	Marked trembling and weakness, especially after exercise.
Sneezeweed (*Helenium hoopesii* Gray).	Mountains, meadows, and valleys from Montana to Arizona.	Leaves	Sheep and cattle	Feeding on the plant for 2 weeks or more.	Profuse vomiting and weakness.
Tarweed (*Amsinckia intermedia* F. and M.).	Northwest, principally in eastern Washington, eastern Oregon, and northern Idaho.	Seeds	Horses, cattle, and swine.	Eaten when mixed with wheat chaff or screenings.	Loss of appetite, jaundice, emaciation, and, in horses, a tendency to walk continuously.
Waterhemlock (*Cicuta* sp.)	Wet places throughout the United States.	Roots and rootstocks.	Sheep and cattle	Eating very small quantities	Violent spasms.

[1] Some poisonous species of *Astragalus* are not locoweeds.

of which consisted of toxic plants. In mountainous areas of the East where natural vegetation remains undisturbed, some of the native poisonous plants are still a problem.

In many areas of the West overgrazing has resulted in the impairment or destruction of the most palatable and nutritious forage plants and has permitted the spread of less desirable and poisonous species. The poisonous-plant problems of today are largely confined to the Western States, since there the natural vegetation has not been disturbed by cultivation and poisonous plants are usually well adapted to withstand the semiarid conditions existing over most of those areas.

WHY ANIMALS EAT POISONOUS PLANTS

Poisonous plants usually grow in rather close association with forage plants and are readily accessible to grazing animals. Very few such plants, however, can be considered sufficiently palatable to be eaten in preference to the better class of forage. When animals are allowed free choice they usually select the more desirable forage and avoid the plants that are toxic.

When poisonous plants are harvested with hay or their seeds become mixed with grain, it is difficult for animals to separate the good feed from toxic material, and poisoning frequently results. Toxic plants may be mixed with pasture forage to such an extent as to cause poisoning, but here the animals have a better chance of selecting their feed if given an opportunity. These conditions are usually associated with farming operations and are largely under the control of livestock owners.

Overgrazing of pastures and ranges is probably the greatest single factor in causing losses from poisonous plants. The danger of overgrazing has been greatly increased in many sections during recent years because of moisture deficiencies that have reduced forage production. The result has been increased livestock losses in many areas.

In many instances animals which have been shipped or trailed long distances without sufficient feed and then turned onto ranges that would not be considered dangerous under normal grazing conditions, have suffered excessive losses. This is because hungry animals often feed on whatever is available, including poisonous plants, instead of selecting the better forage.

There is great variation in the toxicity of poisonous plants and in the amounts necessary to cause injury or death. Some act as acute poisons, while others must be eaten over a considerable period of time to produce harmful results. With a majority of poisonous plants, amounts well below the toxic limits may be eaten even for a considerable time with little or no ill effect.

CONTROLLING LOSSES FROM POISONOUS PLANTS

The most effective method for the control of losses from poisonous plants, and one that has been used successfully in many cases, is the eradication of such plants from pastures or ranges where losses occur. In each case, however, the cost of eradication, which may require

work over a period of years, should be checked against the benefits
to be derived. Plowing and cultivation will usually accomplish complete eradication, but in areas such as the grazing lands of the West
this method is not feasible. When eradication is attempted in these
areas it is necessary to remove the plants by hand, by pulling or
grubbing, which is a slow and expensive procedure even under the
most favorable conditions.

In the Western States many poisonous plants have such a wide
distribution over grazing areas of limited value that the cost of
eradication would be much greater than the benefits. However,
larger areas could be made safe for livestock by removing the toxic
plants from limited areas, including trails and watering places, and
such a procedure would be considered practicable. Its value has been
demonstrated especially in larkspur eradication. The method employed in eradication will depend upon the character and growth
habits of the species involved, their association with other plants,
and the type of soil upon which they grow.

Where eradication of poisonous plants is impractical, it is necessary
to work out a system of pasture and range management that will
permit utilization of the forage crop without causing excessive livestock losses. This is largely a matter of preventing overgrazing. If
a sufficient supply of desirable forage is available, less toxic material
will be eaten.

In areas where the winters are not too severe, poisonous plants may
start growth in the fall or early spring and reach such a stage that
they can be grazed before the appearance of other feed. On high
mountain ranges, poisonous plants are often the first to start growth
and may cause poisoning of livestock if too early grazing is practiced.

When pastures or ranges have been stocked to full capacity during
normal years and no reduction in the number of livestock is made
during drought years, it is advisable to supplement the usual forage
with other roughage or concentrates in order to avoid injury to
existing vegetation and losses of animals from poisonous plants.

One class of animals may not graze on certain plants or may not
be injured by them, while others may be susceptible to their toxic
effects. Under such conditions, permitting only the class of animals
least affected to graze may help to avoid considerable loss and at the
same time permit utilization of the range.

The few toxic plants that are palatable, and forage plants such
as the sorghums which become toxic only under certain conditions,
create problems that are difficult to control. Generally, however, it
is not safe for animals to have access to areas where such plants are
available. The plants must be eradicated or the areas fenced off.

In many cases of plant poisoning, treatment of the affected animals is unsatisfactory and may have little effect. It is probable
that most of the damage has been done by the time the animals are
discovered to have been poisoned. The outcome in each case depends
to a very large extent upon the amount of toxic material that has been
eaten and assimilated. Treatment is usually directed toward eliminating any of the toxic substance that still remains in the digestive
tract. In chronic poisoning, recovery may follow a change of feed

especially if green feed is available, and in all cases good care with plenty of water and the right kind of feed will do much to hasten recovery. About the only specific treatment is that described later for poisoning by the cyanogenetic plants, or plants that produce hydrocyanic acid. From the standpoint of economy, prevention is of far greater value than treatment and when properly carried out will pay good returns.

CHEMISTRY OF STOCK-POISONING PLANTS

The chemical character of the constituents of poisonous plants, especially of those compounds that are physiologically active, is of interest from a number of viewpoints. It is desirable to know whether the substance that produces the symptoms in animals poisoned by the plants is an alkaloid, a glucoside, one of the cyanogenetic group, or whether it belongs to some other category. Knowledge of this sort leads to more rational treatment of the affected animals than can be developed from mere observation of the symptoms alone, makes it possible to determine by laboratory examination whether a given sample of the plant is potentially deadly, and also makes it possible to detect the poison in the tissues of animals, thus leading to a diagnosis in obscure or doubtful cases.

Finally these studies are of especial interest to the plant biochemist, who is building up a systematized mass of information concerning the relationships between the botanical classifications of plants and their chemical composition.

Knowing the botanical position of a new species, the chemist can usually guess fairly accurately the type of compounds that will be found upon chemical examination and may be able to advise on methods of treatment of sick animals or the type of pathological lesion likely to be found on post mortem examination.

During the past half century the chemical study of stock-poisoning plants has been carried on intensively by the Department of Agriculture. It was begun under the leadership of V. K. Chesnut (*2*),[2] who besides being a skillful chemist was also a botanist of no small ability. It has been carried on by a number of chemists and pharmacologists since. Added to the knowledge that has been amassed as a result of these labors has been a great accumulation of information contributed by many scientists in the State experiment stations, the universities, and elsewhere. Progress is still being made, for the problems are not all solved, but the achievements already recorded leave no doubt of the ultimate elucidation of all the mysteries of this most complex and at times baffling field.

PLANTS CONTAINING ALKALOIDS

Second in importance as poisonous plants only to the locoweeds, described later, are the larkspurs, which annually exact a heavy toll from livestock breeders (*23*). These plants appear to be attractive to cattle because of the pleasant acidity of the leaves, which is re-

---

[2] Italic numbers in parentheses refer to Literature Cited, p. 371.

freshing in hot weather. The larkspurs contains alkaloids of complex composition which are highly poisonous. The principal poisonous species are tall larkspur (*Delphinium barbeyi*) and low larkspur (*D. menziesii*), though most of the species of this genus are dangerous, especially when the plants are small or when they are available in quantities. A comparatively nontoxic species is *D. occidentale*, which resembles *D. barbeyi* and is often mistaken for it. The resemblance has resulted in some confusion, and stockmen who have based their observations on *D. occidentale*, mistaking it for *D. barbeyi*, have controverted statements that *D. barbeyi* is poisonous. The fact is that although *D. occidentale* contains about 1 percent of an alkaloid, it is a very slightly toxic one, and under range conditions the plant is essentially nontoxic (*12*).

A very widespread genus of plants, especially on the western cattle ranges, is the lupines, known also as blue bonnets, Quaker bonnets, and by other local names. These plants belong to the legume family and are very nutritious. Some species are harmless, at least at some stages of growth, and are excellent feed for grazing animals; others are dangerous at certain times; and some are toxic at any stage of growth. The toxic character of the lupines is due to alkaloids of a group with the peculiarity that slight alterations in the chemical structure of the molecule may convert a very toxic alkaloid into a comparatively nonpoisonous substance and vice versa (*13*). These alterations are of a kind that may readily take place within the plant itself by the process of normal plant chemistry, and this may account for the great variations observed in the toxicity of the growing plants. The first reports that the lupines were poisonous were from Germany, where the plants caused relatively enormous losses during the sixties of the last century—especially the yellow lupine (*Lupinus luteus*). Those outbreaks, however, appear to have been due to molds and not to any substance normal to the plant itself. In this country the somewhat extensive losses of livestock attributed to this genus have been due to alkaloidal poisoning. A large number of studies on this genus have been published both in this country and abroad, and the characters of the active alkaloids have been satisfactorily worked out.

Another group of alkaloid-containing plants of importance to the livestock breeder is deathcamas (a species of *Zygadenus*). This is a grasslike plant which is not conspicuous until it blooms. It received its name because in pioneer times the bulbs were often mistaken, with disastrous results, for the edible camas used by the Indians as food (*21*). Little work has been done on the chemistry of these plants except for the determination of the fact that they contain complex alkaloids. Other alkaloidal plants of importance are the senecios, or groundsels, the alkaloids of which have been examined by several chemists, notably by Manske (*19*). Species of this genus have been responsible for a considerable number of losses in livestock in Texas and other States. Space does not permit more than a mention of such alkaloidal plants as dutchmans-breeches (*Dicentra cucullaria*), spotted waterhemlock, wild tobaccos (*7*, *24*), carol beans, *Crotalaria* (*27*), and *Peganum harmala* (*26*).

PLANTS CONTAINING GLUCOSIDES

A large number of plants owe their poisonous properties to substances classified by the chemist as glucosides. These compounds are characterized by the fact that they contain various sugars combined in the molecule which can be split out by acids and then detected by chemical reagents. The glucosides are a diverse group. Some form soapy solutions with water, and therefore have been called saponins; others are called cyanogenetic glucosides because they develop hydrocyanic, or prussic, acid under certain circumstances; and still others are outside these two categories.

CYANOGENETIC PLANTS

The cyanogenetic glucosides have been responsible for large losses of livestock in many sections of this country. Altogether, a large number of plants are known to possess cyanogenetic characters, but under practical conditions only a few of these are dangerous to livestock.

The more important of the cyanogenetic plants include wild chokecherry (*Prunus virginiana, P. melanocarpa,* and *P. demissa*), sorghum (*Sorghum vulgare*), Sudan grass (*Sorghum vulgare* var. *sudanensis*), Johnson grass (*Sorghum halepense*), flax (*Linum usitatissimum*), and arrowgrass (*Triglochin maritima* and *T. palustris*). The chemistry of the cyanogenetic species has attracted the attention of a number of chemists, and a great many publications have appeared on this subject (*11, 16, 17, 28*).

Wild cherry is always a potential danger in spring and early summer for animals that are unusually hungry, but, like most poisonous plants, it may be eaten in small quantities without causing injury. The leaves of the wild cherry contain a glucoside named prunasin (*34*). In the seeds this is associated with another cyanogenetic glucoside, amygdalin, which also occurs in bitter almonds and in peach kernels. (This was the basis of the use made of peach kernels by the ancient Egyptian priests, who made a poisonous drink of it to execute criminals. "The penalty of the peach" was the expression used to describe the execution.)

The sorghums—*Sorghum vulgare,* Johnson grass, and Sudan grass—owe their poisonous properties to another cyanogenetic glucoside known as dhurrin (*16*). When grown under ordinary conditions, the sorghums are considered very good feed, but when the normal growth has been interrupted by drought, frost, trampling, or other causes, hydrocyanic acid may develop to a point where the plants become toxic. In other words, the quantity of hydrocyanic acid which these plants can develop varies considerably under different conditions as well as with different varieties (*14*). Young and second-growth plants can develop larger quantities than older plants. The potential quantity of hydrocyanic acid diminishes more or less regularly as the plant matures, and when the seed heads are well formed the plants are generally not capable of causing fatal poisoning. But since there is always a possibility that there will be young suckers or branches or second-growth plants in the field at the same time as the ripe plants, poisoning may result if livestock are allowed access to them. After harvest, the stubble sprouts luxuriantly, and these young plants are high in hydrocyanic acid. Many fatalities have resulted where livestock have been allowed to graze on this second growth.

Arrowgrass is only slightly toxic when growing, as it does naturally, where there is plenty of water, but under drought conditions it may become toxic.

When cyanogenetic plants are made into hay it is generally supposed that most of the hydrocyanic acid volatilizes or evaporates, leaving the hay practically nontoxic. In most cases this is undoubtedly true, although occasionally such hay may retain enough acid to make it dangerous, especially for hungry animals.

Wild flax and wild lima beans contain another cyanogenetic glucoside known as linamarin, or phaseolunatin (*17*). It has been reported that wild lima beans have caused many fatalities among human beings in the Tropics. During the World War they were imported into France as feed for cavalry horses and were responsible for several extensive outbreaks of poisoning. Finally the importation of wild lima beans with a hydrocyanic acid content greater than 20 milligrams per 100 grams was forbidden. Cultivated lima beans are not dangerous in this country, since they contain either no hydrocyanic acid or negligibly small quantities.

There are a number of factors that influence the absorption of hydrocyanic acid from plants after it reaches the digestive tract, but the rate at which such plants are eaten and the amount of food already in the stomach are probably the most important.

Hydrocyanic acid is a rapidly acting poison and offers little opportunity for remedial treatment. Recent work has shown, however, that if the victim can be reached in time a combination of sodium thiosulfate and sodium nitrite given intraperitoneally (injected into the lining of the abdomen) or intravenously (injected into the veins) by a veterinarian is an effective remedy against doses of cyanide up to three minimal lethal doses (*5*). The subject is discussed in United States Department of Agriculture Leaflet 88, Poisoning of Livestock by Plants That Produce Hydrocyanic Acid (*11*).

The symptoms of poisoning by cyanogenetic plants consist of uneasiness, rapid respiration, depression, stupor, convulsions, cyanosis of the mucous membranes (which causes them to turn blue), paralysis, and death. The entire process may require only a few minutes or may last for several hours.

When one animal in a group pasturing on plants that might be dangerous shows symptoms of poisoning the others should be removed from the pasture as soon as possible, since these cases usually develop quite rapidly.

Plants Containing Saponins

The saponin-containing plants are represented by some important stock-poisoning species. Among them may be mentioned the bitter rubberweed or bitter actinea (*Actinea ordorata*), an annual that on occasions causes extensive losses of sheep in the Southwest (*4*). Its relative, pingue, or Colorado rubberweed (*Actinea richardsoni*), also owes its deleterious action to a saponin. The seeds of the troublesome weed corncockle (*Agrostemma githago*) contain a mixture of saponins. These seeds sometimes get into wheat and make it dangerous to feed to poultry or livestock.

One of the most interesting compounds of the saponin group is solanine, which contains basic nitrogen and so acts also as an alkaloid. This substance is found in a number of plants, particularly of the genus *Solanum*, to which belong the white potato and the tomato. Chemically it is very complex. The substance is of interest because it occurs in sprouted potatoes and has, at times, caused poisoning of persons who have eaten such tubers. The toxic effects of the American species, bullnettle (*Solanum carolinense*), bittersweet (*S. dulcamara*), and somewhat doubtfully, black nightshade (*S. nigrum*), are referred to solanine.

PLANTS CONTAINING RESINOIDS

A large group includes the somewhat indefinite substances known as resinoids, which are important as the active principles of certain stock-poisoning plants. Of these, the most widespread is the characteristic poison of the ericaceous plants, known as andromedotoxin (*29, 30, 31, 32, 33*). This is a complex substance considered the active principle present in some of the rhododendrons, azaleas, and possibly the laurels. While an empirical formula has been advanced (*18*) for this poison, we have no knowledge of the peculiar structure of the molecule on which the toxic action depends. The active principle of the extremely poisonous waterhemlock (*Cicuta vagans*) is a resinoid.

Poisonous Milkweeds

The active principles of the poisonous milkweeds (*Asclepias* species) also are resinoids (*22*). Very little is known about their chemistry. Among the more important species investigated during past years are *Asclepias galioides*, the whorled milkweed of the Southwest; *A. eriocarpa*, the broadleaf (wooly-pod) milkweed of California; *A. mexicana*, the whorled milkweed of the Western States; and *A. pumila* and *A. verticilata* var. *geyeri*, the whorled milkweeds of the Central and Eastern States. The toxicity of the different species varies greatly and ranges approximately in the order in which they are here listed.

Losses from the whorled milkweed have been especially severe. In one case 400 sheep died within 24 hours after feeding on this plant near Hotchkiss, Colo. In 1917 a loss of 736 sheep out of a band of 1,000 near Cortez, Colo., was traced to the same species. Next to waterhemlock, this has long been considered the most toxic plant in the United States, but recent unpublished work appears to indicate that it is surpassed by another species of milkweed, *A. labriformis*. Through information supplied by stockmen it was evident that

Asclepias labriformis was causing considerable livestock loss. As a result of these reports, experimental investigations have been carried on for the last 3 years through which it has been determined that this species is approximately three times as toxic as *A. galioides*. The toxicity of *A. labriformis* is highest during the early part of the growing season. At this time the usual lethal dose for a 100-pound sheep is about an ounce of green leaves, and for cattle it is even less in proportion to their weight.

The plant loses some of its toxicity at maturity, but the dry leaves still retain a sufficient quantity of the toxic substance to cause heavy livestock losses during the winter and early spring.

The distribution of *Asclepias labriformis* appears to be limited to southeastern Utah, and it is confined largely to sandy areas and along watercourses where the ground contains more than the usual amount of moisture. This species, like other poisonous milkweeds, is not palatable and is eaten by animals only when other feed is not available. Its presence on overgrazed ranges and trails constitutes a hazard that may result in considerable livestock loss at any time of the year.

Eradication of milkweeds from areas especially dangerous to livestock has been attempted and where successfully carried out has proved to be of great value. There is no known remedy for milkweed poisoning. If losses are to be avoided, hungry animals must be kept away from poisonous-milkweed areas or the plants should be eradicated.

The symptoms of milkweed poisoning consist of uneasiness; some lack of muscular coordination; rapid, shallow, noisy respiration due to edema (swellings filled with fluid) of the lungs; and usually rather violent spasms and considerable struggling, with death resulting from respiratory failure. The kidneys are usually affected to a greater extent than other organs.

PLANTS CONTAINING OXALIC ACID

Certain plants contain notable quantities of oxalic acid, and those in which this substance is in sufficient concentration are likely to be dangerous to livestock. Many of the sorrels and docks owe their poisonous character to this acid. The most important plant of this class in the United States is greasewood (*Sarcobatus vermiculatus*), which has frequently caused large losses (*3*) when herds of hungry sheep have been allowed to graze upon it. The dried leaves contain 9.4 percent of oxalic acid combined with sodium and potassium (*6*). Experimental work with this plant showed that sheep must eat a toxic quantity within a comparatively short time to be poisoned. If the plant is eaten slowly, a sheep may consume two to three times the lethal dose in 24 hours without being affected. This results from the surprising ability of the sheep to metabolize oxalic acid in the body, the carbon being excreted as carbon dioxide.

PLANTS CONTAINING TREMETOL

One of the most interesting of all types of plant poisoning is that known as trembles in livestock and milksickness in man (*10*). The condition appeared in backwoods settlements during colonial times and created a veritable panic among the pioneers. It usually occurred in the late summer and early fall, but it might appear in June, and cases of milksickness were diagnosed in January. The cause of the disease was obscure and a great variety of guesses were current among both laymen and the medical profession. In both animals and men the attacks were confined to localities where cattle were kept in wild pastures, and it was noted at an early date that the human and bovine outbreaks occurred simultaneously. Milk was suspected as the carrier of the disease from cattle to man, as it was observed that the suckling young of animals affected with trembles also contracted the disease. Many attempts were made to discover the cause. From early times it was maintained by many that white snakeroot (*Eupatorium rugosum*) [3] was the poisonous plant involved, but chemical analyses made by competent persons failed to reveal any definite poison in the plant. Other observers pointed out that milksickness was unknown in many localities where this plant grew and that it occurred in areas of New Mexico and Arizona where white snakeroot does not grow.

It was eventually determined that in the Southwest trembles is caused by another plant, rayless goldenrod, or jimmyweed (*Aplopappus heterophyllus*). Finally a toxic substance, tremetol (*9*), was isolated from both plants and was shown to cause trembles in sheep. Tremetol is an oily alcohol. The quantity in white snakeroot varies with different localities, and the differences in toxicity observed are doubtless due to this variation.

Finally, butter made from the milk of a cow that had fed on jimmyweed and that had caused milksickness in a family in New Mexico was fed to a sheep. The animal developed a typical case of trembles. The isolation of tremetol and the production of trembles by feeding poisonous butter to the sheep completed the chain of evidence linking the plants to human milksickness and solved a mystery which for over 150 years had baffled physicians and terrorized dwellers in the rural districts.

PLANTS CONTAINING UNKNOWN AND MISCELLANEOUS POISONS

LOCOWEEDS

Of all the stock-poisoning plants the most important from the standpoint of losses are those that belong in the group of locoweeds, species of *Astragalus* and *Oxytropis* (*20*). This group is so important that at one time the term "locoed" was used synonymously with "poisoned," especially in the Western States, and any victim poisoned by eating toxic vegetation was likely to be called "locoed." Indeed there was some difficulty in educating people to distinguish between the true locoism, which is a definite condition, and other types of poisoning such as those caused by the larkspurs and lupines, which

---

[3] E. D. Merrill (*25, p. 293*) has recently shown that the proper name for white snakeroot is *Eupatorium rugosum*. It has been known for some years as *Eupatorium urticaefolium*.

are quite different. The locoweeds have been subjected to chemical examination many times and by many chemists during the past 70 years. The earlier studies have been described by Crawford (*15*). Since that time white locoweed (*Oxytropis lambertii*) has been studied with the result that the active principle was found to belong to none of the recognized groups of poisonous compounds but appears to be of a new type (*8*).

Some members of the genus *Astragalus* have been shown to be nontoxic, and others are known which produce poisoning but not the true locoism. As an example of the first group may be mentioned the red locoweed (*A. drummondii*) and *A. tenellus*, while the second group is represented by *A. tetrapterus*. Nothing is known about the chemistry of these species. A fourth group of the genus depends for its poisonous properties not upon any constituent normally produced by the plant itself but upon an inorganic substance, selenium, which the plants may take up from the soil in the form of a compound and accumulate in dangerous quantities (*1*).

COPPERWEED (*Oxytenia acerosa*)

The plant commonly called copperweed has a rather wide distribution in much of the Colorado Basin and is found growing along streams, water courses, and seepage areas where the soil is strongly alkaline and contains considerable moisture. Copperweed has been suspected for many years of being toxic, but only in recent years has it been experimentally proved to be a poisonous plant.

Both cattle and sheep are affected, but the heaviest loss has been in cattle. The plant increases in toxicity as it reaches maturity, and poisoning usually occurs in the fall when the cattle are being driven down from the summer ranges. The trails over which these cattle are moved are usually overgrazed and contain little or no desirable forage. Under such circumstances, copperweed, which is ordinarily quite unpalatable, may be eaten in sufficient quantities to cause poisoning. Less than ½ pound of green leaves per 100 pounds of animal weight constitutes a lethal dose for cattle, and this amount can be consumed by hungry animals in a short time.

It is doubtful whether treatment is of much value, as most animals that show severe symptoms die. Losses may be prevented, however, by providing suitable feed along the trails and on the ranges so that animals are not compelled to eat the toxic plants.

Eradication of copperweed from especially dangerous areas has been attempted recently, and if the work proves successful it will be of material value to the livestock owners using these areas.

In copperweed poisoning the liver seems to be primarily affected and later the kidneys. The symptoms usually consist of marked depression, weakness, coma, and death without very much struggling. Occasionally an animal will show considerable nervousness and excitement, but this condition is not common, and quite frequently animals are found dead in the morning without having shown symptoms the previous evening.

PAPER FLOWER (*Psilostrophe sparsiflora*)

It has been known for some time that two species of the genus *Psilostrophe* growing in Texas were poisonous and had caused some loss of sheep, but it has been only in the past 3 or 4 years that *P. sparsiflora*, known as greenstem paperflower, has become a problem in northern Arizona, although it has apparently been in this area for a long time. The plant is increasing in density and spreading over a wider area, so that it is becoming increasingly difficult to utilize this range for sheep without excessive losses.

The paperflower occupies a semiarid region that is used largely as an intermediate and winter range, and it appears that overgrazing may have been responsible for the spread of the plant, as well as for the sheep losses that have occurred. It seems probable that cattle do not eat a sufficient quantity of this plant on the range to produce poisoning, since like most other poisonous plants the paperflower is not palatable. Where the forage consists largely of plants low in palatability, it is necessary to move the sheep to uninfested areas as soon as loss starts in order to prevent continued losses. Even then, some deaths usually occur after the animals are moved.

Owing to the abundance of *Psilostrophe sparsiflora* over a rather wide area, eradication, even if it could be accomplished, would not be economically practicable, and the control of sheep losses in this area must depend upon improvement in range conditions.

In paperflower poisoning the kidneys appear to be primarily affected. Poisoning is usually the result of feeding for several days on the plant, and consequently the symptoms may develop rather slowly. The principal symptoms noticed are loss of appetite, marked depression and weakness, and death following a period of partial coma with very little struggling. Affected animals may linger for a week or more before death occurs.

HORSEBRUSH (*Tetradymia glabrata* and *T. canescens*)

It has been known for a good many years that *Tetradymia glabrata* was a poisonous plant which under certain conditions might cause heavy sheep losses. During recent years, *T. canescens* has also been shown to be poisonous to sheep, although rather large amounts are necessary to produce poisoning.

Tetradymia glabrata, commonly called littleleaf horsebrush, spring rabbitbrush, or coal oil brush, which is the more toxic of the two species, has a rather wide distribution in desert areas of western Utah, Nevada, eastern California, southern Oregon, and southwestern Idaho, where numerous bands of sheep range during the winter and early spring.

Tetradymia canescens, sometimes called spineless horsebrush, grows to a limited extent in the same areas as those occupied by *T. glabrata* but is found in greatest abundance at the higher elevations and extends through central Utah to southwestern Wyoming, southwestern Montana, eastern and southern Idaho, eastern Oregon, eastern Washington, eastern California, and to some extent northern New Mexico.

The most toxic stage for both of these plants is during their active growth period, which for *T. glabrata* is April and May and for *T. canescens* May, June, and the early part of July. While these two species of *Tetradymia* are toxic to sheep and may be the direct cause of losses, their most important action as poisonous plants is the production of a disease in sheep known as bighead or in some localities as swellhead. Bighead is essentially a range disease and has been prevalent in many areas of the intermountain region since the early days of the sheep industry. It has probably caused a greater financial loss to the sheep owners in the affected areas than any other disease.

Prior to 1934, when the Department took up the study of the disease, nothing definite was known regarding its cause or prevention. As a result of the experimental investigations that have been carried on for the last 5 years it has been determined that the two plants *T. glabrata* and *T. canescens* are the principal causes of range bighead, and that by proper range and trail management a good part of the loss may be avoided.

Bighead in sheep is somewhat similar to diseases produced by plants in other parts of the United States as well as in foreign countries, but it has a different cause. There are apparently two separate stages in the disease—first a toxic condition produced by the plants and primarily affecting the liver, followed by a swelling or edema, which, as the name implies, affects principally the head. This subcutaneous edema affects only those animals with white or light-colored skins and is the result of photosensitization, or sensitiveness to light. While either white or black sheep may be affected by the toxic substance in the plants and die from this cause, the pigment in the skin of black animals protects them from the effects of the light rays so that photosensitivity does not occur. The same is true of sheep kept in total darkness following the eating of *Tetradymia*. The exact nature of the substance causing photosensitization and the manner in which it gets into the circulation near the body surface are not definitely known.

The areas where bighead occurs correspond with the distribution of the species of *Tetradymia*, but while these plants are the principal cause of range bighead many other factors enter into the production of the disease. The kind and character of the feed on which the sheep subsist at the time the plant is eaten are probably the most important factors in producing the edema or photosensitization.

These plants are among the first to begin growth in the spring and are usually well leaved out by the time sheep start on the trails to the shearing corrals and summer ranges. It is while this movement is taking place that most of the bighead outbreaks occur.

Since the plants are not palatable and are seldom eaten in toxic amounts when good forage is available, sheep may graze normally in an area where *Tetradymia* is abundant with very little danger of bighead, whereas a herd that is being trailed through the same area may develop the disease. This is due largely to hunger.

Stormy weather also is apt to change the feeding habits of animals to such an extent that unpalatable or poisonous plants will be eaten.

Early spring use of ranges before the forage plants are well started may cause sheep to eat *Tetradymia* in sufficient quantities to produce bighead.

Bighead usually appears quite suddenly in a band, and a large number of animals may become affected within a few hours. However, the plants causing the disease are usually eaten from 16 to 24 hours before the symptoms appear.

Prevention of range bighead depends on a knowledge of the distribution of the *Tetradymia* plants. Avoiding *Tetradymia* areas on the ranges or trails when sheep are hungry will eliminate the greatest danger.

Both *T. glabrata* and *T. canescens* have a very wide distribution and in some areas constitute a large share of the vegetation, which makes it practically impossible to avoid the plants entirely, but with an adequate supply of desirable forage and reasonable care in herd management the danger of bighead outbreaks may be greatly reduced.

BRACKEN

Several species of ferns have been suspected of being poisonous to livestock, but owing to their usually low palatability and the fact that they are seldom eaten to any considerable extent when other forage is available they have not generally been considered of much importance as poisonous plants. Experimental investigation has shown, however, that bracken (*Pteridium aquilinum*) may be poisonous to both horses and cattle, and that under certain conditions bracken poisoning may result in rather severe losses.

The bracken fern has a wide distribution throughout many parts of the United States but is most abundant in areas where the soil contains a liberal amount of moisture. The plants thrive in the shade and also in the open, where they are often associated with meadow grasses.

Most of the cases of bracken poisoning reported in horses have been caused by ferns that were cut and cured in meadow hay, while poisoning in cattle is usually the result of grazing on the green plants when other forage becomes scarce. Hay containing ferns is more dangerous during the winter when it constitutes the sole feed, while poisoning from green plants usually occurs during the latter part of the grazing season and until the appearance of frost.

Bracken poisoning does not usually occur until after the animals have been feeding on ferns for 3 or 4 weeks unless the feed consists very largely of these plants. When large daily amounts are consumed the symptoms may appear earlier and be more acute than when the ration contains less of the toxic material. It may happen that the symptoms do not develop until a few days after the animals have been removed from access to the ferns, in which case the loss might be attributed to other causes.

The toxic substances in these ferns apparently have a cumulative effect, so that a period of time must elapse before symptoms become noticeable. The course of the disease and the severity of the symptoms are largely dependent on the amount of the plants consumed daily, although there is some variation in the individual susceptibility of different animals.

The symptoms of bracken poisoning in horses may be emaciation, weakness, staggering, nervousness, and constipation. The temperature may remain nearly normal, although the pulse rate is usually accelerated. The course of the disease may extend over a week or more, and the appetite remains fairly good for some time after symptoms appear.

The symptoms in cattle are usually more acute and may include a very high temperature, rapid loss of flesh, salivation, hemorrhage from the nostrils, small hemorrhagic spots (petechiae) in the membranes of the eyes, nostrils, and mouth, and a bloody diarrhea.

The symptoms of fern poisoning may vary to some extent, but when such a condition is suspected and it is known that the plants are being eaten, a change to other feed should be made.

The mortality rate from bracken poisoning is usually high, and although some benefit may be derived from treatment of the symptoms if it is begun early, no specific cure is known. Prevention is the most satisfactory means of controlling the disease.

LITERATURE CITED

(1) BYERS, HORACE G.
    1935. SELENIUM OCCURRENCE IN THE UNITED STATES, WITH A DISCUSSION OF RELATED TOPICS. U. S. Dept. Agr. Tech. Bul. 482, 47 pp., illus.

(2) CHESNUT, V. K.
    1897. SOME COMMON POISONOUS PLANTS. U. S. Dept. Agr. Yearbook 1896: 137–146, illus.

(3) —— and WILCOX, E. V.
    1901. THE STOCK POISONING PLANTS OF MONTANA: A PRELIMINARY REPORT. U. S. Dept. Agr. Bot. Bul. 26, 150 pp.

(4) CLAWSON, A. B.
    1931. A PRELIMINARY REPORT ON THE POISONOUS EFFECTS OF BITTER RUBBER WEED (ACTINEA ODORATA) ON SHEEP. Jour. Agr. Res. 43: 693–701, illus.

(5) —— COUCH, JAMES F., and BUNYEA, H.
    1935. THE TOXICITY OF SODIUM CYANIDE AND THE EFFICIENCY OF NITRITE-THIOSULPHATE COMBINATION AS A REMEDY FOR POISONED ANIMALS. Wash. Acad. Sci. Jour. 25: 357–361.

(6) COUCH, JAMES F.
    1922. THE TOXIC CONSTITUENT OF GREASEWOOD (SARCOBATUS VERMICULATUS). Amer. Jour. Pharm. 94: 631–641.

(7) ——
    1927. ISOLATION OF NICOTINE FROM NICOTIANA ATTENUATA. Amer. Jour. Pharm. 99: 519–523.

(8) ——
    1929. A CONTRIBUTION TO THE STUDY OF LOCOISM. Jour. Pharmacol. and Expt. Ther. 36: 55–83, illus.

(9) ——
    1929. TREMETOL, THE COMPOUND THAT PRODUCES "TREMBLES" (MILKSICKNESS). Amer. Chem. Soc. Jour. 51: 3617–3619.

(10) ——
    1933. TREMBLES (OR MILKSICKNESS). U. S. Dept. Agr. Cir. 306, 11 pp., illus.

(11) ——
    1934. POISONING OF LIVESTOCK BY PLANTS THAT PRODUCE HYDROCYANIC ACID. U. S. Dept. Agr. Leaflet 88, 4 pp.

(12) COUCH, JAMES F.
    1936. DELTALINE. A NEW ALKALOID FROM DELPHINIUM OCCIDENTALE.   Amer.
        Chem. Soc. Jour. 58: 684–685.
(13) ———
    1940. LUPINE STUDIES. XVI. THE ISOLATION OF NONALUPINE FROM LUPINUS
        ANDERSONII WATS. Amer. Chem. Soc. Jour. 62: 986–987.
(14) ——— BRIESE, REINHOLD R., and MARTIN, J. H.
    1939. HYDROCYANIC ACID CONTENT OF SORGHUM VARIETIES. Wash Acad.
        Sci. Jour. 29: 146–161.
(15) CRAWFORD, ALBERT C.
    1908. BARIUM, A CAUSE OF THE LOCO-WEED DISEASE. U. S. Bur. Plant
        Indus. Bul. 129, 87 pp.
(16) DUNSTAN, WYNDHAM R., and HENRY, THOMAS A.
    1902. CYANOGENESIS IN PLANTS. II. THE GREAT MILLET, SORGHUM VULGARE.
        Philosoph. Trans., Roy. Soc. London Proc., Ser. A, 199: 399–410.
(17) ——— and HENRY, THOMAS A.
    1903. CYANOGENESIS IN PLANTS. PART III.—ON PHASEOLUNATIN, THE CYANO-
        GENETIC GLUCOSIDE OF PHASEOLUS LUNATUS. Roy. Soc. London
        Proc. 72: 285–294.
(18) HARDIKER, S. W.
    1922 ON RHODODENDRON POISONING. Jour. Pharmacol. and Expt. Ther.
        20: 17–44, illus.
(19) MANSKE, RICHARD H. F.
    1931. THE ALKALOIDS OF SENECIO SPECIES. I. THE NECINES AND NECIC ACIDS
        FROM S. RETRORSUS AND S. JACOBAEA. Canad. Jour. Res. 5: 651–
        659.
(20) MARSH, C. DWIGHT.
    1919. THE LOCO-WEED DISEASE. U. S. Dept. Agr. Farmers' Bul. 1054, 19
        pp., illus.
(21) ——— and CLAWSON, A. B.
    1922. THE STOCK-POISONING DEATH CAMAS. U. S. Dept. Agr. Farmers'
        Bul. 1273, 11 pp., illus.
(22) ——— CLAWSON, A. B., COUCH, J. F., and EGGLESTON, W. W.
    1920. THE WHORLED MILKWEED (ASCLEPIAS GALDIOIDES). U. S. Dept. Agr.
        Bul. 800, 40 pp., illus.
(23) ——— CLAWSON, A. B., and MARSH, HADLEIGH.
    1916. LARKSPUR POISONING OF LIVESTOCK. U. S. Dept. Agr. Bul. 365, 90
        pp., illus.
(24) ——— CLAWSON, A. B., and ROE, G. C.
    1927. WILD TOBACCOS (NICOTIANA TRIGONOPHYLLA DUNAL AND NICOTIANA
        ATTENUATA TORREY) AS STOCK-POISONING PLANTS. U. S. Dept.
        Agr. Tech. Bul. 22, 22 pp., illus.
(25) MERRILL, E. D.
    1938. ON HOUTTUYN'S OVERLOOKED BINOMINALS FOR NATIVE OR INTRODUCED
        PLANTS IN EASTERN NORTH AMERICA. Rhodora 40: 288–293, illus.
(26) MORAN, E. A., COUCH, J. F., and CLAWSON, A. B.
    1940. PEGANUM HARMALA, A POISONOUS PLANT IN THE SOUTHWEST. Vet.
        Med. 35: 234–235, illus.
(27) NEAL, W. M., RUSOFF, L. L., and AHMAN, C. F.
    1935. THE ISOLATION AND SOME PROPERTIES OF AN ALKALOID FROM CRO-
        TALARIA SPECTABILIS ROTH. Amer. Chem. Soc. Jour. 57: 2560–
        2561.
(28) PETERS, A. T., SLADE, H. B., and AVERY, SAMUEL.
    1903. POISONING OF CATTLE BY COMMON SORGHUM AND KAFIR CORN. Nebr.
        Agr. Expt. Sta. Bul. 77, 16 pp.
(29) PLUGGE, P. C.
    1883. UEBER ANDROMEDOTOXIN, DEN GIFTIGEN BESTANDTHEIL DER ANDROMEDA
        JAPONICA THUNBERG. Arch. der Pharm. 221: 1–17.
(30) ———
    1883. UEBER DAS VORKOMMEN DES ANDROMEDOTOXINS IN ANDROMEDA POLI-
        FOLIA L. Arch. der Pharm. 221: 813–819.

(31) ———

1885. VORKOMMEN VON ANDROMEDOTOXIN IN VERSCHIEDEN ERICACEEN. Arch.
der Pharm. 223 : 905–917, illus.

(32) ———

1889. FORTGESETZTE UNTERSUCHUNGEN ÜBER DIE VERBREITUNG DES ANDROME-
DOTOXINS IN DER FAMILIE DER ERICACEAE. Arch. der Pharm. 227 :
164–172.

(33) ———

1891. ANDROMEDOTOXINHALTIGE ERACACEEN. Arch. de Pharm. 229 : 552–554.

(34) POWER, FREDERICK BELDING, and MOORE, CHARLES WATSON.

1910. THE CONSTITUENTS OF THE LEAVES OF PRUNUS SEROTINA. [London]
Chem. Soc. Trans. 97 : 1099–1112.

At the time this book went to press, the drugs and other materials mentioned in various articles—chiefly as disinfectants, insecticides, and anthelmintics—were still available for veterinary and medical use. Under war conditions, however, it is possible that some of these materials may become scarce or unavailable. In that case, the reader should obtain professional advice from the Department of Agriculture, the State experiment station, a local veterinarian, or the county agent as to available substitutes.

374

PART 3

Common Diseases and Parasites of Horses and Mules

Equine Encephalomyelitis

BY L. T. GILTNER AND M. S. SHAHAN

THE SAME VIRUS that causes encephalomyelitis in horses can also cause sleeping sickness (encephalitis) in human beings. Both maladies belong in a group of serious diseases of the central nervous system that includes poliomyelitis (infantile paralysis) of human beings. The intensive research work on encephalomyelitis in recent years is both significant and unusually interesting.

IT IS ESTIMATED that since 1930 nearly a million horses and mules in the United States have been affected by infectious encephalomyelitis. The disease, known popularly as sleeping sickness and brain fever, is believed to have been present in this country for several decades, although the specific cause—a filtrable virus—was not discovered here until 1930 (40).[2]

In 1930 and 1931, an estimated 6,000 horses and mules contracted the disease in California alone (39). During the next few years the malady gradually spread eastward through Arizona, Oregon, South Dakota, Colorado, and Nebraska, finally involving every section and practically every State in this country and some of the Canadian Provinces.

In 1933 the disease appeared along the Atlantic seaboard, in Delaware, Maryland, New Jersey, and Virginia. From these cases a type of virus different from that found in the West was identified (41, 21, 57, 67). This so-called eastern type of virus was found to be more deadly than the western type, and in addition it was determined that

---

[1] L. T. Giltner is Senior Veterinarian and M. S. Shahan is Veterinarian, Pathological Division, Bureau of Animal Industry.
[2] Italic numbers in parentheses refer to Literature Cited, p. 388.

recovery from infection with one type did not immunize an animal against the other. The two types are thus what is known as immunologically distinct, even though both produce essentially the same clinical disease. During the years 1930 to 1941 the western type of the disease spread from California to Kentucky and Alabama, being especially prevalent in the watershed of the Mississippi River. The eastern type in the same period spread chiefly along the Atlantic coast into Florida, Georgia, Massachusetts, North Carolina, and South Carolina, inland into Alabama, and along the Gulf coast to Mexico (*46, 71*). So far as is known, the two types of virus have up to the time of writing remained geographically separated, except in Alabama (*59*) and Texas (*46, 71*).

SYMPTOMS

There are certain indications of infectious equine encephalomyelitis and clincially similar diseases that should be known by everyone handling horses, mules, or asses. Nearly every animal that has sleeping sickness develops fever, sleepiness, grinding of the teeth, wobbly gait, and more or less difficulty in chewing and swallowing.

The first indication, fever, is present in practically all cases. The temperature varies from 102° to 107° F. During the early part of the febrile stage, nothing more indicative of illness than lack of spirit or slightly peculiar actions may be noticed, but it is at this time especially that the virus of the disease is present in the blood (*19, 48, 56*) and multiplying rapidly. The disease may then terminate, if the infection is of the so-called inapparent or occult type; or it may progress, causing distinct symptoms of involvement of the central nervous system (brain and spinal cord) and constituting what is known as the frank case. Both types of attack constitute true infections, and a considerable degree of immunity results from either. These observations have been made in both experimental and field cases (*15, 66*). It is believed that during an outbreak many animals, interspersed among the frank cases and the apparently wholly normal animals, develop occult infections. In an epizootic area during an outbreak, animals with this type of the disease may be found in almost any stable.

Sluggishness and drowsiness are early symptoms in the developing case of infectious equine encephalomyelitis. The lips become loose and droopy or are tensed and wrinkled or drawn to one side. Groups of muscles about the head, shoulder, or flank may be seen to twitch spasmodically. With the progress of the disease, the animal stands dejectedly and moves reluctantly with an awkward stumbling or staggering gait (fig. 1). Some affected animals are inclined to back persistently or walk stumblingly in a circle in one direction, the tail switching as they move. Such animals may blunder blindly into obstructions in their path. Whinnying is a common symptom. In many cases there is extreme sensitiveness, as shown by flinching at the slightest touch or by jerking muscular contractions when the animal is excited by unusual sounds. In most cases the animals are stupid and intractable, but a few become wild and unmanageable as in furious rabies. Sometimes sexual excitement occurs.

The dejected "sleeper" when aroused may exhibit momentary interest in feed or water, only soon to lapse into a stupor with unchewed food in the mouth or water trickling from the lips or nostrils. The lips, tongue, or cheeks may be paralyzed, but in most cases the difficulty in swallowing appears to come from inability to coordinate the normal muscular activity; often if the water bucket is held up to the animal and he is repeatedly aroused, he may succeed in obtaining a considerable quantity of water, a small amount at a time.

FIGURE 1.—A horse with a typical case of sleeping sickness. (Courtesy of Veterinary Science Division, University of California.)

During the periods of stupor, grinding of the teeth is common. Stretching of the neck and head in a yawning motion is frequently observed. There is usually a slight watery discharge from the nostrils, and the mouth becomes foul smelling owing to the accumulation and putrefaction of secretions and unswallowed food. If the eye is examined carefully, the membranes will invariably be found to be congested and of a dull yellowish or muddy color. Sometimes small hemorrhages are present.

With the progress of the illness, the animal becomes increasingly gaunt, and there is commonly a prominent ridge due to muscular tenseness along the lower abdominal wall. The digestive and excretory processes are retarded, and more or less constipation or sluggishness of the bowels results. Urine collects in the bladder, which may become greatly distended. Dribbling of urine without normal periodic voiding is common.

In about 1 of every 4 or 5 cases due to the western type of virus and 9 of every 10 cases caused by the eastern type, the animal gradually becomes weaker and weaker, finally collapsing on the ground. Very few of those that go down and are unable to regain their feet unaided recover, though it may be hours or days before the end. During this time they may lie quietly, breathing with a snoring sound, or they may thrash about considerably. Some animals literally bury themselves, digging up the earth with running movements of the legs in their delirium. Marked bruising and swelling develop on the parts of the body in contact with the ground.

If the animal lies quietly, the body temperature is usually normal or only slightly raised at this stage, but if there is much struggling or if complications such as pneumonia or other organic diseases occur there may be considerable fever. Among the animals that survive a typical attack of the disease, a few—the so-called dummies—retain evidence of more or less permanent injury to the brain and spinal cord.[3]

DEVELOPMENT AND SPREAD OF THE DISEASE

Infectious equine encephalomyelitis is essentially an epizootic disease—that is, one occurring in outbreaks that correspond to epidemics among human beings. While scattered or sporadic cases may occur at any time during the warm months, the peak of an epizootic is usually reached during July, August, or September in most sections. The disease invariably disappears after the first sharp frosts of fall. There is only one proved winter case on record, and that occurred in Florida in January during a mild season (*43*).

Sleeping sickness is essentially a disease of pastured animals, occurring only rarely among those continuously stabled. This is considered to be one of the reasons why Army posts and Thoroughbred breeding establishments remain relatively free from it.

The malady strikes hardest in farm and ranch areas along or near a stream, lake, marsh, swamp, or the seashore. In the West, irrigated sections are especially affected, as well as arid regions when unusually heavy rains occur. In the East, the tidewater regions have the most cases. Scattered or sporadic cases may be observed early in the summer and throughout the warm months under conditions of drought. On the other hand, heavy rains that result in the flooding of pastures and waste land and the formation of pools are frequently followed in 2 or 3 weeks by large numbers of cases. Under the latter conditions, extended hot weather also appears to be a factor in promoting the spread of the disease. Both moisture and heat, of course, encourage the breeding and feeding activities of insects.

There is a tendency for the disease to occur sporadically for one or more seasons in a given locality and then, under conditions favorable to it, to become very severe and widespread for one or more seasons. Following a severe and extended epizootic period, the disease may practically or entirely disappear for several years, only to reassert itself later when circumstances again become favorable.

---

[3] Detailed clinical descriptions of the disease are presented in citations, *6, 10, 17, 39, 49.*

During severe outbreaks, 10 percent or more of the horses and mules in an area may show unmistakable signs of the sickness. It is seldom that more than one or a few of the animals on a given farm sicken. Cases are often separated by several miles, and some premises appear to escape altogether. However, the virus probably attacks more animals than is superficially apparent, producing occult infections.

The incubation period of the naturally acquired disease (the time elapsing between entrance of the virus into the body and the appearance of the first symptoms) is believed to vary in length, as does this period in artificially infected animals. In the latter, the first symptoms usually appear 3 to 10 days after the introduction of the virus, depending on the dose and route of injection and on the type of virus. In some unusual cases as long as 3 weeks may elapse.

Although it is generally believed that horses of all ages and breeds are susceptible, there is some evidence to indicate that certain breeds may be less resistant than others (*30*). Certainly animals that have been exposed to the infection through the course of one or more outbreaks may be reasonably assumed to be more resistant as a class than others, such as colts, which have never before encountered the disease. Heredity, age, and nutrition are all suspected of playing a part in the artificially produced disease in mice, and these may be factors in the case of horses also.

Tests with guinea pigs indicate that young animals nursing immune mothers are highly resistant to the disease (*20*). Foals and young horses are believed to be more likely to recover than older horses. There is a widespread opinion among practicing veterinarians, to some extent supported by available data, that mules are less susceptible than horses (*51*).

It is generally believed that the disease is transmitted by bloodsucking insects. It has been found experimentally that at least 11 species of mosquitoes, all of the genus *Aedes*, can be infected, and 10 of these are capable of transmitting the virus (*9, 16, 26, 27, 33, 34, 36, 61*). Some species have been found that are practically incapable of transmitting one type of virus but that infect with the other type with a single bite (*15, 37*). Other species transmit both types with equal facility. Some of these mosquitoes are known to be widely distributed in the United States, others are somewhat restricted in distribution, but all except one species are present to some extent in one or more of the sections where the disease has occurred (*5*). Mosquitoes (*Culex tarsalis*) naturally infected with the western type of virus were discovered in the Yakima Valley, Wash., in 1941 (*16*). Numerous fruitless attempts had been made to find the virus in mosquitoes and other insects (including horseflies, houseflies, stableflies, horn flies, and spinose ear ticks) in nature (*44, 56, 70*) before this important finding was reported.

The virus has been reported as present in so-called assassin bugs (*Triatoma sanguisuga*) (*29*) collected in Kansas where the disease has been prevalent. This bug is relatively infrequently found in comparison with other insects that might be suspected as vectors (carriers) and probably cannot be held solely responsible for the dissemination of the equine disease. The chief importance of finding infection in this species would seem to lie in the probable existence of a reservoir for the virus somewhere among the many kinds of victims of its bite.

The tick that transmits Rocky Mountain spotted fever (*Dermacentor andersoni*) has been found to be capable of transmitting equine encephalomyelitis virus under experimental conditions (*63*). Moreover, it has been shown to transmit the virus from one generation to the next through the eggs and larvae (*64*). Like other ticks, these are relatively long-lived, and it is easy to conceive of their carrying the virus through the winter, or even through several years, and then transmitting it to susceptible species for further propagation, as has been suggested (*62*). The fact that the disease can readily be transmitted under certain conditions by several species of arthropods, particularly mosquitoes, must be accepted. However, that they actually do transmit it under natural conditions, or that they are the sole means of transmission, remains unproved despite very strong circumstantial evidence supporting the theory.

What becomes of the virus with the seasonal subsidence of the disease in horses is unknown. No evidence has yet been presented which proves that horses harbor the virus from one epizootic season to the next. Inasmuch as the virus is capable of surviving for only a relatively short time outside the animal body, it is assumed that it is perpetuated in some species other than the horse, mule, or ass.

Man was suspected as early as 1932 of being susceptible to the virus of sleeping sickness of American horses (*38*), and the possibility that he might act as a reservoir of the virus was considered in 1935 (*66*). The eastern type of equine virus was first actually demonstrated in cases of disease of the brain in man in 1938 (*12, 72*). Other cases, some due to the western type of virus, were subsequently identified (*11, 32*), and it is now an accepted fact that man is susceptible to the disease, which, as far as is known at present, is not immunologically related to the somewhat similar diseases, infantile paralysis (poliomyelitis) and epidemic encephalitis (St. Louis type). In many if not most cases of the equine virus disease in human beings there has been no evidence of contact with horses, and it is assumed that people generally contract the infection from the same source as horses, though a few cases have occurred among laboratory workers and some among persons closely associated with sick horses. Children have been especially affected in some outbreaks. The virus recovered from the brain of a child has produced typical equine encephalomyelitis when injected into susceptible horses. Encephalitis in man due to the equine virus is a very serious disease at any age, but there is a particularly high mortality rate among children affected with the eastern type, and troublesome complications are reported to be common in those surviving. The disease caused by the western type of virus is relatively much less severe than that due to the eastern type. On the other hand, the former has been more widespread. Over 2,000 cases, mostly attributed to the equine virus (western type), were reported from North Dakota, South Dakota, Minnesota, Montana, and Nebraska in 1941.

It has been determined that horses are susceptible to human encephalitis (St. Louis type) virus when artificially inoculated, and in areas where sleeping sickness has been epizootic in horses, people and animals have been found the serum from which was capable of neutralizing the virus of that disease as well as the virus of infectious equine encephalomyelitis (*8, 23, 24, 45*). The assumption is that both viruses may produce the disease in horses and other animals as well as in man and that the two have existed simultaneously in some outbreaks of both the human and the equine disease, although St. Louis encephalitis virus has never been found naturally occurring in equines. The viruses of St. Louis encephalitis and equine encephalomyelitis have both been found in mosquitoes (*Culex tarsalis*) (*16*).

A disease of the central nervous system due to equine encephalomyelitis virus has been found to occur naturally in ring-necked pheasants, pigeons, and prairie chickens (*3, 7*). Thus, it is definitely known that birds are sometimes attacked by the virus of so-called brain fever of horses. This disease has no known connection with the virus disease of chickens known as chick encephalomyelitis or epidemic tremors (*42*).

A disease in ducks in Montana suspected of being encephalomyelitis was investigated in 1938, but the presence of the equine virus was not actually demonstrated (*60*). This outbreak, as well as the proved cases in pigeons, pheasants, and prairie chickens, occurred in an area where sleeping sickness of horses had been prevalent.

It is now known that over 20 species of birds are susceptible to the virus of sleeping sickness when artificially injected. Following inoculation by certain methods, hens and turkeys have been found to develop transitory inapparent infections, with virus circulating in the blood stream (*65*). A similar condition has been shown with certain species of blackbirds and the mourning dove, cowbird, and grackle (*9*). Such birds, without showing obvious indications of infection, may play roles in the spread of the disease as important as or even more important than those of others which, like pigeons and pheasants, develop frank symptoms of encephalomyelitis and have a high death rate from the disease. The list of susceptible birds includes ducks, geese, a species of hawk, blackbirds, the tawny vulture, the white stork, guinea fowl, English sparrow, Gambel sparrow, quail, LeConte thrasher, the junco, the western burrowing owl, the American egret, red-shafted flicker, killdeer, and robin, besides those already mentioned.

Equine encephalomyelitis virus when artificially injected is capable of infecting more species of animals than perhaps any other known virus. About as many species of mammals as of birds have been so infected. In addition to the commonly used laboratory mammals—guinea pigs, white mice, white rats, rabbits, and monkeys—cattle, swine, sheep, goats, dogs, cats, several species of wild mice, rats, and other rodents, including rabbits, gophers, hedgehogs, and woodchucks may be infected. The list also includes weasels, ferrets, and hamsters (ratlike rodents of eastern Europe). Some species appear to be susceptible to both types of virus, while some can be infected with one type but not the other.

Although horses, mules, and human beings are the only mammalian species now known to contract the disease naturally, many others equally susceptible to artificial exposure may eventually be found naturally affected. In fact, the virus has recently been isolated from a wild deer in Montana. The studies being made by several agencies will probably lead to the identification of other naturally infected animals and eventually to important biological reservoirs of the virus.

While it is possible that horses may occasionally contract the disease by inhaling or swallowing virus from affected animals, judging from the observed facts, transmission by such means must be exceedingly rare. Several deliberate attempts to induce the disease in normal horses by putting them in contact with affected horses have failed (*68, 69*). In fact, in all the literature on the disease not one proved instance is mentioned of infection of normal animals by contact with infected animals of any species or with an environment that might have been contaminated. The tentative conclusion, based on the available information, that the disease is chiefly arthropod-borne, is inescapable, although more work remains to be done to prove it.

DIAGNOSIS

The diagnosis of infectious equine encephalomyelitis is based on a study of the symptoms in each case and such features as seasonal occurrence and distribution in the locality. However, because atypical cases do occur and unusual conditions are not infrequently encountered, a specific laboratory diagnosis (*59*) may be required for confirmation of clinical diagnosis or the determination of the type of virus involved.

If virus is sought in the living animal, repeated samplings of the blood very early in the course of the ailment, preferably before symptoms of disease of the nervous system appear, are usually required. The virus is present in the blood stream for only a comparatively short time and then becomes fixed in the brain and spinal cord, only rarely being found elsewhere after that. It is shown to be present by the inoculation of the finely emulsified nervous tissue from the suspected case into any of the available susceptible animals, usually guinea pigs or white mice; or the tissue may be inoculated into hen's eggs containing 9- to 13-day-old living embryos. Symptoms like those seen in horses develop in the guinea pig or mouse in a few days, and death usually results. The inoculated embryo succumbs to the virus in 15 to 24 hours (*18*). The virus is similarly demonstrable in the body of the inoculated animal and in the embryo, and it may be transmitted by inoculation from the original guinea pig, mouse, or embryo to others in long, continuous series.

If a horse or mule has been dead for some time or even prostrate for several days, it may be impossible to demonstrate virus in the tissue of the central nervous system. A few known artificially produced cases also fail to yield virus. It is then necessary to resort to microscopic examination of the tissues (*4, 25, 28, 31*). In the brain and spinal cord, the blood vessels are found to be engorged or swollen, and small hemorrhages, edema, and abnormal accumulations of various types of cells in the spaces surrounding the blood vessels or in other parts of the tissues are present. Varying degrees of degeneration of the nerve cells are to be observed. Somewhat similar but less characteristic changes may be found in the liver.

These changes are not apparent to the naked eye, although very minute hemorrhagic points may be seen in certain parts of the brain. The cerebrospinal fluid (surrounding the brain and spinal cord) is clear but greatly increased in amount and chemically and microscopically abnormal. The throat and nasal passages may be inflamed, and a putrid odor may be present. Usually the lungs are essentially normal, although there may be congestion or even pneumonia, especially in animals that have been down for some time. The stomach usually contains a considerable amount of watery, foul-smelling food material. Evidence of catarrhal inflammation and sluggishness of the bowels are common. The bladder is usually distended with clear, amber-colored, sirupy urine. The liver, instead of being slate-colored as normally, is slightly enlarged and of a dull, yellowish-gray color. The various membranes of the body also are usually dull yellowish, owing to staining with bile. The muscles appear dry and lighter colored than normal as a result of great loss of water (dehydration) by the sick animal. These changes are not necessarily characteristic of sleeping sickness, and unqualified diagnosis of the disease by this means alone is rarely if ever justified, but a thorough post mortem examination is nevertheless often a great assistance to the veterinarian in identifying other diseases that may be responsible in suspected cases.

Experimental studies have been made of the complement-fixation test (involving the use of blood serum, virus, and red blood cells) as applied to sleeping sickness, but it has not yet been generally used in diagnosis (*22, 41*). The blood serum of a convalescing or recovered animal may be tested to determine its power to inactivate or neutralize encephalomyelitis virus (in vitro neutralization test) (*14, 15, 19, 38, 66, 67*). A positive reaction to this test is generally accepted as evidence of past or present infection, the neutralizing substances constituting a form of antibody.

SIMILAR DISEASES AND CONDITIONS

Not all cases of illness in horses and mules in which there is evidence of disturbance of the central nervous system are infectious encephalomyelitis.

Toxic encephalitis, as contrasted with infectious encephalomyelitis, may occur at any time of the year—in the dead of winter as well as in midsummer. However, the commonest form, that known as moldy corn poisoning (*55*), usually makes its appearance in the late fall or the winter in horses or mules that have been fed on moldy, stunted, or otherwise deteriorated or inferior corn. This malady has been responsible for the death of thousands of valuable horses from time to time in several of the Corn Belt States, usually in the months of November to April after an unusually dry summer and heavy fall rains.

The symptoms of moldy corn poisoning are scarcely distinguishable from those of other clinically similar ailments by any but the trained observer. Usually, however, there is no yellowness of the membranes of the body and no great rise in body temperature. At autopsy, areas of softening and degeneration, sometimes microscopic only but more often plainly evident to the naked eye, are usually found in the brain.

Prevention consists in avoiding the feeding of corn or corn fodder about the absolute soundness of which there is the slightest doubt. Other species of animals may tolerate poor corn, but is dangerous to horses in this and other ways. It may be desirable in some instances to muzzle horses being worked in the corn harvest in order to prevent their eating potentially dangerous corn. Although moldiness is considered as an important indication of danger, unfortunately it is not always possible to determine by examination whether a certain lot of corn can be fed with safety. The toxin in bad corn, whatever its nature, appears to be cumulative in effect, and symptoms do not ordinarily develop in less than a month, even though the corn is fed continuously.

There is no specific remedy for the disease, and the medicinal aid given by the veterinarian varies somewhat with the conditions found in each case.

Other toxins or poisons in some deteriorated feeds other than corn, as well as some mineral poisons such as barium, lead, arsenic, phosphorus, and selenium, may cause symptoms attributable to or suggestive of encephalitis. Among the plants that may induce more or less similar symptoms are whorled milkweed, yellow tarweed, poisonhemlock, ragwort, locoweed, ergot-infested paspalum grass, and horsetail. Unripe and green as well as rotten or sprouted potatoes are very dangerous feed for horses or other animals and often produce symptoms suggestive of encephalitis. Certain ticks engorging on various animals, including the horse, sometimes cause a peculiar form of paralysis, which is usually promptly remedied by the removal of the ticks.

Such diseases as anthrax and influenza (shipping fever) sometimes cause encephalitis. Some cases of acute infectious anemia (swamp fever) show symptoms that resemble those of infectious encephalomyelitis. Rabies, a virus disease transmitted by the bite of an infected animal, usually a dog, is a form of encephalitis. Still other infectious diseases may cause symptoms of nervous disease. Even tetanus, or lockjaw, has been diagnosed as infectious encephalomyelitis by untrained persons. Diagnosis and treatment vary according to the nature of the primary disease in question.

Some animals affected by heat stroke or lightning develop spasms, convulsions, or residual paralysis, which must be differentiated from true encephalitis. These, of course, are usually isolated cases.

Tumors of various types and abscesses in the brain arising from bacterial infection may cause symptoms suggesting infectious encephalomyelitis. Close clinical examination and a study of the history of these comparatively rare cases will usually enable the experienced veterinarian to identify the condition. The same may be said of mechanical injuries to the head.

Botulism (*13*) is a disease caused by the ingestion of a toxin produced in feeds under certain conditions by a widely distributed germ known as *Clostridium botulinum*. The chief symptom consists of progressive paralysis, usually beginning in the eyes, tongue, and throat, finally involving the entire body, and resulting in death.

Azoturia, sometimes referred to as Monday morning disease because it commonly occurs in well-fed and underexercised horses after a week end of rest in the stable, has been confused with infectious encephalomyelitis. The disease is discussed in the section on Miscellaneous Diseases of Equines, page 452.

In the last decade, in several States in areas where infectious encephalomyelitis had previously prevailed, a second illness, now called toxic hepatogenous icterus,[4] in some ways resembling sleeping sickness and in others quite different, has appeared during the late fall and early winter 2 weeks to 2 months after epizootics of sleeping

---

[4] The term "toxic hepatogenous icterus" has been proposed to replace the previously used terms "secondary disease" or "X disease." See MOHLER, J. R. REPORT ON INFECTIOUS EQUINE ENCEPHALOMYELITIS IN THE UNITED STATES IN 1939. U. S. Bur. Anim. Indus., 4 pp., illus. 1940. [Mimeographed.]

sickness (*35, 58*). Usually horses affected with this disease have no fever, develop an obstinate constipation and extreme icterus (jaundice), and become very unmanageable, pushing violently against any objects in their path. The affection is extremely acute and the death rate high. Studies conducted to date do not prove that it is infectious, and its true nature is not yet definitely known. Although many of the animals that have developed this affliction had been treated earlier with antiencephalomyelitis serum, some had not.

The chief abnormality found at autopsy is a damaged liver, which shows characteristic changes under the microscope. Success in treatment appears to depend chiefly on early diagnosis and prompt stimulation of the intestinal tract.

CONTROL AND PREVENTION

Although not everything is known about the spread of sleeping sickness, as has been pointed out, nevertheless there are certain justifiable, practical, and apparently effective means of prevention. The selection and application of these measures, singly or collectively, must properly be considered as technical matters. Accordingly, when control of the disease is to be attempted, a licensed veterinary practitioner or authorized veterinary official should be consulted. In the past, much money has been spent needlessly by frantic horse owners for worthless and in some cases even harmful so-called preventives or cures for infectious encephalomyelitis.

(1) Among the means of prevention, vaccination is of first importance. The approved, commercially available vaccine of today consists of artificially infected chick-embryo tissue, in which the power of the virus to produce the disease has been destroyed by the addition of a solution of formaldehyde (*2*). Other products have been tried with more of less success, but all have been displaced by the present one of chick-embryo origin known as encephalomyelitis vaccine. The vaccine is prepared from embryos infected with western, eastern, or both types of virus. Which should be used depends upon the type of virus known to prevail in the locality.

Since the virus is rendered harmless by the presence of formaldehyde in the vaccine, there is no danger of producing the disease in animals injected with the product. It is thus unlike some other products used for the control of animal diseases, but it is not so foolproof that it can be safely and effectively used by everyone. Its proper administration requires the services of a veterinarian who understands that the product deteriorates and becomes less effective, if not worthless, when not properly handled. Then, too, severe reactions and even death have been known to occur following vaccination (*52, 53*). These undesirable results can be largely if not wholly prevented by injecting the vaccine into the skin (*54*) rather than under it or into the muscles, as was once practiced.

While one dose of the vaccine results in an appreciable degree of resistance, it lasts for only a comparatively short time. Accordingly two doses at 7- to 10-day intervals should be given. Unfortunately many farmers do not have their animals vaccinated until the disease has already made its appearance on their farms or in their vicinity, and under these conditions the method is not fully effective. Although vaccination during an outbreak appears to be safe and effective as a last resort, such a procedure cannot be expected to be as advantageous as vaccination before the epizootic season, which extends from July to October in most sections but is somewhat earlier in others. To secure the maximum protection during these months, the two-dose vaccination should preferably be completed not later than early July in most localities. In some areas vaccination in the early spring or even late winter may be advisable. Experimental tests indicate that most vaccinated animals develop immunity within 10 days to 2 weeks after the administration of the second dose of vaccine and retain a sufficient degree of immunity to resist even the severest artificial exposure for 6 months and sometimes even longer (*50, 60*). In order to assure protection, it appears at present that animals should be revaccinated each year.

(2) Second among preventive procedures is the prevention or limitation of bites by bloodsucking insects, particularly mosquitoes. Prevention or control of breeding of the insects, screening of stables, stabling of horses and mules as much as possible, the use of nets, etc., on working animals, and the frequent application to the animals and the premises of repellent compounds are all useful.

(3) All animals affected with the disease should be stabled in screened quarters or kept thoroughly sprayed with an effective repellent, especially in the early stage of the disease when the blood is infectious. If possible, a separate caretaker should be provided for them. Although it is probable that man does not contract the disease from horses or other affected animals by direct contact, those engaged in handling or treating such animals should avoid unnecessary risks, especially from soiling the hands or person with secretions or excretions from the sick animals.

(4) Extermination of rats, mice, and other vermin and exclusion from the places where the horses are kept of pigeons and stray or wild animals are advisable on general principles.

(5) Although rigid general quarantine measures have not been found practical in dealing with encephalomyelitis, the movement of horses or mules from an epizootic area into a clean area should be discouraged. When it is necessary, the animals might well be vaccinated at least 15 days before being moved. Animals going into an infected area from one where the disease has not been prevalent should be similarly treated.

(6) Animals dead of the disease should be promptly disposed of by thorough rendering or burning or deep burial with the addition of quick lime. The stables, sheds, corrals, etc., used by the affected animals should be thoroughly cleaned, and feed boxes, stalls, watering troughs, etc., should be disinfected with either a 2-percent aqueous solution of lye or a 1-percent solution of formalin. The formalin will in time evaporate from the treated surfaces, but lye should be thoroughly removed after a few hours by repeated washing with clean water.

(7) A specific antiencephalomyelitis serum (*19, 20, 38, 47*) is com-

mercially available, and some experimental data indicate that it has some preventive value. Practical considerations, however, considerably restrict its use in the prevention of the disease, and vaccine is preferred in most instances.

Vaccination properly done does not interfere with working or breeding the animals. A few instances of abortion have been reported in pregnant mares vaccinated by the older method, but none following intradermic vaccination. A small, hard swelling may remain at the site of injection for as long as a few weeks, but this does no harm unless it is situated where harness or saddle will rub it, and it is eventually completely resorbed.

Laboratory workers exposed to unusual danger of contracting the infection have been safely vaccinated with a product of the same general type as that used for horses (*1*), but it has not been generally used in epidemic areas.

TREATMENT

If despite well-advised and diligently applied control measures, sleeping sickness or anything resembling it develops in a stable, a veterinarian should be called immediately. Except for antiencephalomyelitis serum, which if used at all must be given very early in the course of the disease and in large, frequently repeated doses, there is no specific treatment. Whether or not serum should be used is strictly a matter for the veterinarian's decision.

Reliance must be placed chiefly on good nursing, with such additional treatment as is recommended by the veterinarian for each individual case. Quiet, cool, comfortable, well-bedded quarters and protection of the animal from the sun and from self-injury are advisable.

If the animal has difficulty in standing, he may be placed in a leaning position against a padded wall or supported in a specially constructed padded frame.

Unnecessary fussing about the animal should be avoided, although almost constant attendance may be required to assist it in supporting itself. Many animals affected with sleeping sickness will not or cannot eat or drink unless the feed and water are held up to them and they are frequently aroused from their stupor. Water in small quantities, frequently given, is most desirable, and if it is not or cannot be swallowed it may be given by stomach tube, by way of the rectum, or into the blood stream in the form of various solutions. Feed is not nearly so important as water. However, when the animal will take small amounts of it, succulent feed may be allowed freely.

On the supposition that horses affected with encephalomyelitis, like humans with encephalitis, have a headache, cold compresses or ice packs are sometimes placed on the poll. This should do no harm and may be of benefit. Although very few animals that have been prostrate for hours or days can be expected to recover, they should be humanely treated if they are not destroyed.

Some cases may be benefited by stimulants; others may require laxatives, evacuation of the bladder by catheterization, or quieting drugs. Such drugs as are given are usually administered either through a stomach tube or hypodermically. No one system of treatment is applicable in all cases. Above all, unguided home treatment, promiscuous drenching, or other administrations which may be suggested by unqualified advisers, should not be attempted. Unwise or injudicious treatment may easily result in the needless loss of the animal. On the other hand, many horses die despite the best efforts of the most experienced and highly qualified veterinarians.

LITERATURE CITED

(1) BEARD, J. W., BEARD, DOROTHY, and FINKELSTEIN, HAROLD.
 1939. HUMAN VACCINATION AGAINST EQUINE ENCEPHALOMYELITIS VIRUS WITH FORMALIZED CHICK EMBRYO VACCINE. Science 90: 215–216.
(2) ———— FINKELSTEIN, HAROLD, SEALY, W. C., and WYCKOFF, R. W. G.
 1938. IMMUNIZATION AGAINST EQUINE ENCEPHALOMYELITIS WITH CHICK EMBRYO VACCINES♦ Science 87: 490.
(3) BEAUDETTE, F. R.
 1939. EQUINE ENCEPHALOMYELITIS IN AVIAN HOSTS. U. S. Live Stock Sanit. Assoc. Proc. 43: 185–203.
(4) BIESTER, H. E., and SCHWARTE, L. H.
 1936. LABORATORY CASE STUDIES OF EQUINE ENCEPHALOMYELITIS. Iowa Vet. 7 (3): 13–17.
(5) BISHOPP, F. C.
 1939. MOSQUITO TRANSMISSION OF ENCEPHALOMYELITIS, OR BRAIN FEVER, OF HORSES. Wash. Acad. Sci. Jour. 29: 495–501.
(6) BREUCKNER, A. L., POELMA, L. J., EVERSON, C. L., and REED, R. C.
 1934. EQUINE ENCEPHALOMYELITIS. Md. Agr. Expt. Sta. Bul. 369, pp. 137–146, illus.
(7) COX, HERALD R., JELLISON, WILLIAM L., and HUGHES, LYNDAHL E.
 1941. ISOLATION OF WESTERN EQUINE ENCEPHALOMYELITIS VIRUS FROM A NATURALLY INFECTED PRAIRIE CHICKEN. U. S. Pub. Health Serv., Pub. Health Rpts. 56: 1905–1906.
(8) ———— PHILLIP, CORNELIUS B., and KILPATRICK, J. W.
 1941. SUSCEPTIBILITY OF HORSES TO ST. LOUIS ENCEPHALOMYELITIS VIRUS. U. S. Pub. Health Serv., Pub. Health Rpts. 56: 1391–1392.
(9) DAVIS, WILLIAM A.
 1940. A SURVEY OF BIRDS AND MOSQUITOES AS HOSTS FOR THE VIRUS OF EASTERN EQUINE ENCEPHALOMYELITIS. Amer. Jour. Hyg., Protozool. and Malariol., Sect. C, 32 (2): 45–59.
(10) FARQUHARSON, JAMES.
 1939. INFECTIOUS EQUINE ENCEPHALOMYELITIS. Amer. Vet. Med. Assoc. Jour. 94 (n. s. 47): 459–465, illus.
(11) FOTHERGILL, L[EROY] D.
 1940. EQUINE ENCEPHALOMYELITIS. *In* Virus and Rickettsial Diseases With Especial Consideration of Their Public Health Significance. Harvard School of Public Health Symposium, pp. 661–683.
(12) ———— DINGLE, JOHN H., and FARBER, SIDNEY.
 1938. HUMAN ENCEPHALITIS CAUSED BY THE VIRUS OF THE EASTERN VARIETY OF EQUINE ENCEPHALOMYELITIS. New England Jour. Med. 219: [411].
(13) GEIGER, J. C., DICKSON, E. C., and MEYER, K. F.
 1922. THE EPIDEMIOLOGY OF BOTULISM. U. S. Pub. Health Serv. Bul. 127, 119 pp., illus.
(14) GILTNER, L. T., and SHAHAN, M. S.
 1933. THE 1933 OUTBREAK OF INFECTIOUS EQUINE ENCEPHALOMYELITIS IN THE EASTERN STATES. North Amer. Vet. 14 (11): 25–27.
(15) ———— and SHAHAN, M. S.
 1936. THE PRESENT STATUS OF INFECTIOUS EQUINE ENCEPHALOMYELITIS IN THE UNITED STATES. Amer. Vet. Med. Assoc. Jour. 88: 363–374.

(16) HAMMON, WILLIAM McD., REEVES, WILLIAM C., BROOKMAN, BERNARD, IZUMI, ERNEST M., and GJULLIN, C. M.
1941. ISOLATION OF THE VIRUSES OF WESTERN EQUINE AND ST. LOUIS ENCEPHALITIS FROM CULEX TARSALIS MOSQUITOES. Science 94: 328–330.
(17) HARING, C. M., HOWARTH, J. A., and MEYER, K. F.
1931. AN INFECTIOUS BRAIN DISEASE OF HORSES AND MULES (ENCEPHALOMYELITIS). Calif. Agr. Expt. Sta. Cir. 322, 14 pp., illus.
(18) HIGBIE, ELIZABETH, and HOWITT, BEATRICE.
1935. THE BEHAVIOR OF THE VIRUS OF EQUINE ENCEPHALOMYELITIS ON THE CHORIOALLANTOIC MEMBRANE OF THE DEVELOPING CHICK. Jour. Bact. 29: 399–406, illus.
(19) HOWITT, BEATRICE F.
1932. EQUINE ENCEPHALOMYELITIS. Jour. Infect. Dis. 51: [493]–510.
(20) ——
1934. IMMUNIZATION OF GUINEA-PIGS TO THE VIRUS OF EQUINE ENCEPHALOMYELITIS. Jour. Infect. Dis. 54: 368–387.
(21) ——
1935. AN IMMUNOLOGICAL STUDY IN LABORATORY ANIMALS OF THIRTEEN DIFFERENT STRAINS OF EQUINE ENCEPHALOMYELITIC VIRUS. Jour. Immunol. 29: 319–341.
(22) ——
1937. THE COMPLEMENT FIXATION REACTION IN EXPERIMENTAL EQUINE ENCEPHALOMYELITIS, LYMPHOCYTIC CHORIOMENINGITIS AND THE ST. LOUIS TYPE OF ENCEPHALITIS. Jour. Immunol. 33: 235–250.
(23) ——
1939. VIRUSES OF EQUINE AND OF ST. LOUIS ENCEPHALITIS IN RELATIONSHIP TO HUMAN INFECTIONS IN CALIFORNIA, 1937–1938. Amer. Jour. Pub. Health 29: 1083–1097, illus.
(24) ——
1940. EQUINE ENCEPHALOMYELITIS; ITS RELATIONSHIP TO MAN AND ANIMALS IN CALIFORNIA. Internatl. Cong. Microbiol. Proc. 3: 302–303.
(25) HURST, E. WESTON.
1934. THE HISTOLOGY OF EQUINE ENCEPHALOMYELITIS. Jour. Expt. Med. 59: 529–542, illus.
(26) KELSER, R. A.
1933. MOSQUITOES AS VECTORS OF THE VIRUS OF EQUINE ENCEPHALOMYELITIS. Amer. Vet. Med. Assoc. Jour. 82 (n. s. 35): 767–771.
(27) ——
1938. TRANSMISSION OF THE VIRUS OF EQUINE ENCEPHALOMYELITIS BY AEDES TAENIORHYNCHUS. Amer. Vet. Med. Assoc. Jour. 92 (n. s. 45): 195–203.
(28) KING, LESTER S.
1938. STUDIES ON EASTERN EQUINE ENCEPHALOMYELITIS. I. HISTOPATHOLOGY OF THE NERVOUS SYSTEM IN THE GUINEA PIG. Jour. Expt. Med. 68: 677–691.
(29) KITSELMAN, CHARLES H., and GRUNDMANN, ALBERT W.
1940. EQUINE ENCEPHALOMYELITIS VIRUS ISOLATED FROM NATURALLY INFECTED TRIATOMA SANGUISUGA LE CONTE. Kans. Agr. Expt. Sta. Tech. Bul. 50, 15 pp., illus.
(30) LAMBERT, W. V., SPEELMAN, S. R., and OSBORN, E. B.
1939. DIFFERENCES IN INCIDENCE OF ENCEPHALOMYELITIS IN HORSES. Jour. Hered. 30: 349–352.
(31) LARSELL, O., HARING, C. M., and MEYER, K. F.
1934. HISTOLOGICAL CHANGES IN THE CENTRAL NERVOUS SYSTEM FOLLOWING EQUINE ENCEPHALOMYELITIS. Amer. Jour. Path. 10: 361–373.
(32) LEAKE, JAMES P.
1941. EPIDEMIC OF INFECTIOUS ENCEPHALITIS. U. S. Pub. Health Serv., Pub. Health Rpts. 56: 1902–1905.
(33) MADSEN, D. E. and KNOWLTON, G. F.
1935. MOSQUITO TRANSMISSION OF EQUINE ENCEPHALOMYELITIS. Amer. Vet. Med. Assoc. Jour. 6 (n. s. 39): 662–666.

(34) MADSEN, D. E., KNOWLTON, G. F., and ROWE, J. A.
1936. FURTHER STUDIES ON TRANSMISSION OF EQUINE ENCEPHALOMYELITIS BY MOSQUITOES. Amer. Vet. Med. Assoc. Jour. 89 (n. s. 42) : 187–196.
(35) MARSH, HADLEIGH.
1937. LOSSES OF UNDETERMINED CAUSE FOLLOWING AN OUTBREAK OF EQUINE ENCEPHALOMYELITIS. Amer. Vet. Med. Assoc. Jour. 91 (n. s. 44) : 88–93.
(36) MERRILL, MALCOLM H., LACAILLADE, C. WM., Jr., TEN BROECK, CARL.
1934. MOSQUITO TRANSMISSION OF EQUINE ENCEPHALOMYELITIS. Science 80: 251–252.
(37) —— and TEN BROECK, CARL.
1935. THE TRANSMISSION OF EQUINE ENCEPHALOMYELITIS VIRUS BY AËDES AEGYPTI. Jour. Expt. Med. 62: 687–695.
(38) MEYER, K. F.
1932. SUMMARY OF RECENT STUDIES ON EQUINE ENCEPHALOMYELITIS. Ann. Inf. Med. 6: 645–654.
(39) ——
1933. EQUINE ENCEPHALOMYELITIS. North Amer. Vet. 14 (6) : 30–48.
(40) —— HARING, C. M., and HOWITT, B.
1931. THE ETIOLOGY OF EPIZOOTIC ENCEPHALOMYELITIS OF HORSES IN THE SAN JOAQUIN VALLEY, 1930. Science 74: 227–228.
(41) MOHLER, WILLIAM M.
1939. COMPLEMENT FIXATION WITH CHICK-EMBRYO ANTIGEN IN EQUINE ENCEPHALOMYELITIS. Amer. Vet. Med. Assoc. Jour. 94 (n. s. 47) : 39–43.
(42) OLITSKY, PETER K.
1939. EXPERIMENTAL STUDIES ON THE VIRUS OF INFECTIOUS AVIAN ENCEPHALO- MYELITIS. Jour. Expt. Med. 70: 565–582, illus.
(43) OSTEEN, O. L.
1939. INFECTIOUS EQUINE ENCEPHALOMYELITIS: MID-WINTER CASE. Amer. Vet. Med. Assoc. Jour. 94 (n. s. 47) : 441–442.
(44) PHILLIP, CORNELIUS B., and COX, HERALD R.
1936. EQUINE ENCEPHALOMYELITIS IN WESTERN MONTANA IN 1936. A BRIEF DISCUSSION OF THE IMPLICATIONS OF ARTHROPOD TRANSMIS- SION. (Abstract) Jour. Parasitol. 22: 542.
(45) —— COX, HERALD R., and FOUNTAIN, JOHN H.
1941. PROTECTIVE ANTIBODIES AGAINST ST. LOUIS ENCEPHALITIS VIRUS IN THE SERUM OF HORSES AND MAN. U. S. Pub. Health Serv., Pub. Health Rpts. 56: 1388–1391.
(46) RANDALL, RAYMOND/and EICHORN, ERVIN A.
1941. WESTWARD SPREAD OF EASTERN TYPE EQUINE ENCEPHALOMYELITIS VIRUS. Amer. Vet. Med. Assoc. Jour. 98: 448.
(47) RECORDS, EDWARD, and VAWTER, LYMAN R.
1933. EQUINE ENCEPHALOMYELITIS ANTISERUM. Amer. Vet. Med. Assoc. Jour. 82 (n. s. 35) : 608–616.
(48) —— and VAWTER, LYMAN R.
1935. EQUINE ENCEPHALOMYELITIS CROSS-IMMUNITY IN HORSES BETWEEN WESTERN AND EASTERN STRAINS OF VIRUS. SUPPLEMENTAL REPORT. Amer. Vet. Med. Assoc. Jour. 86 (n. s. 39) : 773–777.
(49) —— VAWTER, LYMAN, and others.
1933. EQUINE ENCEPHALOMYELITIS. Nev. Agr. Expt. Sta. Bul. 132, 22 pp., illus.
(50) SCHOENING, H. W.
1939. EQUINE ENCEPHALOMYELITIS. Amer. Vet. Med. Assoc. Jour. 95: 268–271.
(51) ——
1940. THE EPIZOOTIOLOGY OF INFECTIOUS EQUINE ENCEPHALOMYELITIS IN THE UNITED STATES. Vet. Bul. 34 (1) : 13–19.
(52) ——
1940. REACTIONS FOLLOWING ADMINISTRATION OF EQUINE ENCEPHALOMYE- LITIS VACCINE. Amer. Vet. Med. Assoc. Jour. 97: 39–40, illus.
(53) —— GILTNER, L. T., and SHAHAN, M. S.
1939. INFECTIOUS EQUINE ENCEPHALOMYELITIS IN 1939. U. S. Live Stock Sanit. Assoc. Proc. 43: 145–150.

(54) SCHOENING, H. W., SHAHAN, M. S., OSTEEN, O. L., and GILTNER, L. T.
1940. STUDIES ON THE INTRADERMAL METHOD OF VACCINATION AGAINST EQUINE ENCEPHALOMYELITIS. Vet. Med. 35: 377–380, illus.
(55) SCHWARTE, L. H., BIESTER, H. E., and MURRAY, CHAS.
1937. A DISEASE OF HORSES CAUSED BY FEEDING MOLDY CORN. Amer. Vet. Med. Assoc. Jour. 90 (n. s. 43) : 76–85, illus.
(56) SHAHAN, M. S., and GILTNER, L. T.
1934. SOME ASPECTS OF INFECTION AND IMMUNITY IN EQUINE ENCEPHALOMYELITIS. Amer. Vet. Med. Assoc. Jour. 84 (n. s. 37) : 928–934.
(57) ――― and GILTNER, L. T.
1935. EQUINE ENCEPHALOMYELITIS STUDIES : 1. CROSS-IMMUNITY TESTS BETWEEN EASTERN AND WESTERN TYPES OF VIRUS. Amer. Vet. Med. Assoc. Jour. 86 (n. s. 39) : 764–772.
(58) ――― GILTNER, L. T., DAVIS, C. L., and HUFFMAN, W. T.
1939. "SECONDARY DISEASE" OCCURRING SUBSEQUENT TO INFECTIOUS EQUINE ENCEPHALOMYELITIS. Vet. Med. 34 : 354–358, illus.
(59) ――― GILTNER, L. T., and OSTEEN, O. L.
1940. THE ISOLATION AND TYPING OF EQUINE ENCEPHALOMYELITIS VIRUS. Cornell Vet. 30 : 151–160.
(60) ――― GILTNER, L. T., and SCHOENING, H. W.
1938. A REVIEW OF THE 1938 OUTBREAK OF INFECTIOUS EQUINE ENCEPHALOMYELITIS IN THE UNITED STATES. U. S. Live Stock Sanit. Assoc. Proc. 42 : 145–157.
(61) SIMMONS, JAMES STEVENS, REYNOLDS, FRANÇOIS H. K., and CORNELL, VIRGIL H.
1936. TRANSMISSION OF THE VIRUS OF EQUINE ENCEPHALOMYELITIS THROUGH AEDES ALBOPICTUS, SKUZE. Amer. Jour. Trop. Med. 16 : 289–302.
(62) SYVERTON, JEROME T.
1940. DISCUSSION ON EPIDEMIOLOGY OF EQUINE ENCEPHALOMYELITIS. Internatl. Cong. Microbiol. Proc. 3 : 306.
(63) ――― and BERRY, GEORGE PACKER.
1936. AN ARTHROPOD VECTOR FOR EQUINE ENCEPHALOMYELITIS, WESTERN STRAIN. Science 84 : 186–187.
(64) ――― and BERRY, GEORGE PACKER.
1941. HEREDITARY TRANSMISSION OF THE WESTERN TYPE OF EQUINE ENCEPHALOMYELITIS VIRUS IN THE WOOD TICK, DERMACENTOR ANDERSONI STILES. Jour. Expt. Med. 73 : 507-530, illus.
(65) TEN BROECK, CARL.
1938. BIRDS AS POSSIBLE CARRIERS OF THE VIRUS OF EQUINE ENCEPHALOMYELITIS. Arch. Path. 25 : 759.
(66) ――― HURST, E. WESTON, and TRAUB, ERICH.
1935. EPIDEMIOLOGY OF EQUINE ENCEPHALOMYELITIS IN THE EASTERN UNITED STATES. Jour. Expt. Med. 62 : 677–685, illus.
(67) ――― and MERRILL, MALCOLM H.
1933. A SEROLOGICAL DIFFERENCE BETWEEN EASTERN AND WESTERN EQUINE ENCEPHALOMYELITIS VIRUS. Soc. Expt. Biol. and Med. Proc. 31 : 217–220.
(68) UNITED STATES BUREAU OF ANIMAL INDUSTRY.
1933. RESEARCH ON DISEASES. *In* Rpt. of the Chief of the Bur. of Anim. Indus. 1933 : 33–34.
(69) ―――
1934. RESEARCH ON DISEASES. *In* Rpt. of the Chief of the Bur. of Anim. Indus. 1934 : 37–38.
(70) ―――
1938. INFECTIOUS EQUINE ENCEPHALOMYELITIS AND RELATED DISEASES. *In* Rpt. of the Chief of the Bur. Anim. Indus. 1938 : 58–59.
(71) ―――
1941. REPORT OF THE CHIEF OF THE BUREAU OF ANIMAL INDUSTRY 1941, 92 pp.
(72) WEBSTER, LESLIE T., and WRIGHT, F. HOWELL.
1938. RECOVERY OF EASTERN EQUINE ENCEPHALOMYELITIS VIRUS FROM BRAIN TISSUE OF HUMAN CASES OF ENCEPHALITIS IN MASSACHUSETTS. Science 88 : 305–306.

Equine Infectious Anemia, or Swamp Fever

BY C. D. STEIN [1]

HUMAN BEINGS have their malaria and horses their swamp fever, but the latter is the more difficult to diagnose and treat. The horse disease is widespread, persistent, and debilitating, and the virus has been known to remain active in an animal for many years. The author suggests practical ways to minimize the damage.

INFECTIOUS ANEMIA, or swamp fever, also known in some sections of the United States as malarial fever, slow fever, and mountain fever, is one of the most serious maladies of the horse, and because of its insidious nature and widespread distribution it has become a problem of world-wide concern.

Infectious anemia is an acute or chronic disease of equines, caused by a filtrable virus that poisons the blood and characterized principally by intermittent fever, marked depression, progressive weakness, loss of weight, edema (dropsylike swelling), congestion and icterus (jaundice) of the visible mucous membranes, and anemia of a transitory or progressive type.

Long recognized as a specific infectious disease of equines, infectious anemia was reported from Europe as early as 1843. It occurs in various parts of Europe, Asia, Africa, and North America (9).[2] Recently the disease has been reported from Venezuela, South America. The disease has existed in the United States for at least 50 years, and since 1900 has been authentically reported in isolated areas from 29 States. In 15 of these States the virus was recovered by horse-inoculation tests, while diagnosis in the other 14 States was based on clinical examination. Since 1932, outbreaks of the disease have been

[1] C. D. Stein is Veterinarian, Pathological Division, Bureau of Animal Industry.
[2] Italic numbers in parentheses refer to Literature Cited, p. 401.

reported from Maryland, Massachusetts, Mississippi, New York, Indiana, Illinois, Michigan, Kansas, Wyoming, Montana, Colorado, Oregon, Idaho, Texas, Virginia, Vermont, and Washington. Since 1935 investigators in the Bureau of Animal Industry have isolated the virus from field cases in New York, Maryland, Virginia, Mississippi, Louisiana, Pennsylvania, California, Texas, and Wyoming.

Because of the difficulty of diagnosis, the disease is probably more widespread than the reports indicate. Generally speaking, it is most prevalent in poorly drained, low-lying sections, but it has been found in wooded sections and on marshy pastures at high altitudes. It also appears to be more prevalent when biting insects are most numerous and during wet years. The disease appears in the active form in May or June and reaches its height in midsummer, usually declining late in the fall. Chronic cases may be seen at all seasons of the year, and it is possible to produce the disease experimentally at any time.

Except in the Mississippi Delta, the disease occurs in the United States mostly as a sporadic infection, isolated cases or outbreaks for the most part being reported from and confined to low-lying and wooded sections in the States where it is known to exist. In the Mississippi Delta the disease has become established among the mules on the large cotton plantations and is of considerable economic importance; occurring principally in the chronic form, it saps the strength of the animals and renders them incapable of regular work in the busy cotton-growing season when they are most needed (5).

CAUSE

Studies and observations of the disease made by Bureau of Animal Industry investigators in the field and under experimental conditions indicate that debilitating influences that lower the resistance of an animal, such as overexertion, extreme heat, high humidity, faulty nutrition, improper care and handling, bad sanitation, impure water supply, and a heavy infestation of intestinal parasites, are not only predisposing factors but also have a marked influence on the progress of the disease in infected animals. Gates (5) in 1939, reporting on the disease in Mississippi, made similar observations.

Although the infectious nature of the disease was known as early as 1859, the causative agent was not definitely established until 1904, when Carre and Vallee (2) demonstrated that it was a filtrable virus. This finding was confirmed by the early investigations of the Bureau and has since been repeatedly substantiated.

Under natural conditions the virus appears to be specific for equines (the horse, mule, and donkey). It may persist in the host for years. It is apparently present in the blood and body tissues of affected animals at all times and may be eliminated with some of the secretions or excretions. The disease can be readily transmitted experimentally to equines by inoculation, beneath the skin or into the blood stream, of whole blood, blood serum, or spleen, brain, or other tissue emulsions. Experiments and transmission tests made by the Bureau with strains of virus isolated from widely separated areas indicate that its virulence is exceedingly variable and appears to be influenced by a number of factors. Among these are the individual susceptibility of the host, frequency of passage—that is, transmission of the disease from one animal to another (in series) at short intervals—method of exposure, source of virus, character of the inoculating substance (inoculum), and debilitating factors affecting the host.

The virus shows considerable resistance against disinfectants, heating, freezing, and drying. Definite findings of Bureau investigators concerning the action of heat and chemicals on the virus have been put into practical use in formulating requirements for the treatment of antiserums prepared from horses, thus safeguarding against dissemination of swamp fever through the use of such biological products. Biological supply houses operating under Government license are now required to heat all antiserums prepared from horses at 58° to 59° C. (136.4° to 138.2° F.) for an hour, which destroys any infectious anemia virus they may contain.

DISSEMINATION AND TRANSMISSION

While dissemination of the disease usually follows the introduction of infected animals into noninfected territory, the common method of transmission in the natural state is not definitely known. Ordinarily the disease appears to spread slowly. During the transportation of great numbers of horses, however, outbreaks may occur when infected animals are moved into new territory where conditions are favorable for transmission and for the exposure of large numbers of normal horses.

A number of investigators who have worked on this problem are of the opinion that the disease is spread principally in pastures where the virus-laden urine and feces of infected animals contaminate the feed and water, but the part that biting insects may play under these conditions cannot be ignored.

Experimental evidence indicates: (1) That the disease is readily transmitted by the injection of blood or tissue emulsions from affected animals into susceptible ones; (2) that minute doses of the virus are infective for susceptible animals; (3) that the body secretions or excretions may contain the virus; (4) that infected mares may transmit the disease to their offspring; (5) that the disease may be transmitted by external parasites, including biting flies and biting lice; (6) that it may spread slowly by long, continuous, intimate contact; and (7) that carriers probably constitute one of the most common sources of the virus in nature and are chiefly concerned in the perpetuation of the disease. In adopting control measures, these factors should all be taken into consideration.

Infectious anemia has been reported in man in a few instances, but it is probable that man is not very susceptible to the disease. Verge (*10*) in 1933 reported the occurrence of two cases in human beings, those of Luhrs in 1920 and Peters in 1924. In the experiments conducted by the Bureau, equines only were found to be susceptible. Attempts to infect calves, sheep, swine, dogs, rabbits, guinea pigs, rats, mice. and pigeons were without success. Similar results have been obtained by various workers (*4*)   Some investigators in foreign countries, however, have reported that a few other species, including young goats, pigs, rabbits, rats, chickens, and doves, can be infected under experimental conditions.

Mules appear to be somewhat more resistant than horses, acquiring the disease mostly in the chronic form.   Balozet (*1*), in 1933, reported from Tunis, North Africa, that the African ass was as susceptible to the virus of infectious anemia as the horse but that the symptoms were more apparent in the horse.   DeKock (*3*) reported a natural outbreak of infectious anemia in donkeys in Natal, South Africa, that assumed a rather virulent character.

FORMS OF THE DISEASE, SYMPTOMS, AND TERMINATION

The clinical symptoms are variable and depend to a great extent on the form the disease assumes.   Infectious anemia may occur as an acute, rapidly fatal disease or, more commonly, as a chronic affection characterized by intermittent attacks of fever, loss of weight, progressive weakness, marked depression, and dropsical swellings on the lower portions of the body and on the legs.   The disease may also exist in a form in which no clinical symptoms are apparent though the affected animal carries virulent virus in the blood stream.

In the acute form of the disease the incubation period following subcutaneous injection (beneath the skin) of infected blood is usually about 12 to 15 days, though it may vary from less than a week to 3 months and possibly longer.   The onset is sudden and is manifested by a rise in temperature, which usually goes to about 105° F. but may reach 108°.   In the acute form the febrile attacks are usually severe and may be more or less continuous or very frequent.   In this connection it should be mentioned that the irregular recurrent fever is one of the chief clinical manifestations of the disease, and in mild cases it sometimes constitutes the only symptom.   Respiration is accelerated and frequently is of the abdominal type.   The animal is dejected, the head hangs low, leg weakness is marked, the body weight is shifted from one leg to another, and the hind feet are frequently placed well forward under the body.   The membranes of the eyes show congestion, followed by brownish to yellowish discoloration.   Feed is refused.   There may be a slight watery discharge from the eyes and nose and, if the weather is extremely warm, profuse sweating.   Frequent urination may also be noted, and in severe cases diarrhea may develop.   The attack usually lasts from 3 to 5 days, after which the temperature returns to normal and the animal appears to be well except for a marked loss of weight.   Occasionally, however, the initial attack may persist until the animal dies.

Dropsical swellings of the sheath, the legs, the chest, and the under surfaces of the body may occur at any time.   These frequently disappear and appear again at the same or other places.   Subsequent attacks usually follow, with intervening periods of normality varying from a few days to many weeks or months.   When the intervals between the attacks of fever are short, the animal seldom lives more than 15 to 30 days. During the attacks of fever and immediately afterward, there is a reduction in the number of red corpuscles in the blood. When this is pronounced, it can be readily demonstrated by drawing some blood into a test tube in the bottom of which a small amount of powdered potassium oxalate or other anticoagulant has been placed to prevent clotting. During the bleeding process the tube should be agitated gently to mix the blood with the anticoagulant. The tube containing the blood sample should be placed in an upright position to permit the red corpuscles to gravitate to the bottom, and after half an hour a comparison of the sedimented red corpuscles with a sample similarly drawn from a normal horse will clearly demonstrate the degree of anemia that exists. During the periods of normality between attacks, the red-corpuscle count is in a great majority of cases normal.

The subacute and chronic forms of the disease differ from the acute in that the attacks are less severe and the intervals between them are longer. The subacute cases may terminate in death during or following one of the attacks, or the reactions may grow less frequent, the animal finally developing into a chronic case or a clinically recovered carrier. In general, the chronic form is manifested by unthriftiness, rough coat, underweight; sluggishness, weakness, dropsical swellings of the lower parts of the body or on the legs, muddy discoloration of the visible mucous membranes, and small hemorrhages on the nictitating membrane (the third eyelid, or haw) and the nasal septum (the partition between the passages of the nose).

As the disease progresses, evidence of anemia may develop, the red-corpuscle count may be extremely low, the blood may appear thin and watery, and in the later stages the visible mucous membranes may become pallid. The pulse may be slow and weak, the heart action may become irregular, and a jugular pulse may be visible. There may be a rapid slowing of the pulse after exercise. Muscular weakness is manifested by a wobbly or rolling staggering gait or by partial paralysis of the hindquarters. In the chronic form of the disease the appetite is for the most part unimpaired and frequently is ravenous, so that the animals may eat continuously if they have access to feed. In spite of the excessive consumption of feed, however, there is a progressive loss of body weight (fig. 1).

Animals affected with this form of the disease can perform some work if handled with care. They are subject, however, to recurring attacks characterized by extreme weakness, knuckling, inability to walk in a straight line, and prominent hemorrhages on the third eyelid. The weakness may become so great that the animal cannot stand without support. With good attention, rest, and supportive treatment, it usually overcomes these periodic attacks and may go back to routine work. Each attack takes its toll of flesh and strength, however, and repetitions, if frequent enough, will so weaken the animal as to render it useless or finally bring about death by exhaustion.

The inactive or latent form of the disease may follow the initial attack, but it is usually preceded by several attacks of fever. This form is observed in animals that have apparently recovered from the acute, subacute, or chronic types of the disease. Animals affected with the disease in the latent form show no clinical symptoms and are known as clinically recovered carriers. The temperature remains normal, and there is no reduction in the red corpuscles or any sign of disease over a period of years, and yet the infectious agent is always present in the blood stream and all the tissues and may be eliminated with the body excretions. Such animals obviously are a menace to other horses that may be near them, since they are veritable reservoirs of infection that for the most part go

FIGURE 1.—The poor condition of this horse is the result of infectious anemia in the chronic form.

unrecognized and uncontrolled. The inactive form of the disease may, however, become active at any time and present all the characteristics of the acute or subacute form. Unusually hard work or any debilitating influence may reactivate the infection.

The Bureau of Animal Industry has under observation a horse that is a good example of the inactive form of infectious anemia. This horse was exposed to the disease August 2, 1935, by being given an injection of filtered blood from two horses known to have infectious anemia. After an incubation period of 12 days, a typical attack of fever occurred, which in turn was followed by two more attacks within a 3-week period. No further attacks occurred over a period of approximately 5 years. During this time the animal remained in good physical condition and showed no symptoms of

disease whatever; yet blood drawn from it at intervals during the
5 years produced infectious anemia when injected into normal horses.
A horse with a similar history that has been infected for approximately 6 years is also being held under observation; although this
animal has shown no clinical symptoms for more than 6 years its blood
remains infectious.

Schalk and Roderick (*7*), of the North Dakota Agricultural Experiment Station, and Scott (*8*), of the Wyoming station, have reported inactive cases that were infectious over even longer periods.

Heath (*6*) in 1931, reporting on transmission experiments carried
on apparently during 1930, presented evidence to show that blood
from an immune carrier (a mare originally infected in 1912), when
injected intravenously into normal horses, produced infectious
anemia in the subacute form.

ANATOMICAL CHANGES

The pathological alterations in the body tissues resulting from artificially
induced infectious anemia are extremely variable. The changes may be very
well marked and plainly visible (in some cases so pronounced as to be striking), or they may be so slight as to escape detection except by those having
considerable experience with the disease. The lesions, which may occur in any
degree of intensity or in any combination, are most commonly observed in
acute and subacute cases and in chronic cases dying during an acute flare-up.

The most constant lesions of swamp fever are hemorrhages of varying sizes
on the serous and mucous membranes of the body, with enlargement and other
changes of the spleen, kidneys, liver, and heart. The hemorrhages are most
frequently found on the parietal and visceral pleura, the pericardium, epicardium,
and endocardium, the parietal and visceral peritoneum, the mucosa of the small
and large intestines, the mucosa of the caecum, and the surface of the spleen
and kidneys.

The spleen for the most part is enlarged. Occasionally it will be found to be
approximately three times its normal size, and the splenic pulp will be soft and
blackish red in color. The liver is frequently enlarged to enormous proportions
and is hard and friable. It may vary from a yellowish-brown, cooked appearance
to a reddish brown. Frequently there is pigmentation of a yellowish-brown or
greenish-gray tinge. In cross section the lobules stand out quite prominently,
presenting a nutmeglike appearance. The kidneys are frequently enlarged, edematous, and lighter in color than normal, and they show numerous hemorrhages
on the surface ranging from the size of a pin point to several millimeters in
diameter. The heart may be enlarged, flabby, and lighter in color than normal,
or it may have a cooked appearance, and it shows hemorrhages over the epicardium, in the myocardium, and on the endocardium. The heart fat frequently
loses its normal consistency and color and becomes soft and gelatinous. The
visceral lymph glands are usually enlarged and edematous and may be impreg-
nated with hemorrhages. Large areas of hemorrhages are found in the marrow
of the long bones, especially of the femur. Yellowish discoloration of the connective tissues and fat may also be evident. As stated before, the lesions are quite
variable.

In those subacute or chronic cases showing clinical manifestations of a progressive anemia, the autopsy may also show pale mucous membranes and light-
colored, thin, watery blood.

For the most part the tissue changes found in the acute and subacute cases are
more extensive and more pronounced than those in the chronic cases. In chronic
cases terminating in death from exhaustion following a protracted illness, lesions
indicative of cachexia (general ill health) are usually observed, such as emaciation, gelatinous infiltration of connective tissue and fat tissue, especially the
fat tissue of the heart, and a blanched appearance of mucous membranes. In
such cases the hemorrhagic infiltration of tissues and degenerative changes of
the organs may be very slight or entirely absent.

In latent cases (symptomless carriers) and chronic cases of a mild type little or no anatomical alteration is observed on autopsy. The most constant and characteristic histopathological findings are round-cell infiltration and a heavy deposition of hemosiderin in the liver and spleen. The post mortem histological findings are of considerable assistance in making a tentative diagnosis.

DIAGNOSIS

Diagnosis of infectious anemia is usually a difficult matter, since there are no symptoms or post mortem changes that can be considered characteristic or peculiar to this disease alone. The only definite means of diagnosis is by horse-inoculation test. Considering collectively the history of the case, clinical symptoms, and blood examinations, diagnosis with a reasonable degree of accuracy can possibly be made in the active form of the disease. For example, a history of rapid loss of flesh, loss of spirit and energy, evidences of muscular weakness with intermittent attacks of fever, congestion of the mucous membranes of the eye, with possibly some degree of jaundice, and dropsical swellings of the lower parts of the body, collectively, are strongly suggestive of infectious anemia. The tentative diagnosis will be further strengthened if during and immediately after the febrile period an examination of the blood shows a diminution in the volume of the red corpuscles, an increase in the rate at which they gravitate, and a decrease of hemoglobin. It must be remembered, however, that in the intervals between the attacks of fever the blood picture, except in cases accompanied by a progressive anemia, usually returns to normal.

Infectious anemia in the inactive form would ordinarily not be detected, since no clinical symptoms would be present to cause suspicion. It should be remembered also that heavy infestation with intestinal parasites, especially strongyles, produces symptoms that are in some respects similar to those of infectious anemia. Microscopic examinations of the feces for the eggs of these parasites and examination of blood films for evidence of eosinophilia (an increase in the number of certain white blood corpuscles) will assist in making a differential diagnosis. It is possible, and in some areas probable, that some horses and mules will be heavily infested with intestinal parasites and at the same time have chronic infectious anemia.

In acute cases occurring in the field, death may occur before the usual train of symptoms develops. The disease in the acute form may be confused with anthrax, influenza, purpura hemorrhagica, acute equine encephalomyelitis, and other acute febrile conditions. In the subacute and chronic forms it may be mistaken for trypanosomiasis (dourine, murrina, and surra) or strongylidosis.

Since the development of practical and reliable means of diagnosis is of primary importance from the standpoint of control, a considerable amount of experimental work on diagnostic procedures has been carried out by the Bureau of Animal Industry. No laboratory blood test was found sufficiently satisfactory to warrant its adoption as a standard diagnostic method, and antigens prepared from the blood, tissues, and urine of affected animals failed to produce a specific response of diagnostic value.

TREATMENT AND CONTROL

Many investigators have unsuccessfully tried to treat the disease with various agents such as arsenic preparations, quinine, various dyes, mercurial preparations, and a number of others. In sections where the disease is endemic, or constantly present, practicing veterinarians employ supportive treatment, using arsenical compounds, principally sodium cacodylate, together with tonics, rest, and abundance of good feed, at the same time eliminating intestinal parasites and other debilitating factors. While such treatment brings about some clinical improvement, it has no lasting value, for the animal remains infected, is subject to febrile attacks, and is a virus carrier. To establish a complete cure, a method of treatment must be found that will not only free the animal of clinical symptoms but completely eliminate the virus from the tissues.

The control of this disease, because of its obscure nature, the difficulty of diagnosis, its resistance to treatment, and its widespread distribution, presents a problem of serious concern to all owners of horses and mules, especially those with a large number of animals.

Preventive vaccination has been attempted without success by a number of investigators, including those in the Bureau of Animal Industry.

The control of infectious anemia depends primarily on the identification of the chronic carriers. While no systematic program can be undertaken until a definite and practical means of diagnosis of chronic carriers is developed, the results of studies by Bureau and other investigators indicate that the following measures constitute the most effective means of control.

When a definite diagnosis of infectious anemia has been made, it is advisable, if practicable, to kill the animal and dispose of the carcass by cremation or deep burial to prevent further spread of the infection. This method of control has been followed in small isolated outbreaks and in establishments keeping large numbers of horses, and it has been effective in preventing the spread of the disease. It is obvious, however, that the method is impracticable in such areas as the Mississippi Delta, where the disease is widely distributed and exists principally in a mild chronic form.

Animals known to be infected and those suspected of having the disease should be isolated from healthy animals.

The common use of equipment that may produce skin abrasions or absorb body excretions or secretions, such as bridles, harness, saddles, blankets, brushes, and currycombs, on both infected and healthy horses is dangerous and should be avoided.

The greatest care should always be used to prevent transmission of the disease from animal to animal by the use of unsterilized instruments, bleeding needles, or hypodermic needles.

Since infected mares may transmit the disease to their offspring, such animals should not be used for breeding purposes.

Infected and healthy animals should not be kept together in small, poorly drained paddocks adjacent to stables and manure dumps.

Where premises are badly contaminated, or a number of cases of the disease have developed on certain pastures, it is advisable to move the animals to new quarters, deeply plow the ground, and fence off the infected areas. Horses or mules should not be permitted on such pastures or premises for at least 6 months.

The maintenance of good sanitary conditions, fly control, systematic control of intestinal parasites, and provision for a supply of pure, fresh drinking water should also receive attention, and under no circumstances should animals be permitted to drink from stagnant pools.

LITERATURE CITED

(1) BALOZET, L.
    1935. SENSIBILITÉ DE L'ANE AFRICAN A L'INOCULATION DU VIRUS DE L'ANÉMIE
        INFECTIEUSE. Soc. de Biol. [Paris] Compt. Rend. 119: 62–65.
(2) CARRÉ, [H. J.], and VALLÉE. [H. P.]
    1904. SUR L'ANÉMIE INFECTIEUSE DU CHEVAL. Acad. des Sci. [Paris] Compt.
        Rend. 139: 1239–1241.
(3) DEKOCK, G. v. D. W.
    1924. A CONTRIBUTION TO THE STUDY OF THE VIRUS, HAEMATOLOGY AND
        PATHOLOGY OF INFECTIOUS ANAEMIA OF EQUINES UNDER SOUTH AFRI-
        CAN CONDITIONS. Union of So. Africa Dept. Agr. Rpts. 9 and 10
        of the Dir. of Vet. Ed. and Res.. 1923. pp. [253]–313, illus.
(4) FRANCIS, M., and MARSTELLER, R. P.
    1908. INFECTIOUS ANEMIA OF THE HORSE. Tex. Agr. Expt. Sta. Bul. 119,
        19 pp., illus.
(5) GATES, WILLIAM L.
    1940. EQUINE INFECTIOUS ANEMIA (SWAMP FEVER). Amer. Vet. Med.
        Assoc. Jour. 96: 195–199.
(6) HEATH, L. M.
    1931. RESEARCH ON SWAMP FEVER OR INFECTIOUS EQUINE ANAEMIA. Canada
        Dept. Agr. Rpt. Vet. Dir. Gen. (1931), App. 4, Path. Div. Rpt.,
        pp. 70–71.
(7) SCHALK, A. F., and RODERICK, L. M.
    1923. HISTORY OF A "SWAMP FEVER" VIRUS CARRIER. N. Dak. Agr. Expt.
        Sta. Bul. 168, 14 pp., illus.
(8) SCOTT, J. W.
    1931. SWAMP FEVER IN HORSES. Wyo. Agr. Expt. Sta. Ann. Rpt. (1930-31)
        41: 38.
(9) TORRANCE, F.
    1902. REPORT ON "SWAMP FEVER" IN HORSES. Canada Min. of Agr. Ann.
        Rpt. 1901-2, p. 135.
(10) VERGE, J.
    1933. L'ANÉMIE INFECTIEUSE DES EQUIDÉS. MALADIE DE VALLÉE. Rec. de
        Méd. Vét. 109: [797]–838, illus.

Periodic Ophthalmia of Horses

BY L. O. MOTT AND H. R. SEIBOLD [1]

SOME EXPERTS estimate that 1 out of every 10 horses and mules in the United States is affected with moon blindness—a recurrent inflammation of the eyes that may end in loss of sight. It has been known for over 2,000 years, but no one yet knows the cause, or how to prevent or cure it. Here is the most recent scientific information about the disease and advice on treatment.

PERIODIC OPHTHALMIA, or moon blindness is a disease of the eye affecting horses, mules, and asses only. Its history dates back more than 2,000 years. The disease was studied in the earliest days of veterinary medicine. Vegetius wrote about it in the fourth century. During the early parts of the eighteenth century several famous veterinarians described the disease and recorded interesting facts about it. Research on a scientific basis, started as early as the latter part of the same century, has been continued up to the present time.

DISTRIBUTION

Available literature records the presence of periodic ophthalmia in England, Germany, France, Italy, South Africa, the Philippine Islands, Central America, and North America. The geographical distribution is probably much more widespread, however, than the literature indicates, because the disease does not cause the death of animals and therefore in most countries is not listed as one of the reportable diseases. Difficulty in diagnosing the disease, together with lack of more complete knowledge regarding its cause, preven-

[1] L. O. Mott and H. R. Seibold are Assistant Veterinarians, Pathological Division, Bureau of Animal Industry.

402

tion, and treatment has given horse owners a somewhat hopeless outlook regarding it. While it continues to exist, it is seldom reported, and its true economic importance is unknown and probably underestimated.

In England it is reported that previous to 1880 the disease was very prevalent but that it has almost disappeared following the establishment of the Royal Commission on the Horse Breeding Industry, which brought about the condemnation for breeding purposes of all sires exhibited at shows if they had the slightest eye abnormality or any other ailment. This is achieved by rigid veterinary inspection.

Germany, France, and Italy have had the disease in a severe epizootic form. In those countries it appeared to be very closely associated with a low altitude. This point was especially noted in the German army during the transferring of horses. The number of horses with diseased eyes decreased or increased according to the altitude of the locality where the horses were stationed. Early cases often remained stationary or apparently recovered following the move to an unaffected area.

In France also the absence of the condition in areas of high altitude was noted, and some extensive experiments with normal young colts were carried out. Some animals from the high altitude were moved to different low altitudes, and animals from low altitudes were moved to high altitudes, with groups of native colts at each altitude retained as control animals. About 50 percent of the animals in the low altitudes became affected, both in the retained and the moved groups, whereas the disease did not appear in the groups at the high altitudes.

During the Boer War, Great Britain purchased a large number of horses and mules from the United States and transported them to South Africa. Within 2 years following the war, 14 percent of these animals had developed periodic ophthalmia. In certain remount stations the incidence of the disease was as high as 48 percent; at the same time a lower percentage of the native animals were affected. The condition had not previously existed in South Africa. Later it gradually disappeared, so that now this region is free of the disease and has been for 30 years.

Panama, which is now reported to have about the same amount of the disease as the United States, until the last 8 years was relatively free of it. It does not exist in Hawaii, but in the Philippine Islands it appears to be almost four times as prevalent as in continental United States.

The disease has been reported to be of little economic importance in Canada.

The disease seems to occur seldom in the western part of the United States. From reports of various surveys made, a line drawn through the middle of the Dakotas, Nebraska, Kansas, Oklahoma, and Texas would about determine its western limit. Almost all of the States east of this line have the disease, and it affects animals at both high and low altitudes.

PREVALENCE

It is rather difficult to estimate the incidence of the disease or the annual economic loss it causes in the United States, but both are undoubtedly very large. Some investigators have estimated that as many as 10 percent of the horses and mules in this country are affected. Limited field investigations conducted by the Bureau of Animal Industry indicate that the incidence of the disease in some of the Middle Atlantic States is much higher than was generally supposed. The rate of incidence in different areas covered varied from 0 to as high as 30 percent. The variation on farms in different areas appears to be closely correlated with the concentration of animals, a higher percentage of affected animals being found on highly productive soils and good farms where more horses and mules are used than on the scattered farms with poor soil, where the percentage of affected animals almost always dropped very noticeably.

A very conservative estimate would set the monetary loss at least at half a million dollars annually.

THEORIES ABOUT THE CAUSE

The cause of periodic ophthalmia is unknown, but theories about it are numerous. Among other superstitions is the idea that wolf teeth are responsible, and to this day many wolf teeth are extracted to satisfy owners who still hold to this idea. Many horsemen discriminate against the use of blind stallions on the ground that the condition itself, or more likely a weakness or predisposition to the disease, is inherited. One investigator cites a stallion 90 to 95 percent of whose offspring contracted the disease, most of them becoming affected at between 3 and 8 years of age. Other investigators have reported that the condition affects one generation and then misses one or more generations before appearing again. Data accumulated by the Bureau of Animal Industry on a recent field survey indicate the possibility of hereditary susceptibility to the disease.

The association of the disease with low altitudes in foreign countries and its absence in the western part of the United States suggest some correlation with environment. However, comparison of accumulated data from farms free of the disease with similar data from farms where it developed, all within an affected area covered by the Bureau of Animal Industry's survey, showed no correlation with environment. This is slight evidence, however, because the farms free of the disease and those on which it existed were both in the same area.

The possibility that nutritional deficiencies, glandular disturbances, or parasites are directly or indirectly responsible for the disease cannot be overlooked in future investigations.

The infection theory has been investigated by many noted scientists who have worked on the disease. Several research workers have produced a disease that resembled periodic ophthalmia by inoculations within the eye, but they failed to secure a recurrence of attacks. In one instance the disease was reported to have been transmitted from animal to animal by the use of germ-free filtrates made from the eyes of active cases. Such findings would point to a filtrable virus as the causative factor, but the work has not been confirmed.

As observed in field investigations carried on by the Bureau of Animal Industry, the disease has all the appearances of an infectious one. It usually appears sporadically within a community or area, sometimes affecting only a few farms and sometimes farms in several counties, but most often affecting from 5 to 30 percent of the animals within a year or two of the same date. Very often following this sporadic appearance of the disease, it will subside and no new cases will develop for years even when blind animals continue to live on the farms. If the condition again occurs, it almost always does so sporadically. On some farms the disease appears to be more persistent, affecting new animals year after year. These cases are relatively uncommon, but they make the picture still more confused.

The fact that the attacks are accompanied by mild fever, localized severe inflammation followed by abatement of acute symptoms, atrophy, and degeneration of the eyeball, together with the field observations mentioned, makes the infection theory seem plausible.

LESIONS AND ANATOMICAL CHANGES

Clinically, the condition is primarily a disease of the eyes. Various authors have suggested the presence of other clinical symptoms and post mortem findings associated with it, but these have not as yet been generally accepted. It is characterized by a recurring inflammation which may affect one eye alone, or both eyes either simultaneously or alternately, or one eye until blindness occurs and then the other eye. The onset of the attack is sudden, usually being noticed first in the morning, the animal having appeared normal the night before. The eyelids are swollen and tender, and the eye is kept closed. A watery discharge runs from the eyes. There is some rise of body temperature, accompanied by other evidences of a generalized disturbance. After a week or 10 days the inflammation subsides, and the eye or eyes either may appear to be little affected or may be chalk white and completely blind. The interval between attacks may vary from a few weeks to several months, and the number of attacks may vary from 1 to 10 or 20, occurring over a period of years.

Blindness following early attacks is usually due to adhesions of the iris to the lens. If these adhesions break down before they are attached too firmly, the lens will usually clear. Following the earlier attacks, an examination of the eye with an ophthalmoscope (an instrument for viewing the interior of the eye) will reveal only a partial opacity or opaque spots on the lens and sometimes a totally cleared lens with practically normal vision.

The cornea or outside surface of the eye is usually cloudy (blue white) during an attack but almost always clears in a few days and usually remains clear even after the animal is totally blind, the chalk-white appearance of the blind eye being due to an opacity of the lens.

The fluid within the eye also presents a cloudy appearance during an attack. Following an attack, this fluid will sometimes slowly clear, often presenting a hazy appearance for weeks following. Frequently an agglutination or clumping of cells within the eye fluid takes place, which looks like sediment or strings floating around whenever disturbed by movement of the head.

The optic disk and retina are less often available for examination in most affected eyes because of other opaque structures in front of them, but in cases where vision is clear or partly clear very little if any change is noticeable.

DIAGNOSIS

The diagnosis of periodic ophthalmia is very difficult, since the cause of the condition is unknown and no laboratory test or testing agent has been made available for diagnostic purposes. Ophthalmoscopic examination for the presence of cataracts, spots on the lens, and any other opacity or cloudiness is the best available method for recognizing an affected animal when little is known about the animal's source or past history. Where the animal's history is complete, a positive diagnosis is much more easily arrived at because of the characteristic attacks and the sporadic appearance of the condition in other animals within the community or the same stable.

A technical description of microscopic changes due to the disease is given at the end of this article. This is based on recent work in the Bureau of Animal Industry.

SUSCEPTIBILITY

There is little variation in the degree of susceptibility of animals of different types, breeds, or sex. Mules are reported to be less susceptible than horses, and the condition has been observed in asses. There is, however, a noticeable age factor. Most horses are 3 or 4 years old or older before they become affected, and the disease not uncommonly develops in horses between 15 and 20 years of age. A few cases develop in 2-year-olds, fewer in yearlings. Very few cases are recorded in sucklings between 6 months and 1 year old, and so far as is known there are no authentic cases recorded in newborn foals or those under 6 months of age.

It has been observed that no young animals under 3 years of age have ever been affected except where the disease made its appearance in a severe epizootic form, affecting several older animals before the young became affected.

PREVENTION AND CONTROL

No preventive or curative measures have been discovered. Prompt attention to the attacks as they occur by a competent veterinarian may materially prolong the sight in the affected eye or eyes. Treatment consists of application of cold compresses to the eye; administration of drugs to dilate the pupil, followed by drugs to contract the pupil, in order to prevent adhesions of the iris to the cornea or to the crystalline lens; and mild laxatives to decrease the pressure within the eyeball indirectly. The animal should be at complete rest in a partly darkened stable.

Intravenous injections of foreign proteins, such as sterile milk and typhoid vaccine, and other products, including some of the salts of arsenic, mercury, and iodine, when used in the early stages of the disease often shorten the period of an attack and help to prolong the sight.

Horsemen and breeders who hope to ward off this disease from their animals could practice no more sound control, considering the present lack of knowledge of its infectiousness and inheritance, than to keep their animals isolated from any possible direct or indirect contact with affected animals and discourage the breeding of affected animals.

HISTOPATHOLOGY—TECHNICAL DESCRIPTION

Although numerous clinical and bacteriological investigations of periodic ophthalmia have been made in the past, histopathological (microscopic) study of this disease has been undertaken only recently. This has been due in part to the technical difficulties encountered in the microscopic examination of diseased equine eyes.

The microscopic lesions of periodic ophthalmia consist of inflammatory and degenerative changes that progress with the course of the disease. The early stages are characterized by iridocyclitis, or inflammation of the ciliary body and iris. The blood vessels of the ciliary body and iris become congested, and large numbers of lymphocytes and plasma cells are found in the connective tissue stroma of these structures. The nonpigmented ciliary epithelium that covers the ciliary processes exhibits marked changes. These epithelial cells become taller than normal. Brushlike bundles of coarse fibrillar structures that stain red with eosin appear within the confines of this layer of cells. These fibrillar structures extend in a direction parallel with the nuclei of the cells and can best be demonstrated with differential staining techniques. Large numbers of lymphoid cells infiltrate between the individual cells of the nonpigmented ciliary epithelium. The general impression gained from these lesions is that the nonpigmented ciliary epithelium is the structure most seriously affected by the unknown agent of periodic ophthalmia at the onset of the disease.

In conjunction with the inflammatory lesions in the ciliary body and iris, the vitreous body and the aqueous humor exhibit changes in character. This is evidenced by the fact that both the aqueous humor and the vitreous body often coagulate after the eye has been placed in formalin instead of remaining watery in consistency. This change may be due to injury of the nonpigmented ciliary epithelium, which is thought to secrete a part of the fluid that occupies the spaces of the eyeball. Large numbers of lymphocytes and plasma cells are found in the vitreous body and aqueous humor and in the spaces between the fibers of the suspensory ligament of the lens (canals of Petit).

As a result of these inflammatory changes, the iris often becomes cemented to the lens (posterior synechia) or to the posterior surface of the cornea (anterior synechia), causing the "fixed pupil" so often encountered on clinical examination. This places the iris under considerable tension, frequently resulting in mechanical injury to the iris when the muscle fibers in this organ contract. Where anterior synechia has occurred, it is not uncommon to find evidence of mechanical injury at the posterior surface of the cornea, namely, rupture of Descemet's membrane and desquamation of the posterior endothelium.

As the disease progresses, the inflammation of the ciliary body becomes less acute. The coarse red fibrils in the nonpigmented ciliary epithelial layer become less numerous, but the cells do not return to their normal state. They may proliferate and assume an irregular arrangement. In some cases they swell to several times their normal size and assume a fine granular appearance. In many cases the ciliary body becomes covered with a fibrocellular inflammatory membrane (cyclitic membrane). This membrane may envelop the posterior surface of the lens and extend across the entire diameter of the eye. A similar membrane may form anterior to the lens (pupillary membrane).

The lens becomes involved as the disease progresses. The lens fibers degenerate, and the epithelium of the lens proliferates, forming a complicated, capsulolenticular cataract. This type of cataract cannot be treated successfully by surgical methods. In many advanced cases the lens has undergone complete liquefaction, and only the capsule can be found on microscopic examination. The lens frequently becomes dislocated owing to injury to its suspensory ligament and to the nonpigmented ciliary epithelium to which this ligament is attached.

Changes in the retina occur simultaneously with changes in the lens. The retina may become completely or partially detached from the choroid coat, or it may remain in place. Regardless of its position, it degenerates. The rods, cones (neuroepithelial elements), and ganglion cells disappear, but the supporting cells (glia cells) persist and may proliferate. Where the retina has become detached, it usually moves forward in the eye and comes to rest just behind the lens. In these cases it may unite with the inflammatory membrane arising from the ciliary body and eventually form a wide band of fibrocellular tissue extending across the diameter of the eye.

As the retina degenerates, the optic nerve degenerates. In advanced chronic cases, nerve fibers cannot be demonstrated in the optic nerve. The funiculi of the nerve appear to be composed of masses of supporting neuroglia tissue (replacement gliosis). The optic nerve head and the nerve fiber layer of the retina are often infiltrated with lymphocytes and plasma cells.

The choroid coat may be congested and to some extent infiltrated with lymphocytes and plasma cells. In advanced cases the choroid appears thickened, perhaps as a result of shrinking of the eyeball.

Lesions of a minor character are found in the cornea. Small capillary blood vessels are often found in the proper substance of the cornea, particularly in the latter stages of the disease. The proper substance of the cornea usually contains an increased number of cellular elements just posterior to the corneal epithelium. The cellular elements consist of an increased number of corneal corpuscles, along with a varying number of polymorphonuclear leucocytes. In some advanced chronic cases the proper substance of the cornea appears thinner than normal.

Shrinking of the eyeball (phthisis bulbi) is a constant lesion of periodic ophthalmia. This is caused by a decreased tension of the ocular fluids, possibly a result of deranged function of the nonpigmented ciliary epithelium. As the disease progresses, this shrinking and distortion of the eyeball is aggravated by contraction of the fibrocellular inflammatory membranes that so often form. In such cases the eyeball becomes greatly reduced in size, and the fundus may become completely filled with newly formed fibrocellular tissue.

Although the inflammatory lesions are most pronounced at the onset of the disease, the degenerative changes are of particular significance. The latter appear to be most pronounced in the epithelial structures of the eye, namely, the nonpigmented epithelium of the ciliary body, the lens, and the neuroepithelial elements of the retina.

Glanders

BY T. W. COLE [1]

DURING the war of 1914–18, the French Army lost enormous numbers of horses because of glanders. This is one of the serious diseases that has been practically eliminated in the United States. The job now is to see that it stays out of our country.

GLANDERS is a serious constitutional disease of equines (horses, asses, and mules) and occasionally of other animals and man. Formerly widespread in the United States, it has been virtually eradicated within the memory of the present generation. Fortunately most other farm animals, including cattle, sheep, goats, and swine, are for all practical purposes immune and require no special consideration in the control and eradication of this highly infectious malady. The disease is caused by a specific micro-organism called *Bacillus mallei* and is usually manifested by nodular lesions of the lungs and to a lesser degree of other organs, as well as by ulcerative lesions of the skin and the mucous membranes of the nasal cavity and respiratory passage. The term "farcy" is at times applied to the form of glanders in which the skin lesions are the more pronounced.

HISTORY

Few if any diseases have a more ancient recorded history. Glanders was recognized by Hippocrates about 450 B. C. and described with considerable accuracy by Apsyrtus, a Greek veterinarian of the time of Constantine the Great, who knew of its contagious character centuries before the microscope was invented. Down through history, war, with its concentration of horse stock, has been responsible for the greatest devastation by glanders. From time to time the Armies of Great Britain and the countries of continental Europe have suffered tremendous losses from the scourge. During the World War 1914–18, in the French Army alone over 58,000 animals

[1] T. W. Cole is Senior Veterinarian and Assistant Chief of the Field Inspection Division, Bureau of Animal Industry.

were officially declared glanderous. Many of these were slaughtered and used for food, but the loss of work stock was enormous.

According to the best information available, the disease was imported into the United States at the close of the eighteenth century and spread with great rapidity as the pioneers moved westward. There have been severe outbreaks at various times among the horses and mules of the United States Army, and the Army was charged with introducing the infection into Mexico during the Mexican War. Before the disease was brought under control by improved sanitary measures and reliable diagnostic tests at the beginning of the present century, any concentration of horses and mules, particularly in the larger cities, was a fertile field for glanders.

At the present time the occurrence of glanders in the United States is almost negligible. For this reason the precautions being taken by the Department of Agriculture to guard against its reintroduction from abroad through careful supervision, including veterinary inspection at designated ports of entry of all importations of susceptible animals, are of great importance, though this is probably not fully appreciated except by those closely connected with the importation of equines.

SYMPTOMS AND LESIONS

The period of incubation, or the time elapsing between the exposure to infection and the appearance of recognized symptoms, may vary from a few days to several months, but under natural conditions it averages about 2 weeks. The disease assumes either an acute or a chronic form. Asses and mules, as a general rule, manifest the acute symptoms, which progress rapidly, whereas horses almost invariably have the chronic or slowly developing type.

For convenient description the principal symptoms and lesions of typical cases may be classified as nasal, pulmonary, and cutaneous. It should be understood, however, that these forms may occur simultaneously.

Nasal form. The first symptom likely to be noticed is a nasal mucous discharge in one or, more rarely, both nostrils, which later becomes copious and purulent (full of pus). Examination of the mucous membrane of the nasal cavity in the early stages should disclose numerous nodules, ranging from the size of bird shot to that of a pea, which are red and quite firm to the touch. These soon break down into ragged-edged ulcers which pour forth a viscous, sticky material, yellowish in color except for an occasional trace of blood. This condition is often present on the membranous covering of the larynx and trachea. When healing takes place the ulcers are replaced by characteristic radiating or star-shaped scar tissue. These symptoms are associated with enlargement of the submaxillary glands under the lower jaw toward the throat, which become indurated, or hardened, as in the acute form of strangles. The condition differs from strangles in that the glands rarely abscess and erupt.

Pulmonary form. The most constant seat of glanderous lesions is the lungs. Seldom if ever are these organs wholly sound when there

is clinical evidence of the disease elsewhere in the body. Attention may be attracted first to the animal's loss of condition and lack of endurance when worked and the sudden bleeding of the nose from destructive pulmonary processes. Painful spasmodic coughing and the resultant dislodgment of a thick mucus discharge from the nostrils very definitely point to lung involvement. In the early stages of typical cases, firm nodules ranging from the size of a small pea to that of a hen's egg may be found embedded in otherwise healthy-appearing lung tissue. At first dark red and slightly translucent, these nodules gradually take on a whitish, opaque appearance. As the disease progresses the affected lung tissue becomes dark red owing to the presence of excess blood, and in later stages areas containing caseous, or cheeselike, masses are in evidence. The lymph glands of the thoracic (chest) cavity become enlarged and develop nodular lesions similar to those occurring in the lungs.

Cutaneous form. The development of nodules and ulcers in the skin and subcutaneous tissue is a common occurrence in glanders. This is the form which is often referred to as farcy. In the skin proper the nodules, which are about the size of a pea, soon break down to form ulcers. The deeper lying indurated nodules of the subcutaneous tissue (beneath the skin), usually on the limbs, chest, and lower abdomen, may reach the size of a walnut. These also disintegrate into ulcers, which are much deeper than those in the skin and exude a purulent material streaked with blood. Upon healing, the ulcers leave radiating scar tissue. The lymphatic vessels in the region of the nodules and ulcers become thickened and stand out like cords. In the meantime a painless swelling, or subcutaneous edema, occurs on the under side of the abdomen and chest and may extend down the limbs, becoming a serious impediment to walking.

DIAGNOSIS AND TREATMENT

The micro-organism responsible for glanders, *Bacillus mallei*, possesses no characteristics by which it may be readily distinguished from many other bacteria that may be present in glanderous discharges. This greatly limits the possibility of making a diagnosis by microscopic examination. Fortunately, reliable diagnosis may be made by use of the mallein test, the serum test, or animal inoculation. The mallein test is made by observing the results of the introduction into the eye of a few drops of a product derived from cultures of the causative organism. This test is the one most commonly used because of the simplicity of its application and its reliability in detecting all forms, including latent cases, with sufficient accuracy to accomplish complete eradication of the disease when followed by proper sanitary measures.

Since the discovery of mallein as a diagnostic agent for glanders, numerous experiments have been conducted to ascertain whether it has any immunizing or curative value. All attempts to build up immunity against glanders in susceptible animals by vaccination have failed. Spontaneous recovery sometimes occurs, but it does not confer immunity against subsequent infection. For this reason treatment of affected animals with either medicines or biological products is not recommended as a means of controlling outbreaks.

METHOD OF ERADICATION

In glanderous equines the causative organism is excreted in large numbers from lesions of the skin, lungs, and respiratory tract. Therefore objects likely to be contaminated with these pus-laden excretions are to be looked upon as especially dangerous in the spread of the disease. Water troughs, pails, feed, mangers, bedding, harness, grooming utensils, and other objects become important factors in transmitting the disease from infected to healthy animals. The reservoir for the infection is the diseased animal, which, rarely recovers. Consequently, animals presenting symptoms resembling those of glanders should be isolated and mallein-tested by a qualified veterinarian. If the test shows that the disease is present, the animal should be destroyed without delay and the exposed premises and equipment thoroughly cleaned and disinfected. The usual procedure in eradicating the disease is to hold all susceptible animals in the community under strict sanitary control until the diagnostic test has been applied to those even remotely exposed and all reactors among them have been disposed of in a safe manner.

Many of the States have laws and regulations which require the prompt reporting of suspected cases of glanders and provide for the payment of indemnity for animals destroyed under official direction.

Dourine

BY T. W. COLE [1]

A DANGEROUS DISEASE of horses and other equines, dourine is similar to syphilis in human beings. Early diagnosis of dourine, by a serum test, has contributed greatly to progress in eradicating the disease.

DOURINE, an Arabic word meaning unclean, denotes a specific infectious disease transmitted from animal to animal almost exclusively by copulation. The disease is also known by a number of other names such as "maladie du coit," "equine syphilis," "genital glanders," and "breeding paralysis." It is contracted under normal conditions only by the horse and ass. The causative organism, *Trypanosoma equiperdum*, is an animal parasite of microscopic size.

HISTORY

That dourine had entered the United States was first definitely recognized in 1886, when an outbreak occurred in the vicinity of Bloomington, Ill., as a result of the importation of a stallion from France for breeding purposes. Rigid control measures were put into effect promptly by State officials after the disease was diagnosed. Unfortunately, prior to official recognition of the disease, infected animals had been moved out of the district, and these no doubt set up new centers of infection. At any rate, after the initial outbreak the disease was detected at irregualr intervals in Nebraska and South Dakota, but it was finally brought under control. In 1906, however, a new center of infection developed in Iowa. Despite the energetic measures adopted by both State and Federal authorities, this outbreak was not curbed until 1911.

The greatest early handicap in combating dourine was the lack of any diagnostic test. In 1912 the complement-fixation blood-serum test, requiring special laboratory facilities and the services of a trained bacteriologist, was perfected. Its use in testing horses imported from countries in which dourine is present has been an im-

---

[1] T. W. Cole is Assistant Chief, Field Inspection Division, Bureau of Animal Industry.

portant aid in guarding against further introduction of the disease from abroad. Through this test dourine has been found over a large area in the West, including Iowa, North Dakota, South Dakota, Nebraska, Colorado, Wyoming, Montana, Idaho, Oregon, California, Nevada, Arizona, and New Mexico. Notable success has been attained in its eradication, and at present (January 1942) the only known areas of infection remaining are in Arizona, California, and Nevada.

SYMPTOMS

The symptoms vary in individual horses and usually appear in two distinct stages. In the first the sexual organs are affected principally, but if the disease progresses into the second or a later chronic stage, nervous disorders become pronounced. The period of incubation, or time elapsing before clinical symptoms appear after exposure to infection, ranges from 8 days to 2 months. At times the initial symptoms are slight and may escape unobserved unless dourine is known to exist in the vicinity.

In the stallion the disease usually begins with a swelling of the prepuce, or sheath, a condition which later spreads forward to the abdomen and backward to the scrotum. If the inflammation extends to the testicles, these parts become enlarged and sensitive to pressure. During this time usually the penis is constantly affected and partially protrudes from its sheath, swollen and discharging a yellowish fluid from the urethra. Small blisters, or vesicles, that appear on the penis and sheath in the early stages soon rupture and form raw, irregular ulcers, singly and in groups. These ulcers heal, leaving permanent white scars which are highly significant in diagnosing the disease by physical examination. While the symptoms are developing, the stallion manifests a repeated desire to urinate, and the breeding instinct is intensified until frequently it becomes inordinate.

In mares the early symptoms are swollen external genitals, causing a gaping vulva which exposes the clitoris in a constant state of erection. Swelling may also occur in the region of the mammary glands. Early symptoms may include manifestations of uneasiness—switching of the tail and frequent voiding of small quantities of urine—resembling prolonged heat. A scant or copious discharge similar to that found in the stallion may be present. Vesicles, or blisters, which appear on the inner mucous membrane and outer skin of the genitals soon rupture, leaving deep-seated ulcers that, when healed, form rather prominent white scars, distinguished by their permanency from the temporary ones produced by other affections, such as coital exanthema.

The second stage of dourine in animals of both sexes is marked by nervous or constitutional disturbances that may not appear for months or even years after the acute symptoms subside. The cutaneous, or skin, lesions, which are essentially secondary, follow the symptoms in the genital organs and appear in the form of urticarial wheals or plaques resembling those in hives. These are highly characteristic. They vary from the size of a dime to that of a dollar or larger and may be round or irregular in form. The wheals are produced by infiltration of serum into the papillary (hair-producing) layer of the skin and cause the hair to stand erect. The commonest locations of these lesions are on the chest, belly, and croup, but they may appear on the neck, shoulders, withers, or other parts of the body. After these small raised areas subside, the skin is not infrequently left depigmented or covered with white hair.

The advanced cases of dourine are characterized by loss of flesh, nervousness, and paralysis. At times the nerves of the face are affected, causing paralysis of one ear, an eyelid, a nostril, or a lip, or of one whole side of the face. However, paralysis most commonly affects the hind legs, causing the animal to stub or drag a toe in walking, with a tendency to knuckling. When paralysis of the hindquarters occurs, the disease usually progresses rapidly. Muscles become weakened and atrophied until the animal can no longer stand, and it goes down and dies in a state of nervous exhaustion.

TREATMENT

Efforts to protect animals by immunization or to develop a satisfactory medicinal treatment for dourine have been disappointing. Unsatisfactory results from lines of treatment found useful in combating other trypanosome infections are apparently due to the failure of drugs to reach and destroy all the causative organisms. Those located in edematous swellings, joint cavities, and other parts of the body escape and give rise to relapses.

Recovery from dourine is always uncertain. A mortality of 50 percent is not uncommon, and in some outbreaks in other countries losses of as many as 70 percent of the animals affected have been reported when the disease was permitted to run its course. Infected mares seldom conceive, and those that do are likely to abort. Affected stallions are usually reservoirs of infection and may spread the disease with great rapidity over large areas. In this country, where the disease has existed only in restricted areas, sanitary conditions demand its eradication.

METHODS OF ERADICATION

Dourine is spread under natural conditions only by the act of coition. Any sanitary measures for its eradication must necessarily include a ban on the breeding of infected animals. An occasional animal may apparently recover, but it remains a potential spreader, for very often infection is present in a dormant state and the excitement of copulation tends to cause its reappearance with renewed vigor. Spaying mares and castrating stallions, especially under range conditions, where the disease has occurred most frequently in the United States, is a temporizing method of control. Such mares may be covered by a stallion, and even after castration infected stallions may spread the disease to healthy mares. The most effective method of eradicating the disease is the prompt destruction of all infected animals.

The Pathological Division of the Bureau of Animal Industry maintains a diagnostic laboratory in Washington, D. C., properly equipped to apply the complement-fixation test for dourine when samples of blood serum are submitted for examination. Preparing serum samples for the test requires skill and experience and should be undertaken only by a qualified veterinarian.

The Bureau of Animal Industry also cooperates with livestock sanitary authorities in dealing with dourine in the field wherever

FIGURE 1.—Wild range horses that have been brought to an enclosure so that they may be tested for dourine. In testing, a blood sample is taken from each animal of breeding age.

it exists. In this work animals are held under strict surveillance until the results of tests are known, and those found harboring infection are promptly destroyed. The usual procedure is for the State and Federal Governments to share equally in the expense of indemnifying the owners for animals destroyed, except on Indian reservations, where the entire expense is borne by the Federal Government (fig. 1). In the eradication programs, animals whose serum gives negative results are classed as free from the disease and released for breeding.

Miscellaneous Diseases of Equines

BY L. O. MOTT, M. S. SHAHAN,
L. T. GILTNER, AND A. H. FRANK [1]

HERE ARE FACTS, particularly from the standpoint
of symptoms, causes, treatment, and prevention, about
a large number of diseases of horses and mules.

INFLUENZA

EQUINE INFLUENZA, also known as shipping fever, pinkeye, catarrhal
fever, epizootic cellulitis, and, among older horsemen, epizooty, is
probably the most contagious and widely distributed disease to which
horses, mules, and asses are susceptible. The death rate, though sometimes as high as 10 percent of the cases, is not so great as that from
some other infectious diseases, but the economic loss entailed by the
incapacity of affected animals for work is in the aggregate serious.
Horses and mules coming through sales stables, stockyards, remount
depots. and other establishments where large numbers of animals from
scattered sources are held together for some time are especially apt
to develop influenza. The symptoms are strikingly like those of
influenza in man or similar conditions in other species although there
is no proved connection.

Fever (103°–106° F.),[2] extreme weakness and depression. rapid
breathing, harsh cough, and watery discharges from the nostrils and
eyes are common early indications of the infection. The conjunctiva.
the lining membrane of the eyelid, becomes yellowish pink in color
(so-called pinkeye). Swelling due to edema (accumulations of the
watery constituents of the blood and lymph) of the legs, abdomen.
and head are common symptoms in many outbreaks. The affected
animal stands in an attitude of extreme dejection, drinks eagerly

[1] L. O. Mott is Assistant Veterinarian, M. S. Shahan is Veterinarian, and L. T. Giltner is
Senior Veterinarian, Pathological Division, and A. H. Frank is Assistant Veterinarian,
Animal Disease Station, Beltsville, Md., Bureau of Animal Industry.
[2] The normal temperature of the horse is 99.5°–100.5° F.

but sparingly, and eats little, in some cases finally refusing feed altogether. Sometimes there is restlessness and continuous shifting of weight from one leg to another, with a cracking sound in the joints.

In uncomplicated cases the temperature returns to normal within a week and gradual recovery follows. On the other hand, a second rise in temperature, often fluctuating, may occur, ushering in more or less serious complications, such as pneumonia, with rapid, labored breathing; inflammation of the stomach and intestines, usually with constipation and later a profuse, fetid diarrhea; inflammation of the kidneys, as usually indicated by frequent but scanty urination; inflammation of the brain, as shown by symptoms of paralysis or twitching and nervous excitability; abscess formation, in the lymph nodes of the body, especially about the head (commonly referred to as strangles); and even degeneration of the heart muscle, with serious changes in the character and rate of the pulse. Severe swellings about the eyes may occur, and sometimes even blindness results.

This disease, like influenza of man and of swine, is caused primarily by a filtrable virus, complications being attributable to miscellaneous bacteria, chiefly streptococci. Excessive hard work, undue exposure, and generally poor hygienic conditions are contributory factors. Symptoms develop as early as 3 days or as late as 2 weeks after exposure.

PREVENTION AND TREATMENT

Horses and mules being brought onto the farm or into the stable from outside sources, especially sales establishments, stockyards, or remount depots, should be held in rigid quarantine, isolated in a separate stable with separate attendants, for 10 to 30 days.

Animals going to market can apparently be protected to some degree by the repeated injection of bacterins, prepared from killed cultures of the bacteria commonly found as so-called secondary invaders in the disease.

Some apparently fully recovered animals may harbor the virus in the blood stream or, in the case of stallions, in the semen, for months and thus be a source of infection of other animals.

The first symptoms of the disease in an animal should immediately lead to its isolation and a thorough cleaning and disinfection of the stable, including troughs, feed boxes, buckets, etc.[3] Although the disease is highly contagious, its spread may be much lessened by promptness in these matters.

Experiments with the object of perfecting a vaccine for prevention and a serum for treatment of influenza are being carried out. So far no specific biological or chemical preventive or cure is available.

The first principle of treatment is absolute rest for the affected animal at the first signs of illness. He should be placed in a freshly bedded, well-ventilated but draft-free stall, and provided with small amounts of nutritious but not heavy feed. Fresh, clean water should

---

[3] See Disinfection and Disinfectants, p. 179.

be kept before him. It may be advisable to keep him blanketed, but this should not prevent regular grooming.

Such medicinal treatment as is given should be restricted to that specifically prescribed by the veterinarian. This may include inhalation of medicated vapor, medicines to regulate the bowels, stimulants, etc. In some cases it may be necessary to feed the animal artificially. This is usually done by introducing feed into the stomach by means of the stomach tube, or it may be introduced rectally. Blood or blood serum from recovered cases may be administered.

Animals should not be returned to work until some days after the temperature has become normal and full strength has returned.

DISTEMPER (STRANGLES)

In past years when traffic in horses and mules was heavy and these animals were used by practically all farmers to haul farm produce and for transportation, equine distemper was widespread and common in the United States. Animals from the countryside came in contact with city delivery horses on streets, in public stables, and at public watering troughs. It was an exceptional horse or mule that reached the age of 5 years without exposure to the infection, and practically every one developed the disease.

Today, there are large numbers of horses on isolated farms that have never been exposed to the infection and are consequently as susceptible as the colts of the previous era. The disease persists to a greater or less extent in stockyards, sales stables, race tracks, and remount depots. Practically every animal held in such places for any length of time is exposed to distemper, as well as to influenza. When a horse or mule is taken from a point of heavy concentration of animals from diverse sources to an isolated farm or breeding stable, the possibility of the infection being carried along is great.

The essential cause of the disease is generally conceded to be the germ known as *Streptococcus equi*, an organism which is easily spread from an affected animal either directly or indirectly by way of watering troughs, feed boxes, mangers, blankets, halters, etc., as well as on the person of the attendant. Cold, poorly ventilated stables, undue exposure to severe weather, and overwork are contributing influences, and the disease is most prevalent during the spring months. The disease affects only solipeds (horses, mules, and asses). Recovered animals generally remain immune for the rest of their lives, except in rare cases when they are exposed to an extremely virulent form of the disease. The main detrimental effects to owners are impairment in the development of colts and loss of the services of working animals, but in some outbreaks the disease may be fatal in as many as 5 percent of the cases.

The onset of the disease is sudden, usually within 3 to 8 days after exposure. The early symptoms are somewhat like those of influenza. There is fever (104°–106° F.), reduced appetite, and great depression. The membranes of the nose become red and dry, and a watery discharge from the nostrils follows. After 1 to 3 days, the discharge becomes very thick and profuse and is expelled in great quantities by snorting or coughing. In a majority of cases there is a hot, painful swelling of the lymph glands (submaxillary) under the lower jaw near the throat. These frequently become abscessed, and a yellow, creamy pus is formed. In uncomplicated cases, the fever drops, appetite returns, and the spirit revives shortly after the abscesses are drained, through either spontaneous rupture or surgical drainage, the disease lasting 2 to 4 weeks.

Complications are common, however, and abscesses may form in other lymph glands in the body, even in the abdominal cavity. Abscesses in the deeper glands and other tissues of the head and throat often obstruct the breathing, and it may be necessary to place a tube in the trachea (windpipe) to avoid suffocation. Pneumonia may result from spread of the infection, often through the inhalation of pus from ruptured glands. Septicemia, or so-called blood-poisoning, not infrequently occurs.

The mortality may be high in young foals, which sometimes contract the disease, and in newborn foals, which may be born with the infection.

TREATMENT AND PREVENTION

The first provision for an animal affected with distemper should be its immediate isolation from other animals in a clean, well-bedded, draft-free stall. All equipment with which it has been in contact should be thoroughly cleaned and disinfected. All discharges, bedding, and excreta from sick animals should be burned or buried.

Complete rest, a constant supply of pure, clean water, and a moderate amount of nutritious, laxative feed should be provided. The fact that mild, sporadic cases often require no further treatment explains the apparent efficacy of many home-compounded and proprietary medicines advertised as specific cures for the disease. As a matter of fact there is no such medicine for strangles. Veterinary attention is, however, frequently desirable and necessary.

As mentioned before, it may be necessary to place a tube in the trachea to prevent suffocation. Lancing the abscesses may be advisable. Medicines designed to aid the discharge of excessive secretions in the air passages are frequently prescribed. Medicated vapors are sometimes used as inhalants. Cloths soaked in hot liquids are frequently applied to the swollen glands. Blood or blood serum from recovered cases is sometimes employed. Stimulants may be indicated.

For the prevention of the disease, a bacterin prepared from cultures of the germs found in cases of the disease is sometimes used. For best results, repeated doses should be given prior to anticipated possible exposure such as could be encountered in the course of shipping or at shows or race meetings. The precaution of quarantining newly purchased animals in a separate, isolated stable for 2 to 4 weeks before allowing contact with the "home" animals is very desirable.

PURPURA HEMORRHAGICA (PETECHIAL FEVER)

Purpura hemorrhagica is a noncontagious affection which commonly follows severe or complicated cases of other diseases of equines, especially influenza and distemper. While the essential cause is unknown, it rarely occurs except after a severe septic infection.

The malady is generally attributed to a decrease in the thrombocytes or platelets (cellular constituents of the blood concerned with clotting) resulting from the presence of poisonous chemical substances in the blood. It occurs in some cases of fistula or poll evil or subsequent to the development of an abscess or of necrosis (death of tissue) anywhere in the body. Sometimes it appears without a known history of any such process. Rarely more than one or at most a few animals in a stable develop the disease. It usually occurs in the spring or early summer following epizootics (outbreaks) of other diseases. Animals under 2 years of age are seldom affected.

The disease is characterized by hemorrhages and edema in the skin, inner membranes, muscle, internal organs, and other tissues of the body. In some particulars the symptoms are somewhat suggestive of swamp fever (equine infectious anemia). The disease usually begins with hemorrhages in the nasal membranes. Later, swellings appear about the lips, eyelids, legs, or lower part of the abdomen. The swellings are cold and painless, usually sharply outlined but sometimes diffuse, invariably pitting under pressure. They may appear suddenly or develop gradually during several days.

The temperature is usually normal or only slightly increased (102°–103° F.), but the pulse is quickened materially. The membranes at the body openings frequently become yellowish in color (icterus, or jaundice). The average course of the disease is 12 to 15 days, but this is variable, and recurrence of the trouble is not uncommon, especially if the animal is worked or vigorously exercised.

Complications are common. Among these are pneumonia, severe inflammations of the stomach or intestines, and severe anemia (deficiency of blood and of red blood cells). All may lead to a prolonged serious illness and death.

In addition to complete rest, hygienic stabling conditions, and reasonable feeding, treatment is directed toward the alleviation of certain symptoms as they develop or can be anticipated in individual cases. Insertion of a trachea tube to facilitate breathing and the use of stimulants are sometimes advisable. The unrestricted use of purgatives is believed to be harmful in most cases. Direct transfusions of blood are commonly employed. Certain drugs are injected into the blood stream by some veterinarians as a part of the treatment.

WOUNDS AND WOUND INFECTIONS

Of all domestic animals the horse is most subject to accidental wounds. Moreover, it is more susceptible to infections than other domestic animals, especially in wounds that are neglected or unwisely handled. Mules are definitely less likely than horses to acquire accidental wounds, but when they do, infection is a potential hazard.

Many of the germs that commonly result in serious trouble are widely distributed in the soil and in forage or manure. Among them are those of the genus *Clostridium*, including *Clostridium septi-*

cum, which is the cause of various types of so-called gas gangrene and malignant edema, and *Clostridium tetani,* the organism that causes tetanus, or lockjaw. These belong to the class of germs known as anaerobes, which thrive in the absence of air. When implanted in injured tissues from which the air is excluded by surface healing or improper dressings, they become especially active and dangerous. Also, they form a spore, or seed form, which is capable of growth even after being for years outside of an animal body. Such germs as streptococci, staphylococci, and some bacteria in the class known as aerobes, which implies their need for air for best growth, are especially apt to cause the formation of pus. In addition to the so-called pure infections induced by a single type of germ, mixed infections involving more than one type may occur.

The skin has the function of assisting in the elimination of body wastes through sweating and also acts as a protective covering for the body. But it is a basic fact that the skin of an animal is never free from germs, some of which are often of a type capable of causing serious trouble. When the skin is broken by a cut, bruise, or even superficial chafing, access to the inner tissues is open to germs from the hair and skin surface or the injuring object. The sound body reacting normally usually overcomes the threatened invasion. But if the resistance of the body tissues is low, if severe injury occurs, or if the germs are especially numerous or virulent in character, infection follows as a matter of course.

The resistance of the animal's body or the character and number of the germs may be such as to result in the confinement of the trouble to the region where the germs gain entrance. In such a localized infection, there will be redness, swelling, and more or less pain, with or without the formation of gas or pus. But if the army of invading organisms succeeds in overcoming the protective forces called into action by the body, a general or systemic infection, known as septicemia or pyemia (blood poisoning), results, and in addition to the local indications, fever, depression, stiffness, loss of appetite, and other evidences of the spread of the germs in the blood occur. Death of the afflicted animal is common, especially if treatment is not promptly instituted.

Tetanus is caused by a powerful toxin, or poison, formed in the body by the specific germ of the disease, *Clostridium tetani.* Practically all animals, including man, are susceptible, the horse, mule, and ass being especially so. Symptoms of tetanus appear in the majority of cases in 1 to 2 weeks after the germs gain entrance to the body, or they may be delayed for months, according to the severity of the primary injury and the degree of infection. On the other hand, young animals especially may develop symptoms in less than a week.

The first signs of the disease are usually observed about the head. Chewing is less forceful than normal, and swallowing is slow and awkward. The nictitating membrane (the so-called inner or third eyelid between the lower eyelid and the eyeball proper) protrudes up on the surface of the eyeball. The rigidity of the muscles due to spasm spreads, sometimes rapidly, from one group of muscles to another. Eating is greatly impaired or even completely prevented (lockjaw), the legs are spread and stiffened, giving the appearance of a sawhorse, the tail is elevated and stiff, and the ears are held rigidly erect. Constipation commonly occurs. The breathing is rapid and forced, the heart action may or may not be quickened, and usually there is little if any fever except in the severe cases, and then near death. The muscles may tend to relax at intervals, only to contract instantly, with the rapidity of a spring, at the slightest noise, a ray of light, or a touch on the body. Death is usually due to sheer exhaustion, paralysis of the vital organs, or pneumonia resulting from inhaling feed, throat secretions, or medicines which have been improperly administered. Animals which recover are often sick for a month or more.

PREVENTION AND TREATMENT

Localized wound infections, septicemia, pyemia, and tetanus are largely preventable. In the first place, sharp objects should not be allowed in the stables, corrals, paddocks, or pastures used by horses. Barbed-wire fencing should be replaced by board or pole fences. Trees and shrubs should be trimmed at intervals, broken or low-hanging limbs being removed. Farm machinery should not remain in the barnyard or field where horses may be free. Scrap metal, wire, boards, nails, etc., should be kept away from all kinds of live-stock as well as horses. Loose nails, screws, hinges, and door fasteners, splintered boards, and other sharp protruding objects should not be permitted in stables or elsewhere where horses are kept.

Quietness and gentleness are especially desirable attributes in stable workers. General cleanliness and hygiene will lessen infections when injuries occur. In some sections tetanus is especially prevalent, so much so that even surgical operations such as must be performed in the stable or barnyard may predispose an animal to the disease. Some truck gardens, heavily manured lands, and swamps are hotbeds for the tetanus organism and its spores. In such locations, the use of tetanus antitoxin in the form of serum is good insurance against the disease in case of any injury to animals, especially horses. Tetanus toxoid, the chemically treated toxin produced by the germ of tetanus, engenders a strong long-standing immunity against the disease. It is employed as a routine matter in some armies and may be advisedly used in certain localities where the disease is commonly prevalent.

The treatment to be used for wounds depends upon the location and extent of the injury and the likelihood of infection. The majority of wounds, although potentially dangerous, do best if left entirely alone awaiting direct attention by the veterinarian. This does not apply in all cases, of course, as, for example, where the injury has caused profuse bleeding. Blood flowing through and over injured tissue in a moderate amount is a natural and desirable development in a wound. The loss of 1 to 2 quarts or even more blood by a robust horse or mule is not in itself dangerous, but if bleeding is long continued, severe weakening or even death may result. In serious cases it may be possible to stop the flow of blood by the direct application of pressure over the part with a pad of sterile gauze or other suitable material. If this fails, and the wound is on a leg or other part to which a tourniquet may be applied, one may be adjusted above the injury. This may be done simply by passing a thick twisted cloth about the leg and tying it loosely. A stick is then inserted in the space between the cloth and the leg and twisted to a degree of tightness sufficient to lessen or stop the bleeding. The tourniquet must not be applied too tightly, and it should be loosened every 20 minutes so that the blood flow beyond the wound is not cut off entirely. Such substances as flour or earth should never be placed in a wound to stop bleeding, nor should turpentine, crude creosote products, or other irritating substances be used as antiseptics.

To avoid further injury it may be necessary to withdraw an object extending into the wound, but care must be taken not to break it off, leaving a fragment deeply embedded in the tissues. Further possible injury and infection should be avoided by confining the animal in clean quarters.

Upon his arrival, the veterinarian first surveys the damage. Then bleeding vessels are picked up by forceps and tied with a suitable ligature. It is usually desirable to clean the skin in the vicinity of the wound, care being taken that the materials used do not drip or run into the wound. Hair, straw, and other foreign materials are picked from the wound with sterile forceps, the hand or fingers never touching the wound directly. Unless exceptionally heavy contamination of the wound has occurred, strong antiseptic solutions are seldom desirable or necessary. Rather, mild substances, such as physiological salt solution (having the same salt content as the body tissues) which 'may be made by adding 1 teaspoonful of common table salt to 1 pint of boiled water, are used to sponge the exposed surfaces of the wound lightly. If the wound is relatively clean and not too extensive or gaping, the muscles and skin may be drawn together by sutures. Some wounds heal better without any bandage; a bandage serves to protect others against further infection or to support the tissues. A heavy bandage serves in some cases to keep various dressing compounds in contact with the wound. In severe, contused wounds, examinations are made for fractures of the underlying bones.

Many neglected wounds of the foot that do not result in immediate lameness may cause extreme lameness some days later through the damming up of inflammatory wound secretions or pus. The sole of the hoof must often be deeply pared away before the site of the wound is discovered. The area of discoloration must then be enlarged to permit the escape of the material resulting from the infection and the application of antiseptic substances. In areas where tetanus is prevalent, such wounds are especially conducive to that disease.

The treatment of tetanus is often not entirely satisfactory; yet occasional cases eventually recover without any treatment. It is first desirable to open the wound through which the infection entered, if this can be located, thoroughly draining it and applying suitable antiseptics. Confinement in a clean, cool, quiet, darkened stall with as little disturbance as possible is advantageous. If tetanus antitoxin is given—and its use is merited for especially valuable animals and in other selected cases—huge and often repeated dosing is usually required. Further, sedatives of various types are commonly employed, and artificial feeding may be required.

Slight wounds or simple abrasions of the skin, if immediately treated with fresh tincture of iodine U. S. P., seldom cause trouble except in tetanus districts.

Wounds in which foreign material is allowed to remain or which are otherwise neglected commonly develop pus, for the elimination of which surgical incision, drainage, and repeated irrigation with antiseptics may be required.

Horses obliged to lean heavily on a high manger or other fixture to obtain feed frequently develop an accumulation of serum (the watery constituent of blood and lymph) in the breast tissues. Successful treatment of these formations, which are usually free from bacteria, commonly requires incision, drainage, and irrigation or packing.

Chronically inflamed wounds, such as wire cuts, sometimes develop excessive scar tissue, known as keloid. Surgical removal is the only generally applicable treatment for such cases.

BREEDING TROUBLES

The broad scope of the term "breeding troubles" is apparent when it is considered that it includes any cause of barrenness in either the mare or the stallion and the abnormal termination of pregnancy in abortions and stillbirths, as well as the problems of foaling. The importance of proper care and management of breeding animals is well emphasized by the vast amount of literature available to the farmer and the breeder in the form of bulletins and farm and breed magazines. Yet, despite this available information, in too many instances the possible generous margin of profit from horse and mule husbandry under normal conditions is lost through careless or ignorant handling of breeding animals. The method of handling animals has a decided influence on their physical condition and health. In normal, healthy individuals, the husbandman can prevent an overnourished or undernourished condition and provide proper exercise, which with good housing and sanitation will do more than anything else to prevent breeding troubles. Regardless of the success of preventive measures, however, he cannot by these methods alone control all the physiological upsets or the invasion of all the diseases which affect sexual activities.

Anatomy and Physiology

The anatomy and physiology of the genital organs of the mare are very complex. Briefly, the genital tract begins at the external opening, known as the vulva, which opens forward into the vagina. The vagina leads into the uterus (womb) through a narrow, thick-walled neck, or cervix. The uterus branches into two so-called horns. Attached to each of these there is a fine tube, the Fallopian tube, designed to convey the egg from the ovary into the uterus, where it is fertilized by one of the multitudinous sperm cells from the male.

The sexual behavior of normal animals is controlled by secretions (hormones) from certain body glands, as discussed elsewhere in this volume (p. 155).

An upset in the secretion of any of the primary sex hormones may produce sterility in either sex. In the female it may interrupt the coordinated sexual rhythm, prevent conception, or induce early or late abortion. Its effect on the male may be manifested by impotency or sluggish activity and sterility. Much has been accomplished in the treatment of glandular deficiency by proper diagnosis and by the administration of the hormone indicated.

Normally, the egg is expelled from the ovary of the mare close to the end of estrus (about 24 or 48 hours before the end of heat) and is capable of becoming fertilized for only about 12 to 24 hours afterward. The spermatozoa live for about 12 to 48 hours in the genital tract of the mare, the time varying with individual stallions. If the sperm of a given stallion is capable of living only about 12 hours, more frequent matings would be necessary in order to obtain a rate of fertility equal to that of a stallion whose sperm would live an average of 48 hours. These facts show the desirability of breeding the mare 1 to 2 days before she goes out of heat. There is no method, except by individual records, to determine the length of the estrus period. In the absence of such records, in order to breed at the proper time one would have to breed a mare every other day through each estrus period in order to insure pregnancy.

Efficiently kept breeding records and observations on fertile animals indicate that the selection of a particular day for breeding during the period of estrus may largely determine the chances of conception. Estrus has been found to vary in duration from 2 to 30 days in different individuals. However, the periods for an individual mare seldom vary in length by more than 1 to 2 days, so they are of sufficient regularity that records can be relied upon for selection of the proper time for mating.

BREEDING HYGIENE

The success of many large, privately owned breeding establishments and Army remount breeding stations must be attributed largely to careful examination and selection of prospective breeding animals, as well as to breeding hygiene. The complete program is quite elaborate, but the basic principles can be given briefly.

To begin with, each mare and stallion is chosen on the basis of suitable ancestry and acceptable conformation as individuals. The animals must be free of transmissible disease, and the genitalia must be normal.

The mares to be bred are examined during an interval between periods of heat to determine that there is no inflammation of the genital tract. The presence of infection may sometimes but not always be indicated by a discharge from the vulva. Consequently, close examination is required.

After the hind parts of the mare have been thoroughly washed with clean, warm water and a mild soap and dried, the veterinarian inspects the vagina and cervix for the presence of infection by the use of a speculum and light. Infection is usually readily recognized from the appearance of the structures and the character of the secretions, but it may be necessary or desirable to obtain a specimen for laboratory examination.

A manual examination is also made of the ovaries and uterus through the walls of the rectum. The presence of large cysts or excessive fibrous tissue in the ovaries, conditions likely to preclude conception, is thus discovered. Such conditions may be corrected by manual treatment or by the use of hormones, but they are sometimes incurable.

If evidence of infection is discovered in the genital organs, the mare is withheld from breeding until the organs become normal. If the mare is bred while the organs are infected, failure to conceive is common, or if the mare does become pregnant, abortion or the delivery of a weak, infected foal may follow.

Mares are also examined after foaling. The genital organs should return to normal within 8 days, and mares normally come into heat in 7 to 12 days. They may be examined on the sixth or seventh day and if found normal may be bred at this early heat. Many large breeding establishments make it a practice not to breed at this time but to wait until the second heat period. Much future trouble, such as infections and abortions, may be avoided by this practice.

The serviceability of the stallion is checked at intervals by microscopic examination and bacteriological cultures of the semen. An infected stallion is not permitted to serve mares, especially clean ones.

The correction of genital infections in mares is, strictly speaking, a veterinarian's task. It is not to be undertaken by a layman through such practices as promiscuous douching and "opening the womb." Some mares become infected by the free entrance of air and foreign matter into the vagina between the lips of a flaccid or gaping vulva. In such cases, the lips are frequently sutured or clipped together along the upper part of the vulva. After healing, the sutures or clips are removed. Such treatment in the fall usually leads to good breeding condition by the following spring. At mating, care must be taken that the closed portion of the vulva is not torn. At foaling time the adhesions are broken down to permit free passage of the foal.

SERVICE

Estrus, or heat, in most cases is determined by teasing the mare with a stallion. One familiar with the habits of horses can determine whether or not the mare will accept the stallion. Some mares, however, do not show outward signs of heat and remain indifferent when brought in contact with the stallion. Heat may also be determined by a vaginal examination with the speculum. Some mares come into heat at very irregular intervals, in extreme cases only every other year. Hormonal treatment may be indicated for such mares.

In preparation for service, or breeding, the external genital organs of the mare are prepared as for vaginal examination, and in addition the tail may be wrapped with a sterile bandage. The stallion should have a similar cleansing, both before and after service, time being taken to remove all sebum adhering to the penis. Careful technique at this time may prevent the introduction of infection into the mare.

There are two methods used to breed mares—normal mating to a stallion or jack and artificial insemination. In either case extreme hygienic precautions should be observed.

After normal mating, as the stallion dismounts, a portion of semen is generally discharged from the penis. A container may be held under the penis to collect the semen for examination.

If artificial insemination is practiced, the stallion is cleansed as for service and allowed to mount a mare and ejaculate into a sterile artificial vagina which is held to one side of the mare at an angle near the vagina. This method has many advantages over normal matings. The semen can be examined to determine its quality before use. A sample may be stored for some time, transported for considerable distances, and divided for the insemination of several mares. The spread of venereal diseases may thus be prevented, and samples may be examined for the presence of infection.

DIAGNOSIS OF PREGNANCY

Pregnancy can be readily diagnosed by an experienced veterinarian by manual examination within a few months after conception. Pregnancy may also be determined between the forty-second and one hundred and twentieth days after conception by the injection of blood serum from the mare into female rabbits or young rats or mice. During this period the pregnant mare's serum contains a hormone which, when injected into the test animals, causes activation of the ovary and enlargement of the uterus. Observations of these changes may be made through operation on the rabbit, which may be used over and over again, and in rats and mice after the animals are killed.

ABORTION

Of all mares that become pregnant, it is estimated that two-thirds will have normal healthy foals and one-third will either abort or produce a weak, infected foal. Under optimum conditions in a given stable, however, the losses should be negligible. The causes of abortion and of weak foals are many. In general, they may be classed as traumatic (due to an injury) and infectious.

The effects of certain active drugs, including some worm repellents, and the eating of some poisonous chemicals and plants and certain spoiled feeds may be mentioned as traumatic causes of abortion. Some types of illness, such as colic and parasitic infestation, may cause abortion. Mares may abort because of severe kicks or blows over the abdomen. Severe exertion and fatigue may endanger the life of the foal, while on the other hand lack of exercise may cause a weakening and break-down of the abdominal wall, with permanent injury to the mare. Light work each day until foaling time is to be recommended.

Bacterial infection is by far the greatest cause of abortions and stillbirths. Generalized infections such as influenza, infectious anemia, and similar febrile conditions may cause abortion. Infections that are localized in the reproductive tract, producing inflammation of the vagina, cervix, uterus, Fallopian tubes, and ovaries, may prevent conception or result in abortion. Infections of the reproductive tract of the male may be transmitted to the female and later cause abortion.

Infection by streptococci alone is said to cause 25 percent of all abortions. Abortions from this cause generally occur during early pregnancy. A large percentage of mares become infected at foaling time and do not overcome the infection before the first heat period, on or about the ninth day after foaling. A stallion may become infected when allowed to serve infected mares and may spread the infection to all the mares he serves. Streptococcic infection can be largely avoided through using noninfected mares and stallions and taking hygienic precautions. The vaginal examination prior to breeding is very essential, as previously mentioned. A bacterial culture should be made from any abnormal condition found at the examination following foaling. The culture is usually prepared from material obtained from the cervix. If the infection does not clear up by the first or second heat period, appropriate douches may be administered with benefit. It may be advisable to resort to the operation for partial closure of the vulva. Routine semen examinations of stallions should be made to detect the presence of infection. It is essential to observe sanitary precautions, especially at foaling. Thorough disinfection of maternity stalls and the use of clean bedding will do much to prevent infection of clean animals.

An organism commonly causing joint ill in foals (*Shigella equirulis*) in some cases is passed from the dam to the fetus in the uterus. This infection is further discussed under Diseases of Newborn Foals.

The causative agent of contagious equine abortion is the organism known as *Salmonella abortivoequina*. Abortions due to this organism may occur at any stage of pregnancy, but usually from the fourth to the eighth month. Diagnosis may be made by examination of the blood for specific agglutinins. The disease may be largely controlled by the elimination of reacting mares and stallions as breeders and the vaccination of pregnant mares with a specific bacterin, especially in localities where abortion is prevalent. Aborting mares should be kept isolated. Discharges and all contaminated bedding, fetal membranes, and dead fetuses should be burned, and stalls should be thoroughly cleaned and disinfected. After a rest period, most mares will overcome the infection.

Large breeding establishments list many abortions under "unknown cause." In some studs as many as 50 percent or more of the mares may abort without showing any signs of illness, and bacterial cultures from the fetus and the mare may be negative. There are some indications that many such abortions may be due to a virus.

DYSTOCIA AND RETAINED PLACENTA

Dystocia (difficult labor) may result in the death of the foal and in extreme cases of the dam as well. While the entire process of labor normally requires a few hours, the actual expulsion of the foal should take place in less than half an hour. For mares requiring a longer time, the advice and assistance of a competent veterinarian should be immediately obtained. In some cases, traction applied to the fetus may be all that is required, but this is always a dangerous practice for one not trained in obstetrics as it may easily lead·to the death of both dam and foal.

The placenta, or fetal membranes, commonly called the afterbirth, should come away in entirety from the mother within 2 hours after the birth of the foal. If any portion remains longer it is because of some abnormality which demands immediate professional attention. Delay in removal of all the placenta frequently results in septicemia (blood poisoning), laminitis (founder), or other serious complications.

DISEASES OF NEWBORN FOALS

The death of newborn foals results not only in the loss of the stud fees, and of expected profit from the colts, but also in waste of the time and care devoted to the mares while in foal. Diseases of the newborn are due chiefly to infection; however, parasitism, faulty nutrition, and poor housing are important factors.

The diseases of foals caused by infection with micro-organisms include navel ill, joint ill (lameness). pyosepticemia (blood poisoning), scours, and pneumonia. Almost any of the organisms causing these infections is capable of producing one or all of the symptoms.

The organisms that have most frequently been found to cause infections of the newborn are *Shigella equirulis* (syn. *Bacterium viscosum equi*), *Escherichia coli*, *Streptococcus*, and *Salmonella abortivoequina*. The last two are also common causes of abortion.

In *Shigella equirulis* infection the disease symptoms may appear at the time of or within 2 or 3 days after birth. There is a sudden onset with extreme prostration. The duration of symptoms is short, and death occurs early. During the course of the disease the pulse, temperature, and respiration are usually increased. Lameness may be pronounced in one or more joints, with visible enlargement. This organism is reported to cause a larger percentage of fatalities of young foals than any other one infection. Its habitat is believed to be in the digestive tract of the pregnant mare.

Symptoms of *Escherichia coli* infection are usually those of an acute septicemia, sometimes in association with inflammation of the joints and umbilicus (navel). Symptoms of infection usually appear at the time of birth or shortly thereafter, and as in the case of calves, in which it is a very serious problem, the mortality rate is high, death usually resulting in 1 to 4 days.

In streptococcic infection the disease usually appears 10 to 14 days after birth, causing lameness and swelling of joints followed by weakness and gradual loss of condition until death, the disease lasting 2 or 3 weeks. Some of the more chronic cases without general symptoms may recover. Streptococci have been found in a large percentage of unbred mares. These mares when bred are likely to abort or produce young that develop infection. This disease at the present time is thought to be one of the most important breeding diseases.

In paratyphoid (*Salmonella abortivoequina*) infection, the course of fatal cases of the disease is quite rapid, from 4 to 6 days, often accompanied by severe and persistent straining.

There is some difference of opinion among authorities as to the chief method of infection, whether it is prenatal (before birth) or postnatal (after birth); however, both types of infection should be considered important.

Prenatal, or intrauterine, infection of the foal takes place in the uterus (womb) of the dam before the foal is born. The infection may be present in the dam before she is bred, or it may be introduced by the stallion if he is infected or if he has previously bred other infected mares. Mechanical introduction of infection may result from unclean hands and equipment of operators, especially laymen who try to dilate the cervix (open up the mare for breeding) or diagnose pregnancy. If prenatal infection does not result in abortion and the mare carries the foal to the end of the gestation period, the colt is often born weak or develops navel ill within a few days and dies; if it does not die it becomes an unthrifty cripple that must be destroyed.

Postnatal infection primarily gains entrance to the body of the foal through the umbilicus after birth. This infection may be picked up from soil, bedding, or stables contaminated by other infected colts or mares that are discharging infective material.

The control of infectious diseases of the newborn foal by rigid sanitation and breeding hygiene is much more successful than treatment of an infected foal. Treatment is often nonspecific owing to the numerous different causes. Even when specific it often has very little therapeutic value owing to the rapid progress of the disease.

Control begins with hygiene before the mare is bred, as described in the previous section on Breeding Troubles.

After delivery, the nostrils of the foal should first be freed of membranes or obstruction of any kind; then the umbilical cord should be separated by traction if it has not separated naturally. This is accomplished by grasping the cord with both hands, pulling in such a manner as to separate it between the hands at a point 2 or 3 inches from the belly of the foal. The cord should not be ligated (tied), as this would prevent drainage. The umbilical stump should then be thoroughly saturated with a suitable disinfectant. Tincture of iodine is commonly used for this purpose. While one attendant holds the foal in a standing position, another holds a cupful of the solution up against its belly with the umbilical stump immersed in the fluid for about a minute. One application of the disinfectant in this manner is sufficient. The foal should be given a warm, nonirritating soap enema if it does not empty the contents of the lower bowel within the first 8 hours. This may be repeated as often as necessary until the normal yellow feces appear. Scours are not so common in foals as in calves. They may result from infection acquired from the udder and teats of the dam if these have become contaminated or from eating feces, straw, grass, and other foreign material or from overloading the stomach as a result of irregular nursing. Such irregularity may occur if the mare is taken away from the colt for a considerable length of time.

Treatment of infectious diseases of the foal, as previously stated, is usually unsuccessful because of the rapid progress of the disease, which does not allow sufficient time for diagnosis of the specific causative agent. Even when the specific cause is known, response to treatment is often unsatisfactory. However, with the first symptoms of sickness or lameness in the newborn foal, veterinary attention and advice are recommended. Blood transfusions from dam to foal have been given in all types of infection, with indications of favorable results.

In streptococcic infection, sulfanilamide has been reported to be of some value, and antistreptococcic serum and bacterins are sometimes used. The serum or bacterin should be specially prepared by a laboratory from the type of streptococcus concerned in the infection of the animals, since products prepared from other types of streptococcus may give no protection.

Except for administration of the dam's blood, treatment for *Shigella equirulis* infection has not proven to be very effective.

In *Escherichia coli* infection, antibacterial serum as used in calves for scours, the use of muzzles, and restriction of the diet may be of value.

Salmonella abortivoequina infection can be largely prevented by vaccinating the dam during the gestation period.

LAMENESS

Lameness frequently delays or even ends the training of show and race horses and commonly impedes farm work. It is, of course, not a disease but rather a manifestation of some structural or functional disorder of some part of the locomotive apparatus. On the other hand, a so-called false lameness is not uncommon in poorly conditioned or unwisely trained animals without any detectable abnormality.

The character and degree of lameness depend upon the nature and extent of the underlying ailments, which are many and varied. In order to determine efficiently the origin of lameness, a thorough knowledge of anatomy and physiology is essential. In addition, it is helpful to recognize that every animal has a natural "way of going," which may or may not appear normal at first glance but which is compatible with the individual's constitution and conformation. Finally, a knowledge of pathology is necessary.

The duration of the lameness and whether it increases or decreases with continued exercise are points to be considered. If necessary the animal should be observed not only at rest but at all gaits if its condition permits. Enlargement or pain upon pressure or movement of any part is indicative of underlying disease. Sometimes X-rays assist in diagnosis. The nerves supplying certain portions of the leg are sometimes anesthetized, temporarily eliminating the sense of pain in the parts and permitting diagnosis through the process of elimination. The character of the lameness, that is, whether it involves support of weight or extension or flexion of the part, gives important clues as to the seat of the underlying trouble.

CAUSES

Lameness or impediments to the normal gait are observed in certain bone diseases, in azoturia, laminitis, lymphangitis, and miscellaneous wounds and diseases of the feet, which are discussed elsewhere in this article. There are numerous other causes. The diseases underlying lameness are chiefly inflammatory in nature. There are inflammations of bones, muscles, tendons, ligaments, joints, nerves, blood vessels, and skin, which may be the result of mechanical injury, infection, or both. Injuries develop either from accidental violence or from strains following forced training, overwork, improper shoeing, poorly fitted harness, and other largely preventable causes. Infection results chiefly from accidents. Some of the more common causes of lameness will be briefly discussed here.

Sprains

In an animal with good conformation and in good condition the muscles, tendons, and ligaments are marvelously coordinated in maintaining the bones in proper position, assisting in support of the body, and furnishing power for smooth movement. Sudden, severe, or prolonged exertion, especially in young or poorly conditioned animals, tends to cause undue strain in certain parts of the body and often produces stretching or laceration of the tissues, constituting what are commonly referred to as sprains. More severe injury may result in actual rupture of one or more of the major muscles, ligaments, or tendons, especially in the leg. In draft animals, sprains may result from the starting of heavy loads, long-continued, heavy hauling, or work where the footing is hard, rough, or slippery. Horses used in such sports as hunting, racing, and polo are frequently injured in this way as a result of overweighting, fast work on a wet track or field or in rough country, improperly balanced shoes, and the sudden stresses which are frequently encountered in competition. Injuries resulting from stumbling, falling, being kicked, or striking hurdles, mangers, etc., frequently occur. The conformation of some animals is faulty, and this, together with improper or incomplete conditioning before heavy work is imposed, may be a basic factor.

The initial injury is inevitably accompanied by more or less swelling and pain, depending on where the injury occurs. Injury of tendons or ligaments frequently involves some damage to the jointlike sheaths in which they are encased at points along their course, and even the periosteum (membranous covering of the bone) or the joints may become irritated. If the processes continue, the parts are apt to become infiltrated with fibrous tissue and even with calcium salts, leading to firm thickening, loss of elasticity, and contraction of the tissues. The continued irritation may lead to a great increase of the synovial fluid in the tendon sheaths or the joints. Sometimes bacteria, derived either from the outside or from some remote focus of infection within the body, invade the injured tissue.

If the initial, acute inflammatory changes do not recede and chronic infiltrations take place, such abnormalities as "bowed tendons," "bucked shins," hygroma (water knee), "calf knees," etc., result. The more extensive and chronic such changes are, the less is the likelihood of restoring the affected animal to complete soundness.

Foals are sometimes born with contracted tendons, as a result of which they are often unable to stand.

Arthritis

Arthritis is an inflammation of an articulation, or joint, between two or more bones. It occurs primarily or secondarily as a result of injury, involving other factors such as conformation, and may or may not be complicated by bacterial invasion. When foreign objects perforate the joint capsule, infection invariably follows. The result is extreme lameness, accompanied by fever and other constitutional disturbances. Chronic arthritis results in enlargement and impaired movement of the joint.

Luxations (Dislocations)

The displacement of bones from their normal coordinated position constitutes a luxation. The patella (kneecap in man), located in the stifle joint, is sometimes displaced upward or outward and either an extreme straightening of the hind leg in a forward position or a relaxed state in which it will not support the body weight results. Such animals are said to be "stifled." Other less frequent luxations occur in the shoulder, knee, fetlock, and hip joints.

Luxation, particularly of the patella, sometimes occurs after debilitating diseases such as influenza and pneumonia. It is encountered in colts with joint ill or rickets, or may result from injury, and in some cases it appears as a congenital defect. Serious injury is the usual cause in the case of joints other than the stifle.

Affections of the Nerves and Blood Vessels

The nerves of the legs are generally fairly well protected from injury by other tissues, but injuries do occasionally occur that result in more or less severe lameness. These lamenesses are to be distinguished from defects in the gait attributable to damage in the central nervous system (brain and spinal cord) such as develops in encephalo-myelitis and other diseases. Injury of the suprascapular nerve results in a bulging of the shoulder and may be the cause of muscular atrophy or wasting, which is commonly known as sweeny, or swinney. In some cases of difficult foaling the obturator nerve on either or both sides may be compressed between the dam's pelvis and some part of the fetus. As a result, the muscles holding the legs in toward the body may be paralyzed and a spreading of one or both legs occurs. Paralysis of the foreleg may follow injury of the brachial or radial nerves. Minor injury leads to awkward use of the leg, while severe injury results in complete limpness of the entire leg. Tumors may press upon the nerves controlling certain muscles, causing symptoms of paralysis.

Normal tone and function of the body muscles is primarily dependent upon the supply of blood they receive. Inflammation of the blood vessels, chiefly the arteries, may occur in the legs as well as other parts of the body as the result of invasion by blood strongyles, or palisade worms. The walls become thickened, and clots form in the iliac, femoral, and other arteries of the leg. Injury may lead to the formation of similar lesions. In consequence, the blood supply to the legs is more or less decreased. Thrombosis, or clot formation, in the iliac artery produces a characteristic type of lameness with which there may be profuse sweating, trembling, widely dilated nostrils, and rapid breathing. The attack may disappear as rapidly as it developed, leaving the animal entirely normal to all appearances, or a part of the clot may be dislodged into the blood stream and become fixed in a vessel in some vital organ, such as the brain, which may cause death. The attacks of lameness somewhat resemble azoturia in appearance, but in this case they may recur at any time, whereas in azoturia there is no relapse.

Fractures and Stringhalt

Fractures or broken bones may result from severe injury or extreme strain. The symptoms are dependent upon the location and extent of the damage. The afflicted animal does not always collapse as a result of the break but nearly always reveals extreme pain when compelled to move. Disturbance of normal alinement and relationship between the bones, crepitation, or grating sounds, when the leg is manipulated, and X-ray findings are elements of diagnosis. Most fractures of the leg bones of horses or mules are not amenable to treatment under ordinary conditions, but in the case of some valuable animals, especially if they are young and tractable, it is practical for the veterinarian to attempt treatment. Unusually ideal conditions, however, are always required.

Stringhalt consists in spasmodic contractions of the muscles of the hind leg as a result of which the foot is pulled or jerked upward. The ailment usually develops slowly, progressively increasing in severity, but it rarely leads to complete loss of serviceability. Most often it affects only one leg, though both hind legs may be involved. The symptoms are likely to be most marked when the affected animal is first taken from the stall or when it is backed. In some cases the flexion of the leg is so sudden and violent that the animal falls to the ground. With continued exercise, the condition tends to improve, finally disappearing after a short time in most cases, only to reassert itself after a period of rest. By some it is considered a form of neurosis; others believe it to be hereditary, and still other theories have been advanced. No known line of treatment is successful in all cases. Various neurectomies (severing of nerves) and tenotomies (severing of tendons) are performed, often with apparent benefit. Medicinal treatment is not known to be of any avail.

PREVENTION AND TREATMENT OF LAMENESS

With good husbandry, including prevention of wounds and wise care of the feet, there is little lameness in horses or mules of sound constitution, free from hereditary defects or seriously inferior conformation. Patience and understanding should always be practiced in training animals. All parts of the harness should be adjusted properly. Measures taken to modify a horse's gait should be developed gradually. These precautions will limit unnecessary strains which might lead to ailments causing lameness. Immediate attention should be given to the slightest indication of lameness. Delay or unwise treatment may lead to needless complications or incurable conditions.

The first principle of the treatment of a lame animal is rest. The second is accurate diagnosis. Third, it should be understood that no one drug, combination of drugs, or system of treatment is applicable to all cases, even of the same one of the many ailments which result in lameness. Rest alone may be all that is required to correct some simple abnormalities. If the nature and site of the trouble have been determined, cold packs may be applied to the part. Again, alternate hot and cold packs or repeated soaking of the part in a saturated solution of Epsom salts may be advisable. Elastic or other bandages are sometimes applied to sprains with benefit. Various astringent lotions are sometimes used.

Irritants or blistering substances applied in the early stages of most lamenesses are harmful. Only when the condition responsible for the lameness fails to respond to rest and conservative treatment or when chronic changes are present should counterirritation be used. It may be advisedly employed to produce a superficial inflammation in the case of chronic lesions of a tendon, tendon sheath, joint, or bone. Cautery, or "firing," may be used either with or without the adjunct of a so-called blistering agent.

Firing is an accepted form of treatment for chronic ailments that do not yield to conservative treatment and rest. It should not be used indiscriminately by the untrained and cannot be expected to result in the complete disappearance of chronic proliferations (abnormal growth) of tissue, including bone. The irons used in this process are of various shapes for different purposes and are heated by electricity, chemicals, or fire. Care and judgment are necessary to be sure that sufficient but not excessive counterirritation results. A blistering ointment is often used following firing. After such treatment it is best to tie up the animal for a few days or until the acute inflammation subsides, after which it is a common practice to remove the shoes, trim the feet, and the put the animal on pasture for a time.

Wounds causing lameness are treated according to their extent and location, with due regard for the control of infection and the preservation or restoration of normal function in the affected part.

Enlargements of joints or tendon sheaths due to an accumulation of fluid are usually treated by withdrawing the fluid under sterile conditions; this in some cases is followed by injection of antiseptic solution and counterirritation or bandaging.

Special manipulations are required to reduce a luxation. This is usually relatively easy to accomplish, but the condition is apt to recur in many cases if the injury is severe or if treatment has been delayed.

Contracted tendons, especially in foals, frequently require surgical attention and the temporary use of specially made supports.

Advanced cases of sweeny in which marked shrinking of the muscle has taken place are commonly treated by injection with various forms of iodine in solution or other substances to stimulate the formation of new tissue.

Some fractures of certain bones, if detected immediately after the injury takes place and if not too great damage has resulted, will heal under competent care. In most cases, however, humane destruction of the animal is advised by the attending veterinarian on practical grounds.

BONE DISEASES

Probably diseases of the bones are responsible for more lay-offs of draft horses and mules than any other one class of ailments. The services of large numbers of racing and other sporting horses are temporarily and in some cases permanently lost through the same cause.

The chief feature of most bone diseases of solipeds is exostosis, or abnormal growth of bone. This arises primarily from faulty feeding which provides an insufficiency of the minerals necessary for the production and preservation of normal bone. Accessory factors are strains and other injuries such as are discussed under the heading Lameness. Animals with defective conformation are particularly apt to develop these conditions. Improper shoeing may be a contributing cause. Finally, heredity is believed to influence the occurrence of at least some bone diseases. Spavin and ringbone are among the diseases that disqualify a stallion or jack for registration for public service, except as an unsound animal, in many States. Unusually nervous animals, even without defects in conformation or ancestry, appear to be subject to spavin.

The spavin considered here is that involving the bones of the tarsus, or hock, rather than so-called bog spavin, which consists of an accumulation of synovial fluid in and around the joint. Bone spavin usually develops gradually. At first the lameness disappears after the animal goes a short distance, only to return after a rest. "Warming out" becomes less frequent as the disease advances, and there are large bony enlargements (exostosis) of the joints. To the experienced observer, the character of the lameness is quite distinctive even in the absence of definite enlargement. The exostosis, which is usually greatest on the inside of the joint, is most easily detected by viewing the hock from between the forelegs, at an angle from near the shoulder, or from behind. The condition is especially prevalent in animals with small, weak hocks.

Ringbone is an exostosis involving the first and second phalangeal bones, that is, those immediately below the fetlock. Animals with short, upright pasterns seem to be especially predisposed to this condition. It is classified as high, low, and in other ways, according to its location and extent. The lameness of ringbone is especially manifested when the affected animal is required to step from side to side. Marked flinching then occurs when weight is borne on the affected leg, even though no lameness may be revealed when the animal goes in a straight line. The lameness is frequently irregular at first, often being overlooked entirely by the driver or rider, but it finally becomes more or less constant and is attended by plainly visible bony enlargement of the pastern.

Sidebones consist of ossification, or formation of bone, in the lateral cartilages, which are attached to the third phalangeal bone within the hoof, extending above the hoof at the coronet (point of junction of skin and hoof). These cartilages, one on each side of each foot, are normally very resilient, forming a shock-absorbing apparatus within the hoof and presumably assisting in the circulation of blood in the foot. The ossification of these structures greatly disturbs the normal elasticity of the internal part of the foot and the changes in its shape which occur under the influence of the weight of the body. The hardening of the cartilages due to the formation of bone has the effect of cramping the structures of the internal part of the foot, and lameness is inevitable. Sidebones are especially frequent in heavy draft types of horses. They occur chiefly in the front feet.

Splints are not, as some laymen believe, due to growth of a great mass of new bone on the cannon, or shank, bone. The condition consists rather of a comparatively limited exostosis between the cannon bone (large metacarpal) and the small splint bones (small metacarpals), which are situated one on each side of the rear surface of the cannon bone, just below the knee. The splint bones are attached to the cannon by ligaments, forming a part of the carpus, or knee, joint at their upper extremity. The trouble begins with inflammation due to strain or injury of the periosteum or the ligamentous attachment between the cannon and split bones. The condition is quite common during the training of young animals, rarely being encountered in those over 6 to 8 years of age.

The animal may walk normally but is very lame at the trot, nodding the head with each step. The bony enlargements which appear some time after lameness begins usually occur on the inside splint bones. They may be the size of a pea or as large as a small ·marble. Before the proliferation of bone occurs, the parts are sensitive to pressure. When, as sometimes happens, the condition develops in both forelegs, the lameness is not readily detectable.

The term "navicular" is used indiscriminately to designate various diseases affecting the structures which form the coffin joint—that between the second and third phalanges within the hoof. More strictly speaking, navicular disease refers to inflammations involving the navicular bone (third sesamoid), the deep flexor tendon, and the bursa podotrochlearis, or navicular bursa. Usually the disease occurs in one forefoot, though sometimes both are affected. Only occasionally does it develop in the hind feet. Lameness is the first indication. The animal is inclined to stumble, and there is a stilted gait due to shortening of the stride. In advanced cases involving only one foot, there is a characteristic "pointing"—advancing the affected foot well in front of its mate when standing.

The general group of bone diseases classed as rickets (rachitis) and bighead (osteoporosis, osteomalacia, and osteitis fibrosa) are discussed in some detail in the article on Nutritional Diseases of Farm Animals, page 323.

Prevention and Treatment of Bone Diseases

Proper feeding is essential for the development of sound bones in horses and mules as well as other animals. It should begin with the dam and is of great importance for the foal and the developing animal.

Horse breeders desirous of producing sound animals should have a thorough understanding of good conformation. For example, in breeding stock, pasterns that are exceptionally long and sloping or too short and upright are to be especially avoided. Small, weak hocks, poorly alined legs, and poor feet also are important contributing factors in lameness, particularly that attributable to bone diseases.

There is considerable evidence that certain bone ailments, notably spavin and ringbone, are especially prevalent in the offspring of certain animals. There is the suggestion of such a hereditary influence in other diseases of the bones. This is reflected in faulty conformation or constitutional weakness.

Care and judgment in the management of horses and mules, including their shoeing, can assist in lessening strains and injuries which may lead directly or indirectly to the disabling bone diseases.

The principles of treatment of bone diseases are outlined under the heading Prevention and Treatment of Lameness. It should be realized, however, that long-continued diseases of the bone frequently result in irreparable damage. Thus, both spavin and ringbone commonly lead to ankylosis, or complete fusion of the bones of a part or all of the involved joint. If the processes of the disease cannot be arrested early by rest and appropriate treatment, permanent damage must be expected to follow. In this event, serviceability rather than soundness is the goal of treatment. Specially designed shoes are frequently prescribed for such cases, in conjunction with changing of the proportions or angles of the hoof by appropriate trimming.

FOOT AILMENTS

"No foot, no horse" concisely expresses a principle well understood
by experienced horsemen. The horse or mule without sound feet is
so apt to be incapacitated, either temporarily or permanently, that
every precaution possible should be taken. A number of troubles
attributable directly or indirectly to improper management or to
faulty conformation are briefly discussed here. More or less lameness develops sooner or later as a result of any of these conditions.

As a preliminary, it may be well to consider the normal foot of
the horse. The hoof of solipeds may well be compared with the
human toenail except that it completely encases the digit. The hoof
consists of a more or less dense, fibrous, horny material derived from
the skin at the coronet (the spongy, padlike tissue just above the hoof
at its junction with the skin). Within this case of horn are bones,
tendons, ligaments, nerves, and an intricate network of blood vessels.
The hoof wall and sole are attached to the underlying structures
by means of so-called sensitive and insensitive laminae. These consist
of minute leaflike structures which are closely united in dovetailed
fashion. Unyielding as the hoof appears to be, it has been proved
that it expands and contracts in synchronized waves when the animal moves on it, particularly at the heels and the coronary cushion.
Even the sole of the foot, which is superimposed over a padlike
structure known as the plantar cushion, flattens out when weight is
borne. The so-called lateral cartilages (described in connection with
sidebones, p. 438) are an important part of this normal expansion
and contraction.

The nutriment for the structures of the foot is received from
the blood, the flow of which is largely controlled by the expansion and contraction of the parts described. The hoof wall
grows at the rate of about one-fourth of an inch a month,
being pushed down from the coronet regularly all around the foot.
Growth is favored by moisture and good nutrition and general health
as well as by exercise. The unshod hoof grows more rapidly than one
with shoes.

The white line at the junction of the wall with the sole marks the
point of union between the minute horny leaves of the sole and those
of the wall. In shoeing, the nails are driven through the hoof at
a point just outside this line. The sole is marked by a deep, V-shaped
cleft, outlined on each side by the bars, which are a continuation of
the wall. The pyramidal or triangle-shaped horny structure within
the lines of the V formed by the bars is known as the frog. The
entire sole of the hoof, as well as the walls, covers highly sensitive
tissue richly supplied with nerves and blood vessels.

By conformation is meant the general form, outline, and arrangement of parts. The conformation of the ideal foot varies somewhat
with the type of animal and even with the breed. Generally speaking, the well-shaped hoof is roughly like a cone from above downward. The print made by the hoof is generally oval, being slightly
greater in length than in width. The walls of the hoof slope gradually and evenly outward from above and are free from deep grooves

or bulges. The substance of the normal hoof is dense and firm but not brittle, and it has a distinctive gloss, the result of a varnishlike substance called periople, which lessens the evaporation of the water normally present in the horn. The bars are well defined, strong, and widely spaced. There is no compressed narrowing of the foot at the heel, and the frog is clean and well-formed.

The feet should be centered on a perpendicular line from the point of the buttocks through the hock and fetlock in the hind leg and from the shoulder through the knee and fetlock in the front leg. Viewed from the side, the axis through the fetlock, pastern, and hoof should consist of a straight, unbroken line forming an angle of about 34° with the base of the foot. The hoof at the heel should generally be approximately one-third as long as in front.

The foot of the mule or ass is considerably smaller and rounder than the foot of the horse. In addition, the pastern is generally more erect, giving the hoof a comparatively "stumpy" appearance.

BRITTLE HOOFS, SPONGY HOOFS, CROOKED FOOT, AND CONTRACTED FOOT

As the term "brittle hoofs" indicates, there may develop an abnormally dry state of the horn. The hoof becomes almost of the consistency of stone and chips and cracks easily. Brittle hoofs tend to encourage contracted heels and lead to difficulties in shoeing. It has been observed that short, cobby animals of certain breeds commonly have this defect. Long-continued dryness or stabling on dry, hard floors is conducive to the trouble. Repeated applications of certain hoof dressings on show animals may be a contributing cause. In cases of brittle hoofs, it is often advisable to remove the shoes, trim the feet, and reshoe, under a veterinarian's supervision whenever possible. The bearing surface should be made as level as possible, and thin nails should be used, placed in the strongest parts of the hoof wall. When a level bearing cannot be established, a hoof cement is sometimes used advantageously. A hoof ointment containing such substances as turpentine, tar, and wax in an oily or fatty base is often beneficial.

The opposite of brittle hoofs, spongy hoofs are characterized by abnormally soft, nonresistant horn. This condition is a common characteristic of certain breeds and is encountered in animals kept on marshy ground and those of a so-called lymphatic type. Such feet are predisposed to canker and corns. Special care must be taken in shoeing spongy or soft hoofs. Excessive paring of the sole and hot fitting of the shoe are special hazards. Animals with such hoofs are prone to develop dry horn and contracted feet unless particular care is taken.

The term "crooked foot" denotes a foot with one side wall higher than the other. Sometimes the hoof wall is curved in or out on one or both sides. This is often attributable to inherited faulty conformation with "toeing in" or "toeing out," but it may be brought about by unequal paring of the foot or by bad shoeing. Gradual lowering of the high side of a crooked foot by repeated trimming will tend to improve the condition, but complete and permanent correction is impossible when the trouble results from faulty conformation of the leg. Special shoes are sometimes applicable, but they should be frequently reset.

Flat feet with low, weak heels, improperly shod feet in which the frog does not receive normal ground pressure, and feet excessively dried out during a long period of dry, hot weather are apt to become contracted, chiefly at the heels. Excessive paring of the bars may also be a factor. Contraction of long standing is obstinate and impractical to treat in many cases. Animals with such feet are often much better off without shoes. Going thus barefooted permits natural pressure on the frog, and spreading of the heels is the natural result. In shoeing, the bars and frog should be let alone as much as possible, and expansion or other special shoes may be applied. Hoof ointments assist in softening the horn, which tends to become hard.

Sand Crack, Corns, and Thrush

Cracks or splits in the hoof wall following the direction of the horn fibers are classified according to their position as toe crack, quarter crack, or sand crack of the frog or sole. Sand crack is attributable fundamentally to faulty conformation, being found also in animals with brittle hoofs. Rasping of the periople from the outer surface of the hoof wall tends to weaken the wall, promoting sand cracks. They sometimes arise also from purely accidental causes in wholly normal hoofs. They are not particularly serious if the underlying sensitive structures are not involved. Unfortunately, the veterinarian is seldom consulted until the injury is deep-seated and lameness is apparent, and treatment is then not always wholly satisfactory.

Sand cracks are treated according to their location and extent. In simple cases, blistering the coronet with an irritating substance will sometimes sufficiently stimulate horn growth to overcome the crack. The margins of the crack may be drawn together by a skilled horseshoer and clamped with a well-placed horseshoe nail or clamps especially designed for the purpose. Special shoeing is sometimes advantageously employed. Grooves may be cut around the crack to immobilize the hoof wall, thus permitting healing. Finally, in complicated cases, the portion of horn involved in the crack may be removed by cutting or burning, but frequent dressing and a protracted rest are necessary until new horn fills the uncovered space.

The term "corn" to the veterinarian indicates the changes that follow the bruising of the sensitive sole of the hoof, usually between the bar and the wall. The injury is more common in the forefeet and on the inner side. The bruise is accompanied by hemorrhage and consequent discoloration from red to brown, greenish, or yellow. There is pain in the swollen structures. A dry corn is one fortunately unattended by excessive inflammatory changes. A considerable amount of inflammatory exudate, or discharge, is present in a moist corn, and pus is found in the suppurating corn.

Corns are considered by most authorities as basically attributable to faults in conformation (wide, flat feet with low heels; high, contracted heels; long or overgrown hoofs). Direct injury in connection with excessive moisture or dryness and stable filth and excessive paring of the sole, bars, or frog by overzealous farriers are also contributing causes.

Treatment of corns is not always satisfactory, especially in cases of very long standing. Paring of the sole is not always advisable but may be necessary for the liberation of pus. When shoes are applied, one of the main objectives is provision of frog pressure. So-called bar shoes are put on after careful leveling of the foot. Suppurating corns may require frequent special dressings.

A degenerative condition of the frog characterized by a black, offensive pus is called thrush. Often the first indication of the trouble to the casual observer is the characteristic stench. Thrush is caused by an infection first of the horn and later of the sensitive structures. The horn is normally resistant to bacterial invasion but may become deteriorated through long-continued exposure to excessively wet or filthy stalls or paddocks or extended exposure to extremely dry footing, especially in cases of contracted feet. Thrush is more common in the hind feet. Lameness nearly always attends it sooner or later. It is necessary first to trim away all the diseased horn, exposing the depths of the process for antiseptic treatment. The foot should be so trimmed or shod as to restore and preserve normal frog pressure.

CANKER, GREASE HEEL, AND QUITTOR

Symptoms of canker are seldom noticed early, as the disease progresses slowly and practically without pain at first. An inflammatory change in the horn-forming tissue causes secretion of a serous fluid instead of the normally produced horny cells. Eventually the frog and even part of the sole may be separated from the underlying sensitive tissue. Instead of normal horn being formed, there is often a fungoid mass. Deep in the tissue surrounding the lesion there is frequently an accumulation of fetid, cheeselike material. As a result of fungoid growth, the horny sole and frog, and sometimes the entire foot, become deformed.

The disease is confused with thrush and by some is considered as an advanced form of that disease. The exact cause remains undetermined. Certain factors, however, appear to be conducive to canker. Continued standing in dampness and filth or any condition which removes the natural counter pressure on the frog may be suspected as a predisposing cause of this disease as well as of thrush.

Canker is a difficult condition to treat in advanced cases. Surgical removal of the abnormal growth followed by application of a hot iron, packing with an antiseptic pad, and shoeing with specially designed canker-dressing shoes are the essentials of the usual procedure.

"Grease heel" is a term commonly applied to an inflammation of the skin of the pastern and fetlock. The specific cause is unknown, but it is usually seen in heavy horses with coarse, thick legs when such horses are kept in damp, insanitary stables or are long subjected to mud and filth without proper cleaning.

At first there are swelling and redness of the skin, with some itching. Later there is an increased secretion from the sebaceous glands in the affected region, over which the hair stands erect, glued together by the oily secretion, which has an offensive odor. The skin, at first moist and painful, tends to become thickened, and finally, after several months, fungoid masses commonly referred to as "grapes" may be formed. The hind legs are more commonly affected.

In treating grease heel it is advisable first to clip closely all hair on the affected areas. The region should then be thoroughly cleaned with mild soap and water. Following this, various astringent, antiseptic substances are applied at regular intervals. In cases of long standing in which wartlike growths are present these must be removed surgically and the wounds suitably dressed until healing takes place.

The opening at the coronet of one or more sinuses, or pus-discharging passages, is called quittor. The pus originates primarily from a necrotic (dead) lateral cartilage; later, any of the internal structures of the foot may be involved.

Infection may gain entrance through calk wounds, inflammatory conditions of the skin over the coronet, a suppurating corn, a puncture wound in the foot, sand cracks, etc. Cartilage is poorly nourished by the blood; when once it is injured and infected, necrosis invariably follows.

There is usually more or less severe inflammatory swelling around the opening, which is painful. Pus of a grayish color, often streaked with blood, is discharged almost constantly. In chronic cases, hoof deformities result from the disturbed circulation in the coronary band. The deeper the sinus and the more copious the discharge, the poorer the chances of recovery.

Treatment depends upon the degree and extent of the damage. In a few cases, simple drainage and antiseptic treatment result favorably. In most, however, a radical surgical operation involving the removal of all diseased tissue becomes necessary. Frequent dressing is required, and the convalescent period may be quite prolonged.

PREVENTION OF FOOT AILMENTS

From the foregoing, it will be seen that most of the foot abnormalities arise either from inherited poor conformation or improper care of the feet. Poor conformation can be largely avoided by proper selection of animals, either for breeding or for work. The inexperienced should not hesitate to consult a veterinarian in this connection. The application of shoes is an unnatural necessity for many, if not most, horses and mules. If improperly done, injury inevitably follows.

Here are some do's and don'ts in taking proper care of the feet of horses and mules:

The feet of stabled animals should be trimmed, removing all excess growth of the hoof wall, at least once a month. Pastured animals should receive this attention at least every 2 months.

Shoes should be reset or replaced every month. Failure to change the shoes results in the natural growth of the hoof carrying the heel too far beneath the foot for proper bearing.

The feet should be thoroughly cleaned with a blunt stick and sponge or brush and water after every day's work. It is considered a bad practice to use the currycomb below the knees or hocks. A brush or cloth is preferable.

The pasterns and fetlocks should receive special attention in grooming each day, particularly after work in mud or snow.

Stalls should be roomy, clean, well-bedded, and well-drained. During protracted dry weather, the hoofs are apt to become excessively dry, especially if the animals stand on concrete or brick floors. If floors are of dirt, considerable care should be taken to keep them smooth and well-graded. If the hoofs show signs of dryness, periodic soaking for an hour or more at a time in clean water is advantageous.

When an animal is shod, rasping the outer wall and cutting the bars, sole, or frog should not be permitted except under a veterinarian's supervision.

Shoes of other than conventional design should not be applied except under the direction of a veterinarian.[4]

SKIN DISEASES

Afflictions of the skin are relatively infrequent in horses and mules except under improper management, which contributes greatly to the occurrence and spread of such diseases, both infectious and noninfectious.

The skin is an integral part of the body as a whole, and, as such, it reflects either general health or abnormality. Thus, excessive sweating (hyperhidrosis) occurs in certain febrile diseases, failure to sweat (anhidrosis) may be an indication of general debility from various causes, and itching (pruritis) may be traceable to dietary excesses or deficiencies. Hematidrosis, or so-called sweating of blood, is not due to the actual secretion of blood by the sweat glands but rather to mixing of blood with the sweat as a result of a general circulatory disease, as in purpura hemorrhagica. Rational feeding and moderate exercise or work, together with general stable hygiene, promote the health of the skin as well as that of the rest of the body, and when diseases of the skin occur under these conditions they are generally attributable to inflammation caused externally by parasites or irritating chemical substances.

Itching may occur in animals as a result of chronic bowel irritation, chronic kidney disease, failure to shed or delay in shedding the coat, or the long-continued feeding of a restricted diet. It is present in some cases of alopecia (falling of the hair) and ringworm, and it is an almost constant symptom in eczema, pediculosis (lousiness), and

---

[4] The elements of conformation and shoeing are discussed in Farmers' Bulletins 779, How to Select a Sound Horse, and 1535, Farm Horseshoeing.

mange. Intense itching frequently occurs in animals developing rabies.

Erythema of the skin, or redness due to congestion of blood, is a result of excessive or exclusive feeding of certain feeds such as clovers, potatoes, and distillers' grains, and in some cases it occurs in animals on an exclusive ration of alfalfa. It may developed during the course of administration of certain drugs, from friction, or from excessive heat, cold, or sunshine. It is seen in eczema and parasitic infestations and in the course of various infectious diseases.

Dandruff, an accumulation of branlike scales on the skin, is observed in eczema, mange, iodine poisoning, louse infestations, and some cases of chronic digestive diseases.

The diagnosis of skin diseases, which is generally essential before satisfactory treatment can be applied, is often very difficult for even the most experienced veterinarian. There are, however, certain more or less common skin diseases with which the horseman should become at least superficially acquainted in order that he may, as far as possible, avoid them and realize the difficulties to be encountered in diagnosis and treatment. A brief discussion of these follows.

ECZEMA, ACNE, AND URTICARIA (HIVES)

Eczema is defined as a superficial, or surface, inflammation of the skin and is classified for descriptive purposes into several types not of special interest in this discussion. It is most common in the spring, especially in old horses, in which it is often chronic. Vesicles (small water blisters), papules (pimples), or dandruff are common indications of the disease. An eruption with more or less severe itching appears over the body generally or on any part of it. When confined to certain areas, it frequently appears first at the base of the tail or mane.

The vesicles rupture, discharging their contents and matting the hair. Rubbing the parts leads to loss of hair and rawness of the skin. Later, crusts or dandruff appear. During the course of the disease, bacterial infection may take place, and deep infiltration by pus sometimes develops. Eczema sometimes affects several horses at a time in the same stable as if it were contagious. It is aggravated by the use of irritating soaps or solutions. Sometimes it appears so much like mange that differentiation can be made only by failure to find mites. The condition tends to improve during cool or cold weather, becoming worse during warm periods.

The causes of eczema are not exactly known, but they are considered to be variable. Accumulations of mud and snow in the coat, insanitary stables, and lack of grooming to remove accumulation of dirt and sweat appear to be accessory factors. Underlying causes may be a basic sensitiveness to certain feeds or chronic digestive disturbances.

Acne is sometimes called summer mange, although it is not actually mange. It consists of an inflammation of the hair follicles and sebaceous glands caused by pus-forming bacteria. The lesions of the disease, which are either small pimples or larger boillike formations, may occur on any part of the body but are more commonly found in parts rubbed by the harness or saddle. The bacteria appear thus to be rubbed into the pores and follicles.

Urticaria is a manifestation of anaphylaxis (an intoxication due to introduction of a substance, usually a protein, to which the animal is sensitive). It is characterized by the sudden appearance of numbers of rounded, elevated areas in the skin over the head and neck or on the body. The circumscribed swellings are attributable to the infiltration of the skin by edema. The condition sometimes appears in several infectious diseases, and in purpura hemorrhagica; as a result of contact with irritants, such as plants of the genus *Urtica* (stinging nettles) or irritating chemicals; following insect bites; as an anaphylactic reaction to certain feeds; or as a result of absorption of toxic substances from the gastrointestinal tract.

Light Sensitization, Ringworm, and Lymphangitis

Light sensitization is manifested almost exclusively in white-skinned or -spotted animals. In the latter, only the white areas are involved. It apparently is induced by the consumption of certain plants, chiefly legumes, the pigments of which under certain conditions form a substance in the blood that sensitizes the body cells to sunlight, resulting in edematous, or watery infiltrations of the skin and underlying tissues. Inflammation of the membranes of the mouth, colic, jaundice, and even symptoms of brain disturbances may also occur.

Following edema of the skin with or without the formation of vesicles, the skin surface becomes dry and encrusted. Itching may occur. Gangrene of the skin (death of the tissue) may result, leading to the sloughing of the tissue and leaving a raw surface which may be attacked by pus-forming bacteria.

The plants most commonly implicated in this trouble, which may affect cattle and other animals as well as horses, include Swedish clover (*Trifolium hybridum*), red clover (*Trifolium pratense*), vetch (*Vicia sativa*), and St. Johnswort (*Hypericum* species).

The remedy is to change the pasture or hay and keep the animals out of the sunshine for a time. In severe cases, mild protective dressings are sometimes applied to the most seriously affected areas of the skin.

Ringworm is a contagious disease caused by certain microscopic molds (*Trichophyta, Microspora*, etc.). The disease may be transmitted to man and other animals.

Rounded, scaly patches with sparse hair occur on the skin of any part of the body, but chiefly the shoulder, breast, flank, croup, back, or head and neck, and less often on the legs or the abdomen. Asbestoslike crusts may be formed, and the skin generally has a grayish or yellowish powdery or warty appearance in the affected regions. After a time the originally affected areas tend to return to normal, the hair grows in and the skin becomes soft and smooth. But new patches appear in adjacent areas, eventually spreading over most of the body. Ringworm in horses usually causes little itching.

The organism responsible for the condition is usually readily demonstrable microscopically, and it can be cultivated in the laboratory from the scales and hairs from the affected skin. Strict sanitation is an essential in the control of ringworm.

In the nutrition of the body the blood itself does not come in direct contact with the tissue cells. The cells are directly nourished through the medium of a fluid known as lymph, which is derived from the blood. Lymph circulates about the body through channels known as lymph vessels. Lymphangitis is an inflammation of these vessels.

Strictly speaking, this condition is not, of course, a disease of the skin, but since its outward manifestations involve the skin, it is included here. There are at least three main forms which affect solipeds—sporadic lymphangitis ("big-leg" or "weed"), ulcerative lymphangitis, and mycotic or epizootic lymphangitis.

Sporadic lymphangitis occurs chiefly in heavy-legged animals which have been held in the stall on full feed for a number of days between periods of work. For this reason, it is sometimes referred to as Monday-morning disease, as is azoturia also. It appears that the lack of usual exercise and continuation of a full ration, especially a highly nitrogenous one, results in slowing the flow of lymph, which in turn leads to a "filling" or "stocking" of one or more of the legs, chiefly the hind legs. Poorly groomed animals with dirty legs or those with cracked heels, thrush, and similar ailments are especially prone to the condition, and it is assumed that the lesions harboring various pus-forming organisms lead to infection of the lymph stream and consequently the vessels. In acute cases there may be fever, chills, and extreme lameness. Drops of yellowish, glairy liquid, resembling white of egg, may accumulate on the leg. This acute stage may last 2 or 3 days, with gradual improvement, or it may persist and lead to a chronic affliction. Some animals appear to recover only to develop the same condition later. Chronic cases develop a permanent thickening of the skin known as elephantiasis.

Ulcerative lymphangitis is attributed to infection by germs known as corynebacteria. In this disease, infection apparently takes place through wounds, chiefly in the feet, the lesions usually being confined to the hind legs, beginning above the fetlocks. In addition to a doughy swelling of the leg, small abscesses develop along the course of the lymph vessels and burst, discharging a yellow or blood-stained pus. The resulting raw ulcers tend to heal in a few weeks, leaving hairless scars. Succeeding crops of abscesses and ulcers appear, and the lymph glands become involved. Even the internal organs may be affected. The causative germ can be cultivated in the laboratory.

Mycotic lymphangitis is attributed to a yeastlike fungus known as *Cryptococcus farciminosus* Rivolta. Infection is believed to take place through wounds on any part of the body, chiefly the legs. The lymph vessels adjacent to the wound become prominent, and nodules varying from the size of a pea to that of a walnut develop along their course. These burst, discharging a thick white or faintly yellow pus, and red ulcers with little tendency to heal are formed. The organism causing the disease can be grown in artificial media.

All of these forms of lymphangitis may resemble glanders, and tests for that disease as well as laboratory examinations may be required for the exact diagnosis.

TREATMENT AND PREVENTION

Accurate diagnosis is an especially important first step in the treatment of diseases of the skin. From the standpoint of symptoms, many of these ailments are identical in the eyes of the layman, while to the veterinarian clear points of differentiation may be readily apparent. However, very close study and laboratory examination are frequently desirable.

Just as any animal suspected of having an infectious disease should be isolated, so should those with any indication of communicable skin diseases. Even though the veterinarian may later determine that the disease is not transmissible to other animals, better care of the affected animal frequently results from its separation from others in the stable.

Because there are few specific remedies for skin diseases and these are not necessarily applicable in all cases of a given affection, no detailed discussion of medical treatment will be attempted here. Suffice it to say that such a preparation as tincture of iodine is not applicable in every case of ringworm, nor is an acceptable mange remedy necessarily effective in the treatment of eczema; in fact, it is more apt to be harmful.

Clean stables and regular grooming are of the greatest importance in promoting general health and preventing and treating diseases of the skin. Regular cleaning of harness, saddles, blankets, grooming equipment, etc., are parts of good husbandry. If communicable skin diseases appear in the stable, disinfection of the equipment becomes necessary.

Noninfectious and nonparasitic skin diseases are often aggravated if not directly caused by poor condition, which can frequently be improved by modifications or complete changes in the diet. Animals not being regularly worked should have some exercise every day, if possible, and the quantity of their ration should be regulated according to their activity.

Prescription and application of medicinal agents should be left to the attending veterinarian.

ABNORMALITIES OF THE TEETH

Deciduous, or milk, teeth, 24 in number, appear in the horse's mouth early in life and are much smaller than the second or permanent set, which number 36 in the mare and 42 in the male horse.[5] The majority of these erupt or replace the deciduous set at 2½ to 4½ years of age. It is during this period of changing teeth that most horses and mules are broken or trained and first used for hard work. The changing of teeth, especially when the temporary molars fail to shed and become firmly fixed caps on the crowns of the emerging

---

[5] The 4 canine (bridle) teeth found in the male are absent or very rudimentary in the mare. The so-called wolf teeth, which sometimes appear one on each side just in front of the first upper grinders, are vestiges of the first premolar teeth of the prehistoric horse.

permanent molars, is accompanied by pain and poor mastication. This trouble, combined with hard work, causes many colts to lose weight rapidly, appear unthrifty, and sometimes develop digestive disturbances (colic) if attention is not given to the teeth. Any unusual occurrence during feeding, such as slobbering, excessive drooling of saliva, sudden cessation of eating, or dropping of food from the mouth, is a symptom indicative of tooth trouble and should be investigated by a thorough examination of the animal's mouth.

The commonest disorders of horses' teeth are alveolar periostitis and uneven teeth.

ALVEOLAR PERIOSTITIS AND UNEVEN TEETH

The spaces occupied by the teeth in the jawbones are known as alveoli. The embedded part of the tooth is attached to the alveolus, or socket, by a layer of tissue known as the alveolar periosteum, an inflammation of which results in alveolar periostitis, which may extend to the dental pulp (the central, soft, gelatinous part of the tooth). Alveolar periostitis is usually caused by food particles and infective material which have gained entrance to the alveoli from the mouth. The food particles and the resulting decomposed infective material in the majority of cases enter the dental pulp from the grinding surface of the molars through improperly closed structures (infundibula) between the grinding surface and the pulp cavity. Infection may also be admitted through imperfect gums, through the spaces between the teeth, or through the exposure of the alveolar periosteum at the time of shedding the temporary molars. Occasionally the disease may result from cystic tumors, nutritional disturbances, or mechanical violence. The progressive involvement of structures is always accompanied by an extremely offensive odor and more or less pain and difficulty in mastication. Abscesses may form deep in the sockets, involving the bony tissues, and may break through, discharging their contents through the skin on the lower jaw or into the sinuses of the upper jaw. In the latter case there may be a nasal discharge. Obstruction of the blood supply may occur and result in desiccation and often splitting of the tooth. Involvement of neighboring teeth and expulsion of the originally infected tooth may also occur.

The fourth superior (upper) molar is most often involved. The fifth and third superior and fourth inferior (lower) molars are less frequently affected, and the remaining molars rarely. The treatment indicated is early extraction under proper anesthesia.

The horse, like other herbivorous animals, has teeth that are specially adapted for intensive wear and differ from those of other animals and man. In the latter groups, the root only is embedded in the bony alveolus, and crown being fully exposed except where covered by the margins of the gums. In herbivorous animals, the crown is for the most part embedded in the bone in young animals, continuing its growth with wear. In extreme old age, even the true root may come into wear.

Enamel and dentine of unequal hardness make up the tooth surface; the latter being softer wears faster and produces the necessary rough grinding surface. When the grinding surfaces of the teeth of old animals have become smooth, the deep portion of the molars with little enamel has come into wear, and the animals should be fed ground. or crushed feeds.

The distance between the two rows of upper grinders is greater than that between the rows of lower grinders. The grinding table of the upper molars is beveled downward toward the cheek and the opposing table of the lower molars slopes upward toward the tongue. This arrangement is well adapted to the lateral movement used by the horse in chewing its coarse feed. In the normal mouth the outer edge of the upper molars and the inner edge of the lower molars are quite sharp. Not infrequently these edges become excessively sharp or jagged and cause considerable injury to the cheeks and tongue, interfering with normal mastication. Such abnormalities may be corrected by appropriate rasping, or so-called floating.

When one or more teeth in a row in either jaw project or extend beyond the normal grinding plane, uneven wear results. This may lead to serious injury to the animal's mouth and cause improper mastication, followed by indigestion, malnutrition, and in the later stages general unthriftiness, loss of strength, and emaciation.

Where the jaw protrudes, the first or last molars may become longer than others in the arcade because of failure to meet normal grinding opposition. The unopposed teeth continue to lengthen until they meet and injure the opposite gum. Likewise when a tooth is missing in an arcade, its opponent tends to elongate. Such abnormal teeth should be cut off to the level of the adjoining teeth at intervals, usually about once a year.

Occasionally the wolf teeth may cause irritation of the gums, and since they serve no useful purpose they may be extracted with benefit.

FISTULA OF THE WITHERS AND POLL EVIL

Fistula of the withers is a general term loosely applied to any chronic, deep-seated inflammation in the region of the withers, usually accompanied by infection. The conditions included under this general heading are inflammation of the ligament (dorsal cervical desmitis), aseptic or septic inflammation of the protective sheath above the spines of the vertebrae (dorsal bursitis), and true fistula of the withers, in which there is infection of all the structures previously mentioned and possibly the ends of the vertebral spines, with one or more external discharging tracts.

There are differences of opinion among authorities as to the cause of fistula of the withers. It is thought by some that injury from blows, contact with feed racks or low doors, or collar pressure may start the inflammation. *Filaria labiato papillosa*, which is an almost invisible threadlike worm, has been recovered from the diseased tissues in numerous cases and is considered by some as the primary cause. In recent years, bacteriological investigations have revealed the presence of another possible cause, *Brucella abortus*, the germ responsible for brucellosis (Bang's disease) in cattle and for undulant fever in man.

Cervical desmitis frequently results from a slipping of the collar on the top part of the neck and may be controlled in the early stages by properly fitting the collar and adjusting the hame tugs at the center of pull on the shoulder. In more advanced cases surgical removal of the diseased part of the ligament and establishment of adequate drainage are essential for recovery.

The control of aseptic supra spinous bursitis, another primary stage of fistula of the withers, should include the removal of factors that may be responsible for external injury such as low feed racks, low doors, and rocks in the paddock where the animals roll. Conservative treatment is usually tried before resorting to the more drastic surgical procedure. The affected area may be shaved and painted with tincture of iodine or some other mild irritant. Internal medication may hasten and favor resorption in some cases. The use of any surgical instrument, such as a knife or needle, in a case of this type is to be avoided except under strictly aseptic conditions.

In those cases in which the contents of the bursea (sac) are septic or where a true fistula is present, the more radical surgical procedure is indicated. Removal of diseased tissue, including all the diseased tracts and pockets, and the establishment of drainage are essential before healing can be complete. Bacterins prepared from cultures of the micro-organisms found in individual cases are now being used experimentally. Control measures include all those previously mentioned in addition to blood testing for brucellosis. A positive blood test would indicate possible *Brucella* infection, the control of which in cattle and swine may help to eliminate the development of future cases.

Poll evil (atlantal bursitis) is a condition similar to fistula of the withers, differing only in that it affects the poll rather than the withers. The anatomical structures, elementary causes, and general methods for control and treatment are essentially the same.

DISEASES CONNECTED WITH MISMANAGEMENT

While most diseases of horses and mules are influenced indirectly in their occurrence and development by various methods of management of the animals, some are so directly connected with certain practices that it may be correctly said that they are caused by the practices in question.

The ailments here discussed include azoturia, heaves, colic, founder, collar and saddle sores, and certain forms of poisoning. In most of these, mismanagement, whether through ignorance, carelessness, or intention, is the direct cause.

AZOTURIA (BLACK WATER, MONDAY-MORNING DISEASE)

Azoturia is a specific disease of the horse, found most frequently in animals of draft type and characterized by sudden stiffening and paralysis of the muscles, usually in the hind legs, profuse sweating, and black or coffee-colored urine. It usually appears shortly after exercise is begun after a day or more of idleness. It occurs chiefly in animals that are receiving full feed and are in good condition and appears most frequently in the spring months.

Numerous theories have been presented concerning the specific cause. Originally the disease was named in the belief, since disproved, that it was due to an excess of nitrogenous substances in the urine. A plausible explanation is based on the lactic acid theory, developed in recent years. Lactic acid is one of the byproducts resulting from the metabolism of glycogen (animal starch) in the muscles. This natural process is accelerated before and during azoturia, according to some investigators. Excessive lactic acid is thought to cause deranged muscular activity, circulatory sluggishness, and muscular exhaustion. A working animal stores a large amount of glycogen in the muscles during a period of idleness, especially if it is kept on full feed, particularly on a high carbohydrate diet. Such an animal may develop an excess of lactic acid in the muscle tissue when returned to work, with consequent danger of azoturia.

Control measures consist in regulation of the diet during rest periods—cutting the ration to a minimum and giving laxative feeds such as bran—and, if possible, allowing the animals to exercise naturally in a paddock.

All animals should be closely watched when resuming work after a lay-off. If the disease develops, successful treatment requires immediate, absolute rest, in a standing position if possible. This means that the animal should not be moved from the spot where it becomes affected unless absolutely necessary, and then by truck or similar means. Such a procedure may require the erection of a temporary shelter, as well as slings for supporting the animal. Medication must vary with the severity of the case, and veterinary service is essential to determine the necessity of sedatives, laxatives, alkalizing drugs, etc., and to advise on the general care of the animal. A large percentage of affected animals that have been down for some time before the beginning of treatment are lost in spite of the best possible care.

HEAVES (BROKEN WIND, ASTHMA)

Heaves is a chronic respiratory disease of the horse characterized by difficult breathing and a dry, wheezing cough, resulting finally in emphysema (infiltration of air into the tissues) of the lung.

While the exact cause is unknown, recent studies indicate that the condition is especially apt to follow chronic inflammatory conditions of the lungs, chiefly bronchitis. Authorities agree that the main source of trouble is associated with the feeding of damaged roughage. The condition very seldom develops in pastured animals or those fed corn fodder or clean hay, but it occurs commonly in animals fed dusty or moldy hay, made from either legumes or grasses. The inhalation of dust from such hay aggravates any respiratory trouble that may be present and is especially provocative in established cases of pulmonary emphysema.

In the respiration characteristic of heaves there is a double lift of the flank, and exhalation of air requires special muscular effort. The symptoms are increased by hard or fast work, large draughts of cold water, sudden changes in weather, protracted heat or cold, and over-feeding, especially of roughages. A change from clean, bright hay to poorer quality feed often aggravates the condition.

There is no specific remedy, although certain arsenic and other tonics are said to be beneficial in some cases. In advanced cases nothing can be done to overcome the extensive pulmonary abnormality. The symptoms in milder cases can be controlled by feeding only sound hay, preferably in a quantity less than is normally given, with the grain ration increased if necessary. Some affected animals improve markedly if they are placed on pasture for several months or if only light work, alternated with periods of pasturing, is given. If questionable fodder must be used, it should be fed in as limited a quantity as possible under individual conditions. Sprinkling the fodder lightly with water will serve to lessen the likelihood of inhalation of dust.

COLIC

The term "colic" is commonly used for abdominal pain and associated symptoms resulting from any one of numerous disorders of the abdominal cavity. In this discussion, acute dilatation of the stomach, tympany (bloat), impaction (stoppage), obstipation (extreme constipation), intestinal obstruction, torsion (twist or gut tie), strangulation, gastrointestinal catarrh, gastroenteritis, and thromboembolic colic, either alone or in combination with one another, are considered.

The most common conditions are acute dilatation or overloading of the stomach, tympany, and impaction of the large intestines and cecum. These conditions are primarily disorders of function without complicating organic changes of the tissues, which may follow, however, if the condition is not relieved. Some functional digestive disturbances may occur unavoidably as a result of organic disease. However, the majority of colic cases are the result of faulty management, especially improper feeding and poor feed. A functional disturbance of one part of the digestive tract, such as that caused by overloading the stomach, may result in rapid involvement of the entire tract. Thus, stasis (atony, or discontinued muscular movements) of the intestines, followed by fermentation (gas formation), obstipation, and autointoxication, finally terminating in organic changes such as catarrh, inflammation, edema, and hemorrhage, may occur.

Some of the more common causes of digestive disturbances are change of feed, overeating, idleness on a full-work diet, fatigue, excessive drinking, defective teeth, greedy eating, spoiled or fibrous indigestible feed, exposure to abrupt changes in weather, and overwork. Sudden change of feed, either of grain or roughage, will invariably cause indigestion in some horses. Though others are less sensitive to a change, it is always good practice to make feed changes gradually over a period of several days. Overeating, resulting from gaining access to the grain bin, a new field, or some other source of unlimited feed, causes acute dilatation of the stomach and intestines. Work animals standing idle on full feed often develop indigestion as a result of intestinal stasis, faulty elimination, and autointoxication.

Fatigue, exhaustion, and overwork cause a reflex paralysis of the digestive system, making animals more susceptible to digestive disturbances. This condition occurs most frequently in the spring when the horses are first put to heavy work and their feed is increased. The trouble may be avoided in many instances by starting the grain ration 5 or 6 weeks before the heavy work begins. The ration should be increased gradually with an increase in exercise, green animals being worked only part time until they are thoroughly hardened.

Excessive drinking after heavy work is frequently followed by symptoms of indigestion. Water should be withheld until the animal has "cooled out." Two or three swallows of water at a time may safely be allowed at frequent intervals during the cooling process.

Defective teeth cause faulty mastication, which may result in improper digestion and absorption of food, followed by general unthriftiness. The teeth should be examined regularly and defects corrected.

Indigestion from greedy eating parallels symptoms from defective teeth because of improper mastication and in addition frequently produces choke—stoppage of the esophagus (gullet). Complications from this condition predispose to other disorders. Stones or coarse wire mesh in the animal's feed box will decrease the amount of food he can take in his mouth and usually force him to eat with less haste.

Feeds that are moldy, sour, filthy, frozen, improperly cured, full of dirt or dust, fibrous, and indigestible are always dangerous.

Exposure during cold, wet, and stormy weather has proved favorable for the development of colic due to reflex digestive paralysis, increased hunger, frozen feeds, and insufficient intake of water. It is a good practice following exposure to rub the animal dry and then give a little water and hay, withholding grain for an hour or two.

Treatment of colic is as variable as the numerous disorders discussed under that name because of the many causes and the different courses the disease may take. It is advisable to get veterinary assistance during the early stages. To reduce danger from falling, kicking, or rolling, the animal should be placed in a large, deeply bedded box stall or moved out of the stable with an attendant. A slow walk will often keep an animal from injuring itself during severe pain and sometimes may help to ease the pain. The giving of drenches, especially through the nose, by inexperienced laymen is inadvisable because of the danger of strangulation, which may be followed by sudden death or mechanical pneumonia. Today most veterinarians use the stomach tube in the treatment of colic. This not only affords immediate relief of most acute stomach colics through the escape of accumulated gas, but it permits washing out the stomach and in addition eliminates the hazards of drenching.

Founder (Laminitis)

Laminitis, or founder, is a serious ailment of the fleshy laminae of the horse's feet which commonly follows heavy overfeeding, chiefly on grains, and also gorging on green plants or any feed so palatable that excessive amounts are consumed. Other causes, such as metritis (inflammation of the uterus) in recently foaled mares, long-continued or hard, fast work on hard footing, or general intoxication (poisoning) may be responsible, but overeating is the principal cause.

Extreme pain and fever (103°–106° F.) are the chief symptoms. Affected animals are very reluctant to move, and when they are compelled to do so there is excrutiating pain as shown by a peculiar crouching gait, indications of anxiety, and trembling. In most cases all four feet are more or less involved, although it may be evident mostly in the front feet, in which case they are extended in front of the body with the weight on the heels. If the hind feet only are involved, all four feet are bunched under the body, the forefeet and the heels of the hind feet supporting the weight. A severe injury in one leg may lead to laminitis in the foot of the opposite side. The affected feet are hot and throbbing, and the arteries along the pastern can be felt with unusual ease. The slightest pressure on the foot causes the animal to snatch it quickly from the ground.

The first principle of treatment is to place the feet in a cold foot bath, with ice if it is available. The attendant can do this pending the arrival of the veterinarian. Prompt purgation is an important part of the treatment in cases due to gorging. In many cases hypodermic medication is indicated. This is one of the few ailments of animals which may be improved by bleeding, but even here bleeding is not applicable to every case. With prompt and proper treatment, the acute symptoms usually begin to subside in a few days, unless complications arise, which may cause death.

Chronic laminitis results in more or less irremediable deformity of the foot. The hoof wall develops deep rings, and the sole drops. Except for suitable shoeing, little can be done in the way of treatment.

COLLAR AND SADDLE SORES

Certain sores must be attributed primarily to poor conditioning of the animal and to an improperly fitted or poorly adjusted collar or saddle. Either a bruise or chafing of the skin when continually irritated leads to the formation of so-called galls, or sitfasts. These consist of necrotic tissue combined with dense fibrous tissue. Any such lesion may be complicated by the presence of infection.

To prevent these sores, the animals should be gradually hardened to work. This conditioning, together with thorough and regular grooming and properly fitted equipment, is usually all that is required.

If sores do form and work is continued, surgical removal with a period of rest for healing usually becomes necessary. Sometimes with a period of rest the newly formed callouses may slough off or become largely resorbed.

POISONING

Aside from the poisoning due to eating certain plants and the intoxications considered in connection with encephalomyelitis, both of which are discussed elsewhere, the chief source of poisoning in horses and mules is the consumption of such common toxic substances as arsenic and lead.

Carelessness in handling arsenical preparations such as grasshopper bait, paris green, and other plant sprays, as well as arsenical dips, is usually the cause of arsenic poisoning in horses and mules, though injudicious administration of arsenical drugs is sometimes responsible.

When large quantities of arsenicals are consumed the symptoms are usually acute. There is a sudden onset of trembling, restlessness, increased thirst, rapid breathing, colic, prostration, staggering, and extreme sickness. In most cases death follows in 2 or 3 hours. Chronic cases result from the consumption of a smaller amount of arsenic over a period of weeks and may show unthriftiness, rough coat, garlic breath, raised red gum lines, lazy action, easy tiring, and partial paralysis of the hind legs. Treatment in acute cases is often ineffective because of the large amount of arsenic consumed and the rapid course of the disease. Animals that have recently consumed the poison should have the stomach contents removed with a stomach tube and circulatory stimulants and peripheral nerve depressants administered. The most valuable antidote is sodium hyposulfite given by mouth or in the blood stream or both. If the veterinarian is not readily available, as much as a handful of the salt may be given in a drench.

Lead, like arsenic, combines with other elements to form various salts, the most common of which are lead acetate (sugar of lead), red oxide of lead, white lead, lead oxide, and arsenate of lead. The toxic salts of lead have a wide variety of uses in agriculture and are made available to animals by careless use of such substances as sprays, dusting powders, and paints.

Acute lead poisoning does not occur in equines as commonly as in cattle. The symptoms are usually those of indigestion, accompanied by a partial paralysis (knuckling of the joints). Chronic lead poisoning has been commonly observed in districts where small amounts of lead may continually be taken into the body through feed, water, or inhaled lead dust. Such districts are found around lead mines, smelters, and orchards or fields where much spraying is done.

The first noticeable symptom of chronic poisoning is some form of paralysis, usually laryngeal, or throat, made apparent by "choking down," or roaring, following exercise. The time necessary for symptoms to develop varies from several months to as long as a few years, depending on the amount of poison and the rate of intake.

Control may be exercised by giving particular attention to keeping animals away from the source of the poison. Feed may be brought in from outside the dangerous districts, water should be frequently tested for lead, and both feed and water should be protected against further contamination from lead sprays or dust. Muzzles may be placed on horses to prevent their eating vegetable matter while working in sprayed orchards and fields.

In districts where horses are continuously exposed to lead and develop chronic poisoning, animals that become unserviceable may be removed to an uncontaminated environment before the disease has progressed too far. Often such animals will recover sufficiently to do general farm work.

During the convalescent period, various forms of medication may be helpful. When the laryngeal paralysis does not improve, it is a more or less common practice to insert a trachea tube, which often enables the animal to do moderate work without difficulty in breathing. In such cases the tube and the opening must be cleaned frequently.

Acute lead poisoning may be treated by administering the chemical antidotes, dilute sulfuric acid, magnesium sulfate, or sodium sulfate, which combine with lead to form insoluble lead salts. Stimulants for paralysis, protectives for inflamed stomach and intestines, and other treatment should be administered when necessary.

Internal Parasites of Horses and Mules

BY AUREL O. FOSTER [1]

SOME 150 KINDS of internal parasites infest horses and mules, and probably no individual animal is ever entirely free of some of them. Fortunately, comparatively few do real damage—but those few can be extremely harmful and sometimes deadly. Here are the facts about a complicated subject.

THE DOMESTIC EQUINES provide shelter and subsistence to approximately 150 kinds of protozoa and worms which live, as internal parasites.[2] There are few horse owners who have not had some first-hand experience with many of these, and nearly everyone is familiar, in one way or another, with at least some of them. Among the protozoa are the blood-inhabiting trypanosomes and piroplasmata, the ciliates of the large bowel, and several miscellaneous species. The parasitic worms include flukes, tapeworms, stomach worms, large roundworms, strongyles, pinworms, lungworms, filariae, and some others.

Some of the worst diseases of equines are caused by these invaders; yet they do not, as a rule, cause specific and spectacular diseases. In every case of harmful parasitism, the damaging effects are essentially of two kinds—general and specific. The general effect, although seldom as obvious, is unquestionably more important than the specific effect from an economic standpoint; it always causes a loss in the functional efficiency of the animal as a working unit. In some instances, as in such a disease as dourine, the specific effects, clinical or pathological or both, definitely indicate the disease. In most cases, however, as best typified, perhaps, by strongylosis, the

[1] Aurel O. Foster is Associate Parasitologist, Zoological Division, Bureau of Animal Industry.
[2] Horse bots as internal parasites of horses and mules are discussed in another article in this volume.

specific effects are subordinated to the net general effect of the parasitism—decreased efficiency. Symptoms in such cases are manifold, but so variable as to preclude definite diagnosis.

The full importance of parasitism is inadequately understood. The parasite itself is ordinarily dealt with as the agent of disease or debility, but it is possible that parasites play some role in the transmission of other serious diseases, provide portals of entry for harmful micro-organisms, or serve as reservoirs of infection for other diseases. Moreover, parasites may be capable in themselves of exerting effects which have not hitherto been noted. Investigations along these lines have only begun.

Equines everywhere appear to be infected with internal parasites. There are, however, important differences in degree and kind of parasitism in different parts of the world and among individual horses and mules. Fortunately, several of the more pathogenic, or disease-producing, species, such as the blood-inhabiting protozoa, are limited in their distribution and incidence. The intestinal protozoa, however, occur everywhere and possibly in every horse and mule. The most numerous of these are the ciliated forms that live chiefly in the colon. They can be detected readily by microscopic examination of a watered drop of fresh manure. Some of the parasitic worms are distributed more or less regionally, but as there are so many kinds of them and they are so unrelated, it is difficult to make any general statement about them. Most of the important nematodes, too, particularly the strongyles, are found wherever there are equines, and it is doubtful whether any horse or mule is entirely free of them, except perhaps for a short period after an efficient anthelmintic has been administered.

Differences in distribution are probably determined, in general, by differences in developmental cycles. For example, the distribution of species which require intermediate hosts for transmission is more limited than that of species which are able to develop during a short period in the open. Also contributing to the distribution of equine parasites is the fact that horses and mules, perhaps more than other domestic animals, have been transported widely for service in war and in colonizing enterprises and for racing and breeding purposes.

Some of the parasites—most of the trypanosomes, for example— are capable of infecting a wide range of mammals, but the majority are so specialized that they can exist only in equine hosts. Some species, indeed, are better adapted to horses and mules than to donkeys, and others prefer donkeys to other equines. In general, horses and mules appear to be about equally susceptible to most parasites, although some kinds, such as the trypanosomes, are more injurious to horses than to mules.

Within their hosts these parasitic organisms exhibit a high degree of adaptability to specific locations. Most of them normally parasitize the alimentary tract, lungs, body cavity, or blood stream. In the alimentary tract, however, some species are exclusively parasites of the stomach, others of the small intestine, and others of the large intestine. Moreover, the several species of strongyles which inhabit

. the large bowel tend to become localized in specific parts of this organ—the cecum, the ventral colon, or the dorsal colon. In addition to the parasites thus localized, several of the species follow various migratory circuits within the host, whereas many are aberrant, or wandering, in their habits. Consequently, scarcely a part or organ of an animal is entirely free from potential parasitic invasion. Thus there are parasites of horses and mules that live on the surface of the body; in the nose, ears, and eyes; in the skin, muscles, ligaments, visceral organs, or body cavity; or elsewhere in the body. It will also become evident from the following discussions that a parasite which in its adult stage normally inhabits one region of the body may, in its immature stages, be responsible for serious injury in an entirely different part.

PROTOZOAN PARASITES

Except for a few species, the protozoa of equines fall into two groups, those that inhabit the blood and those that live in the large bowel. All the important disease-producing agents are in the first group. The latter group embraces a large number of species that are essentially innocuous and may, in some instances, be actually beneficial to their hosts. In general the former require an intermediate host for their transmission or have an otherwise complicated life history, whereas the latter follow a simple, direct developmental cycle. Those of the blood-inhabiting group are chiefly trypanosomes and piroplasmata, which fortunately have a relatively limited distribution. Although herds have been decimated by infection with these organisms, the incidence of infection is usually not high, even in endemic areas, where cases of infection are always present. In contrast, the latter group—those inhabiting the large bowel—is composed principally of ciliates, which are believed to occur in all equines everywhere.

TRYPANOSOME DISEASES

The trypanosomes are by far the most important protozoan parasites of equines. They cause such diseases as dourine, surra, nagana, mal de caderas, and murrina, each of which takes a heavy toll among the equine populations of regions where it has become established.

Dourine is the only one of these trypanosome diseases that occurs in the United States.[3] It is caused by *Trypanosoma equiperdum* and is widely distributed. It differs from other trypanosome infections in that it is essentially chronic rather than acute and is transmitted directly from horse to horse, usually during coitus, without the assistance of an insect or mammalian vector.

Surra, caused by *Trypanosoma evansi*, is the oldest recorded trypanosome disease of equines. It is an acute, usually fatal, infection, running its course generally within a few weeks. It occurs chiefly in central and southern Asia and in the Philippines. Horseflies (*Tabanus*

---

[3] A more detailed account of dourine is given in a separate article of this Yearbook, p. 413.

species) are thought to be the chief vectors, although the method of spread is purely mechanical.

The disease nagana is prevalent in east and central Africa and does not occur elsewhere. The commonest agent of the infection is *Trypanosoma brucei*, a variety of which is the cause of Rhodesian sleeping sickness of man. In equines the disease is usually fatal in a few weeks, being too acute for the characteristic manifestations of sleeping sickness. It is carried from horse to horse by tsetse flies, in which the trypanosome completes a definite cycle of development.

Mal de caderas is related to surra and may be identical with it. It differs from typical surra, however, in the apparent morphology (form and structure) of its causative agent, *Trypanosoma equinum*, and in its distribution. It occurs only in South America and is believed to be transmitted by horseflies and stableflies.

Murrina, like mal de caderas, is similar to surra, and its causative agent, *Trypanosoma hippicum*, is closely related to *T. evansi*. The disease occurs chiefly in Panama, where it is transmitted, at least in part, by bloodsucking vampire bats. Affected animals, if untreated, usually die in a few weeks or months.

PIROPLASMOSIS

Piroplasmosis, also known as tick fever, biliary fever, and hemoglobinuric fever, is an acute febrile condition characterized by jaundice, hemoglobinuria (hemoglobin in the urine), and anemia. It is caused by the presence of microscopic organisms, known as piroplasms of piroplasmata, in the red blood cells. In important respects it is like tick fever of cattle, but it does not occur in the United States. The majority of cases apparently recover, some within a few days or weeks, but the blood usually remains infective for several months or even years. Unlike the trypanosome infections, piroplasmosis confers a reasonably durable immunity. *Nuttallia equi*, the commonest agent of equine piroplasmosis, occurs in Africa, southern Europe, Transcaucasia, southern Asia, and South America. In Africa, it is transmitted by ticks belonging to the genus *Rhipicephalus*. Another species of the organism, *Babesia caballi*, occurs along with *Nuttallia equi* in Italy, India, and Macedonia, and is also found in Russia, Transcaucasia, North Africa, and Panama. This organism also is transmitted by ticks, chiefly species of *Dermacentor* and *Boophilus*.

INTESTINAL CILIATES AND OTHER PROTOZOA

At least 50 species of ciliated intestinal protozoa, belonging to half as many genera, are common inhabitants of the large bowel of equines. There is no acceptable evidence that they cause disease; indeed, various investigators have now and then advanced the hypothesis that these organisms perform some useful service for their hosts. They may, for example, assist the digestive functions by breaking down certain otherwise indigestible materials into substances that can be readily assimilated. Millions of these organisms pass out every day with the feces of an infected animal.

In spite of their universal presence in equines and their striking variety and' abundance, the method of transmission of ciliated intestinal protozoa has not been satisfactorily explained. It is assumed that new hosts are infected by swallowing living organisms in contaminated food and drink, although it is recognized that such organisms, after entering by the mouth, would require certain adaptations in order to reach the cecum or colon.

Besides trypanosomes, piroplasmata, and ciliates, several miscellaneous species of protozoa occur in domestic equines, some more or less commonly. Among these are the muscle-infecting Sarcosporidia, plasmodial parasites of the blood similar to those causing human malaria, flagellates, and Suctoria of the intestine. Of interest are three species of amoebae that are analogous to three similar species occurring in man. They are *Endamoeba gedoelsti* (syn. *E. intestinalis*), the large and presumably harmless amoeba of the colon, comparable to *E. coli* of man; *E. equi*, a smaller colon amoeba; allegedly disease producing, suggesting the form parasitic in man, *E. histolytica;* and *E. gingivalis* var. *equi*, the equine variety of the human oral amoeba. About these very little is known, and only after further study can their importance be evaluated.

HELMINTHIC PARASITES

The helminths, or worm parasites, of equines are more varied and numerous than are the parasitic protozoa, and economically they are immeasurably more important. In contrast to the specific and fatal diseases caused by certain of the protozoa, the damage caused by worms is usually not spectacular; sometimes it is scarcely apparent, and rarely is it an immediate cause of death. Moreover, the symptoms are usually too general to serve for diagnosis. The important net effect of worm parasitism in equines is reduced efficiency. Judged on that basis, it becomes as obvious as it is paradoxical that parasites which kill their host animals are frequently of less economic significance than are those which insidiously undermine their efficiency.

HORSE STRONGYLES AND STRONGYLOSIS

The horse strongyles are a large, unified group of approximately 40 species belonging to a single nematode family, the strongylidae. Most of them are relatively small, less than an inch in length; some are scarcely visible to the unaided eye. These are commonly known as small strongyles, cylicostomes, or *Trichonema* species. A few strongyles are large, as much as 2 inches long, and are usually firmly attached within the host and sucking blood. The front third of these larger worn s frequently contains fresh blood, which gives that part a red color in contrast to the hind portion, which is darker and more or less slate-colored. There are three species of the genus *Strongylus*, which are variously referred to as large strongyles, sclerostomes, palisade worms, red worms, and blood worms. Undoubtedly the widespread economic importance of these parasites largely accounts for the variety of common names applied to them.

All the strongyles have broadly, similar developmental cycles. During their adult life, they live in the large bowel and tend to become localized in one or another part of this relatively limited portion of the digestive tract. The females deposit large numbers of eggs, which leave the host's body with the feces. The eggs can, and probably normally do, develop and hatch while in the bolus of feces. Unlike the eggs of many parasitic nematodes of other hosts, they do not appear to be delayed or inhibited in their development until the feces are diluted with rain water, earth, or some other agent. This adaptation probably protects the eggs and larvae from the damaging effects of such natural factors as sunlight, desiccation, and cold. Embryonic development is rapid, and the first-stage larvae usually hatch during the second day. In 6 to 10 days, the larvae molt twice and become third-stage, infective larvae. The second sheath is retained, probably as further protection against the hazards of an unfavorable environment. First- and second-stage larvae die rapidly when subjected to drying, marked heat or cold, or excessive bacterial action, but the infective larvae may survive for months or even years under these conditions. The infective larvae rest on the upper, more accessible portions of grass blades and are usually swallowed by horses during grazing. Once swallowed, they undergo a developmental cycle within the host many aspects of which are not yet perfectly understood.

Present evidence indicates that the large and small strongyles have certain essential differences in their cycles of migration and development within the host. The large strongyles migrate extensively within the host, and their migrations are associated with some of the most serious aspects of strongylosis. Moreover, it is becoming increasingly evident that the wanderings of the larvae of the three large strongyles take them to different localities in the host's body— *Strongylus equinus* to the pancreas, *S. edentatus* to the lining membranes and visceral supporting tissue of the body cavity, and *S. vulgaris* to the walls of the visceral arteries.

The small strongyles are believed to pass directly to the large intestine, where at least some of them penetrate the mucous membrane and settle down in the intestinal wall for a period of growth. It is doubtful whether all the cylicostomes undergo this tissue stage, since at autopsy fourth- and fifth-stage worms can usually be found both in the cavity of the intestine and encysted in the mucosa.

The palisade worms and their close relatives differ from the cylicostomes also in their mode of life within the large intestine. Most of the palisade worms attach themselves tenaciously to the mucosa and live as bloodsuckers; the cylicostomes, although capable of attachment, are usually found free in the lumen, but on the surface of the fecal mass in close contact with the intestinal lining.

It becomes apparent from what has been said that strongylosis is not a simple condition of parasitism. The bloodsucking activities of the adult large strongyles produce anemia, which in turn gives rise to many of the symptoms that ordinarily accompany severe strongylosis. By shifting their points of attachment, these parasites leave minute hemorrhages and denuded areas which are favorable sites for bacterial colonization. In their larval stages, they cause transient inflammatory and irritative changes throughout the viscera. Many of these ultimately become scars, adhesions, or caseous (cheese-like) nodules. The larvae of *Strongylus vulgaris* cause dilation and obstruction of blood vessels. Colic is a frequent result of the decreased blood supply to the intestine, and verminous inflammation of the inner wall of an artery always impairs the capacity for arduous work. Intermittent lameness is believed to result often from stoppage of the smaller leg arteries occasioned by the liberation of clotted particles from within a tumor of a blood vessel. Sometimes the wall of the vessel ruptures, causing sudden death by internal hemorrhage.

Animals with severe strongylosis exhibit lack of appetite, anemia, and progressive emaciation. The body wall has a tucked-in appearance, and the animal loses condition generally.

The diagnosis of strongylosis is not easy. The presence of the characteristic ova in the feces is evidence of strongylid infestation, but not necessarily an indication of disease. Most horses in reasonably good condition pass a few of these ova. In general, however, a high concentration of strongyle eggs in the feces, combined with loss of condition and an absence of organic or infectious disease, is strong presumptive evidence of strongylosis.

Not all the 40 different kinds of strongyles have ever been found in any one horse or mule, but every animal almost invariably harbors several of them. It is, therefore, legitimate to ask how many kinds of strongyles occur in the average horse and what are the more or less average maximum and minimum numbers. Study of a considerable body of literature indicates that, qualitatively, strongyle infections of equines vary only slightly in different parts of the world and that, quantitatively, the average horse or mule harbors from one-fourth to one-half of the known strongylid species. One or more of the three species of large strongyles are usually present, along with 10 to 12 species of small strongyles. It appears that about 15 species account for the bulk of strongylid parasitism in equines and that the other 25 do not occur in significant numbers.

The characteristic strongyles occurring in the cecum of horses and mules may be said to be *Strongylus vulgaris, S. equinus, Cyathostomum coronatum, Cylicostephanus calicatus,* and *Cylicocyclus nassatus.* The majority of the strongylid fauna in the ventral colon are of the following species: *Cylicocyclus nassatus, Cylicostephanus minutus, C. calicatus, Cylicocercus catinatus, C. pateratus, Cyathostomum labiatum, C. labratum, Triodontophorus minor,* and *Strongylus edentatus.* The typical fauna of the dorsal colon are *Cylicostephanus longibursatus, Cylicocyclus insignie, C. nassatus, Cylicocercus goldi,* and *C. catinatus.*

Of the 36,000 strongyles recovered in one study, it was found that approximately four-fifths were accounted for by fewer than one-fifth of the species, the six commonest—*Cylicocyclus nassatus, C. insigne,*

Cylicostephanus longibursatus, C. calicatus, C. minutus, and *Strongylus vulgaris*—which are of the greatest economic importance.

Data from several studies suggest that equines harboring approximately 1,000 strongyles are lightly infected; that infections of 30,000 to 50,000 are not infrequent and probably do not as a rule produce symptoms; but that infections of over 50,000 are relatively severe and may result in more or less typical strongylosis.

Both the degree and, to a less extent, the kind of parasitism are affected by many factors, some of which it is possible to evaluate to a limited extent. For example, the size of worm infestations depends principally upon the extent of exposure to infection, and this is influenced by conditions of sanitation, feeding, medication, season, and climate. In addition, observational evidence has demonstrated that infections are more severe in younger animals. There are also certain apparent host "preferences" among the strongylids. *Cyathostomum tetracanthum, Cylicocyclus auriculatus,* and *C. elongatus* are characteristically found in donkeys and are relatively rare in horses and mules. *Cylicocercus alveatus* and *Cylicocyclus triramosus* are common only in zebras, but are more often found in donkeys than in horses or mules. *Cylicostephanus poculatus,* typically found in horses, has been recorded once from a mule but never from donkeys or zebras. There is evidence also that some breeds of horses are probably more resistant to intestinal parasites than are others.

OTHER HELMINTHS AND THE DISEASES CAUSED BY THEM

Besides the strongyles, several more or less unrelated helminths, some of which are of considerable economic importance, affect equines. They are the flukes, tapeworms, stomach worms, ascarids, *Strongyloides,* pinworms, lungworms, and filariae.

Flukes

About a dozen species of trematodes, or flukes, have been reported, though not frequently, from the liver, blood vessels, and alimentary tract of horses and mules. Probably none are normal parasites of these animals. Those most commonly found in equines are the well-known liver flukes of sheep and cattle (*Fasciola hepatica* and *F. gigantica*) and certain species of blood flukes, of which *Schistosoma indicum* is the most important. The last occurs in India and Rhodesia but not elsewhere so far as is known.

Tapeworms

About 10 species of cestodes, or tapeworms, have been found in equines, but only 3 are of economic importance. These are *Anoplocephala magna, A. perfoliata,* and *Paranoplocephala mamillana.* The first is the largest of the horse tapeworms, although it seldom exceeds 10 inches in length. Its prominent head bears four conspicuous suckers, and the body is wide and tough. *Anoplocephala magna,* which occurs normally in the small intestine and rarely in the stomach or cecum, is the commonest tapeworm of American horses. Heavy infestations cause intestinal catarrh, with a consequent disturbance of digestive functions sometimes leading to emaciation and anemia.

The so-called lappetted tapeworm (*Anoplocephala perfoliata*) is 1 to 2 inches long and usually lives in the cecum, although it is sometimes encountered in the lower end of the small intestine. It is responsible for characteristic changes in the mucous membrane. The parasites tend to become localized in a small area immediately surrounding the opening of the small intestine into the cecum, the so-called ileocecal valve region. A hundred or more specimens may be encountered within an area with a diameter of 3 or 4 inches. their heads tenaciously attached and their bodies tightly packed against one another. At this site, the mucous membrane undergoes marked irritative and inflammatory changes, the most serious and conspicuous being a rapidly growing granular lesion. This mass of growing tissue with its eroded surface is seldom larger than a tennis ball, but because of its location it progressively obstructs the ileocecal orifice. Sometimes, however, the process is one of making the tissue thinner rather than thicker, and this has led in some instances to perforation of the intestinal wall. Both processes result eventually in the death of the host animal. Although *A. perfoliata* is a widespread parasite of horses, its geographical occurrence is not well known. It appears to be relatively uncommon in continental United States, but it is the most frequently occurring horse tapeworm in some tropical countries, such as Panama and the Philippine Islands.

Paranoplocephala mamillana is known as the dwarf horse tapeworm. It seldom measures more than an inch in length and is relatively delicate. Although of widespread occurrence this tapeworm is seldom found in large numbers. It lives normally in the upper part of the small intestine and is of less economic significance than the two species already discussed.

The developmental cycles of the horse tapeworms have not been completely determined. The segments filled with eggs break off into the fecal mass, and the eggs are liberated either before or after the feces are deposited on the open ground. Judging from the recently determined cycles of a few related species of tapeworms, it appears probable that the eggs are ingested by arthropod intermediate hosts, perhaps certain pasture mites, in which the larval stages develop. This vector, in turn, is eaten by a grazing horse or mule.

Stomach Worms

Of some 9 or 10 kinds of parasitic worms that have been found in the stomachs of horses, 4 are normally parasitic in these hosts and are the causative agents of a complex of lesions which gives rise to a serious condition known as verminous gastritis or inflammation of the stomach. Three of these worms are closely related and are known as *Habronema muscae, H. majus* (syn. *H. microstoma*), and

Draschia (formerly *Habronema*) *megastoma*. They are transmitted by houseflies and small stableflies. The fourth species, *Trichostrongylus axei*, is more frequently a parasite of cattle, sheep, and goats than of equines and is so small that it may be overlooked at post mortem inspection unless a special search is made for it. *T. axei* does not require an intermediate host but infects the definitive host directly, after the manner of the strongyles.

Habronema muscae and *H. majus* are frequently seen on post mortem examination as slender, whitish worms actively whipping about in the stomach contents, especially if the contents are fluid or have been flushed out with water. The majority of specimens, however, live close to the glands of the stomach, embedded in mucus, or sometimes superficially embedded in the lining of the stomach. In this location it is sometimes difficult to discover them unless they are scraped or teased out. Horses harboring 200 or 300 worms generally have some inflammation of the lining of the stomach, and this contributes to gastric irritability, disordered digestion, and sometimes colic.

Draschia megastoma is less frequently found, but has more serious effects than the other species. These worms bury themselves deep in the mucous membrane and the layer beneath it and produce abscesses. Although such lesions are usually called tumors, they have, probably in every instance, a pus-filled or cheeselike core, in which are many worms and a cavernous tract communicating with the stomach. The tissue surrounding the central core shows marked thickening that gives the lesion a tumorous aspect. The diameter of the lesions varies from that of a walnut to that of an orange. Although these so-called tumors may occur in all areas of the glandular lining of the stomach, a preferred site is that portion nearest the border of the upper, nonglandular area. Not infrequently only a single abscess is present, although often there are many of various sizes. Because of their erosive nature, the abscesses produced by *D. megastoma* occasionally cause acute conditions, such as hemorrhage and perforation, but usually the injury is confined to irritative changes and more or less functional damage to the glandular mucuous membrane.

The larvae of the larger stomach worms, especially those of the last-mentioned species, are responsible in part for a relatively common skin disease of horses called summer sores or bursati. Recently this condition has been increasingly referred to as cutaneous habronemiasis. Although the cause and development of this disease are imperfectly understood, available evidence indicates that the larvae are liberated when infected flies feed on skin wounds or sores. The immature worms in the head region of the fly probably escape by way of the fly's mouth when activated by the warmth of the horse's body. These larvae not only irritate the wounds and make them ugly in appearance but seem to prevent them from healing.

Trichostrongylus axei, the small stomach worm, is probably acquired by horses through association with ruminants. It is, however, a sufficiently important parasite of equines to have been considered by many investigators the principal cause of verminous inflammation of the stomach. Its mode of development is roughly similar to that of the strongyles, except that it does not wander in the body of the host and that it produces characteristic changes in the lining of the stomach. The worms are too small to be readily seen, but the infection can frequently be diagnosed on post mortem inspection by the character of the lesions. Not always, however, is infection with this species accompanied by grossly apparent lesions,· and when such lesions are encountered, they may be of a varying nature. In general, stomachs infected with *T. axei* show a number of isolated, raised, buttonlike areas on the glandular mucosa. These may be the size of a dollar and depressed in the center, or they may be very small and inconspicuous. Sometimes the affected area is large and has a plateaulike appearance. In other cases the lesions are narrow at the base and somewhat mushroomed superficially. In all instances the disease process appears to be a progressive growth of tissue in response to irritative action by the worms.

Workers in both Europe and the United States have expressed the view that probably no other affection of equines is so regularly associated with a relatively sudden loss of condition.

The Large Roundworms, or Ascarids

The common roundworm, *Parascaris equorum*, is the largest parasite of equines. Female specimens vary from 6 to 15 inches in length; males, from 5 to 11 inches. When fully grown they have about the diameter of a lead pencil. They live in the small intestine and are typically parasitic in foals and young animals; only rarely are ascarids important in horses over 4 and 5 years of age, although a few specimens may be present in older animals.

The development cycle of the horse ascarid is simple except for a rather complicated migratory circuit within the host. Female worms in the small intestine deposit many eggs, which pass to the outside with the feces. If the weather is warm and the environment not excessively dry, the eggs develop embryos and are infective to horses in about 2 weeks. When the infective eggs are swallowed by grazing horses, the embryos are liberated in the intestine. They rapidly penetrate the gut wall and are taken by the blood stream to the liver and thence through the heart to the lungs. In the lungs, usually about a week after infection, the larvae escape from the blood stream and migrate up the trachea to the pharynx. After being swallowed once more, the worms develop to maturity in the small intestine.

Because ascarids do not attach themselves to the intestinal mucous membranes they are sometimes considered to be relatively innocuous. In reality, however, they have three attributes which make them very dangerous: (1) The migrations of the larvae through the liver and lungs cause extensive injury to these organs. In massive infections, serious inflammation of the liver or lungs may result. (2) The large size of the adult worms makes heavy infections particularly injurious. In foals the presence of large numbers of ascarids is a fairly frequent cause of partial obstruction of the small intestine, and fatalities from complete obstruction or perforation have been recorded. (3) The large roundworms tend to wander about in the intestine and, if the environment becomes unfavorable, to seek escape through whatever channels are accessible. Cases are recorded of invasion and obstruction of the common bile duct and, more frequently, of the escape of worms into the stomach and even out of the body by way of the mouth or anus.

Strongyloides

Very small, slender worms, *Strongyloides westeri*, occur in the small intestine of nursing foals and are believed to be responsible, at least in part, for the high incidence of scouring among these young animals. Mature horses and mules seldom harbor this species.

The parasitic adults live in intimate contact with the lining of the gut and reproduce asexually. Eggs are liberated into the lumen and have already developed embryos when they pass out with the feces. These are usually the first parasite eggs to appear in the feces of young foals. The larvae hatch in a day or so and are capable of undergoing alternative cycles of development, either transforming directly into infective larvae or growing into free-living, bisexual adults. The latter mate in the manure or on the ground, and the females lay eggs which, in turn, develop into larvae that are infective to equines. The entire cycle is completed within a few days. It is not known whether horses acquire infection by direct skin penetration by the larvae, although this is probable, or by ingesting the larvae during grazing or in contaminated water. At post mortem inspection, the presence of *Strongyloides* may be suspected if the mucous membrane of the upper part of the small intestine exhibits localized inflammation and reddening. The worms can be removed by scraping, and a diagnosis can be made with a low-power microscope.

Pinworms

Whitish worms with long slender tails, pinworms (*Oxyuris equi*) are frequently seen in the feces of heavily infected animals. This fact at once suggests a useful method of diagnosing pinworm infection and an important point in the developmental cycle of this parasite. The worms mature in the large intestine, principally in the dorsal colon, the females becoming full of eggs as they proceed along the small colon toward the rectum. Sometimes the females crawl out of the anal opening and then rupture, leaving the eggs glued to the perianal region. The resultant irritation and itching cause the affected animal to rub itself against posts or other objects, and this frequently leads to secondary infection, which accentuates the discomfort. Rubbing may also crush more female worms on the perianal surfaces. Normally, however, the eggs develop on the ground or in manure, and infection is acquired as in the case of the large roundworms.

Male pinworms are much smaller than the females and appear to live principally in the dorsal colon. In this region also are found at post mortem examination many fourth-stage larvae, which are peculiarly equipped with large muscular mouths for attachment to the mucosa and for voracious feeding.

In addition to the perianal injury produced by pinworms, there is the possibility that the eggs or the matrix of the uterine substance in which they are embedded may have some peculiarly irritating property. The fourth-stage larvae are also injurious on account of their mode of life within the colon. Diagnosis can be made by finding the characteristic eggs in perianal scrapings or by the discovery of adult worms in the manure. Tail rubbing is presumptive evidence of infection.

Pinworms of another species, *Probstmayria vivipara*, are frequently present in large numbers in equines, but they are so small as to be scarcly visible to the unaided eye. These are viviparous worms, as their species name implies—that is, the young are born alive, the eggs being hatched within the body of the female—and they can presumably complete their entire cycle of development in the ventral colon of the host. Nothing is known of the injuriousness of this species or of its means of transmission from horse to horse.

Lungworms

Lungworms of the species *Dictyocaulus arnfieldi*, which live in the bronchi and bronchioles of horses, are of scattered occurrence in the United States and elsewhere. In heavy infections they cause a chronic cough and bronchitis, which weaken the host animal.

The females produce eggs with embryos which hatch in the lungs soon after deposition. The embryos are coughed up through the trachea or are carried up by the action of its ciliated lining. Then, in general, they are swallowed and pass out through the alimentary tract, though in some cases they are expelled from the body during coughing or sneezing. The larvae become infective within a week or so and produce infections in new hosts that swallow them. Larvae reach the lungs after a migration somewhat similar to that of the large roundworms and grow to maturity there.

Filariae

Of the several species of filariae which have been described as being found in equines, many are known only by their larval stages (microfilariae) and it is probable that some, at least, are identical. Only two are of common occurrence.

One of these, *Setaria equina*, is the well-known threadworm of the abdominal cavity. It lives normally in intimate association with the supporting tissues of the intestine, but it is sufficiently large (about 4 inches long) and active to be easily detected at post mortem examination. So far as is known, this parasite does not usually produce serious injury. Infections consisting of a dozen or more threadworms are, however, capable of causing inflammation of the lining of the body cavity and effusion of fluid into this region; 10 liters (about 2½ gallons) or more of free fluid may be present in the abdominal cavity as a result. Occasionally, also, the immature forms of this filaria get into the eyes and cause severe disturbance and serious local injury.

The other filarial worm, *Onchocerca reticulata*, parasitizes the ligamentum nuchae (the large tendon supporting the neck) and is believed to have an important role in the development of poll evil and fistulous withers. Not infrequently, infection with this species leaves only chalklike, elongate nodules or bundles buried in the ligamentous tissue. Recent studies suggest that the microfilariae of this parasite are responsible for skin lesions in horses and probably for the condition referred to as dhobie itch.

Both of the species named have indirect life cycles, horses probably acquiring infection from the bites of infected insect hosts. Although the vectors of *Setaria equina* have not been definitely determined, it has been shown by recent studies that *Onchocerca reticulata* is transmitted by tiny biting flies known as midges.

TREATMENT FOR PROTOZOAN DISEASES

Two kinds of agents are used with some success in the treatment of the trypanosome diseases of equines—antimony compounds and synthetic metal-free organic chemicals. The antimony compound first used successfully is tartar emetic (antimony potassium tartrate). Though very effective, this is also very toxic. It is administered by injection into the veins and care must be taken that no trace of the drug gets into the tissues. With colts and shy animals that jump at the prick of the needle, it is difficult to prevent the escape of the drug into surrounding tissue. This will cause swelling and abscess formation and, in the more severe cases, a sloughing of tissue about the site of injection. Principally to avoid these objectionable effects, many other antimony compounds have been tested against the equine trypanosomes. From the evidence available it is impossible to select the most valuable of these substances but a proprietary drug manufactured and sold under the name "Fuadin," [4] may be taken as an example of the advantages and disadvantages that have accrued from this type of investigation. This compound may be given by either intravenous or intramuscular injection, and it is less acutely toxic than tartar emetic. Apparently, however, animals treated with this drug are more likely to relapse than are those treated with tartar emetic. Also Fuadin is the more expensive of the two and is considered uneconomical for use in some localities.

Several arsenicals have also been tested. Arsenic is a metal very similar chemically to antimony. Although some investigators have reported successful results with one or another of the arsenic compounds, the reports suggest that in general they are less effective than are the antimony compounds.

The only synthetic, metal-free, organic compound that has been used extensively and successfully in equine trypanosomiasis is a complex urea derivative. [5] The drug is dissolved in water and injected either intravenously or intramuscularly. Usually the treatment is repeated after a fortnight. The trypanosomes in the peripheral (exterior) circulation are quickly destroyed, and sometimes a complete

---

[4] A 6.7 percent solution of sodium-antimony III bis-pyrocatechin disulfonate of sodium, having a pH of 7, and containing 13.5 percent of trivalent antimony.

[5] This is marketed under many names but is best known as Bayer 205, Germanin, and Naganol.

cure is obtained. Many relapses, however, have followed this treatment, though some of these, and possibly all, may have been caused by organisms that had invaded the spinal fluid prior to treatment or by failure to administer a curative dose of the drug. Some investigators have injected this as well as other drugs directly into the neural canal (in the backbone), which is often a reservoir of infection. Some successes have been reported with this technique, but the method is not practicable on a large scale. In brief, then, this drug may be employed most effectively in early infections but is of limited value in the more advanced cases.

After extensive experience with murrina in Panama, investigators there resorted to a combination of the drug mentioned above with one of the metallic compounds. The intravenous injection of a solution containing 1.3 grams (21 grains) of tartar emetic and 0.5 gram (8 grains) of Bayer 205 has given good results in many cases, but the frequency of relapses makes it impossible to recommend this as a wholly satisfactory method of treatment.

Because of its powerful action in killing trypanosomes, Bayer 205 has been used as a disease preventive with some success. Injections of the drug at triweekly intervals have been found to provide satisfactory protection against infection, but the expense of this procedure is often prohibitive. Moreover, many animals react unfavorably to repeated administrations of this drug.

Many remedies have been tried for piroplasmosis. The most satisfactory seems to be a compound known as acaprin or akiron.[6] It is given either subcutaneously (under the skin) or intramuscularly, and in many cases a single injection is sufficient. In some animals it has caused undesirable side reactions, which, however, are reported to have been avoided to a large extent when the drug was administered in conjunction with a substance known as rephrin. Formerly a proprietary remedy (akiron R) was manufactured that contained rephrin as well as acaprin.

TREATMENT FOR PARASITIC WORMS

For stomach worms (*Habronema* species, and others) and large roundworms (*Parascaris equorum*), carbon disulfide is the most commonly used anthelmintic. The chemical is given to animals after they have fasted 18 hours and is administered in doses of about 6 fluid drams. Ordinarily the drug should be given by stomach tube, but a skillful veterinarian may be able to administer it satisfactorily in capsules. Carbon disulfide is irritating to the membranes of the mouth, and for this reason it must be carefully administered to avoid contact with them. It also causes marked inflammation of the membranes of the stomach and occasionally produces other unfavorable reactions. The latter are sometimes counteracted by a purgative dose of magnesium sulfate, administered some time after the anthelmintic.

The large numbers and wide distribution of strongyles have given rise to the use and development of many anthelmintics for their

---

[6] Chemically, N, N¹-(Bismethyl-chinolylium-methylsulfate-6-).

removal. Most of these remove only part of the worms, whereas others which are effective cause more or less severe intoxication, or poisoning. The traditional drug used against these parasites is oil of chenopodium. It is very effective and quite safe, but animals are usually slow to recover from the after effects. Carbon tetrachloride is also effective but has proved toxic under certain conditions. Normal butylidene chloride, although effective, has never been widely used because of its high cost. A closely related chemical, normal 'butyl chloride, which seems to be equally effective, is less expensive but is unfortunately metabolized in the horse to a very unpleasant smelling substance. All these drugs must be given after an extended fast and must be followed by a purgative.

Workers in the Federal Bureau of Animal Industry have recently introduced a new anthelmintic, phenothiazine, which seems to lack most of the objectionable features of the drugs previously used. It should be given without a preliminary fast and need not be followed by a purgative. This new drug is highly effective for the removal of strongyles, and it is usually nontoxic in therapeutic doses, although a temporary anemia and some jaundice frequently follow its administration. An occasional death is reported to have been caused by phenothiazine, although thousands of horses have been successfully treated. Its contraindications (conditions under which the drug cannot be used safely) and incompatibilities are incompletely determined, but present evidence indicates that the advantages of phenothiazine may far outweigh any disadvantages that might accompany its use. The therapeutic dose is 30 to 50 grams (1 to 1¾ ounces) for an adult equine. It may be administered by capsule, by stomach tube, or by mixing the drug with suitable feedstuffs. It is important that doses be prepared separately for each animal and that animals be dosed individually. Phenothiazine may be made into a satisfactory suspension for use as a drench by mixing one dose of the drug with 20 cubic centimeters (two-thirds ounce) of molasses and adding enough water to make 90 cubic centimeters (3 fluid ounces). In order to obtain a smooth mixture, the water must be added in small quantities and stirred into the molasses-phenothiazine mixture after each addition of the fluid. When medicated feed mixtures are used, the drug may be mixed with almost any suitable ground feed or mixed grain. It is simplest merely to moisten the feed (2 to 2½ quarts of feed to one dose) and mix in the drug. If this medicated mixture is fed in lieu of a regular afternoon feeding, horses will usually consume it during the night.

CONTROL MEASURES

Since most equine parasites owe their perpetuation to the fact that the animals graze or take their feed from the same places that they deposit their feces, a good deal can be accomplished toward reducing parasitism and keeping animals in good condition by providing sanitary stables and good pastures and by avoiding overstocking. Manure should be removed frequently from stables, which should be of good construction and kept clean. Before spreading the manure out as fertilizer, it is important, if practicable, to destroy the parasite eggs and larvae contained in it. Eggs and larvae are killed by spontaneously generated heat if the manure is stored in a specially constructed, insulated box for 2 or 3 weeks before being used. Grain boxes and hay racks should be so placed as to avoid contamination with manure. Attention to these details and periodic medication for worms are the best general measures for keeping horses free from parasites.

Mange in Equines

BY MARION IMES [1]

NATURE, it seems, has ingeniously devised, for each kind of livestock, a set of mites that live at the expense of the host animals and their owners. Here is an account of the creatures that make horses mangy, and how to get rid of these tormenting pests.

MANGE IN EQUINES, also known as scabies, scab, or itch, includes a group of contagious skin diseases affecting horses, asses, and mules. Since for practical purposes the causes, symptoms, diagnosis, and treatment of mange in the three kinds of animals are similar, mange in horses is selected as typical of the disease in the group.

Mange is caused by small insectlike parasites known as mites which live on or in the skin of the host animal. Horses are commonly affected by three different genera of mange mites—*Sarcoptes*, *Psoroptes*, and *Chorioptes*—and each causes a different kind of mange, known as sarcoptic, psoroptic, and chorioptic, respectively.

Mange mites are truly parasitic, as their entire life cycles are passed on the host animal, and they are the sole cause of mange in equines. In obtaining their food from the tissues of the host and carrying on other life processes, the mites cause wounds or lesions in the skin. As each class of mites has distinctive habits, the nature and location of the lesions they cause in the early stages of mange are sufficiently characteristic to aid in making a differential diagnosis—that is, a diagnosis of the specific type of mange in a given case.

CONTAGIOUSNESS OF MANGE

Each species of domesticated animal has its own peculiar varieties of mange mites, and most of the mites from one species of animal cannot live and propagate permanently on a different species. The sarcoptic mites, however, are transmissible from one species of animal to another and some, including the sarcoptic mites of the

[1] Marion Imes is Senior Veterinarian, Zoological Division, Bureau of Animal Industry.

476

horse, from animals to man. Ordinarily when one species of animal contracts the contagion from another species, the mites live only a limited time on the new host.

Mange is usually transmitted by direct contact with infected animals, but equipment used on or around infected animals or other objects in contact with them act as carriers from which the disease may be contracted. Although mange mites cannot complete their life cycles off the host animal, they may live as long as 2 months when dislodged in cool moist places, and the eggs may retain their vitality for about 4 weeks. Since various factors such as exposure to sunlight, dry air, and other conditions affect the longevity of mites and the viability of their eggs when separated from their host, it is not known definitely how long infected premises may remain a source of danger. Practical experience indicates that buildings and corrals are free from infection about 30 days after all infected animals have been removed.

The spread of mange from one animal to another is not limited to any one season of the year, although the mites are usually most active on the host animals during the winter months. The disease spreads rapidly among horses closely confined or crowded together. Animals exposed to sunlight on pasture seldom contract mange or show new lesions. If they are infected, however, the disease will become active under winter conditions.

Mange is very contagious to horses of all ages and classes, and precautions should be taken to prevent the introduction, spread, or harboring of the contagion. Untreated infected animals or objects used on or around such animals should not come in contact with horses free from the disease. If the disease occurs, all horses on the premises should be treated regardless of the number showing infection. All buildings and small inclosures occupied by infected horses and all equipment used on or around such horses, should be cleaned and disinfected. All litter should be removed from buildings and yards and the exposed surfaces should be sprayed with coal-tar-creosote dip or disinfectant (see Disinfection and Disinfectants, p. 179), diluted in accordance with the instructions on the container. Equipment which may carry the mites should be immersed in the disinfectant.

SARCOPTIC MANGE

The minute white or yellowish parasites that cause sarcoptic, or common, mange of horses are known technically as *Sarcoptes scabiei equi*. The full-grown female mite is about one-fiftieth of an inch and the male about one-sixtieth of an inch in length. They are barely visible to the naked eye but are plainly visible under an ordinary hand lens. The general form of the body is more nearly round than oval, and under a high-power microscope a number of short spines projecting backward may be seen on its upper surface. When mature, these mites have four pairs of short thick legs. The first and second pairs near the head extend beyond the margin of the body, but the third and fourth pairs usually are not visible unless the mite is placed on its back or dorsal surface.

The sarcoptic mites penetrate the upper layer of skin and form burrows or galleries in which mating occurs and the eggs are laid. Each female forms a separate burrow and lays from 10 to 25 eggs. The eggs hatch in from 3 to 10 days, and the young mites after passing through several molts begin laying eggs in new burrows when they are 10 to 12 days old. The average period of incubation (from the time the eggs are laid until they hatch) is about 4 days, and the average period from hatching until egg laying begins is about 11 days. A new generation of mites, therefore, may be produced in about 15 days.

The first visible symptoms of sarcoptic mange in horses are the signs the animal manifests of an intense localized itching. The burrows formed by the mites usually extend to the sensitive layer of the skin, and the presence and activities of the parasites in the tissues cause irritation, inflammation, and swelling. Vesicles (blisters) and small nodules, or lumps, are formed in the skin over and around the burrows. The vesicles break and discharge serum which may dry into scales or granules.

The disease may start on any part of the body, but usually the first lesions appear on the neck, shoulders, or head. From these parts they spread until the entire body may become involved. As the disease advances the nodules become closer together, the hair over the lesions stands erect, and some of it drops out. The skin becomes swollen, thick, and dense to the touch and is drawn into wrinkles or folds. The mechanical injury to the skin from rubbing and biting causes large scabs to form. When the mites are not very active the skin may have a dry, leatherlike appearance.

The only certain method of diagnosis is to demonstrate the presence of the mite. If the lesions are moist, the mites can usually be found in scrapings taken from the edge of a fresh lesion or the furrows of the wrinkles. As sarcoptic mites live in the skin and not on the surface, it is necessary to scrape down to the second or sensitive layer of skin to obtain them. When the lesions are dry and the skin has a leatherlike appearance, it is difficult to find the mites.

PSOROPTIC MANGE

The mites, called *Psoroptes communis equi*, which cause psoroptic mange in horses are slightly larger than sarcoptic mites. They are visible to the naked eye, especially when they are placed against a dark background. The general form of the body is oval, and the tapering head is longer than it is broad. When mature, the mites have four pairs of legs, all extending beyond the margin of the body.

The psoroptic mites do not form burrows but live in colonies on the surface of the skin. Each female may deposit as many as 24 eggs, which hatch on the animal in 4 to 7 days. The new generation of mites reach maturity and mate, and the females deposit eggs in from 10 to 12 days from the time of hatching. These stages in the life cycle have an important bearing on the interval between treatments.

Psoroptic mange is more contagious and usually spreads more rapidly than the sarcoptic variety. The disease usually starts on those parts of the body covered thickly by hair. In obtaining their food the mites puncture the skin of the host animal and probably introduce a poisonous secretion into the wound. As the mites increase, many small wounds are made, causing intense itching, inflammation, formation of vesicles, and exudation of serum. The serum on the surface of the lesion becomes mixed with foreign matter, including micro-organisms, and the mass soon hardens into small yellowish or gray-colored scabs. As the scabs form, the mites move to and feed on the healthy skin around the edges of the lesion, and thus the scab-covered wound is gradually enlarged. The scabs may become dark-colored from blood stains and other causes.

Some of the mites move to other parts of the body and form new lesions, and the process is continued until the entire body surface may become involved. As the disease advances, increasingly large areas of skin become denuded of hair and covered with adherent crusts or scabs. The areas of affected skin become thickened and hardened, or else swollen. The severe itching causes the infected animals to rub, bite, or scratch themselves, so that the scabs are often broken and some of them are torn loose, leaving bleeding wounds. Animals with advanced cases of mange become weak and emaciated, and unless relieved by proper treatment, many of them die.

Psoroptic mites may be seen on the skin, but to demonstrate the presence of the mites it is usually necessary to scrape the outer edges of a red moist lesion with a dull knife blade and transfer the scrapings to a smooth black surface, such as a piece of black paper or a painted board. Spreading the scrapings in the warm sun or near artificial heat usually causes the mites to become active, and they can be seen as minute, gray, moving bodies against the dark background. They are quite plainly visible under a low-power hand lens.

CHORIOPTIC MANGE

Chorioptic mange, commonly known as foot or tail mange, is a contagious skin disease caused by mites called *Chorioptes equi*, which closely resemble those of the psoroptic species. The chorioptic mites live on the surface of the skin and cause lesions similar to those of psoroptic mange. One characteristic difference is the location of the lesions, which are usually confined to the lower parts of the limbs or tail, though they may spread over the legs and even the abdomen.

For practical purposes it is not necessary to differentiate between chorioptic and psoroptic mange, as the treatment is the same for both diseases. If the lesions are confined to the lower parts of the limbs, wading tanks instead of dipping vats may be used in treatment.

TREATMENT OF MANGE

In treating horses, asses, and mules for mange the primary purpose is to kill the parasites that cause the disease. As mange mites may be on any or all parts of the skin of infected animals, eradication usually can be effected only by applying medication over the entire surface of the skin. Hand application of suitable remedies delays the spread of mange, but on account of the difficulty of applying treatment by hand over the entire body surface, the method cannot be depended upon to eradicate the disease. Hand applications are of value, however, in connection with spraying or dipping. Lesions that are covered by hard scabs or crusts should be well soaked by hand with warm dip just before the animals are dipped or sprayed.

Dipping, which consists in immersing animals in a medicated liquid that will kill mange mites, is the most effective and dependable method of treating equines for mange. A dipping vat with attached draining pens, corrals, and other necessary structures is commonly called a dipping plant. Dipping plants are usually so arranged that animals enter one end of a vat filled with dip, swim through the liquid, and leave the vat at the opposite end. Cattle-dipping plants [2] are suitable for dipping horses.

In dipping horses the depth of the liquid in the vat is usually maintained at from 70 to 80 inches, or deep enough to swim the tallest animal. Horses carry out of the vat and retain from 2 to 4 quarts of dip each, depending on their size and the condition of their hair. The total estimated quantity to be carried out by the animals to be dipped, plus that required to charge the vat, should equal the total quantity required to complete the dipping if none is lost by leakage or otherwise wasted.

The capacity of the vat is usually obtained by multiplying the average length in inches by the average width, and then multiplying the product by the depth from the dip line to the bottom, measured at the center of the vat. This gives approximately the number of cubic inches of space to be filled with dip. Divide this by 231 (the number of cubic inches in a gallon) and the result will be the number of gallons of dip needed to charge the vat. To obtain the average length and width of a vat with sloping sides, add the measurement at the bottom to that at the dip line and divide by 2.

After the vat is charged, the contents should be well stirred so that the dip may be of uniform strength and temperature throughout. While the animals are in the vat, the head of each one should be submerged or ducked twice for an instant, and if the inner surfaces of the ears are not well soaked they should be hand-treated. Mangy horses are usually held in the dip for 2 to 3 minutes.

When only a few horses are to be treated and a dipping vat is not available, the dip can be applied in the form of a spray. This method is not economical but if the spraying is continued until the entire surface of the skin is well soaked, mange can be eradicated in this way. An orchard spraying outfit or an ordinary hand spray pump is suitable for the purpose.

Two dippings 10 to 12 days apart usually effect eradication of psoroptic and chorioptic mange. The first dipping, if properly done, kills all the mites but does not destroy the eggs. The second dipping,

[2] IMES, MARION. CATTLE SCAB AND METHODS OF CONTROL AND ERADICATION. U. S. Dept. Agr. Farmers' Bul. 1017, 29 pp., illus. 1918.

if timed correctly, kills the new generation of mites before they start laying eggs.

Sarcoptic mites are more difficult to eradicate. One dipping usually does not kill all the mites, probably because the dip does not always reach the bottom of all their burrows and come in contact with all of them. The proper interval between dippings for sarcoptic mange is 6 or 7 days, and four or more dippings or treatments are usually necessary to eradicate the disease in ordinary cases. Old chronic cases which have continued for several years are practically incurable, and animals so infested should be isolated or slaughtered.

Two classes of dips commonly and successfully used are lime-sulfur and nicotine. Both are used warm for dipping horses; the temperature of the dip in the vat is usually maintained at 90° to 95° F. while in use. Prepared dips should be diluted or mixed and used in accordance with the instructions on the label of the container.

Proprietary brands of lime-sulfur are available either as a concentrated liquid, known as liquid lime-sulfur, or as powder or crystals, known as dry lime-sulfur. These products are equal to or even better than the home-made lime-sulfur dip.[3]

The nicotine dips sold under various trade names are effective remedies for mange when diluted with water so that the dip contains not less than 0.05 percent nicotine. If used much stronger, they are likely to injure horses, especially if the animals are warm from exercise or hot weather, or if very hard water is used in diluting the dip. Nicotine dips should not be heated above 110° F.

---

[3] SCHWARTZ, BENJAMIN, IMES, MARION, and WRIGHT, WILLARD H. PARASITES AND PARASITIC DISEASES OF HORSES. U. S. Dept. Agr. Cir. 148, 54 pp., illus. 1930.

Horse Bots and Their Control

BY F. C. BISHOPP AND BENJAMIN SCHWARTZ [1]

FOR SHEER INVENTIVENESS in accomplishing their objects, it would be hard to beat the insects, and it would seem that the devil himself must have invented the methods used by botflies to reach the viscera of horses. Fortunately, man has brains that can be pitted with reasonable success against instinct.

HORSE BOTS are highly specialized parasites that attack horses, mules, asses, and perhaps zebras. Bots do not molest cattle, sheep, or other farm animals, even though they may be grazing in the same pasture with horses. If the horses are removed from such a pasture, the botflies will die without laying their eggs on the other animals.

Occasionally a young horse bot is found in the skin of a human being, who is evidently an accidental and unfavorable host. Under these conditions the bots act very differently from the way they do in horses; they burrow rapidly about in the skin and have never been known to grow to any considerable size or to reach the stomach or intestines, where they normally attach themselves in horses. In the human skin the minute larvae cause severe itching and local irritation. The burrows may traverse the skin for several inches, leaving a raised, reddened, circuitous streak, suggesting in miniature the work of a meadow mole in a field. How the larvae get into human skin is not known, and the cases are rare.

Four distinct species of bots have been found in the United States, but one of them is extremely rare. The other three are serious pests of horses and mules. They are known as the common horse bot,

[1] F. C. Bishopp is Assistant Chief, Bureau of Entomology and Plant Quarantine, and Benjamin Schwartz is Principal Zoologist and Chief of the Zoological Division, Bureau of Animal Industry.

482

or nit fly (*Gastrophilus intestinalis*); the throat bot, or chin fly (*G. nasalis*); and the nose bot, or nose fly (*G. haemorrhoidalis*).[2]

DISTRIBUTION

Horse bots were undoubtedly brought to this country with horses imported from Europe.

The common horse botfly and the throat botfly occur throughout the United States wherever horses are found, but they are much more numerous in some localities than in others. Throat botflies are extremely abundant in the drier parts of the country and at the higher altitudes—that is, above 3,000 feet. The presence of large

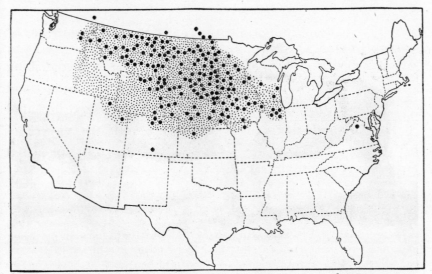

FIGURE 1.—The distribution of the nose botfly in the United States.

numbers of horses in which they may develop favors an abundance of horse bots.

The throat bot appears to have become established in the United States comparatively recently—that is, about 1898. It was first observed in the western part of the Dakotas and in eastern Montana and since that time has spread over much of the region from Illinois to eastern Washington and Oregon, and from southern Canada to central Kansas (fig. 1).

With the free movement of horses and mules from infested areas to various parts of the country, it is surprising that the throat bot has not become more widespread. It is likely that climatic conditions, especially in the eastern and southern States, are not favorable for this species, and this is also probably the reason why the fourth

[2] Further information on the distribution, habits, and methods of controlling bots will be found in publications by Bishopp and Dove (*1*),[3] by Dove (*4*), and by Wells and Knipling (*11*).
[3] Italic numbers in parentheses refer to Literature Cited, p. 491.

species, the European horse bot (*G. inermis*), has not became established in the United States.

LOSSES CAUSED BY HORSE BOTS

Horse owners soon become aware of the presence of horse bots because of the annoyance the flies cause the animals. This is particularly true of the nose botfly, which lays its eggs around the lips of horses. The animal attacked reacts violently; it may toss its head in the air, strike the ground with its front feet, and rub its nose on the ground, the neck yoke, or a barbed-wire fence. If a very

FIGURE 2.—Horses attempt to protect themselves from nose botflies by resting their muzzles on each other's backs.

nervous animal in harness is attacked, it may run away, and sometimes serious damage results. These flies prevent horses on pasture from grazing. The animals usually stand in groups, preferably on the highest spot available, with the nose of one resting on the back of another, as shown in figure 2. Horses are often seen walking or trotting across a pasture with their heads constantly nodding to avoid the attacks of nose flies.

The throat botfly is also very annoying to animals when laying its eggs, but less so than the nose fly. The animals become excited when attacked and often throw their heads violently upward. The common horse botfly is much less disturbing than the other two, although nervous animals are considerably annoyed by it.

Contrary to the belief of many persons, these flies do not sting or otherwise hurt an animal. They undoubtedly cause a tickling sensation when they touch the hairs to lay their eggs, and this is probably very disturbing when the nose fly touches the edges of the lips.

The newly hatched nose bots burrow into the lips and travel around in the mucous lining of the horse's mouth; the young common bots burrow in the tongue; the first-stage throat bots infest the gums. This burrowing habit, first recorded by Dinulescu (*3*) in 1932, causes considerable irritation and perhaps at times interferes with feeding. En route to the stomach, the bots sometimes attach

FIGURE 3.—Some of the bots from a horse's stomach, with a section of the stomach lining in the center showing pits made by bots.

themselves in the pharynx and have been known to cause swelling of the throat sufficient to prevent the passage of food.

In the stomach and intestines, the bots remain attached for several months. At the points of attachment deep pits are formed in the lining membranes (fig. 3), which may serve as places of entry for germs. If the infestation is very heavy, digestion may be seriously interfered with, and clusters of bots attached at the exit end of the stomach may impede the passage of food. These conditions give rise to colic, lowered vitality, and reduced work output. The nose bot has the habit also of reattaching itself in the rectum as it passes out, and there again it causes irritation and itching.

Much of the damage caused by bots in the mouth and digestive tract of horses is not recognized by stock owners, but it is none the less important and causes farmers heavy losses.

LIFE HISTORY AND HABITS

Like other flies, horse bots pass through four distinct stages—the egg, the larva (bot), the pupa, and the adult. The adult botflies are unable to take food; enough is stored up in their bodies in the bot stage to develop the 150 to 300 eggs to be deposited during the short life of the adult fly, whose sole purpose is reproduction. During favorable weather many eggs are laid in a short time.

In 1938 Wells and Knipling (*11*) presented information on the habits and life histories of these common species.

The eggs of all the species are attached to hairs of the host, but there is considerable difference in the place of attachment and also in the shape and color of the eggs (fig. 4). The common botfly lays its eggs on various parts of the animal, but particularly on the inside of the knees; the throat botfly attaches its eggs toward the base of the hairs beneath the jaws; and the nose botfly deposits its eggs on the short hairs on the lips. The egg of the last species has a stalk on the base that extends well down into the hair follicle.

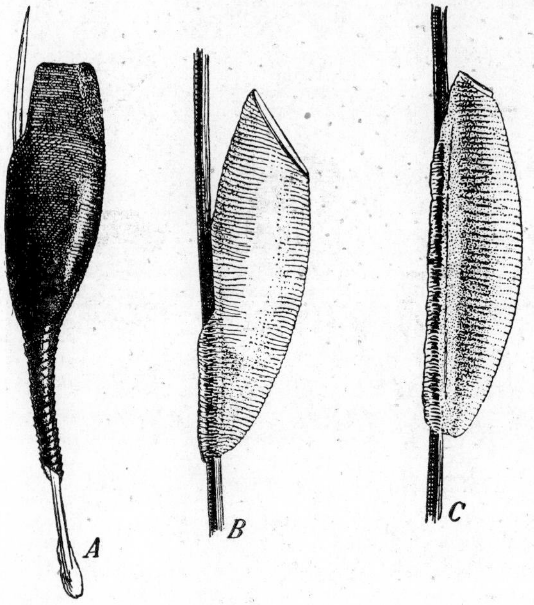

FIGURE 4.—Eggs of horse bots, each attached to a horsehair. *A*, Nose bot egg—hair removed with root; *B*, common horse bot egg; *C*, throat bot egg. Greatly enlarged.

The egg-laying habits of the three species of botflies prevalent in this country are also different. The common botfly hovers around the legs of the horse with its a b d o m e n curved under, depositing egg after egg. It is a large fly resembling a bee, with the wings conspicuously spotted (fig. 5). The other two species have plain, clear wings, are slightly smaller and darker in color, and fly more rapidly. In depositing eggs they usually approach quickly, hover beneath the head for an instant, and then suddenly dart at the lips or at some spot beneath the jaws, according to the species. Usually only a single egg is laid at each strike.

The eggs of the throat botfly hatch in about 6 days, and the young bots immediately crawl into the horse's mouth. Schroeder (*9*) has shown that they soon establish themselves in pockets between the molar teeth, where they grow and molt to the second stage. After

3 to 4 weeks in the mouth they pass to the stomach and intestine, where they attach themselves in the pyloric, or exit, end of the stomach and in the duodenum just below the stomach.

The eggs of the nose botfly hatch in 2 to 4 days, and the minute spiny larvae penetrate the skin of the horse's lips and work toward the mucous lining, where they continue to burrow for more than a month before passing to the stomach.

The eggs of the common botfly are ready to hatch 7 days after being laid on the horse's legs, but hatching does not take place until they are rubbed by the warm lips of the horse. The bots may lie quietly in the eggs as long as 3 months awaiting this stimulus. When the horse bites the spot where the eggs are embedded, it warms them, and the bots push off the egg cap and adhere to the animal's moist lips. They soon penetrate the mucous covering of the lips and tongue. Wehr (*10*) found that they burrow there for about a month before going to the stomach. During this time they molt, or cast their skins, and increase considerably in size.

All three species of bots remain attached to the lining of the digestive tract for 8 to 11 months, during which time they grow to robust tough-skinned bots about three-quarters of

FIGURE 5.—Common horse botfly, or nit fly.

an inch in length. The young bots are distinctly reddish, which may indicate that they feed on blood. When mature, the throat bots are a dirty white and the common bots and nose bots pinkish. The bots of the last species take on a distinctly greenish color just before leaving the animal. When grown, the bots release their hold and pass out with the excrement, except that the nose bots reattach themselves in the rectum for a few days before dropping to the ground. They are often seen attached to the edge of the anus, from which they protrude.

The mature bots differ somewhat in size as well as color, and the species are easily distinguished by differences in their spiny armature (fig. 6).

When the bots reach the ground they seek any protection at hand, or they may burrow just beneath the surface of the soil. In 1 to 4 days the outer skin of the bot contracts and hardens, forming a protecting case in which the change from the sluggish, repulsive maggot to an active, ornate fly takes place. The duration of the pupal, or resting, stage is similar in each species and lasts from 20 to 70 days, depending on the temperature.

In general, botflies are most abundant in late summer and fall, although in the North Central States they may begin activity about the middle of June. In southwestern Texas, the common botfly has a period of activity in the spring that ends when hot dry summer weather sets in; the flies appear again in the fall. Botfly activity ceases with the advent of freezing weather. In the warmer parts of Texas it may extend well into December.

PROTECTING HORSES AGAINST BOTFLIES

Since botflies do not feed, there is no way of attracting them to traps or poisoned baits. Animals are given little protection by the use of repellents, and nets and fringes also are of little value.

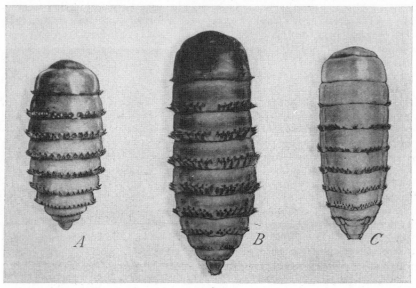

FIGURE 6.—The three species of bots, when full-grown, can be distinguished by their size, color, and the arrangement of spines on their bodies: *A,* Nose bot; *B,* common bot; *C,* throat bot.

As the throat botfly deposits its eggs beneath the jaws and the nose botfly on the lips, covering those areas when the flies are active largely prevents infestation and also greatly relieves animals from annoyance by the flies. It is difficult to provide such protection for animals on pasture, although protective devices have been used even there. While animals are in harness, the throat botfly can be largely warded off by placing a piece of burlap beneath the jaws with one end attached to the throatlatch and the other to the bit rings.

Various types of protectors against the nose botfly are in use. One of the simplest and best is a piece of belting, or even of an old automobile-tire casing, 4 to 6 inches wide. This is attached at each end by a string or by snaps (fig. 7). The protector should not be drawn tightly against the mouth, and it should be long enough to cover the lips entirely, including the corners.

The incubation period, especially that of the throat bot and the nose fly, is so short that control by destruction of the eggs is impractical because of the frequency with which an ovicide would have to be applied. Moreover, no effective egg-destroying agent has been found for these two species.

The incubation period of the common horse bot is longer, but the eggs are very resistant to destruction. Kerosene oil and creosote dips, often recommended as washes for the destruction of the eggs or nits of this species, are of little value. However, a simple and effective method of destroying the eggs in the fall was discovered by Wells and Knipling (*11*). It consists of applying water at a temperature of 105° to 110° F. with a sponge or swab. Applying the warm water with vigorous rubbing causes a high percentage of the eggs to hatch, and the larvae quickly die.

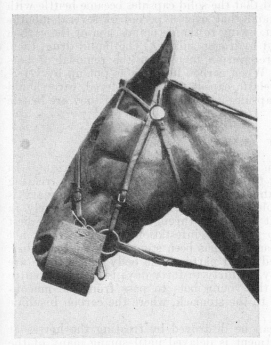

FIGURE 7.—A piece of belting attached to the bit rings is the best protector against nose botfly attack.

TREATMENT FOR THE REMOVAL OF BOTS

Of the remedies that have been proposed from time to time for the removal of botfly larvae from the stomach and upper part of the intestines of horses and mules, only carbon bisulfide has withstood the test of rigid, critical, and painstaking experimentation (*5, 6, 7, 8*). A 6-dram dose, administered by stomach tube or in gelatin capsules, has become the standard treatment for a horse weighing about 1,000 pounds. For horses of other weights the dose is computed on the basis of 1.5 fluid drams (6 cubic centimeters) for each 250 pounds of weight.

This treatment should be administered not earlier than 1 month after the first killing frost, following a fast of 18 hours, and no purgative should be given. Although carbon bisulfide is a toxic substance, it is quite safe for horses provided it is given with due caution by a competent veterinarian. The volatile liquid produces a limited area of inflammation in the stomach of a horse or mule, but this is not known to have serious consequences and disappears in a week or two. When the capsule is administered by inexperienced persons, however, there is danger that it may break in the mouth, with alarming and possibly dangerous consequences. This treatment destroys practically all of the bots in the digestive tract, and also many of the large roundworms that may be there.

Mass or solid capsules containing carbon bisulfide adsorbed on magnesium carbonate came into vogue a number of years ago as a substitute for the liquid carbon bisulfide. Critical tests by Bozicevich and Underwood (*2*) on seven horses showed that the solid capsule was not nearly so dependable as the liquid drug. These investigators also observed that the solid capsules became brittle with age and finally cracked and that over a period of several months they diminished in weight, owing to the decomposition of the carbon bisulfide and the escape of hydrogen sulfide. The liquid drug, then, is considered the best preparation to use for the removal of bots from horses and mules. When carbon bisulfide as put up by veterinary supply houses in gelatin capsules is administered, care should be taken to see that the capsules are still flexible. If they are brittle they should not be used.

TIME OF YEAR FOR TREATMENT

The time of year when the treatment is given is important. In most parts of the country the greatest success is obtained by treating during December and January. In the extreme South, January is preferable. It is desirable, of course, to remove the bots early in the season in order to put the horses through the winter in the best condition possible, but to prevent reinfestation, treatment must not be given until all botfly activity has been stopped by cold weather. Hot water is then applied to all parts of the body where there are eggs of the common botfly. Thirty to forty days is then allowed to elapse to give time for the young bots to pass from the mucous membranes of the mouth to the stomach, where the carbon bisulfide can reach and kill them.

Although many bots can be destroyed by treating the horses at any time of year, if treatment is delayed until spring many of the bots may have matured and passed out, and some of the nose bots may have passed down into the lower intestine, where they are less readily reached by medication.

COMMUNITY CAMPAIGNS

One of the most practical developments in medication for the removal of bots from equines is the community or area campaign for eradication by medicinal treatment of horses and mules. In the Middle West, the South, and elsewhere, these campaigns have been carried out with considerable success. As a rule, area or community treatment is supported and arranged for by the county agent or farm adviser. Under ideal conditions, all the horses in a given area are treated at the same time and at one place or in a limited number of places where the animals are assembled. The treatment is administered by veterinarians, practically all of the veterinarians in the community participating in the work. So far as can be ascertained, there has been no dissatisfaction with this method on the part of the veterinarians administering the treatments or of the farmers engaging in such cooperative efforts. In all instances liquid carbon bisulfide in capsules is administered to the horses, which have been kept on a fast for 18 hours. Area or community treatment has great advantages over individual treatment not only because it affords professional services at a minimum price but also because it may pave the way for complete eradication of bots from horses and mules in the area.

LITERATURE CITED

(1) BISHOPP, F. C., and DOVE, W. E.
    1926. THE HORSE BOTS AND THEIR CONTROL. U. S. Dept. Agr. Farmers' Bul. 1503, 14 pp., illus.
(2) BOZICEVICH, JOHN, and UNDERWOOD, PAUL C.
    1932. CRITICAL EXPERIMENTS WITH SOLID CARBON DISULPHIDE CAPSULES FOR THE TREATMENT OF GASTROPHILUS SPP. IN THE HORSE. Vet. Med. 27: 360–364, illus.
(3) DINULESCU, G.
    1932. RECHERCHES SUR LA BIOLOGIE DES GASTROPHILES, ANATOMIE, PHYSIOLOGIE, CYCLE ÉVOLUTIF. Ann. des Sci. Nat., Zool., ser. X, t. XV, fasc. 1, 183 pp., illus.
(4) DOVE, W. E.
    1918. SOME BIOLOGICAL AND CONTROL STUDIES OF GASTROPHILUS HAEMORRHOIDALIS AND OTHER BOTS OF HORSES. U. S. Dept. Agr. Bul. 597, 52 pp., illus.
(5) HALL, MAURICE C.
    1917. NOTES IN REGARD TO BOTS, GASTROPHILUS SPP.' Amer. Vet. Med. Assoc. Jour. (n. s. 5) 52: 177–184.
(6) ——— and AVERY, LAURENCE.
    1919. THE USE OF CARBON BISULPHIDE IN INFESTATIONS WITH BOTS. Amer. Vet. Med. Assoc. Jour. (n. s. 9) 56: 265–270.
(7) ——— SMEAD, MORGAN J., and WOLF, CHARLES F.
    1919. STUDIES ON ANTHELMINTICS. II. THE ANTHELMINTIC AND INSECTICIDAL VALUE OF CARBON BISULPHIDE AGAINST GASTRO-INTESTINAL PARASITES OF THE HORSE. Amer. Vet. Med. Assoc. Jour. (n. s. 8) 55: 543–549.
(8) PERRONCITO, E., and BOSSO, G.
    1894. EXPÉRIENCES SUR LA RÉSISTANCE VITALE DES LARVES D'OESTRE (GASTROPHILUS EQUI). Rec. de Méd. Vét. (8) 1 (21) : 657–665.
(9) SCHROEDER, H. O.
    1940. HABITS OF THE LARVAE OF GASTROPHILUS NASALIS (L) IN THE MOUTH OF THE HORSE. Jour. Econ. Ent. 33: 382–384.
(10) WEHR, EVERETT E.
    1933. OBSERVATIONS ON THE LENGTH OF TIME FIRST-STAGE LARVAE OF GASTROPHILUS INTESTINALIS REMAIN IN THE TONGUE OF THE HORSE. North Amer. Vet. 14 (10) : 35–41.
(11) WELLS, R. W., and KNIPLING, E. F.
    1938. A REPORT OF SOME RECENT STUDIES ON SPECIES OF GASTROPHILUS OCCURRING IN HORSES IN THE UNITED STATES. Iowa State Col. Jour. Sci. 12: 181–203, illus.

Some Insect Pests of Horses and Mules

BY F. C. BISHOPP [1]

HERE IS condensed and practical information about several enemies of the horse and mule, including mosquitoes, sand flies (punkies), houseflies, horseflies, deer flies, buffalo gnats (blackflies), fleas, lice, and ticks. Special attention is given to control measures.

A CONSIDERABLE NUMBER of insects and insect relatives attack equines in addition to the horse bots, stableflies, ticks, screwworms, and mange mites discussed in other articles in this book. Some of them, such as the biting and sucking lice of horses and mules, are specific; some, like the tropical horse tick, attack other animals but prefer to feed on equines; and many others feed on various warm-blooded animals without seeming to prefer any one kind.

A number of such pests at times become so abundant locally as to have serious effects on horses, causing poor condition, lower work output, difficulty in handling, and even death.

MOSQUITOES AND SAND FLIES

Many kinds of mosquitoes and sand flies, or punkies, attack horses and mules. As a rule, a moderate number of these insects do not greatly annoy horses; but the presence of large numbers sometimes constitutes a serious problem, especially among high-strung animals such as race horses. Difficulties due to these insects have been encountered at meets and fairs held during the late spring and early fall in cities along the south Atlantic coast.

Screening the stables gives some protection against mosquitoes. Sand flies, however, readily pass through ordinary screens, and smudges and sprays are resorted to for relief from them. Painting the screens in the evening with a mixture of 1 part pyrethrum extract

---

[1] F. C. Bishopp is Assistant Chief, Bureau of Entomology and Plant Quarantine.

concentrate and 20 parts lubricating oil (S. A. E. 5), together with the use of a pyrethrum-kerosene spray in the buildings, is effective.[2] Pasturing the horses on high ground free from dense woods and underbrush reduces the mosquito and sand fly hazards outdoors.

Eliminating stagnant water in and near pastures, emptying and cleaning water troughs frequently, and, in salt marsh areas, ditching the parts of the marsh known to produce mosquitoes are effective steps in preventing trouble. Since there are many species of mosquitoes and they have widely divergent habits, control measures must be modified to fit the situation. After stagnant water has been eliminated as far as practicable, the principal lines of attack are: (1) Apply No. 2 fuel oil lightly to the surface pools where mosquito wigglers are found; (2) keep livestock on high, open pastures when mosquitoes are abundant; (3) keep valuable animals in screened barns; (4) use kerosene-pyrethrum sprays to kill the mosquitoes on animals and in the barns; and (5) make smudges in which stock may find protection during severe mosquito outbreaks.

In this brief account it is not possible to discuss all the different methods of controlling mosquitoes. The reader is therefore referred to other published articles that supply more details (*1, 4, 7*).[3]

The fact should not be lost sight of that at least eight American species of mosquitoes have been shown to be capable of carrying equine encephalomyelitis. Epizootics, or severe outbreaks, of this disease are usually concurrent with mosquito outbreaks, and protecting animals from mosquito attack appears to be of some value in preventing the disease.

THE HOUSEFLY

The housefly is not of great importance as an enemy of the horse, but, if not controlled, it breeds in tremendous numbers in horse manure. The presence of this insect in abundance is a serious hazard to human health.

The housefly annoys horses by its persistent efforts to feed on body secretions, particularly those of the eyes. This leads to the suspicion that the flies may transmit certain infectious eye diseases. The housefly is an intermediate host and transmitter of the roundworm parasite of equines, *Habronema muscae* (*8*), and it has also been shown to be capable of transmitting mastitis of cattle.

The control of houseflies depends on the proper disposal of manure and vegetable refuse (*5*). Scattering such materials thinly over fields soon to be plowed is the most satisfactory method of handling them. Manure may be stored in fly-tight manure pits or on racks over water. Treating manure with borax at the rate of 11 ounces to each 8 bushels also checks fly breeding. If the manure is to be used as a fertilizer, borax should not be used in excess of this amount. Care should be exercised not to apply too large an amount of treated manure to soil, since applications heavier than 15 tons per acre are likely to injure some crops on certain soil types.

---

[2] United States Bureau of Entomology and Plant Quarantine. sand flies and punkies. U. S. Bur. Ent. and Plant Quar. Cir. E–441, 3 pp. 1938. [Processed.]
[3] Italic numbers in parentheses refer to Literature Cited, p. 499.

The use of properly baited fly traps as well as of kerosene-pyrethrum fly sprays is an important supplemental control measure. Instructions for making a thoroughly practical fly trap will be found in Farmers' Bulletin 734, Flytraps and Their Operation.

HORSEFLIES AND DEERFLIES

The blood-sucking insects known as horseflies and deer flies are often very troublesome to horses. Their bites are painful, and when the insects are numerous, they draw considerable blood. They also act as carriers of anthrax, the Asiatic disease surra, and possibly other equine maladies.

There are many kinds of horseflies and deer flies of various sizes and colors (fig. 1). Some are relatively small, not more than half an inch in length, while others are three times that size and very robust.

FIGURE 1.—A species of horsefly. Three times natural size.

These pests are widely distributed in this country, being found in greatest numbers in marshy or swampy areas and along streams, where they breed. The eggs are laid on plants growing in or over the water or on stones in streams. After hatching, the larvae drop into the water and burrow into the mud or gravel, where they feed on small, soft-bodied animals. After nearly a year they pupate in the moist soil near the water, and soon the adult insects emerge. The adults are strong, fast fliers and may be found several miles away from water, but they are usually more abundant near it.

As the breeding habits suggest, control is very difficult. Draining swamps and seepage areas along streams, deepening and straightening the edges of lakes and ponds, and preventing accumulations of waste irrigation water in low places in meadows tend to reduce the number of horseflies.

When these pests are abundant, animals in harness may be given some relief by the use of burlap coverings. Darkened sheds and smudges offer some protection to livestock not being worked. Horseflies are not easily repelled, and as the individual flies usually remain on the animals for only very short periods, fly sprays are of little value.

BUFFALO GNATS

Buffalo gnats, or blackflies, are pests of nearly all warm-blooded animals, but certain species prefer certain hosts. They are small, rather heavy-set, humpbacked flies, or gnats (fig. 2). The bites they inflict on human beings are often very irritating; when there are many bites, the face and arms may become swollen, and severe generalized symptoms may result. Livestock are greatly annoyed by the bites of these insects. In severe outbreaks of the southern buffalo gnat in the lower Mississippi Valley many mules die, cattle and horses are reduced in flesh, milk flow is cut, and the coats of the animals become rough and unsightly.

Buffalo gnats breed only in running water. The larvae attach themselves to sticks, logs, stones, and aquatic plants in the faster flowing parts of streams. Stones or dams over which water is rushing are often literally covered with the larvae, which, when full-grown, are from one-third to one-half inch in length. The larvae usually require several months to develop; then they pupate in cornucopialike structures which they spin on rocks in the water. The gnats burst out of the pupa skins and in some way reach the surface of the rough water and fly off.

The adult females appear to require one or more meals of blood before eggs develop. These are laid in a gelatinous mass on stones or twigs at the water's surface or, as in the case of the southern buffalo gnat, are dropped singly on the water as the females dip to the surface from the swarm of gnats dancing over it. Bradley (*2*) has found that the eggs of the southern buffalo gnat sink to the bottom and do not hatch until the following spring when floods occur again. The eggs of most species hatch in a few days.

FIGURE 2.—Adult buffalo gnat, or blackfly. Much enlarged.

The southern buffalo gnat usually appears in swarms in the lower Mississippi Valley during the first warm period of late winter or early spring. If the floods are widespread and the weather continues warm, tremendous numbers of gnats emerge. After a few weeks the gnats disappear, sometimes very suddenly.

The turkey gnat (*Eusimulium meridionale*), which usually appears later in the spring than does the southern buffalo gnat, attacks livestock to a limited extent but is especially destructive to poultry.

Preventing the breeding of the southern buffalo gnat is very difficult. Controlling floodwaters by holding them within dikes reduces the extent of breeding, and it is advisable to remove from streams logs, brush, and other obstructions to which the gnats can attach themselves. The removal of stones is sometimes practicable in more northerly streams where buffalo gnats breed. It is also helpful to install a series of dams to still the water where it normally ripples over stones.

In small streams near horse-breeding farms or vacation resorts where gnats are troublesome, emulsified pyrethrum concentrate may be used to kill the larvae. This material is very destructive to fish and other desirable aquatic life and therefore should be used only by an experienced person. If fish are present, nets must be placed across the stream to prevent them from drifting downstream with the treated water and thus being killed.

Smudges are commonly resorted to, especially in gnat areas in the South, and are helpful in protecting both livestock and human beings from severe attack.

Horses, mules, and cattle may be protected to some extent by being kept on high, open pastures as far from flooded streams as possible. Animals should be watched and removed to protected places promptly if a severe outbreak of gnats occurs, since the initial attack usually is the one that causes death.

Immunizing animals by inoculating them with "gnat extract," made from crushed and filtered gnats, has been tried by Georgévitch (*3*) with a species causing great losses in the Danube Valley. This method appears to have some promise, but further experimental work is necessary to determine its true value.

Many concoctions have been used as repellents to protect human beings and animals from gnats, but none is very satisfactory. One of those most commonly used on animals is crankcase oil with a little pine tar added. The difficulty most farmers experience with oils and greases is that after their continued use animals often become overheated when worked in the sun, the hair being shed in patches, and the skin sometimes being badly burned. In an effort to avoid these ill effects Bradley conducted some tests of nonoily materials and found the following formula to be promising as a protection against the southern buffalo gnat: Boil ½ pound of soap in 1 gallon of water and slowly add 6 ounces of pine-tar oil (specific gravity 1.065) while stirring vigorously; add 1 pint of this mixture to 2½ gallons of water; mop the animals with it in the morning and spray them lightly several times during the way. Another repellent, developed by Schwardt (*9*), is made by emulsifying 3 quarts of cylinder oil with 1 pint of fish-oil soap. This stock emulsion is diluted with 1 gallon of water and mopped or sprayed on the animals.

FLEAS AND LICE

Fleas, especially the human flea, sometimes worry mules and horses considerably. These insects breed in barns, and their attacks frequently become so severe as to prevent horses and mules from standing in the barn even while eating. Methods of dealing with the pests in barns are discussed in the article on fleas, page 1188 of this volume.

Lice not infrequently become so numerous on horses and mules as to make them unthrifty and rough-coated. Of the three kinds of lice found on equines, the bloodsucking species known as *Haematopinus asini* is the most injurious. This louse is about one-eighth of an inch in length and has an elongate head (fig. 3). The other two species, known as *Trichodectes pilosus* and *T. parumpilosus*, have rounded heads and are usually yellowish or reddish brown. They have biting mouth parts and feed on skin scales. Sometimes they become incredibly numerous and seriously irritate horses, causing them to rub against objects, and to kick and stamp.

The species of lice mentioned confine their attacks to members of the horse family and remain on the host animal continuously. The young lice closely resemble the adults except that they are smaller and paler.

When removed from the host animal, the sucking lice are short-lived, living a maximum of 3 days under natural conditions. The biting lice, if kept on bunches of hair, may live for 10 days, but the majority of them die in 3 to 6 days. The eggs, or nits, are firmly attached to the horse's hair. The incubation period of the sucking louse is about 2 weeks and that of the biting lice is somewhat shorter. The sucking louse reaches maturity and the female begins laying eggs 11 or 12 days after hatching.

Lice are particularly abundant during the winter, when infestations may become very heavy before they are observed. Even when no control steps are taken, the lice diminish in numbers when the hair is shed in the spring. However, a few of the parasites remain on the animals, usually in the mane and tail, throughout the summer, and from these the infestation builds up again the next winter.

FIGURE 3.—Sucking louse of the horse and donkey. Much enlarged.

The presence of lice in large numbers is usually made known when the animal begins to rub itself against objects. The top of the tail is often made nearly bare in this way, and patches of hair are rubbed from the neck, shoulders, and flanks. Lice may pass from one animal to another by direct contact or by being rubbed off in corrals or barns.

A number of insecticides, if properly applied, are effective in killing lice, but since none of them will destroy the eggs, it is necessary to treat infested animals at least twice to delouse them entirely. The irregularity in the time required for eggs to hatch and for the lice to mature makes it difficult to set an exact period between dippings. Schwartz, Imes, and Wright (*10, p. 37*) state that "experience has shown that two dippings with an interval of 14 to 16 days usually can be depended on to control both sucking and biting lice."

TICKS

Several kinds of ticks attack horses and mules. One, called the tropical horse tick (*Dermacentor nitens*), prefers equines to other animals. The others attack various kinds of domestic and wild animals.

The tropical horse tick is found in the extreme southern part of Texas and in tropical America. It attaches itself mainly in the ears of the animal but may be found in the foretop and mane or elsewhere on the head and neck.

The Gulf coast tick, technically *Amblyomma maculatum*, in the adult stage attaches itself in the outer ear. The long beak of this tick makes a severe wound, and when a group of the ticks puncture an ear it becomes inflamed, thickened, and sore. Not infrequently screwworm flies are attracted to the infested ears, and their larvae burrow into the tissues. If the screwworms are killed in time the animal's life may be saved, but frequently cartilage is destroyed and the ears droop. When this occurs the animal is said to be gotch-eared.

FIGURE 4.—Ear tick nymph, fully engorged. Much enlarged.

The spinose ear tick (*Ornithodoros megnini*) attaches itself when in the seed-tick stage deep in the external ear. This tick is prevalent in the arid and semiarid Southwest. It is often present in such numbers as to fill the bottom of the ear and cause much annoyance; infested animals shake their heads, the ears and head are sensitive, and the animals are often hard to bridle. Heavy infestations result in loss of flesh and an unthrifty appearance.

The seed ticks of this species molt and become nymphs in 7 to 12 days without leaving the ears. The nymphs become fully engorged (fig. 4) and grow to about one-third of an inch long in 1 to 6 months; then they drop off the animal and crawl up a post, barn wall, or tree, where they find a hiding place and molt their spiny skins. The adults mate, and the females lay eggs in the hiding places. The eggs hatch in about 3 weeks, and the active seed ticks are then ready to attach themselves in the ears of an animal.

The two species of winter ticks, *Dermacentor albipictus* and *D. nigrolineatus*, are widely distributed in this country. They appear to prefer horses and elk as hosts but also attack other domestic and wild animals. They frequently become so numerous, especially on range horses, as to cause extreme debility or even death. The seed ticks of these species become active late in the fall and attach themselves then or during warm periods in the winter or early spring. The ticks remain on the host during their two molts, and the females become engorged and drop off about 30 days after the seed ticks became attached.

The cattle tick (*Boophilus annulatus*) often attacks horses and mules as well as bovines. Some individual animals appear to be very favorable hosts for this tick, while others are infested with few if any of them. For further discussion of this pest, see the article on Cattle Tick Fever, page 572.

The American dog tick (*Dermacentor variabilis*) attaches itself to horses and human beings as well as to dogs and many other species of animals. On well-groomed horses this tick becomes attached mainly in the mane and tail and on the fetlocks. The ticks cause much irritation but are not known to carry any equine disease. (See the article on this tick as a pest of dogs, p. 1180.)

A number of other species of ticks are important as pests of horses in certain localities, among them the black-legged tick (*Ixodes ricinus scapularis*), the Pacific coast tick (*Dermacentor occidentalis*), the lone star tick (*Amblyomma americanum*), and the cayenne tick (*A. cajennense*).

Control measures for ticks must be fitted to the habits of the particular species. Horses infested with the ear tick and the Gulf coast tick may be freed of these pests by treating the ears with a mixture of 2 parts of pine tar and 1 part of cottonseed oil. In order to reach all the ear ticks, it is necessary to work the material into the ear or to break up the mass of ticks, as described by Imes (*6*). The liquid should not be allowed to run down the side of the face, as it may cause shedding of the hair. Applications every 2 to 4 weeks will usually keep either of these species under complete control. The same treatment is effective in controlling the tropical horse tick.

Dipping in an arsenical solution, as mentioned on page 575 of this volume, is the most satisfactory way of destroying cattle ticks and other species that infest various parts of the animal other than the ears. The short period of engorgement and the general host relations of such species as the cayenne tick, the lone star tick, and the black-legged tick make complete control by dipping impossible. The winter ticks are more resistant to arsenical dips than the cattle tick, and many of them survive dipping in the standard-strength arsenical solution. Two dippings at 14-day intervals in a solution containing 0.22 percent arsenic trioxide will destroy most of the ticks if the animal is not exposed to reinfestation. Mopping infested animals with a mixture of 2 ounces of finely ground derris containing 5 percent rotenone, 2 ounces of neutral soap, and 1 gallon of water would probably kill all the ticks with which the wash is brought in contact. This wash is also effective for the American dog tick. Clipping helps to keep ticks off saddle horses, and dusting derris or cube powder in the mane and fetlocks also helps to hold down infestations.

LITERATURE CITED

(1) BISHOPP, F. C.
    1939. DOMESTIC MOSQUITOES. U. S. Dept. Agr. Leaflet 186, 8 pp., illus.
(2) BRADLEY, G. H.
    1935. THE HATCHING OF EGGS OF THE SOUTHERN BUFFALO GNAT. Science 82: 277–278.

(3) GEORGÉVITCH, JIVOIN.
   1923. NOUVELLES RECHERCHES SUR LA MOUCHE DE GOLOURATZ. [Paris] Acad
      des Sci. Compt. Rend. 176: 1500–1502.
(4) HERMS, WILLIAM BRODBECK, and GRAY, HAROLD FARNSWORTH.
   1940. MOSQUITO CONTROL. 317 pp., illus. New York.
(5) HOWARD, L. O., and BISHOPP, F. C.
   1926. THE HOUSE FLY AND HOW TO SUPPRESS IT. U. S. Dept. Agr. Farmers'
      Bul. 1408, 17 pp., illus. (Revised.)
(6) IMES, MARION.
   1918. THE SPINOSE EAR TICK. U. S. Dept. Agr. Farmers' Bul. 980, 8 pp.,
      illus.
(7) KING, W. V., BRADLEY, G. H., and McNEEL, T. E.
   1939. THE MOSQUITOES OF THE SOUTHEASTERN STATES. U. S. Dept Agr.
      Misc. Pub. 336, 91 pp., illus.
(8) RANSOM, B. H.
   1913. THE LIFE HISTORY OF HABRONEMA MUSCAE (CARTER), A PARASITE OF THE
      HORSE TRANSMITTED BY THE HOUSE FLY. U. S. Bur. Anim. Indus.
      163, 36 pp., illus.
(9) SCHWARDT, H. H.
   1935. LUBRICATING OIL EMULSION AS A BUFFALO GNAT REPELLENT. Kans.
      Ent. Soc. Jour. 8: 141.
(10) SCHWARTZ, BENJAMIN, IMES, MARION, and WRIGHT, W. W.
   1936. PARASITES AND PARISITIC DISEASES OF HORSES. U. S. Dept. Agr. Cir.
      148, 55 pp., illus. (Revised.)

Brucellosis of Cattle

BY ELMER LASH AND H. M. O'REAR [1]

THE DAMAGE done to herds by brucellosis of cattle, the rapidity with which it spreads, and the fact that the *Brucella* germ causes undulant fever in man make this disease especially important. A few years ago a Nation-wide campaign to eradicate it was begun; recently a new method of calfhood vaccination became a weapon in this campaign.

BRUCELLOSIS, an insidious disease commonly referred to as contagious abortion or Bang's disease, has caused heavy losses to the cattle industry every year, largely through reduced milk production, the oss of calves by premature birth, and sterility. Brucellosis may spread very rapidly in a susceptible herd, many of the animals contracting the disease within a few weeks after they are exposed to the causative agent.

The disease is caused by a germ known as *Brucella abortus*, which is introduced into healthy herds by the addition of infected cows or infected pregnant heifers.

Brucella germs may be in the uterus or the udder of cows, in the generative organs of bulls, in certain lymph glands and joints, and in the intestines and other organs of newly born calves. Diseased cows eliminate the germs in the fetus, afterbirth, and uterine discharges for limited periods, and in the milk for prolonged periods. The malady appears to be commonly acquired through the mouth in feed and drink contaminated with the germs, or by licking infected animals, contaminated mangers, or other objects to which the germs may adhere. The skin and the membranes lining the eyelids may also provide an entrance for the abortion germ. Proof that bulls transmit the disease through the act of service is lacking.

It was not until 1896 that the organism responsible for bovine brucellosis was discovered by Professor Bang, noted Danish research worker. The existence of such a malady has been known for more

---

[1] Elmer Lash is Assistant Chief and H. M. O'Rear is Senior Veterinarian, Tuberculosis Eradication Division, Bureau of Animal Industry.

than 100 years in the United States, however. For more than 40 years Department of Agriculture research workers have been continually engaged in investigations directed toward finding a cure or a means to control and eventually eradicate bovine brucellosis. Alice Evans, while an employee of the Department, did notable work in connection with brucellosis in discovering the similarity between the organism that causes abortion in cows and the corresponding organism in goats that causes undulant, or Malta, fever in human beings.

BRUCELLA ABORTUS AND HUMAN HEALTH

In recent years it has been shown that undulant fever in man may be caused by the same germs that cause brucellosis in cattle, swine, and goats. A large number of cases of undulant fever contracted from raw milk containing *Brucella abortus* have been reported. Handling infected pork products is also a means by which undulant fever is transmitted to man, as is the handling of discharges and aborted fetuses from infected animals. Though undulant fever would not be classed as a major health problem, it is nevertheless one to be reckoned with, and it can be reduced materially through the eradication of the disease in cattle. Dairymen and breeders of meat animals are aware of the possibility that human beings may contract undulant fever from raw milk, meat, and dairy products infected with brucellosis germs, and of the influence this may have on the market for their products. The simple precautions of pasteurizing milk and cooking meat, however, make these foods safe for human consumption.

SYMPTOMS OF BRUCELLOSIS

The symptoms of brucellosis in cattle are rather inconstant and indefinite. Abortion is probably the most widely known and most readily observed symptom, but it may easily be misinterpreted, since not all cows that abort are affected with the disease. Moreover, the prompt recognition of the disease in affected herds is made more difficult by the fact that many animals that have it never abort. Sterility is usually a serious trouble in herds infected with *Brucella abortus*, but it does not constitute definite evidence of such infection. The retention of the afterbirth, likewise, does not definitely indicate the presence of the disease, as this condition, too, may occur when brucellosis is absent. None of these symptoms prove the presence or absence of the malady, but they may well be regarded as justifying suspicion and calling for prompt action. This is particularly true of abortion; until a definite diagnosis with the blood-agglutination test can be made, it is advisable to infer that an aborting animal is affected with the disease and to take action accordingly.

DIAGNOSIS

In the blood stream of an animal infected with brucellosis there is an antibody, a substance known as agglutinin. When blood serum containing this substance is brought in contact with a suspension of

Brucella organisms (called an antigen), it causes the organisms to adhere to one another and form clumps. This action, known as agglutination, is the basis for the test used in diagnosing brucellosis in the living animal.

To obtain the serum for a test, a sterile needle is inserted through a disinfected spot of skin into the jugular vein of the animal, and a small amount of blood is drawn into a sterile test tube or small bottle. This is allowed to set for a few hours, until the serum separates from the blood clot. A carefully measured amount of the serum is then mixed with a carefully measured amount of antigen for the test. There are two methods of making the test, the tube method and the plate method, and either one is remarkably accurate when conducted by an experienced operator.

LOSSES FROM BRUCELLOSIS

Although it is difficult to determine the financial losses caused by this insidious disease even approximately, estimates, based mostly on actual losses in various communities, have varied from 30 million dollars annually to much larger amounts. No definite, detailed survey taking into account the tremendous intangible losses has yet been made, and hence all estimates have probably fallen far short of the real situation. It is not enough to figure the probable value of a calf that is born dead or that is weak and soon dies, the shrinkage of beef in the beef animal, the diminished production of milk in the dairy animal, the temporary or permanent sterility that may follow the infection, and, not infrequently, the loss of the cow itself through infection; there is also the financial loss that the breeder of selected purebred cattle suffers from interference with his breeding program because of the presence of the disease in his herd.

A careful study of a herd maintained at an experiment station showed that the loss per cow in milk production alone was over $100 a year. In another study it was determined that the loss resulting from abortion in a good commercial-grade herd of 16 cows was about $135 annually, and in a typical purebred herd, $486. Veterinarians and cattle breeders know the wide distribution and economic importance of brucellosis, and the trouble it has caused them makes them more interested in it than in any other infectious disease of cattle. From general observation and special studies, it is known that at the time the cooperative State and Federal campaign to eradicate brucellosis was inaugurated in July 1934 the disease was more widespread than it had been some years before.

REMEDIES WORTHLESS

There is no drug, chemical, or medicinal compound that has been proved to be effective in the prevention or cure of brucellosis, but livestock owners of this country have spent large sums annually for worthless remedies in an effort to stop abortion in their cattle due to bovine brucellosis. These remedies have gained popularity because in most instances they are used and their value is judged at a time when the disease has run its course and is becoming chronic. At this stage abortions can be expected to decrease as a result of acquired immunity, and a large percentage of the cows produce apparently normal calves. Perhaps no other disease is so deceptive in its apparent response to treatment as brucellosis. Though the Department had frequently warned the public that no drug or combination of drugs had been found to be effective in combating this malady in cattle, traffic in so-called cures continued for a time to flourish. It was decided therefore, in 1936, to conduct some experiments with two of the remedies that had been widely advertised. One hundred heifers were selected to be the subjects of the experiments, which were carefully controlled. The two products were proved to have no value whatever in preventing abortion or curing brucellosis in cattle.

CONTROL AND ERADICATION

Brucellosis of cattle may be controlled in several ways, the method used depending on herd conditions and the severity and extent of the disease in the herd. Four methods of control have been used successfully: Test and slaughter, calfhood vaccination with a culture of reduced virulence, sanitary control or herd management, and test and segregation.

THE TEST-AND-SLAUGHTER METHOD

Since 1896 methods of control have been established, but unfortunately none of those thus far receiving recognition are easy of operation or inexpensive. Consequently, there was little organized effort to control the disease until July 1934, when funds were made available by Congress for a cattle-reduction program associated with the severe drought of that year. Since such a program was to be inaugurated, it seemed logical to direct it in part toward the elimination of diseased cattle, and part of the funds were allotted for this purpose. Thus in July 1934 the present brucellosis control and eradication project was begun in cooperation with the livestock sanitary officials of the various States. Since then the cattle owners' losses have been gradually reduced and are now very much less than they were at that time. Figure 1 shows the estimated extent of infection by States at the beginning of the project.

The plan promulgated at the beginning of the campaign, when it was estimated that there were 10 million surplus cattle in the United States, called for subjecting all dairy and breeding cattle over 6 months of age to a blood-agglutination test. It also provided for the slaughter of the animals that reacted to the test, since it is accepted as a fact that such animals are affected with bovine brucellosis.

This was a huge undertaking. It was necessary to draw a sample of blood from each animal under supervision and forward the samples to a laboratory for test. A corps of technicians had to be trained to make the tests, and in order to meet the emergency the laboratories of many of the States were expanded and new ones established. The Department purchased a number of trailer laboratories that have proved very satisfactory. They are usually set up in the county seat where cattle owners may see the blood of their animals being tested and thus gain a clearer understanding of the methods employed to detect diseased animals. High-school teachers and students are invited to view the work conducted in the trailer laboratories, and this has proved very interesting as well as educational to the young people.

When work was inaugurated in the cooperative eradication of bovine brucellosis and until more cattle owners understood the advantages to be derived from a herd free from this disease, only scattered herds were tested. Then, as owners who had freed their herds of the malady realized that bovine brucellosis is easily spread from one farm to another, there were urgent requests to test all cattle in an area and destroy diseased animals that might serve as reservoirs of

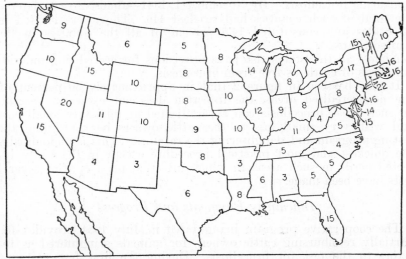

FIGURE 1.—The figure in each State represents the estimated percentage of brucellosis in cattle when Federal-State eradication work began in July 1934. The average estimated extent of infection among all cattle in the United States was 10 percent.

infection from which the disease might be carried back into the tested herds. Acting on these requests and requests from owners whose herds had not been tested, many of the States took up cooperative eradication work on an area basis.

The Area Plan

Under the area plan, all the cattle in an area, except steers and calves under 6 months of age, are tested and the reactors removed and slaughtered. Retests are applied at the proper intervals. The owners are given instructions as to the sanitary methods to follow, since proper sanitation is a very important factor in eliminating the disease. In December 1939 the plan of designating areas as practically free of brucellosis was inaugurated. Whenever the tests of all cattle in a county 6 months of age and over, except steers, indicate that the percentage of cattle with positive reactions does not exceed 1 percent of those tested and that the number of infected herds does not exceed 5 percent of the total number, the regulations provide that such a county may be declared a "modified accredited Bang's disease-free area" for 3 years by the cooperating State and Federal officials in charge of the work, provided all infected herds are placed in quarantine. The cattle in these herds must be re-tested for the disease at intervals of 30 to 90 days until all of them pass two successive negative tests, and they must also pass a third negative test not less than 6 months from the date of the second. The reactors in any test are of course removed from the herds and disposed of in accordance with the State and Federal regulations. On February 1, 1940, the first counties—209 in 17 States—were declared modified accredited areas in recognition of progress made in combating brucellosis. By November 1, 1941—almost 2 years later— the total of such counties had reached 446. They were located in 23 States and constituted 14.5 percent of all the counties in the United States.

Almost all the States also have provisions for accrediting individual herds of cattle as free from brucellosis.

It may be seen in figure 2 that in approximately 50 percent of the nonaccredited areas, the infection does not exceed 2 percent. In such areas brucellosis can be eradicated at relatively small cost and with very small loss to the cattle owners by continuing the testing program and slaughtering the reactors. This is undoubtedly the quickest and most practical procedure except in the badly infected herds in such areas in which infection persists after several tests have been made.

Indemnity Payments and Progress

The cooperative program inaugurated in July 1934 provides for partially reimbursing cattle owners for animals slaughtered as reactors to the test for brucellosis. During the first few years of the campaign the Federal Government provided a major part of the indemnity payments. Since May 1, 1939, however, the Bureau of Animal Industry has been forbidden by Federal statute to make indemnity payments to owners for the slaughter of reactors unless the State or municipality pays a sum equal to or greater than that paid by the Bureau. Federal payment is made on the basis of one-third of the difference between the appraised value and the salvage value, but this amount is not to exceed the amount paid by the State, and it is not to exceed $25 for a grade and $50 for a purebred animal.

During the first 7 years in which this project was conducted, agglutination blood tests, including retests, were applied to approximately 48,117,000 cattle and disclosed about 2,134,000 reactors. At the end of the 7-year period, approximately 1,184,000 herds, containing about 13,933,000 cattle, were under supervision throughout the United States for the control and eradication of brucellosis. About 1,175,000 cattle were in the herds of cattlemen who had applied for the test and were on the waiting list.

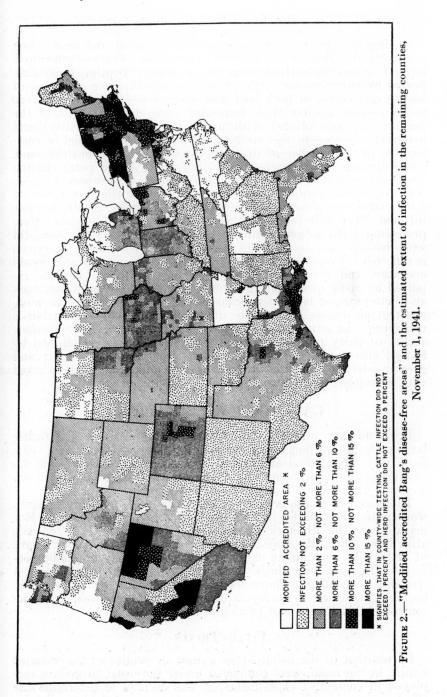

FIGURE 2.—"Modified accredited Bang's disease-free areas" and the estimated extent of infection in the remaining counties, November 1, 1941.

☐ MODIFIED ACCREDITED AREA *

▨ INFECTION NOT EXCEEDING 2 %

▨ MORE THAN 2% NOT MORE THAN 6 %

▨ MORE THAN 6% NOT MORE THAN 10 %

▨ MORE THAN 10% NOT MORE THAN 15 %

■ MORE THAN 15 %

* SIGNIFIES THAT IN COUNTY-WIDE TESTING, CATTLE INFECTION DID NOT EXCEED 1 PERCENT AND HERD INFECTION DID NOT EXCEED 5 PERCENT

Benefits of the Campaign

During the progress of the cooperative control and eradication campaign the Bureau of Animal Industry has received numerous reports of benefits derived from the program. Typical benefits reported by participating cattle owners include thriftier condition of herds; calf crops, in both beef and dairy herds, approximately 20 to 25 percent greater than formerly; noticeable decreases in the number of cows affected with udder troubles and sterility; and material increases in the milk production of herds, roughly comparable to the number of diseased cows replaced by healthy ones. The following report interestingly illustrates this last point: In the first test, applied to 8.304 cattle, 2,319 reactors were reported, or an infection at the rate of 27.9 percent. Four years later the test of 7,403 cattle in the same area disclosed 59 reactors, or 0.8 percent infected. The milk report of this area showed that 7.403 cows were producing 1,430 gallons more milk a day than the 8,304 cows did when brucellosis infection was active. The benefit to the dairymen is reflected not only in increased milk production but also in lowered operation and maintenance costs. Among additional benefits reported by cattle owners are greater marketability of breeding stock and better prices, because purchasers are becoming more and more insistent on disease-free sources of animals and State legislation is restricting the entry of untested breeding stock; greater marketability of dairy products, because legal restrictions are imposed by States, cities, and towns on products from untested herds; and greater safety to human health, because raw milk from herds infected with brucellosis may transmit undulant fever.

CALFHOOD VACCINATION

For a number of years studies have been in progress on a rather large scale for the purpose of determining the possibilities of a comparatively safe method of preventive vaccination with a vaccine developed in the laboratories of the Bureau of Animal Industry from a culture of the *Brucella* organism of low virulence.

This vaccine has also been subjected to rigid tests by many research workers in other similar institutions, with encouraging results. For many years the livestock interests and livestock sanitary officials alike have shared the hope that eventually some satisfactory means of artificially immunizing cattle against this malady might be perfected. Because brucellosis, particularly in dairy cattle, has a tremendous economic importance in addition to its human or public health significance, the prospect of another practical weapon in the control of this disease is of particular significance.

FIELD TRIALS

In addition to the information gained in studies of the vaccine, which, in the main, were conducted under the usual procedure employed in controlled experiments, it was decided to determine the effectiveness of calfhood vaccination under natural field conditions.

A field project was started in January 1936 to determine the value of the vaccine when applied to calves under natural conditions and the feasibility of a vaccinating procedure as a practical means of controlling brucellosis.

Since the project was to be conducted cooperatively in privately owned herds, the usual experimental procedure of maintaining control animals was omitted. The herds selected, therefore, were chosen from those in which the disease was shown by the blood-agglutination test to be present in a sufficient number of animals to insure adequate exposure of the vaccinated animals to the disease, and no herd containing less than 15 percent of positive reactors was accepted. Finally, 260 herds, containing approximately 19,000 cattle, were selected in 24 States. In the initial test applied to these herds, 29.2 percent of positive reactors and 8.4 percent of suspicious animals were disclosed. The suspects and reactors were retained in each herd for a time, after which the practice was adopted of eliminating a few each year as the vaccinated animals came into production and could serve as replacements. The vaccinated animals were permitted to mingle constantly with the infected members of the herd, and the usual sanitary practices employed in animal disease control were not applied in these herds. The only means of control employed was the vaccination of calves between 5 and 7 months of age with *Brucella abortus* vaccine strain 19.

A summary of the results during the first 4½ years of the study, covering three pregnancies of the vaccinated animals, is as follows: In these herds 13,854 calves were vaccinated when between the ages of 5 and 7 months. There were 8,182 calvings of which 7,872, or 96.2 percent, were normal, and only 310, or 3.8 percent, were abortions. Of the 310 animals that aborted, 182, or 58.7 percent, were negative to the test after calving, and 128, or 41.3 percent, showed either a positive or a suspicious reaction. Consequently, on the basis of the blood-agglutination test, only 128 abortions, or 1.6 percent of the 8,182 calvings, could be attributed to brucellosis. Of the 1,346 animals that calved normally and showed either a positive or a suspicious reaction to the test after calving, approximately 500, or 37.1 percent, were negative on the first retest applied 6 months later. Of the first group of 97 animals that calved normally during the first pregnancy and gave a suspicious or positive reaction to the test after calving, 75, or 77.3 percent, had returned to a negative reaction on the fifth retest, applied 2½ years later.

The results of the field trials as well as those of experiments with calfhood vaccination with *Brucella abortus* strain 19 showed that this method of control is very effective as far as calf production is concerned and markedly effective in actually preventing infection. Accordingly, the results of the field study were presented to the United States Live Stock Sanitary Association during its annual meeting in Chicago in December 1940, and a general plan for the official recognition of calfhood vaccination as an aid in cooperative brucellosis control was proposed by the Chief of the Bureau of Animal Industry. According to the provisions of the plan, calfhood vaccination, as well as the test-and-slaughter method of eradication, may be used in States where the proper officials deem conditions favorable, dependent on acceptance of the plan by the proper authorities in such States. Many of the States have adopted plans for using calfhood vaccination in the control of brucellosis in cattle, and interested cattle owners should consult their State veterinarian or State livestock sanitary officials before having the vaccine used in their herds.

The aim in the use of vaccine in a brucellosis-infected herd should be directed toward the eradication of the disease rather than merely toward the assurance of a calf crop. The eradication of the disease is possible only through the removal of the animals that continue to show an agglutination reaction on repeated tests. The reacting animals may be removed immediately, if necessary, or gradually as vaccinated replacements become available. It should be obvious, therefore, that two things are necessary in this connection: (1) That vaccination should be confined to calves between 4 and 8 months of age, and (2) that periodic blood tests should be made of the entire herd. To obtain the desired results, the administration of the vaccine and subsequent care of the affected herd should be entrusted to a qualified veterinarian.

SANITARY CONTROL OR HERD MANAGEMENT

Another plan of control that is both practical and economical should not be overlooked. This is the sanitary control method, with special relation to herd management, which, though it involves extra work, pays splendid dividends. In many herds the disease has been controlled by this method, which has two requirements: (1) A maternity barn, shed, or stall sufficiently removed from buildings housing the other cattle to prevent direct exposure to infection, and (2) a close, daily observation of each pregnant animal, especially first-term heifers. At the first indication of approaching calving or signs of abortion, the animal should be placed in the maternity barn and kept from the remainder of the herd until abortion or calving has occurred and discharge has ceased. Persons caring for these animals should carefully wash their hands with soap and water and thoroughly disinfect their boots or shoes before leaving the building. Implements used for feeding and watering should not be used anywhere else. The aborted fetus and afterbirth should be burned or buried with quicklime. Additional sanitary treatment should be given to aborting animals before they are returned to the herd, and they should not be bred for at least 3 months. These sanitary control measures, when used in conjunction with the test-and-slaughter method or vaccination, greatly increase the efficiency of the latter two through the removal of possibilities of exposure.

TEST-AND-SEGREGATION METHOD

This method consists in segregating the reactors to the blood-agglutination test in a separate herd apart from the nonreactors. Separate premises are necessary for each group. Retests at frequent intervals are made of the nonreacting group in order that infection may be detected in the beginning stage and the reacting animals, if any, removed. Many valuable herds have been freed from infection by this method, but there are several reasons why it is not a desirable one: (1) Only a few owners can provide facilities for two herds; (2) it is usually some time before the reacting herd can be disposed of; and (3) a single act of negligence in the care of the nonreacting herd may result in undoing several years' effort.

PREVENTION

The old adage, "An ounce of prevention is worth a pound of cure," is sound advice in regard to brucellosis, and no possibility of preventing infection from gaining entrance to a normal herd should be overlooked. Undoubtedly the chief way in which this disease is introduced into a herd is through replacements or additions, especially of pregnant heifers or cows. All animals added to a herd should be negative to the agglutination test or be purchased from herds accredited as being free from brucellosis, and it is advisable to keep them from direct contact with the herd for a period of 3 months and not admit them to the herd until they react negatively to the test. Animals shown at fairs and livestock shows may be exposed to infection, and it is advisable to test them several months after their return. Drainage from adjacent infected premises should be diverted, if possible, and small sluggish streams flowing through and from premises known to be infected should be fenced off. The proper pasteurization of milk will make it safe for feeding. Stockmen should be careful in visiting farms where infectious diseases exist, as the germs may be brought home on shoes or clothing.

Johne's Disease

BY B. T. SIMMS, WILLIAM M. MOHLER,
H. W. JOHNSON [1]

THE WORD "INSIDIOUS" can truly be applied to
Johne's disease. It creeps up unobserved, the symptoms are mild at first and the end is death. It is one
of the most difficult of diseases to eradicate from a
herd—and apparently it is increasing in the United
States. The authors tell what is known and what is
not known about it.

JOHNE'S DISEASE, or paratuberculosis, is a chronic infection characterized principally by inflammation of the intestines, loss of condition, and diarrhea. It attacks cattle and sheep and has been reported in goats, deer, and horses. So far as is known, man is not
susceptible. The disease is very widespread, having been observed
in practically every country where cattle are raised on a large scale.
It occurs very frequently in districts such as western continental
Europe and the British Isles, where intensive dairying is practiced.

While Johne's disease has been found in both beef and dairy cattle
in every part of the United States, accurate figures showing its
extent in this country are not available. Both tests of live cattle
with johnin (a diagnostic agent similar to tuberculin, prepared
from cultures of the causative bacillus) and examinations of slaughtered cattle at packing plants have indicated that the disease is
much more prevalent than most veterinarians and livestock sanitary
authorities have realized. About 5,000 head of cattle, most of which
were in dairy herds, were tested recently in the Southeastern States,
and over 100 percent gave positive reactions.

There are very few records of the occurrence of the disease in
sheep in the United States, but only a few investigators have
examined sheep for the disease.

---

[1] B. T. Simms is Director and H. W. Johnson is Associate Veterinarian, Regional Animal
Disease Research Laboratory, Auburn, Ala., and William M. Mohler is Senior Veterinarian,
Pathological Division, Bureau of Animal Industry.

CAUSE OF THE DISEASE

The causative agent of Johne's disease is a bacillus named *Myco-bacterium paratuberculosis*, which is usually found in scrapings from affected parts of the intestinal mucous membrane and in the mesenteric lymph glands.[2] This organism does not grow readily on the commonly used laboratory culture media. Even on media especially adapted to it, it grows very slowly when first isolated from the tissues of diseased animals; hence obtaining cultures is a difficult and laborious procedure. After growing on laboratory media for several generations, however, the organism becomes adapted to such media and grows fairly well. So far as is known, it does not multiply outside the body of a host animal.

Attempts at infecting laboratory animals have met with little success. If the organisms are suspended in oil and injected intra-peritoneally (into the lining of the abdominal cavity) into guinea pigs, local lesions, or tissue injuries, usually develop on the liver, spleen, and omentum, but a progressive disease does not follow. The rabbit gives even less response. The chicken appears to be somewhat more susceptible than the guinea pig, but shows little evidence of a progressive disease.

MODE OF INFECTION

Since the Johne's disease organism lives in the mucous membrane of the intestines of infected cattle and sheep, large numbers may be present in the feces of diseased animals, and it is generally believed that this is the principal source of infection. Exposure may come from direct contact between infected and susceptible animals or through the use by susceptible animals of pens, pastures, corrals, or barns that have been contaminated by diseased cattle or sheep. A contaminated water supply may be a potent source of the disease.

It is very generally believed that young animals are more susceptible than mature ones and that the route of infection is through the digestive tract.

In most herds the disease spreads rather slowly. Even where Johne's disease has been known to be present for many years and there has been no segregation of the infected cattle, it is rather unusual to find as many as half the herd affected.

Several months to several years may pass following exposure before infected cattle show clinical symptoms. Many such animals carry large numbers of the Johne's disease organism in their intestines and may be potent in spreading the disease.

SYMPTOMS

Symptoms of Johne's disease are seldom observed in cattle under 1 to 2 years of age; there are very few records of the disease in steers or in heifers before their first calves are born. Probably the ordeal of freshening makes the infected cow more susceptible to

---

[2] *Mycobacterium paratuberculosis* is aerobic, nonmotile, sporeless, and acid-fast.

the ravages of paratuberculosis, for the clinical symptoms often appear for the first time within 2 to 5 or 6 weeks following calving.

The symptoms that are considered typical consist in gradual loss of flesh to the point of emaciation, and intermittent diarrhea becoming gradually worse. In most instances the temperature remains practically normal. The appetite is usually fairly good until the disease is well advanced, and there is little or no apparent disturbance of the respiratory, circulatory, and urinary systems. During attacks of diarrhea there is some increase in thirst. The decline in general condition is usually accompanied by a roughening of the coat and drying of the skin. Diarrhea may not appear until the animal has lost considerable weight. The semiliquid or liquid feces are usually free from blood and in most instances do not have a very foul odor until the disease is well advanced. Large numbers of gas bubbles may appear in the feces, but this is not very common. There may seem to be improvement, but it is usually very temporary. The tendency is for the attacks of diarrhea to become more frequent and severe until death occurs.

DIAGNOSIS

Diagnosis of Johne's disease has always been somewhat difficult. Many infected animals that may be active spreaders of the disease show no clinical symptoms. Even those exhibiting symptoms may be suspected of suffering from malnutrition, parasitism, chronic indigestion, or chronic poisoning. Attempts at finding acid-fast organisms in either the feces or scrapings from the rectum are sometimes successful, but in many known cases results have been negative.

The use of diagnostic agents similar to tuberculin has given encouraging results. The materials used and the methods of injection have varied with different workers. Twort and Ingram prepared johnin in the same manner as tuberculin and injected it subcutaneously (under the skin). Hastings, Beach, and Hadley used avian tuberculin subcutaneously, and Hagan and Zeissig injected it intravenously (into the veins). The reactions from these injections are a rise in temperature and, in some animals, a general systemic upset.

Intradermic injections (into, not under the skin) of johnin in infected cattle have resulted in local reactions comparable to those seen in tuberculous cattle following the intradermic injection of tuberculin. The reactions appeared in 1 to 3 days and disappeared slowly, but the seventy-second hour after injection is apparently the best time to observe results. The minimal enlargement that is considered a reaction to johnin is smaller than that interpreted as a reaction in tuberculin testing, and the swelling also tends to be somewhat more diffuse than that in tuberculin reactors. Observations indicate that the intradermic injection of johnin does not cause a physical break-down in infected animals.

Practically all workers agree that animals that react to any of the Johne's disease tests are, in a high percentage of the cases, infected. The weakness in diagnosis with the tests is that some infected animals fail to react.

Since the organism causing Johne's disease is similar to that causing tuberculosis, there has been much interest in the possibility that animals affected with one of these diseases might react to tests for the other. Some cattle that have given typical reactions when tested with tuberculin have shown the presence of Johne's disease instead of tuberculosis on post mortem examination. In some herds cattle with no visible lesions have repeatedly reacted to tuberculin over a period of years, and it has been established that paratuberculosis is present in such reactors.

TREATMENT

No satisfactory method of treating cattle affected with Johne's disease has been found. Some animals respond temporarily to a change in feed and treatment with intestinal astringents soon after symptoms appear. Some veterinarians have recommended that animals showing clinical symptoms be taken off pasture and given dry, nutritious feed, while others state that an alleviation of symptoms is frequently observed if affected cattle are placed on good pasture. All agree that any improvement is soon followed by a recurrence of symptoms. Practically all cattle that develop clinical symptoms die within a period that varies between 1 month and 2 years. It is usually recommended, therefore, that animals showing symptoms of Johne's disease be sold for beef while they are still in good condition. Since the disease is not transmissible to man and the lesions do not involve any of the edible parts, the carcasses of affected cattle in good condition at the time of slaughter, if they show no indication of any other disease, are passed as wholesome food.

POST MORTEM FINDINGS

The pathology of Johne's disease is restricted to the digestive tract and adjacent lymphatic glands. Both the location and the type of the lesions vary somewhat in animals of different ages. In young calves the entire small intestine may be involved, while in mature animals the lesions are usually restricted to the ileum, cecum, colon, and rectum. In calves the principal changes observed on autopsy are those accompanying acute congestion. There is redness and some swelling of the mucous membrane of the affected portion of the small intestine. In some cases only a small area is involved.

The changes found in mature cattle indicate a much more chronic disease. The lesions consist principally of a marked thickening of the affected mucous membrane, with some reddened patches and some enlargement of the adjacent lymph nodes. In severe cases of long standing the mucous membrane may be 2 to 5 times its normal thickness. The thickened portions lie in folds, as if the lining membrane were too large. There may be few or many reddened patches, and they vary greatly in size and characteristics. Some are rather sharply outlined; others are diffuse. In some cases these changes involve the mucous membrane of almost the entire ileum, cecum, colon, and rectum, while in others only a small area may be affected. In mature cattle, lesions are found most frequently in close proximity to the ileo-cecal valve. Smears made from the thickened and reddened areas may reveal typical slender, rod-shaped, acid-fast bacteria, usually occurring in nests or clumps.

In some infected animals the organisms are very plentiful, while in others they are very scarce. There seems to be little relation between the severity of the lesions and the number of bacteria found on smears from them. Neither is there any marked relationship between the severity of the symptoms and the extent of the lesions. Some of the most severe advanced cases may have very slight lesions.

The thickening and fold formation just described are not necessarily indicative of Johne's disease. Such changes have been found in the mucous membranes of the intestines of many cattle which had passed johnin tests and in which the paratuberculosis organisms could not be found. It has been impossible to differentiate by macroscopic examination of the tissues between the lesions in cattle free from Johne's disease and those in affected cattle.

In sheep there are even fewer changes than in cattle. Reacting sheep in which Johne's disease organisms have been demonstrated have had only a slight thickening or reddenning of the mucosa of the intestines. Lesions have not been found in any other organs of sheep.

CONTROL AND ERADICATION

Since there is no known method of treating Johne's disease successfully, any effective control must consist in preventing exposure of susceptible, healthy animals. Owners of herds of cattle in which the disease has not appeared should take every precaution to prevent its introduction. If it is necessary to introduce new animals into a herd, they should be procured from reputable breeders, and it would be well to make special inquiry concerning Johne's disease. Such a breeder can usually furnish a statement from an accredited veterinarian concerning the health of the herd from which purchases are contemplated, with a specific statement in regard to clinical symptoms of Johne's disease. Though such precautions may seem unnecessary, it is much less expensive in both time and money to prevent the introduction of this insidious disease than to eradicate it after it becomes established in a herd.

The owner of any herd in which losses from Johne's disease are occurring should realize that, unless it is controlled, it is likely to become increasingly destructive until the herd becomes. economically unprofitable. He should realize, too, that it is one of the most difficult of the infectious diseases to eradicate and that eradication will probably require at least 2 years of constant effort. The mere removal of cattle showing clinical symptoms will not usually bring relief, for too many apparently healthy animals are potential spreaders of the organisms. Although the johnin test is still not perfect, it has enough merit to justify. its use in infected herds. The control program that is most likely to succeed would include testing at regular intervals, preferably every 3 to 6 months; removing all reactors whether or not they were showing symptoms; cleaning and disinfecting thoroughly after any affected or reacting animal is removed from a barn or lot; and, most important of all, rearing young breeding stock in quarters that have not been used by mature animals.

Some cattle showing typical symptoms fail to react to the test. In any successful control program all such animals must be considered sources of infection.

Stanchions, stalls, barns, pens, and corrals in which affected cattle have been kept should be thoroughly cleaned, and all wood or concrete mangers, drinking troughs, and floors should be soaked for several hours in some disinfectant approved for tuberculosis-eradication work. Pens and corrals which have been used for such animals should have all the manure and at least 4 inches of the top-soil removed. This should be either buried or placed in a field to which cattle will not have access. Care should be taken that drainage from such a field does not contaminate pastures, streams, or pens that may be used by healthy cattle.

Since the organisms of Johne's disease are excreted in the feces, special precautions should be taken to prevent contamination of any feed or water with cattle droppings. Cattle should not be allowed in feed alleys. Brooms for cleaning gutters, floors, and stanchion platforms should be used for this purpose only, and a different set should be used for the mangers, feed alleys, and feed trucks. Caretakers should be careful not to contaminate hay, grain, silage, or other feed with infective material carried on their feet. All too frequently herdsmen climb into a haymow or a silo without cleaning their boots or shoes.

Water from pools, ponds, sloughs, and streams that receive surface drainage from lots or pastures that have been used by an infected herd is unsafe. On infected premises great care should be taken to prevent contamination of any pails or buckets from which young calves are to be fed.

During the past several years cattlemen have from time to time raised the question of the desirability of regulations requiring testing for Johne's disease as a prerequisite for interstate shipment. Livestock sanitary officials and authorities seem agreed that such a requirement is not now advisable because definite information that such tests are reliable is lacking. In several States indemnities for cattle slaughtered on account of Johne's disease are paid on the same basis as the indemnities for slaughtered tuberculous cattle. The Bureau of Animal Industry has been granted authority by Congress to pay indemnity to cattle owners for animals that are slaughtered because of reaction to the johnin test, and the payments are made on the same basis as those on tuberculous cattle. Indemnity funds have been available for this purpose since July 1, 1927, and a number of livestock owners have received benefits from them.

Although specific figures are not available to prove it, many veterinarians and livestock sanitary officers believe that Johne's disease is increasing in the United States and that unless something is done to stop the increase the disease will become as serious a menace in this country as it is in some parts of Europe. Much more research is necessary, however, before definite knowledge that can be used to control and eradicate the disease completely will be available.

Bovine Mastitis

BY W. T. MILLER [1]

BOVINE MASTITIS is responsible for enormous losses, through reduced milk production and in other ways, in our dairy herds. Here is a sound program of control based on early detection of the disease, segregation of diseased cows, and use of sanitary measures.

BOVINE MASTITIS is an extremely serious disease of dairy cattle. The annual economic loss to dairymen from loss of cows, decreased milk production, and poor-quality milk is tremendous. In addition, certain human diseases can be contracted through the use of unpasteurized milk from affected cows. To reduce these losses and to improve both the quantity and quality of milk are of the greatest importance at this time.

Mastitis means inflammation of the udder from any cause. There are two forms of the disease, acute and chronic. The latter is the more common, but it is not readily recognized. The acute form, commonly known as garget, is familiar to every dairyman. The affected quarter is reddened, swollen, hot, and painful. The secretion is very much reduced and varies from a watery, blood-tinged fluid containing a few solid particles to thick, yellow, ropy material.

In the past an attack of acute mastitis was thought to be temporary, and it was believed that when it passed, recovery was complete. Actually, in most cases the acute symptoms represent a flare-up of the chronic form already present in the quarter. Recovery from an acute attack usually means a return to the chronic state.

When the average dairy herd is examined for mastitis, it is not unusual to find the chronic form of the disease in one or more quarters of the udders of half the cows. Because of the lack of easily recognized symptoms the owner may be unaware of the extent of the disease. On inquiry, however, the infected cows will be found to have had acute attacks, as a rule at the beginning or end of a lactation period. They are usually short milkers.

---

[1] W. T. Miller is Veterinarian, Animal Disease Station, Bureau of Animal Industry.

Mastitis is an infectious disease. Certain kinds of bacteria enter the opening into the teat canal, travel up the canal, and lodge in the milk cistern at the base of the teat, where they cause a mild or low-grade inflammation. In the course of time the bacteria spread to other parts of the gland, and the inflammation extends until finally the entire quarter is affected. Acute attacks usually occur as the infection progresses.

As a result of the inflammation, the composition of the milk is changed. Although the milk may appear normal, the percentages of butterfat. lactose (milk sugar), casein, and possibly other elements are decreased. On the other hand the number of leucocytes, the salt content, the number of bacteria, and the products resulting from inflammation and bacterial activity increase. A change in the character of the udder tissue itself also occurs. The normal secretory tissue is gradually replaced by nonsecretory, scar (fibrous) tissue. Finally the quarter loses its soft, pliable quality, and hard areas, circumscribed or diffuse, appear in the vicinity of the milk cistern. In advanced cases the quarter becomes hardened throughout, and there is an almost complete loss of secretory tissue.

With the change in the character of the udder tissue, milk production drops. which accounts for shortened lactation periods. The time required for this change to occur varies considerably, depending on the virulence of the invading bacteria, the natural resistance of the animal. the number of acute attacks, and management and feeding practices. In some cases of chronic mastitis the animal may pass through a number of lactation periods before the disease manifests itself. On the other hand, many cows become entirely useless in a comparatively short time.

BACTERIA CAUSING MASTITIS

Bovine mastitis can be caused by a number of different kinds of bacteria. Of greatest importance are the streptococci, including several species that are responsible for such diseases in man as scarlet fever and septic sore throat. Fortunately, infection with these species occurs infrequently and usually as a result of the bacteria having been carried to the end of the teat on the hands of an infected milker. Bacteria of these species do not tend to spread through the herd. On the other hand the streptococci most commonly found in mastitis rarely cause disease in man. However, they spread readily from cow to cow on the milkers' hands or the cups of the milking machine. Once established these streptococci usually remain in the quarter for the rest of the life of the animal. An infected cow is therefore a constant source of danger for the other cows in the herd.

Next in importance as a cause of mastitis are the staphylococci. Several species are known, and they undoubtedly cause many more cases of mastitis than is generally realized. Staphylococci, like streptococci. cause the chronic form of the disease, but they are not likely to persist in the udder for as long a time as the streptococci. Acute attacks which may terminate in the death of the animal occur frequently in staphylococcal mastitis.

Various other types of bacteria are found in occasional outbreaks of the disease. For the most part these types cause acute mastitis accompanied by systemic disturbance, and not infrequently the animal dies. In most cases of this kind the infection leaves the udder after recovery. When these outbreaks occur, they constitute a serious problem through loss of function of quarters and death of cows. Fortunately they appear only sporadically.

DIAGNOSIS

Early detection of diseased cows is extremely important. Acute attacks of mastitis can be diagnosed readily by clinical symptoms, but the chronic form presents some difficulty. Tests that largely solve this problem are now available. Diagnosis of mastitis in individual cows and recommendations for controlling the spread of the disease are functions of the veterinarian. Responsibility for carrying out sanitary measures, early detection of subsequent cases of mastitis, and proper disposition of diseased animals rests with the owner or herdsman. It is essential, therefore, that he should have some knowledge of the more common tests and understand their significance.

Tests for easy routine use must be easily applied and reasonably accurate. Two such tests are now in use in many herds. One is the strip-cup test. In this test several streams of milk are drawn from a quarter onto a fine-mesh wire screen immediately before the animal is milked. The appearance of clots or flakes or of watery or off-color milk on the screen is evidence of mastitis. As in other tests of similar nature, the accuracy of results obtained with the strip-cup test improves with frequent usage. To obtain best results the cup should be used before each milking, or once a day at the very least. With this test mastitis can frequently be detected in previously healthy cows, and bad milk can be kept out of the general supply.

The second test is the bromthymol-blue, or thybromol, test. Changes in the milk are detected by variations in color when the dye solution from which the test derives its name is mixed with it. Milk drawn from a healthy quarter is slightly acid. When a few drops of the dye are added to it, a pale yellowish-green color results. Milk from a diseased quarter is alkaline, and this is indicated by a green color when the dye is added. Different shades of green may be encountered, depending on the degree of alkalinity. The more alkaline the milk, the darker the shade of green becomes. An intense yellow may be observed occasionally. This indicates a very acid condition and is usually accompanied by gross alteration in the appearance of the secretion. Frequent use of the brom-thymol-blue test also increases its effectiveness materially.

PREVENTION

Since curative measures are not entirely effective, a program for controlling the spread of mastitis bacteria from diseased to healthy cows affords an effective and practical means of dealing with the disease. In most cases the bacteria are carried on the milkers' hands or in the teat cups of the milking machine. When a healthy animal is milked immediately after an infected one, the mastitis bacteria are left on the teats of the healthy cow, in which repeated exposure will eventually produce the disease.

The purpose of the control program, therefore, is to avoid exposure of healthy cows during milking. Detection of all cows with mastitis is the first step. Cows with extensive induration (hardening) of the udder should be removed immediately from the herd. They are unprofitable for milk production, are subject to recurrent acute attacks, and provide a constant source of infection for other cows in the herd. The remaining diseased and healthy animals should then be separated into two groups. Complete segregation of the groups in separate barns with separate milkers is the most desirable arrangement. This is not absolutely necessary, however, if strict attention is given to the order of milking and other essential details of the program.

The group of cows with healthy udders must always be milked before the infected group. When first-calf heifers are added to the herd, they should be placed with the clean cows unless they show signs of mastitis. Few heifers come into lactation infected with mastitis bacteria. Cows placed in the two groups should be maintained in them through subsequent lactation periods unless evidence of mastitis is found in members of the healthy group. Should the routine tests indicate the presence of mastitis in a healthy cow, it must be placed in the diseased group without delay. Once in the infected group, the animal must be kept there as long as it stays in the herd. Infected cows should be sold as soon as they become unprofitable or if they suffer recurrent acute attacks.

Certain sanitary measures must be included in the program along with strict observance of the milking order. Individual cloths dipped in fresh hypochlorite solution (200 to 400 parts of chlorine per million) should be used to wipe the udder, teats, and flanks of each cow before milking. These cloths must never be replaced in this solution after use. Between milkings they should be washed, sterilized by boiling or steaming, and dried. After the cow is milked, each teat must be dipped in a small quantity of fresh hypochlorite solution of the strength indicated. This removes the drop of milk from the end of the teat and also repels flies. The solution should be discarded after being used for one cow.

Proper feeding must also be considered. Feeding a high-protein grain ration must be avoided, particularly for cows with mastitis or exposed to the disease. Such feed apparently overstimulates the udder and predisposes it to infection, while infected cows receiving such a ration are more subject to acute attacks and the secretion of abnormal milk. These recurrent attacks lead to more rapid deterioration of the udder. When cows with mild cases of chronic mastitis are fed and managed properly, they may remain in the herd for some time as profitable producers, but they must always be recognized as a source of danger to healthy cows.

Protection of the udder from injury and infection is of equal importance. Adequate stall space and ample bedding are absolute necessities to protect the teats and udder from being stepped on and from being bruised or chilled when the animals lie down. Floors and passageways should be so constructed as to give the cows good footing. To keep down infection, floors and stalls must be washed regularly and disinfected with 3- to 5-percent lye solution. As an additional safeguard, liberal use of lime or superphosphate in back of the stalls and in the gutters is important.

Blackleg

BY WILLIAM M. MOHLER [1]

BLACKLEG, one of the most infectious of diseases and one that usually proves fatal, affects young cattle particularly. It can be prevented by vaccination. Proper disposal of animals that have died of the disease is very important.

BLACKLEG, also known as quarter ill, symptomatic anthrax, emphysematous anthrax, and black quarter, is an acute infectious and usually fatal disease which attacks young cattle between 6 months and 2 years of age. Goats and sheep are susceptible to and occasionally contract the disease, but other animals appear to be immune.

This disease is caused by *Clostridium chauvoei*, which is an anaerobic micro-organism, that is, one that develops rapidly only in the absence of oxygen. These organisms are in the form of short rods and produce spores that are very resistant to destruction by heat, cold, drying, or chemical disinfectants. Usually the organism gains entrance into the body of the animal through small cuts or punctures in the skin; large cuts or open wounds are not favorable for growth of the organism. In some cases the organism may enter the body through abrasions in the mucuous membranes of the tongue, mouth cavity, or throat.

In localities where blackleg occurs frequently, it is the young cattle, especially those between the ages of 6 and 18 months, that are usually infected. Calves 4 to 5 months old sometimes become infected, but an increase in the number of cases is noted with an increase in age. Very young animals evidently have an inherited or natural immunity which gradually wears off as they approach 6 months of age. The disease is seldom contracted by cattle past 2 years of age, and almost absolute immunity is noted after 3 years.

SYMPTOMS

The symptoms of blackleg are so characteristic that it is possible to recognize the disease easily. The first symptoms to be noted are

---

[1] William M. Mohler is Senior Veterinarian, Pathological Division, Bureau of Animal Industry.

high fever, loss of appetite, and a suspension of rumination, followed by great depression. Breathing becomes more rapid than normal. In most cases the animal has difficulty in moving about, and it frequently lies down. Rapidly developing swellings or tumors in the tissues under the skin are characteristic. They may appear on the neck and shoulders, beneath the breast, and on the flanks and thighs, and in some instances they appear on the gums, the base of the tongue, and the wall of the pharynx. The tumors are accompanied by severe febrile symptoms. At first small and painful to the touch, they rapidly increase in size and may cover a considerable part of the body. Upon pressure the tumors make a peculiar crackling sound which is due to the collection of gas formed by the causative micro-organisms.

As the swellings increase in size, the symptoms become more intense. The temperature may reach 107° F., and the respiration may increase to 140 or more a minute. The animal is unable to rise, the extremities become cold, and the temperature usually falls and may become subnormal shortly before death. Violent convulsions and trembling of the muscles are noted before death. Although there are some recoveries, death generally occurs in 12 to 36 hours after the first appearance of the disease.

The carcass of an animal dead from blackleg soon becomes distended by gas, partly through fermentation in the gastrointestinal tract and partly through the formation of gas in the tissue under the skin. Marked distention is noted in the region of the blackleg tumors and where there is loose tissue, especially between the shoulder and the chest and on the outer surface of the hindquarters. In many instances this distention causes the legs on the upper side to stand out straight from the body. Shortly after death a dark, blood-colored, frothy discharge flows from the nostrils and anus. An incision made through the skin into the affected muscle tissue fails to demonstrate any decomposition, but it is possible to detect a characteristic sweetish-sour odor.

The skin covering the blackleg tumors is affected with dry gangrene. The distended muscles, which are easily torn, are dark brown or black, and the spaces surrounding them are filled with bloody liquid and gas. The blood in the badly affected parts of the body is thick and charged with gas and has a disagreeable odor. In the remaining parts of the carcass the blood is normal and coagulates easily after death, forming a solid clot. Hemorrhages are found on the heart and lungs. The spleen is always normal, but congestion is noted in the liver.

Thus it may be seen that a post-mortem examination should serve to distinguish blackleg from other diseases. Nevertheless, though a diagnosis may be made at autopsy, it is sometimes advisable to send specimens from affected animals to the laboratory for a conclusive diagnosis.

TREATMENT AND PREVENTION

Medicinal treatment of animals has thus far proved unavailing. The only reliable and effective means known for protecting animals against blackleg is vaccination, which has been thoroughly tried and proved to be reliable.

Vaccines for protection against blackleg have been greatly improved in recent years. Those produced at the present time include blackleg bacterin, natural aggressin, cultural aggressin, cultural vaccine, and tissue vaccine. These vaccines are used extensively in the United States and give excellent results, as they confer immunity without producing any vaccination disease.

As vaccine is a preventive and not a curative agent, it is useless to vaccinate an animal after the symptoms of blackleg have developed. The immunity conferred by vaccination varies according to the kind of vaccine used and may last 12 to 18 months or longer.

Antiblackleg serum is produced for treating calves already affected with blackleg, as well as for creating a temporary passive immunity in exposed animals in an infected herd. At present the product is rarely used in the United States, but if it is available at the onset of the disease it may be efficacious in some cases.

When blackleg occurs on a ranch or farm it is of the utmost importance that owners of cattle in the district realize that every animal affected with the disease may be the means of propagating and disseminating the infection. Losses may not occur immediately on infected premises; in some cases they occur only after a lapse of years. It is recommended, therefore, that every effort be made to reduce the danger of infection by taking appropriate measures to dispose of all dead animals and with them the infection they carry. The carcass should be entirely destroyed by burning if this is possible. Otherwise a hole 6 feet deep should be dug and the body placed therein and well covered with quicklime before the earth is filled in. Any place where the animal was lying should be thoroughly sprinkled with a strong disinfectant, such as a solution of commercial lye and hydrated lime (2½ pounds of lye and 2½ pounds of lime in 8½ gallons of water).

The eradication of blackleg infection from pastures is difficult. In most cases it is impossible to pasture livestock on other land long enough for the infection to die out. It appears, therefore, that vaccination is the only practicable and effective means of protecting cattle against blackleg. If vaccine is used year after year to prevent the development of new cases over a long period, it is possible that the old infection will finally disappear.

Shipping Fever, or Hemorrhagic Septicemia

BY C. D. STEIN [1]

THE AUTHOR calls this the most serious of a group of cattle maladies that are commonly associated with the hardships and hazards of shipping—that is, the handling, neglect, or exposure of animals in transit or shortly afterward. It is an infectious disease which often terminates in death. The losses from shipping fever can be greatly reduced by careful management in shipping. Vaccination with bacterins at least 10 days before shipping or injection of antiserum may reduce losses.

SHIPPING FEVER, or stockyard fever, is an infectious disease of cattle usually attended with a high mortality. Its medical name, "hemorrhagic septicemia," was given it because it is a septicemia, or poisoning, of the blood (and hence often runs a short, fatal course), and hemorrhages in the body tissues and organs of animals dead from the disease are usually an outstanding characteristic.

The disease occurs in cattle in all parts of the United States. The losses appear to be greatest among young animals, especially those that are thin and poorly nourished. A large number of outbreaks of hemorrhagic septicemia in cattle are associated with the shipment of animals from one point to another by rail or truck and their passage through public stockyards. The vitality of an animal is lowered by the hardships of transit, and its resistance to infection is decreased. The disease is therefore a serious problem to both shippers and receivers of cattle. In some years very considerable losses occur, whereas in other years they may be slight.

---

[1] C. D. Stein is Associate Veterinarian, Pathological Division, Bureau of Animal Industry.

It is generally believed that weather conditions influence the prevalence of the disease, since cattle appear to suffer from it most in the fall, winter, and early spring during particularly changeable or inclement weather. After prolonged travel under such weather conditions, for example, they may arrive on the farm of the purchaser in a run-down condition, though they had appeared perfectly healthy when purchased in the stockyards. Overcrowding, irregularity in feeding and watering, hard driving, lack of rest and proper shelter, and the general excitement associated with shipping are other devitalizing factors that may play a part in reducing normal vigor and increasing the susceptibility to shipping fever.

CAUSE

The primary cause of hemorrhagic septicemia in cattle has not been definitely determined, and there is a difference of opinion both among practicing veterinarians and among research workers.

According to the older school of thought, the principal causative factor is the germ *Pasteurella boviseptica*. The organism has been found in the air passages of normal animals, and organisms closely resembling it are widely distributed in nature. The theory is that such organisms become virulent under certain conditions and that animals harboring them readily develop so-called shipping fever when their natural resistance is lowered.

According to the newer school of thought, the hemorrhagic septicemia organism probably plays a secondary role, like that of diphtheroids, streptococci, and *Bacillus coli* organisms, and there is another primary infective agent concerned in the production of the disease. The nature of this agent is not known, but it is thought by some to be a virus. When cattle are received after a hard railroad journey many of them may manifest symptoms of the disease, and local stock that come in contact with the affected animals very often become infected. Just what part the contamination of yards, buildings, and equipment by affected cattle plays in setting up the disease in noninfected animals is not known, but undoubtedly this is a source of danger. It is worthy of note that the coexistence of two factors (a virus and a bacterium) as necessary causative agents in certain infectious diseases has been recognized in recent years, notably in the case of swine influenza.

SYMPTOMS AND LESIONS

Shipping fever in cattle usually develops very rapidly and lasts from 2 to 8 days or longer. Affected animals first show an elevation of body temperature, ranging from 104° to 107° F., accompanied by loss of appetite, mucopurulent discharge from the nose, an occasional hacking cough, swollen, watery eyes, general depression, gaunt appearance, stiffened gait, and sometimes diarrhea (fig. 1). Within 3 to 5 days after the first symptoms appear, affected animals may develop pneumonia and die in 48 to 72 hours; or the disease may assume a chronic course, and the sick animals may linger on for several weeks. In mild attacks, affected animals may recover in a week or two.

During the course of the disease other symptoms may occur. Swelling may appear beneath the skin of the head, throat, or dewlap. These enlargements are somewhat soft and pit on pressure. The tongue is often extensively swollen, and the animal drools and slobbers because of the irritation to its tongue and throat. There may be difficulty in breathing, depending on the degree of involvement of the air passages and the lungs. Muscular trembling may be evident. There may be a blood-stained discharge from the nostrils, and strings of mucus may hang from the mouth. Examination of the nostrils often reveals the presence of many small hemorrhages, or blood spots, just beneath their lining membranes.

FIGURE 1.—A steer affected with hemorrhagic septicemia, showing typical attitude of dejection.

There is an intestinal form of the disease in which the changes are found chiefly in the abdominal cavity. This form may develop after the disease has appeared in the lungs. The stomach, intestines, and kidneys and the lymph glands belonging to them become studded with hemorrhages of various sizes, and the intestines become intensely inflamed. Diarrhea sets in, and shreds of mucus and bloody droppings are passed. The intestinal form is rare; most cases show severe involvement of the lungs and the symptoms of croupous pneumonia. The animals may stand with their forelegs wide apart in order to breathe more freely. They lose flesh very rapidly, their abdomens become "tucked up," and the eyes quickly become sunken. A stagger-ing gait, caused by extreme weakness, is sometimes noticed.

On post mortem examination the following anatomical changes may be observed in the carcass of an animal dead of hemorrhagic septicemia: Swellings of doughy consistency, containing jellylike material tinged with blood, may be found under the skin. If these swellings occur in the region of the shoulder or flank, they are some-times mistaken for those of blackleg. The lymph glands are en-larged and hemorrhagic (injected with blood). The mucous membranes lining the nose, throat, and air passages of the lungs are inflamed and may contain blood-stained mucus. Hemorrhages may be observed in the fat tissue around the kidneys and in the serous membranes of the internal organs.

When the disease is chiefly in the chest, the lungs are darkened in color, and their fibrous tissues are much thickened owing to the collection of bloody serum in their meshes. There may be solidifi-cation of one or more lobes (pneumonia). The diaphragm, heart sac, and heart walls show numerous bloody points and larger collec-tions of blood.

In the intestinal form, hemorrhages of the intestines are present, and there is sloughing of the lining of the intestinal wall, as a result of which the intestinal contents are wrapped in a covering of bloody mucus.

In acute forms of the disease the animals may die suddenly, and in such cases the changes are not very marked although bacteri-ological examination of the body fluids may demonstrate the pres-ence of hemorrhagic septicemia organisms.

DIAGNOSIS

It is often difficult to diagnose hemorrhagic septicemia because of its similarity to certain other disease conditions encountered in cattle. Owing to its acute course, high fever, and rapid termination, the disease may be mistaken for anthrax, malignant edema, or black-leg. While certain characteristic features of these diseases may aid in making a tentative diagnosis, a bacteriologic examination which in-cludes both cultural tests and inoculation of laboratory animals is sometimes necessary to detect the nature of the disease and especially to differentiate it from others.

Other conditions in cattle, such as coccidiosis, cornstalk disease, lead poisoning, sweetclover poisoning, and other forms of vegetable poisoning, may be mistaken for hemorrhagic septicemia. In an outbreak of suspected hemorrhagic septicemia, diagnosis, treat-ment, and methods of control should be left to an experienced veterinarian.

CONTROL AND PREVENTION

In considering measures for the control and prevention of this disease, it is important to remember that hemorrhagic septicemia is the most serious of a group of cattle maladies that commonly result from mishandling, neglect, or exposure of animals in transit or shortly after their arrival at their destination. Hence the elimination of predisposing factors, such as overdriving, overcrowding, overfeeding, and lack of rest, water, feed, and proper shelter during transit, is stressed. Suggestions for reduction of losses due to hemorrhagic septicemia and other diseases of cattle incident to shipping will be found in the following recommendations from United States Department of Agriculture Leaflet 38, Maintaining the Health of Livestock in Transit:[2]

Avoid hard driving and allow ample time for rest before loading. On arrival at the pens, the animals should not be allowed to fill up on water, but should first have rest and be fed some native grass or nonlegume hay.

Avoid overcrowding cattle in the cars. In cold weather, bed the car well. In very severe weather, in northern latitudes, it may be well to line the side walls of the car with heavy paper, especially if the cattle are young or unthrifty.

Give feed and water at proper intervals en route. When unloaded for feed, water, and rest, the cattle should have plenty of time to become well rested.

Under the 28-hour law 5 hours' rest is the minimum specified time, and the railroads ordinarily allow that period, exclusive of the time of unloading and reloading. It is better, however, to give stocker and feeder cattle special care, allowing at least 8 hours for feed, water, and rest. * * * Cows in an advanced stage of pregnancy, commonly termed "springers," should receive particular attention.

The common practice of withholding water from animals until they are very thirsty so that later they will take a heavy fill is harmful. It tends to upset the digestive system so seriously that the animals are slow in resuming normal feeding and gain in weight. It is therefore recommended that this damaging practice be discontinued through general agreement among livestock owners and handlers.

In the case of stocker and feeder cattle that pass through the public market, the same attention should be given to the shipments back to the country that has been outlined for the shipments to market. Following the arrival of cattle at their final destination in the country, they should receive special attention and care to help them over the period of lowered vitality resulting from the hardships of travel.

Feeder cattle on arrival should be given a fill of dry roughage, such as timothy hay, prairie hay, or corn stover. After having access to this roughage a few hours, they should have water, but not all they will drink. By the end of the first day, give free access to dry roughage and water.

Most feeder cattle are raised on grasses different from those found in the fattening areas. Therefore, if they are to be pasture fed, let them become accustomed to the new grasses gradually, giving them at first only a few hours' grazing each day, especially if the grass is still green.

If feeder cattle are intended for dry-lot feeding with no pasture available, give them access to cornstalk fields or feed them on corn fodder and hay for from 10 days to 2 weeks before starting them on the fattening rations.

If the cattle arrive in cold weather, especially if it is wet and stormy, provide adequate dry shelter. Severe exposure to cold and dampness combined, during the period of low vitality, is liable to have very serious results. If there is any sign of sickness, segregate diseased animals and keep them quiet.

The use of biological products to prevent hemorrhagic septicemia or to control outbreaks has been successful in many instances, but unsatisfactory results have followed in some outbreaks.

The biological products used are either preventive (bacterin and aggressin) or curative (antiserum). Bacterins or aggressins increase the animal's resistance against hemorrhagic septicemia infection. They produce an active immunity of long duration, usually several

---

[2] MILLER, A. W. MAINTAINING THE HEALTH OF LIVESTOCK IN TRANSIT. U. S. Dept. Agr. Leaflet 38, 8 pp., illus. 1931. (Revised.)

months to a year. It is believed that a high degree of immunity is established in 10 days to 2 weeks after vaccination with either bacterin or aggressin.

For best results feeder and stocker cattle should be treated with bacterin or aggressin at least 10 days before shipment, as the use of these products on animals in transit or a few days after they reach their destination appears to be of little or no value, according to experimental work by the Bureau of Animal Industry and other agencies.[3]

On the other hand, the administration of antihemorrhagic septicemia immune serum, which contains great numbers of immune bodies, produces an immediate increase in resistance to the disease. This is, however, a passive immunity of short duration, lasting only a few weeks.

Since antihemorrhagic septicemia serum furnishes quick protection and also has some curative value, its use in preference to bacterin or aggressin is indicated for treatment of cattle in transit or within a few days after they arrive at their destination, particularly if some of the animals in the shipment show symptoms of the disease.

Anaphylaxis (shock or severe reactions) may sometimes follow the administration of antiserum or bacterins. To avoid this, only homologous serum (that is, serum obtained from bovine species) should be used, and bacterins should preferably be composed of a bacterial suspension in normal (0.8 percent) saline solution free from toxic broth or other foreign protein.

The advisability of using biological products and their administration should be left to a competent veterinarian.

Tests conducted by the Bureau of Animal Industry have shown that both laboratory animals and cattle can be immunized under experimental conditions against hemorrhagic septicemia by either aggressin or bacterin. Cattle, sheep, and laboratory animals can also be immunized by treatment with weakened (attenuated) cultures.

During these experiments, animals vaccinated with aggressin and subsequently exposed to artificial infection remained well. Animals treated with aggressin developed immunity to artificial exposure in as short a period as 4 days, while those treated with bacterin required 9 days to develop immunity. Cattle were found to be resistant to infection 15 months after vaccination with aggressin.

In most cases medicinal treatment of a fully established case of shipping fever is of little value. In visibly sick animals, especially during the early stages of the disease, the administration of large doses of antihemorrhagic septicemia serum (one or two injections of 50 cubic centimeters or more) frequently assists in bringing about

---

[3] To ascertain the value of vaccination in reducing losses from hemorrhagic septicemia in animals in transit, the Bureau of Animal Industry, in cooperation with traders and livestock exchanges, conducted experimental work in the control of hemorrhagic septicemia at certain stockyards in 1924 and 1925. During 1924, 151,475 feeder and stocker cattle were vaccinated by veterinary inspectors. During 1925, in an experiment in which 4,439 animals were handled, 2,234 were vaccinated with aggressin and 2,205 were shipped to their destination without treatment, as controls. The results of these experiments based on incomplete reports received from owners of treated and untreated cattle indicate that the administration of bacterin or aggressin confers little if any immunity on animals in transit, many of which apparently have the disease in the incubative stage. In fact, some of the evidence tends to show that losses were greater in the animals treated with aggressin than in those untreated.

recovery. All apparently well animals should be removed from sick ones and placed in separate, noninfected quarters. If new cases develop among them a few days after their removal, the remaining healthy ones should be removed again to another locality. In that way the unaffected animals can be kept out of danger of further contamination.

The administration of sodium bicarbonate has been reported by some stockmen and veterinarians as being of considerable value in both the treatment and the prevention of this disease. During 1934, 1935, and 1936, sodium bicarbonate administered in the form of a drench, on the feed, or in drinking water at the rate of 1 ounce to each 100 pounds of body weight, was given once a day for 14 days by stockmen and stockyard officials to several thousand cattle. Some of the animals were treated in the stockyards and others after arrival on the home premises following shipment. A large number of untreated animals in both groups were held as controls. Reports received by the Bureau on the results of this treatment showed little difference between the treated and untreated animals in their resistance to shipping fever.

Since hemorrhagic septicemia is an infectious disease, the carcasses of animals that have died of it should be burned or buried. Premises are usually contaminated by infected cattle that have recently passed through some of the larger markets. All stables, sheds, or yards that have contained infected animals should be disinfected. The interior of the stables, especially the mangers and gutters, should be washed with a disinfectant, such as compound cresol solution, 4 ounces to a gallon of water, or carbolic acid, 6 ounces to a gallon of water. For dairy barns, however, where the odor of these disinfectants would be objectionable, milk of lime or some other nonodorous disinfectant may be preferred. The yards may be disinfected by the application of a solution made of 5 ounces of copper sulfate to a gallon of water. The best way to apply disinfectant solutions is with a spray pump such as is used in spraying orchard trees. All refuse and waste material from the stable and barnyard should be removed to a place not accessible to cattle or sheep. The manure should be spread on fields and plowed under. A plentiful supply of light and air should be provided for the contaminated stables. Open fields or pastures are cleansed rapidly by the action of sunlight.

Milk Fever

BY L. T. GILTNER [1]

MILK FEVER, which causes the collapse and sudden
death of high-producing dairy cows at the time of calving, is always accompanied by a serious unbalance in
the mineral content of the blood. Treatment by a
veterinarian, as described in this article, is an almost
certain cure.

MILK FEVER, also called parturient paresis and parturient hypocalcemia, is an affection of cows occurring shortly after calving. It is
characterized by paralysis of the motor and sensory nervous apparatus.
Despite its name, milk fever usually is not accompanied by fever.
There is always, however, a marked and rapid lowering of the blood
calcium, so that the name "parturient hypocalcemia," which means
too little calcium at calving time, is quite appropriate.

Milk fever is one of the most common, widespread, and serious of
the acute afflictions of dairy cows. It affects almost exclusively the
high-producing better nourished animals. It very rarely occurs at
the first calving; sometimes at the second calving; and most frequently
after the birth of the third to seventh calf, or during the prime of life.
The poorly nourished cow is seldom a victim, and difficult calving
(dystocia) is hardly ever followed by milk fever. After the first
attack, the trouble may recur at one or more subsequent calvings.

CAUSE

The early investigations into the cause and nature of milk fever are
of considerable interest to the present-day student for the light they
throw on developments in medical science. Most veterinary writers
today begin their discussions of the earlier studies of the disease with
the work done late in the nineteenth and in the early part of the present
century, when the theory of bacterial infection and systemic intoxication with bacterial toxins associated in some manner with parturition

---

[1] L. T. Giltner is Senior Veterinarian, Pathological Division, Bureau of Animal Industry.

was in vogue. In 1897, Schmidt, a Danish veterinarian, acting on the theory that milk fever resulted from infection of the udder, experimented with injections of a solution of potassium iodide into the udders of cows sick with the disease. Although this treatment proved remarkably successful in his hands, it did not afford a satisfactory explanation of his infection theory, since he later found that when air was introduced into the udder along with the potassium iodide solution equally good results were obtained. In the early years of the present century it was found that oxygen or filtered air alone proved superior to the potassium iodide solution as a treatment. Bacteriologic investigations soon showed conclusively that milk fever was decidedly not a bacterial infection of the udder. However, Schmidt's treatment, or a modification of it—the injection of filtered air into the udder—proved so effective that no further investigations into the cause of the disease were undertaken at that time, since researches on other diseases were deemed more important.

An excellent treatment had been discovered, and when it was carried out skillfully, especially with strict aseptic precautions, milk fever could be readily controlled, or at least when cases occurred they could be cured. Research workers were apparently content to let matters stand, even though the underlying cause of the strange malady remained obscure.

Finally, however, in 1925, Dryerre and Greig [2] proposed the theory that milk fever is an expression of an acute deficiency of calcium in the blood. Studies of the blood of cows affected with the disease revealed that there was a marked fall from the normal calcium level. Moreover, when calcium in the form of calcium gluconate solution was injected intravenously in an appropriate dose into cows suffering from milk fever, a cure was promptly effected. Why, then, does inflation of the udder with potassium iodide, oxygen, or filtered air have a curative effect? Greig [3] explains this as follows: "The effect is a mechanical one in that it elicits mammary distention and so prevents the further interchange of calcium from the blood to the gland acini [the microscopic saclike elements of the gland]. There is also reason to believe that the calcium, which is heavily concentrated in the gland, is forced back into the blood as the result of the mammary distention."

Chemical studies have revealed other abnormalities in the blood of cattle suffering from milk fever. In some cases hypermagnesemia (increase in blood magnesium) has been found, in others, hypomagnesemia (decrease in blood magnesium). A decrease in phosphorus and an increase in blood sugar (hyperglycemia) have also been observed.

In the normal animal all of the various blood constituents are maintained at a very constant level through the proper coordination of the body's complex and delicate glandular mechanism. The discovery of the changes in the blood brought about by the disordered functioning of this mechanism during milk fever has been of immense importance

[2] DRYERRE, HENRY, and GREIG, J. RUSSELL. MILK FEVER: ITS POSSIBLE ASSOCIATION WITH DERANGEMENTS IN THE INTERNAL SECRETIONS. Vet. Rec. 5: [225]–231. 1925.
[3] GREIG, J. RUSSELL. THE NATURE OF MILK FEVER. 11th Internatl. Vet. Cong. Rpt. 3: 306–324, illus. 1930.

in pointing the way to effective treatment, but the basic causes of the break-down of the mechanism have not yet been fully brought to light.

SYMPTOMS

The earliest stages in the development of an attack of milk fever are frequently not noted or pass unrecognized by the casual observer. The first symptoms, depression and disinclination to move about or to eat, may set in as early as 6 hours after calving, but more often they begin anytime from about the twelfth hour to the third or fourth day. Although milk fever symptoms may at times appear before parturition or even several weeks afterwards, such cases may be involved with other affections common to the parturient or post-parturient state, and the diagnosis should be confirmed by laboratory aid. Cases have been observed in which the animal appeared excited and highly nervous for a short time, with twitching of the muscles and jerking of the legs and head, but the classical picture of milk fever begins, as already stated, with depression, and this is followed by collapse and complete loss of consciousness. The animal lies with its head turned to one side, the eyes are dull and expressionless, the membrane covering the eye is reddened, the muzzle is dry, the extremities are cold, and the body temperature is usually below normal.

Udall [4] states that one of the most constant and characteristic signs in milk fever is a tonic spasm of the muscles of the neck, giving the neck a distinct lateral kink. This symptom is seen more frequently than the turning of the head to the side. Throughout an attack the animal ceases to feed or ruminate, and all body functions are at low ebb. The pulse and breathing are accelerated, the breathing often being labored and accompanied by groaning. Bloating is not uncommon. The most frequent complications of milk fever are pneumonia, which generally occurs as a result of inhaling food material regurgitated from the paunch while the animal is lying down, and septic inflammation of the womb from various causes. Animals that are not appropriately treated usually die within several hours to a few days.

PREVENTION AND TREATMENT

Among the serious cattle plagues, milk fever is unique in that its treatment when properly carried out is remarkably successful, while practical and effective preventive measures are lacking. Of the suggested means of prevention, the injection of a solution of a calcium salt directly after calving is worthy of mention, as is also the practice of partial instead of complete milking during the first several days after calving. Obviously, however, the former procedure is more or less experimental and not practical, and the latter may lead to mastitis. Special measures should be taken to insure an adequate ration for and proper care of the pregnant and parturient cow.

As already mentioned, however, there are two methods of treatment that are efficacious if properly carried out, but to insure success, treat-

---

[4] UDALL, D. H. THE PRACTICE OF VETERINARY MEDICINE. Ed. 3, 672 pp., illus. Ithaca, N. Y. 1939.

ment must be instituted as early as possible. The procedure preferred by veterinarians consists in intravenously injecting calcium gluconate in 20-percent solution. It is sometimes necessary to repeat the injection one or more times to effect a cure. Solutions of other calcium salts may also be used, but care must be taken that the solution does not enter the tissues surrounding the vein, since this causes severe irritation, often leading to swellings or sloughing. The injection should not be made under the skin.

The alternate procedure, consisting of inflation of the udder with filtered air, must be undertaken with great care so as to avoid introducing infection by contaminating the teat canal. Equipment must be kept sterile and ready for use at all times. Before beginning the actual inflation, a clean sterile cloth is placed under the udder, the udder and the teats are cleansed with warm soapy water and dried with a sterile towel, and the teats and their orifices are disinfected. Each quarter is fully distended with air, and the teat is tied with a flat tape or bandage which is removed after not more than 3 or 4 hours. During an attack the animal should not be permitted to lie on its side, since there is danger of pneumonia from inhaling regurgitated paunch contents; bracing the animal so that it rests on its brisket will prevent this.

Usually with either the calcium-injection or the air-inflation treatment the response is rapid. In complicated cases the animal returns to consciousness in less than an hour and is often on its feet in 2 to 4 hours after treatment. The body temperature and the digestive and eliminatory functions return to normal, as evidenced by the resumption of rumination, defecation, and urination. In certain cases both procedures may be used, the one assisting the other in bringing about recovery. When medication in addition to the calcium salts is deemed necessary, the veterinarian always administers it by the vein, or hypodermically, and not by a drench, since there is danger that the medicine might pass down the windpipe and cause pneumonia. When treatments fail it is usually because there are complications, such as septic inflammation of the womb, pneumonia, or some serious involvement of the digestive organs.

Miscellaneous Diseases of Cattle

BY G. T. CREECH, R. L. KNUDSON, AND O. L. OSTEEN [1]

HERE is information regarding the nature, causes, symptoms, prevention, and control of white scours, acetonemia, pseudorabies (mad itch), common warts, epithelioma (cancer eye), tumors of the lymph glands (lymphocytoma), lumpy jaw (actinomycosis and actinobacillosis), nasal granuloma (snoring disease), and specific ophthalmia (pinkeye).

WHITE SCOURS (INFECTIOUS DIARRHEA, OR ACUTE DYSENTERY)

The condition commonly referred to as white scours is an acute, contagious, infectious disease of young or newborn calves, characterized by a profuse diarrhea and rapid exhaustion. The majority of animals affected are very young, less than 5 days old; the disease is not uncommon in calves less than 48 hours old. In severe outbreaks, however, it has been known to spread to older calves. The percentage of recoveries is very small, with or without treatment.

White scours is primarily an infectious diarrhea that later affects the entire system. The disease is due to an invasion of the intestinal tract by certain types of micro-organisms, particularly varieties of the colon bacillus, which are widely distributed in nature.

Outbreaks of this disease may occur at any season of the year, but it is most common in stabled animals during the fall and winter months. In some cases it may begin in the fall and increase in severity and in number of animals affected until spring.

[1] G. T. Creech is Senior Veterinarian, R. L. Knudson is Assistant Veterinarian, and O. L. Osteen is Associate Veterinarian, Pathological Division, Bureau of Animal Industry. The sections on White Scours, Acetonemia, and Pseudorabies were prepared by Dr. Knudson, and those on Calf Diphtheria, Pneumonia, and Choke by Dr. Osteen.

Infection may take place through either the navel cord or the digestive tract. Calves may become infected in various ways during birth, by sucking a contaminated udder, from the contaminated hands of attendants, by exposure to contaminated stable litter, or by contact with sick calves in nearby pens. These possible sources of infection should be kept in mind in relation to control measures to be discussed later.

Symptoms of the disease vary somewhat in individual cases. At birth, the calf may appear normal, or occasionally it may be weak or dull, but in 48 to 72 hours, or later, a profuse yellowish-white diarrhea with a very pungent and disagreeable odor develops. At the same time it may be noticed that the animal appears dull and listless. The eyes may be drawn back in the sockets, and lack luster. Stiffness of gait is not uncommon. The hair coat quite often appears rough and the skin dry. The hindquarters may be covered with the discharge from the bowels, and in severe cases there may be loss of hair over the parts affected, with considerable irritation and inflammation of the skin. The abdomen may show a tucked-up or gaunt appearance in very young calves, while in older animals there may be more or less distention from large quantities of milk previously consumed. Affected calves have a tendency to sleep much of the time, and the appetite is very poor. Depending upon the severity of the attack, there may be increasing prostration until death ensues. While all or a part of the symptoms described are seen in the majority of cases, in some instances there may be a rather sudden attack, the animal dying in a few hours, and occasionally a calf may be found dead without any definite signs of previous illness.

In making a diagnosis of this disease, it is at times quite difficult to distinguish between white scours and diarrhea due to other causes, particularly those of a dietary nature, such as overfeeding, irregular feeding, use of unclean utensils, feeding cold milk, and too rapid changes in feed, or exposure to cold drafts and cold, damp floors. When a number of calves are affected, as a precautionary measure the contagious form of white scours should always be considered as a possibility until diagnosed as some other form of diarrhea.

A calf that has succumbed to white scours will show soiled hindquarters from the bowel discharges, and the carcass will be emaciated. An odor peculiar to the disease may also be noticed. On autopsy, small hemorrhages may be found on the serous linings—thin lining membranes—of the body cavities and also in the region of the heart. There seems to be a localization of lesions, or tissue changes, in the digestive tract, and slight to severe hemorrhages will be found on the lining of the stomach and small intestine. There may be varying amounts of free blood in the bowel. The contents of the intestinal tract are a dirty yellowish-gray color and have a fetid odor. The intestines may be distended with gas. Varying amounts of a red-colored fluid may be present in the body cavities. It is probable that not all the tissue changes described will be present in each individual case, those occurring depending somewhat on the severity of the infection and the length of time the animal has been affected. In some instances marked lesions may be absent, whereas in long-continued cases there may be infection of the joints, pneumonia, and inflammation of the serous linings of the body cavities. Foreign substances, such as bedding and hair, may be found in the stomach.

PREVENTION AND CONTROL MEASURES

Medicinal treatment begun after the onset of diarrheal symptoms is usually of little avail. A hyperimmune calf-scour serum given as a preventive treatment soon after birth will aid in preventing heavy losses but is of little value after infection has taken place. In some instances a bacterin (made of killed organisms) has been used to inoculate pregnant cows, but little is known regarding the efficacy of such treatment at the present time.

In combating this disease, the owner should remember that the all-important thing is to prevent primary infection of the newborn calf. This can be accomplished only by strict sanitary measures—that is, by providing the greatest possible cleanliness at the time of birth and during the first few days of life, when the animal is most susceptible to the infection. A large box stall or maternity stall that can be readily cleaned and disinfected at frequent intervals should be provided for the cow at the time of parturition. Shortly before the time of calving, the external genitals, hindquarters, tail, and udder should be thoroughly cleaned and disinfected with a 3-percent solution of liquor cresolis compositus (see p. 186). Just before the udder is disinfected, a few streams of milk should be drawn into a vessel (not onto the stable floor) and discarded. As soon as possible after the calf is delivered, its navel should be disinfected with fresh tincture of iodine. Also, before the calf suckles, its mouth may be washed out with a 4-percent solution of boric acid.

The maternity stall should be kept clean by periodic removal of all litter and frequent renewal of the bedding. This is very important, as most calves have a habit of chewing the bedding or other foreign substances, and the infective organisms may thus gain entrance to the digestive tract. It is well known that the first instinct of a normal calf is to obtain food from its mother. This first food is colostral milk, the secretion of the mammary gland of the cow immediately after calving. Colostrum is somewhat different in composition from milk that is secreted later; it aids in cleaning out the digestive tract and also gives the calf resistance against harmful bacteria that may gain entrance to the intestinal canal.

The adoption of some system of regular feeding of calves is essential, since even in an apparently healthy calf an overloaded stomach may result in severe indigestion, which may lower its resistance to such an extent that it becomes susceptible to the causative agent of white scours. Once the infection has gained a foothold in the herd, it is likely to spread to other calves in the same group.

A plan for the care and feeding of very young calves is as follows: For the first 12 hours the calf remains with the dam and obtains colostrum without restraint, since, as a general rule, the calf is not strong enough to overeat. At the end of 12 hours a muzzle is applied and all feed withheld for 24 hours. For 30 days the muzzle

is not removed except while the calf is feeding. The allowance of
the dam's milk for the first feeding day is 5 to 6 percent of the calf's
body weight. This is divided into three feedings, to each of which
is added an equal amount of limewater. The mixture is heated to
100° F. and fed in a sterilized pail. For the second feeding day,
the quantity of dam's milk to be given is 6 or 7 percent of the calf's
weight.

The amount of limewater at each feeding should never be more
than 1 pint. At the end of the first week, the calf may receive a
quantity of milk daily equal to 8 to 12 percent of its body weight.
Feed is given in individual pails morning, noon, and night, with
a pint of limewater at each feeding. The pails should always be
cleaned and sterilized before being used.

It may be advisable during the first week to take the calf's temperature every day before the noon feeding. If it is 103° F. or
more, give an enema, using a 1-percent solution of liquor cresolis
compositus, and administer 3 ounces of liquid petrolatum by mouth.
Feed should be withheld until the temperature is normal.

Calves showing symptoms of the disease should be isolated; their
feces, which contain the infective agent, should be destroyed; and
the stables should be frequently disinfected. Also, all tools and
equipment used around the pens should be cleaned and disinfected.
The sick calves should be given a dose of 4 to 6 ounces of castor oil,
followed by 1 ounce of sodium bicarbonate in a half pint of water,
combined with 3 drams of aromatic spirits of ammonia. Coffee may
be given as a stimulant, and the strength of the calf can be preserved
by feeding raw eggs in pasteurized milk. Limewater may be given
at frequent intervals. Decoctions of linseed, barley, oats, etc., may
also be given. From 5 to 10 drops of liquor cresolis compositus in
a pint of warm water may be administered as an intestinal
disinfectant.

In case of serious losses from this disease, a veterinarian should be
consulted immediately.

ACETONEMIA (KETOSIS, OR CHRONIC MILK FEVER)

For many years the condition now recognized as acetonemia has
been observed in dairy cows during the lactation or milking period.
Because of certain nervous symptoms somewhat like those of milk
fever, acetonemia was thought to be an atypical form of that disease
and has been occasionally referred to as chronic milk fever. The disease is discussed in the article on Nutritional Diseases of Cattle, page
668. It might be added here that most uncomplicated cases respond
quickly and make a rapid recovery following the administration of
one or more treatments with dextrose, the required number varying in
different animals. The dosage of dextrose is 500 cubic centimeters of
a 40-percent solution given daily, either intravenously (in the veins)
or subcutaneously (under the skin), and this treatment may be continued for several days or until there is definite evidence of improvement. Well-marked cases of acetonemia, whether complicated or not,
should be treated by a qualified veterinarian.

PSEUDORABIES (MAD ITCH)

Pseudorabies is an infectious disease of cattle characterized by intense pruritis (itching) and paralysis, which usually results in death in 12 to 48 hours. The disease was first described by Aujeszky in Hungary in 1902, and because of symptoms suggestive of rabies, it was designated pseudorabies. The marked evidence of itching in affected animals has led cattle owners in this country to call it mad itch. It is also known as infectious bulbar paralysis and Aujeszky's disease. The disease is now known to be present on both the North and South American Continents, particularly in Brazil and the United States. In this country it has probably existed in the Middle West for a considerable time.

In 1930, Shope (*13*)[2] described an outbreak of mad itch in cattle in Iowa. Subsequent reports of outbreaks in the same State were made by Murray (*11*), Rossing (*12*), and other veterinarians. The disease has also been observed occasionally in other parts of the country.

The mortality rate in outbreaks of mad itch is quite high; most of the cattle affected die. The economic losses have not been very great, however, owing to the rather limited extent of the infection in this country up to the present.

In his studies of the disease, Shope (*13*) found it to be due to a filtrable virus, and in his experimental comparisons of the virus of the disease in this country with that of the European disease he reached a tentative conclusion that the causative agents of the two diseases were probably the same, with certain demonstrable differences in the two strains of viruses.

Recently Morrill and Graham (*10*) reported a spontaneous outbreak of mad itch in a herd of cattle in Illinois. These investigators made some very interesting experimental studies of the disease and reported the isolation from the spinal cord of a steer of a filtrable virus which was indistinguishable from the virus of the European disease.

The virus is most concentrated in the tissue fluids at the point of inoculation and in the brain tissues. In Europe the causative virus has been found with considerable regularity in the blood of affected animals. In the United States Shope found the virus in certain organs such as the lungs and liver of experimental animals, as well as in the brain and certain other tissues, but he found it difficult to demonstrate the virus in the blood.

The natural mode of infection is not definitely known. Available evidence indicates that the disease is not contagious, that is, it is not spread from animal to animal by contact, and that infection probably takes place through injury or abrasions of the skin on some part of the body, probably most frequently in the region of the head and neck, though somewhat less frequently the skin lesions are observed on certain parts of the buttocks and thighs. The disease also affects swine, which may become carriers of the infection and are therefore

---

[2] Italic numbers in parentheses refer to Literature Cited, p. 563.

believed to be potential spreaders of the disease among cattle. It is also rather common among rats, and it is thought probable that these animals may become carriers. Some observers are of the opinion that the frequent head lesions, or injuries, are caused by the bites of infected rats and that it is very probable that domestic animals may be infected in this manner. The fact that the disease is usually limited to certain herds and premises also tends to confirm the opinion that rats are a probable source of infection.

The symptoms vary somewhat in individual cases. Usually there is a marked rise of temperature, which may reach 108° or 109° F. There may be loss of appetite. Among the first symptoms to be noted is increased alertness or nervousness, which is quickly followed by an intense itching, shown by the animals continually licking or rubbing an area of skin on some part of the body—perhaps on the hindquarters or in the region of the head. The licking may become so vigorous as to produce a rasping sound. As the itching becomes more intense, the licking or rubbing of the affected area evidently does not allay the irritation, and the animal begins to rub violently against any objects in the vicinity, such as barbed wire or posts, and in some cases may even bite or gnaw itself. Some animals may bellow loudly, kick spasmodically with the hind legs, and occasionally run violently into objects. There is usually excessive salivation or drooling of saliva from the mouth. As a result of the rubbing and mechanical injury, the skin is denuded of hair, and raw, bleeding surfaces are seen. The skin becomes markedly thickened, and a fluid may ooze from the area, which eventually becomes a raw, bleeding surface. Occasionally the animal may appear depressed and sleepy. Unsteadiness of gait and possibly paralysis of the hindquarters develop. The affected animals become progressively weaker, and death follows in 12 to 48 hours, sometimes preceded by an increasing evidence of paralysis or irregular convulsions, violent tossing of the head, loud groaning, and shallow breathing. In occasional cases the animal may not show all the symptoms described, and in some instances the intense itching may be entirely absent. In these cases the affected animals may be ill for several days and toward the end have convulsions, drool at the mouth, and grind the teeth.

On autopsy the denuded area of skin will be found to be dark, thickened, and leathery in appearance, and a serous, bloody, and sometimes gelatinous fluid is seen infiltrating the tissues under the skin. If the animal has been down for a considerable length of time before death, there may be edema, or watery swelling, of the lungs. Occasionally petechiae (pin-point hemorrhages) are seen in the heart and pericardium, and the amount of fluid in the heart sac is increased. These heart lesions have led in some instances to confusing the disease with hemorrhagic septicemia. In the central nervous system there may be congestion and small hemorrhages of the meninges, or brain coverings. No organic lesions are found on autopsy that can be considered as characteristic or definitely diagnostic of the disease.

The disease may be differentiated from rabies chiefly by its rapid and fatal course and the usual severe itching, which is not in evidence in rabies. Furious attacks and aggressive behavior on the part of affected animals, common in rabies, are seldom seen in pseudorabies, and the virus is not found in the saliva, as it is in rabies.

There is no known treatment for the disease, and prevention will likewise continue to be a difficult problem until more information is available concerning the means by which animals become infected. When the disease appears in a herd, as a precautionary procedure the healthy cattle should be separated from the sick and removed to different barns or pastures, and the quarters occupied by the sick animals should be thoroughly cleaned and disinfected. Hogs should not be permitted to run with the cattle. A campaign of rat extermination would also be of extreme importance on premises where there have been outbreaks of mad itch in cattle.

THE MORE COMMON TYPES OF TUMORS IN CATTLE

Cattle are subject to a variety of tumors, most of which are of rare occurrence. It is the intention here to consider rather briefly only three of the types that are more frequently encountered, namely, papilloma, or common wart; epithelioma, commonly referred to as cancer eye; and a group of internal lymphoid tumors, which are particularly characterized by hyperplasia, or enlargement of the various lymph glands of the body.

PAPILLOMA, OR COMMON WARTS

The common wart, verruca vulgaris, is a specific type of epithelial (skin) overgrowth, nonmalignant in character. Warts are of common occurrence in animals and in man. Adults may be affected by them, but the young are far more susceptible.

Warts on cattle, particularly calves and yearlings, are quite common. They are found on many parts of the body, but their location depends somewhat on the age of the animal. In cows, warts usually occur on the udder or teats, whereas in calves under 1 year of age they are seen most frequently on various parts of the head—on the ears, and around the eyes and mouth—and on the sides of the neck and shoulders.

Warts may spread from the original location to different parts of the body and may eventually cover large areas of the skin. Occasionally, particularly on young cattle, they become large and pendulous (fig. 1) and as a result sap the strength and stunt the growth of the animals. Their chief damage, however, is to calf skins and cattle hides after tanning. The tanned hides have roughened and weak spots where the warts occurred on the skin, and they frequently contain numerous pits or holes in places where the skin was thickly studded with warts, as on the shoulders. These defects give a moth-eaten appearance to the finished leather, and the parts affected are considered worthless.

The reduction in the value of hides because of warts usually varies from a small percentage to 25 percent and sometimes more, depending on the extent of skin areas affected. Cattle buyers make discounts for warty animals purchased in the markets. Since a considerable number of animals are affected with warts and the hides of many of

FIGURE 1.—A heifer about 18 months old with a natural case of common warts.

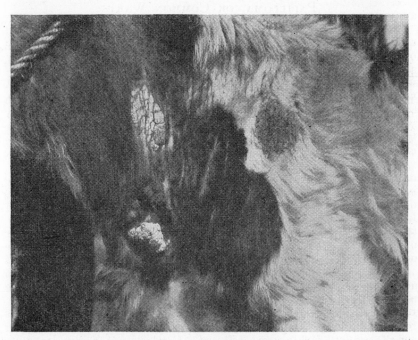

FIGURE 2.—Warts produced on a calf by skin inoculation with filtered material obtained from the warts on the heifer shown in figure 1.

them are greatly reduced in value, the yearly loss in leather is doubtless large, although no definite figures are available.

Warts vary greatly in shape and size. They may be thin, long, and club-shaped, an inch or more in length, and occur singly or in clusters, or they may become large cauliflowerlike tumors several inches in diameter, in extreme cases weighing several pounds. Occasionally they occur as broad, slightly elevated masses. They may be either hard or soft. The large cauliflowerlike growths are usually soft and show a tendency to bleed and slough, and frequently they give off offensive odors.

Common warts in cattle have been shown by experiments to be infectious. The infective agent is what is known as a filtrable virus, meaning that it will pass through an earthen, germ-retaining filter. By experimental skin inoculations with wart material, these growths can be produced with a fair degree of regularity in healthy cattle under 1 year of age (fig. 2). Under ordinary circumstances, infection is thought to take place through injuries to the skin when the injured part comes in contact with warty animals, rubbing posts, fences, buildings, or any structure which an affected animal has touched.

Treatment and Prevention

Warts occasionally disappear without treatment of any kind, especially as animals become older. Most cases, however, require definite and systematic treatment.

Warts that are small at the place of attachment may be removed by either clipping them off with sterile scissors or tying a sterile thread or slender cord tightly around the wart near the base so that it will slough off in a few days. The stumps of the warts should be touched with either glacial acetic acid or tincture of iodine. Tying off is recommended also for warts which because of their size are likely to contain a number of blood vessels that would bleed if the warts were removed by cutting. The roots or bases of such warts also should be treated with glacial acetic acid or silver nitrate. The removal of extremely large warts by surgical means should be performed by a veterinarian. Before warts become excessively large they may be destroyed by daily applications of glacial acetic acid or tincture of iodine. Before applying acetic acid, protect the healthy skin immediately surrounding the warts by thoroughly greasing with petrolatum or lard, taking care not to grease the warts since that would protect them also from the acid. Small warts, such as those on the udders of cows, will sometimes disappear if kept soft by daily applications of sweet oil or castor oil.

If warts are numerous and cover large areas of the body, it may be advisable to give internal treatment also. The usual internal treatment for various skin disorders, including warts, is arsenic in the form of Fowler's solution. The dose is 1 tablespoonful twice daily for cattle 6 to 12 months of age. This method, however, should be considered only an indirect treatment, and it should be used only under the supervision of a veterinarian. Since arsenic may pass into the milk, Fowler's solution should not be given to milking cows.

A wart vaccine is now being used to some extent, with reports of rather favorable results. The treatment is still in the experimental stage, however, and further observations will be required to determine its efficacy.

Preventive measures consist in removing all warty cattle, particularly calves and yearlings, from the herd and cleaning and disinfecting all exposed stables, pens, chutes, and rubbing posts. In dairy herds, cows with warts on their teats and udders should be milked last, and the milkers should be careful to wash and disinfect their hands thoroughly after each milking to prevent the possible spread of the virus from one animal to another. The essential point to keep in mind is that these growths are infectious, or catching.

EPITHELIOMA (CARCINOMA, OR CANCER EYE)

Epithelioma of the eyes of cattle, more commonly referred to as cancer eye, is a cancerous or malignant type of tumor which primarily attacks the eye or related tissues. This eye tumor appears to be somewhat more prevalent in the West and Southwest than elsewhere in the United States, although it may be seen in all parts of the country.

As in the case of other malignant tumors, the specific cause of epithelioma of the eyes of cattle is not known. A number of possible contributing causes have been suggested, such as irritation of the eyes by dust, sand, insects, or other irritants. The strong rays of the sun also have been mentioned as a possible cause, particularly in the case of the Hereford breed of cattle, which appears to be particularly susceptible to cancer eye. The theory is that the lack of protective pigment, or coloring matter, in the eye membranes and skin surrounding the eyes in this breed results in a sensitization of the tissues to sunlight, and the irritation thus set up may lead to the cancerous condition. While it seems logical that irritation may play some part as a causative factor in cancer eye, nothing of a specific nature has been definitely proved.

The growth may have its origin in the membrana nictitans, at the inner canthus, or angle, of the eye, in the mucous lining of the lids, or in the front part, or cornea, of the eyeball. It may appear at first as a small reddish mass with a tendency as it becomes larger to assume a funguslike or papillary (nipplelike) appearance. Such growths are very sensitive and susceptible to injury and when injured bleed freely. The eye proper is not usually affected in the early stages, but eventually it becomes involved, and the sight is destroyed. The tumorous mass usually becomes infected with bacteria, a condition that is followed by suppuration or pus formation, and extensive destruction of tissues, accompanied by a very foul odor. In the warm months it is not unusual to see these eye growths infested by the larvae, or maggots, of the screwworm fly. The eye is eventually completely destroyed by the growth, which then spreads to the surrounding tissues, involving both the soft structures and the bone of the orbit (fig. 3). As the growth becomes more extensive, the bones of the nose and head may be affected.

In the more advanced or long-standing cases, the cancerous cells are disseminated through metastasis, or transference to other tissues and organs, chiefly by way of the lymph stream. The parotid lymph gland, which lies in rather close proximity to the eye, soon becomes involved, and the growth may spread to other lymph glands of the head and neck regions through lymph drainage. By the same means of distribution, or metastasis, the lungs may become involved and in some cases the liver and other organs.

In all advanced cases of cancer eye there is a drain on the animal's vitality. There may be absorption of toxins from the infected tumor, resulting in decline in general condition and emaciation. C a t t l e owners should always bear in mind that epithelioma of the eye is definitely cancerous, or malignant, in all cases a n d eventually w i l l spread to other tissues and cause the death of the animal unless this is prevented through e a r l y operative procedure.

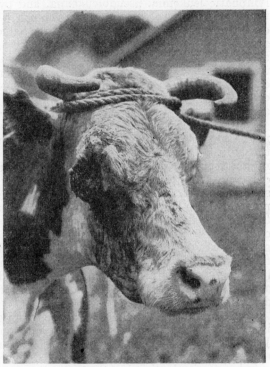

FIGURE 3.—Epithelioma, or cancer eye, in a cow. Note that the eye is completely destroyed and that the growth involves the surrounding tissues.

Little can be done to alleviate the condition after the tumor has become extensive enough to involve the entire eye and adjacent tissues. In such cases, if the animal is still in fair condition, it should be sent to market for slaughter, subject to inspection. Under Federal meat-inspection regulations, if the tumor is still localized, or confined largely to the eye structures, and has not involved the lymph glands, the head is condemned and the remainder of the carcass passed for food.

Operative procedure consists in the total removal of the cancerous tissue, together with removal (enucleation) of the eyeball, which is likely to be involved after the growth is well established. It is extremely important that the operation be performed as soon as a definite diagnosis of cancer eye has been made. When it has been performed early enough, the results have usually been quite satisfactory. Needless to say, such operations should be performed by a veterinarian who is thoroughly skilled and fully equipped to carry out the necessary technical procedure.

Lymphocytoma, Lymphatic Leukemia, and Pseudoleukemia

There is a third group of tumors of rather common occurrence in cattle which are lymphoid in nature—that is, they primarily affect the lymphoid tissue, and the lymph glands in particular, which usually show marked hyperplasia, or enlargement. These internal neoplasms, or morbid growths, are malignant in character and have been referred to by pathologists as lymphoma, lymphocytoma, lymphosarcoma, lymphatic leukemia, pseudoleukemia, and by various other designations. While there is a marked resemblance in the gross appearance of all the conditions designated by these names and also in the microscopical appearance in many instances, occasional slight differences are seen in the cell structure, and this accounts for the variation in terminology. There is still much confusion regarding the proper classification of these lymphoid conditions—whether they should be classified as several distinct varieties of new growths or be placed in a single group.[3]

One of the first indications of the disease usually observed is a noticeable enlargement of the superficial lymph glands (those near the surface), particularly the submaxillary gland, situated in the region of the throat, the prescapular gland, just in front of the shoulder, and the precrural gland, in the flank region (fig. 4). The supramammary lymph gland, which is above and behind the udder, may also be enlarged. As a result of metastasis, or dissemination of the tumor material to other tissues and organs, there may be evidences of general disturbance such as irregular heart action, difficult breathing, general weakness, and progressive emaciation. In the later stages there is loss of appetite, extreme weakness, and finally death. These lymphoid conditions are usually chronic and terminate in death in a number of weeks to several months after the first evidence of the disease is noted.

On autopsy the lymph glands will be found greatly enlarged. There is usually an edematous or watery condition of the various tissues. When the disease has extended to the different organs, there may be marked enlargement of the spleen, and light or grayish areas or spots may be seen in the tissue of the heart, liver, and kidney. Occasionally growths may be seen in the stomachs, and in cows the uterus may be affected. Nodular tumor growths are found in the body cavities in some cases.

It may sometimes be necessary to differentiate the lymphoid conditions from certain other diseases in which the lymph glands become enlarged, such as tuberculosis and actinomycosis (described later in this same article). The possibility of tuberculosis may be eliminated through the tuberculin test, and examinations for actinomycosis or other infectious conditions may be made through a biopsy, or re-

---

[3] Feldman (7) places these lymphoid tumors in the general class of lymphoblastoma. While there is a persistent similarity in most of these new growths, certain exceptions are encountered in which there are rather definite variations. One such exception is found in cases of true leukemia, in which there is a definite change in the ratio of blood cells or a marked increase in the white blood corpuscles. These cases are rather rare (4). Another definite deviation from the usual type has been reported more recently by Bengston (2) of the Bureau of Animal Industry. This type was found to be more definitely sarcomatous in nature, and he designated it as reticulum sarcoma.

Figure 4.—A cow with lymphatic leukemia. Note the greatly enlarged lymph glands—the prescapular, in front of the shoulder, and the precrural, in the flank region.

moval from the living animal by surgery of a portion of an enlarged gland for laboratory examination, culturing, etc. Blood examinations are also valuable aids in diagnosing leukemia.

There are no known methods of treatment or prevention of these lymphoid conditions, which are fatal to all animals affected.

ACTINOMYCOSIS AND ACTINOBACILLOSIS

For many years most of the tumorlike swellings or enlargements of the tissues of the head and throat in cattle, commonly referred to as lumpy jaw, big jaw, and wooden tongue, were diagnosed as actinomycosis. It is now known that there is another infectious condition, technically referred to as actinobacillosis, particularly involving the soft tissues, in which the tissue changes are very similar to those in actinomycosis. The two diseases are due to entirely different types of micro-organisms, the causative agent in actinomycosis being *Actinomyces bovis*, the ray fungus, and in actinobacillosis, *Actinobacillus lignieresi*. Frequently certain types of pyogenic, or pus-producing, bacteria are also associated with these infections.

Actinomycosis and actinobacillosis are both chronic infectious diseases, and the former tendency to confuse them or consider them as one disease was due largely to the marked similarity of the lesions, or tissue changes, and also possibly to the fact that the causative organisms, as seen microscopically in pus preparations and sections from the affected tissues, have a similar club formation and rosette arrangement. It seems logical, therefore, to consider the two types together and at the same time to indicate any specific points of difference between them.

Brief descriptions of the microscopic findings, and also of certain details disclosed by autopsy, are given at the end of this section, page 553.

Actinomycosis and actinobacillosis affect cattle in all parts of the United States, possibly being somewhat more prevalent in the West than elsewhere. Fatalities are comparatively few, and the diseases are ordinarily not considered of great economic importance. The records of the Federal meat-inspection service indicate, however, that these infections are responsible for considerable losses every year from condemnation of affected carcasses and parts of carcasses.

The infective organisms are widespread in nature and gain entrance to the tissues most frequently through injuries or abrasions of the mucous membranes of the mouth cavity and throat region. It has been assumed that *Actinomyces*, or the ray fungus, is present on grasses and grains and that the sharp awns of grains and certain grasses, such as foxtail, are the means by which the organisms are introduced into the deeper tissues of the mouth through the mucous membrane. The gums of cattle are very sensitive and more or less lacerated during the teething period, and in all probability this affords a means of entrance for such infections in many cases, since actinomycotic infections are seen most frequently in young cattle during the period of changing teeth.

Some observers are of the opinion that the mouth may be the chief normal habitat of these organisms, and that they invade the tissues and produce disease only under unusual conditions or following irritation and injuries to the mucous membranes. In areas in the Southwest where the fruit of the cactus is eaten by cattle, it is thought probable that many cases of actinomycotic infection are due to injuries of the mucous membrane of the mouth by the small cactus spines, or spicules.

Lesions of Actinomycosis

Actinomycosis may occur in the soft tissues but as a rule is confined to the bones of the head, particularly the maxillae, or jawbones, the lower jawbone being most frequently involved. The nasal bones are occasionally involved when the upper jaw is affected, and this may result in difficult breathing. The bone lesions produced are those of a rarefying ostitis—that is, the bone becomes enlarged and rarefied, or spongy. The small cavities in the spongy bone are filled with pus. The palate and gums adjacent to the involved bone become swollen and inflamed, and the teeth may become loosened. The bony growth may extend outward through the soft tissues and skin, eventually appearing on the external surface as a mass of granulation tissue, or funguslike growths, with a foul odor. The infection may also extend inward, resulting in similar lesions, cauliflowerlike masses of inflamed tissue containing openings or cavities which discharge a sticky yellowish or creamy pus in which can be seen very minute, pale-yellow grains, the so-called sulfur granules characteristic of this type of infection.

Lesions of Actinobacillosis

So far as is known at the present time, the lesions of actinobacillosis are confined to the soft tissues. In the tissues of the head or cervical (neck) region, the lesions are characterized by movable swellings, or tumefactions, under the skin, varying from the size of a walnut to that of an egg or larger. The lymph glands of the cervical region may be involved and much enlarged. The consistency of the tumor formations may vary somewhat in the different tissues, the firmness of the growth depending on the amount of fibrous connective tissue present. These abscessed enlargements eventually break through the skin, discharging a creamy pus. Frequently the opening or discharging cavity becomes filled with reddish granulomatous (funguslike) tissue.

The tongue is often involved in actinobacillosis, and there may or may not be ulceration. The ulcers most frequently have their beginning at the transverse depression, or so-called groove, on the upper surface of the tongue. They usually show as round or oval depressed areas with elevated, irregular, and ragged edges. The ulcerations are frequently covered with debris such as hairs and vegetable matter, and there is usually a foul odor.

Sometimes when the tongue is involved there may also be ulcerations of the mucous membrane and abscess formation in the region of the pharynx, larynx, and trachea. The lymph glands of the throat region may also be affected. When the tongue is extensively involved in the chronic inflammatory process, there is a very marked increase in the fibrous tissue of the organ (fibrosis), and as a result the tongue becomes increasingly hard and immobile and may protrude from the mouth; this condition has given rise to the term "wooden tongue." The tongue is manipulated with great difficulty, and there is almost constant drooling of saliva. Eventually there is practically a complete loss of prehension, or ability to take feed into the mouth, mastication is seriously interfered with, the animal becomes weak and greatly emaciated, and it may die of exhaustion.

Lesions in the pharynx may take the form of mushroomlike growths or pendulous masses, which in some cases may completely fill the pharyngeal cavity, seriously interfering with swallowing and breathing.

In addition to the external lesions described, there may also be a distribution of the infection to various internal organs and tissues, including the lungs, liver, kidneys, spleen, brain, mammary gland, testes, urinary bladder, muscles, and serous linings of the body cavities. Cases in which the skin and subcutaneous tissues of different parts of the body and the extremities were infected have also been reported.

Infection of the peritoneum—the membrane lining the cavity of the abdomen—is not uncommon in cattle, and three such cases were reported by Creech (*3*) some years ago in calves approximately 8 weeks old. Owing to the age of the animals, these were unusually interesting cases. No other lesions were found, and the portal of entry of the infective agent was not determined.

SYMPTOMS, PREVENTION, AND TREATMENT

The course of both of these diseases is always slow or chronic in character, extending over a period of months or even several years.

The general effects depend largely on the location of the lesions and their interference with the natural functions of the body. For example, when the jawbones are involved, there may be loss of teeth and consequent interference with chewing. Growths in the pharynx may inhibit swallowing and cause difficult breathing or partial suffocation. The difficulties caused by involvement of the tongue, particularly in the more marked cases of wooden tongue, have already been mentioned. Such interference with the body functions naturally leads to depletion and emaciation. Otherwise, localized lesions do not seem definitely to affect the general health of the diseased animals.

Prevention of actinomycosis and actinobacillosis is somewhat difficult in the absence of definite knowledge as to how animals contract these diseases. Available information indicates that they are probably infectious rather than contagious in character. It has been found extremely difficult to transmit actinomycosis by experimental inoculation, but less difficulty has been experienced in transmitting actinobacillosis. While there is little evidence to indicate that the infections are directly transmissible from animal to animal, either actinomycosis or actinobacillosis may affect large groups of animals in the same herd. This suggests that if the disease is not contagious, all the animals contracted it from the same source, possibly the feed. Regardless of the mode of infection, animals with lesions from which discharging pus may contaminate the feed or surrounding objects should not be permitted to remain in pastures or feed lots with healthy cattle.

Treatment of actinomycosis is not very satisfactory, largely because of the nature of the lesions involving the bone tisses, but actinobacillosis yields quite readily to treatment in most cases. The most satisfactory treatment is to give iodine, usually in the form of sodium or potassium iodide, in doses of 1½ to 2½ drams daily, dissolved in water and administered as a drench. When there are lesions of the tongue or pharynx, care must be used to see that none of the drug reaches the lungs, as this may cause pneumonia. After a week or 10 days, the treated animals may show indications of the cumulative effect of the drug, or iodism, evidenced by a flow of tears, catarrh of the nose, loss of appetite, and scurfy skin. When such symptoms appear, treatments should be discontinued for a few days or a week, after which they may be resumed. Definite curative results may be expected to appear in 2 to 6 weeks, the length of time varying in different cases. Some cases do not respond to the treatment, and if no definite evidence of improvement is seen after 3 or 4 weeks, the treatment should be discontinued. It is inadvisable to administer potassium iodide to cows that are lactating, as the drug is secreted in the milk and also tends to reduce the amount. Also the drug should not be given to cows in advanced pregnancy, as it may cause abortion.

Tincture of iodine may be applied externally to the enlargements, or Lugol's solution of iodine may be injected in the region of the swellings. The large cutaneous tumors may be incised, the contents, or necrotic material, removed, and the incision packed with gauze saturated with tincture of iodine.

Surgery would be indicated in some cases, particularly when the tumor formations are so situated that removal may be readily accomplished.

In these diseases it is always advisable to consult a veterinarian and be guided by his opinion as to the required method of treatment in each individual case. A veterinarian's services should, of course, be obtained in all cases in which surgery is indicated.

While some cases of slight actinomycotic infection of the bone may yield to the iodine treatment, it will usually prove more economical to fatten animals so affected for slaughter.

Since man is susceptible to both actinomycosis and actinobacillosis, animals with these diseases sent to market for slaughter ought always to be inspected by a veterinarian in order to determine the suitability of the carcasses for food.

The Federal meat-inspection regulations require the condemnation of the entire carcasses of cattle showing generalized lesions of actinomycosis or actinobacillosis. If the carcasses of affected animals otherwise show a well-nourished condition and the lesions are strictly localized in certain tissues of the body, they may be passed for food after the removal and condemnation of the parts or organs affected. When the head and tongue are affected, both must be condemned. In cases in which the lesions of the jaw are very slight and strictly localized, with no indications whatever of extension of infection to the surrounding and related tissues, the tongue, if entirely free from the disease, may be passed for food.

Findings on Microscopic Examination and Autopsy

Microscopically as well as in visible details, the lesions of actinomycosis and actinobacillosis as seen in tissue sections are very similar, consisting of granulation tissue composed of lymphoid and epithelioid cells and usually numbers of giant cells, with centers of focal necrosis and possibly some calcification. In the degenerated areas will be seen heavy infiltrations of polymorphonuclear leucocytes—the most common type of white blood cells—and some plasma cells. The cellular tissue is surrounded by zones of fibrous tissue.

Within the meshwork of the fibrous formations in actinobacillosis are small cavities or pockets filled with cellular elements or puslike material in which can be seen small yellowish granules similar to those described in actinomycosis. These are the colonies of organisms. If the small granules are examined under the microscope either in press preparations from the pus or in tissue sections, they will be seen as rounded masses with club-shaped radiations that give them a rosette appearance. In most respects the appearance of the rosettes in both types of infection is quite similar with ordinary staining, but with special staining, as with Gram stain, the actinomyces give positive results, or retain the stain, while the actinobacilli give negative results, or fail to retain the stain. In the former, fungus mycelia may be seen, while in the latter only bacteria or bacilli are present. As a rule the rosettes are larger in actinomycosis than in actinobacillosis.

Affected tongue foci, on sectioning, will be seen to contain yellowish, sticky, puslike material. Nodular formations, or small lumps, and fistulous (tubelike) tracts or cavities may be seen in the muscular substance of the tongue in some cases.

In the lungs the disease is manifested as grayish or grayish-yellow nodular masses which contain a thick puslike material and fragments of tissue (detritus). In some cases the lesions may be seen as grayish, soft, moist, areas. On sectioning the affected lung tissue, the yellowish grains or sulfur granules, previously referred to, may be seen distributed through the lesions, which aids in differentiating this type of infection from tuberculosis. In advanced cases the lesions may assume the form of soft, grayish-yellow masses, enclosed in a membrane, and several inches in diameter, in which portions of the affected tissue may be broken down or semifluid. The lymph glands associated with the lungs may also be affected.

Somewhat similar lesions are found in the liver and other organs, the general character of the tissue changes depending somewhat on the amount of connective tissue present and the extent of necrosis and disintegration of the tissues affected.

NASAL GRANULOMA (SNORING DISEASE)

Nasal granuloma, as the name indicates, is a disease of the nasal cavities of cattle in which there is thickening of the nasal mucous lining. The condition causes more or less interference with the passage of air in breathing, resulting in a peculiar snoring sound; hence the more common name snoring disease.

Nasal granuloma has existed among the cattle of India for a long time, but it had not been observed in any other country until a similar disease was reported in 1933 to be present in the United States (5). The disease was first discovered in this country in a dairy herd at the Iberia Livestock Experiment Station, at Jeanerette, La. It had apparently existed in this herd for 4 or 5 years prior to the time studies made of the disease were reported. Subsequently the disease has been observed in several other herds in Louisiana but apparently has not been definitely recognized in any other part of the country.

While there may be a loss of general condition in affected animals in the more advanced stages of the disease, so far as is known, fatalities seldom occur. Since the disease is also very limited in extent, it may be considered of minor economic importance at the present time.

Nasal granuloma occurs in India in two forms. One is parasitic in nature, being caused by a schistosome worm, or fluke, while the other form is caused by a sporozoan organism (one that reproduces by means of spores) of the genus *Rhinosporidium*. The specific cause of the disease in the United States has not been definitely determined. Bacteriological studies and examinations for the presence of parasites have thus far given entirely negative results. Experimental animal inoculations have likewise failed to yield any specific information with regard to the cause of the disease.

The first symptoms usually noticed are sneezing and nasal discharge of a mucopurulent material—a mixture of mucus and pus (fig. 5). In the more acute cases this material is frequently mixed with blood and may also contain small portions of destroyed mucous membrane. The bloody discharges may be seen on the stable floor or on the grass or ground where the affected animals have been pastured.

As the disease progresses, difficult breathing is noticed and a peculiar droning sound, or snoring, can be heard for some distance. The affected cattle show a characteristic wrinkling of the skin surrounding the wing of the nostril, resulting from the extra effort required in breathing because of the partial closing or obstruction of the nasal cavity. The difficult breathing is more pronounced during the warm months, and the disease tends to subside or becomes more or less dormant during the cool season.

Certain treatments for this disease have been tried without very marked success. None have given permanent relief, and further ex-

FIGURE 5.—Cow first found to be affected with nasal granuloma at the Iberia Livestock Experiment Station. Note the characteristic expansion of the nostril and the nasal discharge.

perimentation is probably required to find a satisfactory or specific treatment.

The lesions or tissue changes are confined strictly to the nasal mucous membrane and rarely extend beyond the first 3 inches of the anterior nares, or nostrils. The lesions may extend entirely around the nasal cavity, including the mucosa of the nasal septum, or wall separating the nostrils.

In the more acute cases the mucosa becomes markedly congested, and this is followed by hemorrhages and sloughing, leaving small denuded areas from which blood or a mixture of blood and mucus escapes from time to time. In addition to the more acute changes the nasal mucosa becomes thickly studded with numerous small, grayish, tuberclelike nodules varying in size (fig. 6). In cases of long duration there is marked thickening of the nasal mucosa, due to the extensive chronic fibrous changes.

Histological Changes

While the histological changes are essentially those characteristic of granulation tissue, the lesions vary somewhat with the stage of the disease.

In the newer nodules the invading cells are chiefly round, or migratory, cells and leucocytes. As the disease progresses, fibroblasts become more evident, and groups or masses of eosinophile cells are seen distributed through the newly formed fibrous structure. Finally in the chronic stage the entire affected portion of the mucosa may undergo fibrosis. Certain other changes, such as

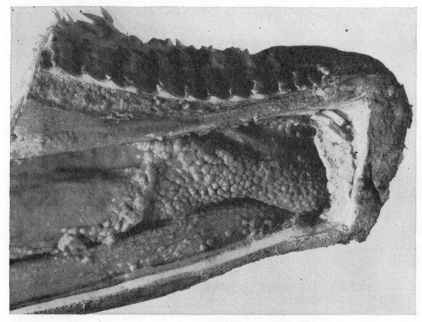

FIGURE 6.—Nodular lesions in the nasal cavity of a cow affected with nasal granuloma.

perivascular infiltration, endarteritis, degeneration, and vacuolization of the mucous glands, have also been noted. Few well-formed giant cells have been observed in sections.

In occasional sections made from the more acute nodular lesions a limited number of small round bodies, fairly definite in outline, have appeared. Some of these showed slightly serrated borders, and a number of the bodies seemed to be nucleated. Some were also surrounded by a brownish-pigmented circle or capsule. Small bodies which were thought to be similar in character also have been found in fresh preparations of the nodular material. Dikmans (6) observed similar small bodies in his studies of the disease and expressed the opinion that they probably had an etiological relation to the disease and possibly were related to the genus *Rhinosporidium*.

GOITER

Goiter is characterized by enlargement of the thyroid glands, which are situated in the region of the throat. While it may occur in adult cattle in the goiter districts, the general health of such animals does not appeared to be impaired (8). The chief significance of goiter in cattle and other animals is as a disease of the newborn. The condition and its prevention are discussed in the article on Nutritional Diseases of Farm Animals, page 332.

SPECIFIC OPHTHALMIA
(INFECTIOUS CONJUNCTIVITIS,
INFECTIOUS KERATITIS, OR PINKEYE)

Inflammatory conditions of the eyes of cattle are referred to medically as ophthalmia, conjunctivitis, and keratitis, the term used depending somewhat on the parts of the eye involved or the extent of the inflammation. The common name for all of these is pinkeye. Most frequently these inflammatory conditions have their beginning as a conjunctivitis, or inflammation of the conjunctiva, which is the lining membrane of the eyelids and also covers the visible part of the eyeball. When the inflammation becomes more extensive and involves the deeper structures of the cornea—the front or transparent portion of the eye—the condition is referred to as keratitis.

The disease is quite widespread throughout the country. As with other diseases of an enzootic nature (that is, prevalent in various districts), it is difficult to explain why it becomes more widespread and virulent during certain years and in certain localities. Whether seasonal and environmental conditions may influence such outbreaks is not definitely known. Although it is apparently not confined to any particular season, the disease is rarely observed during the winter months. It affects old and young animals alike.

There are practically no fatalities from the disease, but it has an economic aspect because it results in poor condition, loss of body weight, reduction in milk secretion, and general lowering of production when a large number of animals are affected.

Available evidence as obtained from outbreaks in certain herds indicates that these marked inflammatory conditions of the eyes of cattle are infectious in nature, but it is also very probable that certain predisposing factors play a rather important part—for example, dust, pollen, strong sunlight, and irritation or injury caused by insects or by contact with grasses, weeds, stubble, etc. Any irritation or injury makes the eye tissues more susceptible to infection.

A number of different types of bacteria have been found to be associated with the disease, more particularly the pyogenic or pus-producing group of organisms such as staphylococci, streptococci, and pyogenic bacilli. The hay bacillus (*Bacillus subtilis*) and organisms of the hemorrhagic septicemia group have been mentioned as possible causes. It has been difficult, however, to incriminate any particular organism as the specific causative agent.

As evidence of the infectious nature of the disease, the Kansas State Agricultural Experiment Station (*9*) reported the experimental transmission of keratitis by the inoculation of the eyes of susceptible calves with lachrymal secretions or discharges from the eyes of diseased calves. The inoculated calves developed the eye disease after an incubation period of 3 to 18 days. Filtered eye secretions from affected calves failed to produce the disease in susceptible animals (the use of bacteria-retaining filters would remove any bacteria present). These investigators also isolated a number of different types of bacteria from the diseased eyes of calves, but they were apparently unable to relate any one organism definitely to the disease.

According to further observations of the Kansas investigators, one attack of the disease does not confer immunity. Affected calves held in dark stalls recovered without treatment after 3 to 4 weeks if the disease had not advanced to the point of ulceration of the cornea.

Among the first symptoms observed are a flow of tears and avoidance of light or a tendency to keep the eyes closed. Severe conjunctivitis or reddening of the conjunctiva develops. The eyelids become swollen, hot, and sensitive to the touch. The lachrymal discharge from the eyes soon becomes mixed with pus and may be streaked with blood. The skin of the face becomes soiled by the constant discharge from the eyes. As the inflammation progresses, there is involvement of the deeper structures of the eye, particularly the cornea. There is an early cloudiness or opacity of the cornea, which may also be covered by an inflammatory deposit, and eventually corneal ulcers (ulcerative keratitis). There may be spontaneous recovery in some cases in which the inflammatory changes are not too far advanced, while in others the disease may become more deep-seated. In the more advanced cases there may be abscess formation of the cornea and possibly in the anterior chamber of the eye. Perforation of the cornea may occur with consequent loss of sight. In extreme cases there may be practically complete destruction of the eye.

There is usually some general disturbance, as evidenced by a rise of temperature, partial loss of appetite, suspended rumination, decrease in the milk secretion, and indications of increasing debility in advanced cases.

Prevention and treatment will probably remain more or less unsatisfactory until more definite information is available concerning the specific or primary cause of the condition. It is definitely known, however, as previously indicated, that a number of different types of organisms are associated with the disease and are capable of causing much damage once they have gained entrance to the tissues of the eye. Whether such bacteria are primary causative factors or secondary invaders, it is extremely important that prompt steps be taken for early treatment of the infectious condition in order to prevent possible permanent damage to the eyes or loss of sight.

TREATMENT

In view of the probably infectious nature of the disease, when the eye affection appears in the herd all unaffected cattle should be moved promptly to other barns or pastures if this is feasible. The diseased cattle should be housed in dark stables or sheds and provided with plenty of fresh drinking water and soft, succulent feed. Depending on the size of the animal, administer 1 to 1½ pounds of Epsom salts dissolved in water.

Cocaine may be applied to the eyes when there is evidence of pain. A 1-percent solution of silver nitrate has given very good results as an eye lotion. This is applied every other day until there are definite indications of improvement, then every third or fourth day until the inflammation subsides. The silver nitrate solution should be fresh when used, and may be applied to the eyes with a soft cotton swab, care being taken not to cause further irritation by undue rubbing or pressure. Less satisfactory results are obtained from applications of boracic acid solution. A more recent treatment recommended for keratitis is mercurochrome. Bardens (*1*) reported having obtained very satisfactory results with mercurochrome in 1- to 4-percent solutions dropped in the eyes several times daily. The stronger solution is recommended in cases of ulceration of the cornea. It is claimed to be less irritating to the eyes than the silver preparations.

Bardens also gives considerable credit to the mixed bacterins for keratitis, used simultaneously with the local mercurochrome treatment. The initial dose of the bacterin was 10 cubic centimeters, increased by 5 to 10 cubic centimeters daily until a maximum of 20 was reached. He found that two doses of bacterin were usually sufficient to correct the condition in dairy cattle.

It appears to be the consensus of opinion among veterinarians that more satisfactory results are obtained in the treatment of the disease when the mixed keratitis bacterins are used in conjunction with local treatments with the mercurochrome or silver nitrate solutions.

The treatments suggested, particularly the bacterin treatments, should be administered by a veterinarian, and, as in other infectious or contagious diseases, when an outbreak of pinkeye occurs in a herd the owner should promptly consult his local veterinarian and follow his instructions with regard to the best procedure for the eradication of the disease from the herd.

CALF DIPHTHERIA

Calf diphtheria is an acute infectious disease of suckling calves characterized by the formation of a diphtheritic false membrane on the mucous lining of the mouth and pharynx (throat). The disease is confined largely to young suckling calves, sometimes attacking them as early as the third or fourth day after birth, although in severe outbreaks mature animals may become affected. The mortality from the disease is very high. Calf diphtheria is also known as necrotic stomatitis, gangrenous stomatitis, ulcerative stomatitis, necrotic laryngitis, malignant stomatitis, and sore mouth.

The disease is caused by a specific organism, *Actinomyces necrophorus*, which is widespread in nature. The organism is strictly anaerobic; that is, it grows only in the absence of oxygen. It gains entrance through wounds in the mucous membrane, or lining, of the mouth. Such injuries are usually caused by sharp-pointed particles of food or other objects. Infection may also occur during the eruption of the first teeth after birth. The parts of the mouth most often affected at the beginning of the disease are the base or sides of the tongue, the inside of the cheeks adjacent to the molar teeth, and the lips. If the infection persists, however, the lesions, or tissue injuries, may spread to the hard palate, the gums, the pharynx, the nasal passages, the trachea (windpipe), and the lungs.

Occasionally only one or two animals in a herd may be affected, but in other instances as many as 70 percent may show evidence of the disease.

The first symptoms appear 3 to 5 days after the causative organism gains entrance to the tissues. The affected animal appears depressed, and even suckling calves will refuse feed. Drooling of saliva and swallowing movements may be noted. At times a swelling may be observed on the side of the cheek or in the region of the throat. The animal becomes weak and loses flesh rapidly. Where the lesions have become extensive, involving the larynx and nasal passages, there are wheezing, coughing, and labored breathing. A sticky, yellowish to greenish-yellow discharge from the nostrils may also be noticed. At this stage of the disease the animal is greatly depressed, extremely weak, and emaciated, and lies down continuously. Slobbering is profuse, and the tongue is swollen and sometimes protrudes from the mouth, which has a very offensive odor.

Soon after gaining entrance to the tissues of the mouth, the causative organism multiplies rapidly, and a poisonous substance, or toxin, is elaborated. This toxin destroys the invaded tissues, resulting in extensive ulceration of the mucous lining of the mouth cavity. In the mouth of an affected animal there may be one or more ulcers on the mucosa of the cheek, on the base of the tongue, or along the sides of the tongue. The destroyed tissue has a grayish-yellow appearance, and around the borders of the ulcer the tissue will be slightly raised, reddened, and granulated in appearance. An exudation, or discharge, of albuminous material from the ulcerated areas combines with the dead cellular elements to form a fibrinous mass, or membrane, than gradually becomes dry, friable (crumbly), and cheesy. This degenerated tissue sticks tightly and can be scraped or peeled off only with difficulty.

As the disease process spreads, the lesions may involve the deeper tissue structures to a depth of an inch or more. Usually in these cases, there is no tendency toward spontaneous healing, and the untreated lesions continue to spread and involve very large areas of the mouth, tongue, larynx (upper part of the windpipe), pharynx, and nasal cavities. In cases of long standing the infection becomes more or less generalized, and lesions may be found in the lungs, stomach, intestines, and liver. In the very acute form of the disease, the animal may die within a week. The cause of death is toxemia, or blood poisoning, resulting from the infection rather than the local effects of the disease. In less acute outbreaks, affected animals may live a number of weeks and show extensive lesions.

In mild cases, if the sick animals are given prompt attention in the early stages, treatment may bring about recovery. On the other hand, in the highly virulent outbreaks in which there is extensive involvment of the tissues, treatment is of little avail.

Prevention is of the greatest importance and consists in segregating the sick from the healthy animals, thoroughly cleaning and disinfecting the stables and sheds, and carefully examining the healthy animals each day for immediate detection of new cases, which should be, isolated as soon as they are found.

Treatment consists in removing the dead tissue from the affected areas and painting the ulcerated surfaces with appropriate medicinal agents, such as a 5-percent solution of potassium permanganate or tincture of iodine. The mouth of an affected calf should be washed frequently with warm water. The strength of the animal should be maintained by feeding nutritious food, such as eggs and milk. As in other serious animal diseases, it is advisable to obtain the services of a veterinarian and follow his directions regarding preventive measures and treatment.

PNEUMONIA

Pneumonia is an inflammation of the lungs in which the air sacs fill up with an inflammatory exudate or discharge. As a result, parts of the lung tissue become solidified and airless. The general character and extent of the pneumonia lesions, or injuries to the tissue, depend largely on the cause and the particular type of pneumonia in individual cases.

Pneumonia may be caused by specific infections, by certain environmental conditions, such as chilling due to exposure, which reduces the defensive forces of the body against disease, or by the presence of parasites. Pneumonia caused by parasitism, however, is very rare in cattle. The presence of foreign material in the lungs also may cause what is called mechanical pneumonia; this may, for example, follow treatment by drenching for some other disease.

In any one of its various forms, pneumonia usually progresses through several stages, terminating either in recovery or in the death of the animal.

As a primary disease, pneumonia usually follows chilling caused by exposure to cold winds and rain or to cold, damp quarters. Calves readily contract the disease when exposed directly to drafts when indoors. Overcrowding of young animals in quarters where the air becomes foul, followed by exposure to outside conditions, is also thought to cause pneumonia. When pneumonia is caused by specific types of infection, it is generally a secondary condition accompanying some other disease. It occurs as one of the symptoms of a number of specific diseases of cattle.

Pneumonia is usually characterized in the beginning by dullness, lack of appetite, high temperature, which may reach 107° F., rapid and shallow respiration, and dilated nostrils. The pulse is strong and hard, becoming more rapid as the disease progresses. A cough may or may not be present in the early stages. The muzzle is hot and dry. The coat is usually rough and the skin rather dry. Constipation may or may not be present, but usually, as the disease progresses, diarrhea occurs. The animal assumes positions that facilitate easier breathing; it may stand with the forefeet spread apart, for example, or rest on the sternum when lying down.

On close examination, sounds may be heard over the chest wall, varying from a slight wheezing noise to a gurgling or splashing sound, depending on the stage to which the disease has developed and also on the amount of lung tissue involved. A discharge from the nostrils may be present, varying from a small quantity of clear fluid to a large amount of sticky, pale yellow material. The course of the disease is variable. Death may follow within a few days after the onset of symptoms, recovery may occur in an equally short time, or the disease may become chronic and persist for several weeks.

In the diagnosis of pneumonia, a history of drenching for some other condition would be strongly indicative of the mechanical type. When only one animal in a herd is affected and there is no suspicion of a contagious or infectious disease, the primary type of pneumonia, as from exposure, would be suspected.

In the treatment of pneumonia, good hygienic surroundings, protection from drafts, wind, and rain, and other provisions for the comfort of the animal are essential. When the animal is on the road to recovery, palatable, easily digested foods in small amounts should be given frequently. Medicinal treatment consists in giving various tonics and stimulants. The application of counterirritants, such as mustard plasters, is practiced by many. No specific treatment in the form of sera and vaccines, as in the case of human pneumonia, has been developed, though the administration of specific antisera may be beneficial if the pneumonia is secondary to some specific infectious disease for which the specific antiserum is available. There are reports of very beneficial results in pneumonic conditions from the use of large injections of blood from normal cattle. In recent years considerable experimental work has been done in the treatment of pneumonia with the sulfonamide drugs. Although some encouraging results have been reported, further studies must be carried out before specific recommendations regarding the use of these drugs can be made.

Since pneumonia is encountered in so many forms and stages, the proper treatment of the disease is a problem for the trained veterinarian.

CHOKE

Choke in cattle is caused by an attempt to swallow large objects without thoroughly chewing them. Swallowing food without completely chewing it is characteristic of cattle. Such food materials as ears of corn, beets, apples, turnips, pieces of cabbage or cabbage stumps, and potatoes, are the principal causes of choke. Foreign bodies, such as balls, pieces of metal, glass, and even table forks, have been found to be responsible for choke. Some animals, however, may have certain defects or alterations of the normal structure of the esophagus or gullet, such as a narrowing or constriction at some point, and when such an animal is hungry and eats greedily, even soft foods like meal, bran, or pulp may become lodged in the esophagus and cause choke.

The object swallowed that causes choke may be located either in the neck or in the chest portion of the esophagus, and it may or may not be large enough to completely obstruct the passage of water to the stomach and air to the lungs. The symptoms and the gravity of the condition depend largely on the character, size, and location of the obstruction. Generally, the first symptoms observed are restlessness, salivation, retching, forced swallowing movements, and coughing. The animal will not attempt to eat or drink, particularly if the obstruction is lodged in the part of the gullet in the region of the neck. Bloating will occur eventually, adding to the discomfort of the animal. If the offending object is located in the chest portion of the esophagus or if it is small enough in size to allow passage of gas and air, the early symptoms may not be particularly alarming, and the animal may even try to eat or drink. The food is promptly regurgitated, and coughing and retching follow.

Treatment to remove the obstruction will depend on its location, size, and character. If the object is an article of food lodged in the neck portion of the esophagus, it should be forced upward as gently as possible to the pharynx, at the back of the mouth cavity, by placing a hand on either side of the neck, along the jugular furrow, and pressing upward against the object. When it reaches the pharynx it can be removed by the hand through the animal's mouth.

If the object is in the chest portion of the esophagus, its removal will require a different procedure. The use of a stomach tube with a slender rod called a probang inserted at the end has proved quite efficient for this purpose. The tube, which is flexible and one-half to 1 inch in diameter, with an aperture for the insertion of the wooden probang, will follow the natural curvature of the neck. It should first be lubricated with linseed oil or some other harmless oil, then carefully inserted through the mouth into the esophagus, and gently pushed downward until the obstruction is encountered. Firm but gentle continuous pressure is then applied. If it is impossible to push the object on into the rumen, or first stomach, by this method, operative procedure, requiring the services of a veterinarian, may be necessary.

A doubled-wire loop, sufficiently heavy or stiff to allow manipulation, is frequently used by veterinarians in removing foreign objects from the esophagus of cattle, regardless of the location.

Rough procedures, such as pushing too hard with the tube and probang or trying to crush an object such as an apple or beet between blocks of wood or bricks, are to be avoided, since there is danger of causing serious injury to the tissues of the throat that may result in the death of the animal. When there is bloating or distension of the rumen with gas, it may be necessary to alleviate this condition before attempting to remove the obstruction from the esophagus. Sometimes it is possible to pass the tube with the probang inserted past the object and into the rumen. The probang is then withdrawn, permitting quantities of gas to escape and relieving the condition. In other cases it may be necessary to insert a trochar, or surgical probe, through the abdominal wall in order to bring about relief.

The symptoms of choke in most cases are quite alarming, but sudden death seldom occurs. The object may sometimes become dislodged in 1 to 2 days without mechanical assistance of any kind. During this time, of course, bloat develops and must necessarily be relieved occasionally. In the case of a valuable animal, the assistance of a veterinarian should be obtained promptly.

LITERATURE CITED

(1) BARDENS, G. W.
    1938. TREATMENT OF INFECTIOUS KERATITIS WITH MERCUROCHROME. Amer. Vet. Med. Assoc. Jour. 93 : 35–36.
(2) BENGSTON, JOHN S.
    1938. PRIMARY RETICULUM CELL SARCOMA OF THE LYMPH NODES OF A COW WITH WIDESPREAD METASTASES. Amer. Jour. Path. 14: 365–376.
(3) CREECH, G. T.
    1935. PRIMARY ACTINOMYCOSIS OF THE PERITONEUM OF YOUNG CALVES. Bur. Vet. 11 (4) : [1]–2, illus.

(4) CREECH, G. T., and BUNYEA, HUBERT.
1929. EXPERIMENTAL STUDIES OF BOVINE LEUKEMIA. Jour. Agr. Res. 38: 395–404, illus.
(5) —— and MILLER, F. W.
1933. NASAL GRANULOMA IN CATTLE. Vet. Med. 28 : 279–284, illus.
(6) DIKMANS, G.
1934. NASAL GRANULOMA IN CATTLE IN LOUISIANA. North Amer. Vet. 15 (9) : 20–24, illus.
(7) FELDMAN, WILLIAM HUGH.
1932. NEOPLASMS OF DOMESTICATED ANIMALS. 410 pp., illus. Philadelphia and London.
(8) KALKUS, J. W.
1920. A STUDY OF GOITRE AND ASSOCIATED CONDITIONS IN DOMESTIC ANIMALS. Wash. Agr. Expt. Sta. Bul. 156, 48 pp., illus.
(9) KANSAS AGRICULTURAL EXPERIMENT STATION.
1938. FEEDER CATTLE INVESTIGATIONS. Kans. Agr. Expt. Sta. Bien. Rpt. (1936–38) 9 : 113–114.
(10) MORRILL, C. C., and GRAHAM, ROBERT.
1941. AN OUTBREAK OF BOVINE PSEUDORABIES, OR MAD ITCH. Amer. Jour. Vet. Res. 2 (2) : 35–40, illus.
(11) MURRAY, CHAS.
1933. MAD ITCH. Cornell Vet. 23 : 303–305, illus.
(12) ROSSING, T. E.
1936. A CASE OF PSEUDO RABIES (MAD ITCH). Fort Dodge Bio-chemic Rev. 7 (3) : 20–21, illus.
(13) SHOPE, RICHARD E.
1931. AN EXPERIMENTAL STUDY OF "MAD ITCH," WITH ESPECIAL REFERENCE TO ITS RELATIONSHIP TO PSEUDORABIES. Jour. Expt. Med. 54 : 233–248.

Cattle Coccidiosis

BY DONALD C. BOUGHTON [1]

AN INFECTIOUS intestinal disease caused by a minute parasite, coccidiosis sometimes causes heavy losses among calves. An uninfected calf is the exception rather than the rule, because carriers of the disease are everywhere. There is no cure, but careful management and sanitation can go a long way toward prevention.

BOVINE COCCIDIOSIS is an infectious disease of cattle, known in its spectacular form as bloody scours or red diarrhea because of the characteristic bloody fecal discharges seen in severe cases. The disease is of economic importance in many parts of the world, including the United States. (*1, 12, 15*).[2] To the outright loss from fatal infections, which may take a heavy toll among calves, must be added the no less significant loss from retarded growth and general unthriftiness among survivors of nonfatal infections, many of which go undiagnosed because marked clinical symptoms are lacking.

NATURE OF THE DISEASE

Coccidiosis is essentially intestinal malaria. The microscopic, one-celled animal parasites, called coccidia, that cause it are close relatives of malaria organisms. As in malaria, a knowledge of the two-phase life cycle of the parasites is of fundamental importance. Whereas the malaria parasites utilize the blood cells, the coccidia invade the intestinal lining of their victim. The injury to the host occurs during this phase of the coccidian life cycle. After a period of multiplication within the intestinal tissues, coccidia produce resistant forms, known as oöcysts, which are discharged in the feces. Outside the animal they live a nonparasitic existence until picked up by a new

[1] Donald C. Boughton is Associate Protozoologist, Regional Animal Disease Research Laboratory, Auburn, Ala., Bureau of Animal Industry.
[2] Italic numbers in parentheses refer to Literature Cited, p. 570.

victim. This second phase is obviously responsible for the transmission of the disease. Malaria parasites, on the other hand, are trapped in the blood stream and require the aid of a mosquito to make the transfer from one host to another.

A significant feature of bovine coccidiosis is that the massive multiplication of the parasites within the host does not continue indefinitely but is culminated rather abruptly with the discharge of large numbers of oöcysts. Following natural exposure or experimental inoculation, the oöcysts appear in the dung in from 1 to 3 weeks, depending on the species of coccidia involved. Reproduction of the parasites appears to be self-limited (*14*). Possibly the length of the multiplication period may be affected by host reaction (*15*). In any event, at least two points of practical significance depend upon this limitation on multiplication. In the first place, infection is often of short duration and recovery consequently spontaneous. Claims for successful treatment must be judged in the light of this fact. Second, the final number of coccidia within the host's tissues at the end of the multiplication period is likely to be smaller if only a few infective oöcysts were ingested. Other things being equal, small numbers of coccidia produce less damage than large numbers. The severity of an infection, therefore, depends on the number of parasites introduced into the intestinal lining.

Acute outbreaks of bovine coccidiosis often appear where young animals are crowded together. This is in line with the general observation that coccidiosis becomes of economic importance wherever mass production of animals involves crowding of the host population (*14*). Groups of calves confined in small lots are more often heavily infected than calves on pasture. Acute infections may appear among yearlings confined in feed lots at the end of the grazing season. Two factors are generally held to be responsible for outbreaks when young or previously unexposed older animals are confined in close quarters: (1) Such animals have less resistance than those that have already experienced infection, and (2) they are exposed to a relatively high concentration of parasites.

INJURIES PRODUCED AND SYMPTOMS

The injuries produced by coccidiosis in cattle result directly or indirectly from massive multiplication (asexual reproduction) of coccidia within the linings of the small intestine, cecum, colon, or rectum. Resulting gross lesions include: (1) Loss of surface epithelium, or lining membrane; (2) thickening of the mucous membrane, with the formation of irregular, whitish ridges; and (3) hemorrhages, which may be petechial—of pinpoint size—in mild cases and diffuse in acute cases. Catarrhal enteritis (intestinal inflammation) is often present in both the small and the large intestines.

Symptoms associated with this condition are bloody diarrhea, anemia, weakness, and general emaciation. Severe straining accompanies the voiding of feces, which may consist primarily of stringy masses of mucus and blood. Secondary bacterial infection—another disease coming on top of the first one—is a common sequel. Pneumonia often develops. An animal that does not die within a week or two after the onset of an acute attack may be expected to recover rather promptly from the diarrhea and improve gradually in general condition.

Calves, often during the second month of life, may suffer from rather severe but nonfatal coccidial infections which fail to produce marked symptoms. There is a more or less persistent nonbloody diarrhea, which has often been mistaken for a prolongation of white scours. Affected animals are unthrifty and often fail to make normal gains in weight.

TRANSMISSION

The ultimate source of the parasites causing bovine coccidiosis is an infected bovine host. Formerly it was thought that all coccidia found in the various domestic and wild animals belonged to the same species. Sparrows, for example, were accused (*8*), falsely, as it was shown later (*4*), of harboring poultry coccidia. Cross-infection experiments, however, have proved that with a few exceptions the different coccidia are specific to their own hosts. None of the species of cattle coccidia tested have been found to infect other animals, such as rabbits, sheep, goats, swine, guinea pigs, rats, mice, and chickens (*7, 15, 18*). Coccidial infections of nonbovine origin have not been demonstrated in cattle, which are undoubtedly exposed while grazing to coccidia of various invertebrate, avian, and mammalian hosts.

Coccidial infection in cattle that do not show clinical symptoms is common. Surveys of wild and domesticated animals have revealed high percentages of infected individuals (*2, 3, 9, 10, 11, 12*). As a matter of fact, an uninfected calf is the exception rather than the rule. Although special concentration techniques may be required to discover the coccidia, they can often be found in healthy adult cattle, and the actual number of oöcysts discharged during a given period, say a month, is enormous. Such healthy animals harboring the organisms are known as carriers of coccidiosis. The carrier state probably involves repeated infection and, possibly to a limited extent, the prolongation of low-grade parasite reproduction following an attack. Second and subsequent infections, under ordinary management practices, are usually milder than first infections, presumably because resistance is increased and exposure is reduced. Carriers are a constant source of oöcysts.

Bovine coccidiosis is transmitted by means of the infective oöcysts, which, as already pointed out, must be of bovine origin. Following the parasitic phase within the host, undeveloped oöcysts are discharged in the feces. Large numbers are characteristic of severe, nonfatal infections; small numbers may be discharged by carriers, presumably as the result of mild reinfection with the same species or new infections with different species. The majority of the oöcysts from a single infection may often be eliminated in the short period of 3 to 6 days.

Before an oöcyst becomes infective, the living material within the cyst wall must undergo a development (sporulation) which requires 2 to 6 days under the most favorable conditions of oxygen and moisture (*3, 15, 16*). This is a vulnerable period in the coccidian life cycle during which sanitary measures can operate successfully. If manure were removed daily, the freshly passed oöcysts would not have time to become infective. Oöcysts are resistant and can remain alive for several months in fecal material in a barn or pasture. Large numbers are often plastered on the coat of a calf befouled with manure, where they are readily accessible to the calf's tongue. Oöcysts can be destroyed by drying and by strong disinfectants. Strong solutions of lye or bichloride of mercury are effective when applied to walls and floors by means of a stiff brush. When an infective oöcyst is ingested by a susceptible calf, the cyst wall is digested, releasing eight small forms (sporozoites) within. The latter penetrate the cells of the lining membrane of the digestive tract, where they begin parasitic multiplication.

SPECIES OF COCCIDIA INVOLVED

There are at least 10 species of bovine coccidia (*3, 13*). This fact complicates and at the same time helps to clarify studies on bovine coccidiosis; generalizations regarding the disease must be qualified and conflicting observations interpreted on the basis of the individual species involved. It is believed that all the species belong to the genus *Eimeria*, the report of a bovine *Isospora* (*5*) not having been verified. At present, species differentiation is based on the following traits: (1) Characteristics of the oöcyst, such as size, shape, color, micropyle, residual body; (2) structure of sporocysts; (3) sporulation time; (4) specific immunities developed; and (5) length of time between inoculation and appearance of oöcysts. The following species are recognized at present: *E. alabamensis*, *E. auburnensis*, *E. bovis*, *E. brasiliensis*, *E. bukidnonensis*, *E. canadensis*, *E. cylindrica*, *E. ellipsoidalis*, *E. subspherica*, *E. zürnii*. Description of tissue stages and the relative pathological significance of individual species await further investigation. There is evidence, however, which indicates that certain species, notably *E. zürnii*, *E. ellipsoidalis*, and *E. bovis*, are of greater economic importance than the others (*1, 3, 15*, and unpublished data).

CONTROL AND TREATMENT

Control of coccidial infection and prevention of clinical coccidiosis are based upon two fundamental facts—(1) coccidiosis carriers are universally present, and (2) excessive exposure to coccidia is particularly harmful to young stock. Sanitary measures and management practices must be designed to prevent young calves from ingesting large numbers of infective oöcysts.

A very common serious mistake is to introduce young calves directly into a group of calves of various ages confined in close quarters. Such conditions are ideal for producing severe infections, as the following typical chain of events indicates: Since coccidia, distributed by carriers, are universally present, the first few calves in a given lot are bound to pick up a few stray oöcysts. As a result, these calves develop nonclinical infections and discharge large numbers of oöcysts. Calves subsequently added to the group are exposed to increasingly large numbers of oöcysts, and their infections and discharges, in turn, raise the parasite population to a dangerous level.

Isolation of young dairy calves, as in individual box stalls, does much to prevent heavy infections. Daily removal of manure and wet, contaminated bedding is important. Precautions must be taken to avoid the introduction of fecal material from other places by the shoes of the caretaker, for example, at feeding time. The use of individual milk pails, cleaned thoroughly between feedings, is advantageous. Calves up to 6 weeks of age should not be removed from their stalls, even during the short period required for cleaning, unless special care is taken to prevent contact with other cattle and unsterilized objects.

Where isolation of dairy calves is impractical and the quarters are not cleaned daily, segregation of calves by ages is helpful. For example, separate pens for different age groups may be provided as follows: (1) For calves under 3 weeks old, (2) for calves 3 to 6 weeks old, (3) for calves 6 weeks to 3 months old, and (4) for calves over 3 months old. The two youngest groups require particular attention. The upper age limit of the third group is chosen more for convenience in caring for the animals than for any practical advantage in reducing coccidial infection.

The first pen, shed, or lot, assigned to the youngest group, is used exclusively for these animals, calves of all other ages being excluded at all times. Upon reaching the 3-week age limit, all calves are removed promptly from the first pen and placed in the second pen. Because oöcysts are rarely discharged by calves under 3 weeks of age, the first pen can be kept free from large numbers of oöcysts. Newborn calves subsequently introduced are spared severe infections, which have serious consequences in very young animals, and are given an opportunity to gain in bodily vigor and to begin normal growth before being exposed to the older animals in the second pen. Nonclinical infections may be expected to develop in the first few calves introduced into the second pen; the short stay here is designed to prevent the excessive accumulation of infective oöcysts which might otherwise take place as the calves subsequently introduced become infected.

It goes without saying that sanitary measures are not to be abandoned upon the adoption of some such age-segregation plan. It is profitable to go to some pains to protect calves against severe coccidiosis in the early weeks of life, inasmuch as thereafter they are usually able to withstand the coccidial infections to which they will almost certainly be subjected.

Where large herds of beef or dairy stock are fed outdoors, the wet, muddy ground around haystacks, feed sheds, and watering troughs presents a special problem. Low spots should be filled in and proper drainage provided so as to permit the ground to dry out from time to time. Manure should be picked up daily if practicable. If contamination proves to be excessive, a change of feeding place is indicated.

Treatment is entirely for the relief of symptoms and includes the judicious administration of astringents and intestinal antiseptics and measures designed to prevent reinfection and maintain bodily vigor. A specific drug for bovine coccidiosis is not known. The beneficial results claimed for various types of drug treatments that have been employed from time to time (*6, 17*) may often be due in reality to spontaneous cure under favorable hygienic conditions. Recent experiments made by the writer with sulfaguanidine, however, suggest that this drug holds promise for the future.

LITERATURE CITED

(1) BECKER, ELERY R.
    1934. COCCIDIA AND COCCIDIOSIS OF DOMESTICATED, GAME AND LABORATORY ANIMALS AND OF MAN. 147 pp., illus. Ames, Iowa. (Iowa State Col., Div. of Indus. Sci., Monog. 2.)
(2) BOUGHTON, DONALD C.
    1937. NOTES ON AVIAN COCCIDIOSIS. Auk 54: 500–509, illus.
(3) CHRISTENSEN, JOHN F.
    1941. THE OÖCYSTS OF COCCIDIA FROM DOMESTIC CATTLE IN ALABAMA (U. S. A.), WITH DESCRIPTIONS OF TWO NEW SPECIES. Jour. Parasitol. 27: 203–220, illus.
(4) CLELAND, J. B.
    1914. INTESTINAL COCCIDIOSIS IN HOUSE SPARROWS (PASSER DOMESTICUS) IN NEW SOUTH WALES. *In* 3d Rpt. Govt. Bur. of Microbiol., New South Wales (1912), p. 134.
(5) COOPER, HUGH, and GULATI, AMARNATH.
    1926. ON THE OCCURRENCE OF ISOSPORA AND BALANTIDIUM IN CATTLE. India Dept. Agr. Mem., Vet. Ser., 3: 191–193, illus.
(6) FRANK, E. R.
    1926. COCCIDIOSIS IN FEEDER CATTLE. Amer. Vet. Med. Assoc. Jour. 69: 729–733.
(7) GUILLEBEAU, A.
    1893. UEBER DAS VORKOMMEN VON COCCIDIUM OVIFORME BEI DER ROTEN RUHR DES RINDES. (Referat) Zentbl. f. Bakt. [etc.] Originale (I) 14: 467–468.
(8) HADLEY, PHILIP B.
    1910. STUDIES IN AVIAN COCCIDIOSIS. III. COCCIDIOSIS IN THE ENGLISH SPARROW AND OTHER WILD BIRDS. Zentbl. f. Bakt. [etc.] Originale (I) 56: 522–523.
(9) MARSH, HADLEIGH.
    1938. HEALTHY CATTLE AS CARRIERS OF COCCIDIA. Amer. Vet. Med. Assoc. Jour. (n. s. 45) 92 (2): 184–194, illus.
(10) ROBERTSON, ANDREW.
    1931. COCCIDIOSIS IN CALVES. Vet. Jour. 87: 312–325; 351–385, illus.
(11) SKIDMORE, LOUIS V.
    1933. BOVINE COCCIDIA CARRIERS. (Abstract) Jour. Parasitol. 20: 126.
(12) SMITH, THEOBALD, and GRAYBILL, H. W.
    1918. COCCIDIOSIS IN YOUNG CALVES. Jour. Expt. Med. 28: 89–108, illus.
(13) TORRES, SILVIO, and RAMOS, J. ILDEFONSO.
    1939. EIMERIAS DOS BOVINOS EM PERNAMBUCO. Arquivos do Inst. de Pesquisas Agronomicas 2: [79]–96, illus.
(14) TYZZER, ERNEST EDWARD.
    1929. COCCIDIOSIS IN GALLINACEOUS BIRDS. Amer. Jour. Hyg. 10: 269–383, illus.
(15) WILSON, IRE DONAKER.
    1931. STUDY OF BOVINE COCCIDIOSIS. Va. Agr. Expt. Sta., Tech. Bul. 42, 42 pp., illus.

(16) WILSON, IRE DONAKER, and MORLEY, L. C.
  1933. STUDY OF BOVINE COCCIDIOSIS. Amer. Vet. Med. Assoc. Jour. 82:
    826–850.
(17) YAKIMOFF, W. L.
  1927. LE TRAITEMENT DE LA COCCIDIOSE DES BOVIDÉS PAR L'ICHTHARGAN.
    Soc. de Path. Exot. Bul. 20: 588–589.
(18) ——— and GALOUZO, J. G.
  1927. ZUR FRAGE ÜBER RINDERCOCCIDIEN. Arch. f. Protistenk. 58: 185–200,
    illus.

Cattle Tick Fever

BY W. M. MAC KELLAR [1]

"THE FIGHT to eliminate the cattle fever tick from the United States is probably the most extensive and sustained campaign ever made on any of man's parasitic enemies." Today 99 percent of the formerly infested area has been freed; the once appalling losses have been practically eliminated.

In 1906 a concerted effort to eradicate the cattle fever tick from the United States was begun. At that time and for more than a century before, this infectious disease of cattle and the parasite that transmits it were the most serious obstacles faced by the cattle industry in 15 Southern and Southwestern States the combined area of which constitutes nearly one-fourth of the United States. Conservative estimates in the early 1900's placed the losses directly and indirectly chargeable to this plague at $40,000,000 annually.

At different times and places the disease has been known by many different names. The one by which it has been best known in the United States is "Texas fever," but this name is misleading because it gives the wholly erroneous impression that the disease originated in Texas or that it is confined to that State. It has also been known as red water, black water, southern cattle fever, acclimation fever, murrain, bloody murrain, Mexican fever, Spanish fever, splenic or splenetic fever, hemaglobinuria, bovine piroplasmosis, and bovine malaria. Since in natural infection the disease is transmitted by one means only, the bite of the cattle fever tick (*Boophilus annulatus*), "cattle tick fever" would seem to describe it best, and this is the name now in general use in the United States.

SYMPTOMS

Cattle tick fever is a specific infectious disease of the blood of cattle, caused by the development and activity of minute animal parasites

---

[1] W. M. MacKellar is Principal Veterinarian and Chief, Division of Tick Eradication and Special Diseases, Bureau of Animal Industry.

known as piroplasms, which are conveyed to the animals by the cattle fever tick. The disease is characterized by high fever, destruction of red corpuscles, enlarged spleen, engorged liver, thick flaky bile, more or less jaundice, emaciation, and death in 10 percent of the chronic to 90 per cent of the acute cases. A peculiarity of the disease is 'that the animals responsible for its spread are apparently healthy, while those that become diseased do not as a rule convey the infection to others.

A NOTABLE DISCOVERY IN MEDICAL SCIENCE

Just when or where cattle tick fever first made its appearance in the United States is not known. The generally accepted theory is that it was introduced into the West Indies and Mexico during the Spanish colonization of those countries and from there reached the southern part of the United States. What seems to be the earliest report in this country of a disease which was undoubtedly cattle tick fever was made in 1796; in August of that year there was an outbreak of a cattle disease in Lancaster County, Pa., which was attributed to a drove of cattle previously brought from South Carolina. In every instance in which these southern cattle mingled with native cattle the disease was contracted by the latter, and in one instance it was supposed to have been caused by merely placing Pennsylvania cattle on ground where the southern cattle had been penned. It was also noted that outbreaks of this strange malady invariably occurred in summer and would disappear with the first heavy frost, and that the southern cattle apparently responsible for spreading the disease seemed to be in perfect health.

About the middle of the nineteenth century similar accounts of this trouble in the West and Southwest began to be heard. This was the period of the great trail movement of cattle from Texas to the stock-raising sections of the West, and because of the enormous losses that followed in the wake of these overland movements the name of Texas became linked with the malady. Laws and regulations aimed at controlling these movements and preventing the spread of the disease were enacted by several States, but notwithstanding these local efforts the borderline of the infected area continued to advance northward. This finally led to the conclusion that the problem was of national interest, and that if the cattle industry of the North was to be protected it would be necessary for the Federal Government to establish control measures dividing the infected areas from the free areas and regulating the movement of all cattle from the areas where the disease existed.

With this in view, in 1883 a survey was undertaken in an effort to locate the northern limits of the infection, and on July 3, 1889, by order of the Secretary of Agriculture, the first national quarantine order establishing a Federal quarantine line and controlling the movement of southern cattle was issued. This quarantine and the strict enforcement of regulations to permit the shipment of southern cattle to northern markets for immediate slaughter only and under special quarantine restrictions proved quite effective in checking the spread of the disease but did little to improve conditions in the quarantine area.

During this time many scientists were conducting investigations in an effort to solve the baffling problems presented by the disease, and in 1889 investigators of the Bureau of Animal Industry had the distinction of being the first to recognize and describe as protozoa the intracellular parasites that are the direct causative agents.

Some observing cattlemen of the West had for a long time advanced the theory that Texas fever was caused by ticks, which were carried to and scattered on the northern pastures by southern cattle. Others ridiculed this theory. The Bureau of Animal Industry decided to investigate it, and the conclusive experiments conducted by its scientists Dr. Theobald Smith and Dr. Fred L. Kilborne in 1889 and 1890 established the fact that cattle tick infestation was necessary in the transmission of the disease. They thus showed irrefutably and for the first time that an infectious disease could be transmitted by an intermediate host or carrier from one animal to another. About that time Dr. Cooper Curtice, also of the Bureau of Animal Industry, made noteworthy contributions to knowledge of this subject by his studies and description of the life history of the cattle tick. This pioneer work opened a new field in medical science and pointed the way for studies that later solved the problems of the spread of such diseases as malaria, yellow fever, Rocky Mountain spotted fever, typhus, and others.

THE TICK-ERADICATION CAMPAIGN

There are in the United States two varieties of the cattle fever tick which are responsible for the spread of tick fever—the North American fever tick (*Boophilus annulatus*), which formerly infested most of the quarantined area, and the tropical variety of the same tick, *Boophilus annulatus* var. *microplus*, found in Florida, Puerto Rico, and areas adjacent to the Gulf coast. This tropical variety has frequently been taken from deer, and its ability to perpetuate itself on these wild animals has greatly complicated the eradication problem and delayed completion of tick eradication in some of the large swampy areas of Florida.

Without the tick the disease is of little importance and would probably die out. Recognition of this fact naturally led to investigation as to the feasibility of tick eradication, and this resulted in 1906 in the inauguration of a campaign to eliminate cattle ticks from the United States. This work, in which State officials, livestock owners, and the Bureau of Animal Industry have cooperated, has continued to the present time. When the cooperative project was undertaken, 985 counties in 15 Southern and Southwestern States were under Federal quarantine because of tick infestation (fig. 1). By December 15, 1940, the tick-eradication campaign had reduced this area to 2 quarantined counties in Florida, where the presence of tick-infested deer has delayed completion of the work, and to parts of 8 counties adjacent to the Rio Grande in Texas, where infestation continues to filter in on stray and smuggled animals from Mexico.

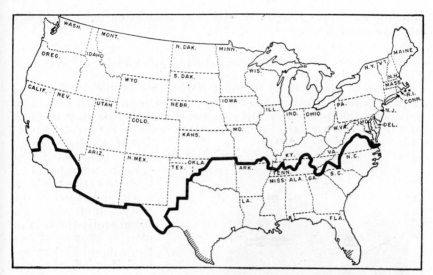

FIGURE 1.—The heavy black line shows the northern boundary of the tick-infested territory at the beginning of tick eradication in 1906. The shaded patches in Florida and Texas indicate the location of quarantined areas December 15, 1941.

Medicinal treatment of cattle sick with tick fever had usually been unsatisfactory, and it was generally believed in the United States that the disease and other losses chargeable to the tick could be satisfactorily and finally disposed of only by its complete elimination. Official work since 1906 has had that end in view. It was sometimes desirable, however, to ship well-bred cattle to infected districts in the South or to export them to tick-infested countries. These cattle, therefore, were immunized so that they could be introduced into the infected areas with comparatively little loss from the fever. Immunity was obtained by introducing the microparasite into the system by blood inoculation. It was found that young animals 6 to 15 months old best withstood this treatment and were more readily and completely immunized than older animals.

The eradication of the fever ticks is accomplished by killing them on the pastures and on the cattle. Pastures may be rendered tick-free by excluding all the host animals—cattle, horses, and mules—until all the ticks on the ground have died of starvation. The other and more common method is to let the cattle remain on the infested pastures and disinfect the animals at regular intervals, usually every 2 weeks, by dipping in an arsenical solution. This prevents the engorged female ticks from dropping to the ground alive and reinfesting the pastures. The seed ticks that are on the ground and those that hatch from eggs laid by females already there will get on the cattle from time to time and be destroyed by the dipping, while those that fail to find a host will starve to death. The length of time it will be necessary to continue the systematic dipping to insure eradication varies somewhat with the time of year the dipping starts and with the thoroughness of the work. The most satisfactory results have followed when dipping began in March and was continued at 14-day intervals until November.

LOSSES DUE DIRECTLY TO CATTLE TICKS

The cattle fever tick is of great importance as the only natural agent by which cattle tick fever is transmitted from animal to animal, and eradication of the tick will result in eliminating the disease. But even if this were not the case, the damage done by the tick as an external parasite would more than justify the trouble and expense of the eradication effort.

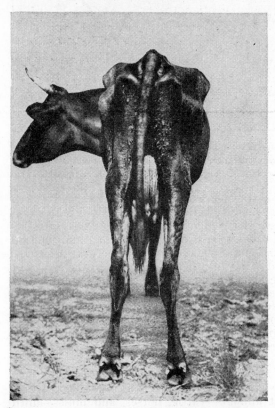

The only food of the cattle fever tick is blood, and the loss of the blood it takes from cattle in its rapid development impoverishes the animals (fig. 2). Heavy infestation means that cattle must have more feed merely to meet the demands of the parasites; the growth of young animals is retarded, and they may remain thin, weak, and stunted (fig. 3, *A*). In dairy cows, the milk flow is greatly reduced.

Since May 1, 1928, the interstate shipment of tick-infested cattle for any purpose has been prohibited. This has necessitated t h e trouble and expense of dipping the cattle and freeing them of ticks before s h i p m e n t. Formerly cattle coming from an infested district and sold in the

FIGURE 2.—A cow emaciated by heavy infestation with the cattle fever tick. This condition was once common in cattle throughout the South, but it is no longer seen in the United States.

"southern pens" at northern markets brought from ½ to 1½ cents a pound less than the quoted market prices. The cars used in shipping southern cattle had to be cleaned and disinfected, which added to the cost of transportation. The handicap placed on cattle raisers as a result of the decreased value of their stock averaged, at the figure quoted, from $3 to $9 a head, allowing an average weight of 600 pounds for all classes of cattle. This decreased value was re-

FIGURE 3.—*A*, A typical herd of ticky cattle; *B*, improved cattle in an area freed of ticks.

flected in the valuation of all cattle in the quarantined area, and the value of the infested ranges and pastures was also lowered, reducing the assets of the whole section. Tick infestation not only lessened the value of the live animals but caused their hides to be graded as of No. 4 quality. The same hide if free from ticks would grade No. 2, and the difference in price between these two grades is 3 to 5 cents a pound. Since a steer hide weighs about 42 pounds, the presence of ticks caused a loss in the hide alone of $1.25 to $2.10. The losses sustained by southern purchasers of northern purebred cattle with which to improve the native stock was another important item. About 10 percent of such cattle, even if immunized, would die of cattle tick fever, and 60 percent or more would succumb if they were not so treated.

THE GREATEST OF ALL CAMPAIGNS AGAINST PARASITES

The fight to eliminate the cattle fever tick from the United States is probably the most extensive and sustained attack ever made on any of man's parasitic enemies. It has resulted in freeing approximately 99 percent of the area formerly infested and has almost entirely eliminated the appalling losses once caused by the tick in the beef and dairy industries of the South. Death losses from tick fever have been practically eliminated. The last report of an outbreak of the disease was in August 1939. Special pens for southern cattle at northern market centers are a thing of the past; southern cattle now move to market or elsewhere without restrictions and compete on an equal basis with stock from other parts of the country (fig. 3, *B*). Purebred breeding animals for the improvement of native cattle may now be shipped to any part of the South without fear of loss from tick fever, and this has resulted in a marked improvement in recent years in the quality of southern cattle. The total cost to the cooperating State, county, and Federal Governments of eliminating this pest will amount to little more than the toll taken from the South in a single year by the cattle fever tick before eradication was undertaken.

Anaplasmosis:
A Disease of Cattle

BY GEORGE W. STILES [1]

ANAPLASMOSIS is a serious blood disease of cattle, and it is slowly spreading to new areas. Much has been found out about the ways in which it is transmitted, but a preventive or a cure is still to be discovered by research.

ANAPLASMOSIS was probably introduced into the United States by the Spaniards at the same time that splenic or cattle tick fever entered this country (*13*).[2] The disease, which is not transmissible to man, chiefly affects cattle, although the antelope, black wildebeest, blesbok, buffalo, camel, deer, duiker, elk, goat, and sheep are reported to be susceptible.

Mature cattle are more subject to infection than young animals. Although calves doubtless acquire mild cases, they are seldom observed to be sick or dying in anaplasmosis-infected herds. Cattle of all breeds may acquire the disease. Some immunity appears to develop in herds in which anaplasmosis has long been prevalent, but a few authentic cases have been reported of a second attack after a year in cows that have recovered.

Anaplasmosis is generally considered to be a tropical or semitropical disease, but it also occurs in localities that have low winter temperatures. It has been reported from Africa, Argentina, Brazil and several other South American countries, Cochin-China, France, Italy, Java, the Philippine Islands, the Union of Soviet Socialist Republics, and the Island of Taiwan.

In the United States the malady is known to exist in 23 States— Alabama, Arizona, Arkansas, California, Colorado, Delaware, Flor-

[1] George W. Stiles is Bacteriologist in Charge, Branch Pathological Laboratory, Denver, Colo., Bureau of Animal Industry.
[2] Italic numbers in parentheses refer to Literature Cited, p. 586.

579

ida, Georgia, Idaho, Kansas, Louisiana, Maryland, Mississippi, Missouri, Montana, Nevada, North Carolina, Ohio, Oklahoma, Oregon, Texas, Virginia, and Wyoming. It may be present but unrecognized in other States. It is slowly spreading to new areas.

The incidence of anaplasmosis seems to be influenced by climatic conditions favorable to insects and ticks that carry the infection. In the United States natural outbreaks usually occur during the summer and fall. Occasionally cases develop in winter in the South. On the Pacific coast the infection, carried by ticks, is common in winter and spring. The disease occurs more frequently in timbered or brushy wet areas than on dry treeless plains, where most species of ticks, horseflies, and mosquitoes are less abundant. Excessive rainfall, floods, irrigation ditches, and marshes provide favorable conditions for the propagation of insects and hence opportunities for the transmission of the disease.

NATURE AND SYMPTOMS OF THE DISEASE

Anaplasmosis is an infectious disease caused by a minute parasite which invades the red blood cells and destroys a large number of them, so that the blood becomes pale and watery. Under natural conditions the microparasite is carried from infected to healthy animals by ticks, horseflies, mosquitoes, and probably other biting insects, as well as by unclean surgical procedures. (An account of the results of research on the transmission of the disease is given at the end of this article.)

In 1910 Theiler (25), of South Africa, described the parasites that cause anaplasmosis as minute, specklike, protozoan bodies in the red cells of the blood and named them *Anaplasma marginale* because of their position near the margin of the cells. Theiler also observed a variety, *A. centrale*, centrally located in the cells and less virulent than the marginal type.[3]

Red blood cells may contain one to three, or even more, microparasites (fig. 1). Early in the course of anaplasmosis only a few of the blood cells contain the parasites, but as the disease progresses the temperature rises, ranging from 103° to 107° F. (normal range 100.5° to 102.5°) and the number of red cells involved rapidly increases. Later the temperature drops to normal and may even be subnormal at the time of death. In convalescent cases, the number of parasites lessens, but red cells containing fine granular bodies called stipple cells appear. Cells of this type also occur in other forms of anemia.

In typical cases the heart action is rapid and pounding, with a pulse rate of 70 to 140 a minute (normal range 40 to 70). In severe cases the red-cell blood count usually drops from a normal of

---

[3] Some workers claim that the causative agent is a type of filtrable virus notwithstanding the fact that filtered blood from sick animals fails to reproduce the disease. Dikmans (3) holds that the causative agent may be either a "reaction product," due to a virus, or a "parasite *sui generis*." Du Toit (4) says "It is difficult to ascertain why there has been so much reluctance to accept the parasitic theory of anaplasmosis. * * * If we take all the known facts about anaplasmosis into consideration, we come to' the conclusion that the simplest and most natural view to take is that this disease is caused by *Anaplasma marginale* and that this organism probably belongs to the Protozoa."

about 5 to 7 million per cubic millimeter of blood to 2 million or less. In normal cattle the hemoglobin or blood-color test is approximately 80 (Tallquist scale), whereas in sick animals a color test of 20 to 30 is not uncommon.

In an advanced case the breathing is labored and difficult and the muzzle is dry. There are marked depression, tremors of the muscles, loss of appetite, and a great reduction in the milk flow. The skin, teats, udder, vagina, whites of the eyes, and all visible membranes become pale and yellow. Pica, or depraved appetite, evi-

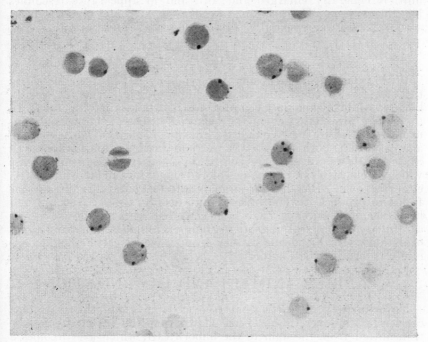

Figure 1.—Red blood cells from a field case of anaplasmosis. The black dots near the margins of the cells are *Anaplasma marginale.* × 1,200.

denced by the eating of bones or dirt, is not uncommon. Sick animals may show brain symptoms and an inclination to fight.

Dribbling urination is common in anaplasmosis, but the urine is not bloody or wine-colored. Sick cattle are usually constipated, and abortion often occurs in advanced pregnancy. Death may follow within 1 or several days after the clinical symptoms of the disease appear. Recovery is usually slow.

There is a wide range in the death rate of affected herds. Sometimes from out of a considerable number infected in a herd only one cow may die, but the average death rate usually varies from 25 to 60 percent of the infected animals. When microscopic examination of the blood from a sick cow shows that 40 to 60 percent of the red cells contain marginal bodies, it is probable that the animal will die; if the number of infected red cells is only 10 to 20 percent, it is more likely to recover.

On post mortem examination, cattle dead of anaplasmosis usually show a marked yellow discoloration of the skin, teats, and visible mucous membranes. Often the heart is flabby, and hemorrhagic blotches may appear on its surface. The blood is thin and watery, and the lungs are usually pale and filled with air bubbles. The liver is enlarged and jaundiced, and contents of the bile bladder are dark green, granular, and gelatinous in appearance. The spleen, or milt, is generally enlarged and soft, and in appearance resembles blackberry jam. The urine may be concentrated and slightly darkened. The bowels generally show a catarrhal condition.

DIAGNOSIS

Within quarantine areas anaplasmosis may be mistaken for cattle tick fever. In the latter disease, however, the urine is usually bloody, while in anaplasmosis discolored urine is not the rule. In the Rocky Mountain region the bacterial disease icterohemoglobinuria, described by Vawter and Records (27), may be confused with anaplasmosis; both diseases cause jaundice. In the Midwestern States cattle of all ages are subject to a fairly widespread disease which is characterized by wine-colored urine but about which little else is known. Blood from animals affected with this disease has failed to produce it when injected into healthy cows. Anthrax and hemorrhagic septicemia have been confused with anaplasmosis. A careful bacteriological and microscopic examination and animal inoculations with blood and tissues from infected cattle should definitely determine the diagnosis.

CARRIER ANIMALS AND IMMUNIZATION

Unfortunately all cattle that recover from anaplasmosis become carriers. Moreover, it has been shown that the infection may be transmitted from the dam to the unborn calf, which also becomes a carrier. At the Beltsville, Md., station the Bureau of Animal Industry has a cow that is still a proved carrier 13 years after recovery from anaplasmosis. When introduced into clean herds, such animals serve as sources of infection, particularly if ticks or other vectors are present.

In areas where the disease exists only in scattered herds it is prudent to fatten all animals that recover and ship them for slaughter, thus reducing the sources of new infection. In areas where the infection is widespread, involving many herds, the slaughter plan is not altogether practical. The sick animals are treated, and those that recover are kept in the herd. The owner should try, however, in every possible way, to prevent the spread of the disease by mechanical or other means.

In some foreign countries, a procedure known as premunition is used to make cattle resistant to anaplasmosis. A small dose of blood from a known carrier is inoculated into the susceptible animal, preferably at an early age (under 6 months) since calves do not react so severely as adult cattle. The vaccinated animals become immune but also become carriers, so that immunization by such vaccination is not recommended in the United States. A number of vaccines prepared by methods designed to destroy the infective agent have been used experimentally, but none have proved successful.

TREATMENT

The treatment of anaplasmosis is largely a veterinary problem, but the owner can give valuable assistance. Sick animals should be kept in the shade and given plenty of clean water, a little appetizing green feed, and protection against flies and mosquitoes. Good nursing is vital. Unnecessary or rough handling of sick cattle, especially range animals, may cause or hasten their death. In drenching cattle with salts, linseed oil, or other drugs, care should be taken to prevent the liquid from entering the lungs. Since cattle sick with anaplasmosis are usually constipated, mild saline purges are indicated. Animals that drink a great deal of water freely often recover; therefore, if affected animals do not drink water copiously, large quantities should be given by means of a stomach tube. When weakness develops, veterinarians often use hypodermic injections of camphor or strychnin.

Many drugs are used for the treatment of anaplasmosis. Among these, sodium cacodylate has its advocates, but its value has not been proved by controlled experiments. Injecting carrier cattle with a 10-percent solution of this drug in doses of 30 and 40 grains per 100 pounds of body weight was ineffective in freeing the animals of the microparasites (26). A modified sodium cacodylate treatment suggested by Boynton (2) consists in the intravenous injection of 1 liter of 5-percent dextrose in distilled water, to which has been added sufficient sodium cacodylate solution to make a dosage of 25 to 30 grains per 100 pounds of body weight. The cacodylate solution consisted of 4.5 grains of the drug per cubic centimeter of water. The required number of cubic centimeters of this solution was added immediately before injection.

Encouraging results from the intravenous injection of 2- to 4-percent mercurochrome have been reported by Dykstra and other veterinarians (5). A desirable mild purging action follows the use of this drug.

According to Koger (10) large quantities of whole citrated blood from healthy bovines injected intravenously seem to reduce the mortality, especially if given early in the course of the disease. (Citrated blood is blood drawn from a healthy animal into a sodium citrate solution which prevents coagulation and thus facilitates its injection.)

Continued efforts are being made to perfect some specific remedy with which to control and treat anaplasmosis.

DETAILS CONCERNING THE TRANSMISSION OF ANAPLASMOSIS

MECHANICAL SPREAD BY UNCLEAN SURGERY

During 15 years of field and laboratory experience with anaplasmosis in various parts of the United States, the writer (23) has learned of and diagnosed many cases of the disease in herds harboring carriers. The cases followed dehorning or other surgical procedures in which sanitary precautions were not observed.

In temperate climates dehorning and tipping (6, 12) are usually done during the cool months to escape screwworm or other fly infestations. Even then, many cases of anaplasmosis have developed following these operations, probably because appropriate precautions were not taken to disinfect instruments between operations.

That contaminated instruments and hypodermic needles can transmit anaplasmosis is supported by experiments by Rees (16), who spread the disease by lancet pricks. Sanborn, Stiles, and Moe (20) reproduced infection by injecting 0.025 cubic centimeter of blood from an acute case intradermically into a healthy cow. Anaplasmosis may be transmitted from carrier animals by unclean needles used in vaccination or in drawing blood, by nose tongs, and by castration, slitting of the ears, or other surgical procedures.

It is essential that sterile instruments be used for every animal to be bled, injected, or operated upon. A sufficient number of bleeding needles should be provided, and they should be kept clean and sanitary. Used needles, saws, and other instruments should first be washed in cold water to remove blood and then sterilized by boiling for several minutes in water containing 2 percent of washing soda. When facilities for boiling are not available, the cleaned instruments and needles may be immersed for 15 minutes or longer in a 2-percent lye solution, which must be freshly prepared each day and kept covered, as it deteriorates upon exposure to the air. After being removed from the lye solution, the needles may be dipped in a 2-percent compound solution of cresol, 2-percent formalin, or 60- to 70-percent alcohol.

NATURAL MEANS OF TRANSMISSION

Investigators working in various parts of the world have shown that anaplasmosis can be experimentally transmitted from diseased to healthy cattle by ticks, horseflies, and mosquitoes. Additional research will doubtless reveal other vectors.

Several research workers have shown that the following 18 species of ticks are capable of transmitting anaplasmosis experimentally:

SCIENTIFIC NAME	COMMON NAME
Boophilus annulatus	Cattle fever tick
B. decoloratus	Blue tick
B. microplus	None
Dermacentor albipictus	Winter tick
D. andersoni	Rocky Mountain spotted fever tick
D. occidentalis	Western dog tick
D. variabilis	American dog tick
Hyalomma lusitanicum	None
H. aegyptium	Bont-leg tick
Ixodes ricinus	Castor-bean tick
I. scapularis	Common shoulder tick
Ornithodorus lahorensis	None
Rhipicephalus appendiculatus	Common brown tick
R. bursa	Common brown tick
R. evertsi	Red-legged tick or red tick
R. sanguineus	Brown dog tick
R. simus	Black pitted tick
Argas persicus [4]	Chicken tick

[4] D. E. Howell and associates, Oklahoma Agricultural Experiment Station, unpublished data.

In his original work (1910), Theiler (*25*) showed that *Boophilus decoloratus* not only transmitted the disease called red water in South Africa but also anaplasmosis, and that *Rhipicephalus simus* spread the same disease. In 1930 Rees (*15*) first experimentally incriminated *R. sanguineus* in this country as a carrier of anaplasmosis, and he later transmitted the disease in the same manner with *Dermacentor andersoni, D. variabilis* and *Ixodes scapularis* (*17*).

In Du Toit's article on anaplasmosis (*4*), presented at the Twelfth International Veterinary Congress in 1934, he mentioned that several species of ticks had been reported by different workers as transmitting this disease. Rozeboom, Stiles, and Moe (*18*) report transmission by *Dermacentor andersoni*, and Stiles (*24*) records 17 ticks as vectors. From California, Boynton, Herms, Howell, and Woods (*1*) reported in 1936 the successful transmission of anaplasmosis by *D. andersoni*, confirming the work of Rees. They also reported

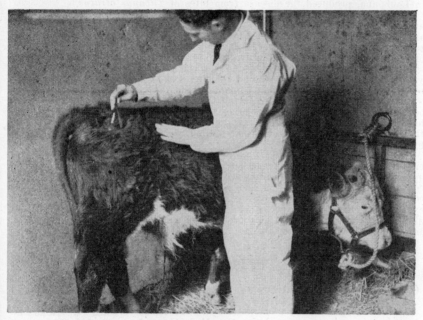

FIGURE 2.—A glass funnel is used to permit horseflies to feed on cattle in experiments on the transmission of anaplasmosis at the Oklahoma Agricultural Experiment Station.

for the first time a new species, *D. albipictus*, and a definite biological transmission of anaplasmosis by *D. occidentalis*. The disease was transmitted through both male and female ticks naturally infected with *D. andersoni* in 1938 by Sanborn, Stiles, and Moe (*20*) and in 1940 hereditary transmission with the female of the species was accomplished by Howell, Stiles, and Moe (*8*).

Horseflies also have been proved to be mechanical carriers of anaplasmosis. In many localities where the disease exists, large numbers of horseflies (tabanids) abound and home-made traps and commercial sprays are often employed to control them. In discussing these conditions, Sanborn et al. (*19*) state: "A study of field conditions, the prevalence of Tabanids, their occurrence, habits and distribution has been found to correspond closely to that of anaplasmosis. This is particularly true in swampy regions near ponds, inundated areas along rivers, lowlands of creeks, and in wooded areas. These are the places where horseflies breed and develop, and where the greatest annoyance to livestock occurs."

The first successful transmission of anaplasmosis by horseflies was accomplished by Sanborn, Stiles, Moe, and Orr (*21*). Subsequently their findings were corroborated and summarized by Howell, Sanborn, Rozeboom, Stiles, and Moe (*7*), who showed that seven species of horseflies can transmit the disease experimentally: *Tabanus sulcifrons, T. abactor, T. venustus, T. equalis, T. erythraeus, T. americanus,* and *T. oklahomensis.*

In part the summary referred to states: "Fewer bites are required if the infecting animal is in the acute stage of the disease than if it is a carrier. Bites obtained five or more minutes after the infective feed were not able to transfer anaplasmosis to healthy animals." These findings may partly explain the sporadic nature of the disease and the apparent slowness of its spread.

In Florida in 1933 Sanders (*22*) incriminated *Tabanus fumipennis* and *Stomoxys calcitrans* as vectors, and Morris, Martin, and Oglesby (*14*), working in Louisiana, produced the disease from bites of *Tabanus atratus.*

Experiments conducted by Lotze and Yiengst (*11*) during the summer of 1941 at the Beltsville Research Center indicated conclusively that after feeding on an infected bull *Tabanus sulcifrons* transmitted anaplasmosis to three healthy cows within a period of 24 to 28 days. These large biting flies were of one of the seven species used by Sanborn et al. (fig. 2.)

Since mosquitoes are known vectors of certain diseases, including malaria, yellow fever, fowl pox, and equine sleeping sickness, these insects also were tested for their ability to transmit anaplasmosis.

Mosquitoes are often present during the anaplasmosis season in large numbers and cause considerable annoyance to cattle. The genus *Psorophora* often breeds in transient pools where cattle graze, and since they are vicious biters, they were suspected of transmitting the disease. That they do so was proved by experimental feedings.

During the summer of 1940 Howell, Stiles, and Moe (*9*) were the first workers to demonstrate the transmission of anaplasmosis by mosquitoes. In one instance 1,525 mosquitoes, *Psorophora columbiae* and *P. ciliata,* were fed on a cow with a clinical case of anaplasmosis and then allowed to feed on a healthy cow, which developed a typical case of anaplasmosis after 38 days. A second experiment, using three species of mosquitoes, *P. ciliata, P. columbiae,* and *Aedes aegypti,* resulted in a positive case of anaplasmosis 58 days after the first feeding, or 38 days after the last of 241 feedings.

LITERATURE CITED

(1) BOYNTON, WILLIAM HUTCHINS, HERMS, WILLIAM B., HOWELL, D. E., and WOODS, GLADYS M.
   1936. ANAPLASMOSIS TRANSMISSION BY THREE SPECIES OF TICKS IN CALIFORNIA. Amer. Vet. Med. Assoc. Jour. 88: 500–502.
(2) —— WOOD, F. W., and WOODS, GLADYS M.
   1937. A NOTE ON TREATMENT OF ANAPLASMOSIS. North Amer. Vet. 18 (5) : 29–30.
(3) DIKMANS, G.
   1933. ANAPLASMOSIS. V. THE NATURE OF ANAPLASMA. Amer. Vet. Med. Assoc. Jour. 83: 101–104.
(4) DU TOIT, P. J.
   1934. ANAPLASMOSIS. 12th Internatl. Vet. Cong. Proc. 3: 325–345.
(5) DYKSTRA, R. R., LIENHARDT, H. F., PYLE, C. A., and FARLEY, H.
   1938. STUDIES IN ANAPLASMOSIS. (Abstract) Expt. Sta. Rec. 79: 392.
(6) HILTS, W. H.
   1928. ANAPLASMOSIS IN CATTLE FOLLOWING DEHORNING. Cornell Vet. 18: 330–332.
(7) HOWELL, D. E., SANBORN, C. E., ROZEBOOM, L. E., and others.
   1941. THE TRANSMISSION OF ANAPLASMOSIS BY HORSEFLIES (TABANIDAE). Okla. Agr. Expt. Sta. Tech. Bul. T–11, 23 pp.
(8) —— STILES, GEO. W., and MOE, LEWIS H.
   1941. THE HEREDITARY TRANSMISSION OF ANAPLASMOSIS BY DERMACENTOR ANDERSONI STILES. Amer. Vet. Med. Assoc. Res. Jour . 2: 165–166.

(9) HOWELL, D. E., STILES, GEO. W., and MOE, LEWIS H.
  1941. THE TRANSMISSION OF ANAPLASMOSIS BY MOSQUITOES (CULCIDAE).
    Amer. Vet. Med. Assoc. Jour. 99: 107–109.
(10) KOGER, R. B.
  1941. WHOLE BLOOD IN THE TREATMENT OF ANAPLASMOSIS. Vet. Med. 36:
    316–318, illus.
(11) LOTZE, JOHN C., and YIENGST, MARVIN J.
  1941. MECHANICAL TRANSMISSION OF BOVINE ANAPLASMOSIS BY THE HORSE-
    FLY TABANUS SULCIFRONS (MACQUART). Amer. Jour. Vet. Res.
    2: 323–326, illus.
(12) MOE, LEWIS H., STILES, GEO. W., and HOWELL, D. E.
  1940. ANAPLASMOSIS TRANSMITTED BY TIPPING THE HORNS OF CATTLE.
    Amer. Vet. Med. Assoc. Jour. 97: 450–451.
(13) MOHLER, JOHN R.
  1932. TICK FEVER. U. S. Dept. Agr. Farmers' Bul. 1625, 29 pp., illus.
    (Revised.)
(14) MORRIS, HARRY, MARTIN, J. A., and OGLESBY, W. T.
  1936. AN ATTEMPT TO TRANSMIT ANAPLASMOSIS BY BITING FLIES. Amer.
    Vet. Med. Assoc. Jour. 89: 169–175.
(15) REES, CHARLES W.
  1930. THE EXPERIMENTAL TRANSMISSION OF ANAPLASMOSIS BY RHIPICEPHA-
    LUS SANGUINEUS. North Amer. Vet. 2 (8) : 17–20, illus.
(16) ———
  1930. EXPERIMENTAL TRANSMISSION OF BOVINE ANAPLASMOSIS AND PIROPLAS-
    MOSIS BY MEANS OF AN INFECTED LANCET. North Amer. Vet.
    2 (10) : 17–20.
(17) ———
  1934. TRANSMISSION OF ANAPLASMOSIS BY VARIOUS SPECIES OF TICKS. U. S.
    Dept. Agr. Tech. Bul. 418, 17 pp., illus.
(18) ROZEBOOM, LLOYD E., STILES, GEO. W., and MOE, LEWIS H.
  1940. ANAPLASMOSIS TRANSMISSION BY DERMACENTOR ANDERSONI STILES.
    Jour. Parasitol. 26: 95–100.
(19) SANBORN, C. E., STILES, GEORGE W., and MOE, LEWIS H.
  1932. PRELIMINARY EXPERIMENTS IN THE TRANSMISSION OF ANAPLASMOSIS
    BY HORSEFLIES. Okla. Agr. Expt. Sta. Bul. 204, 15 pp., illus.
(20) ——— STILES, GEO. W., and MOE, LEWIS H.
  1938. ANAPLASMOSIS TRANSMISSION BY NATURALLY INFECTED DERMACENTOR
    ANDERSONI MALE AND FEMALE TICKS. North Amer. Vet. 19 (1) :
    31–33.
(21) ——— STILES, GEORGE W., MOE, LEWIS H., and ORR, HARRY W.
  1930. TRANSMISSION OF ANAPLASMOSIS BY FLIES. *In* Okla. Agr. Expt.
    Sta. Rpt. 1926–30 (Research Leads to Farm Progress), pp.
    254–264, illus.
(22) SANDERS, D. A.
  1933. NOTES ON THE EXPERIMENTAL TRANSMISSION OF BOVINE ANAPLAS-
    MOSIS IN FLORIDA. Amer. Vet. Med. Assoc. Jour. 83: 799–805.
(23) STILES, GEO. W., JR.
  1936. MECHANICAL TRANSMISSION OF ANAPLASMOSIS BY UNCLEAN INSTRU-
    MENTS. North Amer. Vet. 17 (6) : 39–41.
(24) ———
  1939. ANAPLASMOSIS IN CATTLE. U. S. Dept. Agr. Cir. 154, 10 pp., illus.
    (Revised.)
(25) THEILER, A.
  1910. ANAPLASMA MARGINALE, THE MARGINAL POINTS IN THE BLOOD OF CATTLE
    SUFFERING FROM A SPECIFIC DISEASE. Transvaal Govt. Vet. Bact.
    Rpt., 1908–9: 7–64, illus.
(26) UNITED STATES BUREAU OF ANIMAL INDUSTRY.
  1941. REPORT OF THE CHIEF OF THE BUREAU OF ANIMAL INDUSTRY 1941.
    92 pp.
(27) VAWTER, L. R., and RECORDS, EDWARD.
  1926. RECENT STUDIES ON ICTERO-HEMOGLOBINURIA OF CATTLE. Amer. Vet.
    Med. Assoc. Jour. 68: 494–513, illus.

Cattle Scab
and Its Control

BY RUDOLPH SNYDER [1]

COMMON SCAB of cattle, once widespread and serious in this country, has been almost eradicated, but sarcoptic scab, once rare, is now becoming a real menace. These and the two other types of cattle scab are discussed in this article.

IN HIS annual report for 1902, the Chief of the Bureau of Animal Industry referred to numerous inquiries about a disease commonly known as Texas itch. As the disease appears to have been more prevalent in other sections of the country than in Texas, it seems strange that this name was applied to it. At that time the disease was apparently fairly common among the range cattle of the West and Northwest, and it had also been heard of in other parts of the country. Investigation showed that the condition was scabies, a contagious skin disease commonly known as scab, mange, or itch, caused by insectlike parasites called mites.

There are four species of the scabies parasite which affect cattle, and they belong to four different genera—*Psoroptes, Sarcoptes, Chorioptes*, and *Demodex*. The psoroptic mites, which cause common scab, live in groups or colonies on the surface of the skin, and the lesions, or damage to tissues they cause, spread in all directions from the spot first affected. The sarcoptic mites, which cause what is known in some regions as barn itch, bore into the skin, each female making a separate gallery in which she lays her eggs. The chorioptic mites live in groups on the surface of the skin and usually remain localized on the legs or tail with little or no tendency to spread. The demodectic mites are microscopic in size and are more like worms than typical mites; they live in the hair follicles and sebaceous (sweat and oil) glands and cause smooth spherical swellings, or pustules, in the skin.

[1] Rudolph Snyder is Senior Veterinarian and Assistant Chief of the Interstate Inspection Division, Bureau of Animal Industry.

588

PSOROPTIC, OR COMMON, SCAB

The mites causing psoroptic, or common, scab of cattle were encountered throughout the range and semirange States in the early 1900's. Although not so dangerous a disease as sarcoptic scab, psoroptic scab caused more extensive losses to the livestock industry because of its greater prevalence. It occasionally occurs on cattle in farming communities in various parts of the country, and, unless properly treated, it causes great losses through reduction in weight, failure of young stock to thrive and gain weight normally, and an increase in the death rate, especially among cattle in a state of poor nutrition and low vitality when they are exposed to inclement weather.

The mites that cause common cattle scab are small white or yellowish parasites known technically as *Psoroptes equi bovis*, or perhaps more often as *Psoroptes communis bovis*. The female when full grown measures about one-fortieth and the male about one-fiftieth of an inch in length. They are visible to the naked eye, especially when placed on a dark background. The entire life cycle is passed on the body of a host animal. Each female may deposit 15 to 24 eggs, which hatch after 3 or 4 days' incubation. The young mites reach maturity and mate, and the females of the new generation deposit eggs in 10 to 12 days.

The mites may attack any part of the body that is thickly covered with hair. The first symptom of the disease is usually an intense itching of the skin on the withers, on the top of the neck just in front of the withers, or around the root of the tail. From these points the lesions spread over the back and sides and, unless checked, may involve practically the entire body.

The most certain diagnosis consists in demonstrating the presence of the parasite that causes the disease. This may be done by scraping the outer edges of the infected areas with a blunt-edged knife and transferring the scrapings to a smooth black surface, such as a piece of black paper. Spreading the scrapings in the warm sun or near artificial heat usually causes the mites to become active, and they can be seen as minute, gray, moving bodies against the dark background. Well-advanced cases of scab are usually easy to diagnose, but the disease should never be allowed to reach this stage; in the early stages it yields readily to proper treatment, but if allowed to spread it will entail heavy losses.

The transmissibility of the disease is not limited to any one season of the year, although cattle on green, succulent feed and in a thriving condition seldom contract scab. In fact, in the spring, when infected cattle are turned out on green grass, the old coat of hair is shed, and the disease often seems to have been cured. It will usually break out again, however, with the coming of cold, stormy weather.

Although the infected animal is the most important factor in spreading cattle mites, infected premises should not be overlooked. Owing to the varying conditions that may affect the ability of the mite and its eggs to remain alive when separated from a host, it is impossible to state definitely how long premises may remain infectious after the removal of the cattle. Hence, it is advisable to clean and disinfect all infected sheds, barns, yards, or small inclosures thoroughly before using them for clean or dipped cattle. There are a number of cresylic disinfectants which when diluted in accordance with instructions on the container are suitable for this purpose. (See the article on Disinfection and Disinfectants, p. 179.)

CONTROL MEASURES

The only rational way to treat cattle scabies is to use some external application that will kill the parasites without injuring the animals. Dipping is the method most commonly used to accomplish this. It consists in immersing the animals in a medicated liquid that will thoroughly wet the entire surface of the body and kill the parasites. It is the only method recognized by the Bureau of Animal Industry in the official treatment of scabby cattle because it is the most practical and effective. Dipping plants are usually arranged so that the cattle enter one end of a vat filled with the dip, swim through it, and leave the vat at the opposite end. The dips commonly used by the Bureau of Animal Industry and permitted for use in official dipping of cattle for scabies are lime-sulfur solution and a nicotine solution.

The stages in the life cycle of the mite have an important bearing on the interval which should elapse between treatments for common scab. Dipping properly done will kill the mites but cannot be depended upon to destroy all the eggs, and the animals should be dipped a second time before the newly hatched mites have had time to develop and deposit eggs. Practical experience has shown that the interval between the first and second dippings should be 10 to 12 days, although in some instances this may be safely extended to a maximum of 14 days.

During 1903 some preliminary inspections and dippings were carried out, and in 1904 regulations were issued which placed in quarantine that part of the United States lying west of the Mississippi River and the eastern boundary of Minnesota. This quarantine specified the manner in which cattle could be shipped to other States from the area. In 1905 the quarantine was modified to include only those areas in which the disease was prevalent. During that year a large force was placed in the field by the Bureau of Animal Industry to make inspections and supervise the dipping of exposed and infected animals. From 1904 to 1911 cattle scabies seemed to be increasing rapidly in many States, but after 1911 the effects of the systematic eradication measures carried on by the Bureau in cooperation with the livestock sanitary officials of the various States became apparent. The common variety of cattle scabies has been practically eradicated, and at the present time no territory is under Federal quarantine for this disease.

SARCOPTIC SCAB

Sarcoptic scab or mange, or barn itch, is found more or less frequently on both farm and range cattle throughout the country. Owing to its comparative rarity, it was not formerly considered of much importance in the United States, but during the last few years it has been increasing and must now be considered a major problem. The disease is more serious than common scab because it is more severe in its effects and more difficult to eradicate. It sometimes develops in purebred cattle, and animals from purebred herds may carry the infection although they may not show visible symptoms of scabies at the time they are shipped. Purebred bulls of the beef breeds seem to be especially susceptible and may be an important factor in spreading the disease. The breeder of purebred cattle who supplies bulls for building up range and farm herds finds his business very nearly ruined when sarcoptic scabies develops in his herd. In dairy herds it may seriously affect milk production and throw the balance on the wrong side of the ledger. The disease can be eradicated, however, and if proper methods are adopted before it reaches an advanced stage the losses can be reduced to a minimum.

The parasites *Sarcoptes scabiei* var. *caprae*, which cause sarcoptic scab, resemble in a general way the common scab mites. The entire life cycle is passed on the body of the host animal, but the sarcoptic mites do not remain on the surface; they penetrate the outer layer of the skin and excavate burrows or galleries in which mating occurs and the eggs are laid. When egg laying is completed the female dies in her burrow.

The mites prefer locations where the skin is tender and the hair is thin. In the early stages of the disease the lesions are usually found on the inner surfaces of the thighs, the under side of the neck or brisket, or around the root of the tail. From these parts the entire surface of the body may become involved.

Sarcoptic scab is transmissible from one species of animal to another and also from animals to man. Sarcoptic mites of the horse, sheep, goat, and cat may live on cattle, while those of the horse, dog, and hog are known to be readily transmissible to man; but ordinarily, when one species contracts the contagion from another species, the mites live only a short time on the newly infected animal. Sarcoptic scab of cattle is contagious to all classes of cattle and is transmitted by direct contact with animals or objects that are carriers of the mites.

It is evident, therefore, that all stables and small enclosures occupied by mangy cattle and all implements and coverings, such as currycombs, brushes, and blankets, should be cleaned and disinfected before they are used for clean or dipped cattle. The cleaning and disinfection should be done in the same manner as for common scab.

Probably on account of their burrowing habit, sarcoptic mites are much more difficult to eradicate than the common scab mites. The dips recommended for the latter will kill sarcoptic mites if the liquid comes in contact with them, but it may not reach all the mites at one application. Persistent, thorough, and frequent application of the dip will effect a cure, however, especially if all infected parts are scrubbed well with a brush and soaked with dipping solution just prior to the first dipping. Experience has shown that four dippings in either a lime-sulfur or a nicotine dip will cure sarcoptic scab in cattle. The interval between dippings should be 6 to 10 days.

One dipping in crude petroleum usually cures sarcoptic scab, as it seems to destroy the eggs as well as the mites. A serious drawback to its use as a dip for cattle, however, is that in some cases it is injurious to the animals.

CHORIOPTIC, OR SYMBIOTIC, SCAB

Chorioptic, or symbiotic, scab occurs occasionally in cattle, but it is of less importance than either of the two varieties already described. It is caused by a mite called *Chorioptes bovis*, which under a high-power magnifying glass closely resembles the common scab mite. Though it usually spreads very slowly, the disease is contagious to all classes of cattle. The mites live on the surface of the skin and produce lesions resembling those of common scab. The lesions are usually found on the tail or legs and generally remain localized. For practical purposes it is not necessary to distinguish between chorioptic and common scab, because the same treatment is recommended for both.

DEMODECTIC MANGE

Until about 1923 demodectic, or follicular, mange of cattle, caused by the mite called *Demodex bovis*, was not often recognized in the United States. Owing to the damage to leather caused by demodectic mange lesions, however, an investigation was made in 1927 to determine the extent of the disease, and numerous cases were reported from 14 States, most of which were in old cows of the dairy breeds. The lesions of demodectic mange in cattle appear as nodules, or small lumps, most often in the skin of the neck, shoulders, breast, and dewlap, and sometimes in other parts of the body. Demodectic mange may progress rapidly on an animal until the nodules appear nearly everywhere in the skin, or there may be no alteration in the number and size of the nodules during a period of several years. Ordinarily the disease does not spread rapidly from an infected animal to others in the herd, but precautions should be taken to prevent possible spread by isolating infected animals. There is no known practical remedy for demodectic mange in cattle, although frequent dippings delay the progress of the disease and may cure mild cases.

Tapeworm and Roundworm Parasites of Cattle

BY DALE A. PORTER [1]

SEVENTY or more species of tapeworms and roundworms infest cattle, some causing serious losses. Here
are facts about the more important, including methods
of prevention and treatment. The article on worm
parasites of sheep should also be read by those interested, practically and scientifically, in cattle worms.

THE TAPEWORM and roundworm parasites reported to affect cattle
throughout the world comprise over 70 different species. Although
some species occur infrequently and others are comparatively harmless
to their bovine hosts, some exact a heavy annual toll from the beef
and dairy industries. Losses are due to deaths from gross parasitism,
lowered vitality and resultant poor growth and performance, and
condemnation, in the course of meat inspection, of carcasses or edible
parts as a result of invasion by parasites.

Members of these two groups of parasites—tapeworms and roundworms—vary considerably in their location, structure, and harmful-
ness.

The cestodes, or tapeworms, of cattle are found as adults in the
intestine and as larval forms in the muscles, liver, lungs, and other
viscera. The adults are elongated, flattened worms consisting of a
head and a chain of segments, each having both male and female
reproductive organs, and terminal segments containing mature eggs.
The larval forms, commonly referred to as bladder worms because
they resemble a bladder in shape, are intermediate asexual stages of
tapeworms that live as adults in the intestines of man and other
animals. The bladder worms vary in diameter from one-fourth inch
in the case of the beef bladder worm (*Cysticercus bovis*) to as much
as 6 inches in the case of the hydatid cysts (*Echinococcus granulosus*).

[1] Dale A. Porter is Associate Parasitologist, Regional Animal Disease Research Laboratory, Auburn, Ala., Bureau of Animal Industry.

Although migration is common during development, the adult roundworms, or nematodes, to be discussed in this article occur in the digestive tract or lungs. Some roundworms, the lungworms and stomach worms, for example, are named for the location in which they are commonly found. The roundworms are elongated, cylindrical, unsegmented worms and may be characterized as threadlike or hairlike. The sexes are generally separate, and the males are usually smaller than the females.

Significant facts about the more common tapeworm and roundworm parasites of cattle and their control are discussed briefly in the following pages. The parasites of cattle are closely related to, and in some instances specifically identical with, those occurring in sheep, and from the standpoint of present knowledge more facts have been determined concerning parasitism in the latter host. Hence the reader should also refer to the article on Internal Parasites of Sheep and Goats, page 859.

CESTODA, OR TAPEWORMS

ADULT TAPEWORMS IN THE INTESTINE

Cattle in this country are known to harbor two species of tapeworms, *Moniezia benedeni* and *M. expansa*, both of which are common and sometimes serious pests of sheep also. The worms are whitish to yellowish in color and when mature may be several feet long and as much as three-fourths of an inch wide. The life history of *M. benedeni* is probably similar to that of *M. expansa*. The latter is transmitted by means of a tiny grass mite prevalent on pastures, particularly in damp areas. The mites eat the tapeworm eggs passed in the manure of cattle or sheep harboring the adult worms. The egg develops into a larval tapeworm within the mite, and when the mite is eaten by cattle the larval tapeworm is digested out and settles down in the small intestine, eventually reaching the adult stage (*8, 17, 18*).[2] As the worm grows, the terminal segments become filled with eggs that escape into the intestine and pass out in the droppings. The mature terminal segments, either individually or several together, are occasionally seen in the droppings of calves, particularly when they have diarrhea, and this aids in diagnosing the parasites.

It is generally believed that tapeworms do less damage in cattle than in sheep. Older animals are seldom affected, but young calves may harbor several of the worms, which may cause enough intestinal irritation to interfere with digestion and thus make the calves weak and unthrifty.

TAPEWORM CYSTS IN THE LIVER AND OTHER VISCERA

The hydatid (*Echinococcus aranulosus*) and the thin-necked bladder worm (*Cysticercus tenuicollis*) are the intermediate stages of two

---

[2] Italic numbers in parentheses refer to Literature Cited, p. 603.

tapeworms, *Taenia echinococcus* and *T. hydatigena*, which as adults are parasites in the intestines of dogs, wolves, and other canines. Closely related zoologically, their life histories are essentially similar. The canine hosts acquire the adult worms as a result of eating the cysts in dead animals or in offal from slaughtered animals. Cattle in turn acquire the larvae as a result of swallowing tapeworm eggs eliminated in the droppings of parasitized canines that have access to cattle pastures. The eggs hatch in the small intestine, and the embryo enters the intestinal wall, to be distributed by the blood stream to the preferred sites of development in the body. These bladder worms are found more frequently in sheep and swine than in cattle.

The hydatid forms fluid-filled, tumorlike cysts ranging up to several inches in diameter in the liver, lungs, and other organs. The bovine host is seldom suspected of harboring these parasites during life, although there may be pulmonary or digestive disturbances, depending upon the location of the cysts. Even the presence of large numbers of cysts which may have caused extensive tissue destruction is usually discovered only at slaughter.

The thin-necked bladder worm, *Cysticercus tenuicollis*, occurs embedded in the liver, attached to other abdominal organs, or free in the body cavity. The parasite looks like a sac full of clear liquid, usually about 1 inch in diameter. As in the case of the hydatid, the occurrence of this parasite in cattle cannot be diagnosed during life. A few bladder worms apparently have little or no effect on the host, and large numbers involving extensive liver damage by the immature larval form, as described in the case of sheep, have not been observed in cattle.

Tapeworm Cysts in the Muscles

The beef tapeworm (*Taenia saginata*), in the adult stage a parasite of man, occurs in cattle in the larval, or bladder worm, stage and is then known as *Cysticercus bovis*.

The condition in cattle caused by this worm is commonly referred to as beef measles. The cysticercus consists of a head, a neck, and a fluid-filled bladder within which the head and neck are inserted or sheathed. The worms appear as oval white vesicles about the size of a pea and occur throughout the muscles of the body but most frequently in the heart, muscles of mastication, diaphragm, and tongue. The life cycle involves an alternation between the two hosts, human beings and cattle. Infection of man is brought about by eating the bladder worm in raw or incompletely cooked beef; cattle in turn acquire the larvae as a result of swallowing the tapeworm eggs with drinking water or forage that has become contaminated with the excreta of the human tapeworm carrier. The small larvae hatch from the eggs in the stomach. Upon reaching the intestine they burrow into the gut wall and are carried by the blood stream, aided probably by their own movements, to various locations in the body. Development to the infective cystic stage has been estimated to take from 7 to 18 weeks. Numerous cases of cysticercosis, or measles, detected under Federal meat-inspection procedure have been traced back to contacts with human carriers on farms and ranches.

Usually there are no definite symptoms associated with measles in cattle, and diagnosis depends on finding the cysts in the animals on post mortem examination. The economic importance of the parasite is in its relationship to human health. On account of the danger to human health from eating measly beef, precautions are taken to detect the parasite in beef carcasses through Federal and other equally thorough meat-inspection procedures.

NEMATODA, OR ROUNDWORMS

LUNGWORMS

Lungworms of cattle (*Dictyocaulus viviparus*) are white, threadlike worms 2 to 3 inches long. They inhabit chiefly the medium-sized and smaller bronchial tubes of the lungs. The female worms produce large numbers of eggs which usually hatch in the air passages, liberating larvae which are coughed up, swallowed, and eliminated in the feces. Sometimes the coughed-up eggs hatch in the stomach or intestines, but they often pass unhatched from the host, particularly when there is severe diarrhea.

Under favorable conditions the larvae eliminated with the feces develop to the infective stage in about a week. The infective larvae tend to migrate on grass in warm, wet weather and are taken in with the grass by grazing cattle. The course of development following ingestion of the larvae is believed to be similar to that of the lungworm of sheep (*Dictyocaulus filaria*). In this case the larvae penetrate the intestinal wall and reach the lymph glands, from which they are eventually carried to the lungs. The writer has observed that cattle lungworms mature in 3 to 4 weeks, at which time larvae appear in the feces, and that the worms are apparently capable of living 2 to 4 months within the host.

The worms and their eggs and larvae irritate the lung tissue, producing local inflammation which is manifested by the production of considerable frothy mucus. The extent of the damage to the functioning lung depends largely on the number of parasites present and the age and condition of the host; the parasites occur much more frequently in calves than in mature cattle. In light or moderate cases no symptoms are shown, with the possible exception of an occasional dry cough and poor condition. If the invasion is extensive there are frequent coughing spells, difficult breathing, and progressive weakness. The cases that usually prove fatal are those in which there is extensive involvement of the lungs, particularly as a result of the secondary invasion of bacteria. Such instances are characterized by shallow breathing with the mouth open and the tongue protruded (fig. 1). Death results from exhaustion or suffocation brought on by mechanical blocking of the air passages by worms and the accompanying discharge of mucus and pus.

STOMACH WORMS

Three species of roundworms (*Haemonchus contortus, Ostertagia ostertagi,* and *Trichostrongylus axei*) are common parasites in the abomasum, or fourth stomach, of cattle. Of these the first is the best known and is commonly referred to as the stomach worm or twisted wireworm.

The roundworm *Haemonchus contortus* is ½ inch to 1¼ inches long and about as thick as an ordinary pin. The female worms produce large numbers of eggs, which pass out in the feces and hatch in a few hours under favorable conditions. The larvae, hatching from the egg, undergo two molts, reaching the infective stage in about 4 or 5 days.

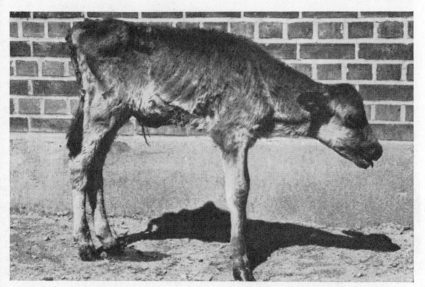

FIGURE 1.—A 2-month-old calf with lungworm disease. Note the open mouth.

The infective larvae retain the last molt or skin and, thus ensheathed, are very resistant to cold and long periods of dryness. When there is rain or dew these larvae crawl up on blades of grass, with which they are swallowed by grazing cattle. The worms become mature in the stomach in 3 to 4 weeks.

Haemonchus contortus apparently affects cattle in the same way that it does sheep, although there may be some differences in the degree of cross transmission between the two hosts. According to Clunies Ross (*5*), lambs may be parasitized readily by *H. contortus* of either ovine (sheep) or bovine origin, whereas calves are parasitized with difficulty by *H. contortus* of bovine origin. As in the case of sheep, younger animals are the ones most seriously affected, although losses may occur occasionally among 3-year-olds (*12*). Among the common symptoms produced by this parasite are loss of flesh, general weakness, and anemia. The anemic condition, due to impoverishment of the

blood from the bloodsucking habit of the worms, may be recognized
by the paleness of the skin and mucous membranes of the mouth and
eyes and the edema, or watery swelling, known as bottle jaw, which
often develops under the jaw (fig. 2). The latter condition is particularly noticeable after the animal has been driven or otherwise
strenuously exercised. Diarrhea has also been considered as symptomatic, but the writer has not observed it in calves showing other clinical symptoms in experimental infections with stomach worms.

Ostertagia ostertagi, another parasite of the fourth stomach of cattle, is also occasionally found in sheep. A small hairlike worm, slightly

FIGURE 2.—A yearling steer with stomach worm disease. Note the submaxillary
edema, or bottle jaw.

over one-fourth of an inch in length, it may often be overlooked. From
what is known, its life history is similar to that of *Haemonchus contortus*. The infective larvae ingested with food reach the abomasum
and there penetrate into the mucous membrane. Development to
maturity takes place in small cystic nodules, or lumps, produced by
the host in an attempt to overcome the invading larvae. Upon reaching maturity the adult worms escape into the stomach leaving the
abandoned nodules to degenerate. The resulting patchy erosion may
be detected as small white circumscribed areas on the stomach lining.
The wall of the stomach may also be extremely thickened and swollen
in severe cases.

In some sections of the United States, notably in the West, this
parasite may replace *Haemonchus contortus* in importance. Stiles
(*15*) considered it to be the chief factor in a severe outbreak of verminous disease in Texas cattle. Several outbreaks of verminous gastritis
(inflammation of the stomach) due to this parasite have been de-

scribed. In outbreaks among yearling animals in which there were several deaths, the symptoms were emaciation, anemia, rough coat, and a diarrhea of varying intensity (*1, 3*). Submaxillary edema (bottle jaw) similar to that seen in cattle haemonchosis has also been reported.

Of the nematode parasites found in the stomachs of cattle, the third species, *Trichostrongylus axei*, is the least specific to a particular host. Large numbers of these parasites, which produce gastritis, have been observed in horses as well as cattle and other ruminants. Available evidence also indicates that this nematode may be transferred from one host species to another (*4, 16, 20*).

The parasites themselves are very slender and only about one-fifth of an inch or less in length. They are found on or in the mucous lining of the stomach, and detecting them usually depends on microscopical examination of scrapings made from the stomach lining. The details of the life history are not fully known, but it has been determined that the host is parasitized by swallowing the infective larvae that develop in the feces of other animals harboring the parasite (*4*).

Injuries to the bovine stomach consist of patchy gastritis in which the lining of the stomach is thickened and thrown into folds (*2*). Such symptoms as severe diarrhea and loss of condition have been associated with the presence of large numbers of these roundworms.

COOPERIDS

Three species of small nematodes (*Cooperia punctata, C. pectinata,* and *C. oncophora*), known collectively as cooperids, occur in cattle in the United States. *C. punctata* has a rather general distribution, having been encountered frequently in both the Northern and the Southern States. *C. pectinata* is prevalent mainly in the South, and *C. oncophora* is more prevalent in the North (*6*).

The adult worms are found on or imbedded in the mucous membrane, predominantly in the upper portion of the small intestine. Hairlike in thickness and about one-quarter inch long, the worms may be overlooked in a superficial examination. The development and transmission of these species are similar to those of the large stomach worm, *Haemonchus contortus*.

It is quite apparent that the cooperids are capable of producing extensive intestinal inflammation in calves. Descriptions given by Hung (*7*) and Dikmans (*6*) indicate that *Cooperia punctata* penetrates the intestinal mucous membrane and the layer beneath, producing a destructive inflammation that is particularly severe where the worms are numerous. Such lesions or tissue injuries appear on examination as accumulations of white or yellow cheesy material (*11*). Seriously affected animals have more or less persistent diarrhea and become emaciated and anemic as the disease progresses.

By reason of their widespread distribution and common occurrence these roundworms may be responsible for more cases of intestinal inflammation and unthriftiness in young cattle than is now generally recognized.

HOOKWORMS

The cattle hookworm, called scientifically *Bunostomum phlebotomum*, belongs to the same family as the hookworms of other animals, including man, and shares the familial reputation of being a bloodsucker. A prevalent parasite of young cattle, this worm occurs normally in the upper small intestine, but it may invade the fourth stomach in small numbers and attach itself to the gastric mucous membrane. The worms attain a length of three-fourths of an inch to an inch and appear pinkish white in the intestine. The eggs of the female hookworm pass from the host in the droppings, hatch, and develop to the infective stage. According to Schwartz (*14*), they hatch in about 96 hours under laboratory conditions at a temperature of 70° to 80° F. The larvae undergo two molts, the third, or infective, stage completing a cycle of development that requires a minimum of 7 days. The infective larvae may be swallowed by cattle while grazing or penetrate the skin and develop to maturity upon reaching the intestine. The details of migration of the lavae following skin penetration are lacking. Probably the route is similar to that of the sheep hookworm (*B. trigonocephalum*), the larvae of which penetrate the skin, migrate to the lungs, presumably by way of the blood stream, and thence to the intestine by way of the windpipe, mouth, and gullet (*10*).

As is common with the hookworms, the adult is provided with mouth parts capable of attaching it to the intestinal mucous membrane. Aside from sucking blood directly from the host, the small lacerations produced by the mouth of the worm may be left bleeding as the worm moves from one place of attachment to another. This species, when present in large numbers, is capable of producing clinical symptoms similar to those produced by the stomach worm, *Haemonchus contortus*. According to Roberts (*12*), the disease runs a well-marked course of weakness, emaciation, intermittent diarrhea, and progressive anemia in which the red-cell count may be reduced as much as 75 percent in severe cases.

NODULAR WORMS

Unlike the intestinal worms discussed previously, the nodular worm, which is known as *Oesophagostomum radiatum*, is found in the large intestine and cecum. This worm is about five-eighths of an inch long and white in color. The eggs of the female are passed with the feces, and larvae are hatched that undergo some development on the ground similar to that of the stomach worm; *Haemonchus contortus*. The infective larvae swallowed by cattle enter the intestinal wall for a period of development and later migrate to the lumen of the intestine to develop to maturity.

The larval parasite and resulting secondary bacterial invasion cause the formation of nodules which, particularly after degeneration to a cheesy state, may be mistaken by inexperienced persons for the lesions of tuberculosis. Although the nodules may be encountered in the bovine omentum (a fold of the lining of the abdominal cavity), they are usually restricted to the posterior (rear) portion of the small intestine and to the large intestine and cecum. These nodules are usually somewhat smaller than those caused by a related species, *Oesophagostomum columbianum*, in sheep, and the general effects of the parasite in cattle are believed to be somewhat less severe. (See Internal Parasites of Sheep and Goats, p. 859.) Such symptoms as anemia, scouring, and emaciation have been correlated with gross parasitism, and because of the permanent nature of the nodules, recovery may be slow.

GENERAL MEASURES FOR CONTROL

Control measures for any parasite depend on complete knowledge of its life history. Studies of the developmental stages usually reveal one in which the parasite is vulnerable to natural or man-made barriers and in which the life cycle may be broken. As research on parasites of cattle continues, control measures should be found which, if not capable of eradicating parasitism, certainly will be instrumental in reducing its toll.

Some general recommendations for the control of the more common tapeworm and roundworm parasites are given below.

Adult tapeworms in the intestine.—The transmission of these tapeworms (*Moniezia* species) involves certain free-living mites as intermediate hosts, but as yet too little is known about their life history or habits to make full recommendations for control. However, since young stock is most often affected, pastures known to be a source of infection should be closed to calves.

Tapeworm cysts of the liver and other viscera.—The control of hydatids and thin-necked bladder worms, both intermediate stages of adult tapeworms in canines, depends on some barrier between dogs and cattle. To effect this barrier, stray dogs and other canines should be kept off farms and suppressed by appropriate measures. Also, dogs belonging on the premises should be kept free of tapeworms by suitable remedies. (See Internal Parasites of Dogs and Cats, p. 1150.) As a precaution against infection of dogs with tapeworms, the viscera of slaughtered cattle, sheep, and hogs should be disposed of in such a manner as to be inaccessible to the dogs.

Tapeworm cysts of the muscles.—To prevent cattle from acquiring the cysticercus of the human tapeworm, *Taenia saginata*, care should be taken that human feces are not disposed of in such a manner as to contaminate the feed and drinking water of the cattle. Prevention of tapeworm in the human being is simple and effective: Cook beef thoroughly.

Roundworm parasites.—In view of the similarity in the development of the free-living stages of the commonly important gastrointestinal roundworms and lungworms of cattle, preventive measures are in general applicable for all species concerned. Any control measures should be set up primarily to reduce the chances that calves and yearlings will become seriously parasitized, since young cattle are the most susceptible.

As moisture favors the development of the eggs and larvae of roundworms, well-drained pastures are preferable, and low, wet areas should be avoided until they are drained. Drinking water should be supplied from wells or flowing streams, preferably in troughs raised above the ground. Pastures that it is impractical to drain should be used only for mature cattle.

Pastures should not be overstocked, and rotation, as often as available forage permits, is highly desirable, since free-living stages of the parasites in a contaminated field will largely succumb in the absence, for a sufficient time, of susceptible hosts.

Young animals being most susceptible to parasitism, calves should be kept as much as possible away from the older stock and the contaminated pastures and quarters where the latter have been confined. As a precaution against further spread of parasitism, any affected cattle should be isolated from the herd for special treatment. Sanitation and good feeding will sometimes stop losses from parasitism even if no medicinal treatment is given.

MEDICINAL TREATMENT

Owing to the similarity of the effects of parasitism in cattle and in sheep the medicinal control of the tapeworm and roundworm parasites of cattle has followed closely the treatments recommended for sheep. In few instances, however, has the efficacy of the drugs been determined by critical tests on cattle; recommendations for their use are based largely on clinical data or the performance of the drugs on related worms in sheep.

A 1-percent solution of copper sulfate has been used for the control of the stomach worm *Haemonchus contortus*. This solution is given as a drench in doses of the following sizes: Calves, 3½ to 4 fluid ounces; yearlings, 6 fluid ounces; 2-year-old and older cattle, 12 to 16 fluid ounces. The addition of 1 ounce of 40-percent nicotine sulfate to a gallon of 1-percent copper sulfate administered in doses of the same sizes as above has also been recommended as a treatment for stomach worms, hookworms, and tapeworms (*Moniezia* species). Mönnig (*9*) reports that a mixture composed of 30 cubic centimeters of 40-percent nicotine sulfate and 30 grams of copper sulfate in 1,800 cubic centimeters of water has given satisfactory results against the tapeworms (*Moniezia*) and stomach worms (*Haemonchus*) in cattle in the field. The mixture is given at the rate of 30 cubic centimeters to each 50 pounds of live weight, with a maximum of 90 cubic centimeters for animals under 2 years of age, and 120 to 150 cubic centimeters, according to size, for those over 2 years old. Crude castor oil is recommended as a purgative to follow this treatment for tapeworms.

Some investigators recommend tetrachlorethylene as a medicinal control for stomach worms, hookworms, and the small intestinal roundworms (*Cooperia* species). This drug may be administered in capsules or as a drench in an emulsion consisting of equal parts of the drug and mineral oil. The dosage of tetrachlorethylene recommended is 10 to 15 cubic centimeters for calves 2 to 4 months old and up to 25 to 30 cubic centimeters for animals 12 to 18 months old (*13*).

The tetrachlorethylene emulsion may be given immediately following the introduction of about 2 cubic centimeters of a 5-percent copper sulfate solution into the mouth (*2*). Recent critical tests (*19*) supplemented by clinical data indicate that phenothiazine may have considerable promise as an anthelmintic for the removal of stomach worms, hookworms, and nodular worms. On the basis of available data, a dose of 20 grams per 100 pounds of live weight, with a maximum individual dose of 60 grams, administered in capsules, is suggested.

Treatment for parasites outside the gastrointestinal tract is unsuccessful. There are no medicinal agents for the removal of tapeworm cysts, and although various chemicals have been administered by inhalation or injection into the windpipe for the removal of lungworms, none has shown effectiveness. Lungworm cases are probably best treated by removing the animals from pasture to clean sanitary quarters and supplying liberal quantities of feed.

While parasitism may be suspected in young cattle in unthrifty condition, malnutrition or other conditions may be present, if not actually responsible. Animals in a weakened condition may react unfavorably to medication, and it is therefore advisable to obtain competent diagnosis and advice before resorting to treatment.

In treating young cattle for parasites it is advisable to treat not only the animals that are seriously affected but also the rest of the herd, since any parasites remaining in the herd become a source of reinfection. Following treatment the animals should if possible be removed to fresh pastures.

LITERATURE CITED

(1) ACKERT, JAMES E., and MULDOON, WILLIAM E.
    1920. STRONGYLOSIS (OSTERTAGIA) IN CATTLE. Amer. Vet. Med. Assoc. Jour. 58: 138–146, illus.
(2) BAKER, DONALD W.
    1939. A NEW SYSTEM OF ANTHELMINTIC CONTROL FOR GASTRO-INTESTINAL PARASITES OF RUMINANTS. Cornell Vet. 29: 192–197, illus.
(3) BARGER, E. H.
    1927. OSTERTAGIA OSTERTAGI IN CALIFORNIA CATTLE, WITH COPPER SULPHATE AN APPARENTLY SUCCESSFUL THERAPEUTIC. Amer. Vet. Med. Assoc. Jour. 71: 560–567, illus.
(4) BRITTON, JOHN W.
    1939. TRICHOSTRONGYLOSIS IN EQUINES. Cornell Vet. 29: 322–330.
(5) CLUNIES ROSS, I.
    1931. THE HOST SPECIFICITY OF HAEMONCHUS CONTORTUS OF SHEEP AND CATTLE. Austral. Jour. Expt. Biol. and Med. Sci. 8: 217–224.
(6) DIKMANS, G.
    1939. PARASITIC ENTERITIS IN CALVES. Vet. Med. 34: 28–30, illus.
(7) HUNG, SEE-LU.
    1926. THE PATHOLOGY OF COOPERIA PUNCTATA INFESTATION IN CALVES. North Amer. Vet. 7 (3): 33–36, illus.
(8) KRULL, WENDELL H.
    1939. ON THE LIFE HISTORY OF MONIEZIA EXPANSA AND CITTOTAENIA SP. (CESTODA: ANOPLOCEPHALIDAE). Helminthol. Soc. Wash. Proc. 6: 10–11.
(9) MÖNNIG, H. O.
    1937. ON THE TOXICITY OF NICOTINE FOR SHEEP AND THE USE OF THE NICOTINE-BLUESTONE DRENCH FOR WORMS IN RUMINANTS. Rev. de Med. Trop. y Parisitol. 3: 3–10.

(10) Ortlepp, R. J.
    1939. OBSERVATIONS ON THE LIFE-HISTORY OF BUNOSTOMUM TRIGONOCEPHA-
        LUM, A HOOKWORM OF SHEEP AND GOATS. Onderstepoort Jour. Vet.
        Sci. and Anim. Indus. 12: 305–318, illus.
(11) Ransom, [B. H.]
    1920. INTESTINAL LESIONS IN CALVES DUE TO COOPERIA PUNCTATA. Jour.
        Parasitol. 7: 96.
(12) Roberts, F. H. S.
    1939. THE GASTRO-INTESTINAL HELMINTHS OF CATTLE IN QUEENSLAND:
        THEIR DISTRIBUTION AND PATHOGENIC IMPORTANCE. Roy. Soc.
        Queensland Proc. (1938) 50: 46–54, illus.
(13) ———
    1940. PARASITIC WORM DISEASES OF CATTLE. Queensland Dept. Agr. and
        Stock, Div. Ent. and Plant Pathol. Advisory Leaflet 26, 20 pp.,
        illus.
(14) Schwartz, Benjamin.
    1924. PREPARASITIC STAGES IN THE LIFE HISTORY OF THE CATTLE HOOKWORM
        (BUSTOMUM PHLEBOTOMUM). Jour. Agr. Res. 29: 451–458, illus.
(15) Stiles, Ch. Wardell.
    1901. VERMINOUS DISEASES OF CATTLE, SHEEP, AND GOATS IN TEXAS. U. S.
        Dept. Agr., Bur. Anim. Indus., Ann. Rpt. 17 (1900): 356–379.
(16) Stoll, Norman R.
    1936. OBSERVATIONS ON CATTLE NEMATODE INFECTIONS, WITH A DEMONSTRA-
        TION OF THEIR SECONDARY TRANSMISSION TO GRAZING SHEEP. Jour.
        Parasitol. 22: 386–407.
(17) ———
    1938. TAPEWORM STUDIES VII. VARIATION IN PASTURE INFESTATION WITH
        M. EXPANSA. Jour. Parasitol. 24: 527–545, illus.
(18) Stunkard, Horace W.
    1937. THE LIFE CYCLE OF MONIEZIA EXPANSA. Science 86: 312.
(19) Swanson, L. E., Porter, D. A., and Connelly, J. W.
    1940. EFFICACY OF NONCONDITIONAL PHENOTHIAZINE IN REMOVING WORMS
        FROM ALIMENTARY CANAL OF CATTLE. Amer. Vet. Med. Assoc.
        Jour. 96: 704–707.
(20) Taylor, E. L.
    1937. PARASITIC GASTRITIS. THE TRANSFERENCE OF THE CAUSATIVE HEL-
        MINTHS FROM SHEEP TO CATTLE. Vet. Jour. 93: 353–355.

At the time this book went to press, the drugs
and other materials mentioned in various articles—chiefly as disinfectants, insecticides, and
anthelmintics—were still available for veterinary and medical use. Under war conditions,
however, it is possible that some of these materials may become scarce or unavailable. In
that case, the reader should obtain professional
advice from the Department of Agriculture, the
State experiment station, a local veterinarian,
or the county agent as to available substitutes.

Bovine Genital Trichomoniasis

BY G. DIKMANS [1]

ONLY WITHIN recent years were the wriggling micro-organisms known as trichomonads discovered to be a cause of abortion, sterility, and breeding difficulties in cattle. Prevention depends on a careful system of management, described in this article.

BOVINE GENITAL TRICHOMONIASIS is a disease of cattle characterized by difficulties in breeding, early abortions, temporary sterility, and pyometra (accumulation of pus in the uterus), without an accompanying fever.

The causative organism, technically named *Trichomonas foetus*, was first observed in association with genital disease of cattle by Mazzanti (5) [2] in Italy in 1900. He found it in the genital tracts of two cows and one heifer that were slaughtered because of permanent sterility. He considered it to be the cause of the sterility and named it *Trichomonas uterovaginalis vitulae*. The literature contains no further reference to trichomonads in connection with genital disease of cattle until 1925, when Drescher (3) reported finding them in pure culture in a bovine fetus aborted at 7 months. This rather striking 25-year lapse was probably due to the fact that since Bang's discovery in 1897 (2) of the organism causing infectious abortion in cattle, the idea that genital disease of cattle manifested by abortion, uterine infection, and sterility was Bang's disease, or brucellosis, dominated the thinking of veterinarians in this field. Only when breeding troubles occurred in the demonstrated absence of *Brucella abortus* were they attributed to other causes, such as coital exanthema (9).

---

[1] G. Dikmans is Parasitologist, Zoological Division, Bureau of Animal Industry.
[2] Italic numbers in parentheses refer to Literature Cited, p. 610.

605

Drescher's report was followed by other reports of similar findings, but they did not settle the problem of the relationship of the trichomonads to genital disease of cattle. Trichomonads had previously been reported from man and various animals. Some investigators considered them harmless, others as organisms responsible for the disease processes in which they were found, while a third group appeared to be of the opinion that trichomonads were secondary invaders unable to initiate pathological conditions but able to aggravate such conditions after they had become established.

Riedmüller in 1928 (*10*) reported finding trichomonads in nine aborted bovine fetuses. In two of these he found the organism in pure culture, in one he found both trichomonads and *Brucella abortus*, and in the remaining six he found trichomonads in association with other bacterial organisms. He described and drew the trichomonad and named it *Trichomonas foetus*.

Experiments conducted by Riedmüller, Abelein, Witte, and Kuest, reported in papers published between 1928 and 1934, showed that (1) trichomonads were found in aborted bovine fetuses, fetal membranes, and fetal fluids, and in the uterine and vaginal secretions of animals suffering from a condition known as infectious uterine catarrh; (2) these trichomonads both when mixed with bacterial organisms and in pure cultures were able to produce abortion in experimentally infected guinea pigs and cattle; (3) trichomonads occurred in the sheaths of bulls which on clinical and other grounds could be considered as responsible for genital disease of cattle mainfested by abortion, pyometra, and sterility; (4) the trichomonads could be transmitted from male to female and vice versa during coition; and (5) these manifestations of genital disease occurred in the absence of Bang's disease and coital exanthema.

In carefully controlled experiments Rees and his coworkers (*6, 7, 8*) in the United States were able to infect heifers and further demonstrate the ability of trichomonads to produce delayed conception, pyometra, and sterility. A bull was also infected through service with

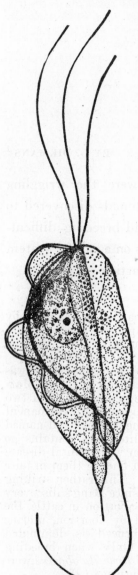

FIGURE 1.—The protozoan *Trichomonas foetus*. Greatly magnified.

an infected heifer, and this bull was subsequently used to infect cows and heifers.

Since 1925 the disease has been reported from several different countries—Germany, France, Italy, the Netherlands, Denmark, Norway, Japan, South Africa, Argentina, Mexico, and the United States. The first report of the occurrence of the disease in the United States was made by Emmerson in 1932 (*4*). Since then it has been reported by various authors from different parts of the country.

The protozoan that causes the disease (fig. 1) is a one-celled microscopic organism with three threadlike whips (flagella) at the front and one at the hind end. An undulating membrane at the back extends almost the entire length of the body. When examined alive, the organism moves across the field of vision of the microscope with an undulating motion; at times it turns and twists and assumes shapes varying from pear-shaped to oval or rounded. The rapidity of its movements depends to some extent on the medium in which it is examined.

SYMPTOMS AND DIAGNOSIS

Although *Trichomonas foetus* has been reported as occurring in the vagina of virgin heifers and in the prepuce of a young bull which, so far as known, had never been used for breeding purposes, the usual mode of transmission is by coitus.

As a result of infection one of several things may happen: (1) The animal may fail to conceive; (2) conception may take place and be followed by abortion; (3) the fetus may die and instead of being expelled may become macerated, while the uterus becomes filled with a characteristic thin, grayish-white, almost odorless fluid; or (4) a normal gestation and birth may occur in spite of infection.

Animals that fail to conceive may develop a uterine infection manifested by a vaginal discharge. This discharge may be continuous, or it may be intermittent, occurring chiefly during estrual periods, which may become irregular.

Abortion due to trichomoniasis may occur at any time during the period of gestation, but it usually takes place 8 to 16 weeks after coition. There are no signs of estrum during this period. A few days before abortion there is often a vaginal discharge. At times instead of a fetus only a small quantity of whitish mucoid fluid is expelled. The abortion may pass unobserved, especially if it occurs at night, in a dark stable, or on pasture. A few days after such an abortion the animal usually comes in heat, and this is often the first indication of infection.

When the fetus becomes macerated and is not expelled, the animal generally behaves like one normally pregnant. It shows no signs of illness, but the usual outward signs normally indicating approaching parturition fail to appear. At the end of the period of gestation there is no calf, and on examination the uterus is found to be filled with the fluid described.

Inflammation of the prepuce accompanied by pus formation and discharge has been reported in recently infected bulls. On examination the preputial mucosa and penis were found to be inflamed and to contain many small nodules similar to those occurring in bulls affected with nodular venereal disease.[3] In bulls the infection usually becomes chronic.

The breeding troubles mentioned very often follow the introduction into the herd of a new bull or new cow; hence the breeding histories of both the individual animals affected and of the herd are of material assistance in arriving at a correct diagnosis. Demonstration of the presence of the organism in vaginal or uterine discharges is necessary, however, to make the diagnosis complete. The immediate microscopic examination of material taken from the vagina or the sheath is the most direct method of making a diagnosis. When direct microscopic examination fails to reveal the organisms, as it frequently does, culturing the material may prove to be of great assistance.

One method of diagnosing trichomoniasis in the bull consists in the examination, 14 to 21 days after service, of heifers which have been bred for the first time. If trichomoniasis is being transmitted by the bulls under examination, the infection in the heifers will be vaginal at that time and the organisms can usually be readily demonstrated in samples of vaginal secretions. This method has been used with good results in herds having a breeding history indicative of trichomoniasis but in which the presence of trichomonads could not be demonstrated in the older animals. The two principal advantages of the method are that infection can be detected with relative ease and that it can be ascertained with certainty which bull or bulls are infected and transmitting the infection in the herd.

A tentative diagnosis of trichomoniasis can be made on the basis of the breeding history of the herd and of the individual animals. A demonstration of the presence of *Trichomonas foetus* in the suspected animals makes the diagnosis certain. Failure to demonstrate the presence of the organism when the herd history is strongly suggestive of trichomoniasis does not mean that the disease is not present; it may simply mean that the examination was not made at the right time and should be repeated.

TREATMENT, PREVENTION, AND CONTROL

There is no specific medicinal treatment for infected animals, and the disease should be handled like any other form of genital infection of cattle.

Cows that abort early in the period of gestation usually recover spontaneously. Such animals should be given a period of sexual rest for about 3 months. Cows showing persistent uterine discharge should be treated for the relief of this symptom. In some cases in which the fetus dies as a result of infection but is not expelled and the uterus becomes filled with fluid, the cervix relaxes when the end of the normal period of gestation approaches and the uterine contents are discharged. In other cases the cervix remains tightly closed, and the only practical way of determining the status of the animal is by manual examination through the rectum. In these cases the uterus should be emptied and douched in the usual manner.

---

[3] Trichomonads have been reported as occurring in the epididymis and in the ampullae of the vasa deferentia where these enter the urethra ; they have also been found in the anterior portion of the urethra.

Cows that, as a result of trichomonad infection, fail to conceive after repeated services should be given sexual rest until after two or three normal estrual cycles. They should receive such treatment as a veterinarian recommends.

Infected bulls have been considered incurable, and their destruction has been advocated as a means of eliminating sources of infection. This advice, while theoretically sound, is not always practical. Abelein (*1*) in 1938 described a treatment that has been used with apparent success in a few cases. It consists in injecting, under spinal anesthesia, 50 to 100 cubic centimeters of a 0.1-percent solution of trypaflavine into the urethra and rubbing a 0.5-percent trypaflavine salve into the inner surface of the prepuce. The treatment should be repeated in a week. Washing the penis of bulls infected with trichomonads with a warm 5-percent oxyquinoline sulfate solution (*11*) once every 8 to 10 days for a period of 3 months has also been reported as a successful method of treatment.

While the medicinal treatment of individual infected animals, whenever such treatment is necessary, is the problem of the attending veterinarian, the prevention of the disease and the handling of a herd into which it has been introduced are largely problems of management. Since the disease is spread principally by coitus, it should be quite apparent that the utmost caution should be exercised in the buying of mature animals as permanent additions to the herd. The breeding histories of all such animals, both male and female, and of the herds from which they come should be carefully examined. Bulls with poor breeding records, no matter what their blood lines may be, should not be admitted to the herd except with great caution.

Bringing cows known as hard or difficult breeders onto the premises for breeding purposes may be fraught with danger. It should be determined if possible why the animals are difficult breeders by securing information on the breeding conditions prevailing in the herd from which the animals came.

Permitting cows to be bred away from home may be equally dangerous. An animal may acquire trichomoniasis in the process and later serve as a source of infection in the home herd.

As a rule the disease is well established and a number of animals are infected before the owner or manager becomes aware of it. Since infection is spread by coitus and chronically infected bulls have been considered incurable, a practice followed in certain infected herds is advisable. This consists in restricting the use of infected bulls to cows that either have passed through an attack of the disease or have already been exposed to it. In large herds where a number of bulls are used and there is reason to believe that all of them are infected, the services of each bull can be restricted to certain groups of cows. New, uninfected bulls should be provided for cows that are definitely known not to be infected and to heifers coming of breeding age.

The few cases of trichomoniasis reported in unbred, virgin heifers have occurred in groups of heifers which had been in close contact with infected cows. The presence of trichomonad infection in these heifers is explained on the theory that infection was acquired by contact. There is at the present time no experimental evidence that contact infection can occur, but in order to be on the safe side, it is suggested that the calves and heifers in infected herds be definitely separated from the animals known to be infected.

RECOMMENDATIONS

The precautions that can and should be taken by herd owners and managers to prevent the introduction of trichomoniasis into their herds and to minimize the effects of the disease after it has been introduced may be summarized as follows:

(1) No mature animal should be bought as a permanent addition to the herd without a thorough investigation of its breeding record and of the herd from which it comes.

(2) No outside animals should be brought onto the premises for breeding purposes without knowledge of their breeding history and that of the herds from which they come.

(3) Cows should not be bred outside of the herd and away from the premises without taking similar precautions.

(4) If breeding troubles and difficulties occur in the herd, a veterinarian should be consulted. If after examination and consultation it is determined that the trouble is due to trichomoniasis, breeding operations should be stopped for a time and available records should be studied in order to determine which animals are infected and which may reasonably be suspected of being infected.

(5) The use of bulls known to be or suspected of being infected should be restricted to cows that have undergone an attack of the disease or have previously been exposed to infection.

(6) A new bull should be provided for heifers coming to breeding age and for the cows that have not been exposed.

LITERATURE CITED

(1) ABELEIN, R.
    1938. BEHANDLUNG VON BULLEN MIT TRICHOMONADEN. Deutsche Tierärztl. Wchnschr. 46: [721]–724, illus.
(2) BANG, B.
    1897. THE ETIOLOGY OF EPIZOOTIC ABORTION. Jour. Compar. Path. and Ther. 10: 125–149, illus.
(3) DRESCHER, [L.]
    1926. VERWERFEN UND JUNGTIERSTERBEN BEI SCHAFEN, SCHWEINEN, ZIEGEN. Ber. über die dritte Jahrestagung der Fachtierärzte. Bekämpf. Aufzuchtkrankheiten (1925), pp. 190–196.
(4) EMMERSON, M. A.
    1932. TRICHOMONIASIS IN CATTLE. A PRELIMINARY REPORT. Amer. Vet. Med. Assoc. Jour. 81: 636–640.
(5) MAZZANTI, E.
    1900. DUE OSSERVAZIONE ZOOPARASSITOLOGICHE. OSSERVAZIONE 2ª. DI UN NUOVO FLAGELLATO NELLA VITELLA. - R. Soc. ed Accad. Vet. Ital. Torino, Gior. 49: 629–631.
(6) REES, CHARLES W.
    1937. OBTAINING BACTERIA-FREE PURE LINES OF TRICHOMONAS FOETUS BY MEANS OF MICROISOLATION. Amer. Jour. Hyg. 26: 283–291.

(7) REES, CHARLES W.
  1938. OBSERVATIONS ON BOVINE VENEREAL TRICHOMONIASIS. Vet. Med. 33:
    321–334, illus.
(8) REES, CHARLES W., and GARLICK, GEORGE G.
  1939. EXPERIMENTAL TRANSMISSION OF BOVINE VENEREAL TRICHOMONIASIS.
    Jour. Agr. Res. 59: 769–775.
(9) REISINGER, L.
  1928. UNTERSUCHUNGEN ÜBER EIN IN ÖSTERREICH GEHÄUFT AUFTRETENDES,
    JEDOCH NICHT DURCH DEN BANSCHEN BAZILLUS VERURSACHTES VER-
    WERFEN DER RINDER. Wien. Tierärztl. Monatsschr. 15: [49]–58,
    102–111, 169–178.
(10) RIEDMÜLLER, L.
  1928. UEBER DIE MORPHOLOGIE, UEBERTRAGUNGSVERSUCHE UND KLINISCHE
    BEDEUTUNG DER BEIM SPORADISCHEN ABORTUS DES RINDES VORKOM-
    MENDEN TRICHOMONADEN. Centbl. f. Bakt. [etc.], Originale I,
    108: 103–118, illus.
(11) SCHMIDT, H., TURK, R. D!, and SHEPARDSON, C. N.
  1937. TRICHOMONAD ABORTION IN CATTLE. Tex. Agr. Expt. Sta. Ann. Rpt.
    (1937) 50: 14–15.

Cattle Grubs, or Heel Flies

BY E. W. LAAKE, F. C. BISHOPP,
AND R. W. WELLS [1]

THE ANNUAL LOSSES attributed to cattle grubs
are estimated conservatively at 50 million dollars a
year, but some authorities believe they are twice that
high. At any rate, this enemy of beef and dairy producers deserves serious attention. The methods that
entomologists have worked out to combat it are
described in this article.

CATTLE GRUBS, also called wolves or warbles, are the maggot stage of
insects known as heel flies, warble flies, or gadflies. Such grubs do a
great deal of damage that affects cattlemen, dairymen, packers, tan-
ners, and finally, consumers. In the United States there are two
species with similar habits. The common cattle grub (*Hypoderma
lineatum* DeVill.) has become established in every State, but the
northern cattle grub (*Hypoderma bovis* DeGeer) has not yet been
found in the South.

LIFE HISTORY OF THE CATTLE GRUB

Heel flies (fig. 1) develop from grubs that have dropped from the
backs of cattle. The common heel flies appear during the first warm
days of spring, and their activity increases as the season advances,
until at the end of about 6 weeks the last of them has disappeared.

The eggs, of which one fly often deposits as many as 300, are
cemented skillfully to hair close to the skin of the animal, usually
low on the legs, particularly just above the hoof (hence the name
"heel fly"), but frequently, if the animal is lying down, on the

[1] E. W. Laake is Senior Entomologist, F. C. Bishopp, Assistant Chief, and R. W. Wells,
Associate Entomologist, Bureau of Entomology and Plant Quarantine.

escutcheon and along the hair of the udder and the belly. The eggs of the common cattle grub are usually attached one above another (fig. 2) and those of the northern species singly. The warmth of the host's body enables the eggs to hatch within 3 to 5 days, and the tiny larvae (fig. 3) emerging from the eggshells force their way at once through the skin and into the deeper tissues. There the larvae move about constantly but slowly for about 9 months, feeding and growing. They have been found in many locations within the host,

FIGURE 1.—The common heel fly, female. Enlarged about 2½ times.

particularly in the connective tissue on the surface of the organs in the abdomen and between the mucous and muscular layers of the gullet and spinal canal.[2]

The northern heel flies do not appear so early, and their activity is extended over a longer period. The grubs of this species are most abundant in the backs of cattle after those of the common heel fly have practically disappeared. Not uncommonly a few of the northern grubs are found in cattle even in August; this overlapping prolongs the fly season in the Northern States and complicates the grub problem there.

---

[2] BISHOPP, F. C., LAAKE, E. W., BRUNDRETT, H. M., and WELLS, R. W. THE CATTLE GRUBS OR OX WARBLES, THEIR BIOLOGIES AND SUGGESTIONS FOR CONTROL. U. S. Dept. Agr., Dept. Bul. 1369. 120 pp., illus. 1926.
  BISHOPP, F. C., LAAKE, E. W., and WELLS, R. W. CATTLE GRUBS OR HEEL FLIES WITH SUGGESTIONS FOR THEIR CONTROL. U. S. Dept. Agr. Farmers' Bul. 1596, 22 pp., illus. 1936. (Revised.)

FIGURE 2.—Eggs of the common heel fly attached to a hair. Greatly enlarged.

The male and female flies live only a few days, rarely longer than a week. They have no need of food and no mouth parts with which to eat. After mating, the females have only one purpose—to deposit their eggs on the hairs of cattle. They do not sting or inflict any pain, as many persons believe. Feeling their touch or sensing their presence, however, cattle are instinctively terrorized.

FIGURE 3.—First-stage larva of the common heel fly. Greatly enlarged.

After approximately 9 months the larvae arrive at the back of the animal, where each larva makes a hole through the skin (fig. 4). Shortly thereafter a pocket, or cyst, developed from the tissues of the host, forms around the larva, and in this the larva remains for 5 weeks or longer. It molts twice after it reaches the back (figs. 5 and 6). As it grows, it causes a swelling, which usually becomes conspicuous, so that a grubby back has a lumpy appearance. After the second molt the white larva begins to darken, turning yellow, then light brown, then dark brown, and finally black

FIGURE 4.—A cow with holes in its back where grubs are located.

when it is about ready to leave the host. Working its way out of the animal's back, it drops to the ground, where it becomes a pupa. If the temperature is not too low, the grubs crawl about for a while before pupating; some go slightly under the surface of the soil, some creep into shallow crevices or underneath leaves or clods, but many have been observed to pupate fully exposed on the surface. In any case, the onset of pupation is not delayed by a search for shelter but begins wherever the larva may be when the temperature is favorable, and the process progresses until the fly is ready to emerge from the pupa case (fig. 7). The period of pupation is affected largely by the temperature and varies from 6 to 10 weeks in the natural environment. The shortest pupal period recorded is about 18 days at a constant temperature of 85° F.

FIGURE 5.—The second instar (stage between molts) of the grub after the first molt in the back. Much enlarged.

Thus the parasite is capable of passing abruptly from a long period within a warm host to a period of comparatively severe exposure on the ground, where metamorphosis takes place and the new generation reaches adulthood.

SEASONAL OCCURRENCE

In the central part of Texas, heel fly activity has been known to begin on the first warm days of February and to extend until the middle of March. Farther south it begins somewhat earlier; farther north, later. Thus, if a person started walking at San Antonio, Tex., on February 1 and reached Vermont by the first of August,

FIGURE 6.—The third, or final, instar of the grub after the second molt in the back. From left to right, the changes in size and pigmentation as growth proceeds. About natural size.

he might see heel flies active on every warm day along his route. When all grubs have dropped from the backs of cattle at Fort Worth, Tex., they have scarcely begun to appear in the backs of cattle in the northern part of Iowa.

NATURE AND AMOUNT OF LOSSES

The annual losses attributable to the heel fly and its larvae are estimated to amount to at least 50 million dollars, and some investigators put them as high as 100 million dollars. Considering the various ways in which the losses occur, it is evident that the toll is very heavy and that the estimates given are not exaggerated.

The activity of one heel fly is at times sufficient to stampede an entire herd of placid cattle. The fly settles on the hoof or lower leg

FIGURE 7.—The pupa case after the fly has emerged. Somewhat enlarged.

of one of the herd to deposit an egg; the animal shows apprehension, then fear, and finally starts on a mad rush to elude the fly, tail hoisted in a gesture which to all cattle unmistakably means the presence of a heel fly. In the subsequent scramble, the animals may rush over cliffs and through fences. A common refuge is a mudhole or swamp, where frequently many cattle become hopelessly bogged. In addition to incurring immediate casualties, the animals may huddle in shade or stand in water, refusing to feed throughout the day, so that they lose or fail to gain weight, as many ranchers can testify. Calves are deprived of milk, and the dairyman suffers a heavy loss through decline in milk production, which can be readily estimated. Particularly striking are the losses on large ranches where the cattle are disturbed by heel flies when they are weak from winter conditions and some have baby calves.

Various types of irritation result when the larvae enter the tissues and while they remain. When a large number of grubs are accumulating in the back they cause edema, or swelling, often followed by pus formation. Death occasionally follows. The carcasses of cattle slaughtered before the grubs have reached the back exhibit in the affected areas yellowish, watery patches known to butchers as jellied or licked beef. This has to be trimmed away and discarded. Even though the quality of the meat is not affected, the trimming disfigures the carcass and reduces its salability. Another loss to packers is caused by the presence of the young grubs in the gullet, or weasand. The grubs have to be trimmed off, and many weasands, which otherwise would be used for sausage casings, are punctured and made valueless.

Grubs cause tremendous losses in leather. Commonly as many as 40 and occasionally 100 or more grub holes are found in a hide. Even after the grubs leave the back, the scars remain for several months, impairing the quality of the skin for leather. Records collected by the Institute of American Meat Packers at one plant and its subsidiaries over a 4-year period show that 42 percent of all hides were grubby. According to trade custom, if a hide has as many as 5 grub holes it is classed as grade No. 2 and is subject to a discount of 1 cent a pound. A hide with many grub holes is not considered worth tanning and is sold for byproducts.

CONTROL MEASURES

Scientists in many countries have proposed methods for controlling cattle grubs, and much attention has been given to the development of effective and practical control methods.

The heel fly is not found in certain areas in the United States—in the Red River Valley of the North, in Minnesota and North Dakota, or in the southern part of Florida. Investigators of the Department

FIGURE 8.—Applying cube-sulfur wash to the backs of cattle with a brush for the control of cattle grubs.

of Agriculture have concluded that the soils of the Red River Valley are so impervious and the terrain so level that the pupae from grubs dropped from infested cattle brought into this area are kept thoroughly wet while on the ground and thus are killed.

Many substances have been applied to cattle to keep away heel flies and to kill the eggs deposited on the legs of the animals. All have been found to be either ineffective or impractical.

Extensive work on the problem indicates that the best time for attacking the pest is when the grubs are in the backs of the cattle and accessible through the holes they have cut through the skin. Each grub that is permitted to mature and drop to the ground may become a fly, and each female fly is capable of laying hundreds of eggs. Squeezing the grubs out with the hands or extracting them with forceps, if carried out systematically on isolated herds, will keep the pests under control. In some areas in closely settled foreign countries, this method is reputed to have eradicated the grubs. Cattlemen in the United States, however, have found it too slow and difficult for general adoption, although some dairymen have practically eliminated the pest from their herds in this way. Among individual animals and breeds there is much variation in the ease with which the

FIGURE 9.—Cube-sulfur spray being applied to the backs of cattle with a power sprayer for control of cattle grubs.

grubs can be extracted by hand. They are far more easily removed from animals of the Island breeds than from most others.

Research workers of the Bureau of Entomology and Plant Quarantine have experimented with many substances that can be easily applied to the backs of cattle for killing the grubs before they leave the animals, and some have been found to be very effective. The most satisfactory are cube powder and derris powder, the finely ground roots of tropical plants widely used as insecticides. The insecticidal element in these powders, known as rotenone, usually varies in amount from 2 to 6 percent; material containing 5 percent is recommended. When the powder is properly applied, practically every grub is killed, and no injury to the animal results. Some of the dead grubs slip out of the back; the others are absorbed by the animal. The powders have been used extensively by dairymen, farmers, and ranchers in many parts of the United States; and where they are used systematically, there has been a very marked reduction in the numbers of heel flies and grubs.

The insecticide may be applied dry, by sifting it lightly over the back and rubbing it into the coat of hair with the hands; the process is made easier and the effectiveness of the drug is increased if it is mixed with equal parts by weight of wettable sulfur (325 mesh). Another effective method is to mix the drug in water and apply it thoroughly as a wash with a stiff brush (fig. 8). The easiest, quickest, and most economical method, however, especially for treating a large number of cattle, is to use a power-operated, high-pressure orchard sprayer, controlling the cattle in a chute, as shown in figure 9. For this treatment the following formula is recommended:

Cube or derris powder (5 percent rotenone)_____ 5 pounds
Wettable sulfur_____ 10 pounds
Water _____ 100 gallons

The nozzle is adjusted to produce a medium-fine spray, and the operator stands on a walkway beside the chute, high enough up so that he can readily direct the spray downward with force on the back of each animal. By this method a crew of 6 men can handle and treat about 100 cattle an hour, the number depending on the arrangement and convenience of the pens and chute. The spraying method is more economical in quantity of material required than either of the other two.

Detailed information on methods of controlling cattle grubs is presented in Bureau of Entomology and Plant Quarantine Circular E–496.[3]

---

[3] WELLS, R. W. THE USE OF DERRIS AND CUBE WASHES IN THE CONTROL OF CATTLE GRUBS. U. S. Bur. Ent. and Plant Quar. Cir. E–496. 5 pp. 1940. [Processed.]

At the time this book went to press, the drugs and other materials mentioned in various articles—chiefly as disinfectants, insecticides, and anthelmintics—were still available for veterinary and medical use. Under war conditions, however, it is possible that some of these materials may become scarce or unavailable. In that case, the reader should obtain professional advice from the Department of Agriculture, the State experiment station, a local veterinarian, or the county agent as to available substitutes.

The Stablefly

BY F. C. BISHOPP AND E. W. LAAKE [1]

MOST PEOPLE in temperate climates are familiar
with the stablefly, or biting housefly, which lives on
blood, maddens animals, makes vicious attacks on
human beings, and can spread some serious diseases.
What can be done to get rid of it?

THE STABLEFLY (*Stomoxys calcitrans*), also called the stock fly, the
biting housefly, and, in the Southeastern States, the dog fly, is found
in all the temperate regions of the world. The adults, both male
and female, are vicious bloodsuckers with long, piercing mouth parts
that on penetrating the skin cause considerable pain to animals or
human beings. This fly has been shown to be capable of carrying
such livestock diseases as anthrax, swamp fever, and surra, as well as
infantile paralysis of man.

Although the stablefly is principally an annoyance to man and
animals, in large outbreaks it may kill horses and cattle by causing
them continuous worry and loss of blood. In some localities—along
beaches, for example—it has seriously affected resort interests and
lowered the value of real estate by driving people away. It is difficult
to control horses when these flies become very numerous; the condition
of the animals is impaired, their efficiency is greatly decreased, and
farm operations are often seriously hampered. Favorite points of
attack by the stablefly are the ears of dogs, hogs, and rabbits, which
become raw and swollen when numerous punctures are inflicted. The
milk production of dairy herds is lowered during every stablefly
season, the decrease amounting to as much as 50 percent in seasons
when the numbers of flies become large. During such seasons dairy
cows and other domestic animals have been known to lose as much
as 10 to 15 percent of their weight. The continuous attacks of the
flies cause constant fighting and restlessness among the animals, and
in seeking natural protection they frequently resort to mudholes or
swamps, where they may stand for hours, often developing swollen
feet and even becoming mired. Such losses and methods of avoiding
them have been discussed in a number of publications.[2]

---

[1] F. C. Bishopp is Assistant Chief and E. W. Laake is Senior Entomologist, Bureau of
Entomology and Plant Quarantine.
[2] See p. 621 for footnote.

LIFE HISTORY AND HABITS

The life history of the stablefly is like that of other true flies in that it has four stages—egg, larva, pupa, and adult fly.

The eggs (fig. 1, *A*) are creamy white, elongate oval, and about one twenty-fifth of an inch long. The adult females lay the eggs in loose masses or singly on fermenting organic matter such as straw or manure. The flies appear to have a keen sense of smell by which they can quickly detect fermenting vegetation or fresh manure. Usually they crawl into the loose vegetation and deposit their eggs in suitably moist material. The egg hatches in 1 to 3 days, producing a tiny, creamy-white maggot, or larva.

Because of careful selection of a breeding place by the parent fly, the larvae have no difficulty in finding ample food nearby. They feed and grow until they are mature, when they are a third to a half inch long (fig. 1, *B*). During moist warm weather larvae may grow to maturity in 6 or 7 days, but during cool weather this may require a month or more. While developing, they undergo two molts and increase in size but do not change their general appearance. The character and abundance of food, the amount of moisture present, and the heat generated by the fermenting vegetation greatly influence the development of the larvae. When mature, they seek a moist, protected place and change to pupae.

The pupa (fig 1, *C*) is formed simply by a shortening and thickening of the larva and is transformed directly into the adult fly. The period required for this transformation varies from 5 to 20 days or longer, depending on climatic conditions. Immediately after pupation, the pupa is yellowish or orange in color, but as it ages it darkens, first to light brown and finally to dark brown or almost black.

The fly (fig. 1, *D*) emerges from the pupal case by splitting open one end and forcing its way out. It then crawls up to the surface of the medium in which the pupa was buried, expands its wings, grooms itself for a while, and takes off on its first flight.

The flies usually feed on blood once a day, but during long, hot summer days may feed twice daily. They also suck moisture from vegetation, manure, and fermenting materials. During cold weather they may not feed for several days, but as soon as the weather becomes warm they resume their attacks upon animals.

Laboratory-reared flies begin mating when they are 2 to 3 days old, and well-fed females begin laying eggs by the time they are 5 days old. A female usually lays several egg masses, each containing from a few to about 50 eggs. After laying a mass of eggs, the fly must have one to three meals before another mass is developed. Stableflies have been kept alive for a month and a half in laboratory cages, and one female under observation laid as many as 600 eggs.

Stableflies are swift, strong fliers. They sometimes follow animals

[2] BISHOPP, F. C. THE STABLE FLY (STOMOXYS CALCITRANS L.), AN IMPORTANT LIVE STOCK PEST. Jour. Econ. Ent. 6: 112–127, illus. 1913.
BISHOPP, F. C. THE STABLE FLY: HOW TO PREVENT ITS LOSSES AND ITS ANNOYANCE TO LIVESTOCK. U. S. Dept. Agr. Farmers' Bul. 1097, 23 pp., illus. 1920. (Revised, 1939.)
UNITED STATES BUREAU OF ENTOMOLOGY AND PLANT QUARANTINE. STABLE FLIES. U. S. Bur. Ent. and Plant Quar., Insects in Relation to National Defense Cir. 17, 12 pp., illus. 1941. [Processed.]

FIGURE 1.—The stablefly: *A*, Eggs; *B*, larva; *C*, pupa; and *D*, adult.   Greatly enlarged.

for miles, making repeated efforts to bite. That these flies are capable of long flights has been demonstrated by experiments in which large numbers were marked with coloring material and then released. Some of the marked flies were recaptured at distances up to 52 miles from the point of release. It appears from field observations that the flies drift with prevailing winds.

Ordinarily stablefly attacks are confined to the lower parts of an animal's body, particularly the outer sides of the front legs (fig. 2), where the animal's tail is less likely to dislodge them. When the flies are very abundant, however, t h e y may attack all parts of the body. Unmolested flies usually engorge to repletion in 2 to 5 minutes. When full, they rest on a nearby object to digest the meal.

More detailed information on the life history and habits of this pest has been published by Bishopp,[3] Hewitt,[4] and Mitzmain.[5]

CONTROL MEASURES

The elimination of man - made breeding places is of first importance in controlling the stablefly.

In the Grain Belt, straw, especially oat straw, is the chief medium in which flies breed in enormous numbers. The combine has been a bless-

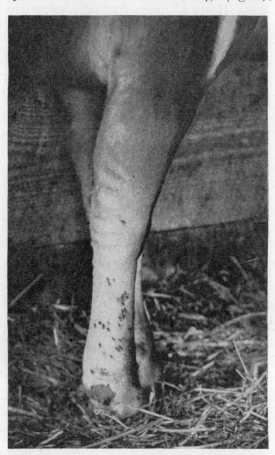

FIGURE 2.—Stableflies on the forelegs of an animal, a favorite place of attack.

ing in eliminating a considerable amount of this breeding material, but where combines are not used, much straw is still being stacked.

[3] See footnote 2, p. 621, first citation.
[4] HEWITT, C. GORDON. OBSERVATIONS ON THE FEEDING HABITS OF THE STABLE FLY, STOMOXYS CALCITRANS L. Roy. Soc. Canada Trans. (1914), Ser. 3, Sect. IV, 8 : 37–42, illus. 1914.
[5] MITZMAIN, M. BRUIN. THE BIONOMICS OF STOMOXYS CALITRANS LINNAEUS ; A PRELIMINARY ACCOUNT. Philippine Jour. Sci. (B) 8 : 29–48. 1913.

Immediate baling of straw that is desired for feeding and bedding purposes is of paramount importance in controlling this fly in the Grain Belt. The stalk butts left after baling should be well scattered. Where baling is impossible, proper stacking of the straw at threshing time so as to prevent the rains from penetrating it will greatly reduce stablefly breeding (fig. 3).

Manure, especially when mixed with straw, corn husks, silage, and alfalfa in barnyards or feed lots, provides a breeding place for many flies. Heaps of grass clippings, celery trimmings, or other decaying vegetation in pastures or fields are also fertile breeding places. All this material should be scattered thinly at least once a week, or preferably twice, so that it may dry quickly. Neither stableflies nor houseflies can breed in dry vegetable matter, and few are able to develop in moist or wet vegetable matter or manure when it is scattered thinly.

In areas where peanuts are grown extensively for the nuts, the litter

FIGURE 3.—A strawstack being constructed to prevent breeding of stableflies.

left in piles after the nuts are harvested has been found by Dove and Simmons [6] to serve as a breeding place for great numbers of stableflies. It is advisable to scatter this litter and plow it under immediately after the peanuts are harvested.

It has also been discovered recently that bay grasses washed up in windrows on certain beaches along the Gulf coast by high tides and storms serve as natural breeding material for stableflies. Experiments conducted by Simmons and Dove [7] have shown that a mixture of 1 part of creosote oil and 3 parts of No. 2 fuel oil driven deep into

[6] DOVE, W. E., and SIMMONS, S. W. CONTROL OF DOG FLY BREEDING IN PEANUT LITTER. U. S. Bur. Ent. and Plant Quar. Cir. E-542. 4 pp. 1941. [Processed.]
[7] SIMMONS, S. W., and DOVE, W. E. CONTROL OF DOG FLY BREEDING IN BEACH DEPOSITS OF MARINE GRASSES. U. S. Bur. Ent. and Plant Quar. Cir. E-541, 8 pp. 1941. [Processed.]

the windrows by a power sprayer, using at least 300 pounds pressure, makes such material unsuitable as a breeding place.

Stableflies that develop in natural breeding material beyond man's control can be effectively reduced in numbers by secondary control methods such as traps and sprays. Traps cannot be depended upon, however, for complete control.

The Hodge window trap and electric grids properly installed in barn windows will catch or electrocute most of the flies carried into the barns on animals. It should be remembered, however, that stableflies remain on animals for only relatively short periods while they feed, and therefore only those flies that happen to be on an animal when it goes into the barn will be caught.

The cattle fly trap developed by the Bureau of Entomology and Plant Quarantine, which is highly effective in ridding cattle of horn flies (see p. 629 of this volume), will also catch considerable numbers of stableflies provided cattle go through this trap once or twice daily on their way to water, to feed, or into the dairy barn; but here again only the flies that happen to be on the animals at the moment they pass through the trap will be caught.

Sprays are undoubtedly the best secondary means for controlling stableflies. Rotenone-oil sprays and pyrethrum-oil sprays properly made not only kill all the flies on an animal at the time of spraying but also leave a residue on the coat which will kill flies attacking the animal within several hours. Rotenone is extracted from the roots of derris and cube plants and pyrethrins from the flowers of pyrethrum plants. Each of these extracts is a powerful insect poison, and both are now widely marketed in concentrated form. Five percent of either of the extracts in an odorless, water-white kerosene, also commonly known as a light spray oil, makes an excellent spray. Sprays containing 10 percent of these concentrated extracts in a light spray oil are even more effective, since they afford almost perfect protection for a day or more, instead of only several hours, after spraying. If the animals are sprayed while their hair is dry, rain will not remove much of the toxic residues, since both of these insect poisons are practically insoluble in water. Three-fourths to one and one-half ounces of the spray, depending on the size of the animal, is sufficient for good coverage if it is lightly but uniformly applied with a good atomizer or hand sprayer. Since stableflies bite mostly on the legs and lower parts of the body, it is particularly important that these parts be completely covered by the spray. Sprays are also effective in controlling horn flies and reducing the number of houseflies.

The Horn Fly

BY W. G. BRUCE [1]

IT CAN BE a serious matter when 4,000 to 10,000 stabbing flies stay on an animal day and night, each taking two meals of blood a day. Here are the facts about a particularly vicious insect and how to combat it.

PROBABLY no fly is more familiar to the cattlemen of the United States than the small black, bloodsucking horn fly (*Haematobia irritans*), also known as the cattle fly, stock fly, cow fly, and third-party fly. Throughout the summer months these pestiferous flies congregate by the hundreds, often by the thousands, on the backs, shoulders, and bellies of cattle (fig. 1), and the continuous stabbing by the hundreds of stilettolike mouth parts of the insects causes the animals endless misery. The tormented cattle often refuse to graze during the day and seek protection by hiding in the brush or tall grass until nightfall, when horn flies are less active.

The injury to cattle caused by horn flies is due to irritation and worry, loss of blood, reduced vitality, and the production of sores that become infested with screwworms. Like all flies that bite intermittently, the horn fly is also a potential disease carrier.

The interruption to the feeding and rest of cattle interferes with normal digestion, and this, together with the loss of blood and the expenditure of energy in fighting the flies, results in loss of flesh and reduced milk production.

Horn flies usually feed twice a day, sometimes more frequently. While the loss of blood caused by one fly may appear negligible. the total loss caused by thousands of these pests infesting a herd of cattle may be illustrated by the following example. On a ranch in Texas where there are about 500 head of cattle, the usual horn fly infestation is approximately 4,000 flies to each animal. The loss of blood from this herd is roughly 7 quarts a day, or about 2,713 pounds, or 312 gallons, a year.

It is difficult to estimate the economic loss due to horn fly attacks, but it is probably not less than 3 million dollars annually. The horn

[1] W. G. Bruce is Associate Entomologist, Division of Insects Affecting Man and Animals, Bureau of Entomology and Plant Quarantine.

fly may not be the most serious pest attacking cattle, but certainly it is one that inflicts considerable damage and should be controlled.

DESCRIPTION AND HABITS

The horn fly is about half the size of the common housefly or the common stablefly, but unlike these two larger flies it remains on the cattle throughout the day and night. One peculiar characteristic of the horn fly is its habit of always resting with the head pointed downward.

Horn flies confine their attacks chiefly to cattle, but they are not

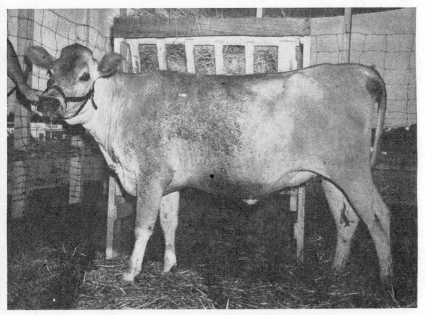

FIGURE 1.—A heifer heavily infested with horn flies.

uncommon on sheep. Occasionally they attack goats, horses, mules, dogs, and, more rarely, human beings. The numbers of horn flies on cattle vary considerably in different localities and at different times of the year. Infestations of 4,000 flies per head are common on cattle in parts of Texas and Oklahoma, and frequently as many as 10,000 have been seen on one animal. The most favorable climatic condition for horn fly development is warm, damp, cloudy weather; hot, dry weather or cold weather is unfavorable to the flies. In general it may be stated that temperature determines the presence of horn flies and moisture conditions determine their abundance.

Horn flies leave the cow only to lay eggs. When a cow infested with horn flies voids a dropping, a large number of the flies immediately swarm to it, and practically all of them crawl beneath it. Here they lay their shiny brown eggs and within 5 to 10 minutes return to the cow. Protected from the sun and rain, the eggs hatch into tiny white maggots in about 16 hours. These maggots immediately crawl into the dropping, where they feed and grow. Ordinarily they become full-grown in 4 days; then they crawl down into the lower part of the dropping or into the soil to pupate.

In pupating, the maggot draws itself up into a small barrel-shaped object, and the outer skin becomes hard and brownish. Inside the hard brown shell the maggot is transformed into a fly. About 6 days after the pupal case is formed, it splits open at one end, and a horn fly emerges.

The newly emerged fly is short, leggy, wingless, and dark-colored, resembling a small spider more than it does a fly. It crawls rapidly away, seeking a favorable place to complete its development, and finally comes to rest somewhere out of the wind, at or near the top of an upright blade of grass or on the side of the dropping. It then starts to distend the abdomen, an operation that requires about 5 minutes. Then follows the unfolding of the wings, slowly at first, until they are about a third unfolded, then quite rapidly. This takes about 2 minutes and is followed by a rather prolonged grooming of the wings with the hind legs. Immediately after the wings are unfolded the body of the fly becomes a light ash-gray color. After 4 or 5 minutes the color begins to darken, and 10 minutes later the fly has assumed its final dark-gray color. About 1 hour after the fly emerges from its pupal case it attempts a few short trial flights and then seeks the nearest cow, upon which it settles.

Mating of horn flies has been observed as early as the second day after emergence, and fertile eggs were deposited 1 day later. On an average, the change from egg to adult, during the summer months, takes 9 to 12 days. The adult horn fly lives about 7 weeks, during which time a female is capable of producing 375 to 400 eggs.

CONTROL MEASURES

Fortunately there are several methods by which horn flies can be controlled. The one chosen on a particular farm will depend upon the system of livestock management.

One of the first practical measures is to destroy the maggots in the cattle droppings. This may be accomplished by dragging brush or a spike-tooth harrow over the pasture to break up the droppings, or by scattering them with a manure fork or shovel so that they will dry out rapidly and the maggots will not be able to survive. This method of horn fly control is feasible only in small pastures.

The accumulations of cattle manure around barns should be hauled to the fields and spread thinly, preferably by the use of a manure spreader, at least three times a week.

Horn flies are easily killed by most of the livestock sprays now in common use. These sprays are ordinarily made by mixing an extract of pyrethrum with kerosene oil. An economical and efficient spray can be made from any of the various forms of pyrethrum extract sold by reliable dealers by mixing it with the oil according to the directions on the container. Thorough spraying with a good hand or power sprayer, one that will generate a fine mist, is necessary for effective control. In spraying cattle with pyrethrum sprays for horn flies, it is not necessary to direct the spray onto the animal. It is better to generate a fine mist around the animal, especially around the legs and under the belly.

Repellents are often recommended for protecting cattle from horn flies, but they are impractical; it is almost impossible to apply repellents to cattle on the range, and the use of these materials, which usually have obnoxious odors and will taint the milk, is not desirable on dairy cows.

An effective cattle fly trap for the control of horn flies has been developed by the Bureau of Entomology and Plant Quarantine.[2] The trap (fig. 2) is constructed in a gateway of a fence surrounding the water supply or in a lane or other place where cattle will be com-

FIGURE 2.—A cow passing through a cattle fly trap.

pelled to pass through it daily on their way to and from water, feed, or some frequented place. The framework of the trap is 7 feet wide, 6 feet high, and 10 feet long. The passageway through the trap is 33 inches wide and is lined along the sides with heavy, large-mesh wire fencing. On each side of the passageway, set behind the fencing, are three trapping elements made of 18-mesh screen in modified tent-trap construction—that is, the screen on the side of the element facing the passageway is folded in a series of Z's. At the inner fold of each Z is a series of holes through which the flies enter the trapping

[2] BRUCE, W. G. A CATTLE FLY TRAP FOR THE CONTROL OF HORN FLIES. U. S. Bur. Ent. and Plant Quar. Cir. E–498, 6 pp., illus. 1940. [Processed.]

element. Two sets of curtains and eight weighted strips are used to
dislodge the flies from the animals. As an animal passes through the
trap, the curtains brush the flies from its back and sides, and the
weighted strips flap around the legs and belly, dislodging flies not
reached by the curtains. The flies attempt to escape through the
trapping elements and are captured. The trap is, under many circumstances, the most efficient, economical, and practical method of horn
fly control.

Some experimental work has been done on the internal medication
of cattle for the control of horn fly larvae in the droppings.[3] The
idea was to administer by mouth chemicals that would pass out in the
droppings and make them poisonous to horn fly larvae. Some of
the chemicals proved to be effective, but they cannot yet be recommended for general use. Rotenone (an extract of derris, cube, and
other substances) was the most effective material tested; when administered to cattle daily at the rate of 0.4 gram per 100 pounds of body
weight of the animal, it killed all the larvae in the droppings. Zinc
oxide, a cheap, common chemical, was also effective when fed daily
at the rate of 1.5 grams per 100 pounds of body weight. Neither
rotenone nor zinc oxide had any apparent harmful effect on the cattle.

---

[3] BRUCE, W. G. THE MEDICATION OF CATTLE FOR THE CONTROL OF HORN FLIES. Kans.
Ent. Soc. Jour. 13 (2) : 41–43. 1940.

Cattle Lice

BY O. G. BABCOCK AND E. C. CUSHING [1]

THERE ARE four kinds of lice that make the lives of cattle miserable and in severe attacks reduce gains and put the animals off condition. Here these pests are described, together with the best methods for get• ting rid of them.

SEVERAL SPECIES OF LICE prey upon calves and mature cattle throughout the United States. They also attack buffaloes and cattaloes (a hybrid between the buffalo and domestic cattle). The damage they do to animals varies greatly according to the degree of infestation.

In general the number of lice infesting cattle increases slowly during the fall months, then much more rapidly during the winter and spring. Often the animals become literally covered with lice and louse eggs before the louse population begins to decline with the advent of hot weather. This may be true for any one or all of the species present. White or light-colored cattle may be so heavily infested as to appear black.

It has been claimed that certain breeds of cattle are more subject to lousiness than others and that Jerseys are the least likely to be infested. Observations indicate, however, that no particular breed is more immune to the attacks of these pests than others.

Heavily infested cattle may in rare cases succumb, but usually the loss takes the form of a reduction of flesh in full-grown animals and slow growth in calves. The mature animals on feed do not make proper gains in weight; they do not eat well, and their vitality is greatly lowered. Their generally unthrifty condition is indicated by a depressed attitude and a mangy appearance of the coat and skin brought about partly by constant rubbing, which results in loss of hair in patches, chronic sores, and bleeding wounds. During the winter such animals suffer severely. Lousy animals make a poor showing at fairs and stock shows.

[1] O. G. Babcock is Associate Entomologist and E. C. Cushing is Principal Entomologist, Division of Insects Affecting Man and Animals, Bureau of Entomology and Plant Quarantine.

SPECIES OF CATTLE LICE

Four species of lice are known to infest cattle in the United States.
Only one, the red louse, *Bovicola bovis* (see fig. 1), is a biting
louse; the others suck blood. The biting louse obtains its food by
chewing hairs and particles of skin. It is small and reddish in color
when mature, the abdomen having reddish bands running crosswise.
These lice, especially in the late spring and often during the summer,
will sometimes literally cover an
animal, and when feed is short on
the range calves have been known
to die from the effects of such infestations. Young calves infested
with the lice are often severely
stunted in growth.

Two of the three species of
bloodsucking lice that attack cattle are commonly referred to as
blue lice. One, *Lingonathus vituli*
(fig. 2), is very common and is dis-
ributed throughout the United
States. The other, called *Sole-
nopsis capillatus*, is probably more
widely distributed than is usually
supposed. This louse is a little
shorter than the other blue louse
but very closely resembles it in
general appearance.

These blue, or long-nosed, lice
develop in patches on different
parts of the body and can be very
easily seen, especially on the noses
of white-faced animals.

FIGURE 1.—A biting louse, *Bovicola bovis*,
dorsal view.

Another louse, resembling and
related to the hog louse but smaller,
is known as the short-nosed, or bull-nosed, ox louse (*Haematopinus
eurysternus*). The young lice of this species closely resemble the
blue lice in general appearance and are often mistaken for them. The
young lice usually attach themselves in dense masses or patches on
the animal. If not too much disturbed, they remain attached for the
purpose of sucking blood until they are sexually mature, when they
crawl about over the animal and reattach themselves to any suitable
host that may come in contact with it. This is the usual way in which
infestation spreads among cattle. The red and blue lice spread in the
same manner, except that they remain attached only for short periods
while feeding.

According to Lamson,[2] the eggs of the red louse hatch in 5 to 7

---

[2] LAMSON, G. H., Jr. CATTLE LICE AND THEIR CONTROL. Conn. (Storrs) Agr. Expt. Sta.
Bul. 97, pp. [395]-414, illus. 1918.

days, and the development of the louse to sexual maturity requires 15 to 18 days, whereas the eggs of the common blue louse, *Linognathus vituli*, incubate in 8 to 14 days, and the young louse reaches sexual maturity 11 to 18 days later.

In Texas it has been found that a high percentage of the eggs of the short-nosed ox louse normally hatch in 16½ days, though a considerable number require more than 17 days and a few have been found to take as many as 33 days. Imes[3] reports the egg-hatching period as varying from 11 to 18 days, a range that is not surprising, since louse eggs are often exposed to very hot or very cold weather in different parts of the country. After hatching, this louse reaches sexual maturity in 13 to 23 days. The mature female

FIGURE 2.—Long-nosed, or blue, louse (*Linognathus vituli*), dorsal view.

may deposit 30 to 35 eggs during her lifetime.

CONTROL MEASURES

The remedies suggested for eradicating cattle lice are many and varied, but most of them have very little if any practical merit. No remedy now known can be considered perfect in all respects.

Dipping is the best method of applying insecticides to cattle for the control of lice. For this purpose it is best to provide a well-constructed concrete vat set in the ground (fig. 3), with suitable chutes and pens for handling the cattle as they are dipped. Such vats are designed primarily for use with large herds or where many small producers can use the same vat. A long vat with straight sides has proved most satisfactory. The most desirable type is approximately 26 to 30 feet long, 30 to 36 inches wide, and 70 to 80 inches from the water or dip line to the bottom of the vat. This type of vat is also used for dipping cattle to control mange and ticks. For delousing a few animals, insecticides in solution may be applied with a bucket pump or other standard sprayer, or dry insecticides may be applied with a shaker can and worked into the hair by hand, as described later. Every animal dipped will carry out from a quart to a gallon of dip, depending on its size and the length and condition of its hair.

It is advisable before dipping to see that all projecting nails, splinters, and broken boards around chutes and corrals are removed. Other precautions are not to dip any animal while it is overheated and, in cold weather, to do the dipping early enough in the day to allow the animals time to dry before evening. Special care must be taken to avoid heating the animal when arsenic dips are used.

If electric prod poles are to be used in handling the animals, two are generally better than one. Properly handled, these poles are a

---

[3] IMES, MARION. CATTLE LICE AND HOW TO ERADICATE THEM. U. S. Dept. Agr. Farmers' Bul. 909, 24 pp., illus. 1925. (Revised, 1940.)

great advantage, but they should be used only on animals in the chute; using the poles on animals in the crowding pens may cause them to mill around and become vicious, and some of them may jump the corral.

The following dip has so far proved very efficient and safe as well as practical: 325-mesh or finer wettable sulfur, 100 pounds; either cube or derris containing not less than 5 percent of rotenone, 10 pounds; water, 1,000 gallons. The water is put in the vat first, and the other ingredients are added to it just before the cattle are dipped. The derris or cube may be put into the water first, then the wettable sulfur; or the cube or derris may be mixed with some of the wettable sulfur in a separate tub, the mixture being added to the water in the vat and the remaining sulfur then put in.

Since the rotenone in derris or cube begins to break down after a few days' use, the dip is good for only 5 or 6 days, after which, if more dipping is to be done, a new charge of cube or derris should be put in, but no more sulfur. It is best, however, at the time of the second dipping to clean out the vat and refill it with an entirely fresh mixture.

FIGURE 3.—A dipping vat for cattle, filled to the dip line.

To insure a satisfactory degree of control, every animal must have its head well ducked at least once during each dipping. The average cattle vat will hold 2,000 to 3,700 gallons of dip, but a capacity of 2,500 gallons seems to be about the most desirable for comparatively small herds.

Owing to the wide variation in the hatching period of louse eggs, it is difficult to arrange a system of dipping that will insure absolute eradication. It has been found, however, that the following dipping schedule is practical and will give a high degree of control:

First dipping—preferably early in the fall.
Second dipping—12 to 14 days later.
Third dipping—17 to 21 days after the first dipping.

Weather conditions will often prevent a third dipping of range cattle at the proper interval. Actual experience has shown that two dippings 17 to 21 days apart will generally give good control. It may not completely eradicate the lice, owing to the fact that on heavily infested animals it is difficult to get every louse wet with the insecticide; again, a few eggs may not hatch until after the second dipping. Louse eggs are not killed by the dip described, nor will arsenical dips kill them.

A number of other insecticidal solutions have been used successfully for cattle louse control, but the sulfur-cube dip is especially effective against the short-nosed ox louse, which is the species most resistant to insecticides.

Coal-tar-creosote dips are effective if used in soft water and at proper strengths.

Nicotine sulfate is also widely used for controlling cattle lice. It is diluted with water in accordance with directions on the container so that the solution contains 0.05 percent nicotine. This dip is very poisonous to livestock, and injury may result if it is made stronger than this.

Arsenical dips are widely employed against cattle lice, but neither they nor a dip of elemental sulfur alone will satisfactorily control the short-nosed ox louse. The efficacy of arsenical dips depends on their sodium arsenite content; they should contain 0.18 percent sodium arsenite. For further information on the use of arsenical dips see Farmers' Bulletin 909, Cattle Lice and How To Eradicate Them.

Oil dips are not generally recommended even though they are saponified, or mixed with soap.

If only a few animals are to be treated they may be sprayed or dusted with the sulfur and cube mixture. This method is especially desirable for 4-H Club calves or when no vat is available. While one person is working the pump, another can direct the spray and at the same time rub it into the skin. Very low or moderate pressure in the spray pump is better than high pressure, which will make the animal uneasy, nervous, and often unruly. In spraying, every part of the animal must be wet, including dew-claws, end of tail, belly, and inside of legs.

For the dry treatment—which must be used in cold weather, especially in winter in the Northern States, even if there are a considerable number of animals to be treated—a mixture consisting of 1 pound of either derris or cube containing 5 percent rotenone, plus 9 pounds of 325-mesh wettable or nonwettable sulfur or some of the inert siliceous carriers may be used. The dust-gun method of application has not proved very satisfactory, but hand treatment, although it requires more material and time to apply, is practical and safe. If this method is used, the mixture must be well rubbed into the skin all over the animal. Animals should be treated again in 12 to 14 days and a third time 17 to 21 days after the first treatment.

Cattle Injuries Caused by Ingesting Foreign Objects

BY L. T. GILTNER AND JOHN A. PATTON [1]

DON'T LEAVE your watch where the cow can get it; she may think it is an appetizer. Cattle manage to swallow an amazing number of things that cause serious trouble with their insides.

FOR SOME UNKNOWN REASON, cattle have a tendency to chew and swallow foreign objects. Among those which have been found in their stomachs are pieces of baling wire and barbed wire, bristles from wire brushes, hairpins, hatpins, knitting needles, pocketknives, different kinds of nails including horseshoe and roofing nails, staples, and scraps of various kinds of metals with sharp ends or cutting edges (fig. 1). Besides such objects as these, which are capable of causing considerable damage, other things which probably cause little injury have also been found in bovine stomachs, such as coins, metal tags and badges, watch chains, parts of watches, keys and key chains, buttons, beads, rings, charms, and nceklaces.

On reaching the first stomach or rumen—more commonly called the paunch—an occasional foreign body may pierce the stomach wall. In most cases, however, the object passes on to the second stomach, or reticulum, from which it may penetrate the surrounding or related tissues (fig. 2).

After penetrating the wall of the reticulum, a pointed object may go in one of several directions. In rare cases such an object has been known to work its way through to the external surface of the body. Occasionally it passes toward the liver, causing injury to that organ. The most frequent direction, however, is frontward, toward the heart. This is thought to be due in part to the breathing and chest action,

---

[1] L. T. Giltner is Senior Veterinarian, Pathological Division, and John A. Patton is Veterinarian, Meat Inspection Division, Bureau of Animal Industry.

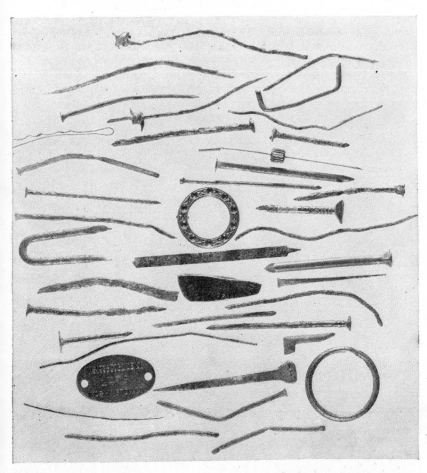

FIGURE 1.—Metal objects recovered from the stomachs of cattle, including pieces of wire, various kinds of nails, staples, a key ring, a bleeding needle, metal tags, and other miscellaneous articles.

FIGURE 2.—A portion of a cow's diaphragm which has been penetrated by a piece of wire.

together with the muscular contractions of the reticulum. The reticulum lies in close proximity to the pericardium, or heart sac, from which it is separated only by the thin diaphragm. After passing through the wall of the reticulum and the diaphragm, the sharp object continues to be forced forward, piercing the heart sac, and may eventually reach and cause injury to the heart itself (fig. 3). In

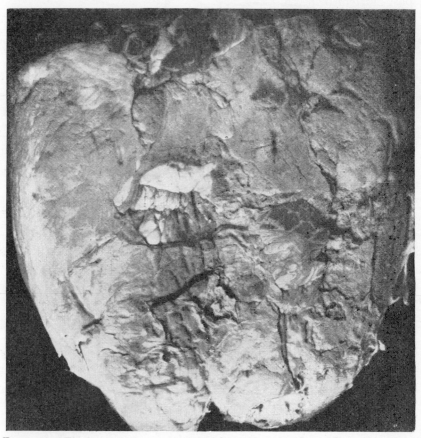

FIGURE 3.—The heart from a cow with traumatic pericarditis. Note the piece of wire embedded in the heart wall and also the roughened and thickened condition of the myocardium (the muscular part of the wall of the heart) resulting from the chronic inflammatory changes.

fact, foreign objects in some instances may even invade the heart cavities.

The condition resulting from penetration of the tissues of the heart region by foreign objects is called traumatic pericarditis, which means injury resulting in extreme inflammatory changes in the pericardium, or heart sac, and related tissues. Such injuries lead to a train of symptoms and complications which in most cases are extremely serious.

SYMPTOMS

Symptoms are not always readily apparent, as is indicated by the fact that of the cattle condemned on account of pericarditis under Federal meat inspection, fewer than 10 percent of the live animals shows evidences of the condition, which becomes apparent only on post mortem inspection.

When recognized the symptoms may vary somewhat, depending on the location and extent of the injury resulting from the presence of the foreign object. At first there may be only some evidence of digestive disturbance. In some cases there may be tympanites, or distention of the rumen, eructations of gas, and indications of colicky pains. The animal may show an anxious expression, avoid motion. and keep the back arched. Pain may be evidenced by grunting on sudden motion. The head is stretched forward, elbows spread outward, and hind feet drawn under the abdomen. The pulse is rapid and the breathing short, difficult, and abdominal in character. There is loss of appetite and little tendency to rumination. In the more advanced cases there are marked frictional heart sounds which may be heard at a distance of several yards and which afford a valuable diagnostic symptom. Frequently there is also a certain amount of liquid around the heart, and in these cases a gurgling or splashing sound is heard in addition to the frictional sound. The presence of large amounts of fluid may cause a venous distention, noticeable in the jugular veins, which stand out like cords on the neck and in which wavelike motions may be seen following the heartbeats.

In the later stages, edematous (dropsical) swellings develop on the chest, dewlap, and anterior (front) abdominal region. There may be some rise of temperature. As the symptoms increase, respiration becomes more labored, and complications such as pneumonia may occur. Diarrhea is in evidence in some animals. A general loss of condition and emaciation occur. The disease may run a course of several weeks to several months after the first symptoms are observed, but cases of spontaneous recovery are rare. Death may result from direct injury to the heart by the foreign object or from complications resulting from infections.

TREATMENT

In certain cases, surgical intervention has given very good results and has brought about some spectacular recoveries. The success of surgical treatment depends on the skill of the operator and the proper selection of cases. Some experienced veterinarians have achieved considerable success in diagnosing and selecting suitable cases for removal of the offending foreign body by an operation. Obviously, advanced cases or those in which there is a fever or other evidence of marked poisoning of the system should not be chosen.

Medicinal treatment is of little or no value, and when a radical operation cannot be undertaken, it is most economical to slaughter the affected animal as soon as possible after a diagnosis has been made.

POST MORTEM FINDINGS

On autopsy the foreign body may be found penetrating the heart wall or free in the accumulated fluid in the pericardial cavity. In some instances the object may pass through the heart wall into a ventricle. Usually the heart sac is much thickened as a result of the inflammatory changes and may in some cases be more or less attached to the heart. Also, as a result of these chronic fibrous changes, the pericardium, diaphragm, and reticulum may have firmly adhered to one another. A clear or cloudy fluid exudate, or discharge, may be present, but most frequently the heart sac is filled with a creamy pus, due to the invasion of pus-producing bacteria which usually accompany these injuries. The puslike material may have an offensive odor.

Most cases of pericarditis caused by foreign bodies are found on post morten inspection at slaughtering establishments. In some cases there have been no outward symptoms to indicate the presence of heart lesions, or tissue injuries. found after slaughter. Because of the extensive heart lesions, the large amount of pus, the possibility of absorption, and the generalized pyemic conditions, or distribution of the infection through the body, many of the carcasses so affected are condemned at slaughtering establishments under Federal inspection.

When symptoms of pericarditis are discernible in cattle shipped to market, such animals are sold on a subject-to-slaughter agreement. which means a loss to the owner. Cattle that exhibit no external evidence of the condition but are later condemned become a loss to the packer. Because of the large percentage of condemnation in such cases, traumatic pericarditis is a problem of considerable economic importance. At one station under Federal supervision, for example. it accounted for 22 percent of all condemnations for inflammatory diseases in cattle.

P. B. Becker, of the Florida Agricultural Experiment Station, has reported, in a personal communication, that 59 out of 1,097 dairy bulls on which careful records were kept died from traumatic pericarditis or other traumatisms of stomach, liver, lungs, or other organs caused by nails, baling wire. or other foreign bodies. In 1940, post mortem examinations conducted by Federal veterinarians on 128,979 cattle slaughtered at one station revealed 6,385 abscessed livers, in 120 (approximately 2 percent) of which pieces of wire or nails were found.

PREVENTIVE MEASURES

Since treatment is of little avail. preventive measures become of extreme importance. Because of the tendency of cattle to pick up various metallic objects, cattle owners, dairymen in particular, should make a special effort to rid their premises as far as may be practicable of the more common metal objects, particularly baling wire; barbed wire, staples, nails of all kinds, and any scraps of tin or other metal that might cause injury if swallowed by animals. It should be possible very largely to prevent traumatic pericarditis in herds by giving thorough and systematic attention to keeping the surroundings free from such objects, particularly around dairies, barns, and feed lots.

The importance of paying attention to such details as the careful collecting and safe disposal of all materials that may cause injury when ingested by cattle cannot be stressed too strongly. When repair work is being done about barns, sheds, or yards, nails, staples, and pieces of barbed-wire or other wire fencing that necessarily become scattered about should be gathered up before the cattle are readmitted. That this pays good dividends is shown by a single example out of many that have come to the attention of the Bureau of Animal Industry. On one large dairy farm under the supervision of a veterinarian, traumatic pericarditis was common and caused the loss of a number of very valuable cattle during a period of about 10 years. After the inauguration of a strict system of surveillance over the "foreign-body enemy" the trouble disappeared, and no new cases have since occurred there.

Paint Poisoning in Cattle

BY L. T. GILTNER [1]

CATTLE ARE POISONED by lead paint much more often than most people realize. The author of this article has made a special study of the problem and describes the causes, symptoms, prevention, and treatment.

IN THIS DISCUSSION, paint poisoning refers to the poisoning that results from the ingestion of any of the lead-containing paints. It is the lead in the paint that causes the trouble.

Cattle may also take into their bodies poisonous quantities of lead from many sources other than paint. Lotions, ointments, and salves contain lead and, when applied externally for the treatment of sores, inflammatory conditions, and parasitism, may be licked off, or the lead may be absorbed through wounds. Lead shot or bullets are sometimes taken up by cattle grazing near shooting ranges; as few as 300 shot have proved fatal to a cow. Herbage in the vicinity of smelters may be covered with a layer of dust containing lead, and the forage plants in such areas may take up lead from the soil. The effluent from smelters may contaminate streams with considerable quantities of lead. Dangerous amounts may be deposited on vegetation in orchards sprayed with lead arsenate solution or other solutions containing lead; the danger is particularly great if the herbage is grazed before rain has fallen. Old batteries, the exhaust fumes from gasoline engines using tetraethyl lead gasoline, and boiled linseed oil are sources of lead to which cattle may at times have access. Soft water conducted through lead pipes and sour feeds such as mashes and milk in leaden containers are sometimes sources of lead poisoning. Finally, mistakes sometimes made in dispensing medicines have caused lead poisoning; for example, sugar of lead (lead acetate) has been mistaken for Glauber's salt or common salt, and white lead has been erroneously used for chalk.

[1] L. T. Giltner is Senior Veterinarian, Pathological Division, Bureau of Animal Industry.

Paint, however, is by far the most common source of lead poisoning in cattle. These animals are fond of licking paint, especially fresh paint, from fences, posts, gates, the exterior of barns, or the walls, partitions, stanchions, and other parts of stables. Also they frequently find discarded paint cans, buckets, or other containers and lick enough paint from them to cause fatal poisoning.

Of all the domestic animals, cattle are the most sensitive to lead poisoning in relation to their size, calves being especially susceptible. Fröhner[2] states that horses can tolerate 10 times larger quantities of lead than cattle can; he gives the following list of the amounts of sugar of lead that are fatal for certain animals: Cattle, 50 to 100 grams; horses, 500 to 750 grams; sheep and goats, 20 to 25 grams; swine and dogs, 10 to 25 grams.

More farm animals are poisoned by lead than by any of the other metallic poisons, and the losses among cattle are greater than the combined losses of all other species. Because of the universal use of paint, the danger of lead poisoning of cattle exists in every farming community. Individual cases in both calves and mature cattle occur frequently, and it is not uncommon for a large percentage of a herd to be affected.

Lead acts as a local corrosive irritant to the mucous lining of the stomach and intestines. After being absorbed, it acts on the psychic, motor, and vasomotor centers of the brain. (The vasomotor nerves control the dilation and contraction of the blood vessels.) Most cases of lead poisoning in cattle are of the acute type resulting from the consumption of large quantities of lead at one time.

The first symptoms are usually marked salivation, slobbering, choking, colic, and suppression of the appetite and milk secretion. Diarrhea may occur, but constipation is much more common, and bloating often ensues. The symptoms arising from derangement of the central nervous system are most striking and characteristic, although they are often confused with those caused by agencies other than lead. There is a pronounced trembling, accompanied by champing of the jaws, attacks similar to those of epilepsy, and a tendency to walk in circles or to push blindly forward into fences or other obstacles. Frequently the affected animals show symptoms of mania, running about wildly with all indications of blindness and colliding with or breaking down objects in their path. Death may occur suddenly during or following such an attack, or there may be sleepiness, weakness, paralysis of the hindquarters or other parts of the body, and eventually deep coma and death. Animals fatally affected seldom live more than a few days.

Poisoning occasionally occurs in the chronic form as a result of ingestion of small quantities of lead over a long period. In such cases there is a general disturbance of the nutrition of the body, with progressive wasting and general weakness. There may be intermittent attacks of colic, staggering, uncoordinated movements, stiffness of the joints, and convulsive seizures. Sometimes there are pustular eruptions in the skin, accompanied by more or less itching. Blind-

[2] FRÖHNER, EUGEN. LEHRBUCH DER TOXIKOLOGIE FÜR TIERÄRZTE. Dritte Auflage, 391 pp. Stuttgart. 1910.

ness, wasting of the muscles, ulceration of the mucous membrane of the mouth cavity, abortion, and sterility are not uncommon.

In acute cases of lead poisoning, the lining membrane of the stomach and intestines will be found to be reddened and inflamed, with areas of ulceration. The mucous membrane of the intestine has a grayish to black discoloration. The intestines are contracted, and the outer surface may be rather pale in color. When the brain cavity or the spinal canal is opened, an excessive amount of fluid pours out, and both brain and spinal cord appear congested. Small blood spots are seen frequently on the surface of the heart or under the membrane lining the chest cavity and covering the lungs. In chronic lead poisoning, the body is in a poorly nourished condition, and the internal organs, particularly the kidneys, appear shrunken, owing to growth of connective tissue that has to some extent replaced the softer glandular tissue.

At times the symptoms and post mortem findings do not suffice to establish a diagnosis, and laboratory methods must be used. For this purpose not only the stomach contents but also a generous part of the liver should be supplied to the chemist for analysis. Lead is readily absorbed and very slowly excreted from the body, being stored in the liver, central nervous system, pancreas, and bones. In cases of true lead poisoning, the recovery of lead from such organs as the liver by chemical analysis is therefore not difficult.

Poisoning by lead from paint or other sources is nearly always the direct result of carelessness or mismanagement. When any painting job is to be done about the farm, cattle should be kept away from the newly painted surfaces, and the containers used for mixing the paint as well as the original containers should be carefully disposed of on completion of the work. When the interior of the stable is to be painted, particularly such objects as the stanchions, a nonlead paint that is not poisonous should be used; in general, a good whitewash is quite satisfactory for large wall areas. Before new paint is applied, the surfaces should be scraped to remove old paint scales, which should be safely disposed of.

The animals should not be allowed access to any other sources of lead such as those mentioned at the beginning of this article. Since treatment is usually not very satisfactory, preventive measures are particularly important and should be kept in mind by the stock owner.

The medical treatment of lead poisoning is to a large extent symptomatic. When an animal is in a state of great excitement, the veterinarian usually administers such hypnotics or anticonvulsants as chloral hydrate. After the animal has become paralyzed, such agents should not be employed. One of the commonest antidotes is Epsom salts, in a purgative dose; these salts bring about a precipitation of the lead in the form of an insoluble lead compound and tend to prevent further absorption. In recent years veterinarians have obtained some favorable responses through the intravenous injection of calcium gluconate.

Nutritional Diseases
of Cattle

BY LOUIS L. MADSEN[1]

A DISCUSSION of the symptons, causes, prevention, and treatment of disorders due to mineral deficiencies, vitamin deficiencies, and certain other conditions associated with nutrition in cattle.

FAULTY NUTRITION is often responsible, directly or indirectly, for large economic losses in the cattle industry. Recognition of this has stimulated research in this field, and much is being accomplished.

It is becoming evident that the so-called nutritional diseases that occur under practical conditions on the farm or range are not always fatal. Undoubtedly, greater losses result from decrease in rate of growth and economy of production, reproductive failures, and increased susceptibility to certain infectious and parasitic diseases than from death. The vital role of nutrition in maintaining health in cattle and other farm animals has been recognized for many years, and this accounts for the careful attention given by livestock producers and veterinarians to providing an adequate diet as a part of the program for the treatment or prevention of many diseases.

In feeding studies much attention is given to comparing the rate of gain or the economy of production of milk or butterfat in animals fed certain feeds or feed combinations. Extensive tables of feed values are being compiled, and it is becoming increasingly evident that the value of a feed for any given purpose depends on its content of essential nutrients, which can now be determined to a large extent by chemical analysis. With this knowledge at hand it is possible to supplement deficient rations with the necessary essential nutrients—minerals, vitamins, or protein—and obtain good results with feeds which, when fed alone, have a relatively low value or even cause nutritional diseases. Knowledge of the essential nutrients has also

---

[1] Louis L. Madsen is Nutritionist, Animal Nutrition Division, Bureau of Animal Industry.

led to improved methods of growing, harvesting, storing, and processing feeds in order to increase or preserve nutritive values. Recognition of these facts has often made it possible for a thriving cattle industry to be built up in sections where cattle feeding for either dairy or beef purposes was not entirely successful because of some rather obscure factors that limited the growth or production or affected the health of the animals.

Some nutritional diseases are due to a deficiency of essential nutrients and others to overfeeding or dietary imbalance or the presence of toxic substances in the feed. Characteristic symptoms of many nutritional diseases of cattle are now well established, and by study and observation livestock men and others concerned can learn to recognize these conditions and overcome them before serious losses result. Prevention, however, is the most successful means of control.

Before the common nutritional diseases are considered, it is important to emphasize that in many cases the results obtained in overcoming them have been so dramatic that some minerals and vitamins have come to be popularly regarded as almost in the nature of stimulating drugs or medicines. This is a mistaken point of view and has often led to unnecessary expense and disappointment when more of the essential factors are added to an already adequate ration. Results from increasing the intake of essential substances are obtained only when the ration is deficient in them. Furthermore, when a ration is deficient in several essential nutrients, all of them must be supplied for optimum results.

THE MINERAL-DEFICIENCY DISEASES

The minerals which have received the most attention in cattle-nutrition studies are phosphorus, calcium, magnesium, sodium and chlorine, iodine, iron, copper, and cobalt. Other minerals such as fluorine and selenium have been investigated largely from the standpoint of their toxicity. The mineral-deficiency diseases and the conditions caused by toxic minerals usually produce fairly typical symptoms and gross alterations in the body tissues. Blood and tissue analyses as well as microscopic examination of tissues are further aids to diagnosis.

CALCIUM AND PHOSPHORUS DEFICIENCY

The first symptom usually noted in cattle receiving too little phosphorus or calcium is a depraved appetite (pica), particularly evident in phosphorus deficiency (*51*).[2] Phosphorus-deficient cattle frequently chew and eat bones (osteophagia) or other material such as wood, hair, putrid flesh, soil, rocks, leather, feathers, etc., in an effort to get additional phosphorus (fig. 1). Consumption of putrid bones, flesh, and other carcass material may lead to toxic symptoms and death from botulism if the material is infected with *Clostridium botulinum*, as is often the case. Loin disease of cattle in Texas and lamsiekte of sheep and cattle in South Africa are

---

[2] Italic numbers in parenthesis refer to Literature Cited, p. 670.

caused by toxin obtained in putrid material consumed in an effort to satisfy the craving for phosphorus. As the deficiency progresses, there are marked loss of appetite, emaciation, lowered efficiency of food utilization, weak bones, stiff joints (creeps), decreased milk flow, failure to come in heat normally, small calf crop, and a generally unthrifty appearance.

When laboratory facilities are available, phosphorus deficiency can be diagnosed either by analyzing the forage accessible to the cattle or by blood analysis for phosphorus. A large decrease in total

FIGURE 1.—Phosphorus-deficient cattle often chew bones and other nonfood material in an effort to remedy the deficiency.

inorganic phosphorus in the blood is the first indication of phosphorus deficiency.

Calcium deficiency in cattle, including lactating dairy cows, is very rare, especially when the animals are fed rations containing liberal amounts of roughage. Isolated cases of calcium deficiency may occur, however, under unusual feeding conditions. Becker, Neal, and Shealy (9) report that dairy cows on low calcium rations frequently suffered bone fractures and gave less milk than when adequate calcium supplements were fed. The calcium-deficient cows remained in good condition, however, and did not show lethargy and stiffness, which is characteristic of advanced phosphorus deficiency. Adult cattle usually show only a slight decrease in blood calcium when they are on calcium-deficient rations; younger animals show a greater decrease, but it is practically never as great as the decrease in blood phosphorus in phosphorus deficiency.

An inadequate phosphorus or calcium intake over a long period leads to a gradual decrease in the body reserves of these elements. The largest reserve of calcium and phosphorus is in the bones, and if abnormal demands are made on this storage depot to meet the requirements of the body, the deficiency symptoms described may gradually develop. In general, during periods of rapid growth and heavy lactation cattle use more calcium and phosphorus than at any other time. Dairy cows frequently secrete more calcium and phosphorus in their milk during periods of heavy lactation than is obtained from the feed consumed. The extra calcium and phosphorus come from the bones. Any deficit is usually made good later when the milk flow declines or during the succeeding dry period.

Phosphorus deficiency is much more common in cattle than calcium deficiency. Cattle grazing in range areas or on farm pastures may develop phosphorus deficiency during periods of drought, especially in regions where the available soil phosphorus is rather low. When the feed supply is restricted owing to drought, overgrazing, or other causes, there may be a phosphorus shortage that would not ordinarily develop if ample forage was available.

In some sections of the country many dairy and beef cattle are fed primarily on roughage, such as alfalfa, with little or no grain to supplement it. Alfalfa is not usually rich enough in phosphorus to be depended upon as the sole source of this mineral, particularly if it is grown under conditions of relatively low soil fertility and low soil moisture. Most hays are even lower in phosphorus than alfalfa. In sugar-beet-producing areas, beet pulp is fed in addition to hay. Any beet byproduct is very low in phosphorus, as is corn silage; so a combination of either one with hay is apt to lead to a deficiency of this mineral. Wintering animals in stubble fields with free access only to cereal straw, corn fodder, prairie hay, or other similar low-phosphorus feeds may also lead to phosphorus deficiency unless some cereal grains, protein concentrates, or a phosphorus-rich mineral mixture is supplied. Pregnant and lactating cows or young growing animals are more susceptible to phosphorus deficiency than mature stock cattle.

Prevention and Treatment

Calcium and phosphorus deficiency can usually be avoided or overcome by giving animals an adequate supply of these minerals through the use of feeds that are good sources, the feeding of calcium- and phosphorus-rich mineral supplements, or increasing the mineral content and yield of available forage by fertilizing the soil on which the crops are grown.

Investigations of the Bureau of Animal Industry in cooperation with the Texas Agricultural Experiment Station and the King Ranch in south Texas have shown that many cattle in the Gulf coast area graze on phosphorus-deficient or semi-phosphorus-deficient ranges. Preliminary results obtained in these experiments by hand-feeding a mineral mixture rich in phosphorus to beef cattle on phosphorus-deficient range are given in table 1. The phosphorus supplements consisted of bonemeal and disodium phosphate. They were fed individually so as to supply the dry cows with 6.5 grams of phosphorus and the lactating cows with 14.3 grams of phosphorus per head daily, in addition to that received from range forage. It is obvious from the data that feeding a phosphorus supplement costing $2.60 per cow per year raised the calf crop considerably, improved the growth rate of calves, and increased the value of the calves at weaning time by an average of $10.44 and that of the yearling heifers by an average of $12.19. It is obvious also that adequate feeding of existing herds is a rapid and economical means of increasing beef production.

TABLE 1.—*Preliminary comparisons of gains and other production data on cows and calves fed a phosphorus supplement and on similar cattle receiving only range vegetation* [1]

Item	Cattle fed phosphorus supplement in addition to the range forage	Cattle on range fed no additional phosphorus
Calf crop (2-year average)--percent--	83	58
Cows producing calves for 2 consecutive years--------------------do----	72	21
Average weaning weight of calves---------------------------------pounds--	499	421
Average weaning weight of calves prorated to all cows------------do----	448	320
Value of calf at weaning time [2]--------------------------------dollars--	39.92	29.48
Weight of heifers at 1 year of age--------------------------------pounds--	541	441
Value of yearling heifers less cost of supplement fed from weaning to 1 year [2]--dollars--	43.06	30.87
Annual cost of phosphorus supplement per cow------------------do----	2.60	---------------

[1] Data obtained by Bureau of Animal Industry, Texas Agricultural Experiment Station, and the King Ranch, Kingsville, Tex., cooperating.

[2] Calves from cows fed phosphorus supplement were valued at 8 cents a pound and those from the cows that received no additional phosphorus were valued at 7 cents a pound.

Under practical range conditions, phosphorus supplements are usually fed free choice. Soluble phosphorus salts such as disodium phosphate, may be given in the drinking water if the source of water can be controlled. The experience of H. Welch, of the Montana Agricultural Experiment Station, in supplying range cattle with phosphorus supplements indicates some of the problems involved. He writes: [3]

We have been using bonemeal and other phosphorus-containing supplements for approximately 20 years in the Montana phosphate-deficient areas. Feeding bonemeal without salt has 2 principal drawbacks. One is that when put out in a box for range cattle, it blows out badly in windy areas: salt helps to bind it together and prevents this blowing. Second, in any bunch of bone-chewing cattle there are several individuals that refuse to eat bonemeal at all unless mixed with salt. Another objection to pure bonemeal is that after it becomes damp the flies will soon deposit eggs, and the bonemeal will become a mass of fly larvae. However, some cattlemen do use the bonemeal in separate compartments of the salt box.

Extensive experiments with disodium phosphate, either straight or mixed with salt, in our hands, have not been as satisfactory as with bonemeal. As far as we can tell, the disodium phosphate is tasteless, but the cattle almost univer-sally found it unpalatable. The same was true of monocalcium phosphate, of

[3] Communication to the Animal Nutrition Division, Bureau of Animal Industry.

phosphate rock origin, containing up to 45 percent P_2O_5, which proved entirely unpalatable to cattle on account of its acid taste.

I mention all these things because it seems to the casual observer that an existing condition of aphosphorosis [phosphorus deficiency] can be remedied by the use of bonemeal, and that that is all there is to it. In actual fact, however, there are some difficulties in entirely remedying the situation, because of the difficulties encountered in getting an adequate dose of the supplement into the cattle.

Mineral mixtures fed on the range or in farm pastures should be placed in well-constructed boxes that protect the contents as much as possible from blowing out or being wet. A satisfactory mineral box is shown in a recent publication from the Florida Agricultural Experiment Station (*48*).

The phosphorus requirement of lactating dairy cows needs special attention, particularly in areas where there is a deficiency of this mineral in the soil and consequently a low content in the pasture grass and harvested forage. If the cows are fed a liberal amount of grain, including a protein-rich concentrate such as wheat bran, cottonseed, linseed, or soybean meal, and a roughage, their phosphorus and calcium intake is usually adequate. For very heavily producing dairy cows, a mineral mixture of bonemeal and salt or some other calcium-phosphorus supplement may be added to the grain mixture at the rate of 1 to 2 percent when necessary. There is little experimental evidence indicating that increased amounts of calcium in the form of mineral supplements have proved beneficial for either growing or lactating cattle when the animals were receiving liberal quantities of feeds of normal composition.

Lactating animals fed roughage with little or no grain should have access to a mineral mixture such as bonemeal alone or 1 or 2 parts of bonemeal to 1 of common salt, according to the appetites of the animals, in order to insure an adequate phosphorus intake. Ground rock phosphate, either raw or as a superphosphate, is likely to contain too much fluorine and arsenic and should not be used in livestock feeding. Purified phosphate salts are available. Dicalcium phosphate and disodium phosphate are probably the most widely used forms of phosphate salts, but they have often proved to be rather unpalatable to cattle and are therefore most successfully used mixed with salt or as a constituent of a grain mixture. Bonemeal and the other calcium-containing salts mentioned also provide an abundance of calcium, and when these supplements are used it is not necessary to add additional calcium in the form of calcium carbonate. If a ration needs the addition of calcium only, a good grade of ground calcium carbonate or oystershell is usually the cheapest source of this mineral.

PHOSPHORUS DEFICIENCY AND PARTURIENT HEMOGLOBINEMIA OF DAIRY COWS

Madsen and Nielsen (*25, 26*) have described a disease of high-producing dairy cows which most frequently occurs 2 to 3 weeks after the birth of the third to the sixth calf and is characterized by anemia (decrease of red blood cells), hemoglobinemia (hemoglobin or red blood pigment in solution in the serum), hemoglobinuria (hemoglobin in the urine), and general weakness. The disease is common in the intermountain areas of the United States and has been reported from Norway, Sweden, Denmark, Finland, Austria, Ireland, and Scotland. It may be confused with other conditions causing hemoglobinuria.

Madsen and Nielsen show a definite relationship between the occurrence of the disease and the ration fed. The disease is most common during the winter, especially when the cows are fed on alfalfa and sugar-beet pulp. No cases have been observed in beef cows. Other characteristic symptoms are loss of appetite, decrease in milk production, rapid pulse, cold and blanched teats, drooping ears, gaunt appearance, weakness, staggering gait, constipation or diarrhea, depraved appetite, increased water consumption, an odor of acetone on the breath, and, in some cases, milk tinted with hemoglobin. Cows that do not die of the disease usually start to recover after the fifth day of illness, and there is partial or complete recovery in a period varying between a week and several months. Cows fed liberal amounts of grain usually recover faster than those kept on their original ration of alfalfa and beet pulp.

The principal blood findings in this disease are a marked reduction in red blood cells and a very marked drop in inorganic phosphorus content. As already noted, the blood plasma is often tinged with hemoglobin. Treatment consisting of intravenous injection of dibasic sodium phosphate followed by drenches with the same material or with bonemeal have been quite successful. No cases have been observed by these authors where cows were liberally fed with grain during the lactation period. Regular feeding of a mineral supplement such as bonemeal is also indicated, particularly with low-phosphorous feeds such as beet pulp.

MAGNESIUM DEFICIENCY IN CALVES

When young calves are fed on milk without forage or a grain supplement for more than a few weeks, they invariably develop a severe disorder characterized by irritability, nervousness, and loss of appetite. In later stages the animals have convulsions. Duncan and associates (*14*) in describing this symptom state:

The animal, apparently temporarily blinded, will run into obstacles, or becoming confused will turn in circles until its balance is completely destroyed. As the convulsions become more violent, the calf may fall on its side with the legs rigid and alternately extended and contracted; there is frothing at the mouth and profuse salivation. These attacks may last continuously for several minutes or, intermittently, for a longer time. Young calves seem to be able to withstand several such convulsions but older calves usually succumb to the first attack.

Such symptoms are associated with low blood magnesium. Moore and coworkers (*31*), in connection with the Michigan work on magnesium, have described the lesions (tissue changes) in calves fed rations low in magnesium. The principal findings were calcification of the yellow elastic fibers of the endocardium (membrane lining the interior of the heart), in the walls of the larger veins and arteries, on the surface of the diaphragm, and in the trabeculae (fibrous bands extending into the interior) and capsule of the spleen. Degeneration and calcification were also found in the Purkinje system (conducting fibers) of the heart. Kidney and liver damage was also found in some cases. These workers suggest a possible relationship between

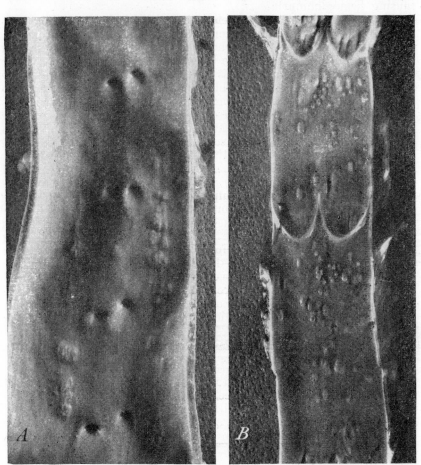

FIGURE 2.—Calves suffering from magnesium deficiency frequently have calcification of the blood vessels: *A*, Calcification of the aorta; *B*, calcification of the jugular vein. (Courtesy of Michigan Agricultural Experiment Station.)

diets low in magnesium and arteriosclerosis of human beings. (Typical blood-vessel lesions found in calves suffering from magnesium deficiency are shown in fig. 2.)

Ordinary diets of forage and grains contain enough magnesium that disorders due to magnesium deficiency are not likely to occur in calves under practical conditions unless they are fed too long on milk without access to supplementary feeds. Feeds rich in magnesium are legume and grass hays, cottonseed, linseed and soybean meal, wheat bran, wheat middlings, beet pulp, and hominy feed. Huffman and Duncan (*22*) report that 15 to 20 milligrams of magnesium as magnesium carbonate ($MgCO_3$) or magnesium oxide (MgO) per pound of body weight maintained plasma magnesium values and prevented the manifestations of magnesium deficiency. Under the same conditions 8 to 10 milligrams of magnesium from natural feeds per pound of body weight was equally effective, indicating that the magnesium of natural feeds is more readily utilized by calves.

GRASS TETANY

Grass tetany is a highly fatal disease of cattle characterized biochemically by lowered blood magnesium and calcium. It occurs most often within 2 weeks after the animals have been turned out to good pasture. The disease has received more attention in Holland, Great Britain, and New Zealand than elsewhere, although it is known to occur also in the United States (*28, 45*). A somewhat similar condition has been described in sheep and horses.

Sjollema (*49*) describes this condition vividly:

Usually the initial signs are nervousness, restlessness, grazing apart from the herd, lack of appetite, muscle-twitching, unsteady gait, spreading of the hind limbs, gnashing of the teeth, rolling of the eyes, an anxious or wild look resulting from abnormal eye muscle contraction, frothing at the mouth and abundant salivation. Some animals low continuously. The ears stand erect, and certain muscles, e. g. those of the tail, are in tetanic contraction. Abnormal contraction of the neck muscles causes a backward thrust of the head and similar contraction of the masticatory muscles results in trismus [lockjaw] . . . clonic-tonic convulsions [alternate rigidity and relaxation] appear, and the animal strikes heavily with all four limbs. During these cramps the animal is in a state of intense excitement, and alternately falls down and gets up with a jerk, the attempt to rise being often unsuccessful. The animals also run against walls, into ditches, etc., violent cramps being easily induced. The excitement is often followed by a paretic [paralytic] or comatose state of depression.

The cause of this condition is still obscure, but it is probably not a simple magnesium deficiency, since pasture grass is a good source of this mineral. Young, fast-growing pasture grass on well-fertilized pastures is suspected by some to contain an unbalanced content of minerals or toxic products which cause the disease. Sjollema (*49*) believes that heavy grain feeding in winter, together with limited roughage consumption, predisposes cattle to this disease, since such rations are usually low in calcium and high in phosphorus. A condition called grass tetany is reported by Quin (*45*) to occur in Kansas, Nebraska, and Oklahoma among cattle turned out to young lush pastures of rye, wheat, or barley; no blood studies are reported. Metzger (*28*) states that, with few exceptions, the cases reported in Kentucky occur in cows grazing on young, rapidly growing grass, and the record rainfall during the spring of 1935 caused a marked increase in the number of cases.

Since the disease is often rapidly fatal, there may not be sufficient time for treatment. Intravenous injection of a solution containing calcium chloride and magnesium chloride, which of course requires the services of a qualified veterinarian, has given good results (*49*). After the injection, it is advisable to keep the animal quiet and feed it only dry hay. Taking cattle off pasture at night for the first 2 weeks or so and giving them a feeding of hay has been recommended as a preventive measure.

SALT (SODIUM CHLORIDE) DEFICIENCY

Such common feeds as forages, grains, and grain byproducts ordinarily do not contain enough sodium and chlorine to meet the needs of farm animals. Milk production, hot weather, and hard work with excessive sweating increase the salt requirement. Symptoms of salt deficiency in dairy cows are loss of appetite, salt hunger, rough hair coat, and a rapid decline in condition and milk yield. Special attention should be given to providing an adequate supplement of salt, which may be supplied in granulated, flake, rock, or block form. Animals will usually consume more in the granulated or flake than in the solid form. Potassium or sodium iodide when needed, bonemeal, and ground limestone are frequently mixed together with salt and fed free choice or included in the grain mixture. On the range, boxes containing salt or general mineral mixtures should be protected from rain as much as possible, and enough boxes should be supplied so that even the very timid animals will have ample opportunity to obtain some. Animals that have been deprived of salt for a considerable period should not be given all they will eat at once, but should first be hand-fed limited amounts for several days, or harmful results may follow.

POTASSIUM DEFICIENCY IN CALVES

Salts of potassium are also required by the body for normal nutrition, but any practical diet usually contains an ample quantity of this mineral. Experimental semipurified rations containing 0.10 to 0.12 percent of potassium have been fed to calves, beginning at 160 days of age, by Sykes and Alfredson (*50*). They report finding lowered serum potassium, which promptly increased when additional potassium was fed, while the calcium, phosphorus, and magnesium values were not altered from normal. A striking result of their studies was the finding that three of the four calves used developed marked changes in the heart, determined by the electrocardiograph. Histological (cell) changes were also found in the Purkinje system (conducting tissue) of the right and left ventricles.

THE TRACE MINERALS IN CATTLE NUTRITION

Iodine Deficiency and Goiter

Iodine deficiency in cattle nutrition, as in that of other animals, is largely a sectional problem. The areas of the greatest iodine deficiency are in the Northwest and in the North Central States around the Great Lakes. The symptoms and prevention of this nutritional disease in cattle and other livestock are discussed in the. article on Nutritional Diseases of Farm Animals, page 332.

Nutritional Anemia (*Iron, Copper, and Cobalt Deficiency*)

For many years a condition occurring in cattle in Florida, known as salt sick, and a similar or identical malady in Michigan, called Grand Traverse, or lake-shore disease, have caused considerable loss to the cattle industry in certain areas of these States. Affected animals gradually lose their appetites and become emaciated and weak. Some have a depraved appetite. Diarrhea or severe constipation may be present. The blood is pale, owing to its low content of hemoglobin (red blood pigment). Young cattle fail to grow normally and if they survive do not reach normal adult size. Sexual maturity is delayed,

FIGURE 3.—These two purebred Jersey bulls were fed a ration of natal grass hay and shelled corn from cobalt-deficient land, with skim milk. The addition of 5 milligrams of cobalt daily to the ration of the animal on the left resulted in its weighing 550 pounds at 15 months of age, while the maximum weight of the animal on the right at 16 months of age was 350 pounds. (Courtesy of W. M. Neal, Florida Agricultural Experiment Station.)

and reproduction and lactation are very unsatisfactory. After death the liver, kidneys, and other tissues are pale, and the heart muscle is flabby. The disease is most prevalent in young cattle over 6 months of age and in heifers calving for the first time. Cattle of all ages and both sexes may be affected when the animals are restricted to deficient ranges.

Recent studies indicate that salt-sick animals are frequently suffering from a deficiency of one or more minerals, and possibly other factors also. Copper deficiency and cobalt deficiency may occur separately or overlap in some areas. In Michigan the condition is due essentially to cobalt deficiency.

Neal and Ahmann (*33*), of Florida, describe the symptoms of cobalt deficiency in calves (fig. 3) fed a ration of natal grass hay, shelled corn, and dried skim milk as follows: Affected cattle usually show a long rough coat of hair, scaliness of the skin, listlessness, retarded development of sexual characteristics, gauntness due to loss of appetite (much less marked when liquid skim milk is a part of the ration), and muscular atrophy. The erythrocyte (red blood corpuscle) count may be above average, and the hemoglobin concentration equal to or above that in animals receiving cobalt and making normal growth. The amount of hemoglobin per erythrocyte, or per volume of erythrocytes, is reduced. The condition would be classified as a microcytic hypochromic anemia (an anemia characterized by undersized red blood corpuscles and too little hemoglobin). The spleen is shriveled and fibrous and the heart of normal size but very flabby.

Copper deficiency also causes nutritional anemia, loss of appetite, slow growth, lowered fertility, and occasionally bleaching of the hair coat in cattle. Further studies will undoubtedly yield additional information on how deficiencies of copper and cobalt, and possibly of other trace minerals, may be differentiated.

Workers at the Florida experiment station have demonstrated that the forage and soil are usually lower in iron, calcium, magnesium, and phosphorus in areas where salt sick occurs than in areas where cattle are not affected with nutritional anemia (*35*). Iron deficiency has been thought to be a cause of this disease, but recent studies tend to give more weight to the possibility of a deficiency of cobalt or copper or both.[4] In Michigan the cobalt content of the hay grown in affected areas is considerably lower than that of hay from farms where the disease does not develop.

Considerable success has been attained in treating and preventing anemia in cattle by supplying iron, cobalt, or copper salts along with common salt for use as a lick. Advanced cases have also been successfully treated by drenching animals with these salts in solution. There is some indication that the responses obtained from feeding iron salts are due at least in part to the cobalt impurity which these salts frequently contain. Cases of Grand Traverse disease in Michigan respond well to a cobalt supplement alone (*3*).

In Florida supplements of 5 to 10 milligrams of cobalt a day markedly improved the growth of calves on a cobalt-deficient ration. Calves fed supplements of ferric ammonium sulfate and copper sulfate developed deficiency symptoms sooner than individuals on the basal ration only, while those receiving supplements of cobalt or of iron, copper, and cobalt appeared normal (*34*). Cobalt deficiency in the feeds of Florida is associated with certain soil types (Norfolk series) low in cobalt; it may also be associated with copper deficiency.

Whenever salt-sick cattle fail to respond to the usual supplement of iron and copper, it has been recommended by the Florida Agricultural Experiment Station[5] that cobalt be added to the mineral mixture.

---

[4] Communication to the Animal Nutrition Division from W. M. Neal, of the Florida Agricultural Experiment Station.
[5] COBALT IN THE TREATMENT AND PREVENTION OF SALT SICK. Fla. Agr. Expt. Sta. [1] p. 1937. [Processed.]

For advanced cases the following treatment is recommended:

Dissolve 10 grams of cobalt chloride or cobalt sulfate in one gallon of water. Give mature animals 6 ounces * * * as a drench once weekly for three or four weeks. Calves should be given 3 ounces, and other animals in proportion.

For prevention of the disease:

Add one pound of cobalt chloride or cobalt sulfate to each ton of the regular salt sick mixture (100 lbs. of salt, 25 lbs. of red oxide of iron, and 1 lb. of powdered copper sulfate). A recommended manner of making this addition is to dissolve 22 grams of the cobalt salt in a small amount of water and spray it over 100 lbs. of the salt sick mineral with a fly sprayer or atomizer. It should be mixed thoroughly so that animals taking it will secure a uniform amount. This should be offered in protected mineral boxes at all times.

TOXIC MINERALS

SELENIUM AND FLUORINE POISONING

Losses due to consumption of plants containing toxic amounts of selenium occur among livestock on the ranges and ranch lands of the Great Plains, particularly in South Dakota, Wyoming, and Nebraska. Other States that undoubtedly have a more or less serious selenium problem are North Dakota, Kansas, Oklahoma, Texas, New Mexico, Arizona, Colorado, Utah, and Montana.

Symptoms of chronic poisoning are described by Moxon (*32*) and also in the article on Nutritional Diseases of Farm Animals, page 323.

An acute attack may lead to so-called blind staggers, as commonly reported from Wyoming. This name for the disease is misleading, since the animals do not always become blind or stagger, but they do have a tendency to stray, stumble over objects in their way, and bump into objects and attempt to push them over rather than walk around them. In the last stages paralysis may set in and the animal dies with symptoms of abdominal pain, grinding of the teeth, and respiratory failure.

Prevention of selenium poisoning involves keeping animals away from areas that produce toxic plants, not always an easy matter.

Treatment of alkali disease, or blind staggers, is not entirely successful, since the injury caused by selenium is often permanent. The Wyoming station (*4*) reports success in treating blind staggers in the early stages by hypodermic injections of strychnine and drenching with warm water. The treatment should be carried out by a competent veterinarian. Changing the ration of the animal to selenium-free grain, a protein-rich concentrate, and good hay will do much to favor recovery if the damage to the internal organs has not been too great. Recent work at the South Dakota experiment station indicates that small amounts of arsenic (12 to 15 parts per million) in the feed or drinking water are effective in treating selenium poisoning in cattle as well as in dogs and chickens.

Fluorine poisoning in cattle is most frequently the result of feeding such products as raw phosphatic limestone as a mineral supplement. A purified product low in fluorine is now available for livestock feeding. Areas of excessive fluorine are mentioned in the article on Nutritional Diseases of Farm Animals, page 338.

Fluorine poisoning as seen in cattle is usually of the chronic type caused by the consumption of a small amount of fluorine over a considerable period. In mineral-feeding investigations with dairy cattle, Reed and Huffman (*46*), of Michigan, and Phillips, Hart, and Bohstedt (*42*), of Wisconsin, have observed the harmful effects of feeding raw rock phosphate in amounts ranging from 0.625 percent to 2.5 percent of the grain mixture. In the Michigan studies the health of the animals declined, and their teeth became badly worn. The condition of the teeth was first discovered when the animals were about 2½ years of age. At this time the animals began to lap cold water when drinking; if the water was warmed to body temperature they would drink freely. The jawbones and leg bones became abnormally thick and rough. Other symptoms noted were loss of appetite, progressive emaciation, decreased milk yield, delay of estrum after parturition, and lowered birth weight of calves. These may have been secondary effects due to the poor condition of the animals.'

Animals usually recover to some extent if the period of fluorine feeding has not been too long and damage to the body is not too severe. The source of excessive fluorine in the ration should be removed. Cattle with excessively worn and defective teeth have difficulty in eating dried roughage but many improve considerably if turned out to pasture.

VITAMIN-DEFICIENCY DISEASES OF CATTLE

Cattle and other ruminants are unique among animals in their vitamin requirements. According to present knowledge, vitamin A or its precursor, carotene, and vitamin D are the only vitamins that must be furnished in order to prevent characteristic nutritional diseases. Nearly all of the recognized vitamin B factors are known to be synthesized by bacteria in the digestive tract of these animals, but information is still lacking on whether this source is entirely adequate under all conditions. Vitamin C is also synthesized in the body by cattle. Recent studies have indicated that under certain conditions the formation of vitamin C may be inadequate, but under such circumstances a dietary source of vitamin C is apparently of no benefit, and injection of the vitamin appears necessary to maintain successful reproduction. Most cattle feeds are rich in vitamin E, but there is no conclusive evidence that this vitamin is essential.

Fortunately most cattle feeds such as green pasture grass, hay, silage of good quality, and cereal grains are rich in the known vitamins. The essential vitamins should be furnished to cattle in ordinary feeds whenever possible. An understanding of the conditions under which vitamin deficiencies are likely to occur and prompt recognition of early symptoms of deficiency are essential to eliminate the large losses caused by these diseases.

VITAMIN A DEFICIENCY

Vitamin A deficiency is the most common vitamin-deficiency disease of cattle (*18*). It has been reported from the Southern States, where cottonseed meal and hulls are fed, from the West and Southwest, where large numbers of cattle are grazed on ranges that become deficient in carotene-rich forage because of drought or overstocking, and from the Midwest and sections where corn or cereal grains, beet byproducts, cereal hay and straw, or old hay or poorly cured forage are used to fatten cattle. The practice of wintering cattle in stubblefields with access to a straw stack without a supplement of well-cured hay which has retained a good green color may also lead to a deficiency of this vitamin, particularly in young, growing cattle or pregnant animals.

Symptoms of vitamin A deficiency appear in cattle of all ages after they have been for an extended period on a ration containing too little carotene or vitamin A. One of the first symptoms of the deficiency that can be detected in fattening cattle or adult animals is night blindness, or an inability of the animals to see well in dim light, as during the late evening. This can be detected by driving the cattle about in a corral and noting whether they bump into the fence or each other or stumble over objects placed in their way. Several stages or degrees of night blindness can be recognized, and the condition may progress to total blindness unless the deficiency is corrected.

Night blindness results from inability of the animal to regenerate sufficient visual purple, a light-sensitive pigment of the retina, which is a compound of vitamin A and a protein. In young animals night blindness may progress rapidly to permanent blindness owing to injury to the optic nerve. Simple night blindness can usually be cured, but injury to the optic nerve is likely to result in permanent damage. In the advanced stages of vitamin A deficiency the eye is very sensitive to bright light. Animals are somewhat dazzled, blinking abnormally or keeping their eyes closed when exposed to bright sunlight. An excessive secretion of tears, which run out over the face and jaw, is often seen. In total blindness the pupil is fully dilated, and in some cases the cornea may ulcerate or become opaque.

Swelling of the legs and forequarters (commonly called anasarca) is often found in cattle showing symptoms of vitamin A deficiency (fig. 4). This condition has been observed in a large number of fat cattle coming from the Corn Belt in the Middle West. Other symptoms noted in this condition are rapid respiration, stiffness or lameness, night blindness, total blindness, convulsions, loss of appetite, and loss of weight. Death occurs in advanced cases. When such animals are slaughtered, an extensive edema (waterlogged condition) of the fat and muscle tissues is found, a condition that occurs in dry-lot-fed cattle that have been on low-carotene rations for 10 to 18 months or longer. The animals recover within a few weeks if well-cured alfalfa hay is added to the ration (*11*).

Cows and bulls may lose their reproductive ability in advanced vitamin A deficiency, but the interruption of sexual activity or damage to the sexual organs is not always permanent. The usual course is for the cows to conceive and later to either abort or give birth to weak or blind calves, which often fail to survive. Cows that have deficient calves may remain apparently normal themselves, even though they are receiving an insufficient amount of carotene for normal reproduction.

Hart and Guilbert (*19*) report that retention of the placenta is common in vitamin-A-deficient cows.

Calves suffer from vitamin A deficiency within a few weeks after birth unless their ration is adequate in this factor. Calves deficient at birth are often blind and weak, slow to get up, and very wobbly on their legs. They may have convulsions shortly after birth, and these often continue intermittently with increasing severity until death (fig. 5). Such calves frequently suffer from diarrhea (or occasionally constipation) and may develop respiratory disorders such as pneumonia. Blindness usually develops in the later stages. As the de-

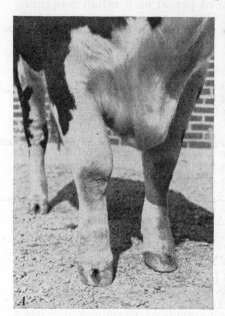

FIGURE 4.—*A*, Swelling (generalized edema, or anasarca) of the legs, brisket, and shoulders is often associated with vitamin A deficiency; *B*, after liberal doses of vitamin A or a ration of well-cured hay the edema usually disappears.

ficiency progresses, the coat becomes rough, the appetite is poor, and growth is slow, or there is loss in weight. Examination of calves that die from vitamin A deficiency usually reveals that blindness is due to stenosis of the optic nerve (*29*), while a cystic pituitary with considerable destruction of glandular tissue [6] and white spotted kidneys (*30*) may also be found.

Cause, Prevention, and Treatment

An inadequate carotene intake over a period long enough to permit almost complete exhaustion of the body stores of preformed vitamin A and carotene is the principal cause of vitamin A deficiency in cattle.

[6] Madsen, Louis L., Hall, S. R., and Converse, H. T. Unpublished data, Bur. Anim. Indus. and Bur. Dairy Indus.

Since forage, either fresh or cured, is the chief source of carotene for cattle, the kind, quality, and amount of forage consumed are the first factors to investigate if vitamin A deficiency is suspected.

During extended periods of drought, pasture and range herbage becomes scarce and is also lower than usual in carotene, protein, and phosphorus. Consequently cattle grazing under such conditions are subjected to a shortage of carotene and other essential factors. Carotene deficiency is an important economic problem in the West, South, and Southwest, where large numbers of beef cattle are grazed on ranges which may become deficient in carotene-containing forage because of insufficient rainfall. Feeder cattle raised under these conditions may show symptoms of vitamin A deficiency or have such a low body storage of vitamin A and carotene that they develop this deficiency later during the fattening period.

In work of the Bureau of Animal Industry in cooperation with the Texas Agricultural Experiment Station it was found that the time required for the development of night blindness in cattle fed a carotene-deficient ration

FIGURE 5.—If a cow's ration is low in carotene during the gestation period, her calf may be blind and weak at birth. *A,* This cow is in good condition and shows no evidence of vitamin A deficiency other than low blood carotene and vitamin A. Her calf was normal in size and condition but was unable to stand alone and had frequent convulsions. *B* shows the characteristic attitude during a convulsion. *C,* Abnormal position of front legs. This calf could not stand alone until 4 days of age and survived only 4 weeks.

varied considerably, depending on the age of the animals and their previous nutritional history. Older animals on carotene-rich feeds accumulate a larger supply of carotene than younger animals, and consequently deficiency symptoms appear first in the young animals on a vitamin-A-deficient diet. During grazing seasons of abundant rainfall all animals have a larger storage of carotene than during periods of drought. In this work, reported by Riggs (*47*), yearling steer calves showed symptoms of vitamin A depletion within 128 to 266 days, with an average of 178 ± 37 days, while younger calves (3 to 5 months old) developed night blindness within 46 to 61 days during 1939, and steers of the same age developed these symptoms within 65 to 131 days during 1939–40. In work of the Bureau of Animal Industry at Beltsville, Md., symptoms of vitamin A deficiency became evident in a group of yearling Hereford heifers as early as 60 days after they came off good pasture and were given a carotene-deficient ration.

Carotene requirements for fattening beef cattle have been investigated at the Texas Agricultural Experiment Station in cooperation with the Bureau of Animal Industry. Steer calves used in the experiments were first largely depleted of their vitamin A reserves and were then divided into five groups and fed sufficient alfalfa-leaf meal at five levels of carotene intake so as to provide 1,250 to 5,000 micrograms of carotene per 100 pounds of body weight daily. No significant differences were found in rate of gain, carcass weight, or carcass grade after a 140-day fattening period. Steers fed the 1,250- and 1,500-microgram level remained completely night blind, and night blindness persisted in some of the steers fed the 2,500- and 3,000-microgram levels. Steers fed 5,000 micrograms of carotene per 100 pounds of body weight became essentially normal.

The condition of fattening animals is not necessarily an indication of inadequate carotene intake, since animals may be critically low in this factor and yet appear to be in good condition. This deficiency never occurs in cattle fattened on good pasture, but it should be guarded against in lot-fed cattle receiving heavy rations of grain with roughages of relatively low carotene content. Vitamin A deficiency can be avoided or corrected in fattening cattle by feeding at least 2 to 3 pounds of new green, leafy (preferably legume) hay daily to each animal.

Carotene or vitamin A requirements for normal reproduction are much higher than for the prevention of night blindness (see the article Nutritional Diseases of Farm Animals, p. 342) or other common symptoms of vitamin A deficiency. For dairy cattle, Converse and Meigs [7] found that normal calvings resulted when timothy, clover, or alfalfa hay was fed without pasture if the hay was of high quality and rich in carotene. In a limited number of experiments a carotene intake of 80 to 100 milligrams appeared sufficient, and a daily intake of 50 to 60 milligrams resulted in the birth of many weak or dead calves. They point out that in order for clover and timothy hay to be graded U. S. No. 1 the hay must have 45 percent

---

[7] CONVERSE, H. T., and MEIGS, EDWARD B. THE CAROTENE REQUIREMENTS OF DAIRY CATTLE FOR NORMAL REPRODUCTION. U. S. Bur. Dairy Indus. BDIM–827, [4] pp. 1938. [Processed.]

or more of green color. Carotene analyses made during these studies at Beltsville on clover and timothy hay with 50 percent of green color (slightly more than is required for U. S. No. 1) resulted in values of 18 to 20 milligrams of carotene per kilogram (2.2 pounds) of hay. Under the conditions of the experiment, it is estimated that 4½ kilograms (about 10 pounds) of this high-quality hay daily would supply sufficient carotene for normal reproduction.

In some preliminary studies by Davis and Madsen (*12a*), 60 micrograms of carotene per kilogram of body weight (about 2,727 micrograms per 100 pounds of body weight) was found to be sufficient for beef heifers to produce calves which were apparently normal at birth. Calves born to beef heifers receiving 30 and 45 micrograms of carotene per kilogram of body weight were weak or blind at birth and had other symptoms of vitamin A deficiency.

Work in the Bureau of Dairy Industry at Beltsville, Md., has also shown that the minimum amount of carotene and vitamin A needed for the cure of night blindness in cattle does not furnish enough for normal growth and health in young calves. The vitamin A needs of calves are summarized by Converse and Meigs,[8] as follows:

The experiment shows: (1) That when skim milk is fed even after a month on whole milk, calves should receive some well-cured green hay as a source of vitamin A unless cod-liver oil or some other supplement is furnished; (2) that too much dependence should not be placed on whole milk feeding to supply vitamin A unless the milk comes from cows on pasture; (3) that milk does vary widely enough in its vitamin A content to indicate needed caution in its selection for calf feeding; (4) that whole milk in the calf ration is needed more for its vitamin A content than for its fat or energy; and (5) that 20 to 25 cubic centimeters of animal-feeding cod-liver oil or 15 milligrams of carotene roughly equals the vitamin A requirement of growing calves during the milk-feeding age.

Feeds low in carotene, which should be supplemented with carotene-rich feeds if fed to cattle over an extended period, are cottonseed meal and hulls, linseed and soybean meals, wheat, oats, barley, corn (white or yellow), sorghum grains, beet pulp and molasses, cereal straw, corn stover, low-grade legume or grass hays, range herbage during extended periods of drought, and hays held in storage more than 1 year. Feeds rich in carotene are green pasture (grass, legume, or browse), high-grade green, leafy hay (legume, grass, or cereal) of the current year's crop, well-made silage (corn, grass, or legume), and new high-grade alfalfa meal.

The Vitamin B Complex in Bovine Nutrition

Interest concerning the role of the vitamin B complex in the nutrition of cattle dates back to the early work of Theiler and associates in South Africa (*52*), reported in 1915. They suggested after some rice-feeding experiments in which small amounts of roughage were also fed that:

It may be that cattle are capable of synthesizing their own vitamins in virtue of the extensive bacterial flora of their intestinal tract—a sort of commensal symbiosis.

---

[8] CONVERSE, H. T., and MEIGS, EDWARD B.   CAROTENE AND VITAMIN A IN THE NUTRITION OF DAIRY CALVES.   U. S. Bur. Dairy Indus. BDIM–645, 4 pp.   1934.   [Processed.]

This hypothesis was investigated later by workers at the Pennsylvania experiment station (*5*) and was shown to be true for what was then called vitamin B. The workers were successful in obtaining apparently normal growth, gestation, and parturition in dairy heifers on a ration that was low in vitamin B as determined by rat growth. Successful lactation was never obtained for more than several weeks, however. The reason for failure in lactation has never been satisfactorily explained. The work was carried out before the complex nature or chemical properties of the vitamin B group were known. Recent work has confirmed the original observation of vitamin synthesis in the digestive tract of ruminants, and considerable information is now available on the formation of the individual members of the B complex. (See the article on Nutritional Diseases of Farm Animals, p. 344.)

The question whether synthesis of the vitamin B complex in the digestive tract of cattle is sufficient to meet their needs under all circumstances has not been solved in all details. The report from the Kenya Colony (*12*) that "sweating sickness" in calves, characterized by clinical symptoms similar to those of blacktongue in dogs and pellagra in human beings, is interesting in this regard. Rapid recovery from this disease follows treatment with bakers' yeast or liver extract. Newman and Savage (*36*) have noted improved results by including dried brewers' yeast and cereal-yeast feed in a dry calf starter fed to young calves that received a limited amount of milk. Baker (*2*) describes beneficial results from feeding yeast to calves that were in an advanced state of malnutrition and debility as a result of diarrhea, followed by constipation and loss of appetite due to gastrointestinal parasitism (trichostrongylosis). After the animals had gained in appetite and strength, anthelmintic (worm) treatment was successfully administered, and the animals made remarkable recoveries.

Fortunately most feeds of good quality commonly used in cattle feeding are usually good sources of most of the individual vitamins of the B complex. Circumstances may upset their intake however, and other conditions such as infectious diseases, heavy gastrointestinal parasitism, or other disturbances may have a modifying influence on the synthesis of essential factors in the digestive tract. More research on this subject is necessary.

Vitamin C (Ascorbic Acid) and Breeding Efficiency

It has been the belief for a long time that farm animals as a group, including poultry, usually synthesize enough vitamin C to meet their requirements, but recent studies indicate that this is not always true. Phillips and coworkers (*44*), at the Wisconsin station, have shown that calves on a carotene-deficient ration do not maintain normal levels of vitamin C in their blood plasma or urine. Later work (*43*) indicated that the breeding efficiency of some bulls with low fertility could be markedly improved by subcutaneous injections of ascorbic acid. Directions for ascorbic acid therapy of slow-breeding bulls have recently been published (*41*). The average dose recommended is 5 milligrams of ascorbic acid per kilogram (2.2 pounds) of body weight or 1 to 2 grams per 1,000 pounds of body weight injected at 3- to 4-day intervals for 5 or 6 weeks or until the bull shows improvement. Preliminary work also indicates that vitamin C treatment of cows that fail to conceive may also be beneficial in some cases (*1*).

VITAMIN D DEFICIENCY

Vitamin D is essential for normal calcium and phosphorus metabolism in both young and adult cattle. Vitamin D deficiency is most apt to occur during the winter season, when the sun's rays are less potent in ultraviolet light, or during periods of barn feeding when the animals do not have access to either sunshine or sun-cured roughage. Bone deformities are probably the most easily recognized feature of the nutritional disease; however, vitamin D deficiency leads to important changes in the body fluids and other tissues also. Vitamin D deficiency in cattle is very rare except under experimental conditions.

The symptoms of rickets and of osteomalacia have been described in considerable detail in the article on Nutritional Diseases of Farm Animals, page 325.

Vitamin D in any form is suitable for the cure or prevention of rickets in calves. Duncan and Huffman (*13, 21*) have demonstrated the effectiveness of sunshine and sun-cured roughage in curing and preventing rickets experimentally produced in calves. One to two pounds of sun-cured alfalfa a day prevented rickets in calves up to 195 days of age. However, in work at the Pennsylvania experiment station (*7*) 1 pound of sun-cured alfalfa did not have sufficient antirachitic potency to produce a well-calcified skeleton in young calves kept away from direct sunshine over a 6-month feeding period. Two pounds of good sun-cured timothy a day was found to prevent rickets up to 1 year of age, while 3 pounds of hay cured rickets in an animal at 9 months of age. Bechtel and associates (*8*) found that calves would not eat enough corn silage to prevent rickets when an experimental basal ration low in vitamin D was fed, but that in older animals consuming 15 to 20 pounds of silage rachitic symptoms were alleviated in 3 out of 4 cases. Bechdel and coworkers (*6, 7*) found that 3 to 5 pounds of oat straw or 2½ pounds of sun-cured alfalfa prevented rickets, while up to 2½ pounds of night-harvested, machine-dried alfalfa or alfalfa machine-dried immediately after cutting in the daytime was ineffective. Ultraviolet irradiation of the basal ration or irradiation of the calves themselves cured rickets, while feeding cod-liver-oil concentrate or irradiated yeast at the rate of 300 U. S. P. units of vitamin D per 100 pounds of body weight or more per day prevented rickets in calves from birth to 7 months of age. Long, Huffman, and Duncan (*23*) found that only 0.3 to 0.4 U. S. P. units of vitamin D per pound of body weight was necessary to prevent rickets in the growing calf when winter and early spring milk was the sole source of vitamin D, if normal plasma magnesium values were maintained.

Daily exposure to the sun during the summer protects calves against rickets, but during cloudy weather in the late fall and winter extra vitamin D may be needed if roughage of low quality is fed and if the calves are kept inside for long periods because of bad weather. The vitamin D requirements of adult cattle can be readily satisfied by regular exposure to sunshine, together with a liberal amount of sun-cured roughage as normally fed in practical rations.

VITAMIN E AND STERILITY IN CATTLE

Benefits from wheat-germ oil (rich in vitamin E) in the treatment of noninfectious barrenness of cattle has been reported particularly under certain feeding conditions found in Denmark and elsewhere (see the article on Nutritional Diseases of Farm Animals, p. 346), but supporting data are rather meager and often conflicting. Under conditions in the United States, wheat-germ-oil treatment for sterility in cows has produced some confusing results. The Oregon experiment station reports (*10*):

Extensive experiments have been made to test the value of giving cows injections of the antisterility vitamin E which is being extensively advertised as somewhat of a cure-all for difficult breeding. Although earlier trials have indicated these might have some value, further and more extensive tests, using herds at the state hospitals in Salem and Pendleton, have given results too indefinite for conclusions to be drawn.

Research workers have not been able to establish satisfactorily that vitamin E is a dietary essential of calves, cows, or bulls. The technical difficulties and expense involved in preparing vitamin-E-free experimental diets in the quantities needed have limited the studies with cattle.

Since most cattle feeds are good sources of vitamin E, a natural deficiency of the vitamin in balanced rations would, of course, normally be rare (*20*, *40*).

Determination of the need of including vitamin-E-rich concentrates in cattle rations in order to insure fertility and overcome certain forms of sterility awaits further work.

MISCELLANEOUS NUTRITIONAL DISEASES AND DISORDERS OF CATTLE

URINARY CALCULI (UROLITHIASIS)

Cattle frequently suffer from the formation of crystalline deposits or stonelike concretions in the urinary tract. The size, number, and location of the calculi mainly determine whether or not symptoms of the condition become evident.

Newsom (*37*) summarizes some of the causes of urinary calculi and discusses them under the headings of water, vitamin A, mineral unbalance, reaction, hyperparathyroidism (overactivity of the parathyroid gland), infection, and urinary irritation. It is evident from the list of factors that may influence calculi formation that the problem is complex. Evidence that dietary factors are concerned is definite, but it should be kept in mind that other factors may be involved, and also that there are many different types and kinds of calculi.

Newsom points out that calculi are more common in winter, when water is limited or lacking because of freezing weather. The case for vitamin A deficiency as a cause of calculi formation in cattle is not complete, although some rations that tend to favor calculi formation may be low in this factor. An unbalanced mineral intake, particularly of calcium, phosphorus, and magnesium, is believed to influence calculi formation in cattle to a considerable degree.

In cooperative experiments of the Bureau of Animal Industry and the Texas Agricultural Experiment Station conducted at Big Spring, Tex., a serious calculi problem has developed in steers fattened on milo grain, cottonseed meal, and sorgo silage. Such rations are naturally high in magnesium. Steers given high levels of calcium, furnished either as pulverized oystershell or bonemeal had fewer calculi than those receiving less calcium and more magnesium. The work is being continued, with special emphasis on the ratio and quantity of calcium, phosphorus, and magnesium in the diet.

Symptoms and treatment are discussed in the article on Nutritional Diseases of Farm Animals, page 347.

BLOAT

Bloat is a troublesome disorder of cattle that is often the cause of heavy losses. The disease is usually of a sporadic nature; when due to overeating or consuming spoiled feeds, it may be considered as nutritional; but other conditions, such as occlusion of the openings of the forestomachs with hair balls or other foreign bodies, and factors that interfere with normal rumination and intestinal movements, may also be involved. Bloating may occur suddenly or may appear in some individuals more or less regularly after each feeding.

Bloat is due to an excessive accumulation in the rumen of gases probably formed to a large extent by bacterial action. The conditions that favor the kind and amount of gas produced in the rumen and the factors that inhibit its normal removal are not completely understood. Recent studies have indicated that the pressure of the gas in the rumen, which results in a distention of the organ, causing pressure on other vital organs such as the heart and lungs, is not the sole cause of death in bloated animals. Adsorption of toxic gases from the rumen also produces distressing symptoms and may cause death (*38*).

A number of precautions for controlling or preventing bloat have been advocated, but practically none have proved to be of much value under experimental tests. It is generally agreed, however, that legume pastures (alfalfa, clovers, etc.) are more likely to cause bloating than is grass. A young, lush growth of legumes appears to be more dangerous than the mature forage. Pasture that is wet with dew is often said to be particularly dangerous. Before turning hungry animals on legume pasture, it may be worth while to give them a good feed of dry hay so they will not gorge themselves on green forage.

It is possible that soil conditions under which a feed is grown may also influence its tendency to produce bloat. McIntosh (*24*) states that—

The farmers who have the least trouble with bloating are those whose alfalfa fields are in a high state of fertility, while those who have the greatest amount of trouble are farmers whose pasture land is in a worn-out condition.

His theory has not been critically tested, but it is no doubt worthy of careful consideration. The determination of the chemical characteristics of feeds that cause bloat and a more accurate definition of the environmental and physiological factors concerned in this disease are important problems for further study.

Fattening cattle or heavy-milking cows that receive large quantities of grain also have a tendency to bloat. In cattle-fattening experiments, Osland and coworkers (*39*) at the Colorado experiment station report that—

* * * barley, when fed alone in a grain, cottonseed cake, and hay ration, is not a safe feed for calves because of its tendency to cause bloat, even though it is fed at the rate of only 1 percent of their live weight or less. The addition of cheap, bulky carbonaceous feeds such as wet beet pulp, silage, or potatoes has proved effective in checking digestive troubles but has failed to prevent bloats entirely.

Similar results were obtained by the Bureau of Animal Industry in cooperation with the Montana experiment station. A large proportion of steer calves fattened on barley and alfalfa were found to suffer from bloat or other digestive disturbances that caused scouring or going off feed. Feeding a grain ration consisting of an equal amount of barley and dried molasses-beet pulp, however, resulted in no serious cases of bloat or other digestive disorders. In these experiments bloat was usually treated by drenching the animals with as much as 12 ounces of raw linseed oil.

In severe cases of bloat, puncturing the paunch with a trocar may be necessary. This operation may injure the animal if not done properly, and it should be performed by a qualified veterinarian whenever possible. Further treatment to stop fermentation in the paunch and restore normal gastrointestinal activity may also be prescribed.

KETOSIS

The metabolic disorder of cattle in which there is an abnormal quantity of ketone bodies (acetone, acetoacetic acid, and beta-hydroxybutyric acid) in the blood, urine, and milk is an important problem in the dairy industry. The disease causes a loss of condition in affected animals, a marked decline in milk flow, and the production of a characteristic off-flavored milk. Duncan, Huffman, and Tobin (*15*) studied this condition in a herd of Jersey cows under farm conditions, many of which were seriously affected with the disease. The disorder was apparently associated with feeding a ration of poor-quality soybean hay, corn silage, and a small amount of grain during the fall and winter. The disease was described as follows:

The occurrence of the disturbance in the health and milk production of the cows became most pronounced within two to six weeks following a normal parturition. It was the owner's opinion that the cows were in good nutritional condition before calving and that all had begun to produce large quantities of milk. He also observed that the cows lost appetite gradually, rapidly decreased in milk production, became constipated, hide-bound, listless, and emaciated in appearance. He reported that the barn had a peculiar odor at times.

Cows in the most critical condition were given chloral hydrate (1 dram in 12 ounces of warm water 3 times a day for 1 day), and this was repeated later in severe cases. The ration of all the animals was changed. Liberal quantities of alfalfa hay of medium quality and cornstalks were fed instead of the soybean hay and silage previously used. Severely affected cows were given 1 to 2 pounds of corn sugar or molasses and the grain was increased to 5 pounds a day. The new feeding schedule resulted in marked improvement within 2 weeks in most cases, as shown by improvement in appetite and general condition and by a decrease of the ketone bodies in the blood, urine, and milk as determined by chemical analyses.

Duncan and coworkers and others have reached the general conclusion that ketosis may be reduced in stall-fed animals by feeding hay of a good quality together with a liberal supply of grain. In addition, high-producing individuals should have some feed that is a source of quickly available sugar, such as molasses. Turning animals to pasture also resulted in recovery. An extract from the anterior lobe of the pituitary, and even vitamin B_1, have been reported to be of use in the treatment of this disease.

Overeating and Undernutrition

Cattle, like other farm animals, are adversely affected by overeating. (See the article on Nutritional Diseases of Farm Animals, p. 348.) When this occurs, the regular ration, except water, should be withheld for a day or two, and they should be slowly brought back on feed, a small amount of palatable roughage being given first, with gradual introduction of the grain mixture as the appetite returns. If there is severe constipation after an attack of diarrhea, it should be treated as soon as possible with Epsom salts, raw linseed oil or pure mineral oil. The advice and help of a qualified veterinarian may prevent serious consequences if it is obtained early enough.

Lactating dairy cows are occasionally overfed when record-breaking production is desired. Symptoms of overeating are loss of appetite, dullness, diarrhea, distention of the rumen (bloat), and a marked drop in the milk yield. Milk fever (see p. 533) occurs most often in heavily fed, high-producing animals. In an effort to force apparently normal animals to maximum performance or above, drugs are occasionally prescribed to stimulate appetite, a practice that should be discouraged. The record may be attained, but the productive life and reproductive ability of the animal may thereby be permanently injured. Losses due to overeating can best be controlled or prevented by careful feeding, with strict attention to the appetites of the animals.

Underfeeding may be harmful to the animal body and is frequently uneconomical (*27*). Undernutrition may come from either quantitative or qualitative deficiencies in the ration or from both. (See Nutritional Diseases of Farm Animals, p. 349.)

Losses from livestock consuming poisonous plants on the range are usually largest during periods of drought or when the range is overgrazed. Shortage of water is as serious or more so than a lack of feed. Forsling (*16*) discusses the dangers of overstocking.

Hart (*17*) points out that "profitable livestock management does not include allowing animals to border on starvation or failure to supply sufficient quantities of essential substances until symptoms appear."

LITERATURE CITED

(1) ANONYMOUS.
  1940. "HARD TO SETTLE" COWS RESPOND TO VITAMIN C INJECTIONS. Wis. Agr. Expt. Sta. Ann. Rept. (Bul. 450) : 37–38, illus.
(2) BAKER, DONALD W.
  1941. YEAST AS AN ADJUNCT TO THE ANTHELMINTIC TREATMENT OF ADVANCED CASES OF TRICHOSTRONGYLOSIS IN CALVES. Cornell Vet. 31 : 13–16.
(3) BALTZER, A. C., KILLHAM, B. J., DUNCAN, C. W., and HUFFMAN, C. F.
  1941. A COBALT DEFICIENCY DISEASE OBSERVED IN SOME MICHIGAN CATTLE. Mich. Agr. Expt. Sta. Quart. Bul. 24 : 68–70.
(4) BEATH, O. A., DRAIZE, J. H., and GILBERT, C. S.
  1934. PLANTS POISONOUS TO LIVESTOCK. Wyo. Agr. Expt. Sta. Bul. 200, 84 pp., illus.
(5) BECHDEL, S. I., ECKLES, C. H., and PALMER, L. S.
  1926. THE VITAMIN B REQUIREMENT OF THE CALF. Jour. Dairy Sci. 9 : 409–438, illus.
(6) ——— HILSTON, W. W., GUERRANT, N. B., and DUTCHER, R. A.
  1938. THE VITAMIN D REQUIREMENT OF DAIRY CALVES. Pa. Agr. Expt. Sta. Bul. 364, 26 pp., illus.
(7) ——— LANDSBURG, K. G., and HILL, O. J.
  1933. RICKETS IN CALVES. Pa. Agr. Expt. Sta. Tech. Bul. 291, 41 pp., illus.
(8) BECHTEL, H. ERNEST, HUFFMAN, C. F., DUNCAN, C. W., and HOPPERT, C. A.
  1936. VITAMIN D STUDIES IN CATTLE, IV. CORN SILAGE AS A SOURCE OF VITAMIN D FOR DAIRY CATTLE. Jour. Dairy Sci. 19 : 359–372.
(9) BECKER, R. B., NEAL, W. M., and SHEALY, A. L.
  1934. EFFECT OF CALCIUM-DEFICIENT ROUGHAGES UPON MILK YIELD AND BONE STRENGTH IN CATTLE. Jour. Dairy Sci. 17 : 1–10, illus.
(10) BESSE, RALPH S.
  1938. DAIRY CATTLE DISEASES. Oreg. Agr. Expt. Sta. Bien. Rpt. 1936–38 (Bul. 359) : 58–59.
(11) CREECH, G. T., and MADSEN, L. L.
  1942. GENERALIZED EDEMA, OR THE SO-CALLED ANASARCA IN CATTLE. Bur. Vet. 18 : 1–3, illus.
(12) DAUBNEY, R.
  1936. REPORT OF THE CHIEF VETERINARY RESEARCH OFFICER FOR THE YEAR 1934 : SWEATING SICKNESS IN CALVES. Kenya Colony Dept. Agr. Ann. Rpt. 3 : 31–32.
(12a) DAVIS, RUSSELL E., and MADSEN, LOUIS L.
  1941. CAROTENE AND VITAMIN A IN CATTLE BLOOD PLASMA, WITH OBSERVATIONS ON REPRODUCTIVE PERFORMANCE AT RESTRICTED LEVELS OF CAROTENE INTAKE. Jour. Nutr. 21 : 135–146, illus.
(13) DUNCAN, C. W., and HUFFMAN, C. F.
  1936. VITAMIN D STUDIES IN CATTLE. III. INFLUENCE OF SOLAR ULTRAVIOLET RADIATION UPON THE BLOOD CHEMISTRY AND MINERAL METABOLISM OF DAIRY CALVES. Jour. Dairy Sci. 19 : 291–303.

(14) DUNCAN, C. W., HUFFMAN, C. F., and ROBINSON, C. F.
 1935. MAGNESIUM STUDIES IN CALVES. I. TETANY PRODUCED BY A RATION
  OF MILK OR MILK WITH VARIOUS SUPPLEMENTS. Jour. Biol. Chem.
  108 : 35–44.
(15) ——HUFFMAN, C. F., and TOBIN, H. A.
 1939. A CHEMICAL STUDY OF KETOSIS IN A DAIRY HERD. Amer. Vet. Med.
  Assoc. Jour. 95 : 690–700.
(16) FORSLING, C. L.
 1924. SAVING LIVESTOCK FROM STARVATION ON SOUTHWESTERN RANGES.
  U. S. Dept. Agr. Farmers' Bul. 1428, 22 pp., illus.
(17) HART, GEORGE H.
 1938. DIETARY DEFICIENCIES AND RELATED SYMPTOMATOLOGY IN DOMESTIC
  ANIMALS. Amer. Vet. Med. Assoc. Jour. 92 : 503–515.
(18) ——
 1940. VITAMIN A DEFICIENCY AND REQUIREMENTS OF FARM MAMMALS.
  Nutr. Abs. and Rev. 10 : [261]–272.
(19) —— and GUILBERT, H. R.
 1933. VITAMIN-A DEFICIENCY AS RELATED TO REPRODUCTION IN RANGE CATTLE.
  Calif. Agr. Expt. Sta. Bul. 560, 30 pp., illus.
(20) HATHAWAY, I. L., and DAVIS, H. P.
 1934. THE VITAMIN B CONTENT OF CERTAIN DAIRY FEEDS. Nebr. Agr. Expt.
  Sta. Res. Bul. 73, 7 pp.
(21) HUFFMAN, C. F., and DUNCAN, C. W.
 1935. VITAMIN D STUDIES IN CATTLE. I. THE ANTIRACHITIC VALUE OF HAY
  IN THE RATION OF DAIRY CATTLE. Jour. Dairy Sci. 18 : 511–526.
(22) —— and DUNCAN, C. W.
 1936. MAGNESIUM CARBONATE AND MAGNESIUM OXIDE SUPPLEMENTS TO A
  WHOLE MILK RATION FOR DAIRY CALVES. (Abstract) Jour. Dairy
  Sci. 19 : 440–441.
(23) LONG, JOHN W., HUFFMAN, C. F., and DUNCAN, C. W.
 1936. A STUDY OF THE VITAMIN D REQUIREMENTS OF CALVES WHEN NATURAL
  MILK FURNISHED THE SOLE SOURCE OF THE ANTIRACHITIC FACTOR.
  Milk Plant Monthly 25 (7) : 30–36, 72, illus.
(24) McINTOSH, R. A.
 1938. THE INDIGESTIONS OF RUMINANTS WITH SPECIAL REFERENCE TO TREAT-
  MENT. Cornell Vet. 28 : 161–169.
(25) MADSEN, D. E., and NIELSEN, H. M.
 1939. PARTURIENT HEMOGLOBINEMIA OF DAIRY COWS. Amer. Vet. Med.
  Assoc. Jour. 94 : 577–586, illus.
(26) —— and NIELSEN, H. M.
 1940. THE RELATIONSHIP OF PARTURIENT HEMOGLOBINEMIA OF DAIRY COWS
  TO APHOSPHOROSIS. North Amer. Vet. 21 : 81–89, illus.
(27) MADSEN, LOUIS L.
 1939. FACTORS AFFECTING MAINTENANCE NUTRITION, FEED UTILIZATION, AND
  HEALTH OF FARM ANIMALS. U. S. Dept. Agr. Yearbook (Food
  and Life) 1939 : 431–449, illus.
(28) METZGER, H. J.
 1936. A CASE OF TETANY WITH HYPOMAGNESEMIA IN A DAIRY COW. Cornell
  Vet. 26 : 353–356.
(29) MOORE, L. A.
 1939. RELATIONSHIP BETWEEN CAROTENE, BLINDNESS DUE TO CONSTRICTION
  OF THE OPTIC NERVE, PAPILLARY EDEMA AND NYCTALOPIA IN CALVES.
  Jour. Nutr. 17 : 443–459, illus.
(30) —— and HALLMAN, E. T.
 1936. PRODUCTION OF WHITE SPOTTED KIDNEYS IN CALVES. (Abstract of
  paper) Jour. Dairy Sci. 19 : 434–435.
(31) —— HALLMAN, E. T., and SHOLL, L. B.
 1938. CARDIOVASCULAR AND OTHER LESIONS IN CALVES FED DIETS LOW IN
  MAGNESIUM. Arch. Path. 26 : 820–838, illus.
(32) MOXON, ALVIN L.
 1937. ALKALI DISEASE OR SELENIUM POISONING. S. Dak. Agr. Expt. Sta.
  Bul. 311, 91 pp., illus.

(33) NEAL, W. M., and AHMANN, C. F.
　　1937. COBALT AS AN ESSENTIAL ELEMENT IN ANIMAL NUTRITION. Science 86: 225–226, illus.
(34) —— and AHMANN, C. F.
　　1937. THE ESSENTIALITY OF COBALT IN BOVINE NUTRITION. Jour. Dairy Sci. 20: 741–753, illus.
(35) —— and BECKER, R. B.
　　1933. THE COMPOSITION OF FEEDSTUFFS IN RELATION TO NUTRITIONAL ANEMIA IN CATTLE. Jour. Agr. Res. 47: 249–255.
(36) NEWMAN, PAUL E., and SAVAGE, E. S.
　　1938. THE USE OF YEAST IN CALF MEALS AND PELLETS. Jour. Dairy Sci. 21: 161–167, illus.
(37) NEWSOM, I. E.
　　1938. URINARY CALCULI WITH SPECIAL REFERENCE TO CATTLE AND SHEEP. Amer. Vet. Med. Assoc. Jour. 92: 495–502.
(38) OLSON, T. M.
　　1940. BLOAT IN DAIRY CATTLE. Jour. Dairy Sci. 23: 343–353.
(39) OSLAND, H. B., MAYNARD, E. J., and MORTON, GEORGE E.
　　1936. COLORADO FATTENING RATIONS FOR CATTLE. Colo. Agr. Expt. Sta. Bul. 422, 120 pp., illus.
(40) PALMER, L. S., NELSON, J. W., and GULLICKSON, T. W.
　　1940. VITAMIN E POTENCY OF CERTAIN FOODSTUFFS. (Abstract of paper) Jour. Dairy Sci. 23: 571–572.
(41) PHILLIPS, PAUL H.
　　1940. DIRECTIONS FOR THE ASCORBIC ACID THERAPY OF SLOW-BREEDING BULLS. Amer. Vet. Med. Assoc. Jour. 97: 165–166.
(42) —— HART, E. B., and BOHSTEDT, G.
　　1934. CHRONIC TOXICOSIS IN DAIRY COWS DUE TO THE INGESTION OF FLUORINE Wis. Agr. Expt. Sta. Res. Bul. 123, 30 pp., illus.
(43) —— LARDY, H. A. HEIZER, E. E., and RUPEL, I. W.
　　1940. SPERM STIMULATION IN THE BULL THROUGH THE SUBCUTANEOUS ADMINISTRATION OF ASCORBIC ACID. Jour. Dairy Sci. 23: 873–878.
(44) —— RUPEL, I. W., OLESON, J. J., and BOHSTEDT, G.
　　1938. THE EFFECTS OF AN ATYPICAL BLINDNESS-PRODUCING RATION UPON THE VITAMIN K AND C CONTENT OF CALF BLOOD. Amer. Soc. Anim. Prod. Proc. 31: 320–327, illus.
(45) QUIN, A. H.
　　1939. SOME FACTORS INVOLVED IN THE DEFICIENCY DISEASES. Amer. Vet. Med. Assoc. Jour. 94: 621–626.
(46) REED, O. E., and HUFFMAN, C. F.
　　1930. THE RESULTS OF A FIVE-YEAR MINERAL FEEDING INVESTIGATION WITH DAIRY CATTLE. Mich. Agr. Expt. Sta. Tech. Bul. 105, 63 pp., illus.
(47) RIGGS, J. K.
　　1940. THE LENGTH OF TIME REQUIRED FOR DEPLETION OF VITAMIN A RESERVES IN RANGE CATTLE. Jour. Nutr. 20: 491–500.
(48) SHEELY, W. J., and SHEALY, A. L.
　　1940. BEEF PRODUCTION IN FLORIDA. Fla. Univ. Agr. Ext. Bul. 104, 35 pp., illus.
(49) SJOLLEMA, B.
　　1932. NUTRITIONAL AND METABOLIC DISORDERS IN CATTLE. Nutr. Abs. and Rev. 1: 621–632.
(50) SYKES, J. F., and ALFREDSON, B. V.
　　1940. STUDIES ON THE BOVINE ELECTROCARDIOGRAM. I. ELECTROCARDIOGRAPHIC CHANGES IN CALVES ON LOW POTASSIUM RATIONS. Soc. Expt. Biol. and Med. Proc. 43: 575–579, illus.
(51) THEILER, SIR ARNOLD, and GREEN, HENRY H.
　　1932. APHOSPHOROSIS IN RUMINANTS. Nutr. Abs. and Rev. 1: 359–385.
(52) —— GREEN, HENRY HAMILTON, and VILJOEN, PHILIP RUDOLPH.
　　1915. CONTRIBUTION TO THE STUDY OF DEFICIENCY DISEASE, WITH SPECIAL REFERENCE TO THE LAMZIEKTE PROBLEM IN SOUTH AFRICA. Union So. Africa Dept. Agr., Dir. Vet. Res. Rpt. 3–4: 7–68.

Hog Cholera

BY C. N. McBRYDE [1]

IN ITS EFFECTS on swine, hog cholera can be compared only with some of the diseases that used to wipe out whole communities of human beings before the days of modern medicine. The discovery of a serum that would produce immunity against this disease was an event of major importance to the livestock industry. Here a pioneer in the fight against hog cholera tells what it is and what can be done about it.

HOG CHOLERA is a devastating livestock disease that has caused enormous economic losses in the United States for over a century. It recurs from year to year but during certain periods has been unusually prevalent. The first such period on record reached its climax in 1887, the second in 1896, and a third in 1913. During these periods hog producers suffered enormous losses, and in some localities the swine population was almost wiped out. In the fall of 1926 the disease again became unusually prevalent in parts of the Middle West. The supply of preventive serum on hand at that time was inadequate to meet the unusual demand, and losses in some sections were very heavy.

The direct monetary value of hogs destroyed by cholera in the United States has amounted to as much as 65 million dollars in a single year, and the average annual loss during any 10-year period prior to 1914 was probably not less than 20 million dollars. If the indirect losses could be computed, the totals would be greatly increased.

The estimated number of hogs dying from cholera in the United States from 1884 to 1940 inclusive are shown in figure 1. According to data available, the disease killed more than 13 percent of the swine in the country in 1896. Again in 1913 more than 10 percent

---

[1] C. N. McBryde was in charge of the Field Station, Pathological Division, Ames, Iowa, Bureau of Animal Industry, until March 1, 1942, when he retired.

of the hogs in the United States died of cholera. Since 1914, except for 1926, as noted previously, the general trend of losses from hog cholera has been downward as a result of the increasing use of anti-hog-cholera serum.

It does not appear to be definitely established whether hog cholera originated in America or in Europe. According to some authorities the disease existed in Europe long before it was recognized in this country, and it seems not unlikely that the contagion may have been imported from there, as was pleuropneumonia of cattle. It was first reported in the United States in southern Ohio in 1833 and soon spread throughout the country. By 1853 no less than 90 separate areas of infection were known to exist, and the malady was becoming

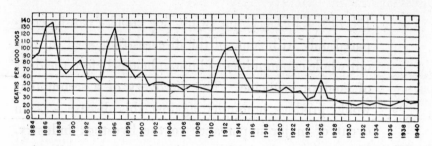

FIGURE 1.—Estimated death losses of hogs from hog cholera in the United States 1884–1940.

much dreaded by swine breeders. Hog cholera now occurs in every State in the Union and in practically all parts of the world where hogs are raised. In Canada and Australia, however, the losses from the disease are said to be comparatively small in proportion to the number of pigs raised.

THE CAUSE OF HOG CHOLERA

Hog cholera has been under investigation by the United States Department of Agriculture since 1878. Because of its very great importance to the livestock industry it was one of the first diseases to be studied experimentally by the Bureau of Animal Industry after its establishment in 1884.

As a result of early studies carried out in the laboratories of the Bureau of Animal Industry of the United States Department of Agriculture, it seemed to be definitely established in 1885 that a bacterium, or bacillus, resembling the germ that causes typhoid fever in man, was the cause of hog cholera. For nearly 20 years this germ, which came to be called the hog cholera bacillus, was quite generally accepted by research workers in the field of animal diseases as the cause of hog cholera. Later studies by the Bureau of Animal Industry, however, proved that this germ is not the true cause of the disease and established the fact that it is caused by a virus.

The virus of hog cholera cannot be seen with the most powerful microscopes in use today, and it passes readily through the pores

of very fine filters which hold back all visible bacteria. It is therefore called an ultramicroscopic virus and a filtrable virus. Attempts
to grow the virus outside of the animal body generally have been
unsuccessful. However, Carl Tenbroeck, director of the Department
of Animal Pathology of the Rockefeller Institute, has recently reported
that he has been able to grow the virus by methods similar to those
previously described by Hecke, a German investigator.

The discovery that hog cholera is caused by a filtrable, ultramicroscopic virus was very important in the study of this disease. It upset
all previous concepts regarding the nature of the disease and served
to explain earlier failures to obtain an effective vaccine or serum.
It also paved the way for subsequent studies that finally led to the
discovery of a successful preventive serum.

SYMPTOMS AND DIAGNOSIS

Hog cholera is a highly infectious and contagious disease. It
affects swine of all ages and is usually acute, although it sometimes
pursues a subacute or chronic course. It is characterized by a sudden
onset, loss of appetite, fever, and weakness. The mortality rate of the
acute form is usually high, and entire herds have been wiped out by
it within a short time. Pigs affected with the disease in the subacute
or chronic form may linger for some time before they succumb.
Spontaneous recovery is rare.

All breeds of swine are subject to the disease. At one time it was
thought that the mulefoot, or single-toed, hog was immune, but this
was proved to be a fallacy by experimental inoculation of these
animals.

When the disease makes its appearance in a herd, the first symptoms
noted are loss of appetite in one or more animals, which either refuse
to come up to feed with the rest of the herd or come to the feed trough,
nibble at their feed, and then turn away. In animals experimentally
infected, fever usually develops a day or two before visible symptoms
are noted.

The affected animals separate themselves from the rest of the herd
and soon show signs of weakness, especially in the hind legs, which are
frequently crossed, resulting in a peculiar wobbling, scissorslike gait.
The fever rises rapidly in the acute cases, and the animals may become
very thirsty. Frequently there is a conjunctivitis, characterized by a
thick, gummy secretion, which at times may almost glue the eyelids
shut. The sick pigs usually die within 7 to 10 days.

In diagnosing hog cholera, the temperature of the affected animals
is of much importance. The normal temperature of swine under ordinary weather conditions, when the animals are at rest and not excited,
ranges from 101° to 103° F. When cholera is present in a herd, it is
not uncommon to find a large proportion of the hogs with temperatures of 104° to 107° F., or even higher. The body temperature
usually falls in the later stages of the disease and frequently becomes
subnormal shortly before death.

A pig sick with hog cholera has a rather characteristic appearance.
The animal stands in a listless, dejected attitude with the head droop-

ing downward and the tail hanging straight and limp. As a field man of the Bureau of Animal Industry expressed it, the animal appears to be lost in thought (fig. 2).

In most cases it is not possible to know when the infection actually reaches a farm herd, but once the disease makes its appearance it spreads more or less rapidly throughout the herd if no treatment is given. A large part of the herd does not sicken suddenly, however, as is the case in an outbreak of swine influenza, or "hog flu."

FIGURE 2.—Pigs suffering from acute hog cholera. The sickest animals are lying down; the others stand in the characteristic attitude, with heads down and tails limp.

In the course of virus production at the Bureau of Animal Industry station at Ames, Iowa, hog cholera virus was injected into the bodies of 100 susceptible shotes. The shortest incubation period (the time between the entrance of the virus into the body of the animal and the appearance of visible symptoms) was 3 days and the longest 5 days, the average being about 4 days. When susceptible swine are exposed by contact, it is impossible to determine just when infection takes place, but visible symptoms are rarely observed within less than 5 or 6 days after such exposure.

SEASONAL OCCURRENCE

Hog cholera has a rather marked seasonal incidence. In the Middle West it is essentially a disease of the late summer and fall, as shown in figure 3. During the winter months outbreaks are sporadic, and the disease never becomes epidemic as in the summer and fall. In the South, where the winters are mild and the temperature more or less uniform, severe outbreaks of hog cholera may occur at any season of the year.

Before the discovery of a preventive serum, the disease often swept through the countryside, causing devastating losses. During the fall months, looking across the prairies of the Middle West, one could often

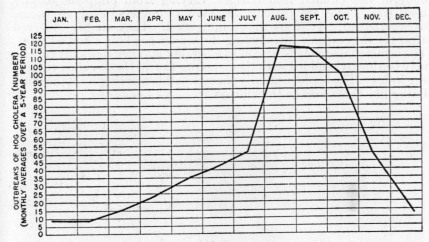

FIGURE 3.—Seasonal occurrence of hog cholera in Iowa, based on a 5-year record, 1928-32.

see smoke ascending from perhaps half a dozen farms where pigs dead of cholera were being burned. The writer recalls such sights in 1904 to 1906, the early years of his field work with cholera in Iowa and Nebraska.

POST MORTEM FINDINGS

The skin of the under surface of the body and behind the ears is frequently bright red at the height of the disease and later may become dark purplish.

The changes that take place in the lymph glands of hogs with cholera are usually quite striking and are of considerable diagnostic importance. These glands are normally gray, but in hog cholera they become enlarged and show marked reddening. When the glands are cut through, it is often found that the reddening is confined to the margin and does not extend throughout the body of the gland. The lymph glands are quite generally affected. The ones usually found on post mortem examination to be diseased are those in the neck near the angle of the jaw, those in the groin, and those in the mesentery, or thin membrane which supports the intestines.

The lungs show small hemorrhagic spots on the outer surface, varying in size from that of bird shot to that of a small pea and usually bright red in color. Another frequent lesion, or tissue injury, is caused by the collapse of lung lobules, giving rise to larger areas of a dark-red or purplish color.

The spleen, or milt, is usually engorged with blood, darker than normal, and often soft and easily torn. Not infrequently dark, raised, ovoid areas a quarter of an inch or more long are seen along the border of the spleen.

The kidneys usually show characteristic lesions in the form of small, more or less circular hemorrhages, varying from pin-point to pin-head size. These are perhaps the most characteristic of all lesions of hog cholera. They are shown in figure 4. They are best observed after the thin capsule surrounding the kidney has been stripped away. The hemorrhages may be few in number, but at other times the surface may be thickly studded with them, giving rise to the so-called turkey-egg kidney. The bladder usually shows small hemorrhages on the inner lining like those seen on the kidneys.

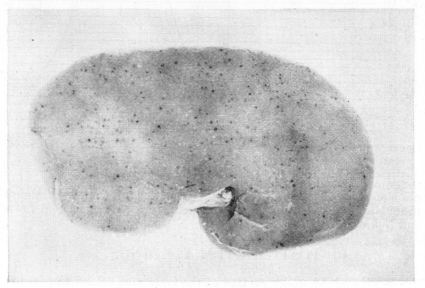

FIGURE 4.—Hog kidney showing lesions characteristic of acute hog cholera.

The intestines sometimes show small red hemorrhages on the outer surfaces and also on the inner lining. The lining of the upper part of the large intestine often shows a diffused reddening. In the subacute or chronic cases the lining of the large intestine often becomes ulcerated, and this is especially noticeable where the small intestine joins the large intestine. Distinct, raised ulcers may occur in the large intestine. When well-defined, these are called button ulcers.

Marked variation in the extent of the lesions is a peculiarity of the disease. At times they may be so slight as to be scarcely noticeable; again, they may be very extensive and very striking. Since tissues and organs of hogs dying from other causes may present an appearance very similar to that described for hogs dead of cholera, it is not advisable for a farmer to attempt to determine the cause of death by cutting open a dead hog. A veterinarian should always be called in when disease appears in a herd.

MODES OF INFECTION

That the sick pig is a potent factor in the spread of hog cholera has long been known, but the manner in which the virus is thrown off from the animal body has not been so well understood. Experiments conducted at the Bureau field station at Ames, Iowa, have demonstrated that the virus is present in the circulating blood of the sick animal and also in the various secretions and excretions. It was found in the circulating blood of a sick pig as early as the first day after experimental infection. The virus was found in the eye and nose secretions and the fecal matter by the third day and in the urine by the fourth day. It is apparent that the cholera-infected pig may be a source of danger during the period of incubation, that is, before the development of visible symptoms of the disease. In purchasing new stock, therefore, the farmer should segregate such animals and keep them under observation for at least 2 weeks before adding them to his herd.

At one time it was thought that birds, especially pigeons, might be an important factor in spreading the disease. Farmers were accordingly advised to destroy their flocks of these birds. That belief was purely theoretical, however, and was proved false by carefully conducted experiments in which susceptible pigs were exposed for long periods to pigeons which passed back and forth from a pen only 10 feet away that contained pigs sick and dying of hog cholera. Although pigeons were shown not to be concerned in the dissemination of hog cholera, it is not unlikely that crows and buzzards may act as carriers of the disease, for these birds may carry away and later drop portions of cholera-diseased carcasses upon which they have fed.

The virus has been found to remain active throughout the winter in the carcasses of cholera-infected pigs buried late in the fall in Iowa. Unburied carcasses of infected pigs were found to remain infectious for 11 weeks during cold weather. In earlier times such carcasses were undoubtedly a potential menace, but nowadays dead animals on farms are usually picked up promptly by trucks operated by rendering plants. If such service is not available, all carcasses of hogs should be burned or else buried deeply and covered with quicklime. During the warm summer months, both buried and unburied carcasses undergo rapid putrefaction, and the virus is soon destroyed. In warm weather, after the virus leaves the animal body in the secretions and excretions, it is quickly inactivated, but in cold weather it may survive for a much longer time. Contaminated pens were found to harbor the infection for as long as 4 weeks during the winter season, whereas in summer they were sometimes no longer infectious after 24 hours. The rapid disappearance of the virus from contaminated pens in hot weather is probably a result of putrefactive and fermentative changes taking place in the litter. Sunlight is also potent in the destruction of disease organisms.

Cured meats are unquestionably a source of danger when fed as scraps in garbage, since the virus has been found to survive in hams taken from cholera-infected hogs cured by both the dry-salt and brine methods.

A study of insects as possible carriers of hog cholera was made

some years ago at the field station at Ames. The species studied
included the common hog louse, the housefly, the biting stablefly, the
buffalo gnat, and several species of mosquitoes. Extensive experiments demonstrated quite conclusively that both the housefly and the
stablefly were capable of transferring the virus of hog cholera from
sick to well pigs. The results for the other insects were negative.

The housefly commonly feeds on the highly virulent eye secretions
of hogs suffering from cholera as well as on the infectious blood from
wounds or cuts. Since experiments by the United States Bureau of
Entomology and Plant Quarantine have demonstrated that houseflies
can travel as far as 12 miles in 48 hours, it is plain that these flies may
contribute to the rapid spread of hog cholera from farm to farm.

It was demonstrated that the virus of hog cholera may be transmitted from sick to well pigs through the bite of the stablefly. Not
much is known as to the flight habits of stableflies except that they will
follow a team of horses for a considerable distance along a highway.
After engorging themselves with blood, they have a habit of resting
for a while on the vegetation along the roadside and then following
another team of horses. In such relays they may travel a considerable
distance. In the late fall, too, the flies may enter the open windows
of automobiles and thus be transported long distances. Weekly counts
of flies trapped on dairy farms near Ames were made during the
summer and early fall for several years. Curves or graphs plotted to
show the prevalence of the biting flies were found to correspond very
closely to those showing the incidence of hog cholera during the several
years in which the fly counts were made. Insect transmission provides the most satisfactory explanation of the rapid spread of hog
cholera during an outbreak and the fact that it frequently seems to
jump from one farm to another, often skipping over intervening
farms.

IMPORTANCE OF SANITATION AND CARE
IN THE PREVENTION OF DISEASE

Sanitation, proper feeding, and good care are of the greatest importance in successful swine raising.

A recent survey by an authority on swine diseases has revealed,
however, that only about one-third of the farmers of this country
follow good practices in feeding and housing their swine.

Poor feeding undoubtedly tends to lower the resistance of livestock to many infectious diseases. Recent experimental work indicates, for example, that a ration lacking in certain vitamins may
be a hitherto unsuspected factor in certain intestinal troubles of
swine. Poor housing is a predisposing factor in pneumonia, influenza,
and other respiratory disturbances.

Sanitation is probably the most neglected factor in swine raising,
and its lack undoubtedly contributes to the occurrence of filth-borne
intestinal diseases. The practice of using old hog lots year after
year should be discontinued. When pigs are allowed to run in such
lots they are almost certain to pick up the eggs of intestinal parasites

and the germs of disease, and as a result the farmer will have a lot of unthrifty, unprofitable pigs on his hands.

Among the ailments of swine the intestinal diseases are next in importance to hog cholera. They not only cause an enormous direct loss but are also responsible for a large indirect loss. The simultaneous vaccination of such infected herds with serum and virus for immunization against hog cholera is likely to be followed by bad results.

In 1927 the Bureau of Animal Industry, through carefully conducted experiments carried out in McLean County, Ill., developed what has become known as the McLean County system of swine sanitation. While the system was developed primarily for the protection of swine against infestation with the ascaris, or common roundworm, it has also served to protect them against the filth-borne bacterial diseases. In this way it has proved a valuable adjunct in the successful immunization of swine against hog cholera.

Considering the great importance of sanitation and care in the prevention of swine diseases and their bearing on hog cholera, interested farmers should refer to the article in this volume in which the McLean County system is described (p. 774).

PREVENTION OF HOG CHOLERA

Many preparations composed of various drugs and chemicals have been exploited from time to time as preventives of or remedies for hog cholera, but all such products tested by Federal and State institutions have been found worthless. Farmers are therefore warned against investing their money in such preparations.

Many so-called tonics also are advertised as able to do wonders for hogs. Some of them may have some value as conditioners, but none are of any value in the prevention or cure of hog cholera.

ANTI-HOG-CHOLERA SERUM

After the discovery that hog cholera is caused by a filtrable, or ultramicroscopic, virus, a few preliminary experiments looking toward production of a protective serum were carried out in 1903 at the Bureau of Animal Industry experiment station at Bethesda, Md. Results were not satisfactory, and the experiments were laid aside on account of other work. In 1905 the experiments were resumed at the Bureau field station at Ames, Iowa. A successful preventive serum was finally developed there and was given a practical trial on farms in the vicinity of Ames in 1907.

The method of preparing the serum was patented, and all rights were dedicated to the public. Notice of the successful results was sent to every State, with an invitation to send representatives to the Bureau station at Ames to observe the methods of preparing and administering the serum. Twenty-five States accepted this invitation in 1908. During the years immediately following these demonstrations, a number of States began production and distribution of the new serum to farmers within their borders. At the same time or shortly after the preparation and sale of the serum were undertaken by commercial concerns, and when these firms became well established serum production by the States was discontinued.

The serum is prepared by injecting large immune hogs with virulent blood obtained from pigs sick of cholera. A very minute quantity of such blood would cause the death of a susceptible hog, but even large doses are harmless to an immune hog. After the immune hogs are injected with virulent blood they are called hyperimmunes, since their immunity is increased by this procedure. After a suitable interval, the hyperimmune hog is bled by cutting off a portion of its tail. Several bleedings are made in this manner. This blood contains large quantities of protective substances termed antibodies. Anti-hog-cholera serum is prepared by removing the fibrin and cells from the blood and adding a small amount of preservative to the clear serum.

The efficacy of anti-hog-cholera serum in the prevention of hog cholera is now universally recognized, and the serum is used in all parts of the world where hogs are raised. It is not a cure for hog cholera and should be used only as a preventive, although it seems to have some curative value if administered in the very early stages of the disease.

When given alone, the serum produces only a temporary immunity, which may be lost within a few weeks. When the serum is given in conjunction with a small amount of virus or virulent blood, however, a solid, or lasting, immunity is produced which usually persists throughout the lifetime of the animal. Because of the permanence of the immunity, this method of administering the serum, known as simultaneous inoculation, or serum-virus immunization, is generally employed in the immunization of herds of swine. The serum may be injected under the skin of the flank or in the axillary space between the foreleg and body. In small pigs some practitioners favor injecting the serum into the abdominal cavity of small pigs, while it may be injected behind the ear in large animals. The two methods most commonly employed in giving the serum and virus are shown in figure 5, *A* and *B*.

The dose of serum varies with the weight of the animal. The minimum doses prescribed by the Bureau of Animal Industry are shown on all commercial labels. If cholera has appeared in a herd before treatment is given, the amount of serum should be increased by half. . Because the dose increases with the weight of the animal, it is more economical to immunize swine against cholera when they are small. When pigs are left unvaccinated there is also additional risk of loss. Many farmers therefore make it a routine practice to have each year's crop of pigs immunized while young. Immunization at about weaning time is recommended.

Since an active virus is used in simultaneous, or serum-virus, immunization—commonly termed vaccination—it is of the utmost importance that the animals receiving this treatment be perfectly healthy and free from disease. After treatment, there is a period of lowered resistance in the animals, owing to the fact that the virus circulates in the blood for 2 or 3 weeks after vaccination. If the animals are perfectly healthy at the time of treatment, are not harboring any infection and are not exposed to infection shortly after treatment,

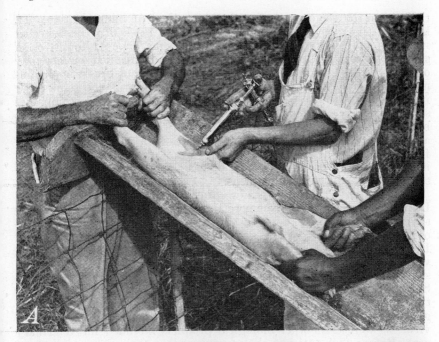

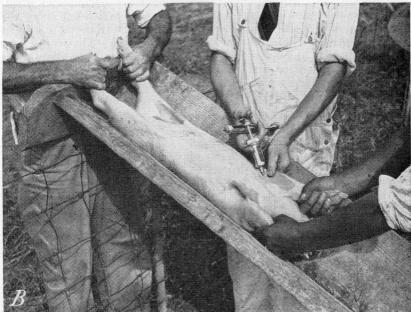

FIGURE 5.—*A*, Injecting a pig with anti-hog-cholera serum beneath the skin in the flank. *B*, Injecting virus in the axillary space between the foreleg and the body.

there is no danger connected with this method of immunization. If, however, the pigs happen to be harboring a masked or unsuspected infection at the time of treatment or become exposed to infection shortly thereafter, trouble may develop, and so-called breaks may occur. Such unfortunate occurrences are really not breaks in immunity but result from the combined action of the virus and some other infective agent. The period of lowered resistance which accompanies serum-virus treatment results from a decrease in the number of white blood cells, which are known to be one of the main defenses of the animal body against infection. The decrease in white cells has been found to be less when large doses of serum are given, and therefore it is advisable to give ample doses of serum in carrying out the simultaneous, or serum-virus, treatment.

Anti-hog-cholera serum is now produced on a large scale in the United States by many commercial plants throughout the country, the majority of which, however, are located in the hog-raising States of the Middle West, where suitable animals are readily obtainable. In 1913 Congress passed an act placing these plants under the supervision of the United States Bureau of Animal Industry. A new division was accordingly established, designated as the Division of Virus-Serum Control, which maintains a rigid supervision, through its trained veterinary and lay inspectors, of all commercial plants engaged in the production of anti-hog-cholera serum and hog cholera virus, as well as of other biological products intended for veterinary use. Before any anti-hog-cholera serum leaves a commercial plant, samples are subjected to rigid tests for potency, carried out under the supervision of Federal veterinary inspectors. Samples of all virus used with anti-hog-cholera serum are likewise tested. The swine raiser who has his pigs immunized against hog cholera is, therefore, sure of having standardized and reliable products used on his herd, provided the veterinarian who does the work has handled the products in a proper manner after receiving them from the producer.

CRYSTAL-VIOLET VACCINE

Scientific workers in the Bureau of Animal Industry have sought for many years to develop a protective vaccine from which the disease-producing properties of the active virus would be completely eliminated.

Much time and work have been devoted to the preparation and testing of experimental vaccines at the station at Ames during the last 15 or 20 years. Various chemical agents have been used in the preparation of vaccines, and in some cases effective vaccines were obtained. The results were not uniform and consistent, however, until crystal violet, an aniline dye, was tried as an attenuating, or weakening, agent with a view to reducing virulence. It was found that the addition of this chemical to virus-infected blood entirely eliminated the disease-producing property of the virus without affecting its antigenic, or immunizing, property.

The new immunizing agent so developed was subjected to carefully controlled experimental tests at the Bureau field station and has been used successfully on more than 12,000 pigs in 236 farm herds in the vicinity of Ames. Pigs treated with this vaccine show no visible reaction, and there is no danger of introducing hog cholera on noninfected premises through its use. The absence of any reaction period following the administration of crystal-violet vaccine, with no apparent loss of appetite and no necessity for change of ration, provided a good one is being supplied, insures an uninterrupted gain in weight. In turn this should effect somewhat earlier marketing than is possible with pigs receiving serum-virus treatment, which usually necessitates a reduction in the feed for a time.

Although the duration of the immunity following treatment with crystal-violet vaccine has not been definitely established, it seems to protect swine against hog cholera satisfactorily through the fattening period or up to the usual market age, which is about 8 months in Iowa. Unfortunately there is an interval of 2 or 3 weeks between the administration of the vaccine and complete establishment of immunity, and this will naturally limit its use to some extent in veterinary practice, for it could not be used in a community where hog cholera is prevalent. For the same reason, the vaccine could not be used on garbage-feeding ranches where the pigs are farrowed on the ranch. It might be used, however, on garbage-feeding ranches which bring in pigs from the outside if the pigs receiving the vaccine are held in quarantine for 3 weeks and fed on grain before being put on the garbage ration. The vaccine cannot, therefore, entirely supplant the serum-virus method of immunization, but it may find a field of usefulness in the treatment of farm herds in the spring and early summer before hog cholera becomes prevalent. It should also afford a somewhat cheaper and safer means of protection than simultaneous immunization.

The new vaccine is now being distributed in considerable amounts to veterinary practitioners in Iowa, Illinois, and several Eastern States, and a better appraisal of its true value can be made when these extended field trials have been completed.

As in the case of anti-hog-cholera serum, the Government has obtained a patent on crystal-violet vaccine with all rights dedicated to the public.

Swine Erysipelas

BY H. W. SCHOENING,
C. G. GREY, AND O. L. OSTEEN [1]

IT WAS ONLY 20 years ago that swine erysipelas was first definitely recognized in this country. Ten years ago it was found to be an acute herd infection in certain areas. Will it become as serious a disease here as it has been in certain parts of Europe? The developments outlined in this article will be watched with interest by producers.

SWINE ERYSIPELAS has for many years been one of the most important diseases of swine in continental Europe and in England. The causative agent was discovered by Pasteur and Thuillier in 1882 and 1883.[2] Loeffler, working at about the same time, studied the organism but did not publish his observations until 1886.[3] It is of interest to note that in 1879 Koch discovered the mouse septicemia bacillus (*Bacillus murisepticus*),[2] which is considered to be identical with the swine erysipelas bacillus.

In the United States, the specific organism of swine erysipelas, technically named *Erysipelothrix rhusiopathiae*, was first isolated in 1921 by Creech,[4] of the Bureau of Animal Industry, from a lesion, or tissue injury, in a hog that came from Texas. The organism was obtained from a specimen of skin showing a typical "diamond skin" lesion. Such lesions, typical of those described in European countries as the result of an infection with swine erysipelas, had been observed in the United States for many years, but the disease was called diamond-skin disease. Swine erysipelas was not considered to be present in this country before the discovery of the organism by Creech. After Creech's discovery other workers isolated the organism from lesions in

---

[1] H. W. Schoening is Chief, C. G. Grey is Assistant Veterinarian, and O. L. Osteen is Associate Veterinarian, Pathological Division, Bureau of Animal Industry.
[2] PREISZ, HUGO. ROTLAUF DER SCHWEINE. *In* Handbuch der pathogenen Mikroorganismen 6: 1–36, illus. 1913.
[3] LOEFFLER. EXPERIMENTELLE UNTERSUCHUNGEN ÜBER SCHWEINE-ROTHLAUF. [Germany] K. Gsndhtsamt. Arb. 1: [46]–55. 1886.
[4] CREECH, G. T. THE BACILLUS OF SWINE ERYSIPELAS ISOLATED FROM URTICARIAL LESIONS OF SWINE IN THE UNITED STATES. Amer. Vet. Med. Assoc. Jour. 59: 139–150, illus. 1921.

the joints and some other parts of the bodies of swine. It was then recognized definitely that swine erysipelas existed, apparently in a chronic form, in certain parts of the United States.

Beginning in 1930 the disease was recognized as an acute herd infection in South Dakota, Nebraska, and other States of the Corn Belt, and since that time it has continued to be a more or less serious disease of swine in certain areas in those States.

NATURE AND CAUSE OF THE DISEASE

Swine erysipelas is an insidious disease, and the manner in which it spreads is not entirely understood. It is quite likely, however, that the disease requires considerable time to make any appreciable headway in certain areas or in a new territory. In certain parts of the United States it has probably existed in a chronic form for many years, gradually increasing in virulence in certain areas until, when favorable conditions prevailed, it manifested itself in the explosive, or acute, type.

Breed,[5] reporting on the distribution of swine erysipelas in the United States, stated that the organism had been identified as a cause of swine maladies in 28 of 46 States; from two States no reports were received. While the infection appears to be confined principally to the Corn Belt, it perhaps exists in many other States in a chronic, low-grade form.

That the disease flourishes under certain conditions is apparent from the European literature and from observations made in this country. The disease occurs most often during the spring, summer, and fall, but it has been observed in the United States in every month and every season. An explanation for this is that in this country sows farrow every month of the year, and thus there is a continuous supply of new pigs susceptible to the infection.

Swine of all ages are susceptible to the disease, from suckling pigs to adult animals. The causative organism has also been found to affect a variety of birds and animals, including man. Horses, cattle, sheep, dogs, ducks, chickens, turkeys, mud hens, and parrots have been reported to be susceptible. In certain parts of this country, the disease has been of economic importance in sheep and turkeys. That the organism is quite infective to man is evidenced by the number of cases reported in the literature. Veterinarians, butchers, and livestock handlers have frequently been infected. Infection among laboratory workers is not uncommon, while numerous cases have been recorded among workers in bone factories. The so-called fish handlers' disease has been found to be caused by infection with the swine-erysipelas organism, which has been found on the skin of many salt-water fish.

Although it does not bear spores, the erysipelas organism is very resistant to adverse conditions, owing, it is claimed, to a waxy substance it contains. A culture of the organism that was experimentally dried on a glass surface and kept at 98° F. remained alive for a month. In a cool, dark place also it remained active for a month. In smears

[5] BREED, FRANK. SWINE ERYSIPELAS, ITS DISTRIBUTION, INCREASING IMPORTANCE AND CONTROL. U. S. Live Stock Sanit. Assoc. Proc. 41: 344–355. 1937.

on glass exposed to direct sunlight, the organism survived only 2 days.
Under laboratory conditions in various types of media, it has a very
long life. Nocard and Leclainche [6] state that organisms remain alive
for 17 days in water. The organism is very sensitive to heat, however. At 111° F. it is destroyed in 4 days, at 125° F. in 15 minutes,
and at 130° to 137° F.—far below ordinary cooking temperatures—
in several minutes.

Living erysipelas organisms have been found in putrid material
after 4 months. In the flesh of swine, the organisms are quite resistant to destruction, and Preisz [7] reports living organisms in a
carcass that had been buried for 280 days. The organisms are only
slowly destroyed by salting and pickling, and they also have been
found alive after 26 days in strong brine. Salting hams with salt
and saltpeter failed to destroy their virulence in 30 days. Organisms
added to pickling fluid were still virulent after 170 days. On the
other hand, the organism is not resistant to the action of disinfectants.
It is killed by solutions of phenol in 15 minutes, while formalin and
ordinary lye readily destroy it.

In areas where the disease is found, the organism exists in the soil
as a saprophyte, living on dead or decaying organic matter. Evidence has been presented to show that it can multiply in the soil under
certain conditions and that sandy soils rich in lime and humus are
especially favorable.

These facts are evidently important in outbreaks of the disease.
Since the organism can survive for long periods in certain soils, the
recurrence of swine erysipelas can readily be brought about by favorable conditions. It appears that on some farms where infection
exists the disease may recur irregularly over a period of several years,
though this may not happen on other farms where the soil is similarly
infected. No satisfactory explanation has been made for these differences. Once an infection has appeared on a farm, however, a potential
danger exists that it will reappear in subsequent years.

It is not definitely known whether infection proceeds directly from
animal to animal or whether the organisms excreted by an infected
animal must pass some part of their life outside the animal body or
otherwise undergo some change before they are capable of reproducing
the disease. It is generally agreed that cultures of the organism
can reproduce the disease only with the greatest difficulty when injected
into swine. It is also generally held that some unknown factor in
addition to the organism itself is necessary to bring about infection.
The experience of Bureau of Animal Industry pathologists supports
this idea. Several years ago, for example, two healthy hogs were
placed in contact with two hogs affected with a chronic form of swine
erysipelas. The four animals were housed in a small enclosure on a
concrete floor. After almost 3 months the normal animals remained
healthy. Soil was then placed on the concrete floor. About 2½
months later both the normal hogs developed the disease and died
within a week of each other. *Erysipelothrix rhusiopathiae* was recovered from the organs of the dead animals.

[6] Nocard, Ed., and Leclainche, E. LES MALADIES MICROBIENNES DES ANIMAUX. Ed. 3,
rev. and enl. 2 v. Paris. 1903.
[7] See reference in footnote 2, p. 686.

During an acute attack of the disease, the causative agent can be found in the blood, urine, and feces, and the surroundings of the animals soon become heavily contaminated. Animals affected with the chronic form of the disease may also pass it on to others.

It has been shown that the swine erysipelas organism may be harbored in some parts of the bodies of apparently healthy animals, such as the tonsils and parts of the intestinal tract. Possibly this is a result of a previous infection and recovery, or the organisms may have been picked up from contaminated soil without infection resulting. Such animals may possibly be dangerous to others, or they may subsequently develop the disease themselves.

SYMPTOMS

Acute swine erysipelas is characterized by its sudden onset, and many swine in the herd may be affected at the same time. Only a few may be visibly sick, while a number of others may run high temperatures—105°–110° F. Affected hogs lie in their bedding, but it may be noted that their eyes are clear and active—every move an attendant makes is watched, but they are very reluctant to move themselves. If forcibly disturbed, they start off with considerable activity but protest with loud squeals. Since the tissues of the joints are involved in the disease process, many of the affected swine are undoubtedly in pain when they walk. They make an effort to keep their feet under them, which makes the backbone appear long and strongly arched. After moving about a bit, they drop down on their bedding again. Where considerable swelling at a joint is noted, there may be exostoses (bony growths), which do not disappear when the disease subsides. Animals thus affected are the so-called knotty-legged hogs, or chronics, which harbor the disease organisms in their joints and may act as spreaders of the infection.

Several of the hogs may die quite suddenly. They may appear well at feeding time one evening and be found dead the next morning. There have been cases where entire herds have died, but this is rather rare at present in this country, although it is not so uncommon in unvaccinated herds in swine erysipelas districts of Europe. As a rule only a few hogs die, some make a complete recovery, and the rest may remain unthrifty chronics.

In hogs acutely ill with swine erysipelas, shortness of breath caused by pulmonary edema—a waterlogged condition of the lungs—may be noted. At times swellings about the snout make breathing very difficult. Nausea and vomiting are not uncommon symptoms. Some 24 to 48 hours after the onset of the disease irregular red patches, which are neither tender to the touch nor swollen, may be noted on the lighter parts of the skin. Such areas may remain localized or may enlarge and run together until the greater part of the body surface is involved. Death is sudden, usually preceded by respiratory distress (labored breathing) brought about by pulmonary edema and heart weakness. The temperature drops, and the mucous membranes become cyanotic (blue).

The so-called diamond skin, skin with regular rhomboidal lesions (fig. 1), sometimes appears in acute cases in which the affected swine die within 3 days after the onset of the disease. Such lesions on the skin are, however, usually associated with a less severe type of swine

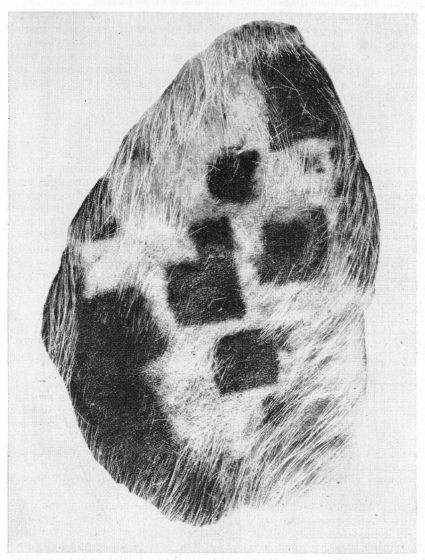

FIGURE 1.—Rhomboidal, or diamond-shaped, skin lesions of swine erysipelas. This specimen of skin was taken from a hog which was inoculated on October 11 and died on October 14.

erysipelas, in which the symptoms are of a milder character and rapidly subside after the appearance of the characteristic skin eruption. Unless complications set in, hogs affected with the mild type of erysipelas usually recover within 2 weeks. Where the diamond-skin lesions extend over considerable areas, however, there may be a dry gangrenous sloughing of large portions of skin. The ears and tail are often lost in this way. Loss of the tail, which is the more frequent; may be the only apparent evidence of infection, past or present. Skin lesions are difficult to see except on the lighter colored breeds of hogs or on the light parts of dark breeds.

The swine that do not die of the disease are often left in such a condition that they are unprofitable to the owner. Many have swollen joints, and these animals are discounted by the packer-buyers. Others that do not have enlarged joints may appear dehydrated (dried up), and these are called race-horse pigs by some owners. Such hogs eat a great deal but do not fatten as soon or as well as normal hogs. Joint trouble may appear as an independent manifestation of the disease. All the joints may be enlarged, but those of the knee, hock, and toes are most frequently affected.

At times the only indication of infection in a herd is a dry, scaly eczema (skin eruption), which is nonparasitic in character and fails to clear up in response to changes of feed or the use of dips and oils. Such lesions disappear as a rule upon the administration of specific antiserum, alone or in combination with living culture, as described later.

DIAGNOSIS

The diagnosis of swine erysipelas presents many difficulties, but in areas where it has become prevalent veterinarians, through clinical observations supported by laboratory findings, have been able to recognize it with a fair degree of accuracy. The disease is at times confusing, however, because it may manifest itself in so many ways. The problem is one for the consideration of a veterinarian.

Symptoms and manifestations that aid in diagnosis are the sudden onset, typical skin discolorations, dehydration (dried-up appearance) of the skin, curled ears, stub tails, evidence of pain on moving, reluctance to move unless forcibly aroused, enlarged joints, scaly eczema, swellings on ears, snout, legs, and elsewhere, sloughed ears and sloughing of patches of skin, and high temperature. The eyes may be clear and the squeal vigorous.

Specimens from suspected outbreaks of swine erysipelas should be forwarded to a diagnostic laboratory for bacteriological examination. Such laboratories are maintained by many of the States to aid in diagnosing and controlling diseases and ailments of livestock and poultry.

Since the definite diagnosis of swine erysipelas is very difficult from a clinical standpoint, attention has been given in recent years to the development of serological methods of diagnosis. These depend on the reaction of whole blood or blood serum in a laboratory test. The Bureau of Animal Industry started working on this problem in 1932 and, after considerable experimentation both in the laboratory and in the field, has developed the rapid-plate agglutination test, which, within limits, has proved a valuable aid in diagnosis.

In using the test it is quite important to recognize its limitations and interpret the results properly. Definitely positive reaction in swine indicates either infection with or exposure to the specific microorganism. Swine that have recently received injections of the specific antiserum also give positive results as early as 24 hours after the administration of the test, and this reaction may persist for some weeks. The test has little value, therefore, in the case of animals that recently received the specific antiserum.

Positive reactions may possibly be obtained in animals that show no clinical evidence of the disease, which may be explained by the fact that swine erysipelas organisms may be harbored in the body of an animal without producing any visible lesions or symptoms. It is also possible that there may be obscure joint lesions that are the result of erysipelas infection. Experimental work has shown that on a very thorough post mortem examination, most of the apparently normal hogs kept on premises known to be infected and showing a positive reaction to the test will exhibit lesions in one or more joints. By bacteriological examination of a number of these animals it has been possible in most instances to isolate the swine erysipelas organism. Bureau pathologists have found that animals showing visible joint lesions on clinical examination give a strongly positive reaction to the test and that the organisms is easily recovered from such animals. Animals that react less strongly may simply be harboring it.

Generally speaking, the test is considered to be more applicable to herd diagnosis than to the diagnosis of the disease in individual animals, and for the present its use should be restricted to persons qualified to make proper interpretations. When erysipelas is suspected in a herd, a number of animals should be tested and the diagnosis should not be made until the representative serological picture of the herd can be obtained. The fact should be kept in mind that the chronic form of swine erysipelas may be present in a herd that is also affected with some other acute disease, and a positive reaction does not necessarily shut out the possibility of some other infection also being present.

CONTROL MEASURES

Since swine erysipelas is propagated in the infected animal and apparently also in the soil, when it appears on a farm to determine the best procedure to follow is a difficult problem. As has been previously stated, the organism may live in the soil for a considerable period, although it can be destroyed in hogpens by the usual cleaning and disinfection.

Since the disease often manifests itself in a low-grade type of infection and since it has been shown that animals affected with this chronic form may under certain circumstances pass it on to normal hogs, it is apparent that such animals should be removed from the herd.

Anti-swine-erysipelas serum has been available for some years, but, while effective, it has certain limitations. The immunity produced by the injection of serum cannot be expected to last more than 2 or 3 weeks. Likewise the serum is effective only when given very early in the acute stage of the disease. After the disease once establishes itself and becomes chronic, the value of the serum is very limited.

In European countries use is made of an active-immunization procedure, which includes administration of both a live culture of the causative agent and hyperimmune serum—the so-called simultaneous method of immunization. This method has not been considered to be applicable for general use in this country because the live culture might set up new centers of infection in cases of mistaken diagnosis of swine erysipelas. In certain sections of the Corn Belt, however, the disease has progressed to such an extent that a large-scale experiment in which the simultaneous method of vaccination is used under restricted conditions is now being conducted cooperatively by several of the State livestock sanitary authorities, the State experiment stations, and the Federal Bureau of Animal Industry. Certain herds are vaccinated with the serum and culture, and accurate records are kept of the results. The plan is to run this project for several years before a final decision is reached as to the applicability of the serum-and-culture method of vaccination in the United States. The results so far have been very satisfactory, but sufficient time has not yet elapsed to get full information.

In handling diseases of swine, owners should always get in contact with State and local veterinarians, and this is particularly important in combating actual or suspected outbreaks of swine erysipelas.

RELATION TO ARTHRITIS

Considerable experimental work and field observations over a period of years have shown that the swine erysipelas organism has a marked predilection for the joints, even in the early stages of the disease while it is still acute. Arthritis may result from an acute attack of swine erysipelas or from a low-grade infection in which the animal may not be noticeably sick at any time but may later have enlarged joints.

The term "arthritis" designates an inflammation of the joint, whether or not the joint is enlarged. Post mortem examination of a large number of hogs has revealed that those affected with the arthritic form of swine erysipelas may show extensive damage to one or more joints, including the articular surfaces and the joint capsules, with no visible enlargement.

It was demonstrated by Ward [8] as early as 1922 that cases of arthritis in swine were caused by infection with the swine erysipelas organism. Since swine arthritis has become widespread in recent years, it was thought advisable to seek additional information which would give some idea as to the distribution of the disease in various parts of the country. Accordingly, beginning in 1939, specimens of arthritic lesions in swine were obtained from a number of meat-inspection centers in various parts of the country with information as to the origin of the hogs from which the specimens were obtained. Up to the date of writing a total of 572 joints had been received and examined bacteriologically. The swine erysipelas organism was recovered from

[8] WARD, ARCHIBALD R. THE ETIOLOGY OF POLYARTHRITIS IN SWINE. Amer. Vet. Med. Assoc. Jour. 61 : 155–161. 1922.

444 of these, or 77.62 percent, and it is probable that the percentage would have been higher had it been practical to make extensive cultural tests of all the affected joints. The swine from which these specimens were obtained (swine with erysipelas) had their origin in 114 counties in 16 States (Iowa, Nebraska, Minnesota, South Dakota, Texas, Oklahoma, Arkansas, Tennessee, Mississippi, Alabama, Florida, Virginia, Maryland, Pennsylvania, Kansas, and Missouri); but the greatest number came from the Corn Belt.

DIFFERENTIAL DIAGNOSIS

The principal disease with which swine erysipelas might be confused is hog cholera. In acute swine erysipelas the onset of the attack is as a rule more sudden and abrupt and its course more rapid ·than in hog cholera, and body temperatures are generally higher. In swine erysipelas the animal gives more evidence of pain on being handled than in hog cholera. In swine affected with erysipelas the eyes remain clear and active, while in those with cholera they become dull and gummy.

There may sometimes be confusion in the picture presented by a post mortem examination, but usually in hog cholera the lymph nodes assume a dark-red or marbled discoloration, while in swine erysipelas there may be little change in color but marked evidence of edema, though at times a cherry-red to violet discoloration may be noted.

In uncomplicated hog cholera the spleen remains normal in size; in swine erysipelas it usually shows some enlargement. In hog cholera accompanied by certain bacterial infections, however, enlargement of the spleen may be noted.

In hog cholera intestinal lesions are more commonly found in the large intestine. In swine erysipelas they are more commonly observed in the small intestine.

Enteritis of Swine

BY C. N. DALE [1]

THREE VERY SERIOUS FORMS of intestinal inflammation—necrotic enteritis, swine dysentery, and enteritis of young pigs—are considered here. The first two are especially deadly in combination with hog cholera. Everything that is known about these maladies indicates that the heavy losses they cause could be largely prevented by really good swine husbandry.

THE TERM "enteritis" means an inflammation of the intestines. There are many kinds of enteritis affecting swine, and they vary in intensity. Two of the most serious are necrotic enteritis and swine dysentery.

NECROTIC ENTERITIS

Necrotic enteritis has until recently been considered an infectious disease of swine caused by the micro-organism *Salmonella choleraesuis*. Lately, however, the relation of swine nutrition to the development of this disease has been given prominent attention. The results of investigations now in progress in different sections of the country may clarify the question of the cause of the disease.

Necrotic enteritis has also been called necro, paratyphoid, caseous enteritis, and infectious necrotic enteritis. The term "necrotic enteritis" means an inflammation of the intestines (enteritis) characterized by dead cells or tissue (necrosis). Besides being a specific disease of swine, necrotic enteritis is also a condition associated with other diseases.

THE CAUSAL ORGANISM

The disease was first described as early as 1866 (*4*).[2] Later it was associated with hog cholera. After it had been determined that hog cholera was caused by a filtrable virus, further investigation revealed that necrotic enteritis occurred as an independent disease and was

---

[1] C. N. Dale is Associate Veterinarian, Pathological Division, Bureau of Animal Industry.
[2] Italic numbers in parentheses refer to Literature Cited, p. 702.

caused by the micro-organism *Salmonella choleraesuis* (literally, swine-cholera *Salmonella*) which has also been called *Bacterium choleraesuis*, *Bacillus suipestifer*, and still later *Salmonella suipestifer*.

In the United States, Murray and associates (*5, 6*) and Biester and associates (*1*) have described extensive investigations of the disease. These investigators were able to produce it in more than 100 pigs by feeding them cultures of the organism. They also isolated the causal organism from all of the field cases that were investigated. A number of other investigators have also shown that necrotic enteritis can be produced by feeding cultures.

Examinations of the bacterial flora of the intestines of apparently healthy swine for the presence of the paratyphoid organism show that relatively few normal pigs harbor the organism. It has been found in a sufficient number, however, to indicate that there may be a carrier type in which the organism is present without causing any appreciable injury. Some change may take place in such an animal that may provide conditions necessary for the organism to become active.

The organism is known to be highly virulent in the presence of hog cholera infection. Thus, when a pig that has been harboring the *Salmonella* organism without appreciable damage becomes infected with hog cholera virus, the paratyphoid organism invades the body tissues and produces definite lesions. Animals affected with both hog cholera virus and *Salmonella choleraesuis* generally die within 5 to 7 days, whereas hog cholera infection alone usually requires about 15 days to cause death. The combined infections spread from animal to animal, producing a very severe, fatal disease. *S. choleraesuis* has been considered to play a part in so-called hog cholera "breaks" (see the article on Hog Cholera, p. 673), and the greatest precautions should be taken in immunizing pigs with hog cholera virus and anti-hog-cholera serum when there is a possibility that this paratyphoid organism is present in the herd.

Knowledge of the role which the *Salmonella choleraesuis* organism plays when associated with hog cholera, although far from complete, is quite extensive, but the information available on its association with other diseases and conditions is more limited. Two forms of the primary *Salmonella choleraesuis* infection are generally recognized—acute and chronic. It is the chronic form of the infection which has been specifically known as necrotic enteritis.

SYMPTOMS

Necrotic enteritis generally begins with a rise in temperature, diminished appetite, and diarrhea. A number of factors may bring about variation in the intensity of these symptoms, and during the initial stage the trouble may frequently be diagnosed as hog cholera. If this diagnosis is followed by the administration of hog cholera virus and anti-hog-cholera serum together, the results may be disastrous. Sick pigs and many deaths may be expected. Post mortem examinations will probably reveal lesions, or tissue injuries, due to hog cholera, and the conclusion will be drawn that before the animals were treated the latter disease had progressed too far for the treatment to save them. This is one of the cases in which the services of a veterinarian are needed. Necrotic enteritis in its early stages may be similar to various other acute diseases besides hog cholera, and even with the most careful investigation it may be impossible to determine the exact nature of the trouble. Control measures will be determined by the definiteness and accuracy of the diagnosis.

After the first few days the temperature of pigs affected with necrotic enteritis may return to normal and their appetite improve, but the animals become unthrifty and fail to put on weight normally. Emaciation, weakness, prostration, and death often follow, particularly when no efforts at control are made.

LESIONS

It is generally accepted that the lesions revealed by post mortem examination in cases of necrotic enteritis are confined chiefly to the gastrointestinal canal (the stomach and intestines) and are characteristic of the disease. However, many of the lymph glands, particularly those of the stomach and intestines, may be enlarged and reddened and may contain a larger amount of fluid than normal, which gives them a gelatinous appearance. The tonsils may show varying degrees of tissue destruction. The intensity of the involvement of the stomach also varies. In some cases the lining of the stomach is normal; in others the alterations may vary from slight or marked inflammation to extensive destruction of tissue. The small intestines may also fail to reveal any significant injury, but cases are observed in which the lesions vary from slight irritation to definite tissue destruction. The outstanding and most characteristic lesions of the disease are found in the large intestines, the walls of which are generally much thicker than normal. The lining shows the characteristic patches of dead tissue, varying in size from small circular spots to extensive areas involving several feet of the bowel. The entire lining can be easily scraped off. The dead tissue may slough and be mixed with the intestinal contents.

Variation in intensity of the symptoms and lesions is explained by a number of factors. (1) As in the case of many other disease-producing organisms, different strains of the *Salmonella* organism vary in their virulence or ability to produce disease. (2) Repeated passage through animals may increase the virulence of the organism. (3) The severity of the disease may vary with the number of the organisms taken into the animal's body and the frequency with which they are introduced. (4) Among individual animals and groups of animals there are variations in resistance to infection owing to numerous debilitating factors.

CONTROL MEASURES

Various remedies have been used for necrotic enteritis, but reports indicate that as a whole they have been unsatisfactory. No known medicinal preparation has sufficient merit to be recommended as a specific treatment.

Experience has shown that it is more profitable to adopt adequate preventive measures than to attempt treatment after the disease has appeared in a herd. Rigid sanitation, as commonly recommended for the control of roundworms in pigs (see p. 774 of this volume), has proved to be quite effective in the prevention of necrotic enteritis. It is advisable to adhere to standard methods of swine production and to supply adequate rations so as to avoid the introduction of factors that might lower resistance to infection. When the disease has become established in a herd, separating the apparently healthy pigs from the sick ones and placing the former in clean quarters or on ground not previously used for swine often checks the spread of the infection.

RELATION OF NUTRITION TO NECROTIC ENTERITIS

Much has been written recently on the relation of nutrition to necrotic enteritis in swine. Because of the interpretations given to certain nutritional investigations on rations deficient in pellagra-preventive (P–P) factors, many persons believe that necrotic enteritis is primarily due to a nutritional deficiency and that the addition of liver, yeast, and particularly nicotinic acid to the ration constitutes a cure and preventive. This view overlooks the importance of the *Salmonella choleraesuis* organism and may result in neglect of sanitation as a control measure. The evidence now available does not appear to be sufficient to justify reliance on adequate nutrition alone to control the disease.

On the basis of present knowledge, the situation may be summarized as follows:

1. Necrotic enteritis is a chronic form of *Salmonella choleraesuis* infection.

2. A vitamin deficiency, presumably of nicotinic acid, will produce in swine pellagra or a pellagralike disease, some aspects of which may be like necrotic enteritis.

3. Pigs affected with this vitamin deficiency may be subject to a more severe or extended attack of necrotic enteritis than pigs not so affected when similarly exposed.

4. When the rations are deficient, nicotinic acid and possibly other factors of the vitamin B complex should be given as a supplement for the prevention and treatment of the deficiency disease.

SWINE DYSENTERY

Although swine dysentery has often been and sometimes still is described as a form of necrotic enteritis, it has become generally recognized as a specific disease. Because of its nature, it has been variously designated as infectious hemorrhagic enteritis, swine typhus, bloody diarrhea, bloody scours, bloody dysentery, bloody flux, black scours, and colitis (inflammation of the colon).

The disease has been reported in many sections of the country but it appears to be more prevalent in the large swine-producing States of the Midwest than elsewhere. Some idea of its extensiveness may be gained from Hofferd's report (*3*) that in a single year some veterinarians estimated death losses up to 1,500 head in their respective practices. The history of the majority of outbreaks generally discloses that the affected animals have been either directly or indirectly in contact with sales barns or public stockyards. Enforcement of sanitary regulations at these places has been reported to have been followed by a decrease in the incidence of the disease in swine from these sources.

Symptoms

Swine dysentery is considered to be an acute infectious disease and its outstanding symptom is usually a profuse bloody diarrhea. The fecal discharge often contains shreds of tissue in addition to varying amounts of blood. The disease starts in a few pigs and more pigs become infected each day. Some go off feed while others show no loss of appetite.

Biester, Schwarte, and McNutt (*2*) reproduced the disease experimentally in normal pigs by feeding them intestinal tissue and the contents of intestines from affected swine. The pigs showed a rise in temperature from the fourth to the seventh day. Diarrhea appeared about the sixth day and the elimination of blood a day or two later. On an average, temperatures in swine dysentery do not exceed 105° F. and some do not show an appreciable variation from normal, or 104° F. (In many other acute infectious diseases, such as hog cholera, swine erysipelas, and *Salmonella choleraesuis* infection, the temperature commonly rises to 107° F. or even higher.)

Some pigs die suddenly after a couple of days of illness while others linger for 2 weeks or even longer. Pigs that recover are stunted and usually unthrifty. Whiting (*7*) in 1924 reported that of 192 pigs exposed by feeding or pen contact, 167 developed the disease, while 25 did not show visible symptoms. All the pigs that did not develop the disease were later fed virulent material and remained healthy. Pigs that have recovered are not considered immune and are subject to repeated attacks. In a herd of young pigs 60 percent or more may die. The number of deaths in a herd of older pigs is usually considerably less. Both cholera-immune and cholera-susceptible pigs may be affected. The use of hog cholera virus and anti-hog-cholera serum for immunization of herds in which swine dysentery exists is generally followed by serious losses. Almost total loss of herds affected with swine dysentery has occurred when the disease has been accompanied by hog cholera.

While swine dysentery generally occurs where sanitation is poor and feeding practices questionable, it has been reported in herds kept under good sanitary conditions and fed rations generally recognized as satisfactory.

It has often been observed that the disease frequently occurs in hogs following cattle, including cattle that had been recently brought to the farm. Some observers think that this is merely coincidence, but others have suggested that cattle may be carriers of the disease. Hofferd (*3*) reports a herd in which the disease recurred whenever corn was added to the diet.

CAUSE AND LESIONS

The cause of swine dysentery has not yet been determined. A germ-free filtrate of intestinal tissues from affected pigs has failed to reproduce the disease when fed to healthy swine. A number of different organisms have been isolated from animals affected with the disease which, when fed to normal pigs, also failed to produce the disease.

Laboratory studies have revealed the presence of the organism *Salmonella choleraesuis* in some outbreaks, but in others it has not been found. This organism may not be instrumental in causing the disease, but since it is the cause of necrotic enteritis it seems probable that its presence in cases of swine dysentery may influence the course and final outcome of the dysentery outbreak. Outbreaks in which this organism is not present may respond to control measures differently from those where it is present.

The lesions found on post mortem examination in the early stages are principally in the large intestine. The lining of the cecum and colon is inflamed and bloody. In later stages, shreds and patches of dead tissue are found adhering to the intestinal wall or loose in the fecal contents. The stomach may also show lesions, but the small intestine is not usually involved. When secondary complications set in, lesions in other parts of the body may be found. These vary with the nature of the complicating factors.

CONTROL MEASURES

Much effort has, been given to control of swine dysentery, and many remedial measures have been used. Each has its advocates, and some may be beneficial in lessening the severity of the disease. None has sufficient merit, however, to be recommended as a specific treatment.

A review of the control methods used indicates that preventive measures give the best results. No means of vaccination or immunization is known. Until more is known about the disease it is necessary to rely on sanitation as a means of prevention. Since the exact nature and sources of the causative factor are unknown, sanitary measures must be very broad and must take in all the probable sources of infection. For instance, since cattle or brood sows may be carriers, preventive measures must include them.

Certain procedures may be practical on one farm and others on another. The advice of a veterinarian should be obtained in formulating an adequate and effective scheme of sanitation. Since affected pigs are obviously a common source of infection, extreme caution should be used when swine from the outside are brought to a farm where there is a herd of healthy pigs. The new group should be isolated and quarantined where they may be observed for at least a week, preferably longer, before being added ·to the healthy group.

If swine dysentary has become established in a herd, the apparently healthy pigs should be separated from the sick ones. When any of the healthy group sicken, they should be removed. On the basis that it is worth while to limit the amount of infected material the pigs can get, some recommend the removal of both groups, sick and healthy, to concrete floors that can be kept thoroughly clean. Others would remove both groups to clean ground. Observations indicate the importance of removing the pigs from the contaminated lots in which they have been running. The contaminated quarters should be cleaned and disinfected before being restocked. It is desirable to wait until the end of the summer before placing pigs in the lots where infection occurred. Good drainage and clean water should be provided. Pigs that have recovered should be sold for slaughter rather than allowed to remain as a possible source of infection for a new group. At all times attention should be given to standard methods of feeding and proper nutrition.

Sanitary officials have given continuous attention to the formulation and enforcement of regulations to minimize the spread of the disease as a result of the transportation of swine through public stockyards and public sales stables.

When the cause of the disease has been determined, modification of the sanitary measures now employed to control it may be warranted.

ENTERITIS AND SCOURS IN BABY PIGS

The annual loss of young pigs in the United States is very large. On many farms it is not unusual for 50 percent or more of the pigs to die during the first few days of life. Reports indicate that most of these have developed enteritis and scours. The trouble has been attributed almost entirely to faulty nutrition and lack of proper housing, care, and sanitation.

The condition is usually recognized by its common symptom, diarrhea. The ailment soon spreads to all the pigs in the litter, particularly when the pens are not cleaned and disinfected. The pigs may scour for a few days, stop suckling, and die or become unthrifty.

While it is a common practice to treat the sick pigs by giving some medicinal preparation, such as castor oil or formalin, this procedure offers little chance of success unless primary attention is given to providing clean quarters, proper care and feeding of the mother, and general sanitation. (See p. 774 of this Yearbook and Farmers' Bulletin 1437, Swine Production.)

An enteritis in baby pigs which has some characteristics not common to the so-called scours has been reported. It has been called the little-pig disease or the 3-day-pig disease. The pigs show symptoms of weakness, unsteady gait, emaciation, roughness of hair, and sometimes a wrinkled appearance of the skin, and most of them are droopy and listless. The number of such pigs that have diarrhea varies.

Post mortem examination reveals a varying degree of enteritis confined largely to the small intestine. The stomach is normal and generally contains curd, which indicates that at birth the pigs were in condition to nurse.

This condition occurs in litters from sows that are fed garbage as well as from sows that are on other rations considered satisfactory. Pigs are usually affected 24 to 72 hours after birth and generally die within 24 to 36 hours after the first symptoms appear. Experimental work so far has failed to reveal the cause. Recent investigations have shown that the blood of affected pigs contains much less blood sugar than that of normal pigs. If the amount of blood sugar was not too low, recoveries often followed injections of glucose solution and forced feeding of milk.

ENTERITIS DUE TO MISCELLANEOUS CAUSES

Inflammation of the intestines is frequently associated with many diseases and ailments caused by protozoa, parasites, bacteria, and viruses, including swine erysipelas, anthrax, and hog cholera. In chronic hog cholera, areas of dead tissue commonly referred to as button ulcers may be observed in the intestines. Various mineral poisons such as lye and copper sulfate also cause enteritis in swine. The control and treatment of these types of enteritis naturally depend on the cause.

LITERATURE CITED

(1) BIESTER, H. E., MURRAY, CHAS., McNUTT, S. H., and PURWIN, PAUL.
    1928. STUDIES ON INFECTIOUS ENTERITIS OF SWINE. II. THE PATHOGENESIS OF
    INFECTIOUS ENTERITIS. Amer. Vet. Med. Assoc. Jour. 72: 1003–
    1022, illus.
(2) —— SCHWARTE, [L. H.], and McNUTT, [S. H.]
    1935. GENERAL CONSIDERATION OF ENTERITIS IN SWINE. Iowa Vet. 6 (5):
    5–7, 22–24.
(3) HOFFERD, R. M.
    1936. SWINE DYSENTERY IN IOWA FROM A FIELD STANDPOINT. Amer. Vet.
    Med. Assoc. Jour. 88: 299–310.
(4) HUTYRA, FRANZ, MAREK, JOSEPH, and MANNINGER, RUDOLPH.
    1938. SPECIAL PATHOLOGY AND THERAPEUTICS OF THE DISEASES OF DOMESTIC
    ANIMALS. Ed. 4, 3 v., illus. London.
(5) MURRAY, CHAS., BIESTER, H. E., PURWIN, PAUL, and McNUTT, S. H.
    1927. STUDIES IN INFECTIOUS ENTERITIS OF SWINE. Amer. Vet. Med. Assoc.
    Jour. 72: 34–65.
(6) MURRAY, CHAS., BIESTER, H. E., PURWIN, PAUL, and McNUTT, S. H.
    1929. STUDIES IN INFECTIOUS ENTERITIS OF SWINE. Amer. Vet. Med. Assoc.
    Jour. 74: 345–356.
(7) WHITING, R. A.
    1924. SWINE DYSENTERY. Amer. Vet. Med. Assoc. Jour. 64: 600–610, illus.

Swine Influenza

BY C. N. DALE [1]

ALTHOUGH swine influenza cannot yet be cured or prevented any more effectively than human influenza can, close study of the disease has led to fundamental discoveries regarding the human malady. The author of this article traces the main points of the story.

SWINE INFLUENZA is an acute, infectious, and highly contagious disease now known to be caused by the combined action of a filtrable virus and a microscopic organism called *Hemophilus influenzae suis*.

The disease is apparently widespread, but it appears to be more prevalent in the Middle West than elsewhere in the United States. The outbreaks generally occur in the fall and early winter and are more numerous in some years than in others. Observations seem to indicate that improper housing with consequent undue exposure to cold and dampness are predisposing conditions. Such exposure may cause viruses harbored by apparently healthy animals to become active.

Once swine influenza appears, it spreads rapidly through the entire herd, and within 48 to 72 hours after the first pig shows symptoms all the animals may be affected. The pigs become listless and go off feed, and there is marked prostration. The breathing is labored and jerky, and the animals appear to be very sick and distressed. Coughing is also observed, there may be a watery discharge from the eyes, and the temperature is usually high. After 5 or 6 days of sickness the animals usually recover rapidly. Complications may retard recovery and increase the mortality, which is generally 1 or 2 percent, although losses as high as 10 percent have been reported.

The tissue injuries evident on post mortem examination generally consist of enlarged, watery, and congested lymph glands in the neck and along the bronchial tubes. The lungs show areas of pneumonia which are often confined to the front lobes.

No vaccine is available for use in the field, and there is no known specific medicinal treatment. Affected animals should be provided with clean, well-bedded, comfortable, and properly ventilated quarters.

---

[1] C. N. Dale is Associate Veterinarian, Pathological Division, Bureau of Animal Industry.

Good care may be helpful in insuring the usual recovery after 6 or 7 days and preventing deaths from secondary complications.

RESEARCH ON SWINE AND HUMAN INFLUENZA

The story of the research work that resulted in identifying the cause of swine influenza is exceptionally interesting and indicative of the nature of the disease. Begun in the Bureau of Animal Industry, this research led to a long series of research projects by medical doctors interested in tracking down the cause of human influenza. Eventually the work was amazingly successful. Swine influenza and human influenza were found to be closely related, and today the outlook for combating this major plague of man is better than ever before.

Swine influenza was first described as a specific disease in 1919 by Koen (*11*),[2] a veterinarian in the Bureau of Animal Industry. The description given then may still be used for clinical diagnosis of the disease as it occurs naturally in the field.

Though many disagreed with Koen that such a disease existed, investigations since then have verified his contention, which he expressed in these words:

I have no apologies to offer for my diagnosis of "flu." Last fall and winter we were confronted with a new condition, if not a new disease. I believe I have as much to support this diagnosis in pigs as the physicians have to support a similar diagnosis in man. The similarity of the epidemic among people and the epizootic among pigs was so close, the reports so frequent, that an outbreak in the family would be followed immediately by an outbreak among the hogs, and vice versa, as to present a most striking coincidence if not suggesting a close relation between the two conditions. It looked like "flu," it presented the identical symptoms of "flu," it terminated like "flu," and until proved it was not "flu" I shall stand by that diagnosis.

During the next 3 or 4 years after Koen's report, the disease as it occurred in the field was described in several publications (*2, 3, 4, 10, 15*). Some of these papers reported bacteriological studies the results of which were negative—that is, the causative agent was not discovered. The descriptions of the disease agreed closely with Koen's, however, although some included symptoms that were not observed by him.

Up to 1931 a few investigations (*8, 14, 30*) had resulted in the isolation of specific micro-organisms that were considered significant as causative agents of the disease, but these findings were not definitely confirmed.

In 1928 McBryde, of the Bureau of Animal Industry, and his associates published a report (*13*) of their investigations on the transmission of the disease. They were able to reproduce the disease by introducing into the noses of healthy pigs mucus from the windpipe and bronchial tubes of animals showing characteristic symptoms of swine influenza. The mucus was mixed with a solution of salt and water. (Such a mixture is called a saline suspension of tracheal and bronchial mucus, and the method of introducing it into the animal is called intranasal instillation.) The disease was also transmitted by the same method with nasal instead of tracheal and bronchial secretions from

---

[2] Italic numbers in parentheses refer to Literature Cited, p. 711.

affected pigs. The disease developed in 65 percent of the animals exposed by these means. When healthy pigs were placed in pens with pigs having the disease, 40 percent of the former came down with it.

McBryde and associates also carried out a small number of experiments to determine whether the cause of the disease was a filtrable virus. In all their investigations, however, intranasal instillations of tracheal and bronchial mucus which had been passed through a fine filter to eliminate bacteria failed to produce the disease in healthy swine.

Experiments That Led to Finding the Cause of Swine Influenza

In 1931 Shope (*17*), of the Rockefeller Institute for Medical Research, reported that swine influenza was caused by the combined action of a filtrable virus and the micro-organism *Hemophilus influenzae suis*.

Shope (*18*) had investigated outbreaks of swine influenza in Iowa in 1928 and again in 1929. Material for laboratory and experimental work was collected from field cases and transported under refrigeration to Princeton, N. J., where the experiments in transmitting the disease to normal swine were conducted. The animals used were obtained in the vicinity of Princeton, an area from which no outbreaks of swine influenza had been reported. Shope called attention to the fact that the normal pigs which McBryde and his associates had used in their transmission experiments were obtained in a locality where the disease had been prevalent, and suggested that some of these pigs might have had a certain degree of immunity. This may have accounted for the failure of some of them to develop the disease after intranasal instillations of nasal and tracheal material from affected pigs or after being in contact with sick pigs.

By intranasal instillation of small amounts of 10- and 20-percent suspensions of bronchial mucus alone or mixtures of suspensions of bronchial mucus, bronchial lymph glands, and diseased lung, Shope was able to establish swine influenza in normal swine. The disease was produced with eight different strains of the material from Iowa. Shope found that some strains induced a more severe and virulent form of swine influenza than others. The mortality in the experimental cases was higher than that which occurs in natural outbreaks.

Lewis and Shope (*12*) made bacteriological studies of these experimental cases of swine influenza. They also examined, as a control group, animals that were not affected with swine influenza but were either normal or infected with hog cholera or pneumonia. By using a special culture medium for growing bacteria they were able to isolate the same organism from the lung, bronchial exudate, or heart blood of almost all the pigs affected with swine influenza. They failed to find the organism in any of the normal swine or those infected with hog cholera or pneumonia. They called the organism *Hemophilus influenzae suis*.

Efforts were made to test the possibility that *Hemophilus influenzae suis* might cause swine influenza. It was instilled intranasally in several normal pigs. Two became ill and showed symptoms that could be those of swine influenza, but most of the pigs showed no symptoms whatever. The results apparently indicated that the organism alone would not cause swine influenza.

Although the results of the filtration experiments of McBryde and his associates (*13*) pointed very strongly to the conclusion that the cause of the disease was not a filtrable virus, these workers considered that the experiments might have been too few in number to be conclusive. Shope (*19*), therefore, carried on further experiments on the basis of the possibility that the cause of swine influenza was a filtrable virus.

Germ-free filtrates of suspensions of lung, bronchial lymph glands, and exudate from pigs' affected with swine influenza were instilled intranasally in 10 normal pigs. At the time these experiments were made Shope did not yet know of the role that the *Hemophilus influenzae suis* organism possibly plays in causing swine influenza. Results from 3 of the 10 pigs exposed were interpreted as being negative. The other 7 showed some evidence to indicate that the filtrate had contained an infectious agent. The disease produced was not typical of swine influenza, however, and Shope gave it the name "filtrate disease." It has been produced experimentally many times since, but has never been known to occur naturally. Possibly the disease does occur but because of its mildness goes unrecognized. Usually there is either no rise in temperature or a slight rise that lasts only a day, instead of the high fever lasting 4 to 6 days in typical swine influenza. In the filtrate disease the symptoms of depression, decreased appetite, and altered breathing were slight, and there was no prostration. Occasionally the pigs had a slight cough. Generally the symptoms were so mild as to be noticed only on close observation.

The filtrate disease was very contagious, and symptoms usually appeared in normal swine 2 days after they were placed in contact with pigs already affected. The post mortem lesions of pigs with the disease were generally similar to those in typical cases of swine influenza but not as extensive.

In cases of disease produced by the filtrate, bacteriological studies failed to reveal the presence of the *Hemophilus influenzae suis* organism. The difference in this respect between animals affected with the filtrate disease and animals affected with typical swine influenza suggested that a combination of this organism and a filtrable virus might be necessary to produce typical swine influenza. When mixtures of the filtrate and the *H. influenzae suis* organism were instilled intranasally in normal swine, cases of typical swine influenza developed. The combined action of these two agents was thus established as the cause of the disease.

Immunity Experiments

Shope (*19*) also carried out experiments which indicated that the majority of animals that recover from the experimentally produced disease become immune. He also showed that the serum of the blood of animals that had recovered would neutralize the virus, or make it harmless. In other words, when a definite amount of serum from a pig that has recovered is added to a similar amount of virus, the mixture when instilled intranasally in a normal pig does not produce swine influenza; but when the same amount of serum from a pig that has not had swine influenza is added to the same amount of virus, the mixture when instilled intranasally in a normal pig does produce swine influenza. This so-called neutralization test is used extensively in the studies of influenza as well as of many other filtrable-virus diseases.

In answer to the question whether organisms other than *Hemophilus influenzæ suis* act with swine influenza virus to cause the disease, Shope called attention to the relatively large number of cases caused by the virus alone in which none of the organisms that are normally present in the respiratory tract were capable of producing swine influenza.

In citing attempts of investigators to determine the possibility that human influenza also is caused by a filtrable virus, Shope (*19*) suggested that the problem be investigated with the idea that the combined action of the *Hemophilus influenzæ* organism commonly found in the human respiratory tract and a filtrable virus might be the cause of influenza in man.

In 1932 Shope (*20*) reported on additional studies on immunity to swine influenza. It was shown that pigs that had recovered from the filtrate disease, acquired either as a result of intranasal instillation of the virus or by contact, became immune to exposure with a mixture of swine influenza virus and the *Hemophilus influenzæ suis* organism—that is, they became immune to typical swine influenza. However, the intranasal instillation of the *H. influenzæ suis* organism alone did not confer such immunity. Shope also showed that the blood serum of pigs that had recovered from the filtrate disease would neutralize a mixture of virus and *H. influenzæ suis*. When such serum was added to the mixture and allowed to stand for an hour, the combined materials failed to produce swine influenza when instilled intranasally into susceptible pigs, but if serum from normal pigs was used the combined material would produce the disease.

It was also demonstrated that when swine influenza virus alone was injected into the muscles of pigs, instead of being introduced by the other methods described, it would not produce swine influenza even though the *Hemophilus influenzæ suis* organism was present in the respiratory passages. Although pigs thus treated were not affected with the disease, they became immune.

CAUSE OF HUMAN INFLUENZA DETERMINED

In 1933 Smith, of the National Institute for Medical Research, London, and his associates (*29*) reported the production of a disease in ferrets by the intranasal instillation of bacteria-free filtrates of throat washings obtained from human patients with influenza. The disease was also transmitted from sick to healthy ferrets either by contact or by direct transfer of nasal washings. Ferrets that had recovered from the disease were found to be immune for some time to subsequent infection with the same strain of virus. As Shope had shown that serum from swine that had recovered from swine influenza would neutralize swine influenza virus, these investigators showed that the serum from ferrets that had recovered from human influenza would likewise neutralize the human influenza virus, as evidenced by the failure of the disease to develop in ferrets when a mixture of the virus and serum were instilled intranasally. By similar tests these workers also demonstrated that serum from human patients after their recovery from influenza would neutralize the human influenza virus, although the results of these tests were not always constant. It was suggested that this inconstancy was a result of their inability to measure the amount of virus in the infective material and the number of neutralizing bodies in the serum used in the mixtures.

COMPARATIVE STUDIES OF SWINE AND HUMAN VIRUSES

Smith obtained, for comparative studies, samples of the swine influenza virus and the *Hemophilus influenzae suis* organism with which Shope had produced influenza in swine. When the swine influenza virus was instilled intranasally in ferrets, it produced a disease that was indistinguishable in its symptoms from that produced by the human influenza virus. The nature of the disease in ferrets was not altered when the swine influenza organism was injected together with the swine influenza virus. When cross-immunity tests in ferrets were made, it was found that the animals that had recovered from the disease produced by the swine virus were solidly immune to the human strain of virus but that ferrets that had recovered from the disease produced by the human virus were not completely immune to the swine virus. The tests did, however, indicate a close relationship between the two strains of viruses.

In 1934 Shope (*21*) showed that the swine influenza virus produces a more severe type of disease in ferrets if it is instilled intranasally when the animals are under ether anesthesia. A specific type of pneumonia would develop in ferrets thus exposed.

Later in 1934, Andrewes, of the National Institute for Medical Research, London, and his associates (*1*) were able to produce a specific disease in mice with both the human and the swine viruses by injecting them intranasally into these animals when they were under ether anesthesia. As in ferrets, the disease produced in mice by the mixture of swine influenza virus and the *Hemophilus influenzae suis* organism, which is necessary for producing typical swine influenza in swine, was no different from that produced by the swine influenza virus alone. It was also shown that mice could be used to test sera for the presence of bodies that would neutralize the viruses. This neutralization test in mice has been used extensively in the studies of influenza that have been carried on since that time.

During the next few years, strains of human influenza virus other than the one isolated by Smith were recovered from outbreaks of influenza in other countries. At first it was thought that these strains were identical, but in 1938 neutralization and immunity tests with 28 strains showed that they were not all alike, although they were definitely related (*28*).

In 1935 Shope (*22*) reported that swine influenza virus could be established directly in mice by intranasal instillation of suspensions of affected swine lung. At the same time experiments showed that mice immunized against specific strains of the human virus were resistant to swine influenza virus. Similar tests showed that mice immunized against the swine influenza virus were resistant to a specific strain of the human virus. Mouse neutralization tests made later showed that various strains of human virus acted differently in their ability to produce antibodies against swine influenza virus.

After the development of the neutralization test in mice, by which the quantity of protective antibodies in human and animal sera could be measured, and the perfecting of the method of isolating the viruses in laboratory animals which proved that there were different strains, it was not long before a vast amount of information resulting from such tests became available for study. Even though a large part of the work has pertained to human influenza, it has often been necessary to include somewhat parallel investigations with the swine influenza virus. Some of the work on human influenza seems particularly significant in the study of swine influenza and indicates the necessity for further research to extend the knowledge of the relationship between the two viruses.

Results of experiments were reported which showed that the sera of animals exposed several times, instead of only once, to either the human or the swine virus contained antibodies against both viruses (*7*).

The results of mouse neutralization tests with samples of human sera showed that a large majority of the samples contained neutralizing bodies (antibodies) against a specific human strain of virus (*6*). A very high proportion of the samples from adults neutralized swine influenza virus, but the samples from children under 12 years of age seldom did (*23*). Two explanations have been offered for the presence of larger amounts of swine influenza antibodies in the sera of adults than of children. One is that the adults have been exposed to human influenza several times, and as a result, as has been shown in experimental animals, antibodies against swine influenza virus have been produced, whereas in children, who presumably have been subjected to only a single attack, such antibodies have not been produced. The other explanation is that the swine influenza virus is the surviving type of the agent that was primarily responsible for the outbreak of human influenza in 1918. Adults who had been exposed to or infected with the virus as it existed at that time developed antibodies against it. Such antibodies were not present in the sera of children, who had not been exposed to that virus.

Neutralization tests with sera from persons living on the island of St. Helena, where an outbreak of influenza occurred in 1936 (*31*), support the idea that the amount of swine influenza antibodies in human serum may increase following an attack of influenza caused by a supposedly human type of virus. No outbreak of influenza had occurred on this island from 1917 to 1921. The sera of individuals living on the island during that period had slight or negligible antibodies when tested in 1935 for either a specific strain of human virus or swine influenza virus. Several months after the 1936 outbreak, tests of the sera from the same individuals revealed that not only had the antibodies for the human virus increased but also that antibodies for the swine strain had been acquired by persons who had none when tested in 1935.

While serological investigations may have no immediately practical application—at least so far—to the handling of field outbreaks of influenza in swine, they serve as basic information for veterinarians and others who are concerned with the origin, spread, and distribution of the swine disease.

ACTION OF THE HUMAN INFLUENZA VIRUS IN SWINE

The human influenza virus when instilled intranasally in young pigs produced a mild illness, and a mixture of the virus and swine influenza organisms produced a more severe illness (*27*). Further investigations (*27*) of the ability of the human influenza virus to produce disease in swine showed that while the symptoms and lesions in swine infected with the human virus alone were indistinguishable from those produced by the swine virus alone, some differences were observed between typical swine influenza and the disease produced by a mixture of the human virus and *Hemophilus influenzae suis*. As outbreaks of a disease with which the human influenza virus is associated may occur in swine in the field, these differences should be recognized, for otherwise such outbreaks may not be correctly diagnosed or may be considered to be atypical cases of swine influenza. In experimental cases produced by the mixture of the human virus and *H. influenzae suis*, the period of fever may be 2 or 3 days shorter than in swine influenza. The animals are depressed and their appetites diminished, but while they may appear listless they do not show the marked prostration so often seen in swine influenza. Respiratory symptoms occur but are less marked than in swine influenza. The results of a few experiments suggest that infection in swine with the human virus may not be readily transmitted to normal swine by contact, but this may not be true in outbreaks in the field.

The actual isolation of the human virus from swine in field outbreaks has not yet been reported. However, mouse neutralization tests of sera from field herds of swine indicate that they are attacked by the human virus (*24*). Sera from older pigs that were on farms during a period when people living there had been affected with the human influenza virus contained antibodies that neutralized the human virus but not the swine virus. Younger swine, farrowed long after the cases of human influenza, did not contain antibodies for either the human or the swine virus.

OTHER RECENT FINDINGS

Scott (*16*), of the School of Veterinary Medicine of the University of Pennsylvania, found that relatively large doses of the hemorrhagic septicemia organism (see the article on p. 726) when instilled intranasally produced no illness in normal swine, whereas a mixture of a small amount of the organism and swine influenza virus produced clinical symptoms that resembled swine influenza. Only a slight feverish reaction resulted from the intranasal instillation of the swine influenza virus alone.

It is known that in the field hemorrhagic septicemia infection is often secondary to or associated with hog cholera. Little is known about the frequency of herd outbreaks in which hemorrhagic septicemia infection may be secondary to or associated with swine influenza.

It has been reported that lungworm larvae (p. 758 of this Yearbook) may act as a reservoir of swine influenza virus from one season to the next (*25*). The virus is harbored by lungworm larvae from pigs with swine influenza during their development in their intermediate host, the earthworm. After the parasite reaches the respiratory tract of a new swine host, swine influenza occurs when the virus is liberated or made active by certain stimuli.

More recently it has been reported that such stimuli to be effective must occur during the late fall, winter, or early spring months (*26*). During the summer these stimuli have not caused swine influenza in pigs harboring lungworms that are carriers of swine influenza virus. As yet there is no explanation for this seasonal variation, but some of the endocrine glands are suspected of being responsible.

SUGGESTED NOMENCLATURE

In order that there may be a common terminology to apply to various types of influenza, it has been suggested (*9*) that the type of virus isolated by Smith be called influenza virus A and the disease it causes influenza A. It was also suggested that since the group of diseases commonly called influenza are not all caused by influenza virus A, the names influenza virus B, C, etc., be given to each specific virus isolated as the cause of the disease it produces. The virus isolated by Francis (*5*), of the New York University College of Medicine, is thus called influenza virus B and produces the disease influenza B. This terminology applies only to human influenza and not to influenza in animals. Consequently the term "swine influenza virus" is retained.

LITERATURE CITED

(1) ANDREWES, C. H., LAIDLAW, P. P., and SMITH, WILSON.
    1934. THE SUSCEPTIBILITY OF MICE TO THE VIRUSES OF HUMAN AND SWINE INFLUENZA. Lancet [London] 227: 859–862.
(2) DIMOCK, W. W., and HEALY, D. J.
    1922. INFLUENZA OF SWINE, "HOG FLU," BRONCHO-PNEUMONIA. North Amer. Vet. 3: 138–141.
(3) DORSET, M., McBRYDE, C. N., and NILES, W. B.
    1922. REMARKS ON "HOG FLU." Amer. Vet. Med. Assoc. Jour. 62: 162–171.
(4) DREHER, W. H.
    1922. SWINE DISEASES AS WE FIND THEM IN THE FIELD. Amer. Vet. Med. Assoc. Jour. 61: 178–181.
(5) FRANCIS, THOMAS, Jr.
    1940. A NEW TYPE OF VIRUS FROM EPIDEMIC INFLUENZA. Science 92: 405–408.

(6) FRANCIS, THOMAS, Jr., and MAGILL, T. P.
1936. THE INCIDENCE OF NEUTRALIZING ANTIBODIES FOR HUMAN INFLUENZA VIRUS IN THE SERUM OF HUMAN INDIVIDUALS OF DIFFERENT AGES. Jour. Expt. Med. 63: 655–668, illus.
(7) ———— and SHOPE, RICHARD E.
1936. NEUTRALIZATION TESTS WITH SERA OF CONVALESCENT OR IMMUNIZED ANIMALS AND THE VIRUSES OF SWINE AND HUMAN INFLUENZA.. Jour. Expt. Med. 63: 645–653.
(8) FULTON, J. S.
1930. HOG INFLUENZA. Amer. Vet. Med. Assoc. Jour. 77: 368–371.
(9) HORSFALL, F. L., Jr., LENNETTE, E. H., RICKARD, E. R., and others.
1940. THE NOMENCLATURE OF INFLUENZA. Lancet [London] 239: 413–414.
(10) KINSLEY, A. T.
1923. SWINE "FLU." Vet. Med. 18: 314.
(11) KOEN, J. S.
1919. A PRACTICAL METHOD FOR FIELD DIAGNOSIS OF SWINE DISEASES. Amer. Jour. Vet. Med. 14: 468–470.
(12) LEWIS, PAUL A., and SHOPE, RICHARD E.
1931. SWINE INFLUENZA. II. A HEMOPHILIC BACILLUS FROM THE RESPIRATORY TRACT OF INFECTED SWINE. Jour. Expt. Med. 54: 361–371.
(13) MCBRYDE, C. N., NILES, W. B., and MOSKEY, H. E.
1928. INVESTIGATIONS ON THE TRANSMISSION AND ETIOLOGY OF HOG FLU. Amer. Vet. Med. Assoc. Jour. 73: 331–346.
(14) MURRAY, CHARLES.
1920. NOTES ON A MICROCOCCUS ISOLATED FROM CASES OF BRONCHO-PNEUMONIA (SO-CALLED "FLU") OF SWINE. Amer. Vet. Med. Assoc. Jour. 57: 539–542.
(15) ————
1921. WHAT IS HOG "FLU." Wallace's Farmer 46: [371], illus.
(16) SCOTT, JOSEPH P.
1938. SWINE INFLUENZA. 13th Internatl. Vet. Cong. Proc. 1: 479–487.
(17) SHOPE, RICHARD E.
1931. THE ETIOLOGY OF SWINE INFLUENZA. Science 73: 214–215.
(18) ————
1931. SWINE INFLUENZA. I. EXPERIMENTAL TRANSMISSION AND PATHOLOGY. Jour. Expt. Med. 54: 349–358.
(19) ————
1931. SWINE INFLUENZA. III. FILTRATION EXPERIMENTS AND ETIOLOGY. Jour. Expt. Med. 54: 373–385.
(20) ————
1932. STUDIES ON IMMUNITY TO SWINE INFLUENZA. Jour. Expt. Med. 56: 575–585.
(21) ————
1934. THE INFECTION OF FERRETS WITH SWINE INFLUENZA VIRUS. Jour. Expt. Med. 60: 49–61.
(22) ————
1935. THE INFECTION OF MICE WITH SWINE INFLUENZA VIRUS. Jour. Expt. Med. 62: 561–572.
(23) ————
1936. THE INCIDENCE OF NEUTRALIZING ANTIBODIES FOR SWINE INFLUENZA VIRUS IN THE SERA OF HUMAN BEINGS OF DIFFERENT AGES. Jour. Expt. Med. 63: 669–684, illus.
(24) ————
1938. SEROLOGICAL EVIDENCE FOR THE OCCURRENCE OF INFECTION WITH HUMAN INFLUENZA VIRUS IN SWINE. Jour. Expt. Med. 67: 739–748.
(25) ————
1939. AN INTERMEDIATE HOST FOR THE SWINE INFLUENZA VIRUS. Science 89: 441–442.
(26) ————
1941. THE INFLUENCE OF HOST AND INTERMEDIATE RESERVOIR HOST IN DETERMINING THE EPIDEMIOLOGIC PATTERN OF BOVINE PSEUDORABIES AND SWINE INFLUENZA. *In* Problems and Trends in Virus Research, Univ. Pa. Bicentennial Conf., pp. 55–66.

(27) SHOPE, RICHARD E., and FRANCIS THOMAS, Jr.
1936. THE SUSCEPTIBILITY OF SWINE TO THE VIRUS OF HUMAN INFLUENZA. Jour. Expt. Med. 64: 791–801, illus.
(28) SMITH, WILSON, and ANDREWES, C. H.
1938. SEROLOGICAL RACES OF INFLUENZA VIRUS. Brit. Jour. Expt. Path. 19: 293–314, illus.
(29) ——— ANDREWES, C. H., and LAIDLAW, P. P.
1933. A VIRUS OBTAINED FROM INFLUENZA PATIENTS. Lancet [London] 225: 66–68, illus.
(30) SPRAY, ROBB SPAULDING.
1922. THE BACTERIA IN NORMAL AND DISEASED LUNGS OF SWINE. Jour. Infec. Dis. 31: 10–21.
(31) STUART-HARRIS, C. H., ANDREWES, C. H., SMITH, WILSON, and others.
1938. A STUDY OF EPIDEMIC INFLUENZA, WITH SPECIAL REFERENCE TO THE 1936–7 EPIDEMIC. [Gt. Brit.] Med. Res. Council, Spec. Rpt. Ser. 228, 151 pp., illus.

Miscellaneous Diseases of Swine

BY G. T. CREECH [1]

FACTS REGARDING the symptoms, causes, prevention, and (where possible) treatment of swine pox, infectious arthritis, necrotic rhinitis and stomatitis, posterior paralysis, pneumonia, mastitis, various skin inflammations, and swine plague are given in this article.

SWINE POX

AVAILABLE INFORMATION indicates that swine pox has probably existed in European countries for a century or more, but the disease has been definitely recognized in this country for only a little over a decade. McNutt, Murray, and Purwin [2] were among the first to recognize and describe the disease in the United States (1928). Since that time others have investigated it, and recently Shope [3] made rather detailed studies with particular reference to the nature of the virus, or causative agent. The disease is fairly prevalent in the Middle West and has also been encountered to some extent in the Eastern States.

Swine pox is an infectious disease which is now known to be caused by two types of virus. This is evidenced by the fact that swine that have recovered from the disease are immune to the particular type of virus that caused the attack but are still susceptible to the other type of virus, to which they have not been exposed. The disease is observed most frequently in very young animals, particularly suckling pigs, and seldom is seen in pigs more than 6 months of age. Some pigs are more resistant to the infection than others; when the pigs in a herd are affected, as a rule there will be a few that show no evidence of the disease.

The symptoms manifested in swine pox depend on the severity of the

[1] G. T. Creech is Senior Veterinarian, Pathological Division, Bureau of Animal Industry.
[2] McNUTT, S. H., MURRAY, CHAS., and PURWIN, PAUL. SWINE POX. Amer. Vet. Med. Assoc. Jour. 74 : 752–761, illus. 1929.
[3] SHOPE, RICHARD E. SWINE POX. Arch. f. die Gesam. Virusforsch. 1 : 457–467, illus. 1940. [Reprinted in Rockefeller Inst. Med. Res. Studies 116 : 397–408.]

attack. In the more acute form there are well-developed symptoms and skin lesions, but in the milder form only slight manifestations of the disease may appear. The symptoms commonly observed in the more acute form are dullness, weakness, loss of appetite, chills, and a rise of several degrees in temperature. In many cases there is a catarrhal discharge from the eyes and nose. In some of the milder cases the skin lesions may develop to some extent without evidence of any general disturbance of the system.

The skin lesions are first noticeable as small reddish areas on various parts of the body, most frequently on the face and ears, in the armpits,

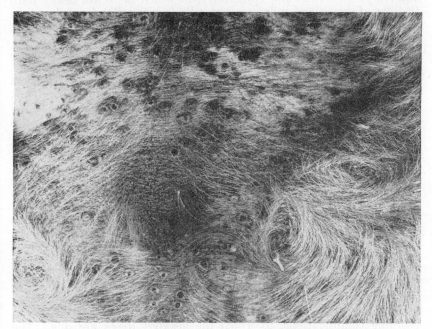

FIGURE 1.—Skin lesions in a typical case of swine pox. Note the characteristic crater-like centers of the eruptions. (Courtesy of H. E. Biester, Iowa Agricultural Experiment Station.)

on the inner surface of the thighs, and on the abdomen. In the more severe cases, much of the skin of the body may be involved, including that of the neck, shoulders, sides, and back. The size of the reddened areas may increase to that of a dime or become even larger. They become raised above the surface of the surrounding skin, developing into rather definite nodular areas, or papules (pimples). After several days, small vesicles, or blisters, are seen at the centers of the papules. The vesicles at first contain a clear fluid which later becomes cloudy and puslike. The blisters cause itching and in rubbing them the pig ruptures many of the vesicles, which may bleed and some of which may become more or less fused together. After several more days, the pustules tend to dry up and the centers shrink and become depressed or craterlike (fig. 1). Later dark scabs form and these eventually drop off or are rubbed off by the pig.

In some of the more acute cases, vesicles which subsequently become ulcers and destroy tissue may form in the mucous lining of the mouth, pharynx (in the upper part of the throat), stomach, intestinal tract, and possibly the trachea (windpipe) and bronchial tubes as well. Certain of the lymph glands, such as the inguinal, in the groin, may become enlarged.

Microscopically, the skin lesions or injuries in swine pox are seen to be of an acute inflammatory nature, involving both the inner and outer layers (dermis and epidermis), in which there are heavy infiltrations of serum and inflammatory cells (white cells) from the blood stream. As a result of the infiltration of serum and cells, the skin in the areas involved is swollen and thickened.

The symptoms, including the skin lesions, and the general course of the disease may vary considerably in individual pigs, the final outcome in many cases depending on possible complications, such as severe diarrhea with rapid exhaustion, bronchitis, and pneumonia. Swine pox can cause considerable damage and possibly severe losses, particularly among the suckling pigs of a herd.

Diagnosis, Treatment, and Prevention

At certain stages, swine pox may be confused with other diseases in which there are skin lesions, such as swine erysipelas and hog cholera. As the disease progresses, however, the characteristic umbilicated, or depressed, centers of the eruptions seen in swine pox should aid in differentiating this disease from the others in most cases. Also, in swine erysipelas lameness or arthritis may develop. In questionable cases laboratory assistance may be necessary in making a definite diagnosis.

No specific treatment for swine pox is known. Proper care of the sick pigs and strict sanitary measures are of chief importance in controlling the disease after it has gained entrance to the herd and in avoiding complications, to which the heaviest losses are due. The sick pigs should be isolated from the remainder of the herd, and the feeding troughs, floors, and walls of pens or hog houses should be thoroughly cleaned and disinfected. Hot lye solution is a very satisfactory disinfectant. The healthy pigs should be removed to clean, sanitary quarters, which in the winter season should be warm and have plenty of bedding. All pigs should have good nourishing food and access to a plentiful supply of fresh drinking water. Proper attention to the herd during the period of sickness will reduce losses from swine pox very considerably.

Shope and other investigators made the important observation that swine pox is not transmitted from sick to healthy pigs by contact. They found that lice carry the virus from animal to animal and may spread the disease throughout an entire herd. The most important preventive measure consists in the prompt and effective eradication of hog lice, as described in the article on page 741.

INFECTIOUS ARTHRITIS

Infectious arthritis, commonly referred to as joint ill or navel ill, is an acute infectious disease of recently farrowed pigs that has been known to hog raisers for a long time. As a rule the disease occurs sporadically and may cause heavy losses in some herds. The disease is characterized by inflammatory changes, with possible abscess formation of the umbilical, or navel, tissues and inflammation of the joints.

Infectious arthritis is caused by different types of germ infections. A number of pyogenic, or pus-producing, micro-organisms, including streptococci, staphylococci, and certain types of the colon bacillus, have been found associated with the disease. In most cases the infecting organisms gain entrance to the body through the tender navel cord soon after birth. They are distributed through the tissues by the blood stream and eventually reach the joints, where they tend to become localized.

While navel ill in young pigs is due specifically to certain types of infection, there are also a number of contributing or predisposing causes, such as improper care, damp, insanitary quarters, and lack of proper bedding on concrete floors.

The manifestations of the disease depend somewhat on the virulence and extent of the infection in individual pigs. In the more typical cases some evidence of inflammation of the umbilicus, or navel, is frequently observed, and in some there are accumulations of pus. The joints are definitely swollen, and when they are opened, the synovial, or joint, membranes will be found to be distended with a turbid or coagulated fluid. In the late stages the joint tissues may be infiltrated with pus. Occasionally the infection will be carried by the circulation to such organs as the liver and spleen, where abscesses may form.

The symptoms of the disease appear most frequently a few days after birth or during the first week of life, but they may be observed occasionally during the second or third week. At first a disinclination to suckle, dullness, and possibly constipation may be noted in the affected pigs, and these symptoms may be followed by diarrhea. There is evidence of lameness, and on examination one or more of the joints will be found to be swollen, hot, and painful. Usually there is marked weakness and rapid emaciation, and as a rule the course of the disease is rather brief, death occurring about the second or third day.

In diagnosing infectious arthritis it may be necessary to differentiate the disease from certain others in which joint lesions, with resulting lameness, may also occur, such as swine erysipelas or swine brucellosis. The presence of associated navel lesions should aid in reaching a definite diagnosis.

No specific treatment for the condition after the pigs have become infected is known. Preventive measures are, therefore, of greatest importance. Infection in most cases follows soiling of the stump of the sensitive navel cord with contaminated material from bedding or floors, a fact that should be emphasized. Consequently, the first and most important step in the prevention of infection of young pigs is to provide clean quarters for sows at farrowing time. In fact infectious arthritis can probably be largely prevented in most herds by providing sanitary surroundings at farrowing time. Clean bedding should be provided for the sow and litter and should be changed rather frequently. The young pigs should be prevented from lying directly on concrete floors. As a definite and practical preventive measure, the navel cords of all pigs should be tied with sterile cord, the end of the cord clipped, and the stump dipped in tincture of iodine as soon as practicable after birth.

During the first few days after farrowing, or until the navel cord has dried up and fallen off, it would also be well to examine the pigs from time to time in order to detect any possible indications of infection as evidenced by inflammation of the navel. When inflammation is noted, the navel should be washed in warm water to which a small amount of cresol has been added and then dusted with powdered alum. Pigs showing evidence of sickness should be given a physic of either Epsom salt or raw linseed oil and should be housed in a warm, dry place, particularly in cold weather. Occasionally pigs seem to recover from the infection, particularly when turned out to pasture, but in a number of such cases a recurrence of the arthritis when the pigs were again housed for fattening has been noted.

In handling the herd as a whole, it is always a good sanitary procedure on removing hogs from the various pens and hog houses to cleanse and disinfect such quarters thoroughly before they are occupied again. A 4-percent hot lye solution may be used as a disinfectant for cleaning and scrubbing the woodwork, floors, etc. Several hours after they are cleaned with the lye, thoroughly wash the quarters with clean water.

NECROTIC RHINITIS AND STOMATITIS

Necrotic rhinitis, or so-called bull nose, is most frequently observed in growing pigs It is characterized by swelling and enlargement of the tissues of the nose and face, including the bony structures, which results in more or less deformity. There are also necrosis, or destruction, and sloughing of the tissues of the snout, lips, and other parts of the mouth.

The condition is infectious and is caused by a micro-organism, *Actinomyces necrophorus.*

Rather widespread in nature, the organisms gain entrance to the tissues in the region of the nose or mouth through wounds or abrasions that may result from blows or fighting, or they enter the lips and gums through injuries caused by certain types of rough feed or by foreign objects such as wire. Filthy surroundings or generally insanitary conditions are very conducive to bull nose infection.

One of the first symptoms noted is a partial loss of appetite. The affected pigs may root in their feed but eat very little. Because the pigs sneeze repeatedly, the condition is commonly referred to by hog owners as sniffles. In sneezing, a certain amount of bloody discharge mixed with clumps of dead tissue may be expelled from the nasal cavities. Many of the affected pigs make a peculiar blowing sound that is considered one of the characteristics of the disease. The snout is enlarged, and lumps or swellings may be seen on some parts of the face. When some of these swellings are opened they are found to contain a cheeselike material which has a disagreeable odor. In many cases the bones of the nose and face are destroyed. In the late stages of the infection the pigs eat with difficulty and gradually become weak and emaciated. If the infection is permitted to continue, it will eventually result in the death of the animals.

Treatment may be undertaken in the very early stages while the swellings on the face are still small or before the infection becomes deep-seated. The swellings should be opened, and as much as possible of the puslike material should be removed. Half-strength tincture of iodine should then be injected into the cavity. It should be understood, however, that after the infection is fairly well established, treatment is in most cases very unsatisfactory or of little avail, largely on account of the involvement and destruction of the bones of the nose and face. In such cases the affected pigs should be destroyed.

If the affected pigs are not destroyed, they should be placed in separate quarters. Occasionally a pig may recover, but as a rule it is advisable to destroy all pigs showing well-marked evidence of infection. The noninfected pigs should be removed to clean sanitary surroundings to prevent the further spread of the infection. The quarters previously occupied by the pigs should be thoroughly cleaned and disinfected, with particular attention to mudholes or damp insanitary parts of hog lots. The use of open pens or hog lots that have been left unoccupied and exposed to direct sunlight for a considerable period and will also prove helpful in overcoming such infections.

Necrotic stomatitis, a type of sore mouth in suckling pigs, is thought to be due to the same cause as necrotic rhinitis. The affected pigs are observed to suckle with some difficulty, and on examining the mouth ulcerated areas with reddish borders and yellowish-white centers are noticeable on the gums, lips, and palate. There are necrosis and sloughing of the tissues, with which a disagreeable odor is associated. Owing to the difficulty of eating as a result of soreness and pain, the affected pigs soon become weak and emaciated.

Treatment of infectious sore mouth, as of necrotic rhinitis, is usually unsatisfactory after the infection has become well established, and in both these conditions primary attention should be directed toward prevention by proper sanitation.

GOITER (HAIRLESS PIGS)

Goiter in swine is rather widely distributed in some parts of the United States, particularly in the Northwest and the Great Lakes region. For a long time the cause of goiter remained obscure, but the disease is now definitely known to be caused by deficiency of iodine in the ration of the sow during the period of pregnancy. (See the article on Nutritional Diseases of Farm Animals, p. 332.)

PARALYSIS OF HINDQUARTERS

Paralysis of the hindquarters is a rather common manifestation of disease in swine. In many cases the cause is obscure, though there have been a number of theories concerning it, and treatment is unsatisfactory.

It has been fairly definitely determined that vitamin deficiencies, including that of vitamin A and possibly others, may cause paralysis in swine. It has also been found that certain inflammatory conditions of the spinal cord and related nerve tissues, presumably due to some type of germ infection, may cause posterior paralysis. In growing pigs and pregnant brood sows, an inadequate mineral supply may result in a soft condition of the bones, making them subject to fracture. and such fractures, either of the spinal vertebrae or of the femur, or thigh bone, may cause symptoms that very closely resemble posterior paralysis. Paralysis sometimes follows parturition in sows that are in run-down condition and are being suckled heavily. Diseased conditions of the spinal cord or vertebrae, such as those caused by tumors, abscesses, and tuberculosis, may result in paralysis. It is also claimed that parasites, such as the kidney worm of swine, may occasionally invade the loin muscles and cause posterior paralysis. Other conditions, such as lack of exercise, lumbago, and rheumatism, are said to be contributing causes.

As a rule posterior paralysis develops gradually. The first indications are a wobbly or unsteady gait and inability of the animal to control the hindquarters. As the condition progresses, walking becomes more difficult and weakness of the hindquarters more pronounced. Finally the animal is unable to stand on the hind feet and drags the hindquarters when forced to move (fig. 2). In exceptional cases, the first symptoms noted may be stamping of the hind feet. or a quick raising or lowering of the feet, which may be followed shortly by definite evidence of paralytic changes and loss of control of the hindquarters. For a time the affected animal may have a very good appetite and fail to show any other functional disturbance. If the paralysis cannot be remedied, however, the animal will eventually refuse feed, develop constipation, and show a general loss of condition.

Because the cause in many cases is obscure, treatment of posterior paralysis is not very satisfactory. Regardless of the cause, however, the first step in treatment is to make the animal as comfortable as possible. If there is evidence of constipation, a dose of Epsom salts or linseed oil should be given. Feed a light diet, such as slop made of milk and bran, and provide clean bedding and an ample supply of fresh drinking water. In some cases massaging of the loin muscles with a good liniment may prove beneficial. If the affected animal is a sow suckling a large litter, the pigs should be weaned. A ration consisting of crushed wheat, bran, and milk made into a slop will prove beneficial in restoring the animal's vitality, depleted by heavy suckling. Sows that have recently farrowed should also have plenty of green feed in the ration to provide the necessary vitamins.

In view of the probability that many cases of posterior paralysis are caused by vitamin and mineral deficiencies, preventive measures consist in providing the animals with a well-balanced ration and meeting their mineral requirements. This may be accomplished by adding green feeds to the usual ration, which is often deficient in the essential vitamin A; if green feeds are not available, fish oils may be substituted. Mineral is supplied by adding steamed bonemeal to the diet. As additional preventive measures, care should be taken to

Figure 2.—The posture of this hog is characteristic of the advanced stage of posterior paralysis. (Courtesy of Charles Murray.)

prevent injury to the pigs, and they should have plenty of exercise and sunlight, and sanitary surroundings at all times.

PNEUMONIA

Pneumonia is rather commonly associated with hog cholera, swine plague, and other acute infectious conditions of swine; it is of much less frequent occurrence as a primary or specific disease. When not associated with other diseases, pneumonia probably occurs most frequently in the septic, or gangrenous, form.

Pneumonia always results from some form of irritation of the lung tissue. The nonspecific types may be due to a number of causative factors, such as exposure to severe weather conditions, the inbreathing of dust or other irritating substances, the introduction of foreign material into the lung as a result of improper drenching, and any form of mechanical injury to the lung tissue.

The various forms of irritation mentioned lead to inflammatory changes and consequent solidification of the lung tissue, so that little air space is left in the parts of the lung involved. In-the advanced stages the lung becomes hepatized, or liverlike, to such an extent that portions of the affected tissue will sink when placed in water.

The acute pneumonias are attended by chills, elevation of temperature, and difficult and rapid breathing with some evidence of pain. The affected hogs frequently appear to be trying to obtain some relief by lying on the chest. In all acute types of pneumonia there is a similarity of symptoms regardless of the specific causative agent. This may tend to cause some confusion, as in cases of hog cholera and other infectious diseases with which pneumonia may be associated. There are, however, certain differentiating features which should be kept in mind when pneumonia is present in a herd. In the ordinary types of pneumonia—that is, those not associated with some other disease—usually only a few animals in the herd are affected, and their temperature seldom exceeds 104° F. (normal for a hog is 101° F.), whereas when pneumonia accompanies such diseases as hog cholera the temperature is usually several degrees higher, and more animals are sick. The disease runs a milder course in the ordinary types, and many of the animals recover, while in cholera the course of the disease is rapid, and most of the affected animals succumb.

Autopsies on hogs dead from pneumonia commonly reveal the solidification of the lung already mentioned. Sometimes puslike material is present, and there may be centers of dead tissue (necrosis) in the lung. There is an absence of congestion, hemorrhages, and similar lesions in other tissues and organs, where they are found in hog cholera. Pneumonia due to lungworms is chronic in type, and as a rule only certain areas of the lung tissue are involved.

Pneumonia may be prevented to a large extent by correct sanitary measures and proper handling of the herd, particularly under severe weather conditions. The quarters where swine are kept should be reasonably sanitary, protected from cold, and properly ventilated without drafts. Hogs should not be permitted to burrow under strawstacks where they are crowded together and become overheated; when they come out from such places into the cold at feeding time, they become chilled, and chilling is very conducive to pneumonia. Feeding hogs on clean concrete floors will aid very materially in preventing worm infestations, which may result in verminous pneumonia.

When pneumonia is known to be present in the herd, proper care and handling are of extreme importance in aiding recovery. The sick hogs should be housed in warm, clean, dry quarters where there is proper ventilation without drafts. A box stall is desirable when available. There should be an ample supply of clean drinking water. A purgative such as Epsom salts should be given early in the disease. If the animals show an inclination to eat, give bran mashes or other kinds of soft sloppy feed.

Since pneumonia is frequently associated with certain acute infectious diseases of swine, owners should be on the alert for possible outbreaks of such serious infections as hog cholera when a considerable number of the animals in a herd are observed to be sick. A veterinarian should be consulted immediately with a view to obtaining a prompt and accurate diagnosis, and his advice with regard to the proper procedure in controlling and preventing the further spread of the disease should be strictly followed. Prompt action in such cases may prevent heavy losses in affected herds.

MASTITIS (MAMMITIS, OR GARGET)

Mastitis, or mammitis, also referred to as garget, is an inflammatory condition of the mammary gland, or udder.

Owing to their location and the conformation of the animal, the mammary glands of swine are predisposed to various kinds of injuries, such as bruises or abrasions from contact with stubble, stones, and other objects. As a result of such injuries, various types of bacteria, particularly pyogenic (pus-producing) organisms, gain entrance to the udder tissues. Organisms may also reach the gland tissues through the teat cavities. The invasion of the infective organisms is followed by inflammation.

The inflamed udder becomes swollen, hot, and painful. Milk that is forced out of the infected gland is clotted or more or less ropy. As the condition progresses, abscesses may form. In some cases there is a general disturbance of the system, resulting in loss of appetite, rise of temperature, and possibly constipation. Owing to the soreness of the affected udder, the sow frequently will not permit the pigs to nurse.

In cases of acute mammitis, alternate hot and cold applications, when practicable, will prove helpful in reducing the inflammation of the udder. The sow should also be given a purgative, such as Epsom salts. If there are open wounds or sores, they should be thoroughly cleaned with warm water, after which either iodized glycerine or antiseptic dusting powders may be applied. In cases of abscess formation, the condition can be satisfactorily relieved only through surgical means. In addition to the acute, more common, pyogenic form of mammitis in swine there are also several other forms, more chronic in character and due to different types of infection, such as actinomycosis, tuberculosis, and botryomycosis.

Actinomycosis of the udder is caused by the actinomyces, or ray fungus, which is widespread in nature, particularly on grains and grasses. Infection of this type is, therefore, most likely to be observed in the udders of sows that have been pasturing on stubble fields. The infective agent gains entrance to the udder tissue through injuries or abrasions of the skin. The lesions are quite similar in appearance to the changes seen in actinomycosis of other tissues and are characterized by tumefactions, or enlargements, which may vary in size from an inch to several inches in diameter. The enlargements may become eroded and rupture, discharging a sticky, granular, light-yellowish pus. Medicinal agents are of little value as treatment, and usually relief must be obtained by removing the entire tumefaction through proper surgical procedure.

In tuberculous mammitis, caused by the tubercle bacillus, technically called *Mycobacterium tuberculosis*, the lesions, or tissue changes, are the same as those observed in tuberculosis in other parts of the body. In these cases the causative organism may have been introduced from outside sources through injuries, or it may have been transmitted through the circulation from a center of infection in some other tissue or organ. If the tuberculous lesions are localized, or confined to the udder tissue, relief may be obtained by surgical means.

This procedure may be followed when the sow is a valuable animal; otherwise it would be safer to slaughter the animal and cremate the carcass in order to prevent the possible further spread of the infection.

Botryomycotic mammitis, which has been attributed to the presence of *Staphylococcus ascoformans*, is of rare occurrence. The lesions are rather similar in their gross appearance to those of actinomycosis, consisting of fibrous tumorlike enlargements containing numbers of pus centers or cavities. Treatment would consist in surgical removal of the enlargements.

The services of a veterinarian should be obtained for all the conditions in which surgical procedure must be resorted to.

SKIN DISEASES OF SWINE

Skin diseases may be classified as parasitic and nonparasitic. Only the latter will be considered here, except insofar as the conditions described may be more or less indirectly the result of parasitic infestation. Diseases and injuries caused by parasites are discussed elsewhere in this volume.

Erythema

Erythema is a reddening of the skin due to congestion of the blood capillaries near the surface, particularly those of the small elevations of the skin or papillae. It may be primary or secondary. The primary type may be the result of various forms of external irritation, including friction, blows, exposure to sunlight, bites by parasites, extreme heat and cold, and chemicals. This type of erythema may also be caused by certain feeds or improper methods of feeding.

The condition is characterized by diffuse reddening of the skin and is, therefore, readily observed only in swine with white or unpigmented skin. The redness disappears on pressure and returns when pressure is removed. The skin feels hot to the touch, and there may be some evidence of pruritis, or itching. Erythema may be the first stage of an inflammatory condition of the skin; otherwise it usually disappears spontaneously after a number of hours, or at most within several days.

Treatment is necessary only when there is considerable itching. Applications of cold water or alcohol give relief. If there is evidence of irritation from rubbing, ordinary dusting powders or zinc ointment may be used. Preventive measures consist in providing proper sanitary conditions, giving careful attention to the feed, and ridding the animals of any lice that may be present.

Erythema occurs as a secondary condition in a number of acute infectious diseases, such as hog cholera, swine plague, and swine erysipelas, and this fact should be kept in mind when the condition is observed in the herd.

Urticaria (Nettle Rash)

Urticaria (called hives in human beings) is a skin affection characterized by slightly raised and reddened areas on the skin surface. Pigs are more frequently affected than mature swine. The condition is thought to be due in many cases to a general disturbance of the system, as in the case of a digestive derangement. Certain feeds—buckwheat, for example—may cause urticaria in older hogs; this is a type of allergy. The condition may also result from external irritations and filthy surroundings.

The reddened areas of the skin are hot, and there is evidence, of itching. In these cases, applications of alcohol or cold water have a good effect. A purgative, such as Epsom salts, is in order. With the necessary corrective measures, including proper diet and the removal of irritating factors, the skin lesions usually heal spontaneously without recourse to treatment of any kind.

ECZEMA

Eczema is observed most frequently in pigs and is comparatively rare in older swine. In this condition there is a definite inflammation of the skin with eruptions on various parts of the body.

Eczema is usually associated with digestive derangement, improper care and feeding, and an insanitary environment. The condition is also seen in pigs that have become weak and emaciated as a result of chronic diseases, such as hog cholera and swine plague. Primary irritation of the skin by lice may also lead to eczema.

Eczema is characterized by erythema, or reddening of the skin, and the formation of small nodules with vesicles, or blisters, and pustules (swellings containing pus). After being ruptured, the vesicles and pustules dry up, forming scabs. At this stage there is intense itching, and as a result of injuries caused by rubbing there may be considerable scaling of the surface layer of skin and consequent inflammatory changes, accompanied by pus, in the deeper skin structures. In the later stages of this condition the skin may become thickened and hard and show cracks and some bleeding.

Eczema may be differentiated from mange by the absence of parasites. In some cases the eczematous lesions may simulate swine pox, though the skin lesions of the latter are rather characteristic.

Treatment consists largely of preventive measures, such as removing or avoiding all predisposing factors, through providing sanitary surroundings and seeing that pigs have good rations. All pigs affected should have a purgative, such as Epsom salts. Zinc ointment and antiseptic dusting powders may be applied to the skin lesions.

SUNBURN AND FROSTBITE

Pigs that have white skin or very little pigment in the skin are susceptible to sunburn on exposure to the direct rays of the sun. At first there will simply be reddening of the skin, but if the exposure is continued a definite dermatitis, or skin inflammation, will develop, with more or less sloughing of the surface layer and eventually thickening and hardening. Pigs so affected do not thrive.

Preventive treatment is self-evident and consists in providing shade to protect the hogs from continued exposure to the direct rays of the sun, particularly during the hot season. Applications of mild antiseptics and ointments would be indicated in cases of considerable destruction of skin tissue.

Pigs farrowed during the cold season, particularly in northern regions, may be frozen when the sows are not properly housed and protected from the cold. The parts most frequently affected are the ears and tail. The frosting of the tissues may result in an inflammatory condition. If the tissues are completely frozen, there will be considerable sloughing of the parts and sometimes the loss of ears and tail.

Occasionally the skin of mature hogs may be frozen as a result of exposure, as during shipping, and this also may result in inflammation and possible sloughing.

Prevention consists in protecting the hogs against extreme weather conditions. Skin lesions caused by freezing may be treated with mild antiseptics and ointments, like similar skin conditions.

SWINE PLAGUE (HEMORRHAGIC SEPTICEMIA)

Swine plague, or hemorrhagic septicemia, is an infectious disease of swin caused by a specific organism, *Pasteurella suiseptica*. The organism is rather widespread in nature and may also be found in the air passages and intestinal tracts of apparently normal hogs.

Swine plague apparently occurs rather frequently in its septicemic (blood-poisoning) form in European countries and hence is recognized there as an independent disease, but in the United States it is seen more often as a complication in certain other diseases, particularly hog cholera. Because of this frequent association with other conditions, there has been some question as to whether swine plague does occur in this country as a specific disease. Although further studies will be required to clear up certain points, present information indicates that it probably does occur independently from time to time, particularly as a pulmonary type of infection, or pneumonia, and usually as scattered cases.

It seems evident that *Pasteurella suiseptica*, which ordinarily is harmless, or nonpathogenic, to healthy swine, becomes capable of producing disease under certain conditions, such as lowered vitality, which make the tissues more susceptible to invasion. The organism may survive for a certain period in insanitary surroundings or in dark places, but it is rather quickly destroyed by sunlight and ordinary disinfectants. The infection is rarely transmitted directly from animal to animal and seldom spreads beyond the herds affected.

A number of factors may result in diminished resistance of swine to hemorrhagic septicemia infection, including exposure to cold, exhaustion from shipping, weaning, poor housing, improper feeding, and different forms of irritation of the lung tissues, as from excessive dust or parasites.

In the uncomplicated form of swine plague, manifested chiefly as pneumonia, the respiratory tract is the channel through which infection commonly takes place. The severity of the symptoms and the extent of the tissue damage depend on the virulence of the infective organism and the resistance of the individual animals.

The symptoms commonly observed in this country are those usually seen in pneumonia. The temperature may rise to possibly 105° F., and there may be rapid and difficult breathing and a spasmodic cough, with a discharge of mucus or mucus and pus from the mouth and nose. In some cases there is conjunctivitis (inflammation of the mucus membranes of the eyes) and a purulent discharge from the eyes. Other symptoms are partial or complete loss of appetite and constipation, which may be followed by a bloody diarrhea. Diffuse reddening of the skin may be noticed. In some cases there is a tendency for the affected hog to sit on its haunches. As the disease progresses, extreme weakness and emaciation occur, and breathing becomes difficult. Finally, complete prostration occurs, and death may ensue in from 1 to 2 weeks. Few hogs make a complete recovery. In those surviving, the disease usually assumes a chronic form in which there is continued difficult breathing, a persistent cough, poor appetite, progressive weakness, emaciation, and in some cases a fetid diarrhea, and after a number of weeks the animals die from exhaustion.

The lesions found on autopsy are chiefly those of pneumonia, or extensive solidification of the lung tissue. The involved tissue may vary from reddish or brown to gray in different portions, and this variation gives the cut surface of the lungs a mottled appearance. Dead areas of lung tissue (necrosis) will be seen, their extent depending somewhat on the length of time the pneumonia has been present. Inflammatory changes in the pleura, or thin membrane covering the lungs, together with a purulent condition, may be seen in some cases The lymph glands associated with the lungs (the bronchial and mediastinal glands) will be hemorrhagic, and in the more chronic cases may contain centers of dead tissue.

DIAGNOSIS AND CONTROL MEASURES

The problem of reaching a definite diagnosis of swine plague is greatly complicated by the fact that it is so frequently associated with hog cholera. It is impossible, through observation, for even an experienced veterinarian to differentiate between the two diseases in herds where there is possibility of the presence of hog cholera. In such cases a definite diagnosis can be made only by demonstrating that the causative organism of swine plague is in the blood or tissues of the affected hogs, and by determining the presence of the virus of hog cholera through swine inoculations with filtered blood from the affected hog. It may also be difficult to differentiate in some cases between pneumonia due to swine plague and some of the more common types of pneumonia in swine.

No specific curative treatment for the disease is known. There are hemorrhagic septicemia serums, aggressins, and bacterins on the market which have been used to some advantage, particularly as preventive agents. The most effective means of prevention, however, consists in practicing proper sanitation. Hog houses and their surroundings should be kept in a reasonably sanitary condition at all times. Since dusty pens in dry weather tend to favor infection, wetting grounds and floors with water or a weak disinfectant from time to time is a helpful preventive measure. Hogs should be properly housed and protected against severe weather conditions during the winter. Treatment of the sick animals is largely a matter of proper care and handling. Sick hogs should be removed from the herd and placed in clean, dry quarters with plenty of fresh air but without drafts. Plenty of clean drinking water should always be available. The feed should be of a soft, sloppy nature and limited in amount until the animals show improved appetite. Recovery is usually slow, and because of the tendency of the disease to become chronic and the continued emaciation and lack of vitality of the affected animals, they may become a total loss to the owner.

When swine plague occurs as a complication of hog cholera, the sick animals should be handled and treated as they would be for the latter disease alone. Under such circumstances it is advisable to consult a veterinarian immediately and follows his recommendations.

At the time this book went to press, the drugs and other materials mentioned in various articles—chiefly as disinfectants, insecticides, and anthelmintics—were still available for veterinary and medical use. Under war conditions, however, it is possible that some of these materials may become scarce or unavailable. In that case, the reader should obtain professional advice from the Department of Agriculture, the State experiment station, a local veterinarian, or the county agent as to available substitutes.

Brucellosis (Infectious Abortion) in Swine

BY ADOLPH EICHHORN [1]

FEWER SWINE than cattle get brucellosis, but on the other hand half the cases of undulant fever in human beings are due to infection with the swine organism; and the latter also causes a more severe disease in human beings than the cattle organism. Systematic eradication of swine brucellosis, then, is a matter of considerable importance in the public interest.

FOLLOWING the epoch-making discovery by the Danish investigator, Bang, in 1896, that abortion in cattle may be induced by the microorganism *Brucella abortus*, the disease, then called contagious abortion, was also found to be present in cattle in the United States. It was not until 1914, however, that a similar disease in swine was reported by Traum, who recovered from the aborted fetuses of a sow an organism similar to that causing abortions in cattle.

Subsequent investigations showed that the organism infecting swine was slightly different from the cattle type. A third type was recovered from goats affected with a similar disease. Therefore the generic name *Brucella* was given to these three closely related germs, the cattle species being called *Br. abortus*, the swine species, *Br. suis*, and the goat species, *Br. melitensis*. The medical term "brucellosis" has been given to the diseases in all animals caused by any and all of the three *Brucella* organisms. More popularly, the three diseases are known respectively as Bang's disease, contagious abortion of swine, and Malta fever of goats.

From recent surveys brucellosis in swine appears to be much more

[1] Adolph Eichhorn is Director, Animal Disease Station, Bureau of Animal Industry.

restricted than brucellosis in cattle, the latter unquestionably being one of the most important diseases affecting the cattle industry. The swine disease, however, may become a very serious menace, not only to the swine industry but also to public health, as will be shown later, unless definite, systematic measures of control or eradication are instituted.

Since Traum's discovery of brucellosis in swine, investigations of the disease have been made by the Bureau of Animal Industry and other research institutions in the United States and foreign countries. In 1922 Schroeder showed that the swine species of the *Brucella* organism possesses greater virulence for guinea pigs than the bovine species of *Brucella*. Subsequent investigations conducted by Schroeder and Cotton, Buck, and others in the United States have shown that cattle thoroughly exposed to infected swine do not contract the disease and develop only a temporary reaction to the blood-agglutination test used to detect the presence of the disease.

While some investigators report that as many as 20 percent of all sows are infected, a more careful survey in Iowa showed that only 2.5 percent in that State reacted to the agglutination test. In other localities in the Middle West approximately the same percentage of infection in hogs as in Iowa, or a lower one, was found.

The disease is usually introduced into a herd through the purchase of an infected animal and may be spread through the ingestion by the animals of aborted fetuses and fetal membranes, as well as through contaminated food and drinking water. Infection through the skin and membranes of the eye might also occur in some instances. The possibility of transmission of the disease from cattle to swine through the eating of aborted cattle fetuses and membranes has been suggested, but experimental evidence shows that swine are extremely resistant to the bovine species of *Brucella*.

LESIONS

Following infection, the germs of the disease are usually present in the blood, through which they reach the lymph glands, spleen, udder, and bones, causing inflammatory conditions at the points of localization. In the male animals the infection frequently causes a severe destructive inflammation of the testicles and seminal vesicles, which results in a marked swelling of the testes and the epididymis—the tubes at the back of the testes—and may affect the general condition of the animal. Boars so affected are frequently defective in breeding capacity, and the infection may result in impotency if both testicles are affected.

As each fetus in the sow is enveloped in a separate membrane, it is not uncommon for some fetuses in a litter to be born fully developed, while others show that death occurred prior to the termination of pregnancy. Most often the fetuses die following the act of abortion, though mummified fetuses are not infrequent, especially when the fetus has died a considerable time before abortion took place. In cases of abortion, the membranes of the sow disclose hemorrhages, and there is a grayish-brown exudate, or discharge similar to that observed in the disease in cattle.

Not infrequently the disease is associated with arthritis, resulting in suppuration (generation of pus) at a joint and erosion, or slow destruction of the cartilage. Abscess formations may be observed in the liver, spleen, and other parts of the body. The bones of the spinal column may become affected, and abscesses may develop which in advanced cases are enclosed in a capsule of connective tissue. These changes may become aggravated and result in deformity of the spine and impairment of locomotion.

SYMPTOMS

The symptoms are not unlike those occurring in cattle. (See Brucellosis of Cattle, p. 501.) A day before abortion, there is swelling of the udder and vulva, and milk makes its appearance in the teats. At times the sow shows illness prior to abortion, lying down a great deal of the time and at other times being restless and uneasy, and not infrequently develops a discharge from the vagina. There is rarely any discharge after abortion, except that when abortion occurs during the early stages of pregnancy there may be a dark-grayish discharge several days afterward. The expulsion of the fetus takes some time, and there is no indication of labor pains. The fetuses are expelled in the enveloping membranes and hence there is no retained placenta, or afterbirth, as is often the case in aborting cows. In some instances inflammation of the uterus follows, but usually the sow makes a rapid recovery. The sow usually comes in heat within a few days after abortion, but as a rule several negative breedings take place before she again becomes pregnant. Animals that have aborted once do not usually do so again. The time of the occurrence of abortion varies considerably and is unquestionably dependent on the time and the virulence of infection, but usually it takes place between the sixtieth and ninetieth days of pregnancy.

DIAGNOSIS

It is very essential to examine the boars carefully in all instances of abortion among swine. Diagnosis is made by isolating the *Brucella* organism from the infected animals and also by the agglutination test. Since the organism grows readily on artificial culture media, its isolation is not difficult. The infection is most frequently found in the genitals of reacting boars and in the stomach contents of aborted fetuses. *Br. suis* is often present in pure culture and may be readily identified by appropriate procedures.

Abortions caused by brucellosis should not be confused with abortions from other causes. Mechanical injuries to the sow, the presence of other infections, and vitamin or mineral deficiencies also may cause abortion. It is essential, therefore, to confirm the diagnosis by the isolation of the organism or by positive blood tests. The blood test is unquestionably the most readily available diagnostic method, but it apparently is not as reliable as the test in cattle.[2] Experiments to establish whether an antigen, or testing agent, produced from swine strains is more reliable than that prepared from bovine strains have not shown any advantage for the former, and therefore the antigen generally employed for testing is prepared from a bovine strain. Other biological tests have been used for the diagnosis of the disease in swine, but they have failed to show any superiority over the agglutination test, or even as much accuracy.

PREVENTION AND CONTROL

There is no specific drug or other chemical agent known for the cure of the infection. As in the case of bovine abortion, various remedies for the prevention and treatment of the disease are being exploited, but in all instances they have failed to show any merit. Attention must therefore be directed toward prevention of the disease. Where the infection is suspected, all animals should be subjected to the blood test. Like brucellosis in cattle, the disease in swine tends to be self-limiting. Animals that have aborted may become immune, or even if they should harbor the infection they carry their fetuses through the normal period of pregnancy. It is advisable, however, after the presence of the infection has been established, to eliminate all reacting animals and subject the rest of the herd to frequent blood tests until there is no evidence of a suspicious or reacting animal. This should be accompanied by adequate sanitary measures.

In its resistance to physical and chemical exposure, *Brucella suis* behaves like the organism of the bovine type. Thus, the article in this book dealing with the disease in cattle should be carefully studied and the sanitary measures recommended for its control should be applied to the elimination of the infection in swine.

While calfhood vaccination for the control of the disease in cattle has given very encouraging results, few experimental data are available on the immunization of swine. In isolated instances cultures prepared from strain 19, used in calf vaccination, have been employed for immunization in swine, but no data are available as to their efficacy. Experimental work is still in progress.

PUBLIC HEALTH HAZARD

From a public health standpoint, human infection with the swine type of *Brucella* is unquestionably more important than human infection with the bovine type. It is a recognized fact that *Brucella melitensis*, the goat type, induces the most severe type of undulant fever, the disease in human beings. Next in order is the swine type, and last, the bovine type. This fact has been established by isolating the various types of organisms from infected human

---

[2] Agglutination in dilutions of 1 to 50 or higher is indicative of infection, and agglutination of 1 to 25 should be considered suspicious. Not infrequently the agglutination test shows no reaction until after the animal has aborted. For details of the test and its interpretation, the reader is referred to Farmers' Bulletin 1871, Brucellosis of Cattle.

beings and observing the severity of the disease caused by each of the three species. It has been estimated by Public Health Service officials that about 50 percent of human infection is due to *Br. suis* and is the result of contact with infected swine on farms or in abattoirs. The frequent occurrence of the disease in human beings in swine-raising localities is indicative of the danger, and the disease often occurs among workers in packing houses as a result of handling carcasses of infected swine. Studies have shown that in the Corn Belt more than half the cases of undulant fever are caused by the swine type and that in regions where the infection in hogs is not common this type of infection in man is less frequent.

Mange of Swine

BY MARION IMES [1]

A SUITABLE DIP, used in a vat or a hog wallow, will get rid of common mange of hogs. The method of treatment is described here, and it is worth putting into practice because when mange takes hold it can be very expensive to the hog owner.

COMMON MANGE OF HOGS is a contagious skin disease which costs swine growers huge sums of money each year, and they pay the bill whether they know it or not. There are no specific data on losses at the farm and feed lot, but as mange stunts the growth of young hogs, delays fattening, and causes some deaths, the estimated losses at these sources probably average about $2 an animal in infected herds. In addition, mangy hogs shipped to market are usually sold at a discount of from 50 cents to $1.50 a hundredweight. The average yield of the principal cuts per hog at packing houses is 35 pounds of hams, 30 pounds of bacon, and 15 pounds of picnics, or a total of 80 pounds of the most valuable parts of the carcass. When the skin over these parts is mangy, the grade and consequently the selling price are lowered—hence the discount on the price of the live hog.

Common mange is more or less prevalent throughout the United States, and the total number of infected hogs is large. The losses, therefore, are sufficiently impressive to emphasize the fact that the disease is a serious menace to the industry. Fortunately there is a brighter side to the picture. Several years ago the Bureau of Animal Industry made an investigation of mange of swine and conducted experiments on treating infected hogs, and the findings showed that the disease yields readily to proper treatment and is easily eradicated.

A contagious disease, however, cannot be eradicated by temporizing or following slipshod methods. Mange is caused by a well-known parasite and is not a filth-borne disease. Good sanitation and careful feeding are essential parts of all successful methods of swine pro-

[1] Marion Imes is Senior Veterinarian, Zoological Division, Bureau of Animal Industry.

duction, but shifting undipped hogs to clean lots, changing or increasing the feed or adding medicines to it, sprinkling dry lime-sulfur in the bedding, or hand treating only the well-developed skin lesions will not eradicate hog mange.

Swine in the United States are affected by two kinds of mange, sarcoptic and demodectic, caused by two different genera of mites—*Sarcoptes* and *Demodex*—which live in the skin of the host animal. The entire life cylces of the mites are passed on the host animal. In obtaining their food from the tissues and blood and preparing suitable places for their various life processes, the mites cause characteristic wounds, or lesions, in the skin. The sarcoptic mites burrow into the skin, each female making a separate gallery in which she lays her eggs. The skin over and around the burrows becomes inflamed, and small vesicles and cone-shaped swellings appear. The demodectic mites, which cause demodectic, or follicular, mange, live in colonies or groups in the hair follicles and sebaceous glands and cause small hard swellings or pimples.

SARCOPTIC MANGE

Sarcoptic, or common, mange occurs in all parts of the United States where hogs are raised. Traffic in breeding stock evidently has been an important factor in spreading the disease. Under conditions favorable to it, mange spreads rapidly unless active measures are taken to control it. Hogs of all classes and ages are susceptible to the infection, but young stock and poorly nourished, older animals of low vitality suffer most.

The mites that cause sarcoptic mange of swine are known as *Sarcoptes scabiei suis*. These mites are small white or yellowish insectlike parasites, visible to the naked eye, especially when they are placed against a dark background. The mature female is about one-fiftieth and the male is about one-sixtieth of an inch in length. They are plainly visible under an ordinary hand lens.

The general form of the body is round, and the bluntly rounded head is as broad as it is long. The mature mites have four pairs of short thick legs, the fourth pair and usually the third pair not extending beyond the margin of the body. Under a high-power microscope a number of short, backward-projecting spines can be seen on the upper surface of the body.

In the burrows or galleries made by the mites in the skin each female may lay from 10 to 25 eggs, which hatch in 3 to 10 days. The mites of the new generation form new burrows and begin laying eggs when they are 10 to 12 days old. The average period of incubation is about 4 days and the average period between hatching and egg laying about 11 days.

SYMPTOMS

The first lesions of sarcoptic mange usually appear on the head of a hog, around the eyes, nose, or ears, where the skin is tender and the hair is thin. From these parts the infection spreads over the neck, shoulders, and back and along the sides, finally involving the entire body. The mites cause irritation, itching, inflammation, and swelling in the sensitive tissues of the skin. Nodules and vesicles appear over and around the burrows. The vesicles break and discharge serum, which usually dries into hard granules or scales. The hair over the lesions stands erect, and some of it drops out.

As the mites multiply and the disease advances, increasingly large areas of skin become involved. The nodules increase in number and are closer together. The mechanical injury to the skin resulting from rubbing and other efforts to relieve the intense itching cause large scabs that may be stained yellowish or reddish by serum or blood. The skin becomes thickened and is thrown into wrinkles or folds. Scrapings taken from moist furrows of the wrinkles usually contain mites. In chronic cases of the moist form of the disease there is a very offensive odor. When the mites are not very active, the surface of the affected skin may be a silver-gray color and have a dry, scurfy, or leatherlike appearance. In such cases the mites are difficult to find.

Positive diagnosis consists in finding the mites, which are the sole cause of the disease, but on account of their burrowing habit this is not always easy. They may be found by deeply scraping the affected area with a blunt-edged knife and examining the scrapings in warm sunshine or near artificial heat, under a low-power magnifying glass. Well-advanced cases of mange are easy to detect, but since the disease should not be allowed to reach this stage, early diagnosis is important. Repeated rubbing, scratching, or biting in one place indicates irritation and itching and should be investigated at once by a close examination of the animal. Disarranged hair indicates the area of skin to be examined. If the skin is thickened and hardened and dried serum or scabs are present, search should be made for mange mites.

CONTAGIOUSNESS

Sarcoptic mange is contagious to all animals of the same species. It is transmissible from one species of animal to another, and in some cases from animals to man. Sarcoptic mites of the hog are known to be transmissible to man. They live only a limited time on the human host but may produce lesions that persist for 30 days or longer and cause extreme annoyance. It is advisable, therefore, to change clothes and bathe after handling mangy hogs.

The disease is usually transmitted among swine by direct contact of uninfected with infected animals, but it may be contracted from infected enclosures, equipment used on or around infected animals, or other objects that are carriers of the mites. Although they cannot propagate except on the host animal, dislodged mites that drop in moist shady places may retain their vitality for 4 weeks or longer during mild weather. Bright sunshine, freezing weather, and lack of moisture usually destroy mites and eggs not on an animal in a few days.

Usually the disease spreads slowly during warm weather, especially when the animals are on pasture, but it spreads rapidly when hogs are closely confined in small enclosures. Exposure to inclement weather, insufficient feed or feed of poor quality, or any other circumstance tending to lessen the vitality or functional activities of the hogs hastens the spread and development of mange. When the mites are active and new lesions are developing, the entire body surface may become involved in about 6 weeks.

Attacks of the disease do not confer immunity, and hogs may become infected any number of times. Since sarcoptic mange is contagious, plans for keeping hogs free from the disease should include precautionary measures against the introduction of infection by such means as bringing undipped animals onto the premises, contact between clean and infected hogs separated only by a wire fence, and allowing hogs to occupy infected premises.

All small enclosures that have been occupied by infected hogs should be cleaned and disinfected before they are used for healthy hogs. Remove all litter, cleaning down to a smooth surface, then spray the exposed surfaces with coal-tar-creosote dip or disinfectant diluted in accordance with the directions on the label of the container. The coal-tar-creosote preparations are sold under many different trade names, and when properly diluted with water they are suitable for use as disinfectants on animals as well as for premises.

TREATMENT

The proper treatment of hogs infected with sarcoptic mange mites consists in killing the parasites without injuring the animals by applying medicated liquids known as dips. Of the several different kinds of effective dips available, oils and lime-sulfur are the ones most commonly and successfully used. These are obtainable ready-prepared for dilution with water, or they may be made by the user. Ready-prepared dips should be diluted and used in accordance with the instructions on the label.

In treating hogs for mange the entire herd should be treated regardless of the number showing visible lesions. To select and treat only those with well-advanced cases of mange will not eradicate the disease, as any member of the herd may at any time carry the parasites temporarily without showing visible lesions. In some cases the disease may be dormant during the summer and early fall months, but with the advent of cold inclement weather it may develop very rapidly. When the weather is too cold for dipping or other effective treatment, rapid spread of the disease may be checked temporarily by hand applications of dips to the worst cases, but mange cannot be eradicated by such methods. Dipping during the mild weather of autumn is good insurance against the risk of loss from mange and the probable additional expense of winter treatment.

Sows heavy with young should not be dipped or oiled within 2 weeks of their farrowing time or too soon after farrowing. When the pigs are 3 weeks old, the sow and pigs may be dipped or treated without undue risk of injury. All the pigs of the litter should be dipped or treated in the same manner as the sow; otherwise she may fail to recognize and to suckle some of them. As mange affects the heads and ears of hogs, it is necessary to submerge, or duck, the head of each hog as it swims through the dip.

Dips

The most effective known dip for sarcoptic or common mange of hogs is crude petroleum or some of the oils derived from it. Unprocessed crude oil is often difficult to obtain and is more expensive than some of the processed oils. The various processed oils vary greatly in the number and relative percentages of their constituents, and there is no fixed standard for oil dips for hogs. The processed oils from which the gasoline and other light hydrocarbons have been removed are usually suitable, but those from which the lubricating oils have been removed are not.

Used lubricating oils, drained from the crankcases of automobiles and other engines, are suitable and effective as dips for hogs, but lubricating oil is not suitable for use on cattle, horses, or sheep. When properly used on hogs, lubricating oil is an effective remedy for mange, it does not injure the animals, and it is usually available at low cost. Several proprietary brands of oil dips are available and are usually effective, but they cost more than crankcase drainings.

In preparing an oil dip, fill the vat with water to within about 6 or 8 inches of the dip line (40 to 48 inches from the bottom) and add sufficient oil to bring the fluid up to that line. The oil floats on the water, forming a layer 6 to 8 inches deep, depending on the quantity added, and as the hogs swim through the vat their bodies become coated with oil. It is not necessary to retard the progress of the animals through the vat. Oil dips are used cold, and one dipping is usually sufficient to eradicate ordinary mange. Hogs with thick adherent scabs from old chronic infections should be dipped two or more times. The proper interval between dippings in oil is about 10 days.

Shade or shelter should be provided for freshly oiled hogs, which should not be exposed to bright, hot sunshine or cold, inclement weather for 24 hours or longer after being oiled. Injury may result also from too much exercise or overheating if the freshly oiled animals are moved rapidly or driven too far.

Lime-sulfur dip is effective in eradicating common mange of hogs when four or more dippings are given at intervals of 6 or 7 days. The temperature of the dip while the animals are in it should be maintained at 95° to 100° F., and visibly infected hogs should be held in the swim 3 minutes. Scrubbing and soaking any lesions covered by hard scabs with warm dip just before the first dipping is recommended.

Proprietary brands of lime-sulfur dip, in the form of concentrated liquid, powder, or crystals, the latter two known as dry lime-sulfur, are available. These products are standardized and are equal to or even better than home-made lime-sulfur dip. Unless the user has proper equipment for preparing the home-made product, the prepared dips are also cheaper.

Methods of Applying Dips

A properly constructed dipping vat or hog wallow [2] is necessary for the proper treatment of any considerable number of hogs. Hog-dipping vats made of galvanized iron, ready for setting in the ground, may be purchased, or vats made of concrete or wood may be constructed on the premises. They are usually arranged so that the hogs enter one end of the vat filled with dip, swim through, and leave the vat at the opposite end, where they enter a draining pen with a watertight sloping floor from which the surplus dip that drips from them flows back into the vat.

The liquid in the vat should be from 40 to 48 inches deep, which is sufficient to swim the tallest animal. A full-grown hog carries out of the vat and retains on an average about 1 quart of dip, and the average quantity for each animal of a mixed herd is about 1½ pints. Adding the quantity of dip carried out and retained by the hogs to the quantity required to charge the vat originally gives the approximate quantity needed to complete the dipping process for a given herd. The capacity of the vat in gallons is obtained by multiplying the average length in inches by the average depth, then the product by the average width, and dividing by 231, the number of cubic inches in a gallon. The average length of a vat with sloping sides is obtained by adding the length in inches at the dip line to the length at the bottom and dividing by 2, and the average width in a similar manner.

If shallow water is available, hogs will wallow in it when the weather is warm, and this habit may be utilized in preventing or curing mange. Adding oil to the water in properly constructed wallows is an inexpensive and satisfactory method of applying oil to hogs.

The water in the wallow should be about 3 inches deep without oil until the hogs become accustomed to using it. Hogs will not wallow in deep water, and when they lie down in wallows they displace a volume of the liquid, which causes the water line to rise. If they cannot easily keep their nostrils above the liquid, they leave the wallow before their bodies are wet on both sides. After the habit of using the wallow is well fixed, oil may be added and the depth of the liquid increased to 5 or 6 inches, depending on the size of the hogs and as observation and experience may indicate. After the bodies of the animals are well coated with oil, the wallow should be drained, cleaned, and recharged with water only. Oil may be added every 10 days until the desired results are obtained.

DEMODECTIC MANGE

The mite known scientifically as *Demodex phylloides*, which is the primary cause of demodectic or follicular mange in hogs, is a minute, wormlike parasite that penetrates into the hair follicles and sebaceous glands of the skin. The mites are microscopic in size, the mature

---

[2] IMES, MARION. HOG LICE AND HOG MANGE: METHODS OF CONTROL AND ERADICATION. U. S. Dept. Agr. Farmers' Bul. 1085, 28 pp., illus. 1920. (Revised, 1937.)

female measuring about one one-hundredth of an inch in length. Positive diagnosis of the disease can be made only by demonstrating the presence of the mites. If the contents of demodex nodules are examined under a microscope, the small wormlike mites are easily identified.

In small numbers demodectic mites apparently do not cause lesions. Although it is difficult to transmit the disease by artificial means, it is classed as contagious. Demodectic mange may spread rapidly on a hog, but the transmission of the disease from one hog to another is usually much slower than the transmission of common or sarcoptic, mange. Ordinarily the disease does not spread to all members of a herd, since many animals are apparently immune, or at least do not contract the disease.

The lesions of demodectic mange appear as small hard nodules, or pimples, in the skin, usually around the eyes or snout, and spread slowly over the under side of the neck, breast, and abdomen, and between the hind legs. The nodules range in size from that of a pinhead to that of a hazelnut and usually contain a material of creamy white color and cheesy consistence. In advanced cases the nodules may rupture and discharge their contents over the hair and skin, and in rare cases suppurating (pus-generating) cavities result.

There is no known practical cure for demodectic mange in hogs, as the cost of treatment is out of proportion to the usual value of the animals. Individual animals that show lesions of demodectic mange should be removed from the herd and disposed of or killed. The rest of the herd should be dipped in oil or coal-tar-creosote dip and the premises cleaned and disinfected in the same manner as for sarcoptic mange.

Hog Lice

BY O. G. BABCOCK AND E. C. CUSHING [1]

WHY LET hogs be tortured by the biggest of all the lice that infest our domestic animals? The remedies are simple, inexpensive, and effective.

HOG LICE are so common that they are often considered as one of the evils that must be endured. These bloodsucking insect parasites, however, are so easily controlled that there is little excuse for letting hogs suffer from the constant irritation they cause, or for the owner to put up with the losses they occasion. Generally these losses are so gradual and continuous that the owner is not aware of them and therefore makes no attempt to keep his animals free of the pests. The injury in heavily infested herds is considerable but it can be eliminated by using a few simple and inexpensive control measures. If young pigs that become infested with lice from their mother are allowed to go untreated until they are old enough to market, there may be a reduction in value of 2 to 6 percent.

The presence of hog lice is easily detected, as this is the largest louse commonly infesting domestic animals in the United States. The adult female is about one-fourth inch long and the male a little shorter. Both sexes are of a grayish color but appear darker on the darker skinned breeds of hogs.

The lice feed frequently and puncture the skin in a different place at each feeding. An animal on which there are only a few of the parasites may be seen to rub and scratch itself on the sides of the pen or on posts, troughs, and other objects. When there is a heavy infestation hogs suffer constant irritation; they are restless and do not eat properly. Ultimately an unthrifty condition results which is sometimes followed by the attacks of other parasites. The constant rubbing and scratching produces sores that do not heal because the lice congregate around the raw tissues and keep them irritated. In the screwworm area these wounds attract screwworms and quickly become infested.

[1] O. G. Babcock is Associate Entomologist and E. C. Cushing is Principal Entomologist, Division of Insects Affecting Man and Animals, Bureau of Entomology and Plant Quarantine.

HOW HOG LICE BREED

Hog lice are parasitic on swine only and spend their entire life on the host. Other animals and even human beings may occasionally transport the insects accidentally from one place to another.

The female deposits the yellowish-white eggs on the bristles of the hog—from 1 to 20 on a bristle—in such places as back of the ears, on the shoulders and neck, and on the flanks. Each mass of eggs is laid within a few seconds, and as many as 90 eggs may be laid by a single female over a 25-day period. Hatching takes place in 12 to 20 days, the eggs at the greatest distance from the body, that is, farthest up the bristles, usually requiring the longest time, especially in cold weather. After emerging from the egg, the transparent young louse becomes fairly active. It seeks the tender skin surface nearest the place where the egg was laid and begins feeding. On hogs that have been heavily infested for some time these tender skin patches become rough and encrusted with scales, beneath which the young lice hide, seeking protection from cold or from extreme heat. Young lice also seek the protection and warmth afforded by the axilla, or hollow between the leg and the body, and the internal parts of the ears. The newly hatched lice become sexually mature in about 10 days, and egg laying may begin on the twelfth day after hatching.

Practically all new infestations occur when the sexually mature females leave the tips of the bristles of their host and attach themselves to the hairs of other hogs with which the host comes in contact. When separated from an animal, hog lice live only 2 or 3 days. Therefore reasonably clean pens, corrals, and premises which have not·held animals for several days are not sources of infestation even though infested hogs may have occupied them previously.

CONTROL MEASURES

The methods for keeping hogs free of lice are economical and easily applied, and they should be used by every hog owner, whether he raises hogs for market or for home consumption. Two of the simplest remedies are crude petroleum in dipping vats and kerosene-oil emulsion applied by hand. Both are effective in killing hog lice and their eggs. Arsenical dips, coal-tar-creosote emulsions, and lime-sulfur dips have certain disadvantages that make them inferior to kerosene emulsion or crude petroleum for this purpose.

Crude petroleum is the most widely used and satisfactory remedy. Unprocessed crude petroleum, the natural crude oil that has not been subjected to any manufacturing process, is probably the most effective, but processed crude petroleum—the residue from the crude oil after the distillation of gasoline and other light hydrocarbons—can be used as a dip and is very effective in eradicating hog lice as well as mange. Processed crude oils vary greatly in the number and relative percentages of their constituents and consequently in their consistency, or thickness. As a rule, the thinner the processed crude oil is, the better it is as a dip for hogs. The thick, heavy residue left after the extraction of the lubricating oils is not suitable.

Small quantities of distillate are sometimes added to the processed crude oil, and the product is sold at a high price as a special oil having a high degree of efficacy in eradicating hog lice and mange. The effectiveness of the processed oil for mange is increased by adding distillate or kerosene in the proportion of 1 gallon to each 10 gallons of the oil. Heavy processed oils should be diluted with distillate until they flow freely from the container at the usual dipping temperature, but the maximum quantity of distillate added should not exceed 20 percent. There are also several proprietary brands of crude-petroleum dip, consisting of processed crude oil to which other ingredients have been added. They are usually effective, but they cost more than the unmedicated crude oil.

Kerosene emulsion may be prepared as follows: Slice and dissolve ½ pound of soap in 1 gallon of water, heating the water until the soap is dissolved. Add 2 gallons of kerosene, churning or agitating the mixture thoroughly until no free kerosene is observed on top of the liquid. This stock solution is then diluted with 11 gallons of soft water to make about a 15-percent emulsion, which will kill hog lice and their eggs if properly applied to the animals. Kerosene emulsion is not recommended for use in dipping vats or hog wallows.

Dipping and Treating

Dipping hogs in especially designed hog-dipping vats is the most effective and economical means of controlling lice when the number of animals is sufficiently large to warrant the construction of a vat. Using a concrete hog wallow (fig. 1) is the next most desirable method of treating large numbers of louse-infested animals. Crude petroleum is the preferred material for use in both vats and wallows.

When the size of hogs using the same wallow varies, the most desirable depth of liquid is 3 to 4 inches. About 1 pint of oil is added to the water in the wallow for each pig and 1 quart for each hog. Usually all hogs will have received sufficient treatment in 24 to 48 hours, after which time the wallow should be drained and charged with fresh water. Arsenical dip is dangerous to use in wallows.

Complete instructions and specifications for building vats and wallows and using crude oil in them are given in Farmers' Bulletin 1085.[2] Anyone contemplating the treatment of hogs by either of these methods should obtain a copy of this publication.

When only a few hogs are to be treated, crude petroleum or kerosene emulsion can be applied by hand. Care should be taken to distribute the insecticide evenly over the entire surface of the head and body of the animal, particular attention being given to the inner surfaces of the ears and to the axillae. The materials can be applied with a brush, mop, or cloth.

Animals should not be treated when they are overheated; and freshly oiled hogs, regardless of the method by which the oil has been applied, should not be forced to move rapidly, or be exposed to bright sunshine, or be allowed to become chilled. The animals should be provided

---

[2] IMES, MARION. HOG LICE AND HOG MANGE: METHODS OF CONTROL AND ERADICATION. U. S. Dept. Agr. Farmers' Bul. 1085, 22 pp., illus. 1937. (Revised.)

with plenty of shade and moved as little as possible for 24 to 48 hours after treatment, depending on temperature. Apparently oil does not injure hogs if proper care is given them, but this is not true of all species of domestic animals.

Rubbing posts and patented hog oilers have been devised that de-

FIGURE 1.—Small home-made concrete hog wallow.

posit a small amount of oil on a part of the skin surface when the animal rubs against them. These devices are useful for keeping louse infestations in check, but since only a small part of each animal's body is treated at one time, they cannot be depended on to eradicate lice from a herd. Thorough hand treatment and the use of dipping vats or medicated wallows are the only methods that will give complete control.

Internal Parasites
of Swine

BY L. A. SPINDLER [1]

THIS ARTICLE discusses all the principal internal
parasites of swine in considerable detail, including the
damage they do, their life histories, and their relative
importance. In equal detail, it outlines systems of
control based on careful scientific investigations and
shows the great saving that can be made by good
management practices.

IN THE COURSE OF CENTURIES swine have come to be afflicted with an
imposing array of internal parasites. In the United States they
cause extensive losses every year. Like a "fifth column," the parasites
seldom give warning of their presence but attack from within, sapping the strength of the host that nourishes and protects them. In
general, parasites may have little effect on mature swine, but in young
animals they can cause serious injuries. By the time their presence
is suspected, they may have undermined the health of the host to such
an extent, by imposing a continuous drain on its vitality and sapping
its strength little by little, that it never fully recovers, is incapable
of normal growth, and makes no profit for the owner.

The extent to which parasites may undermine the health of pigs
is illustrated in figure 1, A and B. Pigs farrowed and kept in permanent, insanitary hog lots may be invaded by parasites even during the
first few days of their existence (21),[2] and at that age infection with
even a few parasites may cause unthriftiness.

Thrifty growth in pigs is of the greatest importance to the swine
raiser; other things being equal, it is an index of profit. Probably
the larger part of the economic losses attributable to swine parasites

[1] L. A. Spindler is Zoologist, Zoological Division, Bureau of Animal Industry.
[2] Italic numbers in parentheses refer to Literature Cited, p. 785.

745

FIGURE 1.—*A*, These large, healthy pigs were protected from the ravages of parasites; *B*, these unthrifty pigs became parasitized soon after they were born.

results from failure of infected pigs to make profitable gains. Death
of pigs from gross parasitism also causes losses.

Unthriftiness and death, moreover, constitute only part of the losses
caused by parasites. Additional losses result from rejection and con-

demnation, under meat-inspection procedures, of edible parts of carcasses that show `the presence of parasites in the tissues or are so injured by them as to be unfit for food. In addition, some parasites, such as certain tapeworms, are transmissible to man, and parts of carcasses invaded by them must be destroyed. Few estimates are available of the extent of losses of this type, but in one packing house the value of parts of carcasses condemned as a result of invasion by parasites, chiefly kidney worms, was estimated at $80,000 annually, or approximately 27 cents per hog slaughtered (8). This is in addition to losses sustained by the producers of these animals as a result of unthriftiness.

More than 50 species of worm and protozoan parasites have been reported as being found in the bodies of swine throughout the world. Fortunately a number of these species occur in swine in the United States only infrequently, and other species, although widespread, are not of major importance under ordinary conditions.

The internal parasites of swine comprise four general groups commonly known as roundworms, flukes, tapeworms, and protozoa. The first three groups are worm parasites, and of these the most numerous are the roundworms. Flukes and tapeworms occur less frequently and are generally considered to be of less importance. The occurrence of protozoa is widespread, and under certain conditions they may be injurious. It must be remembered that all parasites are potentially injurious, though some are generally of minor importance. Almost without exception they invade flesh and other tissues of the body of the living animal. They may block important ducts and passages and thus impair their functions, and they predispose the animal to various diseases. Even the parasites that ordinarily occur in small numbers may under certain conditions become numerous and as a result of such heavy infection sap the strength and vitality of the host animal.

Two methods of combating parasites are open to the swine raiser. One is to administer drugs to expel the parasites from the bodies of the invaded animals. The other is to outwit and outmaneuver these destroyers of health by protecting the animals from invasion—in other words, to raise the pigs under such conditions that they will not become infected.

The administration of drugs has some inherent disadvantages, one of which is that at least one very important parasite occurs in locations in the body where it is beyond the reach of drugs. Another wanders extensively in the tissues of the body and cannot be expelled until it has settled and become mature, by which time it may have undermined the health of the host.

Prevention of infection by measures designed to break the life cycle of the parasite at its weakest point, the stage on the ground, is in the long run the cheapest method of combating the menace. Such a plan involves raising the animals in clean quarters and on clean temporary pastures away from permanent hog lots and permanent pastures, which are hotbeds of infection. It may be accepted as a fact that the extent of parasitism in swine is proportional to the lack of sanitation. Hogs that are fed on the ground may be heavily infected with parasites, since the animals habitually spend much time on the area where they feed, and most of the droppings, which are the conveyors of parasite infection, are deposited on the feeding lot. The menace of permanent hog pastures has been summarized in the slogan "Permanent pastures perpetuate parasites."

The management practices described in the latter part of this article have proved helpful in controlling parasites on farms where they would otherwise constitute a serious problem. The control measures suggested are based on detailed scientific knowledge of the life histories of the parasites. The facts that must be known include the manner in which a parasite propagates, the stage at which it is infective to swine, the ability of the parasite in the infective stage to maintain itself on pastures and hog lots, the conditions under which pigs become infected, the behavior of the parasite in the body of the animal, and the damage it inflicts. Unless a farmer has a knowledge of these facts he can do little to overcome such pests.

Essential features of the life cycles of the most important parasites of swine are given in the discussion that follows.

WORM PARASITES

TAPEWORMS

The Pork Bladder Worm

Tapeworms occur in swine only in the larval stage, in which they are known as bladder worms because they are bladder-shaped. Bladder worms are located primarily in the muscles, but they may also invade other tissues of the body.

An important tapeworm of domestic swine in this country is the pork bladder worm (*Cysticercus cellulosae*), a form of the parasite which occurs in the muscles and produces a condition known as measly pork. The muscles chiefly invaded are those of the heart, head, diaphragm, abdomen, and tongue and those used for chewing. The parasite may also occur in the brain and other nerve tissue.

This pork bladder worm is the larval stage of an important tapeworm of man. Pigs become infected by swallowing the eggs or segments containing eggs that have been passed in the feces of infected human beings. In the intestine of the pig, the tiny embryos contained in the tapeworm eggs break the shells and by means of six tiny hooks with which they are equipped bore into the wall of the intestine, where they penetrate the blood vessels. The blood stream carries them throughout the body. When the hatched embryos, known as larvae, reach the finest blood vessels (capillaries) they force their way through the blood-vessel wall and burrow into the muscles, where they grow rapidly and develop into bladder worms. They appear as glistening white spots in the muscles, each spot being somewhat larger than a grain of tapioca.

In recent years clinical symptoms of tapeworm infection have seldom been observed in pigs, probably because most infections are very light. In severe infections sensitiveness in the snout and paralysis of the tongue, which may seriously interfere with feeding, have been reported. A slight tap on the end of the nose that would not affect a normal pig may cause an infected animal to squeal with pain. Eventually the animal may become unable to eat and may die of starvation. Blindness may sometimes result from the presence of bladder worms in the brain or in the eyes. Feebleness, shortness of breath, diarrhea, prostration, and death have been reported as results of a heavy infection.

Bladder worm infection of swine can be diagnosed with certainty as a rule only after the death of the animal, when the parasites may be seen on the surface of the heart and other muscles. In certain countries where the parasite is prevalent and infections are probably severe, inspection of the tongues of live pigs for bladder worms is frequently practiced.

Fortunately, of late years, only a small proportion of hogs in the United States have been infected with the pork bladder worm (pork measles). For example, only 44 cases of infection of swine with bladder worms occurred in Texas during the period 1902 to 1924 (*9*). From 1930 to 1939, inclusive, only 1 hog out of each 6,000,000 slaughtered under Government supervision was condemned because of infection with this parasite.

The Hydatid

A bladder worm that sometimes occurs in hogs in certain parts of the United States is the hydatid (*Echinococcus granulosus*), the larval stage of an extremely small tapeworm of dogs and wolves. Unlike the parasite that causes pork measles, these bladder worms do not become localized in muscles but are found primarily in the liver and other organs. They vary greatly in size, in many cases being as large as a walnut or larger.

Swine become infected by swallowing the eggs passed in the feces of dogs or wolves harboring the adult tapeworms. The course of infection is then much the same as that followed by pork bladder worms. No specific symptoms have been associated with the presence of these cysts in swine. Owing to their large size and the fact that they displace normal tissue, however, they may be considered as injurious, particularly when located in the liver. They make the affected tissue unfit for use as food.

Human beings also may become infected with hydatids by swallowing the tapeworm eggs. When swine are slaughtered on the farm, any parts containing these bladder worms should be destroyed and not fed to dogs, since the tapeworm-infected dogs would serve as a reservoir for the infection of additional hogs and possibly of human beings.

The Thin-Necked Bladder Worm

A bladder worm that occasionally parasitizes hogs is the larval stage of another tapeworm of dogs known as the thin-necked bladder worm (technically *Taenia hydatigena*). This large bladder worm sometimes occurs embedded in the liver, but more often it is attached to the abdominal organs or free in the abdominal cavity. It is usually about an inch in diameter but may attain larger sizes. Hogs may acquire infection as a result of swallowing eggs in the droppings of infected dogs.

Light infections probably produce little injury, but it has been stated that heavy infections may be fatal to young pigs, since considerable damage is done to the liver by the migrating larvae. No method is known by which the infection can be diagnosed during the life of the animal.

FLUKES

Two species of flukes occur in swine in this country—the lung fluke, *Paragonimus westermanii*, which also occurs in dogs, cats, sheep, and cattle, and occasionally in human beings in other countries, and the liver fluke, *Fasciola hepatica*, which occurs chiefly in cattle and sheep but occasionally in swine. Liver flukes have a complex life history which involves a snail as intermediate host. Hogs become infected as a result of swallowing green forage or water harboring the metacercariae (flukes in the infective stage) which have emerged from the bodies of snails. Flukes in the adult stages may be found in the bile ducts of the liver. Owing to their relatively infrequent occurrence, liver flukes do not ordinarily constitute a serious problem in swine raising.

ROUNDWORMS

Roundworms are the most widespread and undoubtedly the most injurious of the worm parasites that invade the bodies of swine. Almost all organs and tissues of an animal's body may be penetrated by one or more species of roundworms either in their adult or larval (immature) stages. The larvae of some species wander extensively throughout the body of the host and in spite of their small size cause considerable damage to the tissues they invade.

Although a large number of species of roundworms have been reported from swine in the United States, only about 20 species are common. Of these, fortunately, only a few, comparatively, are of major importance under ordinary conditions. The swine raiser should nevertheless remember that even species commonly considered to be of little importance damage the tissues in which they are located and are therefore potentially injurious to the health of the animal. Under any of the various conditions that impair the health of growing pigs, such as inadequate nutrition, severe climatic conditions, and disease, parasites that ordinarily occur in small numbers may become a serious problem.

The roundworms considered to be of least importance under ordinary conditions will be discussed briefly. The more important forms will be treated in some detail as a prelude to a discussion of control measures.

Gullet Worms

The gullet worm (technically *Gongylonema pulchrum*) occurs in the lining of the esophagus, or gullet, and in the tongue. In these locations it appears as a white wavy line just beneath the surface. The female worm is about an inch in length and the male somewhat smaller.

Gullet worms are reported to be prevalent in swine in the Middle Atlantic, the Middle Western, and the Pacific Coast States. In a series of post mortem examinations in which the parasites were looked for, gullet worms were found in the esophagi of 14 percent of the swine examined.

Gullet worms have an indirect life history—that is, their development requires that they live for a time in an intermediate host. Eggs of microscopic size, each containing a tiny embryo, are liberated by the female worm into the mouth or esophagus of the infected pig. The eggs are swallowed and pass through the stomach into the small intestine, where they become mixed in the intestinal contents and are voided in the droppings. Various species of dung beetles and certain cockroaches have been reported as capable of serving as intermediate hosts. The insects swallow the eggs while feeding on feces. In the intestine of an insect the tiny embryos break out of the eggs, bore through the intestinal wall, and get into the body cavity, where in about a month they have developed to a stage infective to swine.

Pigs become infected with gullet worms by swallowing the infected beetles. In the body of the pig the young worms are liberated from the insects and make their way to the esophagus and tongue, which they penetrate and in which they grow to maturity.

So far as is known, there are no symptoms that can be definitely ascribed to infections with gullet worms, and in light infections the effect on the host may be slight.

Gullet worms are of importance from the standpoint of human health. A number of cases of infection of human beings have been reported, and infected hogs may serve as reservoirs of such infection.

Stomach Worms

Three species of worms occur in the stomachs of swine in the United States. Two (*Ascarops strongylina* and *Physocephalus sexalatus*) are known as thick stomach worms. The worms of these species are more or less similar in general appearance, being reddish in color and nearly an inch long in the adult stage. The other species, *Hyostrongylus rubidus*, known as the red stomach worm, is a small, delicate, slender, reddish worm about one-fifth inch in length. Owing to its small size and reddish color, it is difficult to see against the lining of the stomach and may be overlooked by the untrained observer.

Thick stomach worms have an indirect life history and utilize as intermediate hosts a large number of the various species of beetles that feed on dung. The eggs are microscopic in size, practically colorless, and thin-shelled. At the time it is deposited by the female worm each egg contains a tiny embryo. The eggs become mixed with the intestinal contents and pass to the outside with the droppings. Insects feeding on the droppings swallow the eggs, they hatch, and the tiny larvae bore through the intestine into the body cavity of the insect, where during the course of about a month they develop to a stage infective to swine. .Hogs feeding on contaminated ground swallow the beetles. In the stomach of the hog the parasites are freed from the bodies of the beetles by the action of the digestive juices. The young worms make their way into the mucous membrane of the stomach, where they grow to maturity.

When stomach worms are present in small numbers the effect on the host animal may not be very great. Symptoms that have been attributed to the parasites in heavy infections are loss of appetite, restlessness, and a great craving for water. Even when the worms are present in small numbers there is generally a thick mucuslike covering on the stomach wall in which the adult worms are buried. Such a condition may well interfere with digestion and contribute to the general unthriftiness common in parasite-infected swine.

Noticeable injuries sometimes result from penetration of the worms into the wall of the stomach. The worms sometimes penetrate deeply, the hole made being similar in appearance to a pinprick. Such lesions may pave the way for bacterial invasion of the stomach wall.

The occurrence of thick stomach worms is widespread in hogs in the United States. In certain of the Midwestern States as many as 90 percent of the animals examined have been found to harbor the worms, and in the Southeastern States, 50 to 80 percent.

One of the thick stomach worms (*Physocephalus sexalatus*) has the peculiar ability to encyst, or form a protective outer covering, and remain alive in the stomach wall of various animals and birds that are not its normal hosts. When the infected insect is swallowed by such a strange host, the young worms make their way into the stomach wall and there surround themselves by a heavy cyst wall, inside of which they remain dormant. When fed to susceptible pigs, such encysted forms were able to develop into mature worms (*4*). Hence, when steps are taken to control this parasite, consideration must be given to the possibility of its transmission through the medium of snakes, birds, and other small animals that may have become infected and may in turn be eaten by hogs.

Red stomach worms are apparently less common than thick stomach worms. In one section of the United States where the prevalence of these worms has been investigated, as many as 15 to 35 percent of the hogs examined have been found to harbor them.

The life history of the red stomach worm differs from that of the thick stomach worms in that no intermediate host is necessary, the infections being directly acquired. Female worms on the stomach wall produce thin-shelled, partly developed eggs that pass through the intestine of the host and out with its droppings. Development of the eggs then progresses rapidly under favorable conditions of moisture and temperature, and in about 24 to 48 hours a tiny motile embryo has fully formed within the egg. The egg then hatches, and the microscopic larva grows and develops, and reaches a stage infective to swine in about 6 days. During this period of growth the larva undergoes one complete and one partial molt. In other words, it completely sheds the outer covering of the body once, and the second time the outer covering becomes loosened and considerably stretched, and a new covering forms underneath. The old unshed covering serves to protect the larva against drying and other injurious environmental conditions. The larva at this stage is said to be ensheathed and is infective to swine.

The infective larvae live in the feces and on the soil beneath and immediately surrounding the fecal mass. Those that are protected from sunlight and drying live for several weeks or months; as more and more eggs are deposited, the soil eventually teems with larvae.

Hogs become infected by swallowing the infective larvae while feeding around droppings. Upon reaching the stomach of the pig, the young worms begin to grow and in the course of about 20 to 25 days reach maturity. The worms then mate, and the females begin to produce eggs.

The damage produced by red stomach worms is sometimes severe. As shown by a number of investigators, erosion (slow destruction) and ulceration of the mucous membrane of the stomach may occur, with extensive formation of mucus. Symptoms that have been associated with infections include diarrhea, variable appetite, and emaciation; occasionally the animal dies. On the other hand, some investigators consider that the parasite is not particularly harmful unless it is present in association with other disease processes or invades animals whose vitality is depleted, such as young nursing sows or animals fed a deficient diet. Pigs fed an adequate diet and kept under sanitary conditions were not seriously affected by moderate experimental infections, and the worms persisted 6 to 8 months in the absence of reinfections.

Intestinal Threadworms

Adult intestinal threadworms (*Strongyloides ransomi*) are among the smallest of the roundworms that infect swine.

These worm parasites are peculiar in that no males have been found in association with females in the intestine of the swine host. Moreover, in the stages outside the body of the host they may undergo a complex and unusual course of development on soil. The adult female worms are about one-sixth of an inch or less in length. They are whitish and occur embedded more or less deeply in the intestinal tissue, where they may be overlooked even by trained observers.

Intestinal threadworms occur in hogs everywhere. In a series of examinations of swine of all ages, 26 percent were found to harbor these worms. In view of the fact that older animals may develop a resistance to infection, the incidence of the infection in pigs is probably much higher than indicated, since many adult swine were included in the examinations in question. The prevalence of these worms in pigs is illustrated by the fact that they have been found whenever they have been looked for.

Eggs produced by the female threadworms in the intestine of the host usually contain an embryo by the time they reach the exterior. In the feces the microscopic eggs complete their development and hatch within a few hours. The larvae follow one of two courses of development. Some larvae develop within a few days, during which they have undergone one complete and one incomplete molt, to a stage in which they are infective to swine. Others develop into male and female worms, so small as to be almost microscopic, which are not infective to swine. In the latter case the worms mate, and the female produces numerous eggs, from which tiny larvae hatch and soon develop to the infective stage. This dual method of development serves to increase greatly the number of infective larvae on the ground, and hence the probability that pigs will become severely infected is increased.

A pig may become infected by swallowing the infective larvae, or the larvae may penetrate its skin when the animal is rooting or lying on the ground. In either case the larvae get into the blood stream and are carried to the lungs. Here they break out of the tiny blood vessels, get into the air spaces (bronchioles), and crawl up the air passages into the throat, where they are swallowed. During this journey the larvae increase greatly in size. After being swallowed they pass down the esophagus and through the stomach and ultimately reach the small intestine. They attain maturity in about 7 days after entering the body of the animal.

Threadworms in small numbers may have little noticeable effect on pigs fed adequate amounts of a well-balanced diet, even though the infection may persist throughout the life of the animal. The number of threadworm eggs passed in the feces of adult animals that have developed a resistance to infection is usually very small. When the vitality of the animal becomes depleted, however—as in nursing sows, for example—the worms may gain the upper hand and produce vast numbers of eggs. This favors infection of the young pigs. In massive infections pigs may suffer from severe diarrhea. As a result of penetration of the larvae, pigs may also develop a skin eruption, which is usually more severe in young than in older animals. Little is known concerning the number of worms necessary to produce noticeable symptoms in pigs, but it has been estimated that infected pigs that were emaciated and suffering from severe diarrhea harbored 10,000 to 25,000 threadworms in the intestine.

The infective larvae of threadworms are capable of penetrating the unbroken skin of human beings. It has been observed that when large numbers of larvae penetrate at one time, severe itching occurs, followed later by a marked puffiness, which may persist several days, at the site of penetration. Persons walking barefoot over ground infested with infective larvae of threadworms may develop a swelling of the feet as a result of penetration of the larvae. So far as is known, threadworms of swine do not grow to maturity in man.

Nodular Worms

Nodular worms are parasites of the blind gut (cecum) and large intestine and derive their common name from the fact that they produce nodules, or lumps, of varying sizes in the wall of the large intestine and cecum. Nodular worms are perhaps the commonest of the worm parasites of swine. In the southeastern part of the United States, practically all hogs raised under ordinary conditions may be infected.

Nodular worms are slender, whitish to grayish in color, and one-third to one-half inch in length. Four species occur in swine. One (*Oesophagostomum dentatum*) is found in practically all parts of the United States and in southern Canada. The three other species, *O. longicaudum* (the long-tailed nodular worm), *O. brevicaudum* (the short-tailed nodular worm), and *O. georgianum* are found chiefly in the southern part of the United States. The last-named species is found only occasionally. Nodular worms differ from some of the other worm parasites in that they may infect older animals as heavily as younger animals, or even more heavily. An infected animal may harbor several thousand worms.

The various species of nodular worms differ considerably in their effect on the host animal. *Oesophagostomum dentatum* and *O. brevicaudum*, the short-tailed forms, are apparently the least injurious from the standpoint of gross damage to the intestine. The nodules caused by these forms ordinarily are not much larger than the head of a pin and are only moderately inflamed. *O. longicaudum* may produce large nodules that often become secondarily infected with bacteria.

The life histories of all the species of nodular worms are in general quite similar. Since the course of development of the long-tailed form has been worked out in more or less detail, it is used here as an example:

The adult worms of *Oesophagostomum longicaudum* are localized in the cecum and large intestine of the host animal. The females deposit large numbers of partly developed, thin-shelled eggs, which become mixed with the intestinal contents and are eventually eliminated with the droppings. Under favorable conditions of moisture and temperature these eggs develop rapidly in the feces and in about 24 to 48 hours a larva of microscopic size emerges from each. The larvae live in or beneath the pile of fecal material and on the surrounding soil, if it is moist and shaded. After about 3 to 5 days of further development they become infective to swine. The infective larvae are very numerous; in a small lump of feces or a small handful of soil there may be thousands. Infective nodular worm larvae do not like either strong light or complete darkness but prefer a subdued light. If placed in a glass dish containing water half of which is shaded, the larvae will collect at the juncture of the shaded and unshaded portions. When larvae are able to find favorable conditions in nature, as at the base of grass on pastures, they may survive 14 months or longer. They are unable to withstand complete drying longer than a few hours. When the surface of the soil dries, they may migrate downward to the layer of moist soil underneath. When the surface of the soil becomes moist again, they may return upward where the chances of coming in contact with host animals are greater. The larvae also migrate short distances up the stems and blades of grass or other objects wet with dew or rain, and this increases their chances of being swallowed by hogs grazing on the moist grass. Also when feces containing the eggs are buried, as by plowing, the eggs will hatch and the larvae will migrate upward. In plowed fields where the surface of the soil becomes thoroughly dried, however, many of the larvae are apparently unable to reach the surface.

Observations on farms have shown that pigs become infected with nodular worms as a result of swallowing the larvae while feeding on contaminated ground or grazing on contaminated pastures. After being swallowed, the larvae pass through the stomach into the small intestine and thence into the large intestine. By this time the protective sheath has been discarded, and the larvae penetrate into the wall of the large intestine and the blind gut. Despite their small size, frequently they severely injure the tissue immediately surrounding them as they bore into the wall. Often this causes an intense inflammation, and in 48 hours or sooner a small nodule, or elevation, has been formed at the place where the larva penetrated.

Inside the cyst the young worm grows and develops for about 2 to 3 weeks. During this time it increases greatly in size, and the cyst also enlarges. The young worm reaches a stage in which it very closely resembles the adult worm except that it is smaller. It then breaks out of the cyst and moves into the lumen, or cavity, of the intestine, where it continues its development. About 5 to 7 weeks after the infection the worms are fully grown, have mated and begun to produce eggs, and the cycle begins all over again.

The precise effect of nodular worms on pigs has not been definitely ascertained. Most of the information available comes from observations of clinical cases of nodular worm infection. It has been stated that development of the nodules in the intestine may interfere with the proper absorption of food material and consequently affect the health of the host animal. There is also danger of infection of the nodules by bacteria; it is the observation of the writer that marked secondary infection of nodules is common in infections with the long-tailed nodular worm. According to some investigators, there is clinical evidence to suggest that in addition to the irritation produced by the nodules, a toxic substance produced by the worms is absorbed into the system of the host and results in a mild toxemia.

In nodules containing young *Oesophagostomum longicaudum*, a fluid surrounds the worm inside the cyst. As the worm grows, the cyst enlarges greatly, and the amount of fluid increases. Shortly before the worm is ready to move into the lumen of the intestine the cyst wall ruptures and the fluid surrounding the worm escapes and may be absorbed into the system of the animal. Although the amount of fluid in one cyst is probably negligible, the amount from thousands of cysts would be considerable. When large numbers of cysts rupture at about the same time, the animal may well suffer from toxemia if this fluid is absorbed. In this connection it has been possible to detect in the muscle tissue of infected swine the presence of substances similar to those composing the bodies of nodular worms. Although the source of these substances is not definitely known, they may have come in part from the cysts.

The adult worms may also damage the intestine by producing irritation and inflammation, according to some investigators. Weakness, anemia, emaciation, diarrhea, and general unthriftiness have been reported to be common results of infection with these parasites.

An important economic result of nodular worm infection of swine is the unsuitability of the severely infected intestines for use either as sausage casings or as food. In certain parts of the country the large intestines of pigs (chitterlings) constitute a more or less common article of diet. Since the parasites are not known to be transmissible to man, chitterlings showing small numbers of pinhead-sized nodules without inflammation, such as result from infection with *Oesophagostomum dentatum*, are safe for human consumption after the lesions are trimmed out, but inflammation and secondary infection, such as often occur in infections with the long-tailed nodular worm, make the intestine unfit for use as food. Intestines studded with nodules are generally weak and tear easily, and this largely destroys their value for use as sausage casings. It may be considered, then, that nodular worm infections cause considerable losses to the meat industry, which are passed on to the farmer in the form of lower market prices.

Whipworms

Whipworms (*Trichuris suis*) inhabit the blind gut and large intestine of swine. Little is known concerning the prevalence of this parasite except in the Southeastern States, where 23 percent of all the swine examined were found to harbor this parasite, the number of worms ranging from 2 to 163 per animal.

The whipworm is about 1 to 2 inches in length. The body is composed of a long slender part resembling the lash of a whip and a shorter thick part resembling the whip stock; hence the name "whipworm." The slender part of the worm bears the mouth at the tip and is about twice as long as the thick part. The male is slightly smaller than the female, and the end of the thick part of the male is sharply coiled. Whipworms attach themselves to the intestine by sewing the long whiplike part of the body into the tissues.

The eggs deposited by adult female whipworms are keg-shaped and have brownish-colored, thick shells. They are produced in large numbers, become mixed with the intestinal contents of the host, and are then eliminated with the feces. The eggs are undeveloped when passed. They develop in the feces, a tiny embryo forming within each egg, but they do not hatch there; they remain quiescent until they are swallowed by a host animal or until they die. Eggs of whipworms develop slowly. In some cases the development of the larvae requires several months, but under certain conditions of high humidity and temperature, it may be accomplished in about a month.

Pigs become infected with whipworms by swallowing the infective eggs when feeding on soil where they are present. The eggs hatch in the stomach and intestine, and the larvae make their way to the blind gut, where they grow to maturity in about 10 weeks or longer.

Well-fed pigs harboring small numbers of whipworms usually show no recognizable symptoms, and the infection is generally short-lived, lasting only a few weeks. In massive infections growth may be noticeably retarded. The writer has observed heavily infected pigs whose strength appeared to ebb slowly until they finally died. Upon examination, the blind gut of such animals was found to be inflamed, greatly thickened, and festooned with whipworms.

Very little information is available as to how long whipworm eggs will remain alive on soil. It is known, however, that eggs of the whipworm that parasitizes human beings and those of the whipworm of dogs are killed rather quickly by drying and do not live long on soil where shade is lacking and moisture is not abundant. The same is probably true of the eggs of the swine whipworm, since it was observed at the Beltsville Research Center, Beltsville, Md., in the summer of 1940, that whipworm eggs on a hog lot lost their vitality about 2 months after the area was cleared of trees and other vegetation.

The species of whipworm found in human beings is closely related to that found in swine, and for a time the two were thought to be identical. Under certain conditions it was believed human beings might become infected with whipworms as a result of swallowing eggs that had passed out of swine. Recently, however, study of the two forms has confirmed the conclusions of the scientist who originally described the parasite many years ago that the species are separate and distinct. There is, therefore, little likelihood of infection of man with the swine whipworm.

Lungworms

Lungworms are known to be among the most widespread of the parasites that infect swine. Reports indicate that this parasite may be found in swine in all parts of the United States and in Canada. In the southeastern section of the United States 70 percent or more of the swine examined were found to be infected. Lungworms do great damage to young pigs. It is believed by some investigators that they sap the strength of the animal, ruin its appetite, and make it short-winded. There is also evidence to indicate that these parasites may be instrumental in the spread of swine influenza, a very important virus disease (*17*).

Lungworms are whitish, threadlike roundworms that may attain a length of about 2 inches. They commonly occur in the smaller air passages of the lungs (bronchioles) and may be found by cutting off the tips of the lobes of the lungs and squeezing the tissues, which forces the worms out of the bronchioles. In heavy infections the worms may also be found in the larger air passages (trachea and bronchi).

Three species of lungworms belonging to two genera are of common occurrence in swine in this country. The two most common forms, *Metastrongylus elongatus* and *Choerostrongylus pudendotectus*, are usually present in about equal numbers and are of widespread occurrence. The third species, *Metastrongylus salmi*, is found chiefly in swine raised in the South; generally only a small percentage of hogs harbor this form, and the infections are usually very light.

Recently it was found that the life history is indirect and involves as intermediate hosts various species of earthworms, particularly red-striped worms of the genus *Helodrilus*, which are found chiefly in manure piles and rich, feces-contaminated soil. The common garden or orchard earthworm (*Lumbricus*) may also serve as intermediate host.

Female lungworms produce large numbers of thick-shelled eggs each containing a tiny embryo. The eggs are coughed up, swallowed, and eliminated in the feces of the host. Earthworms feeding on the feces swallow the eggs, which hatch in the earthworm's intestine. The tiny lungworm larvae bore into the glandular portion of the intestine (the portion that contains the calciferous glands) and also get into one or all of the five to seven pairs of hearts of the earthworm. In about 3 weeks to a month the lungworm larvae have completed their development and are capable of producing an infection in a pig that swallows the earthworm.

In the body of the pig the lungworm larvae, liberated from the earthworm by the digestive juices, migrate by way of the lymphatic and blood-circulatory systems to the lungs, where they become localized, complete development, and begin to produce eggs in about 1½ months.

Lungworm eggs are long-lived. On soil under favorable conditions of moisture and shade they probably survive for years. Earthworms infected with lungworm larvae have been found in a hog lot abandoned for approximately 4 years. During this time the lot apparently had remained grown up to weeds and the soil had remained moist. Earthworms kept in samples of this soil became infected with lungworms, showing that lungworm eggs were present (*22*). In contrast to this, eggs on dry soil at Beltsville, Md., failed to survive more than 1 month during the summer. The eggs are very resistant to low temperatures when adequate moisture is present and have been found to survive continuous freezing at temperatures of 14° to 20° F. for more than a year. Eggs buried in soil survived for periods of several months where grass or other vegetation was growing and the roots penetrated to the level of the eggs. Where the soil was bare of vegetation the period of survival was much shorter (*7*). Such observations show that areas extensively contaminated with feces of lungworm-infected swine may remain dangerous to susceptible swine for a number of years unless the animals can be prevented from eating the earthworm intermediate hosts.

The presence of lungworms and the feeding of these parasites in the bronchioles of the host are considered to be a source of irritation to the animal. The worms also block up the air passages and interfere mechanically with breathing. One of the most outstanding symptoms of lungworm infection is a cough. Even lightly infected animals may be subject to fits of coughing, which weakens the animal and lowers its vitality. Coughing is more pronounced after exertion of any kind.

The irritation to the lungs arising from the presence of the worms and their feeding, together with the plugging of the bronchioles, results in a consolidation, or hardening, of the lung tissue surrounding the sites occupied by the worms, and hard nodules soon form in the tissue. During the early stages of invasion, hemorrhages may appear on the surface of the lungs. In infections of long standing the tips of the lungs become grayish or whitish and hard.

Animals infected with lungworms frequently tend to go off feed. A change of diet usually remedies this condition for a time, but it may return. Ultimately unthriftiness and failure to grow normally result.

Kidney Worms

The swine kidney worm, technically *Stephanurus dentatus*, causes heavy losses to southern swine raisers and to the meat industry. It is probably one of the most injurious pests with which the producer in the South has to contend and one which he must assiduously combat in order to make swine raising profitable. In the South losses from trimming of infected carcasses and from condemnation of livers, kidneys, and other organs damaged by the parasite have been estimated at approximately 27 cents per animal slaughtered. Since about 10 million hogs raised in the Southern States are slaughtered annually in Government-inspected abattoirs, the annual loss from kidney worms may be estimated at more than 2.7 million dollars. In addition producers suffer losses from arrested growth and development of swine and imperfect utilization of feed, which may result from interference by the parasite with the proper functioning of important organs and tissues.

Although kidney worms are most common in the South, increasing reports of the occurrence of these worms in swine in various parts of the Northern States and even in Canada indicate that the parasite may be spreading northward. If it gains a foothold in breeding swine in the North it may well become a serious problem there.

Kidney worms are thick-bodied black-and-white worms which, when fully grown, may attain a length of 2 inches. Mature worms may be found in the kidneys and in cysts in the ureters (tubes leading from the kidneys to the bladder). In addition to the worms these cysts often contain a greenish or whitish pus. Immature worms invade the liver, kidney fat, blood vessels, lungs, and other locations outside the digestive tract. Wherever they are located, kidney worms destroy vital tissue.

Mature female kidney worms embedded in the kidneys and ureters produce large numbers of dark-colored, partly developed eggs which they deposit in the cavities of the kidneys and of the ureters through perforations in the walls of these tubes. The eggs pass down the ureters into the bladder, where they collect until discharged with the urine. As many as 700,000 to 1,000,000 eggs have been observed in the urine passed by a moderately infected hog in 1 day. Eggs that fall on moist, shaded soil develop rapidly, and in about 24 to 48 hours, depending on temperature conditions, a tiny larva hatches from each egg. The larva develops rapidly and during the course of 3 to 5 days undergoes one complete and one partial molt, after which it is infective to the host animal.

Observations under actual farm conditions have shown that the larvae are extremely exacting in their requirements for shade and moisture (*16*, *19*), as described later.

Swine become infected with kidney worms as a result of swallowing the infective larvae while feeding or rooting in contaminated soil. French scientists first observed that kidney worm larvae may penetrate the skin of pigs. Later this was confirmed by Australian scientists. In the United States, however, it was found that larvae placed on the unbroken skin of pigs were unable to penetrate it. It was finally ascertained that they are able to penetrate the unbroken skin of pigs, provided some object is available against which they can brace themselves in order to force their way in (*20*). Particles of soil or mud sticking to the bodies of swine might provide the necessary condition.

It has been thought that swine may become infected as a result of frequenting wallows contaminated with the urine of animals infected with kidney worms. Careful studies have failed to disclose the presence of larvae in these locations, however.

Having once entered the bodies of swine, kidney worm larvae get into the blood stream and are carried to the liver, lungs, and other organs. Those that arrive in the liver and large blood vessels adjacent to that organ grow and develop to many times their original size over a period that may last 4 or 5 months. During this time the worms in the liver burrow extensively through the tissue, particularly just beneath the capsule (membranous covering), where they leave crooked, bloody tracks. Many of the parasites remain in this organ until they die and degenerate (*14*). Others break out through the liver capsule and migrate among the abdominal organs until they reach the kidney region, where some immediately penetrate the kidneys and ureters and others come to rest in the fat surrounding the kidneys, causing considerable inflammation there.

The time required for the worms to reach maturity in different swine hosts varies considerably. According to some investigators, the worms that become established in the walls of the ureters and in the tissue of the kidney proper begin to produce eggs about 6 or 7 months after first entering the body of the animal. On the other hand, the worms were found to be still immature in a pig slaughtered 12 months after being experimentally infected.

So far as is known there are no readily observable symptoms peculiar to kidney worm infection. Infected animals frequently discharge pus in the urine, particularly when the infection is heavy. However, this has not been found to be a reliable criterion of infection, as it naturally would not occur until the worms had reached the kidneys and set up disorders in those organs, which as previously pointed out might take 6 months or longer. It has been shown that the growth rate of 2- or 3-week-old pigs is markedly retarded following infection (*14*). Posterior paralysis (paralysis of the hindquarters) may sometimes occur as a result of injury to the spinal cord by migrating kidney worms.

The principal injury inflicted by kidney worms occurs in the liver. If the lesions caused by the migrations of the worms have healed, the liver at autopsy appears badly scarred, showing hard grayish areas, which are sometimes small, circumscribed, and more or less shallow and sometimes large and deep. Completely healed lesions often do not contain worms. Incompletely healed and unhealed lesions are usually soft and may contain pus and live worms or dead worms that may be partly disintegrated. In addition, the infected livers are often covered with a fibrinous deposit which sometimes causes them to adhere to adjacent tissue. Similar lesions are often found in lungs and other organs.

Liver destruction retards the growth and impairs the health of the infected animal. According to some observers, death commonly occurs among young pigs as a result of the extensive destruction of the liver tissue and the effects of the marked changes accompanying such destruction (*3*).

As previously mentioned, kidney worms inflict extensive damage on the kidneys and ureters. An important and quite common accompaniment of kidney worm infection is a condition known as hydronephrosis, which was first noted in 1923 by an Australian scientist. This is the result of the destruction of kidney tissue until a portion of it is replaced by a watery cyst. The condition is undoubtedly

FIGURE 2.—Portion of the ureter of a hog infected with kidney worms, two of which are visible.

harmful to the animal, since it hampers the functioning of the kidney. In addition, the presence in the walls of the ureters of cystic cavities containing worms often has the effect of thickening the walls to such an extent that the passage is almost stopped up (fig. 2). The writer has often seen ureters with walls so inflamed and thickened as a result of invasion by kidney worms that a darning needle would scarcely pass through the opening. Such a condition probably results in the retention of a certain amount of urine, which would interfere with the proper functioning of the kidney and therefore impair the health of the animal.

More or less extensive thickening and inflammation of the urinary bladder has been observed by the writer to be common in swine infected with kidney worms. The daily accumulation of eggs in the bladder irritates its delicate tissues. Furthermore, worms frequently become dislodged from their locations in the kidneys and ureters and pass down to the bladder, where they generally rupture and become partly disintegrated, releasing the contents of their bodies, which may also serve to irritate the bladder.

According to Australian investigators, the effect of kidney worms on the general health and condition of an animal may be so great that it becomes possible to pick out the carcasses of infected pigs in abattoirs by their appearance, which is less pleasing and leaner than that of the carcasses of normal pigs. This poor condition is the direct result of unthriftiness and slow growth resulting from various injuries caused by the worms.

Figure 3 illustrates the effect of kidney worms and other parasites on the growth of pigs. The two carcasses shown are of animals the same age; the smaller animal probably became infected with kidney worms early in life, while the larger was raised free of parasites. Retardation of growth caused by kidney worms is a costly matter to the swine raiser, even if considered only from the standpoint of market value. It is evident that the smaller animal the carcass of which is pictured here could be expected to sell for only a small fraction of what the larger animal would bring. Furthermore, during its lifetime it prob-

FIGURE 3.—Carcasses of two pigs the same age. The smaller was infected with kidney worms and other parasites, while the larger had been protected from these pests.

ably consumed as much feed as the larger pig, and perhaps more.

The presence in the liver of worms or lesions makes the invaded tissue unsuitable for food. In light infections, where only a small number of superficial lesions occur in livers, the affected portions can be trimmed out, but even this reduces the market value of the organ. Loin muscles are frequently invaded by kidney worms, necessitating considerable trimming of these valuable parts of carcasses. Occasionally kidney worms migrate to other parts of the muscle structure. The writer has frequently observed lesions in hams made by kidney worms burrowing through the flesh; such meat is unfit for food. Another loss is the spoilage of kidney fat, the so-called leaf fat. Many kidney worms come to rest in the fat surrounding the kidneys, where they irritate the tissues and are soon surrounded by areas of inflammation which make the fat inedible. The pancreas, spleen, lungs, and other organs are also frequently invaded by the worms, and these parts become unfit for use as food.

All such losses are ultimately borne by the farmer in the form of lowered market prices. In some areas where kidney worms and other parasites are prevalent, a blanket reduction in price is made to compensate for losses due to parasites and other diseases and conditions. In the last analysis, therefore, the producer of hogs infected with kidney worms is the principal loser.

In areas where kidney worms are prevalent, and hogs and cattle occupy the same pastures, cattle also sometimes become infected.

Hookworms

Several species of hookworms have been reported as being found in the small intestines of swine the world over. Only one species, technically called *Crassisoma urosubulatum*, however, is common in swine in the United States. It occurs chiefly in the southern part of the country and is a white, fat-bodied worm that may reach a length of about one-fourth of an inch. About 11 percent of the swine examined for this parasite have been found infected. The life history of this hookworm has not been demonstrated in its entirety, although it is probably similar to that of other hookworms. The thin-shelled, partly developed eggs become mixed in the intestinal contents of the host and pass out with the droppings. On soil the eggs complete development and hatch within a few days. The larvae undergo one complete and one incomplete molt, after which they are infective to swine. It is not known how long the larvae will live on soil or how they are affected by sunlight, drying, and other climatic conditions. Infection probably results from swallowing the larvae along with feed and water, although they may also penetrate the skin, as do the larvae of other hookworms.

This hookworm parasite of swine was first seen by an Italian scientist in 1909. He noted that the worms attach themselves to the intestine by sucking a portion of the tissue into their mouths. Since the mouths of the worms are provided with sharp cutting plates, or teeth, they may lacerate the tissues and cause bleeding. It was noted that the worms caused punctiform hemorrhages, and that the presence of the parasites was associated with a catarrhal condition of the intestine.

Since the worms apparently lacerate the tissues and cause hemorrhages, they probably suck blood. When present in large numbers, therefore, they may cause anemia, just as do the hookworms parasitic in other animals. In light infections the worms probably do little noticeable injury. It has been observed that a residuum of infection is sometimes present in the breeding stock on farms and that under certain conditions that are not well understood the pigs become heavily infected. In such cases the worms probably contribute to the general unthriftiness common in parasite-infected animals.

Thorn-Headed Worms

Zoologically, the thorn-headed worms (technically called *Macracanthorhynchus hirudinaceus*) which occur in the large intestine of swine are not true roundworms. These parasites, known as acanthocephalids, are considered by some investigators to be related to both the roundworms and the tapeworms. Unlike the roundworms but like the tapeworms, they have no intestine, and a spiny protuberance at one end serves to attach the worm to the intestine of the host. Like the roundworms, however, they are cylindrical, elongate, and gradually tapering toward the hind end, and the sexes are separate. The female worms may reach an extreme length of 12 or more inches, while the males, which have a small swelling at the end of the tail, are somewhat shorter.

These worms attach themselves to the wall of the small intestine by means of a spiny proboscis, or snout. They may not remain attached to any one spot, however, but may migrate from place to place in the small intestine. At the site of attachment a nodule, or swelling, forms as the result of injury to the tissues by the spiny proboscis; there are usually more nodules than worms present. Fresh nodules are generally inflamed, while older ones may be either hard or secondarily infected with bacteria.

Adult female thorn-headed worms produce numerous thick-shelled, brownish eggs, each containing a fully developed larva. One female may produce as many as 600,000 or more eggs a day at the peak of her egg-producing capacity. The thick shells protect the larvae from drying and from other deleterious environmental conditions. Eggs have been kept in a dried condition for more than a year without apparent effect on the larvae. They are also able to withstand prolonged freezing and may survive temperatures as high as 150° F. The larvae inside the eggs may survive for long periods on soil; eggs on soil at Beltsville, Md., have retained their vitality as long as 4½ years.

Thorn-headed worms have an indirect life cycle. White grubs, the larvae of June bugs (May beetles), rose chafers, and other similar insects may serve as the intermediate hosts. The grubs feeding on manure or on soil contaminated with the feces of infected swine swallow the parasite eggs. The eggs hatch in the intestine of the grub, and within a few hours the tiny larvae penetrate into the wall of the gut. After a period of growth and development lasting about 2 weeks, during which they have greatly increased in size, the parasites migrate into the body cavity of the grub and become sausage-shaped; at this stage they are large enough to be visible to the naked eye. After further growth and development they reach a stage in which they are infective to swine. At this stage they consist chiefly of a large spiny proboscis invaginated into, or sheathed in, a bladderlike appendage so that they somewhat resemble bladder worms.

Development to the infective stage is accomplished in about 7 to 12 weeks, depending on temperature and the stage of development of the host grub; there is evidence that the rate of development of the parasite is speeded up during pupation of the grub. Adult beetles are capable of harboring the parasite in the infective stage.

Swine rooting in manure piles, strawstacks, or the rich soil of barnyards or low-lying pastures may find and swallow white grubs, of which they are very fond; they probably also find and eat the beetles during the season when these insects are common. In the body of the hog the infective thorn-headed worm larvae are freed from the body of the insect by the action of the digestive juices. In the small intestine the larvae extend the proboscis and attach themselves to the wall of the intestine, mate, and began to produce eggs in about 3 to 4 months. In the intestine of the hog the worms may grow at the rate of about an inch a month. Egg-producing maturity is usually reached before the worms attain their full growth.

The effect of thorn-headed worms on swine is not well understood, although it is known that these worms contribute their share to the general unthriftiness that is commonly associated with parasitic infections. Loss of appetite, constipation, and restlessness have been attributed to infection with these worms, and it has been stated that the parasites often kill young pigs. Occasionally the injury inflicted on the intestine by the proboscis is so deep that the intestinal wall is perforated and the delicate lining of the abdominal cavity becomes inflamed, a condition known as peritonitis. There have been cases in which the entire worm has broken through the intestinal wall and entered the body cavity of the animal. Such a condition may well produce a fatal peritonitis.

An important effect of infection by thorn-headed worms is a marked weakening of the small intestine. In some cases the infected intestines have only about half the strength of uninfected intestines. It has been observed that the intestine is often weakest at a point some distance from the worms. The weakened condition of the intestine makes it unfit for use as sausage casings, and this causes financial loss to the packers which may be passed on to the farmer in the form of lowered market prices.

Large Intestinal Roundworms (Ascarids)

The large intestinal roundworm, or ascarid, parasitic in the small intestine of swine, is probably the most commonly observed and one of the most injurious of all the worm parasites of these animals. It is widespread throughout the world. In the United States, from 20 to 74 percent or more of the hogs examined for this parasite have been found to be infected.

The worm is known as *Ascaris lumbricoides* var. *suis* to distinguish it from *A. lumbricoides*, a worm that occurs in human beings and is presumably closely related to the one in swine, from which it cannot be distinguished by any characteristics of form. Usually reddish or pinkish in color, the adult worm is about as thick as an ordinary lead pencil and may reach a length of 12 inches or more.

The normal location of the adult worms is in the small intestine, but wandering adults may occur in the stomach, the large intestine, the bile ducts of the liver, or the gall bladder, and they are often seen in the feces of infected animals. The young (larval) worms migrate extensively in the body of the host and during these migrations appear in the blood stream, the liver, the lungs, and other organs and tissues.

At first the life history of this parasite was not well understood. About 1916 an English investigator found that the life cycle is direct.

A few years later two American scientists confirmed his work and demonstrated the following points by a series of carefully planned experiments:

(1) Eggs eliminated by female worms in the intestines of pigs are undeveloped. When incubated at a temperature of about 33° C. (91° F.), the eggs may complete development in about 10 days. Longer periods are required at lower temperatures.

(2) The embryonated eggs, if swallowed by a suitable host animal, hatch in the small intestine. The young larvae penetrate the wall of the alimentary tract and, apparently aided by the circulation, migrate to the liver and lungs, being found in the liver as early as 2 days after infection and in the lungs 3 days after infection. Larvae are most numerous in the lungs 10 days after the infection, becoming scarce in the liver as they become numerous in the lungs. During the period of migration to the liver and lungs, they may also migrate into the spleen, thyroid, pancreas, and other locations in the body.

(3) In the lungs the larvae, which have developed to 5 to 10 times their original size and may be visible to the unaided eye, break out of the capillaries, migrate up the air passages to the throat, are swallowed, and appear in the small intestine as early as 6 days after infection.

(4) In pigs the ascarids develop to maturity within about 2½ months after infection. Some larvae die during their migrations in the body, and those that settle in organs other than the liver and lungs are relatively short-lived.

The course of migration of ascarid larvae in the body of the pig is illustrated in figure 4.

The eggs of ascarids have a thick, rough shell which makes them resistant to unfavorable environmental conditions. They are therefore able to survive prolonged exposure to freezing temperatures and to drying, and they are killed by few strong chemicals. The eggs are also very long-lived, having been kept alive in the laboratory as long as 5 years. Eggs in cultivated soil have remained alive and been able to infect pigs after approximately 4½ years.

The egg production of adult female ascarids is enormous. It has been estimated that a full-grown female may contain as many as 26 or 27 million eggs, and it has been shown that a single female worm may give off as many as 250,000 eggs a day. This, it can be seen, would result in rapid accumulation of enormous numbers of eggs on the soil where even a few infected hogs are kept. Soil is not necessary for the development of the eggs; they will develop on wood, brick, or concrete floors—in fact, anywhere that slight moisture is present. The eggs are sticky and adhere to the floors and walls of pens, and vigorous cleaning is necessary to dislodge them. When pens are cleaned in the ordinary way, without washing, many eggs remain, and the premises become potential sources of infection.

Although, as pointed out, ascarid eggs are quite resistant to many inimical environment factors, it has been observed that when they are exposed directly to sunlight for a time, many of them die. When eggs are exposed to drying and to sunlight at the same time, the rate of death is more rapid. The undeveloped eggs are the least and the fully developed (embryonated) eggs the most resistant. It was found in tests carried out under tropical conditions that undeveloped eggs protected by a thin layer of water failed to survive exposure to direct sunlight for more than 3 hours, and none survived more than 2¾ hours when exposed in a dried condition. Some fully developed eggs in water survived as long as 9 hours; others in a dried condition were killed by approximately 5 hours' exposure. In temperate climates, where the sunlight is less intense than in the Tropics, the eggs would probably survive longer.

Under natural conditions, eggs are more or less protected by the fecal mass during the early stages of their development when they

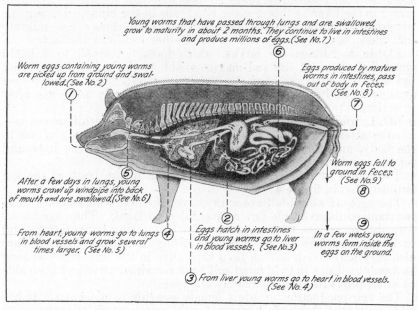

Young worms that have passed through lungs and are swallowed, grow to maturity in about 2 months. They continue to live in intestines and produce millions of eggs.(See No.7):
⑥

Worm eggs containing young worms are picked up from ground and swallowed.(See No. 2)
①

Eggs produced by mature worms in intestines, pass out of body in Feces. (See No.8)
⑦

After a few days in lungs, young worms crawl up windpipe into back of mouth and are swallowed.(See No.6)
⑤

Worm eggs fall to ground in Feces. (See No.9)
⑧

From heart, young worms go to lungs ④ in blood vessels and grow several times larger. (See No. 5)

Eggs hatch in intestines and young worms go to liver in blood vessels. (See No.3)
②

In a few weeks young worms form inside the eggs on the ground.
⑨

③ From liver young worms go to heart in blood vessels. (See No. 4)

FIGURE 4.—The path followed by roundworms in the body of the pig. (After Ransom (12).)

are most susceptible to sunlight and drying. This circumstance together with their increasing resistance to solar radiation as they develop, probably enables some eggs to survive for long periods on soil even though unprotected by vegetation. Nevertheless sunlight and drying are among the most effective of the measures which the farmer has at his disposal in his war on these parasites.

The damage inflicted by ascarids may be sufficiently great at times to cause the death of heavily infected animals. While the effects produced by moderate and light infections are correspondingly less severe, even these may stunt the animal. An instance in which the rate of growth and general condition of a pig infected with ascarids was compared with that of a pig of the same age kept free from these pests illustrates this point (5). At slightly over 3 months of age the worm-free pig weighed 82 pounds and the infected pig, 10¾ pounds. A large part of the visible damage inflicted by these parasites occurs in the liver and lungs and is produced by the larvae in their migrations through the body of the animal. In heavy infections the damage is so extensive that by the time the worms have appeared in the intestines the health of the animal may have been undermined to such an extent that it may never fully recover. During the migration of the larvae through the lungs, the pig may have difficulty in breathing and may contract pneumonia and die. Infected pigs commonly show symptoms known as thumps—labored breathing often accompanied by a deep, harsh cough, which is more pronounced after exertion. Although thumps in young pigs may be caused by conditions other than ascarid infection, this is probably the commonest cause in growing pigs kept on permanent pastures. Small hemorrhages and whitish pneumonic areas may also appear in the lungs after extensive invasion by ascarid larvae.

Although the injuries to the liver heal as a general rule they are sometimes so severe as to leave permanent scars which appear at times as small pearly-white spots. Sometimes these scars are so numerous as to dot the entire surface of the liver. It has been stated that the livers of about 35 percent of the swine slaughtered in some regions show this condition.

The damage produced by the adult worms in the intestine is less spectacular and less definite. Digestive disturbances, capricious appetite, and retarded growth and delevopment have been associated with the presence of adult ascarids in the intestine. In fact, growth may be retarded to such an extent that it is impossible to get the animals to a marketable weight soon enough to be profitable. The presence of the parasites in the intestine is frequently associated with a reddish slime with a distinctive odor on the wall of the intestine.

A frequent result of ascarid infection of swine is a generalized icterus (yellows). Adult worms occasionally migrate into and plug the bile ducts of the liver, stopping the flow of bile into the intestine. The bile is then distributed by the blood stream through the body of the animal, lodges in the tissues, and gives the flesh a yellowish color, making it unfit for food. Since such carcasses are rejected and condemned under Federal and equally competent State and local meat-inspection procedures, the animals are almost a total loss.

PROTOZOAN PARASITES

The most common of the protozoan parasites belong to four general groups known as amoebae, balantidia, coccidia, and sarcosporidia. The amoebae and the balantidia are of especial importance because they are indistinguishable, for the most part, from similar protozoa that sometimes produce dysentery in man. The coccidia that infect swine are distinct from the coccidia that occur in other animals and in man.

The conditions under which protozoa produce harmful effects in pigs are not well understood. Under ordinary conditions they often appear to do little if any damage. However, the pigs generally become infected with these parasites within a few days after they are born, when the young animal is adjusting itself to life and its resistance is low. Hence the parasites may produce injuries that may not be apparent at once but that may show up later in the form of unthriftiness.

AMOEBAE

Several species of amoebae, belonging to the genera *Endamoeba*, *Endolimax*, and *Iodamoeba*, may occur in pigs. The most common are certain species of the *Endamoeba*, three of which are often found in pigs, but considerable difference of opinion exists as to their importance in causing sickness in the young animals. For a number of years investigators have observed these parasites in the intestinal wall of pigs, and some have considered that the organisms act like normal inhabitants of the digestive tract. Others have felt that under certain circumstances the organisms may invade and erode the cells of the intestine, causing dysentery. From time to time outbreaks of dysentery occur in swine that can apparently be attributed to no cause other than amoebae. It has been considered possible also that the pig acts as a reservoir host of the parasite and may be instrumental in bringing about outbreaks of amoebic dysentery in man.

The amoebae may merely live in the cavity of the intestine, or they may invade the tissue cells, where they may well become decidedly harmful. In the intestine the active forms multiply by division of their bodies. Under certain conditions the organism becomes rounded and secretes a heavy cyst wall about itself. Such cysts are microscopic, some of the largest being only about one one-hundred-fiftieth of an inch in diameter. Inside the cyst the amoeba divides until there are, in some cases, as many as eight small parasites instead of one. As this development progresses the cyst passes down the intestine with the feces. By the time it reaches the exterior the development has been completed and the organism is infective to swine.

Swine become infected by swallowing the cysts while feeding on contaminated ground. In the intestine the cyst wall ruptures, releasing the tiny amoebae. Little is known about how long the cysts may remain alive on soil. Since swine often eat fresh feces, however, the infection may be readily acquired in that way.

In severe infections the intestine may become inflamed, and extensive patches of tissue may be destroyed. The parasites burrowing into the wall of the intestine not only erode and destroy patches of tissue but also often rupture small blood vessels which bleed into the intestine. The destruction of the intestinal wall may produce a dysentery in which the feces may be watery and blood-tinged. There is said to be loss of appetite and the infected animal becomes gaunt and has a high fever.

It has been reported that a liquid diet of milk generally brings about a decrease in the numbers of intestinal amoebae in a host.

BALANTIDIA

The balantidia (*Balantidium coli*), though very small in size, are somewhat larger than the amoebae.

When large numbers of balantidia in the active stage are grouped together in water, a trained observer can see them with the unaided eye. In the active stage they have a more or less definite shape, slightly pointed at one end, and are covered with cilia (hairlike structures) by means of which they swim about.

Balantidia are probably the most widespread of the protozoan parasites of pigs, and probably nearly every pig harbors a few of these organisms in its large intestine and blind gut. Considerable difference of opinion exists among investigators as to the actual importance of the parasite as a cause of intestinal disorders in pigs. Some have reported that its presence is frequently associated with severe diarrhea and even dysentery; others maintain that the parasite does little harm.

Although balantidia ordinarily live in the cavity of the intestine in contact with the cells, they may occasionally invade tissue. They multiply by dividing into equal parts, each part becoming a complete organism. As the feces of the host passes down the intestine, some of the parasites are carried to the exterior. Here some may become round and secrete a heavy cyst wall about themselves, while others die. Some encyst before they pass out with the feces. The cysts vary greatly in size; some may be as large as one-fiftieth of an inch in diameter. Pigs become infected by swallowing the cysts. In the intestine of the pig, the cyst wall is dissolved, and the young parasite emerges and begins to multiply. It has been stated that symptoms of intestinal disorders may appear within 10 to 14 days after infection. A diet rich in starchy grains provides conditions favorable for infection, whereas diets rich in proteins are unfavorable.

It has been observed that suckling pigs may become infected with these protozoa within a few days after birth. The infections may not become noticeable, however, until the pigs are weaned or until they begin to eat solid food. When the pigs are living entirely on milk, the parasites may not pass to the exterior. As soon as the young animal begins to eat grain or other solid food, the parasites may be found in the feces. It has been found possible to free pigs of balantidia by placing the animals on a diet of cow's milk exclusively for about a week. However, an infection does not confer immunity to reinfection.

Occasionally severe intestinal disorders accompany infections of pigs with balantidia, and it has been reported that fat hogs are as a rule the most severely infected. There may be marked depression, loss of appetite, and considerable dysentery, with ulceration and inflammation of the intestine. When present, these symptoms certainly indicate that balantidia may be of considerable importance as a cause of unthriftiness in swine.

COCCIDIA

Probably the most important protozoan disease of swine is that known as coccidiosis. The disease is caused by the presence in the large intesine of the organisms known as coccidia (*Eimeria*), several species of which occur in pigs. The parasites occur in the cells lining the wall of the intestine, where they grow and develop. In the resistant stages they are called oöcysts. Oöcysts, which correspond to the eggs of worm parasites, are somewhat egg-shaped, and the largest may be about one one-hundredth of an inch in size. They are discharged into the cavity of the intestine, pass out with the droppings, and undergo a period of development before they become infective to swine. Under favorable conditions of moisture and temperature this development is completed in a few days.

Pigs become infected by swallowing the oöcysts while feeding on contaminated ground. Upon reaching the intestine the oöcysts rupture, each releasing several infective bodies. Each of these is capable of penetrating a cell, where it grows at the expense of the cell and produces a number of new infective bodies, which in turn penetrate other cells. Sooner or later some of these bodies develop into oöcysts, which pass out with the droppings and develop to the infective stage.

Owing to the extensive destruction of tissues that normally occurs during the development of the oöcysts, coccidiosis may be a serious disease in pigs, as it usually is in calves and chicks. It has been stated that the pronounced unthriftiness of pigs that commonly occurs on some farms is attributable to coccidia. It is probably the result of the extensive destruction of intestinal cells, which undoubtedly interferes with the absorption of food. According to some investigators, in heavy infections there is a marked thickening of the intestine, which might also interfere with digestion and the absorption of food and water. Experimentally infected pigs lose weight, and the critical stage of the infection lasts about 3 weeks in such pigs.

A characteristic of coccidiosis is that spontaneous recovery may occur. The animal may be severely sick and large numbers of oöcysts may be passing in the feces, when suddenly it begins to get well and the oöcysts disappear. In some cases, however, the disease becomes chronic after it has passed the critical stage, and the pig may remain permanently weak and unthrifty.

SARCOCYSTIS

Sarcocystis miescheriana is a parasite that is considered by some scientists to be related to and by others to be a member of the protozoa. Heavy infections with this organism are characterized by the presence of small white spots in the muscles which may be almost invisible or nearly as large as the head of a pin. In the spots are tiny elongated sacs containing the extremely small spores of the parasite.

Sarcocystis is quite common in garbage-fed hogs; as many as 75 percent of those examined from some localities have been found infected. The parasite is apparently less common in hogs from sections of the country where grain is customarily fed, as only about 5 percent of the animals from these areas have been found on examination to harbor the parasite. The manner in which hogs become infected is unknown, though there have been several theories. Related parasites occur in rats, mice, cattle, sheep, and rabbits.

The flesh of pigs having massive infections with *Sarcocystis* may be light in color, soft and somewhat watery, and peppered with tiny white spots which are rather indefinite in outline. In older hogs in which the .infections are apparently of long standing, the sacs containing the parasites often become greatly enlarged. In many cases the parasites die, and calcification sets in, which produces a gritty condition of the meat. When the lesions of the infection are so large or so numerous as to be visible to the unaided eye, the meat is unfit for food; it is reported that toxic effects have resulted from eating such meat.

CONTROL OF SWINE PARASITES BY TREATMENT

Treatment for the removal of worm parasites is a valuable aid in the control of these pests, especially when combined with sanitary practices designed to prevent reinfection. Removing adult parasites stops the deposition of eggs which sooner or later reach the soil. Moreover, the animal is relieved of the drain caused by parasitic infection. Treatment, however, has certain limitations. Kidney worms and lungworms cannot be removed by the use of drugs, and there are no entirely effective treatments for the removal of whipworms, thorn-headed worms, and intestinal threadworms. Treatments are generally effective against ascarids, nodular worms, and stomach worms, though no single treatment is entirely effective in removing all of them.

For best results, treatment for the removal of parasites should be administered by or under the direction of a veterinarian, since such treatments often involve the administration of drugs that are rather toxic, or poisonous. Drugs that are injurious to the parasite may also be injurious to the pig, and dosages must be properly adjusted. Whether treatment is needed, the kind of medication to use, the proper dosage and method of administration, and whether the physical condition of the animal is such that the drug can be safely administered are matters that involve specialized training.

The drugs recognized to be most effective are oil of chenopodium (wormseed oil), santonin, hexylresorcinol, phenothiazine, and carbon disulfide. The first three are generally effective against adult ascarids in the small intestine. While not entirely satisfactory as a general anthelmintic for swine, phenothiazine in suitable doses is effective in removing nodular worms and moderately effective in removing adult ascarids. Carbon disulfide has been reported to be effective in removing the red stomach worm and has been recommended for the removal of thick stomach worms. The following are approximate dosages of these drugs for animals weighing 100 pounds: Oil of chenopodium, 2 to 4 cubic centimeters; santonin, 1 to 4 grams; hexylresorcinol, 8 grams; carbon disulfide, 8 to 10 cubic centimeters; phenothiazine, 12 grams. The exact dosages, however, must be carefully calculated on the basis of the body weight and physical condition of the animal to be treated.

The four drugs first named may be administered by means of a dose syringe, or stomach tube, or by capsule, following a period of fasting; a purge must be administered at the time of or immediately following administration of the drug. Phenothiazine can be given either in capsules or mixed with four to eight times its weight of dry ground feed without preliminary fasting; no purge is necessary. By using the medicated feed mixture it is possible to treat several pigs at one time.

It should be remembered that treatment alone will not solve the parasite problem. Removal of parasites does not insure against reinfection, and if the animals are kept on contaminated ground the relief afforded by treatment may be only temporary.

CONTROL OF SWINE PARASITES BY MANAGEMENT

Management practices designed to break the life cycles of swine parasites at their weakest point, the stage on the ground, are in the long run the cheapest and most effective means of combating these pests.

Two systems have been devised and tested by scientists of the Bureau of Animal Industry. One, called the McLean County system of swine sanitation, was designed for the control of ascarids under conditions prevailing in swine-raising sections of the Midwest. The other, a modification of that system, was designed to control kidney worms under conditions prevailing in the Southeastern States. These systems have for their objects (1) the prevention of infection by preventing contact of susceptible animals, as far as possible, with infective stages of the parasites, (2) the utilization of natural forces in destroying parasite eggs and larvae on soil, and (3) simultaneous improvement of the health of the animal through adequate nutrition, since it is recognized that well-fed animals are less likely to become seriously infected than are inadequately fed animals.

The McLean County System of Swine Sanitation

On the basis of the results of investigations on ascarids by scientists in various countries a system of swine sanitation was outlined that would protect pigs from parasite infections during the first few weeks of life (*11*). The plan was then tried out on a practical scale on farms in McLean County, Ill., beginning in the spring of 1920. It was based on the following facts, already brought out in the discussion of ascarids:

(1) Young pigs are more susceptible to the parasite than older hogs. Pigs suffer most severely from infections during the first few weeks of their lives, becoming more resistant as they grow older.

(2) Pigs become infected by swallowing the infective eggs of the parasite, which occur in the feces of hogs or on the soil of places that have been frequented by hogs.

(3) A single full-grown female worm in the intestine of a hog produces several hundred thousand eggs daily, and as a consequence the soil of areas occupied by infected hogs is likely to be teeming with eggs. The feeding habits of hogs are such that they probably swallow large numbers of eggs daily.

(4) Ascarid eggs are sticky and adhere to the walls and floors of

buildings and to the bodies of animals; in these situations they may live for long periods.

(5) Not all adult hogs harbor ascarids even though exposed to infected soil, but the parasites may be found in about one out of every three hogs of breeding age.

Procedures Under the System

It was recognized that in order to protect young pigs against infection it would be necessary to initiate protective measures even before they were born and that from the time of birth to several months of age they would have to be kept entirely away from old hog lots or pastures. The following procedures were therefore devised and tested (*12*):

(1) Clean the farrowing pens thoroughly and then scrub them with scalding water and lye.

Farrowing pens should be of sanitary construction to facilitate cleaning. Shortly before farrowing time the accumulated manure, dirt, and litter should be carefully scraped from the floor, walls, etc., carried away, and either destroyed or plowed under. The entire pen, including walls, floors, guardrails, troughs, etc., should be washed and scrubbed with liberal quantities of very hot water in which lye has been dissolved. If possible, boiling water should be used, for the hotter the water the more effective it will be in destroying parasite eggs. The lye acts as a cleansing agent and helps to remove dirt, in which worm eggs are apt to be lodged.

Recommendations as to the proportion of lye to water vary. Some investigators recommend 1 pound per gallon of water, others 1 pound to 20 gallons. Strong solutions would probably be more effective in removing dirt than would weak solutions. The pen should be scrubbed as the hot lye solution is applied. In the scrubbing, particular attention should be paid to cracks and crevices in floors, walls, troughs, guardrails, and any other places within reach of pigs where parasite eggs may have accumulated. When the pen has been thoroughly scrubbed, it should be rinsed with clean water, and the worker should not reenter the pen; the final rinsing should be accomplished from the outside. The importance of thorough cleansing cannot be overemphasized, as the more thoroughly the job is done the less will be the danger of worm infection.

If there are outside pens in connection with the inside pens, they should also be cleaned if they are of wood or concrete construction; if they have dirt floors, these outside pens should be shut off so as not to be used by the pigs.

If the buildings are not artificially heated, the cleaning should be done in the fall before freezing weather, since it may be difficult to clean properly during cold weather or in early spring or late winter. After being cleaned, the pens should be closed to hogs until farrowing time, and no one should be allowed inside them, as there is always danger of parasite eggs being carried in dirt adhering to shoes.

Cleaning the pens with disinfectants is not recommended, since worm eggs are not killed by most disinfectants.

(2) Clean the sows with warm water and soap just before they are placed in the farrowing pens.

A few days before the sows are due to farrow they should be washed with soap and warm water to remove the mud and dirt that is usually on their skins. Particular attention should be paid to cleaning the udders and sides of the animal where the young pigs will come in close contact with the mother. Immediately after being washed, the sow should be placed in the farrowing pen. It is advisable to wash the sow close to the door of the pen so that she will not have to walk over ground that may be contaminated with worm eggs and thus carry infective material into the pen.

Unless the sows are carefully cleaned before they are placed in the farrowing pens, they may carry with them a multitude of worm eggs and disease germs, so that even within a few hours after the pigs are born they may swallow large numbers of infective agents.

After farrowing, the sows and pigs should not be allowed out of the farrowing pens until they are taken to pasture. Care should be taken by the attendants not to introduce worm eggs into the pens either by entering them wearing dirty shoes or by using dirty troughs or other equipment. Bedding should be changed and the pen cleaned without the attendant entering the pen any more than can be helped.

(3) Haul the pigs and sows from the clean pens to clean pasture.

The young pigs and their mothers may be moved to clean pastures any time after warm weather sets in. It is desirable to make the transfer as soon as convenient (within 2 weeks if possible) in order to get the pigs to clean surroundings before the ascarid eggs that may have been deposited by the sow in the pen have reached the infective stage.

The sows and pigs should be hauled, not driven, to the clean pasture. Use of a stone boat with one crate for the sow and another for the pigs is recommended. Some farmers use a double-decked crate with the upper compartment for the pigs and the lower for the sow (fig. 5). Failure to use caution during the trip from the farrowing house to the pasture may nullify the efforts made in cleaning the sows and pens. A sufficiently large number of worm eggs to cause considerable trouble could be picked up by pigs walking on contaminated ground. An actual example of this was observed by the writer on a farm where a system of sanitation for the control of parasites was being followed. In transferring sows and pigs to a clean pasture the animals were leisurely driven along an old lane for a distance of perhaps 200 yards. This lane had been frequented by hogs at intervals for a period of several years. The majority of the pigs were later found to be infected with ascarids and other parasites.

(4) Keep the young pigs in clean pastures until they are at least 4 months old.

The pasture provided for the sows and pigs should not be a permanent pasture which has recently been used by hogs and may, therefore, be contaminated with worm eggs and larvae. Instead it should be a field that has been under cultivation and sown at the proper time to a suitable forage crop. Legume pastures available in the normal course of crop rotation are desirable, if a different field is devoted to this purpose each year.

In the pasture an individual **A**-type shelter house for each sow and her litter should be provided. This is a small, movable structure built in the form of an **A** with a door at one end. No other hogs should have access to the pasture, and the pigs should not be allowed to run back from the pasture to the barn or lots. If the pigs are thus kept from contaminated places until they are at least 4 months old, there is little likelihood that they will suffer seriously from infections with ascarids. For the best results, however, the animals should be kept away from contaminated areas until they are marketed.

FIGURE 5.—Hauling the sow and pigs to pasture in a double-decked crate with a space for the sow below and a place for the pigs above. (After Ransom (*12*).)

In the case of fall pigs (if not farrowed too late), the same system may be followed with slight modifications. The permanent farrowing house need not be used. If the sows have been on pasture and are not encrusted with dirt and filth, they may be transferred directly to a special temporary pasture and the farrowing may be done in individual **A**-type houses. If the sows have been kept in a hog lot or are encrusted with dirt and filth, they should be washed before being turned into the pasture. In regions not too far north, pigs farrowed by the end of summer will be old enough to be past the ages of greatest susceptibility to ascarid infection before it is necessary to put them into winter quarters that may be more or less contaminated. Even then it is desirable to clean and scrub the hog houses before putting the pigs in them.

Advantages Obtained by Use of the System

When the first practical tests of this system were made on farms, careful records were kept of the number of pigs farrowed, the number of deaths, and the causes of death, together with records of the number of pigs marketed. Following is a summary of reports (*2, 6, 10, 13*) of benefits derived from the use of the system:

(1) More pigs were raised than under the old system of hog raising. In 6 years, on 40 different farms, 6,204 sows farrowed pigs, 39,855 of which were placed on pasture, making an average of 6.4 pigs per litter that survived the farrowing period and reached pasture. Disregarding losses from accidents of various sorts and from hog cholera, the system was 97.8 percent effective in protecting pigs from parasitic and associated hog-lot diseases. Naturally all farmers did not follow the system equally well. On a number of farms where the procedures recommended were closely followed, 1,656 sows farrowed pigs, 10,749 of which reached pasture, an average of 6.5 pigs per litter (*10*).

On the whole, about 76 percent of the pigs farrowed were marketed. Twenty-four percent were lost from all causes, including still-births, accidents, hog cholera, and worms. In contrast, on the farms where the sanitation system was not followed, only about 50 percent of the pigs were marketed (*10*).

(2) Pigs were ready for market earlier.

It was found that pigs raised under the sanitation system were in general ready for market as long as 7 weeks earlier than pigs raised in the ordinary way. It was also found that 4-month-old parasite-free pigs weighed about 28 pounds more on an average than pigs raised on the same farms but not kept under sanitary conditions (*13*).

(3) More pigs were raised per sow.

The system enabled farmers to raise as many pigs as formerly with about two-thirds as many sows. It was estimated (*2*) that if a farmer needed 17 sows to produce two carloads of 84 or 85 pigs each under ordinary conditions, by using the swine sanitation system he could reduce the number of sows to 12. The cost of feed necessary to maintain 5 sows, estimated to be about $30 per sow per year, could thus be saved.

The effectiveness of the swine sanitation system in saving pigs is further illustrated by the following report (*6*): A group of 12 sows farrowed 117 pigs in an old hog lot. Parasitism and other hog-lot diseases reduced the number until only 35 pigs remained to be marketed. The following year the same 12 sows farrowed 95 pigs. By following the program of good feeding, good housing, and clean pastures, 90 of these pigs were raised to market weight.

The fact needs emphasis that if maximum benefit is to be derived from swine sanitation the entire procedure must be followed closely, as lack of thoroughness in any step results in a corresponding decline in effectiveness (*1*). It was observed, for example, that of a group of 160 farmers those who merely cleaned but did not scrub farrowing pens before the sows were put in them raised an average of 5.05 pigs per litter. Those who both cleaned and scrubbed pens raised an average of 5.67 pigs per litter. Still others who cleaned and washed the farrowing pens and also washed the sows raised an average of 6.85 pigs per litter. The owners who followed all these steps and in addition transferred the pigs to clean pastures during the suckling period raised an average of 8 pigs per litter.

An important aspect of parasite control in pigs, which is often overlooked or disregarded by the farmer but which materially increases the effectiveness of any control measure, is the matter of a well-balanced diet provided in adequate amounts for the growing animals. Ordinarily the full-fed pig is the healthiest pig. For one thing, it has more of the vitality necessary to resist or throw off disease agents than a pig on a deficient or inadequate diet. Also the adequacy and sufficiency of the diet have a marked effect on the feeding habits of the pigs, and this in turn directly influences the extent of the parasite infections acquired. Pigs full-fed from self-feeders are less likely to become seriously infected with parasites than scantily fed pigs or pigs fed from ground where the feed comes in contact with feces. Inadequately fed pigs spend much time searching for food on the ground, where it is generally contaminated with agents of disease.

The part that feeding habits may play in parasite infection is indicated by the following observations made in connection with nodular worm infections of pigs on two farms where a system for the control of parasites was being tested (*18*):

On one farm the recommendations were carefully followed except that insufficient feed was made available to the pigs. As a result the animals were constantly hungry and spent a large part of their time rooting and searching for food on ground contaminated with the feces of the sows, which were infected with nodular worms. The pigs were frequently seen eating grains of corn that had passed undigested in the feces of the sows. Examination of such feces and the surrounding soil invariably revealed the presence of infective larvae of nodular worms. At slaughter the intestines of the pigs were found studded with nodules and harboring hundreds of nodular worms.

On the other farm, where the recommended procedures were followed and in addition adequate amounts of a well-balanced diet were made constantly available in self-feeders, the pigs spent little time in rooting and searching for food on the ground. After eating from the self-feeders, the pigs would lie down in the shade until they were hungry again. They were never seen to eat corn passed in the feces of the sows. When slaughtered, the majority of the pigs were found to be free of nodular worms, and the remainder were only slightly infected. In spite of the fact that these animals had as much opportunity as the underfed pigs to become infected with nodular worms, the infections acquired were relatively unimportant owing to their feeding habits.

The influence of adequate nutrition on infection with internal parasites applies also to very young pigs. Young pigs whose mothers do not provide adequate milk soon begin rooting and searching for food on the ground, from which they are likely to acquire infection with parasites, especially those having direct life histories. It has been observed that litters of pigs farrowed in old hog lots by sows that did not provide adequate nourishment for their offspring became infected with parasites during the first few days of their existence. In contrast, some of the pigs farrowed in the same lot by sows that provided adequate milk for their pigs did not become infected for several weeks, and some did not become infected at all during the period they were kept under observation (*21*).

The observations related show that in addition to the recommended procedures for the control of parasites in pigs, two additional precautions can be taken by the farmer which may aid materially in controlling these pests: (1) Select sows for breeding that provide adequate milk for the suckling pigs, especially during the early stages of lactation; in other words, use only sows that are good milkers. (2) As soon as the pigs begin to eat, provide adequate amounts of a well-balanced diet in self-feeders.

KIDNEY WORM CONTROL PLAN

Because kidney worms cannot be removed from the body of the living animal by the use of drugs, it was early recognized that the only way to cope with this parasite was to prevent infection. Although various measures for controlling kidney worms had already been recommended, none was entirely applicable to conditions in the United States. An investigation was therefore begun to ascertain the factors responsible for the spread of kidney worms, such as (1) the distribution and length of survival of the larvae on pastures, (2) the effect of climatic factors on the eggs and larvae, and (3) the conditions under which pigs acquire infection. The investigation was carried out under actual field conditions in one of the Southern States where kidney worms constitute a serious problem, and the following facts were ascertained (*19*):

(1) Infective kidney worm larvae are most abundant in and beneath trash and litter, such as corn husks, etc., that accumulate on feeding grounds. The larvae also occur in lesser numbers on the soil of moist, shaded areas, along fences, under trees, and in and around hog houses and other buildings frequented by hogs. The larvae are widely distributed over pastures where the grass is dense enough to shade the ground and thus retains a certain amount of moisture around the roots. Infective larvae are not common in wallows and do not live long under such conditions.

(2) On soil where they are protected from direct sunlight, drying, and freezing temperatures, kidney worm larvae may persist for 3 months or longer.

(3) Kidney worm larvae are very sensitive to the effects of direct sunlight, under which they fail to survive more than 1 hour even when not subjected also to drying.

(4) Kidney worm eggs deposited by infected animals on unshaded bare soil live only a few hours on sunshiny days. Under these conditions the eggs are apparently killed by the combined effects of the sunlight and drying.

(5) The greatest concentrations of kidney worm eggs occur on the soil beneath accumulated trash and litter on the feeding ground, on soil in the vicinity of farrowing houses and shelters, and on paths

along the fences that surround the pasture. It was observed that on waking and leaving the shelters sows would generally urinate after walking a short distance, thereby contributing to the concentration of eggs on the soil near the farrowing houses and shelters.

(6) The infective larvae may migrate from the soil up the stems and blades of grass at night when the vegetation is wet with dew. As the sun comes up and the grass begins to dry, many of the larvae return to the damp, shaded portions of the grass and to the soil beneath.

(7) Infective larvae are stimulated by moderate heat and will migrate short distances toward a warmer environment.

On the basis of these facts and observations of the habits of swine and of husbandry practices in common use in the region where kidney worms are abundant, a plan of management for sows and litters that has for its object the protection of pigs from infection with kidney worms while they are with the sow was devised (*19*). The objective is accomplished by the use of temporary pastures and a simple arrangement of farrowing equipment (A-type houses, feeding and watering devices, etc.) in relation to the pasture areas so as to take advantage of various climatic factors to insure destruction of the eggs and larvae of kidney worms.

Figure 6 is a photograph of a model of a kidney worm control set-up. The arrangement of equipment shown was designed to insure, as far as possible, that the majority of the kidney worm eggs passed by the sows will fall on places where they cannot survive. It provides under actual farm conditions an effective means of breaking the life cycle of the parasite at its weakest point, the stage on the ground. Tests carried out on farms in the kidney worm belt have shown this arrangement to be an effecive control measure. The bare area must, however, be kept free of trash and vegetation of all kinds.

The sequence of steps to be followed in carrying out this plan has been outlined in detail elsewhere (*15*), but they will be enumerated and briefly discussed here.

(1) Put pregnant sows shortly before farrowing on a pasture that has been especially prepared by being sown to a suitable forage crop.

Temporary pastures of oats, rye, or some other suitable crop should always be utilized for this purpose. The area should be one that has been plowed and had at least one crop grown on it since last being used by hogs. This precaution is to insure destruction of kidney worm larvae and the infective stages of many other parasites.

(2) In sowing, leave an area of bare soil all around the pasture.

The bare area should be about 5 feet wide on each of three sides of the pasture and at least 30 feet wide at one end (fig. 6). The wider portion is to accommodate the farrowing or shelter houses, water barrel, creep for pigs, and feeding pen for sows. The wide area should be at the end of the field most convenient for taking care of the animals without having to cross the entire field.

(3) Keep the bare portions of the field free of all trash, litter, and vegetation.

If trash is allowed to accumulate and grass to grow on the bare area, the purpose of the plan may be defeated, since such accumulations provide protection for the larvae. It may be necessary to cultivate the bare areas from time to time, using a plow disk or some other implement to destroy grass that may start up. The parasite eggs deposited by the sows around the houses and during the course of their wanderings along fence rows will thus be exposed to sunlight and drying, the farmer's best allies in combating parasites.

FIGURE 6.—A model set-up for kidney worm control. At the bottom, close to and facing the fence, are four A-type farrowing houses. Also on the bare area are a creep for the pigs (left-hand corner), a feeding pen for the sows (right-hand corner), and a watering barrel.

(4) A creep large enough for the pigs should be located on the bare area and not in the pasture area.

It is essential that the creep be located on the bare area and that the area surrounding it be kept free of trash and vegetation. This is necessary because sows often remain in the vicinity of the creep when the pigs are feeding and contaminate the surrounding soil with their urine and feces. When the creep is located on the pasture area it has been found that the accumulation of kidney worm larvae around it constitutes a source of infection for the pigs. When the creep is on bare soil, the eggs will be destroyed and will not be important in the spread of kidney worms except during long spells of damp, cloudy weather.

(5) The feeding pen for the sows should be located some distance away from the creep.

It has been found advantageous from the standpoint of parasite control to feed the sows in a separate pen. The pen should be so arranged that the pigs cannot have access to it at any time. The sows should be fed in the pen and should be allowed to remain there for some time after feeding so that they may urinate and defecate where the pigs will not have access to the infective material.

(6) A watering barrel of sanitary construction should be located on the bare strip.

The arrangement should be such that the barrel will not overflow and thus create a wet area around it that might be favorable for the survival of parasite eggs and larvae.

(7) An A-type farrowing house should be provided for each sow.

The farrowing houses should be located on the bare strip at a distance of about 6 feet from and facing the fence. The houses should be placed some distance apart. Trash and litter, such as bedding, should not be allowed to accumulate around the houses to provide shelter for kidney worms. It has been found that larvae of nodular worms often occur inside farrowing houses and beneath shelters in small particles of fecal material carried in on the bodies and feet of the animals. The bedding inside the houses should therefore be changed from time to time in order to remove fecal material that may have been tracked in.

Control of kidney worms is accomplished by this procedure in the following ways:

(1) Since the sows usually urinate not far from their shelter houses (especially after waking), near fences, and near the creep, the kidney worm eggs they excrete fall on soil that remains bare and dry (except during wet seasons) and are destroyed by sunlight and drying. Although the sows frequently urinate while grazing on the pasture area, the eggs are generally so scattered as to reduce the chances of infection materially.

(2) The use of a separate feeding pen for the sows, to which the pigs are never admitted and where the sows are left for a time after feeding, assures that many worm eggs will be concentrated in a location inaccessible to the pigs. Better results may be obtained if the manure is removed from the feeding pen at frequent intervals and disposed of so that the pigs will not come in contact with it.

Feeding the sows in a separate pen is desirable from another standpoint. During the gestation and lactation period, it makes it possible to exercise some control over the diet of the sow with a minimum amount of trouble.

Results Obtained by Use of the System

As a measure of the effect of these management practices in controlling kidney worms, careful post mortem examinations have been made from time to time of swine raised in accordance with the procedures recommended. Examinations were recently made of 525 pigs raised by this plan on farms in southern Georgia and northern Florida. Slight kidney worm lesions were present in the kidneys of only 10 percent of the animals. Only 14 percent of the livers were condemned as unfit for food because of these parasites. Naturally some of the farmers had not adhered strictly to the prescribed plan, and consequently some of the animals became infected. In 21 herds that were raised strictly in accordance with the provisions recommended, all livers were passed for food and the kidneys and kidney fat of all the animals were free of worms.

In marked contrast to those results, in 53,000 hogs raised without any attempt to prevent infection, 92 percent of the livers and all the kidneys and kidney fat were found parasitized with kidney worms and were condemned as unfit for food (*15*).

Other benefits derived from the kidney worm control plan include the raising of more pigs, better and more economical gains, and consequently more profit. Information gleaned from reports of county agents, directors of 4-H Clubs, and extension workers shows that by following the system in its entirety many farmers save more of their pigs and the young animals grow faster than under the old system. According to reports, some farmers have been able to market pigs anywhere from several weeks to as long as 3 months earlier than was customary. For example, it is reported that where the system has been carefully followed and the pigs were force-fed, it has been possible to market them at 200 pounds live weight in 5 months. It has also been stated that pigs grow more uniformly than when raised without attention to sanitation, and that hogs raised free from kidney worms and other parasites often dress out better than wormy hogs. In some cases the carcasses of the worm-free animals have dressed out over 78 percent. The difference is illustrated in figure 3 (p. 763), which shows the carcasses of a worm-free and a wormy hog, each 6 months of age.

Some criticism of the system has been made on the ground that it entails some trouble and expense. Practically the only unusual expense is that of providing shelter houses, water barrels, and feeding pens. However, these need not be elaborate structures and can be built of materials already on the farm. Once constructed, they can be used for many years.

As for the extra effort the system entails, if a farmer depends for part of his income on profit from the hogs he raises, he should consider the raising of the animals as an integral part of his farm program and give as much attention to it as he would to the corn, cotton, peanuts, and other crops he grows. It is well recognized that certain types of land are unsuited for growing grain, forage, or other plant crops and that any attempt to grow these crops on such soil would meet with failure. It should likewise be recognized that certain types of locations, such as permanent pastures, low-lying areas, etc., are unsuited for growing a pig crop. Any attempt to utilize such lands for pigs is likely to meet with partial or complete failure to raise the crop at a profit.

The farmer fights diseases and insects that affect his grain, forage, and fiber crops, and he fertilizes the soil to provide adequate nourishment for the plants to promote maximum growth. The pig crop is no different. The pigs have diseases that should be combated and need adequate nourishment to promote good health and maximum growth.

Pigs cannot be raised successfully on wasteland without attention any more than peanuts or corn can be expected to thrive on swampy or stony ground without proper attention. The farmer who wants to make a profit from his hogs should devote some of his best land to that purpose each year, just as he would to a plant crop on which he expects to make money. The pig crop should receive as careful attention as the plant crop, and it will not only give maximum returns but will also pay extra dividends by enriching the soil.

LITERATURE CITED

(1) ANONYMOUS.
.1926. SWINE SANITATION. (Abstract) Vet. Med. 21: 501.
(2) BURCH, J. W.
1930. THE MISSOURI PLAN OF GROWING THRIFTY PIGS. Mo. Univ. Agr. Col. Cir. 259, 12 pp., illus.
(3) CLUNIES ROSS, I., and KAUZAL, G.
1932. THE LIFE CYCLE OF STEPHANURUS DENTATUS DEISING, 1839: THE KIDNEY WORM OF PIGS. WITH OBSERVATIONS ON ITS ECONOMIC IMPORTANCE IN AUSTRALIA AND SUGGESTIONS FOR ITS CONTROL. Austral. Council Sci. & Indus. Res., Bul. 58, 80 pp., illus.
(4) CRAM, ELOISE B.
1930. BIRDS AS A FACTOR IN THE CONTROL OF A STOMACH WORM OF SWINE. Auk (n.s.) 47: 380–384.
(5) FRANCIONI, J. B., and MORRIS, HARRY.
1930. IT PAYS TO TREAT PIGS FOR WORMS. La. State Univ. Ext. Cir. 96, 10 pp., illus. (Revised.)
(6) GIBSON, J. E.
1931. SWINE-SANITATION PLAN RESULTS IN MORE AND BETTER PIGS PER SOW. U. S. Dept. Agr. Yearbook 1931: 503–505, illus.
(7) KATES, K. C.
1941. OBSERVATIONS ON THE VIABILITY OF EGGS OF LUNGWORMS OF SWINE. Jour. Parasitol. 27: 265–272.
(8) NIGHBERT, E. M., and CONNELLY, J. W.
[1928.] LOSSES THROUGH CONDEMNATIONS DUE TO PARASITES AND PARASITIC CONDITIONS OF SWINE, AND THE EFFECT OF SWINE SANITATION IN THE CONTROL OF KIDNEY WORMS. [Privately printed cir., Swift and Co.],[6] pp.
(9) PRICE, EMMETT W.
1925. THE OCCURRENCE AND DISTRIBUTION OF CYSTICERCUS CELLULOSAE IN TEXAS SWINE. Jour. Parasitol. 12: [81]–83, illus.
(10) RAFFENSPERGER, H. B., and CONNELLY, J. W.
1927. THE SWINE SANITATION SYSTEM AS DEVELOPED BY THE BUREAU OF ANIMAL INDUSTRY IN M'LEAN COUNTY, ILL. U. S. Dept. Agr. Tech. Bul. 44, 20 pp.
(11) [RANSOM, B. H.]
1918. WORMS IN PIGS. U. S. Dept. Agr. Weekly News Letter 5 (35): 5.
(12) ———
1927. THE PREVENTION OF ROUNDWORMS IN PIGS. U. S. Dept. Agr. Leaflet 6, 8 pp., illus.

(13) Robbins, E. T.
1926. CHEAPER AND MORE PROFITABLE PORK THRU SWINE SANITATION. A RE-
VIEW OF THE M'LEAN COUNTY SYSTEM OF SWINE SANITATION ON
ILLINOIS FARMS DURING 1925. Ill. Agr. Expt. Sta. Cir. 306, 16 pp.,
illus.
(14) Schwartz, Benjamin.
1931. SWINE KIDNEY WORM CAUSES LOSS TO SOUTHERN PRODUCERS FROM
CONDEMNED CARCASSES. U. S. Dept. Agr. Yearbook 1931: 499–502,
illus.
(15) ———
1934. CONTROLLING KIDNEY WORMS IN SWINE IN THE SOUTHERN STATES.
U. S. Dept. Agr. Leaflet 108, 6 pp., illus.
(16) ——— and Price, E. W.
1929. THE LIFE HISTORY OF THE SWINE KIDNEY WORM. Science 70: 613–614.
(17) Shope, Richard E.
1939. AN INTERMEDIATE HOST FOR THE SWINE INFLUENZA VIRUS. Science
89: 441–442.
(18) Spindler, L. A.
1933. FIELD STUDIES OF THE LARVAE OF NODULAR WORMS OF SWINE, WITH
SUGGESTIONS FOR CONTROL. North Amer. Vet. 14 (11) : 37–44.
(19) ———
1934. FIELD AND LABORATORY STUDIES ON THE BEHAVIOR OF THE LARVAE OF
THE SWINE KIDNEY WORM, STEPHANURUS DENTATUS. U. S. Dept.
Agr. Tech. Bul. 405, 18 pp.
(20) ———
1934. SKIN PENETRATION EXPERIMENTS WITH THE INFECTIVE LARVAE OF
STEPHANURUS DENTATUS. North Amer. Vet. 15 (10) : 32–36.
(21) ———
1937. INFESTATION OF SUCKLING PIGS WITH HELMINTH PARASITES UNDER
CONDITIONS OF CONSTANT EXPOSURE TO INFECTION. Helminthol. Soc.
Wash. Proc. 4 : 62–63.
(22) ———
1938. PERSISTENCE OF SWINE LUNGWORM LARVAE IN EARTHWORMS. Helminthol. Soc. Wash. Proc. 5 : 63.

At the time this book went to press, the drugs
and other materials mentioned in various articles—chiefly as disinfectants, insecticides, and
anthelmintics—were still available for veterinary and medical use. Under war conditions,
however, it is possible that some of these materials may become scarce or unavailable. In
that case, the reader should obtain professional
advice from the Department of Agriculture, the
State experiment station, a local veterinarian,
or the county agent as to available substitutes.

Trichinosis

BY BENJAMIN SCHWARTZ [1]

RECENT SURVEYS show that far more people in the United States are infected with trichinae—the small worms that settle chiefly in the muscles and cause trichinosis—than was formerly thought to be the case. Human beings get the disease almost entirely from pork. It can be prevented by the methods described in this article.

THE MICROSCOPIC ROUNDWORM PARASITES that occur at times in the muscles of human beings, swine, dogs, cats, rats, mice, and many other omnivorous and carnivorous animals are known to the general public as trichinae and to biologists and medical scientists as *Trichinella spiralis*. These parasites, when present in sufficient numbers in a suitable host, produce a disease known as trichinosis or trichiniasis.

Although trichinosis is probably never diagnosed in swine and seldom in other animals during life, the disease as it appears in man presents a more or less definite chain of symptoms, principally fever, muscular pains, and swelling of the eyelids. It may terminate in death and, in fact, is known to produce fatal results in about 5 percent of the cases. Because infected pork eaten raw or imperfectly cooked is the main source of human trichinosis, the occurrence of trichinae in swine has a far greater significance as a possible hazard to human health than as a cause of sickness in the affected animals.

In the discussion that follows trichinae are considered, therefore, largely as a menace to human health. The public health aspect of swine trichinosis, which has been widely publicized in recent years, has produced considerable repercussions in this country to the detriment of swine producers and the meat industry.

---

[1] Benjamin Schwartz is Chief of the Zoological Division, Bureau of Animal Industry.

THE DISCOVERY THAT TRICHINAE PRODUCE DISEASE

Trichinae were named and described in 1835, a quarter of a century before they were shown definitely to have any influence on human and animal health. There is some reason to believe that these parasites were actually observed in England in 1822 and again in 1828. In fact it appears quite certain that trichinae in their cysts, or capsules, were found in England by Hilton in 1832 in the abdominal muscles of a human cadaver. Hilton, who was a demonstrator in anatomy in Guy's Hospital, London, did not investigate the contents of these cysts, and the credit for doing this for the first time belongs to his fellow countryman, Paget, who made his observations 3 years later. In 1835 Paget, a medical student, discovered, while dissecting the muscles of a human body, small gritty spots that took the keen edge off his scalpel. Fortunately he had enough curiosity to investigate these spots with the aid of a microscope and, with technical assistance from others, determined that the spots were actually cysts containing organisms. He turned the material over to his professor, Sir Richard Owen, who in the same year published an account (*10*)[2] of the encysted parasites now known as *Trichinella spiralis*.

Following their discovery, trichinae, later recognized to be roundworms, continued to be encountered from time to time in dissecting rooms and for the next 25 years were regarded by most medical workers as relatively harmless zoological curiosities. The discovery by Leidy of trichinae in pork in the United States in 1846 (*6*) and a similar discovery in a cat in Germany some time later apparently threw no light on the possible origin of these muscle parasites. How they got into the muscles and how they propagated remained a complete mystery for two and one-half decades following their discovery, though speculation on these points was not lacking.

Like some other important discoveries in parasitology, those relating to trichinae were begun with simple observations that were followed later by experiments to determine the essential facts in the life cycle. In 1851 Herbst published an account of experiments in which he fed to dogs meat from a badger that, presumably, had been infected experimentally with trichinae; some time later he discovered encysted trichinae in the dogs' muscles. Investigations carried out in Germany a few years later by Leuckart, Zenker, and Virchow demonstrated conclusively that trichinae in the muscles of man and animals are actually incompletely developed worms, distinct from all others known up to that time as parasites of man and animals, and capable of undergoing further growth and development in the intestines of suitable hosts. Finally, these three investigators, working at the same time but independently, elucidated the essential facts in the mode of transmission of trichinae and established beyond doubt that the worms that occur in the muscles are the infective stages of parasites that can grow

---

[2] Italic numbers in parentheses refer to Literature Cited, p. 801.

to maturity in the intestines of susceptible host animals that have ingested trichina-infected meat.

That pork is a source of human infection came to light in 1860 under rather dramatic circumstances:

While conducting a necropsy, or post mortem examination, on a 19-year-old girl who died in Dresden, Germany, early in 1860, of a disease that was diagnosed before her death as typhoid fever, Zenker failed to find the usual post mortem picture characteristic of that disease. He found, however, numerous unencysted trichinae in the girl's muscles. Part of this material he sent to Leuckart and part to Virchow, the former an outstanding zoologist and parasitologist and the latter known the world over as the founder of cellular pathology. These investigators determined by animal experimentation that the trichinae found in the muscles of the girl developed to maturity in the intestines of suitable hosts, the mature parasites, in turn, evidently producing a new generation of young worms that ultimately invaded the muscles. Meanwhile Zenker discovered mature trichinae in the girl's intestines. He learned, moreover, that she had eaten raw sausage a month or so before her death. Fortunately some of the sausage was still available in the household where she had been a servant, and an examination showed that it was heavily infected with trichinae. Moreover, Zenker elicited the information that others in the household who had eaten this sausage had also become sick.

Thus in the year 1860 trichinae were shown to be pathogenic (disease producing) to man and capable of causing death; infected pork was shown to be a source of human trichinosis; and the mode of transmission of trichinae from one animal to another was conclusively established by rigid scientific experimentation. Perhaps the strangest occurrence in the unraveling of the story of trichinosis was the demonstration by Leuckart and Virchow, on the same day but quite independently of one another (8), of the presence of unencysted trichinae in the muscles of test animals to which infected meat had been fed several weeks earlier. The unencysted worms which Leuckart found in the muscles of an experimentally infected hog and Virchow found in those of an experimentally infected rabbit were in the same stage of development as those found by Zenker in the muscles of the girl whose death was the first to be definitely recorded in medical literature as due to human trichinosis.

LIFE HISTORY OF TRICHINAE

The life history of trichinae is shown graphically in figure 1. It is evident that infection results from eating meat that harbors trichinae. As a rule, human beings acquire trichinae by eating raw or imperfectly cooked trichinous pork in one form or another; swine become infected by eating offal or garbage containing scraps of raw infected pork or by eating the flesh of infected rats, mice, or other animals (fig. 1, sec. 5) rats and mice, in turn, acquire trichinae by eating raw, trichina-infected pork or other infected meat in garbage or elsewhere, or through cannibalism; dogs, cats, and other carnivorous animals acquire these parasites by eating the flesh of other animals already infected. Regardless of the source of infection, the course of events following the consumption of trichinous meat is briefly as follows:

As the trichina-infected meat is digested in the stomach of a human being, hog, or other suitable host, the encapsulated worms (fig. 1, sec. 4), are freed from their lemon-shaped or spherical capsules, or cysts, which are approximately one-fiftieth of an inch in maximum diameter and therefore microscopic in size. The worms themselves,

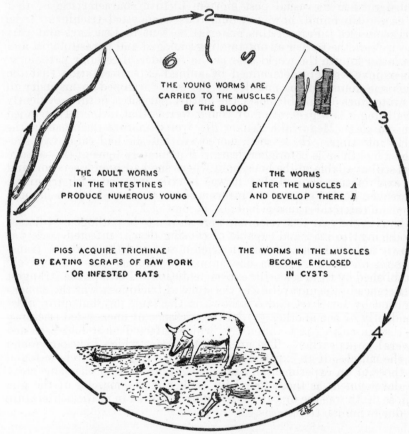

FIGURE 1.—The life cycle of trichinae (*Trichinella spiralis*).

spirally coiled within the cyst, are cylindrical in shape and measure about one twenty-fifth of an inch from end to end. Once they are free in the cavity, or lumen, of the stomach, they pass rapidly into the small intestine and become localized among the folds and villi (minute projections of the inner lining). Here they increase in size and attain sexual maturity in 2 days or earlier (*3*). Following the mating of the sexes, the worms continue to grow, and they attain their maximum size 4 to 5 days later, or 6 to 7 days after they reach the host's stomach. When full grown, the females measure from one-eighth to one-sixth of an inch in length; the males are only about half as long (fig. 1, sec. 1). The fertilized eggs are not discharged by the female worms, as are those of most other parasitic roundworms that occur in man and domestic animals, but develop within the maternal uterus, where they hatch and from which they escape as larvae.

The birth of the larvae begins about 5 days after infection (*3*) and may continue for several weeks; though many more young are born during the first 2 weeks of the worms' fertile period than subsequently. The adult trichinae in the intestine tend to die and pass out after their reproductive functions have been fulfilled, though adult worms have been found several weeks after infection and some of them, at least, may persist for 3 months or so. The newborn larvae (fig. 1, sec. 2), of which several hundred can be deposited by a single female trichina (*9*), measure about one two hundred and fiftieth of an inch in length. Owing to the fact that the female worm is rather deeply imbedded in the intestinal lining, the larvae are deposited directly in the lymph spaces of the intestinal wall. The larvae thus caught in the lymph channels migrate with the lymph stream, ultimately reaching one of the large lymph vessels, known as the thoracic duct. This empties into a large vein, from which the blood flows to the right side of the heart. The larvae are distributed by the circulation from the right side of the heart to the lungs and thence to the left side of the heart and by the arterial circulation to all parts of the body. It is known that trichina larvae reach various tissues and organs but they become localized, for the most part, in the voluntary muscles (the flesh), the fibers of which they penetrate (fig. 1, sec. 3, *A*) and in which they ultimately become encapsulated.

Within 10 to 14 days after their penetration into the muscle fibers the larvae have attained their maximum length, which is 10 times their original length (fig. 1, sec. 3, *B*). Encystment begins about 1 month after infection, and a thin-walled capsule is readily recognizable about 2 weeks later. About 6 months after infection the capsules may begin to calcify, calcium being deposited first at their poles or ends. Living trichinae commonly occur in such calcified capsules. It is not known precisely how long trichina larvae may live within their cysts, but there is reason to believe that they can do so for many years, at least in some cases. Sooner or later, however, the worms within the capsules may calcify and break down into crumbled masses, or they may die before the process of calcification has set in and become absorbed. However, even though the worms remain alive they are incapable of further growth within the capsules. In many respects the live, encysted worms are comparable to seeds which are capable of further development only under favorable conditions. These conditions are fulfilled for trichinae when the flesh, or meat, in which they are present is eaten by an animal in which they are capable of developing to sexual maturity, as previously described.

HOSTS OF TRICHINAE

Trichinae have been recorded from a variety of animals besides those mentioned. Bears, in particular, can play an important role in the transmission of trichinae to man, severe cases of this infection in Europe having been traced to the eating of uncooked bear meat. In the United States there have been instances in which jerked bear meat has been found to be a source of human trichinosis. Various other carnivorous animals, such as the fox, the badger, the martin, the raccoon, the otter, the mongoose, and others are known to be hosts of trichinae. Several wild rodents, such as the mole, the hedgehog, the ground squirrel, and others, also have been reported as hosts of these parasites. In the laboratory, rabbits, guinea pigs, white rats, and mice are readily infected experimentally with trichinae, and much of the available information about these parasites is a result of the experimental infection of these rodents. The herbivorous domestic animals—cattle, sheep, goats, and horses—also are susceptible to experimental infection with trichinae. Under normal conditions, however, these animals would not become infected, since they do not eat meat, and so far as is known, their susceptibility is only of theoretical interest and without any practical significance.

In certain European countries the flesh of various fur-bearing animals, in addition to that of bears, is sometimes eaten raw or incompletely cooked, with the result that some cases of human trichinosis have been traced to this source. In the United States, however, all cases of trichinosis that have been definitely traced to their source, with the exception of a few known to have resulted from eating uncooked bear meat, were found to have been caused by the eating of raw or rare pork or some pork-containing meat food product, such as sausage, insufficiently processed to destroy trichinae. Cases of trichinosis usually occur after parties, picnics, and family gatherings in which raw ham or sausage or some other insufficiently cooked or inadequately cured pork-containing food is eaten by relatively large groups, only those who abstain from eating the food in question escaping infection (*16*).

THE DISEASE

SYMPTOMS

The disease trichinosis manifests itself in man and animals by various symptoms, the severity of which is usually correlated with the number of worms swallowed in the infected meat. The consumption of lightly infected pork or other meat by man or animals produces no visible symptoms unless large quantities of such meat are eaten. On the other hand, the consumption of even relatively small quantities of heavily infected meat may produce serious illness and even death.

The clinical manifestations of trichinosis in swine have been established by experimental feeding of large quantities of trichinous meat. In the severest cases intestinal irritation, fever, muscular pain and stiffness, difficulty in chewing and breathing, and severe emaciation have been noted. In more moderate infections the symptoms are indefinite. Trichinosis in pigs is not diagnosed during the life of these animals, even though the symptoms are striking, for the reason that other, more familiar febrile diseases—that is, diseases accompanied by fever—of swine are characterized by similar clinical manifestations.

In man the clinical picture of trichinosis has been ascertained in various parts of the world since 1860. The classical accounts of this disease as recorded in the medical literature are briefly as follows:

During the development of trichinae in the intestine and the production of their young, known as the stage of ingression, there may be nausea, vomiting, diarrhea, and abdominal pain, or these symptoms may be entirely lacking. Other manifestations during the first week or so of infection are a general torpor, accompanied by weakness, a sensation of tension or pain in the muscles, muscular twitching, and, towards the end of this period, a swelling of the face and eyelids, particularly the latter.

The next stage of the disease, known as the stage of digression, corresponds to the distribution of the larvae throughout the body and their penetration into the muscles. The symptoms of this stage appear after the first week, about 9 days to 2 weeks after initial infection, and continue for the next 2 weeks or so. They are characterized by severe muscular pains, the muscles becoming swollen, hard, and tense. Moving the eyes and the tongue and chewing, breathing, swallowing are likely to be painful because of the penetration of trichina larvae.

The third stage, known as the stage of regression, corresponds to the encystment of the parasites within the muscles and may be accompanied by an intensification of the symptoms of the second stage and the appearance of pronounced swelling of the legs, forearms, abdominal wall, and face. Anemia and cutaneous (skin) eruptions may appear, and pneumonia is a probable complication.

Fever sets in during the first stage, becomes more pronounced during the second stage, and may persist, usually with remissions, for several weeks. Apathy or mental disturbances may set in, and in some cases the mental symptoms may become aggravated to the point of delirium.

The symptoms outlined represent, no doubt, a composite picture of the disease. All of them would not be present in all cases, nor would they appear necessarily in the order mentioned. Actually the clinical picture may show striking variations, as indicated in accounts of a recent outbreak of trichinosis in England (5, 20) involving about 500 clinical and an undetermined number of subclinical cases.

DIAGNOSIS

In a few cases practicing veterinarians have diagnosed trichinosis in pet animals, largely on the basis of fever associated with muscular stiffness. In man a presumptive diagnosis of trichinosis is frequently made on the basis of symptoms, particularly if the clinical manifestations can be traced to the consumption of raw pork or some pork food product not sufficiently processed to destroy trichinae. Not infrequently, however, the clinical manifestations of trichinosis in

man have been confused with those of other febrile diseases, especially typhoid fever, undulant fever, influenza, nephritis, tuberculous
meningitis, gastroenteritis, colitis, rheumatic endocarditis, syphilis,
tuberculosis, and other diseases.

Of the more important diagnostic aids that are used to corroborate
a presumptive diagnosis of trichinosis, eosinophilia (an increase in
certain white blood cells—the eosinophilic leucocytes of the blood),
a positive skin test and blood serum test, and the discovery of trichinae in small pieces of muscle (biopsy material), are the most
important.

INCIDENCE OF TRICHINAE AND OF TRICHINOSIS IN MAN

Investigations conducted in the United States during the last 12
years and still in progress have disclosed a surprisingly high incidence of infecton with trichinae in the general populaton of this
country. The investigations under consideration have been conducted by means of one or both of two techniques: (1) Digesting,
in an incubator, the diaphragm or other muscle tissues, or sizable
portions of them, obtained from the bodies of persons that have died
in hospitals from various causes other than trichinosis, and recovering
any trichinae present from the sediment of the digestive fluid; (2) repeated, painstaking microscopic examinations of fresh preparations
of diaphragm or other muscle tissue in which trichinae are known
to be localized in large numbers.

Queen (*11*) reported in 1931 that the muscle samples from 59 of
344 unselected persons (17.2 percent) who died in Rochester, N. Y.,
and those from 16 of 58 persons (27.6 percent) who died in Boston,
Mass., contained trichinae; other investigators working in or obtaining their material for the most part from large metropolitan hospitals afterward published more or less similar results. In some
of these cases the reported incidences of infection with trichinae
were even more striking than those recorded by Queen. A recent
report issued by the United States Public Health Service (*4*) covers
the examination for trichinae of 2,330 human diaphragms obtained
from hospitals in Washington, D. C., and 670 from various Federal
hospitals in other cities. Of the total number examined, 488 (16.3
percent) were infected with trichinae. It is important to note,
however, that 425 contained trichinae in rather small numbers,
probably too few, in most cases, to have produced any signs of
illness during life. Only 8 of the 488 positive diaphragms contained
more than 100 larvae per gram of muscle tissue examined, and it is
not unlikely that these were from the only individuals who showed
signs of illness caused by trichinae during life. In general, the observations recorded by other investigators in the course of the recent
surveys of over 5,500 human diaphragms also show a high incidence
(14 percent) and a low intensity of infection. Practically none of
the investigators who conducted the surveys were able to obtain from
the medical history of the persons involved any conclusive evidence
of clinical trichinosis during life.

The number of cases of clinical trichinosis in the United States actually recorded as such in the medical literature is very small when compared with the high incidence of infection with trichinae already discussed. In 1938 Sawitz (*13*) concluded from a study of the statistical data published by the United States Public Health Service and records available in medical journals that the total number of cases of clinical trichinosis ever recorded in the United States amounts to between 5,000 and 6,000. It cannot be properly concluded, however, that all cases of trichinosis that have occurred in this country since 1842, when these parasites were first found in the body of a person who had suffered rheumatic pains in the arms and legs, have found their way into medical statistics or into the medical literature (*15*).

Investigations on the incidence of trichinae in human beings in foreign countries, comparable to those made in the United States, are only fragmentary. The recent examination of 200 diaphragm samples from as many persons who died in England from various causes disclosed only two lightly infected ones, thus giving an incidence of 1 percent (*24*). Recently an examination of 420 diaphragms in Canada (*2*) revealed 7 that were infected with trichinae, an incidence of 1.6 percent.

In England up to 1940, the number of cases of clinical trichinosis and those involving the post mortem discovery of trichinae in human cadavers was well below 100 (*24*). Because of this the general opinion has prevailed that that country was singularly free from the disease. However, a serious epidemic of trichinosis came to light in England in December 1940, as previously noted, with an estimated number of at least 500 clinical cases and an undetermined number of nonclinical infections. It is quite evident, therefore, that as long as infected animals exist as a reservoir of the disease, the danger of its spreading to man is ever present.

OCCURRENCE AND FREQUENCY OF TRICHINAE IN SWINE IN THE UNITED STATES

The first recorded discovery of trichinae in swine was made in the United States in 1866 by Leidy, who discovered the cysts while eating a slice of cooked pork in his home in Philadelphia (*7*).

In 1862, 2 years after the discovery of the transmission of trichinae to man as a result of the consumption of raw, infected pork, an epidemic of trichinosis, with the mortality of 16 percent, came to light in a small town in Germany. Two years later another and even more serious epidemic of this disease occurred in another small town in that country, with the result that pork began to acquire the stigma of being capable of producing a serious and painful human disease that had a strikingly high mortality. These and other epidemics of trichinosis in Europe were not without effect on the American meat industry, which by 1879 had developed a rather flourishing export trade to certain countries in Europe. By 1881 Italy, Germany, Austria, and France had promulgated sanitary regulations prohibiting the importation of pork from the United

States because of the alleged danger of acquiring trichinosis from this meat.

It is not surprising, therefore, that under the Federal meat-inspection act of 1891 provision was made for the microscopic examination for trichinae of pork intended for export to foreign countries in order to surmount the sanitary barriers that had been set up against the importation of this commodity from the United States. This led to the systematic microscopic examination of samples of muscle tissue from millions of hogs intended for export, and the microscopists of the Bureau of Animal Industry engaged in this work determined that a small percentage of these animals were actually infected with trichinae. In a total of over 8 million hogs samples of which were examined microscopically from 1898 to 1906, nearly 1.5 percent were found to contain live trichinae, and in addition slightly over 1 percent were found to contain what were, presumably, trichinae in various stages of disintegration.

With the passage of a new meat-inspection act by Congress in 1906, microscopic inspection for trichinae of pork intended for export was discontinued, largely because this inspection was inherently imperfect. According to statements published by European meat-inspection experts, reinspection of samples of pork from this country certified as being free from trichinae in accordance with the results obtained by microscopic inspection here showed some of the pork to be infected. The incidence of trichinae in swine in this country from 1906 up to quite recently was unknown but was assumed to be the same as that brought to light by the systematic microscopic examinations of 1898–1906.

In 1933 the writer initiated an investigation to determine the current frequency of infection of swine with trichinae, using for this purpose a procedure that gives far more accurate results than the microscopic inspection previously used. The new procedure consists in digesting in artificial gastric juice in an incubator the diaphragms of hogs, selected at random, and determining the number of trichinae, if any, present in each diaphragm in relation to the quantity of meat digested. Since the diaphragm is known to be one of the preferred locations of trichinae, it is believed that the procedure outlined establishes the true incidence of these parasites in swine to a higher degree of probability than any other known method of examination.

Out of more than 13,000 diaphragms from as many farm-raised hogs shipped to the most important meat-slaughtering centers of the United States, only 126 (0.95 percent) were found to be infected with trichinae. Nearly two-thirds of these contained the parasites in exceedingly small numbers (only 1 to 5 larvae per 100 grams—about 3½ ounces—of meat), so small, in fact, that it is doubtful whether any method of inspection other than the one used would have resulted in their discovery except by sheer accident. Considering the fact that in microscopic inspection of pork for trichinae only 3 samples from each carcass, each sample about the size of an oat grain and certainly no larger than a small pea, are examined or can be examined satisfactorily from a practical standpoint, it is quite evident that the chances of detecting such light infections are exceedingly slight.

Data not previously published show that out of about 9,000 samples of pork from as many hogs originating on the Atlantic and Pacific seaboards and known to have been fed almost exclusively on untreated garbage, 554 (6.11 percent) were found to be infected. Not only was the incidence of infection in the garbage-fed hogs greater than that in the farm-raised hogs fed forage, grain, and other feeds, but the intensity of infection in the garbage-fed series also was much greater. Only something over one-third of the diaphragms from the garbage-fed-samples contained the very light infections that occurred in about two-thirds of the positive diaphragms of farm-raised hogs. In one series, including nearly 4,500 diaphragms from garbage-fed hogs in one of the Pacific Coast States, the incidence of infection was over 3.5 percent. In another series including over 2,500 diaphragms from as many hogs from one of the Atlantic Seaboard States, the incidence of infection was about 10.5 percent, while in about 2,000 diaphragms from hogs in another State on the Atlantic coast the incidence was nearly 6 percent. It is evident, therefore, that the average frequency of trichinae in garbage-fed hogs is more than 6 times that in farm-raised hogs. Pork from hogs fed garbage is, therefore, a far greater danger to human health than that from hogs raised on the farm and fed on forage, grain, and the usual supplements of tankage and minerals.

In the course of examinations to determine the incidence of trichi-nae in swine fed on different types of feeds, over 2,200 diaphragms were obtained from hogs known to have been fed cooked garbage only. Of these, only 11 (slightly less than 0.5 per cent) were found to be infected, the numbers of trichinae in the positive hogs being very small. It is evident, therefore, that the danger inherent in garbage as a feed for swine, from the standpoint of trichinosis, is the presence in it of pieces of raw pork or other meat containing trichinae. Cooking destroys nearly all of these parasites, as shown by the data just presented, and would destroy all of them if sufficient heat were applied.

The occurrence of trichinae in nearly 1 percent of farm-raised hogs affords conclusive evidence that the animals must have had access at one time or another to offal, garbage, kitchen scraps, or possibly other sources of trichinous meat. In the absence of such sources of infection, these pigs would not acquire trichinae unless, because of some dietary deficiency or other reason, they happened to eat infected rats or mice.

According to information published recently (*14*), trichinae are now exceedingly rare in swine in Germany, as shown by the fact that in 1936 samples of only 135 hogs were found to be infected out of nearly 19 million swine, samples of which were examined under the microscope as a regular routine. The indicated frequency is about 7 infected hogs in every million examined. In Poland, where pork is not microscopically inspected for trichinae, the incidence of these parasites in swine was reported in a German publication in 1941 to be about 70 times greater than in Germany (*14*). In Canada, where swine-husbandry practices are more nearly similar to those prevailing in the United States than are those in European countries, an examination of 995 diaphragms from as many garbage-fed swine from the Provinces of Quebec, Ontario, and Manitoba disclosed 2 that were infected, the incidence being, therefore, 0.2 percent (*1*). This low figure is not surprising since the Dominion laws require the sterilization by heat of all garbage fed to swine. In a previous investigation in Canada involving nearly 2,300 diaphragms the incidence of infection was 0.57 percent, very close to the figure derived from the data on the results of examinations in the United States of diaphragms of swine fed only cooked garbage.

CONTROL OF TRICHINOSIS

Since there is no specific treatment for the removal of adult trichinae from the intestine or for the destruction of their larvae in the blood or muscles before or after their encystment, the major emphasis must be placed on prevention. Preventive measures must be directed against trichinosis in swine as well as in man because the successful control of the infection in pigs will result in a diminution in the number of human cases and might bring about its ultimate elimination from the list of human diseases. Actually, trichinosis in man is an easily preventable disease, since prevention consists merely in thoroughly cooking pork in all its forms. Its persistence despite repeated warnings of the danger inherent in raw pork is proof that warnings have not reached the public or that they have not been heeded by persons whose taste for raw pork in one form or another is such that they will eat it even in the face of the danger of acquiring a painful, serious, and possibly fatal illness.

Different countries have met the problem in different ways, the preventive measures adopted in any particular country being governed to a greater or less extent by the prevailing habits of the population with respect to the cooking and curing of pork and its products. Some countries have no trichinosis problem so far as is known, presumably because their populations do not eat raw pork in any form. Other countries, particularly on the continent of Europe, followed the leadership of Germany and long ago adopted as part of their meat-inspection procedure the plan of microscopic examination of samples of pork from all hogs slaughtered for human consumption, including those slaughtered on the farm for home consumption. In adopting this procedure, the meat-inspection authorities of the countries concerned recognized that they had to cope with the custom of eating pork in the raw state, a habit so deeply rooted in the general population that it could not, in their opinion, be eradicated by education. The countries that have practiced microscopic inspection, particularly Germany and Denmark, point with pride to the fact that, largely as a result of this, the incidence of trichinae in swine has declined steadily and that this decline has been reflected in a sharp diminution of trichinosis in man.

In the United States microscopic inspection for trichinae was resorted to, as previously noted, only in the case of pork intended for export to countries in Europe that made such inspection mandatory. The motives were economic rather than hygienic. At no time did

American meat-inspection authorities give serious consideration to the adoption of microscopic inspection of pork for trichinae as part of the general procedure under Federal meat inspection. Investigations have shown that in numerous instances trichinous pork had been examined microscopically as many as 20 to 30 times before the parasites were found. Since it would be impracticable under any inspection scheme to make so many examinations, the unreliability of inspection for trichinae is quite obvious. Stiles (*23*) determined that out of 6,329 cases of trichinosis that occurred in Germany between 1881 and 1898, 2,042 (over 32 percent) could be traced to pork which had been inspected microscopically and passed as free from trichinae. This evidence shows that microscopic inspection is inherently imperfect and is fraught with the danger of giving persons who are fond of raw pork and its products a false sense of security, encouraging the consumption of raw pork and defeating in a measure the very purpose for which the inspection was intended.

It must be borne in mind that Federal meat inspection in this country is limited to plants that engage in interstate or foreign commerce. Slaughtering and meat-processing plants not engaged in interstate or foreign commerce do not come under the provision of the Meat Inspection Act and are therefore either without inspection or subject only to State or muncipal inspection. Slaughtering done on the farm is exempt from inspection. Since only a few States and comparatively few municipalities have a rigid system of meat inspection, not all pork from hogs slaughtered in this country would be subjected to microscopic inspection even if such inspection were enforced in Government-inspected establishments. Actually, only about 60 percent of the hogs consumed in this country are slaughtered in Federally inspected establishments. It cannot be supposed that consumers would take the trouble in most instances to differentiate between pork inspected microscopically by Federal or other authorities and pork not so inspected. This situation would tend to nullify, at least in part, the good that might result from microscopic inspection of pork for trichinae. In addition, the cost of microscopic inspection by the Federal Government alone would involve an expenditure of about 10 million dollars annually (*17*), approximately twice the present outlay for all Federal meat inspection. In view of the fact that this investment of public funds cannot be expected to yield entirely satisfactory results, for the reasons already given, the drain on the Public Treasury that it would entail hardly appears to be warranted.

Following the publication of results of investigations showing that rabbits experimentally infected with trichinae gave clear-cut reactions to the injection into the skin of various test materials (antigens) prepared from trichina larvae, research work was undertaken by specialists in the Bureau of Animal Industry and elsewhere to determine the feasibility of detecting infection with trichinae in hogs prior to slaughter. Although several workers have recommended, at least by implication, the adoption of this or a similar biological test to weed out trichina-infected swine, the work reported by investigators of the Bureau of Animal Industry (*18, 19, 21, 22*) shows that the skin test, when applied to swine, is not sufficiently specific to warrant its use for the purposes indicated.

In the absence of any known practical method of inspection of hogs for trichinae, the regulations governing meat inspection by the United States Department of Agriculture provide that no article of a kind prepared customarily to be eaten without cooking shall contain any muscle tissue of pork unless this meat has been subjected to a temperature sufficient to destroy all live trichinae, or to other treatment prescribed by the Chief of the Bureau of Animal Industry. The treatments prescribed for all meat food products containing pork muscle tissue that are prepared to be eaten without cooking are (1) heating, (2) special refrigeration, and (3) special processing. When heating is done, it is required that all meat food products of the kinds mentioned must be so heated that they will attain in all parts a temperature of not less than 137° F., this temperature having been determined by investigation to be lethal to trichinae (*12*). The required refrigeration involves the subjection of pork or of articles containing pork muscle tissue to a temperature of not less than 5° F. for a continuous period of not less than 20 days, or the subjection of the meat or articles to lower specified temperatures for shorter specified periods. Special curing methods in lieu of the required heating or refrigeration are designed to effect the destruction of trichinae by the action of curing ingredients, especially salt, by smoking at temperatures lower than 137° F. for definite periods, and by drying. The prescribed curing methods are known, as a result of numerous trials, to be effective in destroying the vitality of trichinae.

All the methods approved by the Bureau of Animal Industry as effective in destroying life in trichinae are based on extensive scientific research carried out in the laboratory and in meat-packing establishments and were subjected to repeated trials before they were adopted for official use. Under Federal meat inspection, therefore, the public is safeguarded against the danger of acquiring trichinosis from meat food products containing pork muscle tissue that are usually eaten without cooking. In preparing fresh pork and ordinary varieties of cured pork that have not been specially processed, under competent inspection, to destroy trichinae, the only safe rule to follow is to cook the pork until it is well done throughout.

Inasmuch as data that have been presented in this article show that garbage-fed hogs have an averge incidence of trichina infections more than six times that of farm-raised hogs and that cooking garbage renders it safe as a swine feed so far as trichinae are concerned, the control of garbage feeding by States and muncipalities through the enforcement of heat-sterilization requirements, or the voluntary adoption by feeders of the practice of sterilizing garbage by heat, would go a long way toward reducing the rather high incidence of trichinae in swine in the United States.

On the farm, three precautions would further reduce the incidence of swine trichinosis: (1) Do not feed offal, kitchen scraps containing raw pork, or the contents of the slop barrel to swine; (2) do not throw dead rats and mice into the hog pens; (3) bury deeply in quicklime or burn the carcasses of hogs and other animals that die on the farm.

These steps, together with the control of garbage feeding indicated above, would eliminate to a large extent practically the only source of human trichinosis in this country.

LITERATURE CITED

(1) CAMERON, THOMAS W. M.
    1940. INVESTIGATIONS ON TRICHINOSIS IN CANADA. III. ON THE INCIDENCE OF TRICHINOSIS IN GARBAGE-FED HOGS. Canad. Jour. Res., Sect. D, Zool. Sci., 18 : 83–85.
(2) EKBAUM, ELLA KUITUNEN.
    1941. THE INCIDENCE OF HUMAN TRICHINOSIS IN TORONTO. (Abstract of paper) Canad. Pub. Health Jour. 32 : 78.
((3) HEMMERT-HALSWICK, ALFRED, and BUGGE, G.
    1934. TRICHINEN UND TRICHINOSE. Ergeb. der Allg. Path. Mensch. u. Tiere 28 : 313–392, illus.
(4) KERR, K. B., JACOBS, LEON, and CUVILLIER, EUGENIA.
    1941. STUDIES ON TRICHINOSIS. XIII. THE INCIDENCE OF HUMAN INFECTION WITH TRICHINAE AS INDICATED BY POST-MORTEM EXAMINATION OF 3,000 DIAPHRAGMS FROM WASHINGTON, D. C., AND 5 EASTERN SEABOARD CITIES. U. S. Pub. Health Serv., Pub. Health Rpts. 56 : 836–855.
(5) LEE, J. E. STANLEY.
    1941. AN OUTBREAK OF TRICHINIASIS IN WOLVERHAMPTON AND DISTRICT. A CLINICAL ACCOUNT OF SEVEN CASES. Brit. Med. Jour. 4180 : 237–240.
(6) LEIDY, JOSEPH.
    1848. [ENTOZOON IN THE SUPERFICIAL PART OF THE EXTENSOR MUSCLES OF THE THIGH OF THE HOG.] (Abstract) Acad. Nat. Sci. Phila. Proc. (1846–47) 3 : 107–108.
(7) ———
    1866. [REMARKS ON TRICHINA.] (Abstract) Acad. Nat. Sci. Phila. Proc. 18 : 9.
(8) LEUCKART, RUDOLF.
    1876. DIE MENSCHLICHEN PARASITEN UND DIE VON IHNEN HERRÜHRENDEN KRANKHEITEN. Bd. 2, 882 pp. Leipzig and Heidelberg.
(9) MATOFF, KONSTANTIN, and WAPZAROWA, MARA.
    1937. WIEVIEL JUNGTRICHINELLEN KANN EINE WEIBLICHE DARMTRICHINELLE GEBÄREN. Ztschr. f. Infektionskrank., Parasitäre Krank. u. Hyg. der Haustiere 51 : 89–98.
(10) OWEN, RICHARD.
    1835. DESCRIPTION OF A MICROSCOPIC ONTOZOON INFESTING THE MUSCLES OF THE HUMAN BODY. [London] Zool. Soc. Trans. 1 : 315–324, illus.
(11) QUEEN, FRANK B.
    1931. THE PREVALENCE OF HUMAN INFECTION WITH TRICHINELLA SPIRALIS. (Abstract of paper) Jour. Parasitol. 18 : 128.
(12) RANSOM, B. H. and SCHWARTZ, BENJAMIN.
    1919. EFFECTS OF HEAT ON TRICHINAE. Jour. Agr. Res. 17 : 201–221.
(13) SAWITZ, WILLI.
    1938. PREVALENCE OF TRICHINOSIS IN THE UNITED STATES. U. S. Pub. Health Serv., Pub. Health Rpts. 53 : 365–383, illus.
(14) SCHAAF, J.
    1941. VORKOMMEN UND VERBREITUNG DER TRICHINOSE IM GENERALGOUVERNE-MENT POLEN. Berlin. u. München. Tierarztl. Wchnschr. Nr. 11 : 131–133.
(15) SCHWARTZ, BENJAMIN.
    1929. TRICHINOSIS, A DISEASE CAUSED BY EATING RAW PORK. U. S. Dept. Agr. Leaflet 34, 8 pp., illus.

802 *Yearbook of Agriculture, 1942*

(16) Schwartz, Benjamin,
1938. ANIMAL PARASITES TRANSMISSIBLE TO MAN. Sci. Monthly 47 : 400–410.
(17) ———
1941. MEAT-INSPECTION ASPECTS OF TRICHINOSIS. Amer. Vet. Med. Assoc. Jour. 98 : 459–461.
(18) ——— and McIntosh, Allen.
1929. SKIN REACTIONS IN EXPERIMENTAL TRICHINOSIS IN PIG. (Abstract of paper) Jour. Parasitol. 16 : 104–105.
(19) ——— McIntosh, Allen, and Mitchell, W. C.
1930. NON-SPECIFIC SKIN REACTIONS IN PIGS TO THE INJECTION OF TRICHINA EXTRACTS. (Abstract of paper) Jour. Parasitol. 17 : 114.
(20) Sheldon, J. H.
1941. AN OUTBREAK OF TRICHINIASIS IN WOLVERHAMPTON AND DISTRICT. Lancet [London] 1 : 203–205.
(21) Spindler, L. A., and Cross, S. X.
1939. INTRACUTANEOUS TESTS FOR THE DETECTION OF TRICHINA INFECTIONS EXPERIMENTALLY AND NATURALLY ACQUIRED BY SWINE. Helminthol. Soc. Wash. Proc. 6 : 37–42.
(22) ——— Cross, S. X., and Avery, J. L.
1941. RESULTS OF INTRACUTANEOUS TESTS FOR THE DETECTION OF TRICHINA INFECTIONS IN SWINE. Helminthol. Soc. Wash. Proc. 8 : 1–5.
(23) Stiles, Charles Wardell.
1901. TRICHINOSIS IN GERMANY. U. S. Bur. Anim. Indus. Bul. 30, pp. 7–192.
(24) Van Someren, Vernon D.
1937. THE OCCURRENCE OF SUBCLINICAL TRICHINOSIS IN BRITAIN. RESULTS FROM 200 LONDON NECROPSIES. Brit. Med. Jour. 4014 : 1162–1165.

Salt Tolerance and Salt Poisoning of Swine

BY N. R. ELLIS [1]

THERE HAS BEEN a good deal of discussion about whether certain cases of poisoning in swine, often fatal, were due to an excess of salt. The author reports the results of a careful investigation to clear up the whole question of how much salt swine can tolerate and what an excessive amount does to them.

COMMON SALT is recognized as one of the chemical substances required in the diet of animals; hence it is good husbandry to include a supply in the rations of livestock. The quantitative requirements vary with the species. Those for swine are regarded as among the lowest. That excessive amounts may be harmful to the extent of being toxic is not at all surprising, since there are recognized limits beyond which various nutritive essentials become a burden, or even toxic, to the animal body. Much of the science of animal nutrition is built around the proper proportioning and balancing of the essential elements of the diet.

"Salt poisoning" is the term frequently used to characterize certain forms of poisoning, often fatal, in swine, which are generally attributed to an excessive intake of sodium chloride. The true cause, particularly the conditions under which severe poisoning may result, remains obscure.

Various reports have listed a number of gross symptoms as characterizing the condition, including extreme nervousness, frothing at the mouth, convulsions, paralysis, diarrhea, vomiting, loss of appetite, extreme thirst, blindness, and finally death. As evidence of the causative agent, case histories have frequently pointed to the consumption of large amounts of salt, especially in the form of brine, by

[1] N. R. Ellis is Senior Chemist in Charge of General Nutrition Investigations, Animal Nutrition Division, Bureau of Animal Industry.

hogs that for extended periods had not received salt as a regular part of their ration. Udall (*11*)[2] has pointed out that the immediate effect of excessive consumption of salt is inflammation of the mucous membrane of the stomach and marked redness.and dryness of that of the mouth. The principal change evident on post mortem examination is gastroenteritis (inflammation of the stomach and intestines).

RESULTS OF STUDIES OF SALT REQUIREMENTS AND SALT TOLERANCE OF SWINE

As a result of feeding investigations on the requirements of swine for salt, the need for small additions to the ration is well recognized. The generally recommended practice is to provide a mineral mixture containing salt in a self-feeder compartment, so that the pigs can satisfy their craving for minerals, or to mix small amounts with the concentrate feeds. The daily requirements are known to be small. Morrison (*7*) recommends not over ¼ pound of salt to 100 pounds of feed mixture. This would allow 5 to 6 grams (less than ¼ ounce) a day per 100 pounds of live weight; when this is added to the salt naturally contained in the average ration, the total would probably seldom exceed 10 grams (about ⅓ ounce).

That salt may be toxic to animals when consumed in large quantities has been recognized as entirely probable for a long time. The lethal, or fatal, dose for poultry has been fairly well established from the work of Mitchell, Card, and Carman (*6*) and others. Concerning the toxic quantity for swine, the results are conflicting. As will be seen in the present review, the case against salt as the cause of poisoning is not clear-cut in spite of the frequent warnings found in textbooks and popular articles on swine feeding. Undoubtedly, gorging with salt has been at least a contributory if not the main factor in a certain number of deaths among swine. In his discussion of salt poisoning in livestock Udall (*11*) states that "swine have been poisoned by drinking brine and by eating garbage that had been pickled in brine." He quotes the toxic dose of salt for swine as ½ to 1 pound.

In reviewing his experiences with salt poisoning, Hofferd (*3*) observes that the most common effects of excessive salt intake over extended periods are inflammation of the kidneys and bladder and hardening of the liver. Acute poisoning was attributed to the consumption of brine. He states that diagnosis is often difficult because of varying symptoms. However, the temperature of affected animals generally remains about normal, and the animals usually show extreme nervousness and evidences of pain as a result of irritation of the kidneys and bladder. Among the instances of poisoning cited was one that occurred on a farm where a commercial mixed cattle feed containing much more salt than the hog feed in use was inadvertently placed in the hog feeders. In another instance a herd of pigs had been vaccinated with both virus and serum, and when a

[2] Italic numbers in parentheses refer to Literature Cited, p. 808.

number of them sickened and became paralyzed the owner placed blocks of medicated salt in the pens. The pigs were observed to eat considerable amounts of the salt, and thereafter a number of the sick ones died. Removal of the salt blocks coincided with cessation of the deaths.

The consumption of salt in the form of brine is singled out by Hofferd and other writers as the chief factor in causing acute poisoning and sudden death of swine. Buffagni (*2*) has reported cases of poisoning in pigs due to a mixture of brine with the concentrate feed. A cow was reported as having been poisoned by 1 kilogram (2⅕ pounds) of salt administered as treatment for a condition diagnosed as indigestion.

Wautié (*13*), describing experimental work on salt and brine poisoning, tells that three pigs fed a brine solution that gave them 60 to 80 grams (2 to 3 ounces) of salt daily were severely affected by the tenth day. The symptoms consisted of stiffness of the legs, absence of reflex response, blindness, and constipation. An injection of calcium gluconate gave relief. Dry salt up to 250 grams (a little over half a pound) a day did not produce the extreme symptoms observed in the pigs given brine. He concluded that salt poisoning depends on the form in which the salt is taken (liquid or solid), the availability of water, the tolerance of the animal, and the type of food it is receiving. The poisoning from brine was thought to be due partly to the presence and action of nitrates, propylamine, and trimethylamine.

In recent years a number of workers have studied the salt tolerance of pigs in relation to their appetite for salt and to optimum and toxic levels. Amounts up to 80 grams (nearly 3 ounces) per animal per day increased the live-weight gains, and an intake of a gram per kilogram of live weight was not toxic, according to Vil'ner et al. (*12*). The ingestion of 100 grams (3½ ounces) a day over a 7-day period had no appreciable effect on the level of chloride in the blood in experiments reported by Marcq and Devuyst (*4*). Another conclusion that appears to be of special significance was that poisoning was difficult to cause experimentally except where secondary disorders were present. Tocher (*10*) concluded that pigs will not consume rations high in salt unless the salt is added gradually. He gave the optimum amount of salt with rations of mixed cereal, as approximately ½ ounce daily per 100 pounds of live weight.

In a study of the effect on swine of fish meals containing large amounts of salt, Rasenack (*8*) observed that pigs weighing 30 to 40 pounds showed signs of injury after consuming 15 grams (over ½ ounce) of salt daily. Serious injury and death did not result, however, until the level reached 75 or 100 grams daily (2½ to 3½ ounces). Another study on fish meal, by Mayrhofer (*5*), indicated that meals with as much as 9 percent of salt can be used without ill effects.

In view of the varying levels of sodium chloride naturally contained in swine rations and the disagreement in the recommendations on the optimum level, Sinclair (*9*) undertook some studies in which the salt additions were varied from none to 3 percent. The calculated daily total sodium chloride intake ranged from less than 0.1 gram in the basal grain ration to approximately 75 grams (2.7 ounces) in the ration with 3 percent of salt added. He estimated the daily sodium chloride requirement for a pig increasing in weight at the rate of 1 pound a day as 1.33 grams (about one-twentieth of an ounce). Apparently the sodium chloride contributed by tankage was sufficient to supply the needs of the pigs fed the grain-tankage diets used by Sinclair (*9*), since additions of salt to the diet did not increase the growth rates or efficiency of feed utilization of the pigs. From the standpoint of salt poisoning, no significant changes due to high salt intake were observed other than increase in water consumption and excessive urination. No changes were observed in the size or appearance of the kidneys, the water content of the muscle tissue, or the dressing percentage.

Interest in the often-repeated warning against salt poisoning led the Rowett Research Institute in Scotland to make a study of salt feeding (*1*). Pigs of 60 to 190 pounds live weight were fed a ration of cereal feeds, skim milk, cod-liver oil, and ground limestone, with different levels of sodium chloride. The pigs refused to eat a ration containing 4.7 percent of salt, and on a 3.3-percent salt level no apparent symptoms of ill health were noted. Further experiences, with pigs starved for 24 and 48 hours, led to the conclusion that pigs are unlikely to succumb to salt poisoning, because they refuse to eat salty feeds. The data on the optimum salt content of the ration for fattening pigs indicated a figure between 0.25 and 0.50 percent, which is in agreement with other published data.

EXPERIMENTS AT THE BELTSVILLE RESEARCH CENTER

A somewhat different picture of the palatability of salt-containing rations, but with no change in the inability to produce toxic effects with any consistency, has been obtained in experiments with fattening pigs (results heretofore unpublished) at the Department of Agriculture Beltsville Research Center, Beltsville, Md. In the first experiment, to a series of six diets, 0, 1, 2, 4, 8, and 12 percent, respectively, of salt was added. Two pigs were fed each diet. The average daily gains of the two pigs on the diet containing 2 percent of salt exceeded those of the other pigs. Increasing levels of salt resulted in decreased feed intake and retardation of gains. Nevertheless, the two pigs on the highest salt level ate sufficient feed to give them an intake of approximately half a pound of salt a day. One of the animals that received the diet with 8 percent of salt showed evidence of salt poisoning on the eighty-sixth day of the experiment. This pig, which had refused its feed for 2 days, when forced to move out of the shelter walked with a hesitant, nervous motion, frothed at the mouth, and champed its teeth. Two hours later, when it was driven with much difficulty to the scale house, the animal was quite evidently blind. Its weight was 160 pounds whereas 3 days previously it had weighed 187 pounds. A total of 1,770 cc. (1¾ quarts) of water was administered by mouth. Five days later when the animal was slaughtered it had fully recovered except for the blindness and weighed 197 pounds. It should be noted that while the development of blindness was attributed to the effects of the salt, the evidence is purely circumstantial. Microscopic examinations on the 12 hogs did not reveal any unusual changes attributable to salt ingestion.

In the second experiment, shotes were fed a ration containing only 0.1 percent of sodium chloride for 3- and 6-week periods and then given access to salt under various conditions, including free access to loose salt, salt mixed in different percentages in the dry feed, and free access to different brine concentrations. In no case were there any unusual effects that could be attributed in any way to salt poisoning. When the salt content of the diet was adjusted to 10 percent, the daily salt intake approximated 150 grams (5½ ounces) per 100 pounds of live weight. At a 15-percent level the feed intake was still not greatly depressed. The salt intake, however, increased in one case to approximately 180 grams (6.3 ounces) and in another to 225 grams (7.9 ounces) per 100 pounds live weight. Thus one animal weighing 218 pounds, after being fed 26 days on the high salt ration, was consistently consuming an average of 8.4 pounds of total ration and 495 grams (1.1 pounds) of salt a day. A daily water consumption of 2.35 gallons at a period when water intake is normally low (December) was apparently sufficient to permit elimination of the salt without ill effects.

When brine solutions of 5- and 10-percent salt concentration were placed before two pigs that had received no added salt in the ration during a preliminary 3-week period, and no other water was furnished, relatively small amounts of the brine were consumed. One pig drank only 6 quarts of the 5-percent brine in 10 days, while the other consumed 5 quarts of 10-percent brine. Thus the daily salt intake was only a small fraction of that when salt was added to the ration. When two more pigs, after a preparatory period of 6 weeks without added salt, were given access to the usual water supply in addition to the brine solutions, the brine consumption was of the same order as that of the pigs limited to brine only, namely, 4 to 5 quarts per 10-day period. The daily intake of salt in brine was thus only 40 to 60 grams (1.4 to 2.1 ounces) daily.

Two pigs were permitted free choice of dry salt without a preliminary salt-starvation period and four others (two in each group) after a 3-week and a 6-week salt-starvation period, respectively. In the first case (no salt-starvation period) the average daily salt intake amounted to only 5.5 grams. After a 3-week preliminary period the salt consumption averaged 12.7 grams a day, and after the 6-week period, 27 grams.

Two other animals were fed basal diets in which the salt content was increased at 7-day intervals by 4 percent each time. By the fifth week, the salt content was 20 percent, and it was maintained at this level for 4 weeks. The pigs grew normally for the first 4 weeks and maintained their weights with small fluctuations for the remaining 4 weeks. The water intake ranged between 6 and 8 gallons per pig per day during this time.

The 12 pigs used in these experiments were apparently in good health at the conclusion of the salt feeding. Several were changed back to the basal diet without salt additions for short periods previous to slaughter. When the pigs were slaughtered and examined, no unusual conditions were observed. Sodium chloride analyses of samples of lean tissue from the hams of the pigs that had received up to 20 percent of salt in their diets showed no significant difference from samples taken from hogs on ordinary diets.

PRACTICAL CONCLUSIONS

Considerable difficulty seems to attend the experimental production of salt poisoning by the direct use of salt. It is unfortunate that critical studies have not been made on the brine solutions that have reportedly caused toxic effects. Such studies might have disclosed the presence of other substances more definitely toxic than sodium chloride. Other secondary factors involving ailments difficult to diagnose are suggested in some of the reports.

Such practices as mixing salt with the mixed feeds in the slop barrel, dumping into the feeding troughs vats of old brine left over from the curing of meats, or adding to the feed batches of salt contaminated with unknown substances should be avoided in the feeding of swine. As already indicated, the salt requirements are so low and salt is so inexpensive that there is little justification for the use of waste products that might in one way or another be the cause of such cases of so-called salt poisoning as do occur.

The available evidence shows that there is considerable latitude in the tolerance of growing and fattening pigs for salt. In certain of the experiments cited, the pigs were induced to consume diets containing large amounts of salt, while in others the animals refused diets with even moderately high levels of salt. Undoubtedly the components of the diet and the previous feeding history play an important part. The low salt requirement of pigs was also emphasized in a number of instances. It would appear that the use of the animal-protein supplements and simple mineral mixtures containing moderate levels of salt such as are generally used by swine feeders in this country will seldom lead to salt hunger, much less to the setting up of conditions favorable to the intake of salt in unfavorable or toxic amounts.

LITERATURE CITED

(1) BLISSETT, A. H.
      [1936.]   SOME RESULTS OF PIG FEEDING EXPERIMENTS OBTAINED AT THE
                 DUTHIE EXPERIMENTAL STOCK FARM, ROWETT RESEARCH INSTITUTE,
                 ABERDEEN. Pig Breeders' Ann. (1935–36) 15: 122–126.
(2) BUFFAGNI, VITTORIO.
      1935.   AVVELENAMENTI DA CLORURO DI SODIO IN SUINI E BOVINI. Profilassi
              8: 53–54.
(3) HOFFERD, R. M.
      1937.   SALT POISONING IN SWINE. Norden News 11 (1) : 6–7.
(4) MARCQ, J., and DEVUYST, A.
      1935.   INTOXICATION DE PORCS À L'ENGRAIS PAR LE SEL MARIN. Inst. Agron.
              et des Stas. de Rech. de Gembloux. Bul. 4: 316–324.

(5) MAYRHOFER, J.
   1931. BEITRAG ZUR FRAGE DER VERFÜTTERUNG SALZHALTIGER FISCHMEHLE.
      Fortschr. der Landw. 7 : 230–231.
(6) MITCHELL, H. H., CARD, L. E., and CARMAN, G. G.
   1926. THE TOXICITY OF SALT FOR CHICKENS. Ill. Agr. Expt. Sta. Bul. 279,
      pp. 135–156, illus.
(7) MORRISON, FRANK BARRON.
   1936. FEEDS AND FEEDING. A HANDBOOK FOR THE STUDENT AND STOCKMAN.
      Ed. 20, unabridged, 1050 pp., illus. Ithaca, N. Y.
(8) RASENACK, OTTO.
   1925. UNTERSUCHUGEN ÜBER DIE WIRKUNG STARK KOCHSALZHALTIGEN FISCH-
      MEHLS AUF SCHWEINE. Arch. f. Wiss. u. Prakt. Tierheilk. 52 :
      297–315.
(9) SINCLAIR, R. D.
   1939. THE SALT REQUIREMENT OF GROWING PIGS. Sci. Agr. 20 : 109–119,
      illus.
(10) TOCHER, J. F.
   1935. THE PROPORTIONS OF CERTAIN POISONOUS SUBSTANCES IN FEEDING
      STUFFS AND THEIR EFFECT ON LIVESTOCK. Vet. Rec. 15 : [447]–480.
(11) UDALL, D. H.
   1939. THE PRACTICE OF VETERINARY MEDICINE. Ed. 3, rev., 672 pp., illus.
      Ithaca, N. Y.
(12) VIL'NER, A., KRASOVSKY, I., and TSELIKE, B.
   1936. [SODIUM CHLORIDE IN PIG FATTENING.] Svinovodstvo Nos. 9 and 10.
      [In Russian. Abstract in Nutr. Abs. and Rev. 7 : 778. 1938.]
(13) WAUTIÉ, A.
   1935. CONTRIBUTION Á L'ÉTUDE DES ACCIDENTS CAUSÉS PAR LE SEL ET LA
      SAUMURE CHEZ LE PORC. Ann. de Méd. Vét. 80 : 253–261.

Nutritional Diseases of Swine

BY LOUIS L. MADSEN [1]

THE SYMPTOMS, causes, and prevention of the mineral and vitamin deficiencies that affect swine—often with serious consequences for the producer—are discussed in this article, which also includes the results of recent experiments with some of the little-known B vitamins.

THE CONTROL OF NUTRITIONAL DISEASES among swine is one of the first essentials in successful pork production. The importance of adequate nutrition is further emphasized by the fact that the cost of feed alone, including pasture, is estimated as making up 65 to 85 percent of the total cost of producing hogs for market. Swine are able to convert a larger proportion of their feed into edible meat and fat than any other farm animal, but errors in diet which slow their growth or lead to poor utilization of feed or the development of nutritional diseases can result in heavy death losses and otherwise seriously interfere with the economical production of pork.

Many nutritional diseases of swine can be readily controlled if feed requirements are understood and the required nutrients are provided. Early recognition of deficiency symptoms and prompt application of curative or preventive measures will frequently prevent heavy losses. A knowledge of the nutritive value of feeds is very helpful in his respect.

Swine are raised under a wide variety of conditions and are fed many kinds of feed. Concentrated feeds make up the bulk of most ordinary rations, but some bulky feeds, such as good pasture plants or a limited amount of well-cured roughage (particularly alfalfa), have proved to be of value as sources of essential nutrients. Pigs

---

[1] Louis L. Madsen is Nutritionist, Animal Nutrition Division, Bureau of Animal Industry.

fed in the dry lot and especially in floored pens depend entirely on their daily allowance of feed to meet their requirements. Such animals are particularly likely to suffer from nutritional diseases unless their ration is carefully selected.

Since this article deals primarily with the nutritional diseases of swine,. for additional information on the nutritive requirements of swine and practices in swine feeding the reader is referred to articles in the 1939 Yearbook of Agriculture (*7, 31*).[2]

THE MINERAL-DEFICIENCY DISEASES OF SWINE

CALCIUM AND PHOSPHORUS DEFICIENCY AND THE INTERRELATIONSHIP OF VITAMIN D

Calcium deficiency is more likely to occur in swine than a deficiency of phosphorus because swine are often fed rations made up largely of grains or grain byproducts, together with some protein-rich concentrates, and these feeds are usually good sources of phosphorus but low in calcium. Vitamin D is closely related to the metabolism of calcium and phosphorus and is therefore considered with the deficiency diseases involving these two minerals.

Rickets

Rickets, a disease of young animals, occurring before the bones cease growing in length, is most often seen in winter and early spring when pigs are kept housed because of inclement weather, but it may occur at any time of the year if the animals are improperly fed and not allowed free access to direct sunlight.

The symptoms of rickets in swine (*22*) are similar to those in other young animals. (See Nutritional Diseases of Farm Animals, p. 323.) Affected animals frequently have a poor appetite and a generally unthrifty appearance, soft, fragile bones, and usually lameness, especially in the advanced stages of the disease. The degree of bone and joint involvement varies; there may be merely a slight stiffness and stilted movements, or the animals may be able only to crawl on their knees; or they may lie on one side, unwilling or unable to get up. The front and hind legs may become bowed, and the joints are frequently enlarged. The pasterns in some pigs become abnormally straight and thickened, while in others they sag until the pigs almost walk on their dewclaws. In standing, the front and hind feet are often brought very close together. The back is usually abnormally arched.

In advanced cases of vitamin D deficiency, blood-serum calcium is usually lowered from a normal value of 10 to 12 milligrams per 100 milliliters to 6 milligrams or less. Blood phosphorus also may be low. At the lower levels of blood calcium, the animals may go into tetanic convulsions, frequently referred to as fits, and sometimes die in convulsions.

---

[2] Italic numbers in parentheses refer to Literature Cited, p. 826.

Symptoms appear earlier and their onset is somewhat more gradual in young weanling pigs than in older animals. Fattening pigs may "go off their feet" rather suddenly. Such animals usually lose appetite quickly, appear sick, and may have marked incoordination of movement or suffer from partial or complete paralysis. Broken or dislocated leg and pelvic bones or fractured vertebrae resulting in pressure on the nerves and spinal cord may be the cause of these symptoms in some cases. The death rate from rickets is not usually very high, but animals suffering from the disease may succumb to pneumonia or other communicable diseases to which they are predisposed by their weakened condition.

CAUSE, PREVENTION, AND TREATMENT

Rickets is usually due to an inadequate intake of calcium or phosphorus or both, or to a faulty proportion of these minerals in the diet, together with a deficiency of vitamin D. A deficiency of vitamin D or of this vitamin and calcium is the chief cause of rickets in swine. Pigs fed indoors on a ration made up largely of cereal grains, without access to palatable sun-cured roughage, direct sunlight, or other source of vitamin D, are therefore very likely to develop this deficiency disease.

An adequate intake of vitamin D cannot compensate for faulty mineral nutrition. The quantitative requirement for vitamin D is lowest, however, when the ratio of calcium to phosphorus lies within the range of 1:1 or 2:1 (2). Too much calcium in the ration interferes with the utilization of phosphorus. An excess in the diet of other minerals, such as salts of iron, magnesium, beryllium, manganese, strontium, thallium, and aluminum, may also interfere with phosphorus assimilation.

Rickets can be readily prevented or cured in the early stages by correcting the diet. Young pigs that have access to direct sunshine store up considerable amounts of vitamin D. It is not safe, however, to depend entirely on stored vitamin D during long feeding periods in confinement unless the pigs are fed in outdoor lots so that direct sunshine is available. When the body stores of this vitamin are largely depleted, rickets will develop. Johnson and Palmer (20) found that colored pigs, when allowed access to fall sunshine before being confined for the winter, stored sufficient vitamin D to protect them from rickets for about 4 to 8 weeks, while white pigs under comparable conditions were protected about twice as long.

The most economical source of vitamin D is direct sunshine, but this may be inadequate in northern latitudes during the winter. High-grade sun-cured legume hay, particularly alfalfa, is a very good source of vitamin D as well as of calcium. Alfalfa of good quality may be fed either free choice in racks or chopped or ground and added to the grain ration at the rate of 5 to 10 percent for fattening pigs and 10 to 15 percent for sows and boars. Artificially dehydrated alfalfa meal is lower in vitamin D than meal made from sun-cured hay. Other hays, such as soybean, lespedeza, sweetclover, red clover, etc., may be used in place of alfalfa, although they are not usually as palatable. When a good grade of hay is not available for winter feeding and available sunshine is limited, vitamin D may be furnished by such supplements as fish oils, fortified oils, and such irradiated products as yeast and activated sterols of animal origin.

Insuring an adequate calcium and phosphorus intake is as important as supplying vitamin D. Many feeds, including buttermilk, skim milk, tankage, fish meal, and meat scraps, are rich in both calcium and phosphorus. Legume pasture and hay furnish an abundance of calcium, while wheat bran and the protein-rich meals such as linseed, cottonseed, and soybean are rich in phosphorus but low in calcium.

The choice of a mineral supplement, if any is needed, depends on the mineral content of the grain ration. Sources of calcium and phosphorus are often fed with common salt. Other essential minerals such as iodine, iron, and copper may be included in such a mixture when necessary. Some suggested mineral mixtures that can be very economically mixed on the farm according to the individual needs of pigs are given in table 1. These mixtures may be fed free choice or added to the ration at the rate of 1 to 1½ pounds to each 100 pounds of grain mixture. Additional salt may be given free choice.

TABLE 1.—*Suggested mineral mixtures for hogs*

Mixture No.	Mineral supplement needed	Suggested mixture		
		Ground limestone	Steamed bonemeal	Common salt
		Pounds	*Pounds*	*Pounds*
1	Very high calcium	75		25
2	Very high calcium; medium phosphorus	50	25	25
3	High calcium; high phosphorus	33⅓	33⅓	33⅓
4	High calcium; very high phosphorus		75	25

Mineral supplement No. 1 should be used when the ration is low in calcium only. Phosphorus in this case must be supplied by the rest of the ration of whole grains, grain byproducts, and protein-rich concentrates. As previously explained, excessive calcium feeding should be avoided. Mineral supplements No. 2 and No. 3 furnish large amounts of calcium and supply phosphorus in addition. Mixture No. 3 is probably the most widely recommended mineral supplement and has been fed with success to swine of all ages as well as to other farm animals. Mineral supplements Nos. 2 and 3 are appropriate for rations that supply less phosphorus and may also be used successfully in the case of young breeding animals with which the total grain allowance is somewhat restricted to avoid excessive fattening. No. 4 furnishes calcium and more phosphorus than No. 2 or No. 3, but this is not often essential when ordinary well-balanced swine rations are fed. Bonemeal is usually more expensive as a source of calcium than a good grade of limestone or oystershell. Defluorinated rock phosphate prepared for animal feeding may also be used as a source of calcium and phosphorus.

Calcium Deficiency in Brood Sows

Breeding swine, particularly pregnant or lactating sows, develop serious symptoms if their ration is deficient in calcium. This deficiency is most common in swine fed in floored pens, without access to pasture, on a ration consisting largely of cereal grains without an appropriate mineral mixture. In a study of the effects of calcium deficiency on the general appearance and reproductive performance of sows and gilts, Evans (8) describes this condition as follows:

* * * the main manifestations of calcium deficiency—as typified by all the pigs in the group—were: (1) Rough scaly skins, dirty in appearance. (2) The pigs were periodically "off their feet" with their legs bending inwards, and developed what appeared to be characteristic signs of rickets. (3) The sows often refused their feed towards parturition, this indicating nutritive disturbances. (4) They had great difficulty in farrowing and could not stand on their feet for two or three days afterwards. (5) No signs of milk could be seen before or after farrowing, and their udder was very flabby especially in comparison with the normal sows. (6) Very few pigs survived at weaning time and even the few left-made very poor live weight gains. It should be observed, however, that the sows themselves when they farrowed appeared to be in good condition.

Hogan (12) in studying the calcium requirement of brood sows found that their rations should contain not less than 0.4 percent of calcium. Sufficient calcium will usually be furnished if 1 to 1½ pounds of mineral mixture No. 1 (table 1) is added to the ordinary ration made up largely of cereal grains.

Good pasture and legume forage should be included in the ration of the brood sow whenever possible. Well-cured legume hay, particularly alfalfa, may be fed in a rack or ground and added to the grain mixture at the rate of 10 to 15 percent. When the ration of the sow contains such feeds as fish meal, tankage, buttermilk, and skim milk in liberal quantities, the intake of calcium and phosphorus is usually adequate, and it is unnecessary to supply these minerals in a special supplement.

Phosphorus Deficiency

As already noted, phosphorus is less likely to be deficient in ordinary swine rations than calcium (the reverse of the situation with cattle). When swine are grazed on pasture or on cultivated root crops with little or no grain and no protein-rich or phosphorus-rich mineral supplement, however, phosphorus deficiency may develop. Aubel, Hughes, and Leinhardt (1) fed swine on low phosphorus rations and reported the following symptoms:

* * * (1) A loss of appetite, (2) a poor utilization of feed and storage of energy, (3) a failure to make normal growth and to develop bone and muscle normally, (4) a lowering of inorganic phosphorus in the blood, and (5) a marked increase in thirst and a corresponding excretion of urine.

The increased water intake and excessive urine output were associated with enlarged kidneys, which were pale in color.[3]

---

[3] On histological examination these "large white kidneys" showed "chronic diffuse nephritis of the parenchymatous type, and presented widened glomerular spaces around the glomerular tufts and also widely distended uriniferous tubules with flattened epithelial cells. A granular debris was present in some of the tubules.

Under the conditions of the experiment, the phosphorus intake was adequate when the ration contained at least 0.27 to 0.3 percent of phosphorus.

Ordinary feeds that are good sources of phosphorus for swine are wheat bran, wheat middlings, and especially the protein-rich concentrates such as tankage, fish meal, and soybean, linseed, cottonseed, and peanut meals. Dairy byproducts, such as skim milk and buttermilk, are good sources of phosphorus as well as of calcium. When phosphorus-rich feeds are used in the ration, it may not be necessary to supply additional quantities of phosphorus. In cases where additional phosphorus is needed, mineral mixtures Nos. 2, 3, or 4 (table 1) may be offered the pigs in a self-feeder. Too much calcium in the ration will adversely affect the utilization of phosphorus.

Nutritional Anemia of Suckling Pigs

Nutritional anemia is one of the principal causes of unthriftiness and death among young swine. It is particularly prevalent in pigs farrowed in late fall, winter, and early spring which, because of inclement weather or for other reasons, are kept confined to floored pens without access to soil or vegetation. The condition usually appears in pigs 1 to 6 weeks of age, with a somewhat higher incidence about the third week of life. Affected pigs show paleness of the skin and the mucous membranes, lack of vigor, sluggishness, failure to gain normally in weight, and unusual fatigue and labored breathing (thumps) on the slightest exertion. Young pigs may be severely anemic and yet appear fairly well developed and fat. Some die suddenly; others linger for several weeks, lose condition, and become emaciated. Post mortem examination reveals watery blood, excessive fluid in body cavities, grayish-yellow, mottled liver, and marked paleness of the muscles, lungs, and kidneys. Pneumonia and digestive disturbances may also occur. Swine that have recovered from anemia frequently show scattered areas of fibrosis— formation of fibrous tissue—in the liver, due presumably to a healing and replacement process following damage during the anemia.

The milk of all animals is extremely poor in iron and copper, and since young swine are born with a limited store of these minerals, a regular supply is needed shortly after birth to meet the needs of increased blood formation and rapid growth. Soil and forage normally supply sufficient quantities of iron and copper, but newborn pigs kept in pens with surfaced floors or in paved lots have no opportunity to get these minerals. Anemia may also be caused by intestinal parasitism or may accompany severe disorders such as necrotic enteritis, but in these cases factors other than primary iron and copper deficiency are involved.

Several methods have proved successful in the control of anemia. Putting the sow and pigs out to pasture as soon as the weather and other conditions are satisfactory is a good way to prevent anemia. A few shovelfuls of sod or soil taken from areas not traversed by swine (to limit parasitic infestation) placed in the pen or lot may also provide ample protection, but it may be better to enrich the soil with iron and copper salts. Willman, McCay, and Morrison (*29*) were successful in preventing anemia in confined suckling pigs by treating them with a saturated solution of dried ferrous sulfate (copperas, 1 pound per quart of water, dissolved as completely as possible with hot water in the following ways: (1) Drenching the pigs once a week until they are 4 or preferably 6 weeks old. (2) Drenching them twice a week until they are 4 weeks old. (3) Swabbing the udder of the sow once daily until the pigs are 6 weeks old.

One-third of a teaspoonful of the solution should be the maximum dose for pigs under 1 week of age. This dosage may be increased until the pigs are receiving 1 teaspoonful when they are about 3 or 4 weeks old. Drenching or swabbing, preferably the latter which is usually the most convenient method of controlling anemia, should be started when the pigs are 3 or 4 days old. It has been observed that too large doses of the iron solution given as a drench to young pigs will cause scours and occasionally vomiting. Treatment may be discontinued whenever the pigs are turned out to pasture. Pigs older than 6 weeks usually are eating enough supplementary feeds to prevent anemia. Extra iron need not be provided in salt mixtures for adult swine except in areas where the soil is deficient in this mineral.

FIGURE 1.—A litter of hairless pigs still-born. The sow that farrowed them received too little iodine (Courtesy of J. W. Kalkus, Western Washington Experiment Station.)

IODINE DEFICIENCY AND THE BIRTH OF WEAK PIGS

A deficiency of iodine in the ration of pregnant sows leads to the birth of weak offspring. The young pigs may be stillborn (fig. 1), or they may be born alive and die shortly afterward (*28*). The symptoms and prevention of this disease in swine and other farm animals are discussed in the article on Nutritional Diseases of Farm Animals, page 332.

MANGANESE DEFICIENCY AND LAMENESS IN PIGS

Miller and coworkers (*24*) describe a lameness in pigs fed rations consisting of yellow corn, tankage, soybean meal, ground alfalfa, and salt. The condition is manifested by stiffness, enlarged hock joints, and crooked legs, as in rickets, but adding calcium and phosphorus or various sources of vitamin D is ineffective in treatment. In initial experiments, manganese sulfate added to the ration at the rate of 50 to 60 parts of manganese per million was effective in preventing the lameness but not in curing it once it was established. Wheat and oats are usually higher in manganese than corn.

TOXIC MINERALS

FLUORINE AND SELENIUM POISONING

Fluorine and selenium poisoning of swine and other livestock is discussed in the article on Nutritional Diseases of Farm Animals. Kick, Bethke, and Edgington (*21*) found that pig rations containing 0.03 percent or more of fluorine derived either from rock phosphate or sodium fluoride were harmful.

Symptoms of fluorine poisoning in swine include slow growth, low feed consumption, stiffness, marked changes in the bones and teeth (fig. 2), increased thirst, and kidney injury. The bones become thicker than normal, break more easily, and are rough, white, and

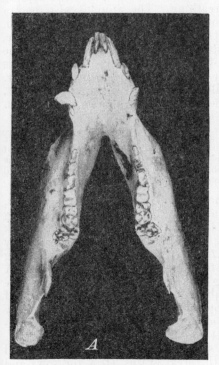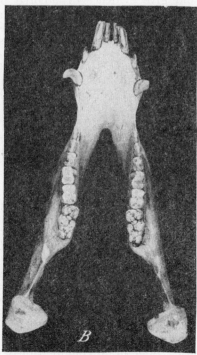

FIGURE 2.—*A*, Thickened jawbone, the result of the consumption of too much fluorine in raw rock phosphate. *B*, A normal jaw, shown for comparison. (Courtesy R. M. Bethke, Ohio Agricultural Experiment Station.)

lusterless. The mandibles (jawbones) are also enlarged and rough.

Swine suffering from the toxic effects of fluorine may improve considerably if the source of fluorine is eliminated from the ration, but they may be permanently injured to some extent.

Moxon (*25*) states that hogs seem to be even more susceptible than cattle and horses to selenium poisoning.

THE VITAMIN-DEFICIENCY DISEASES OF SWINE

VITAMIN A DEFICIENCY

Vitamin A deficiency occurs most commonly in swine fed in dry lots on rations of grain other than yellow corn, without access to green feed, well-cured forage, or other sources of carotene or vitamin A.

One of the earliest indications of the deficiency is night blindness, although Guilbert, Miller, and Hughes (*10*) found that in experimental vitamin A deficiency of swine some of the animals developed partial posterior paralysis before defective night vision had been demonstrated. Hostetler, Foster, and Halverson (*13*) found that pigs suffering from advanced vitamin A deficiency would easily become excited and fall over on one side in a spasm or convulsion, roll their eyes, struggling a little or lying with legs extended, squeal as if in pain, and give evidence of labored breathing. The animals also had a watery discharge from the eyes and were partly or completely blind. Other symptoms are loss of appetite, diarrhea, unthrifty appearance, staggering gait, and in the later stages complete incoordination of the hind limbs due to degeneration of the nerve and spinal cord. Gilts or sows usually show considerable irregularity in breeding behavior. Some fail to breed entirely, while in others, according to Hughes, Aubel, and Lienhardt (*19*), the heat periods are more frequent than normal and of longer duration. They state:

* * * The vulva of some of the gilts in the later stages of the disorder remained swollen as though in continuous œstrum. * * * The ovaries of these sows on examination showed the unusual condition of containing at the same time, ripe Graffian follicles, freshly ruptured follicles, and both new and old *corpora lutea*.

If a sow moderately deficient in vitamin A is bred, it may abort, or a resorption of the fetus may take place. In some cases the young may be born at the regular term but may be either dead or so weak that they die shortly after birth. In such cases the sow frequently fails to lactate normally. Hale (*11*) has made a series of interesting observations on embryonic injury to swine due to maternal vitamin A deficiency previous to and during the early period of gestation. He found various eye defects and abnormalities, including absence of eyes. There were various developmental defects, such as accessory ears, subcutaneous cysts, harelip, cleft palate, faulty kidney development, and malformed hind legs. (Fig 3.)

The value of green pasture or soiling crops (rape, soybeans, field peas, alone or in combination with cereal grains, etc.) for sows and young growing swine cannot be overemphasized. On these feeds the young feeder pigs or breeding animals store up a considerable amount of vitamin A in their bodies, and these stores are utilized to good

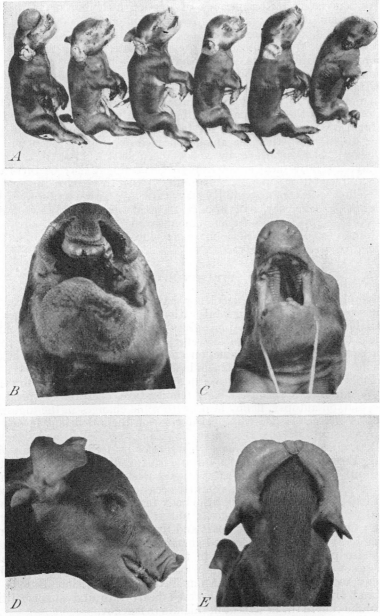

FIGURE 3.—Pigs born to sows that have been fed rations deficient in vitamin A may have various developmental abnormalities, are usually weak at birth, and often die. *A*, A portion of a litter of 10 pigs all born without eyeballs. The pig on the left has a cystic enlargement on the head. *B*, A pig with a double cleft lip. *C*, A pig with a cleft palate. *D* and *E* show an eyeless pig with extra earlike growths. (Courtesy of Fred Hale, Texas Agricultural Experiment Station.)

advantage later during periods of dry-lot fattening or in winter, when the supply of carotene-rich feeds is limited.

Well-cured, green, leafy legume hay, particularly alfalfa, is an excellent source of carotene and prevents acute vitamin A deficiency among swine in dry lots. If the hay is of good quality, a sufficient amount may be eaten if fed in racks; otherwise, 5 to 10 percent of alfalfa meal should be added to the grain ration of young fattening swine or 10 to 15 percent to the ration of breeding animals. When yellow corn is the principal grain fed, it can usually be depended on to furnish enough vitamin A for fattening animals, but there is still some question whether the amount needed for reproduction will be sufficient when furnished by yellow corn only. If a good grade of hay or alfalfa meal is not available, vitamin A may be furnished by cod-liver oil or some other fish oils. Other feeds rich in carotene are yellow sweetpotatoes and yellow carrots. Swine suffering from vitamin A deficiency will usually respond very quickly when the vitamin is supplied in adequate amounts, but animals with advanced symptoms such as marked muscular incoordination or blindness seldom recover completely.

THIAMIN (VITAMIN B₁) DEFICIENCY

Symptoms of thiamin deficiency have recently been produced in swine by feeding experimental rations, but no direct evidence is available to indicate that pigs given ordinary feeds suffer from a deficiency. It is recognized, however, that the requirement for thiamin is very high for reproduction and lactation, though little attention has been given to this problem in the case of swine.

Hughes (*14, 15*) lists decrease in appetite with a tendency towards leg weakness, a lowering of body temperature, decreased respiratory rate, and, on autopsy, flabby heart with some changes in the digestive tract as characteristic symptoms in pigs on diets deficient in one or more vitamins of the B complex. Van Etten, Ellis, and Madsen (*27*) produced thiamin-deficiency symptoms by feeding nursling pigs diets treated with sodium sulfite and sulfur dioxide to destroy the vitamin. They found that after several weeks on the diet the young pigs started to refuse food, vomited occasionally, became emaciated, and had a marked lowering of the body temperature (fig. 4). Death usually occurred within 5 weeks unless thiamin was added to the diet. On autopsy, a flabby heart and liver damage were often found. Some individuals have increased amounts of fluid in the body cavities and also pathological changes in the intestine. Histological (cell) changes were reported in the heart and liver. Electrocardiographic studies recently made in the Animal Nutrition Division, Bureau of Animal Industry, revealed a lowered heart rate and abnormalities of conduction in the heartbeat in thiamin deficiency.

Thiamin deficiency probably never occurs if the diet contains a liberal amount of whole cereal grains or if the animals have access to pasture or well-cured legume forage. Other feeds rich in thiamin are mill byproducts (such as wheat bran), yeast, and legume seeds (such as beans, peas, and peanuts). Increasing the fat in a thiamin-deficient ration lowers the requirement.

RIBOFLAVIN DEFICIENCY

Riboflavin deficiency has been produced experimentally by Hughes (*15*) by feeding a diet low in this factor. He describes the symptoms as slow growth, frequent scours, and walking with difficulty owing to a crippled condition of the legs. Feeding a source of flavin slightly improved the growth and well-being of the pigs, but no improvement was noted in their walking ability. Work in the Bureau of Animal Industry confirmed the fact that riboflavin is

FIGURE 4.—This pig is showing the effects of thiamin (vitamin B₁) deficiency. The main symptoms are lack of appetite, emaciation, lowered body temperature, and slow heart rate.

essential to swine. Nursling pigs fed a riboflavin-deficient diet failed to grow normally, vomited frequently, had severe diarrhea, developed a rough skin and hair coat, had considerable secretion about the eyes, developed a peculiar gait, became very sick, and died (fig. 5).

Hughes (*16*) reports that the minimum daily requirement of riboflavin for young growing swine is between 1 and 3 milligrams per 100 pounds of live weight. The value of dairy byproducts such as skim milk, buttermilk, and whey in swine feeding is probably partly due to their high riboflavin content. Yellow corn, an important swine food, is a fair source of riboflavin. Wheat and barley are lower in this vitamin.

NICOTINIC ACID DEFICIENCY AND NECROTIC ENTERITIS IN SWINE

When nicotinic acid therapy for blacktongue in dogs was announced in the United States, Chick and associates (*3*) in England had two young pigs that had developed a characteristic dietary disease from having been maintained on a Goldberger (pellagra-producing) corn diet. The principal symptoms were severe diarrhea, refusing food, dirty-yellow skin, severe scabby dermatitis (skin inflammation), loss of hair, and a muscular difficulty in the use of the hind legs. Two intramuscular injections of 100 milligrams of nicotinic acid in one pig and three injections in the other at 3-day intervals, followed by a daily allowance of 60 milligrams in the food, produced a striking effect:

The appetite returned within 24 hrs. of the first injection, the diarrhea abated and they began to increase in weight * * * The scabs on the skin began to be detached after 1 week, leaving clean, healthy skin. At the same time, the colour of the animals improved gradually and after 6 weeks of treatment was that of healthy pigs.

FIGURE 5.—Nursling pigs develop riboflavin deficiency within a very short time when given a diet low in this factor. Note poor condition, rough hair coat, and peculiar straight posture of hind legs of this pig.

At the time of this report, about 2 years' work at the Michigan station, started by Madsen and continued by D a v i s, was reported briefly by Gardner (*9*). This preliminary note pointed out that in certain feeding experiments swine developed intestinal disorders resembling necrotic enteritis and that supplementary feeds, such as raw liver, brought about remarkable recovery from the disease. Barley also had a preventive and curative influence. In some cases nicotinic acid was just as beneficial as liver. The Michigan work, later published in detail (*5*), suggests that necrotic enteritis is a secondary complication caused by intestinal invasion by organisms following nicotinic acid deficiency in the pig. It was pointed out, however, that necrotic enteritis probably involved additional dietary factors.

Common swine feeds, such as corn, milk, and milk byproducts and soybean and linseed meals, are relatively low in nicotinic acid. Peanut meal, however, is reported to be high in this factor. Barley is usually higher in nicotinic acid than corn, while wheat and oats have intermediate amounts.

In the Michigan experiments (*5*) more cases of necrotic enteritis developed on the basal ration of corn than when barley was fed.

Supplementing the corn ration with fresh liver (200 grams daily), yeast or liver meal instead of tankage, or changing the grain ration to barley often resulted in curing the condition. It was also found that it was necessary to give as much as 100 to 300 milligrams of nicotinic acid a day in order to prevent or cure the symptoms of necrotic enteritis which were attributed to nicotinic acid deficiency. Successful use of nicotinic acid to treat this condition in swine under farm conditions was reported by the Michigan workers and also by Madison and coworkers (*23*) at the Pennsylvania station.

Because of the widespread losses of pigs due to necrotic enteritis and similar conditions, more work needs to be done to define the relationships of diet and infection as causes of this disease more accurately, as well as to obtain additional information on the content of protective factors in available swine feeds.

PYRIDOXINE (VITAMIN B$_6$) DEFICIENCY

Chick and associates (*4*) fed young swine on a purified diet and noted that the animals developed typical epileptic fits and a microcytic anemia (characterized by small red blood corpuscles) if they were deprived of the fraction of yeast containing vitamin B$_6$. Van Etten, Ellis, and Madsen (*27*), in studies on the thiamin requirement of swine, noted convulsions in swine fed autoclaved (heated) diets, and in later studies of the Bureau of Animal Industry, convulsions and anemia were found to occur in young pigs on both autoclaved and synthetic diets which did not contain crystalline pyridoxine. This deficiency is not apt to occur under farm conditions unless the swine are fed a restricted diet low in this factor or unless the vitamin has been destroyed by unusual treatment of the ration.

Pyridoxine is of little interest at this time in livestock feeding because of its wide distribution in natural foods, including the cereal grains and legumes. Yeast and glandular tissue such as kidney and liver are also good sources. This factor is synthesized by bacteria in the digestive tract of ruminants but must be present in the diets of chickens, dogs, and swine.

PANTOTHENIC ACID DEFICIENCY

Pantothenic acid was first recognized as a growth-promoting factor in yeast. It has now been established as an essential vitamin for several species of animals. Dry-heat treatment of feed readily destroys the factor. Bacteria synthesize this vitamin in the digestive tracts of ruminants, but chickens, dogs, swine, and possibly some other animals require the factor preformed in the diet. Experiments in feeding purified and heat-treated rations at the Beltsville Research Center indicate that young swine on rations deficient in this factor lose their appetite, grow slowly or stop gaining in weight for a time, then lose weight and die (fig. 6). Other prominent symptoms of this deficiency are diarrhea (frequently bloody), loss of hair, weakness and incoordination in the use of the legs, and the formation of a brownish-red incrusted material on the eyelids. Microscopic examination of the nerves and spinal cords from pantothenic-acid-deficient pigs has revealed degeneration of the myelin (sheath) of the nerve fibers similar in all details to that found in pigs that developed incoordination on natural feeds and heat-treated rations (*6*), as described in the following section of this article.

Hughes (*17*) and Hughes and Ittner (*18*) have also studied pantothenic acid deficiency in swine, and they suggest that the minimum requirement for this factor fed as calcium pantothenate lies between 7.8 and 11.8 milligrams daily for each 100 pounds of live weight.

Locomotor Incoordination in Swine Due to Nerve Degeneration

A varying number of pigs fed in pens on rations that have heretofore been considered nutritionally complete—such as yellow corn

FIGURE 6.—Both these pigs were fed the same purified diet except that the pig on the right did not get a supplement of pantothenic acid. This animal has a poor appetite, is weak and emaciated, and suffers from severe diarrhea.

and trio protein mixture (tankage, linseed meal, and alfalfa), with a supplementary mineral mixture—develop incoordination in the use of their legs. This disease was probably first described by Wehrbein in 1916 at the Iowa State College as posterior paralysis and incoordination in movement, associated with degeneration of the sheath of various nerves. Communications to the Bureau of Animal Industry indicate that the disorder is of serious economic importance and is more prevalent during some years than others. It has occurred in the Bureau's herd at the Beltsville Research Center, Beltsville, Md.

Recent work on the problem by Ellis and Madsen (*6*) has shown that feeding normal diets that have been subjected for 30 to 40 hours to dry heat at a temperature of 115°–120° F. greatly increases the incidence of the disease and the severity of myelin degeneration in the nerves and spinal cord (fig. 7). Supplemental or replacement feeds fed with the heated diet have given some encouraging results. Barley, oats, liver, and concentrated milk products have given the most protection. Tests with many other feeds plainly indicate that the dietary factor or factors involved are present in variable or insufficient amounts in many of the common swine feeds. Further work with purified and natural-food diets at the Beltsville Research Center, together with the work of Wintrobe and associates (*30*) and the recent report by Hughes (*17*), indicates that pantothenic acid deficiency is probably one of the causes if not the main cause of this disease.

ACUTE HYPOGLYCEMIA IN NEWBORN PIGS, OR SO-CALLED BABY PIG DISEASE

For a number of years the Illinois Agricultural Experiment Station has been investigating a highly fatal disease of newborn pigs. Sampson, Hester, and Graham (*26*) describe the symptoms of this condition as follows:

In the typical syndrome apparently n o r m a l pigs v a r y i n g from approximately 24 hours to 72 hours old or slightly older show symptoms of shivering, dullness, and anorexia [loss of appetite]. The a n i m a l s have a tendency to isolate themselves and b u r r o w under the bedding. * * * Coincident with the loss of appetite and onset of weakness, the hair coat becomes rough, the skin cold and clammy, and the heart action slow and feeble. Finally the pig lapses into coma. Death of several or all pigs in the litter often occurs within 24 to 36 hours after the first symptoms are manifested.

FIGURE 7.—This pig has marked incoordination in the use of its legs owing to nerve degeneration. The incidence and severity of the disease can be increased by heating the ration.

These investigators report that the affected animals have a marked lowering of the blood sugar, or hypoglycemia, and indicate that the symptoms are probably due to this feature of the disease. In experimental work, baby pigs were found to be highly susceptible to a lowered blood sugar caused by fasting up to about 24 hours after birth. Affected pigs have been successfully treated in the early stages of the disease by repeated intraperitoneal injections of glucose supplemented by hand feeding of sugar solution or milk. Suggested preventive measures include feeding sows and gilts a liberal ration throughout pregnancy and not reducing the amount of grain fed during the last few weeks of the gestation period as commonly practiced. Newborn pigs should be closely watched for the first few days to be sure that they are nursing properly, that the sow has sufficient milk, and that the young pigs do not become chilled. If symptoms develop, hand feeding should be begun immediately.

LITERATURE CITED

(1) AUBEL, E. C., HUGHES, J. S., and LEINHARDT, H. F.
    1936. THE EFFECTS OF LOW-PHOSPHORUS RATIONS ON GROWING PIGS. Jour. Agr. Res. 52: 149–159, illus.
(2) BETHKE, R. M., EDGINGTON, B. H., and KICK, C. H.
    1933. EFFECT OF THE CALCIUM-PHOSPHORUS RELATIONSHIP OF THE RATION ON GROWTH AND BONE FORMATION IN THE PIG. Jour. Agr. Res. 47: 331–338, illus.
(3) CHICK, HARRIETTE; MACRAE, THOMAS FOTHERINGHAM; MARTIN, ARCHER JOHN PORTER; and MARTIN, CHARLES JAMES.
    1938. CURATIVE ACTION OF NICOTINIC ACID ON PIGS SUFFERING FROM THE EFFECTS OF A DIET CONSISTING LARGELY OF MAIZE. Biochem. Jour. 32(1): 10–12, illus.
(4) —— MACRAE, THOMAS FOTHERINGHAM; MARTIN, ARCHER JOHN PORTER; and MARTIN, CHARLES JAMES.
    1938. THE WATER-SOLUBLE B-VITAMINS OTHER THAN ANEURIN (VITAMIN B_1), RIBOFLAVIN AND NICOTINIC ACID REQUIRED BY THE PIG. Biochem. Jour. 32(3): 2207–2224, illus.
(5) DAVIS, G. K., FREEMAN, V. A. and MADSEN, L. L.
    1940. THE RELATION OF NUTRITION TO THE DEVELOPMENT OF NECROTIC ENTERITIS IN SWINE. Mich. Agr. Expt. Sta. Tech. Bul. 170, 23 pp., illus.
(6) ELLIS, N. R., and MADSEN, L. L.
    1941. RELATION OF DIET OF SWINE TO DEVELOPMENT OF LOCOMOTOR INCOORDINATION RESULTING FROM NERVE DEGENERATION. Jour. Agr. Res. 62: 303–316, illus.
(7) —— and ZELLER, J. H.
    1939. NUTRITIVE REQUIREMENTS OF SWINE. U. S. Dept. Agr. Yearbook (Food and Life) 1939: 706–722, illus.
(8) EVANS, R. E.
    1929. PROTEIN AND MINERAL METABOLISM IN PREGNANT SOWS ON A NORMAL OR HIGH CALCIUM DIET COMPARED WITH A CALCIUM-DEFICIENT DIET. Jour. Agr. Sci. [England] 19: 752–798, illus.
(9) GARDNER, V. R.
    1938. NECROTIC ENTERITIS IN SWINE. (Preliminary note) Mich. Agr. Expt. Sta. Rpt. 1937–38: 14.
(10) GUILBERT, H. R., MILLER, R. F., and HUGHES, E. H.
    1937. THE MINIMUM VITAMIN A AND CAROTENE REQUIREMENT OF CATTLE, SHEEP AND SWINE. Jour. Nutr. 13: 543–564.
(11) HALE, FRED.
    1935. THE RELATION OF VITAMIN A TO ANOPHTHALMOS IN PIGS. Amer. Jour. Ophth. 18: 1087–1092, illus.
(12) HOGAN, A. G.
    1932. THE CALCIUM REQUIREMENT OF BROOD SOWS. Mo. Agr. Expt. Sta. Res. Bul. 167, 18 pp., illus.
(13) HOSTETLER, EARL H., FOSTER, J. E., and HALVERSON, J. O.
    1935. VITAMIN A DEFICIENCY—A CAUSE OF LAMENESS AND DEATH AMONG SWINE. N. C. Agr. Expt. Sta. Tech. Bul. 52, 31 pp., illus.
(14) HUGHES, E. H.
    1938. THE VITAMIN-B COMPLEX AS RELATED TO GROWTH AND METABOLISM IN THE PIG. Hilgardia 11: 593–612, illus.
(15) ——
    1939. THE ROLE OF RIBOFLAVIN AND OTHER FACTORS OF THE VITAMIN-B COMPLEX IN THE NUTRITION OF THE PIG. Jour. Nutr. 17: 527–533, illus.
(16) ——
    1940. THE MINIMUM REQUIREMENT OF RIBOFLAVIN FOR THE GROWING PIG. Jour. Nutr. 20: 233–238, illus.
(17) ——
    1942. PANTOTHENIC ACID IN THE NUTRITION OF THE PIG. Jour. Agr. Res. 64: 185–187, illus.

(18) HUGHES, E. H., and ITTNER, N. R.
  1942. THE MINIMUM REQUIREMENT OF PANTOTHENIC ACID FOR THE GROWING PIG. (Abstract of paper) Jour. Anim. Sci. 1: 85.
(19) HUGHES, J. S., AUBEL, C. E., and LIENHARDT, H. F.
  1928. THE IMPORTANCE OF VITAMIN A AND VITAMIN C IN THE RATION OF SWINE, CONCERNING ESPECIALLY THEIR EFFECT ON GROWTH AND REPRODUCTION. Kans. Agr. Expt. Sta. Tech. Bul. 23, 48 pp., illus.
(20) JOHNSON, D. W., and PALMER, L. S.
  1939. INDIVIDUAL AND BREED VARIATIONS IN PIGS ON RATIONS DEVOID OF VITAMIN D. Jour. Agr. Res. 58: 929–940.
(21) KICK, C. H., BETHKE, R. M., and EDGINGTON, B. H.
  1933. EFFECT OF FLUORINE ON THE NUTRITION OF SWINE, WITH SPECIAL REFERENCE TO BONE AND TOOTH COMPOSITION. Jour. Agr. Res. 46: 1023–1037, illus.
(22) LOEFFEL, WM. J., THALMAN, RAY R., OLSON, F. C., and OLSON, F. A.
  1931. STUDIES OF RICKETS IN SWINE. Nebr. Agr. Expt. Sta. Res. Bul. 58, 67 pp., illus.
(23) MADISON, L. C., MILLER, R. C., and KEITH, T. B.
  1939. NICOTINIC ACID IN SWINE NUTRITION. Science 89: 490–491.
(24) MILLER, R. C., KEITH, T. B., MCCARTHY, M. A., and THORP, W. T. S.
  1940. MANGANESE AS A POSSIBLE FACTOR INFLUENCING THE OCCURRENCE OF LAMENESS IN PIGS. Soc. Expt. Biol. and Med. Proc. 45: 50–51.
(25) MOXON, ALVIN L.
  1937. ALKALI DISEASE OR SELENIUM POISONING. S. Dak. Agr. Expt. Sta. Bul. 311, 91 pp., illus.
(26) SAMPSON, JESSE, HESTER, H. R., and GRAHAM, ROBERT.
  1942. STUDIES ON BABY-PIG MORTALITY. II. FURTHER OBSERVATIONS ON ACUTE HYPOGLYCEMIA IN NEWLY BORN PIGS (SO-CALLED BABY-PIG DISEASE). Amer. Vet. Med. Assoc. Jour. 100: 33–37, illus.
(27) VAN ETTEN, CECIL, ELLIS, N. R., and MADSEN, L. L.
  1940. STUDIES ON THE THIAMIN REQUIREMENT OF YOUNG SWINE. Jour. Nutr. 20: 607–625, illus.
(28) WELCH, HOWARD.
  1940. PREVENTION OF GOITER IN FARM ANIMALS. Mont. Agr. Expt. Sta. Cir. 160, 5 pp., illus.
(29) WILLMAN, J. P., MCCAY, C. M., and MORRISON, F. B.
  1932. ANEMIA IN SUCKLING PIGS. Amer. Soc. Anim. Prod. Proc.. 25: 141–145.
(30) WINTROBE, MAXWELL W., MITCHELL, DAVID M., and KOLB, LAWRENCE C.
  1938. SENSORY NEURON DEGENERATION IN VITAMIN DEFICIENCY. DEGENERATION OF THE POSTERIOR COLUMNS OF THE SPINAL CORD, PERIPHERAL NERVES, AND DORSAL ROOT GANGLION CELLS IN YOUNG PIGS FED A DIET CONTAINING THIAMIN (B_1) AND RIBOFLAVIN BUT OTHERWISE DEFICIENT IN VITAMIN B COMPLEX. Jour. Expt. Med. 68: 207–220, illus.
(31) ZELLER, J. H., and ELLIS, N. R.
  1939. PRACTICES IN SWINE FEEDING. U. S. Dept. Agr. Yearbook (Food and Life) 1939: 723–745, illus.

At the time this book went to press, the drugs
and other materials mentioned in various articles—chiefly as disinfectants, insecticides, and
anthelmintics—were still available for veterinary and medical use. Under war conditions,
however, it is possible that some of these materials may become scarce or unavailable. In
that case, the reader should obtain professional
advice from the Department of Agriculture, the
State experiment station, a local veterinarian,
or the county agent as to available substitutes.

Foot Rot of Sheep

BY M. S. SHAHAN [1]

FOOT ROT, due to infection in the hoofs of sheep and goats, is a rather widespread and sometimes serious disease that cripples the animals and causes great suffering. It yields well to combined surgical and medicinal treatment, and much can be done to prevent it.

FOOT ROT is a specific infectious disease that periodically becomes a major hazard to sheep raising and sheep feeding over wide areas in the United States. It has also been reported from many other countries where sheep husbandry is important. In this country the disease is especially troublesome in flocks confined in crowded corrals or pastures, but it occasionally affects range sheep as well, especially during exceptionally wet seasons. Goats are sometimes affected by a similar, if not identical, disease.

SYMPTOMS

Usually the first indication of the disease to be observed is lameness in some of the sheep in the flock or band, but before this becomes marked there is usually reddening and swelling of the skin just above the hoof, between the toes, or at the bulb of the heel. More or less oozing of watery fluid from the inflamed tissues follows, and if the disease is not stopped the sole and walls of the affected foot are undermined by the infectious process. Death of the tissues results in the accumulation of a grayish-yellow, cheesy exudate, or discharge, followed by separation of the hoof from the underlying sensitive tissues. A characteristic foul odor is invariably present.

If the disease is allowed to progress, lameness becomes more and more pronounced. One foot or all may be involved. When both forefeet are affected, the pain may be so intense that the animal kneels to feed. If all four feet are severely affected, the animal may refuse to stand. The infection penetrates deeper and deeper into the tissues

---

[1] M. S. Shahan is Veterinarian, Pathological Division, Bureau of Animal Industry.

until not only the ligaments and tendons but even the bones and joints may be involved. In warm weather the feet may become infested with maggots.

Some severely affected sheep may die, but even the worst cases sometimes gradually improve after several weeks, seeming to recover even without treatment. But within the long, misshapen, and extremely hard hoofs or beneath the fungoid masses that may develop between the toes, the infection often remains, to break out again in the flock. The condition tends to improve when sheep are on dry, well-drained land, but unless it is eliminated by treatment, the disease is likely to persist in affected flocks for months or even years.

CAUSE

Foot rot can be readily transmitted to healthy sheep by inoculating them with exudate from the feet of affected animals. Because the feet of sheep are constantly exposed to the myriads of germs present in soil, manure, and water, bacteriological studies of the disease are difficult. In foot rot, pus-forming bacteria, colon bacilli, spirochetes, and other micro-organisms are frequently present.

The micro-organism known as *Actinomyces necrophorus*, which destroys the tissues it affects, is frequently found in cases of foot rot (*6, 7*),[2] and it is considered by some the essential cause of the disease. An organism known as *Treponema podovis*, or *Spirochaeta penortha*, and by other names is commonly present (*1, 3, 4, 5*). A germ which is known tentatively as *Fusiformis nodosus* has lately been assigned the causative role in the disease (*2*) with a suggestion that other organisms, particularly spirochetes and the tissue-destroying bacillus mentioned, probably act as accessories or secondary factors. The apparent confusion among qualified investigators as to the exact cause of the disease is probably largely due to the indiscriminate use of the term "foot rot" for almost any abnormal condition of the feet associated with lameness.

TREATMENT

Although the cause of the disease may not yet be wholly agreed upon by veterinary investigators, fortunately there are definite principles of treatment which, if followed, are very successful. As with most other animal diseases, it is preferable that treatment and preventive measures be applied by a veterinarian, or at least under the direction and supervision of a veterinarian.

Of primary importance is the immediate examination at the first signs of foot rot of all sheep in the band or flock and the segregation of all animals showing any symptoms. At this time any excessive or abnormal growth of hoof should be pared away with a sharp knife or pruning shears. Hoof nippers may be required in some cases. The object should be not only to restore the normal proportions and contour of the hoof but also to discover so far as possible any evidence of the foot rot infection.

---

[2] Italic numbers in parentheses refer to Literature Cited, p. 833.

In a typical, well-established case the affected animal will usually be found to have deep-seated infections beneath the sole or the hoof wall. Proper treatment demands the removal of such parts of the hoof as are undermined by the typical grayish, dead tissue characteristic of the disease (fig. 1). Trimming sometimes assumes the proportions of a major surgical operation. The tendency of the average untrained or inexperienced person is to trim either too little or too much of the horny hoof. If too little is taken away, the depths of the infected tissue cannot be reached by the antiseptic which is subsequently applied. Too drastic trimming and paring, on the other hand, needlessly injure normal tissues and thus still further delay healing.

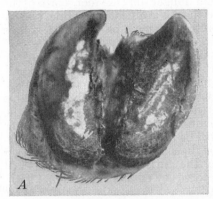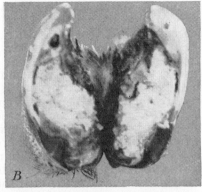

FIGURE 1.—The foot of a sheep affected with foot rot: *A*, Before trimming; *B*, after trimming. (Courtesy of the Montana Agricultural Experiment Station.)

After the feet have been trimmed, a suitable antiseptic should be applied. If a good job of trimming has been done, nearly any efficient antiseptic agent may suffice to curb the infection. If only a few animals are to be treated, their feet may be immersed in a bucket or other receptacle containing the antiseptic, or the antiseptic may be applied by hand. The choice of method, as well as the selection of an antiseptic, depends on the severity and extent of the disease and the facilities available for handling the sheep. **Severely caustic chemicals should never be used by inexperienced persons.**

When large numbers of sheep are to be treated, a trough of wood or other convenient material is usually constructed for use as a foot bath in applying the antiseptic. For most sheep an inside width of about 12 inches and a depth of 6 to 8 inches is adequate. The length of the trough depends on the number of sheep. A 10-foot trough is long enough for a small flock, but one considerably longer is preferable if several hundred sheep are to be treated. The trough may be placed along a corral fence or in a gateway. Converging wing panels or hurdles, either permanent or movable, are usually provided at the entrance to facilitate handling the sheep. Outwardly sloping panels are usually placed at the sides of the trough in a chutelike arrangement. The length of time each sheep should stand in the foot bath depends on the nature and strength of the antiseptic used and the extent of the disease. These matters are best judged by the attending veterinarian. Ordinarily no sheep is kept in the trough for less than 1 minute, and longer than 5 minutes is rarely necessary or advisable. In any event, the animals should be closely watched to insure immersion of the feet and to prevent them from lying down in the trough.

The substance most widely used in treating foot rot is a solution of copper sulfate, or so-called bluestone. The chemical, preferably in powdered form, is dissolved in warm or hot water in 10- to 30-percent solutions (about ⅘ to 2½ pounds per gallon), prepared preferably in enameled or earthenware vessels. When weak solutions are used, the sheep should ordinarily be held longer in the foot bath. The strongest solution may be effective in one application, while two or more treatments at 2- to 4-day intervals may be required if less concentrated solutions are used.

Some cases respond well to treatment with 2- to 10-percent dilutions of formaldehyde solution (U. S. P.). **This, as well as copper sulfate, is very irritating to human beings, as well as to the animals, and it should be handled with care.** Other drugs are applicable in individual cases, depending on the extent of the disease and the facilities available for handling the animals to be treated. The longer treatment is delayed, the greater will be the likelihood of serious loss.

In practice, some use another trough, containing water only, placed at the front end of that containing the antiseptic. This water bath washes dirt from the sheep's feet before they enter the medicinal bath. If the disease is advanced and the feet are extremely sensitive after treatment, they may well be protected by clean, soft dressings and the application of some such substance as oil of pine tar.

PREVENTION

As with other infectious diseases, prevention is much more effective than is treatment after the disease has developed. Because infected sheep are considered the greatest source of infection, any sheep to be added to a flock from outside sources should first be held in quarantine for at least a month. If no indications of foot rot appear by the end of the quarantine period, usually the new animals may safely be added to the flock. Sheep should preferably be procured from a source known to have been free of foot rot for at least 6 months previously. Sheep treated for the disease should not be returned to the flock until it is certain that they are normal. In some cases the most economical procedure may be to sell all affected sheep for slaughter under inspection, thus eliminating the expense of treatment and the hazard of their presence to the healthy sheep.

Barns, sheds, troughs, and corrals that have been used by infected sheep should be thoroughly cleaned and disinfected. (See the article on Disinfection and Disinfectants in this Yearbook, p. 179.) All accumulations of litter and manure should be removed and preferably burned. Infective foot trimmings and dressings also should be disposed of by burning. Muddy corrals and pastures should be drained, if practicable. In severely affected flocks it may be advisable to move all the apparently normal sheep to fresh ground. It is not known exactly how long land used by sheep affected with foot rot remains infectious.. If the soil is light and well-drained, the rainfall limited, and the weather hot with an abundance of sunshine, the infection will probably not survive for more than 2 weeks. Under such conditions corrals may ordinarily be considered safe from the standpoint of foot rot if sheep are excluded for a month. On the other hand, if the soil is heavy and poorly drained and there is much rainfall and a scarcity of sunshine, a considerably longer time may be necessary before sheep can be safely returned. In northern latitudes, infected pastures are generally considered safe if sheep are withheld for 4 months during the usual cold winter season.

If different attendants cannot be provided for the healthy sheep and for those being treated for foot rot, the normal sheep should be cared for first and the others last. After handling affected sheep, attendants should cleanse themselves and disinfect all instruments used.

As an added measure of prevention, the apparently healthy portion of the band is sometimes subjected to the antiseptic foot bath described. When this is done, old solutions that have been used by infected sheep should not be used for the healthy sheep.

CONDITIONS CONFUSED WITH FOOT ROT

Animals compelled to travel long distances over rough, hard, gravelly, or rocky roads or trails, or those pastured on exceptionally dry, sparse pastures, frequently develop foot soreness that may be confused with foot rot. Continuously stabled animals or those pastured on low-lying, swampy lands are apt to develop grotesquely shaped, overgrown hoofs, which should be trimmed periodically to prevent lameness. Sheep pastured on muddy ground often collect caked and dried soil between the toes, with resulting injury to the tissues, which may become more or less severely infected. Sheep on stubblefields not infrequently suffer from local injuries that are likewise avenues for the entrance of nonspecific infections. Injuries due to penetrating wounds usually occur only in one or a few animals at a time and are readily identified. The treatment of all such animals is made easier and more effective if they are confined or isolated, just as they would be if foot rot were present.

LITERATURE CITED

(1) BEVERIDGE, W. I. B.
        1936. A STUDY OF SPIROCHAETA PENORTHA (N. SP.) ISOLATED FROM FOOT-ROT IN SHEEP. Austral. Jour. Expt. Biol. and Med. Sci. 14: [307]–318, illus.
(2) ——
        1941. FOOT-ROT IN SHEEP: A TRANSMISSIBLE DISEASE DUE TO INFECTION WITH FUSIFORMIS NODOSUS (N. SP.). Austral. Council Sci. and Indus. Res. Bul. 140, 56 pp., illus. [Processed.]

(3) Blaizot, Ludoric, and Blaizot, Pierre.
    1928. treponema podovis n. sp., agent pathogène du piétin des moutons. [Paris] Acad. des Sci. Compt. Rend. 187: 911–912.
(4) Howarth, J. A.
    1930. foot rot in sheep. Vet. Med. 25: 186–188, illus.
(5) ————
    1930. the pathogenic significance of spirochetes in some well-known pathological conditions of domestic animals. Amer. Vet. Med. Assoc. Jour. 76: 630–642, illus.
(6) Marsh, Hadleigh, and Tunnicliff, E. A.
    1934. experimental studies of foot-rot in sheep. Mont. Agr. Expt. Sta. Bul. 285, 29 pp., illus.
(7) Mohler, John R., and Washburn, Henry J.
    1904. foot-rot of sheep: its nature, cause, and treatment. U. S. Bur. Anim. Indus. Bul. 63, 39 pp., illus.

Sore Mouth of Sheep and Goats

BY M. S. SHAHAN [1]

SORE MOUTH, a virus disease that attacks young animals especially, is serious partly because it so often leads to complications with other infections. It can be controlled, as this article makes clear, by sanitary measures and the use of preventive vaccination.

SORE MOUTH is widely prevalent among lambs in feed lots and is considered by some authorities to be almost always present to some degree wherever lambs are fattened for the market. The disease also occurs in range bands and farm flocks and not uncommonly affects goats, particularly kids. Technically, it is known as contagious ecthyma.

CAUSE AND SYMPTOMS

Sore mouth is a highly contagious disease caused by a specific filtrable virus (1, 3, 5, 7),[2] which is capable of remaining infective for months in the dried scabs that develop in the course of the illness.

The affection seldom appears in animals over 1 year old. Lambs shipped to the feed lot frequently develop the disease, usually within a week to 10 days after arrival. Small vesicles appear on the lips, gums, or tongue, which are considerably swollen and somewhat reddened. After a few days the vesicles become pustules. These finally rupture, leaving raw, granulating sores, that bleed easily and are encrusted with thick, grayish-brown scabs (fig. 1). Within 3 to 4 weeks the scabs drop off, and the lesions heal, leaving no scars.

This description applies to the typical uncomplicated case. The chief trouble caused by such an infection is the extreme soreness

[1] M. S. Shahan is Veterinarian, Pathological Division, Bureau of Animal Industry.
[2] Italic numbers in parentheses refer to Literature Cited, p. 838.

of the affected parts. Lambs or kids nurse reluctantly, and older animals graze with difficulty and even at the trough may eat sparingly. In consequence growth is more or less impaired, and considerable weight may be lost. Death from the disease is rare.

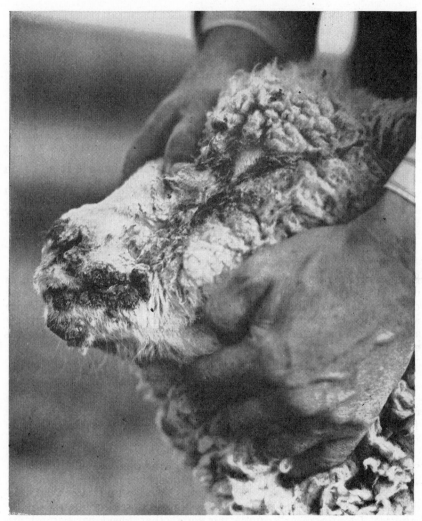

FIGURE 1.—A sheep affected with sore mouth. (Courtesy of the Colorado Agricultural Experiment Station.)

Occasionally bacterial infection, chiefly by *Actinomyces necrophorus*, takes place (*4*). In such instances, areas of dead tissue frequently develop in the stomach and intestines, the liver, or the lungs. The death loss from such so-called secondary infection may reach 50 percent of the animals affected. In some sections of the country, infestations of the lesions, or injuries, of sore mouth with screwworms is a common trouble. (See The Screwworm and Blowfly Problem, p. 313 of this Yearbook.)

The lesions of contagious ecthyma, with or without complicating bacterial infection, sometimes appear on the udders of nursing ewes and goats, and the resulting soreness may lead to the animals' refusing to permit their young to nurse. Then, either through the accumulation of milk in the udder or bacterial infection or both, caked udder, mastitis, or "blue bag" may develop. Sometimes the eyelids are involved, and the sight is threatened. Contagious ecthyma has also been reported to produce lesions on the ears, under the tail, on the inside of the thighs, or in other areas where there is little wool or hair.

PREVENTION

Before the vaccine now used was developed, isolation of affected animals and general sanitation of corrals, barns, sheds, etc., were the only practicable means of controlling sore mouth. These measures are still to be considered effective adjuncts in the prevention and control of the disease, and they may be followed without using vaccine in flocks where the veterinarian considers this procedure advisable.

The vaccine now commercially available was developed at the Texas Agricultural Experiment Station (*1, 2, 7*) between 1932 and 1935. Made from the scabs taken from typical cases, it is similar in nature to smallpox vaccine and is applied to scratches in the skin on the under side of the tail, the inside of the thigh, or elsewhere. Susceptible animals develop takes resembling the lesions of the natural disease, and after recovery they are immune, with relatively few exceptions, for several months to 2 years or longer. Animals that have recovered from the disease itself are similarly immune.

In range areas where the disease is known to prevail, a practical procedure has been to have the lambs or kids vaccinated at the time of marking, that is, when castration, docking, and earmarking are done, though sometimes this may not be wise or convenient for various reasons. It has been found that the disease can be almost entirely prevented in feed-lot sheep if they are vaccinated at least 10 days before being shipped (*2, 6*). Immunity thus has time to develop before exposure to infection during shipping.

Since the scab that falls away from the site of the vaccination contains the causative virus just as does the scab from a natural case, sheep should not be shipped until after the vaccination wounds have completely healed. Delay until then is believed to result also in a more complete resistance to any infection that might be acquired en route. Because the virus may be distributed around premises where vaccine has been used, either through accident in handling the vaccine or the falling of the scabs from the vaccinated animals, vaccine should never be used except in areas or on premises where the disease has been diagnosed by a veterinarian.

The disease spreads so rapidly in feed lots, and occasionally on the range or farm, that vaccination after it appears is rarely practical. There may be some benefit from vaccination, however, if it is done promptly before many of the animals have developed symptoms.

TREATMENT

As indicated in the discussion of symptoms, treatment, except for isolation of the affected animals in clean, roomy quarters, is usually unnecessary. The disease runs its course, and medicinal aid is seldom required and rarely practical. The chief considerations are the prevention of screwworm infestations and secondary infections. If such complications arise, vigorous treatment with selected larvicides and antiseptics is indicated. The foci of bacterial invasion are usually beyond the reach of any known medicinal agent, but the extensive development of such complications can be largely avoided by local antiseptic treatment. If screwworms infest the lesions, they should be promptly removed.

LITERATURE CITED

(1) BOUGHTON, I. B., and HARDY, W. T.
    1934. CONTAGIOUS ECTHYMA (SORE MOUTH) OF SHEEP AND GOATS. Amer. Vet. Med. Assoc. Jour. 85: 150–178, illus.
(2) ——— and HARDY, W. T.
    1935. IMMUNIZATION OF SHEEP AND GOATS AGAINST SORE MOUTH (CONTAGIOUS ECTHYMA). Tex. Agr. Expt. Sta. Bul. 504, 16 pp., illus.
(3) HOWARTH, J. A.
    1929. INFECTIOUS PUSTULAR DERMATITIS OF SHEEP AND GOATS. Amer. Vet. Med. Assoc. Jour. 75: 741–760, illus.
(4) NEWSOM, I. E., and CROSS, FLOYD.
    1931. SOME COMPLICATIONS OF SORE MOUTH IN LAMBS. Amer. Vet. Med. Assoc. Jour. 78: 539–544.
(5) ——— and CROSS, FLOYD.
    1934. SORE MOUTH IN FEEDER LAMBS DUE TO A FILTRABLE VIRUS. Amer. Vet. Med. Assoc. Jour. 84: 233–247, illus.
(6) ——— and THORP, FRANK, JR.
    1938. LAMB DISEASES IN COLORADO FEEDLOTS. Colo. Agr. Expt. Sta. Bul. 448, 42 pp., illus.
(7) SCHMIDT, H., and HARDY, W. T.
    1932. SOREMOUTH (CONTAGIOUS ECTHYMA) IN SHEEP AND GOATS. Tex. Agr. Expt. Sta. Bul. 457, 22 pp., illus.

Miscellaneous Diseases of Sheep and Goats

BY M. S. SHAHAN [1]

HERE is a discussion of some 36 or more diseases and injuries to which sheep and goats are subject. Many of them, it will be noted, can be largely prevented by good management, proper feeding, strict sanitation, and care in ordinary operations involving surgery. The author emphasizes the need for sound veterinary diagnosis.

DISEASES OF THE DIGESTIVE ORGANS

BLOAT, constipation, diarrhea, and enterotoxemia are included among diseases of the digestive organs. All may be largely prevented or controlled by proper feeding.

Bloat, or the accumulation of gas in the stomach or intestines of sheep and goats from fermentation of their contents, is chiefly the result of feeding green, wet, frosted, or damaged feeds, but it may occur after the eating of any feed in large quantities, particularly one to which the animals are not accustomed. Bloat is an evidence of indigestion and in an acute form it is very troublesome and dangerous. To prevent it, sheep should be given only clean, sound feed in amounts that they can satisfactorily digest. If, through inexperience or accident, the trouble occurs in a flock, all the animals should be immediately removed from access to either feed or water. Kneading the paunch through the abdominal wall in the region of the left flank and slowly driving the affected animal may promote passage of the gas. Elevating the forequarters or placing a gag in the mouth may accomplish the same purpose. If a veterinarian is not available, oil of turpentine (1 to 2 teaspoonfuls) or aromatic spirits of am-

---

[1] M. S. Shahan is Veterinarian, Pathological Division, Bureau of Animal Industry.

monia (½ to 1 teaspoonful) in a half pint of water or milk may be given as a drench. A laxative is generally desirable. When death threatens from extreme distention, an opening into the paunch may be made to permit the escape of the gas. This is usually done by the veterinarian with a special instrument known as a trocar and cannula. In an emergency, the operation may be performed by an untrained person, but, whenever possible, instructions should be obtained from a veterinarian before resorting to this. After recovery from acute bloat, the animal should be allowed free access to water but be given only laxative feeds in small amounts for several days.

Constipation, or impaction of feed in the paunch or the other stomachs, may develop as a result of feeding coarse, dry, or indigestible feed or from overfeeding more healthful materials. The remedy is to remove the accumulated feed by means of drugs that stimulate the muscles of the digestive tract, kneading the flanks, introducing water into the stomach through a stomach tube, or, if necessary, by drenching or the administration of appropriate laxatives.

Diarrhea, or watery feces, may be caused by internal parasites such as coccidia or worms, infection by bacteria such as *Salmonella aertrycke* or *Mycobacterium paratuberculosis*, the feeding of green succulent feeds, or excessive consumption of any feed. Prevention and cure depend upon the nature of the underlying cause. Lamb dysentery, paratyphoid dysentery, and Johne's disease are distinctly different from simple diarrhea and are discussed elsewhere in this article.

Enterotoxemia, intoxication or poisoning of intestinal origin, is probably the most frequent cause of losses of lambs in western feed lots. It differs from the Australian disease of the same name (*1*),[2] though the two are similar in some respects. Feed lot enterotoxemia results from the overeating of grains or other concentrates. The immediate cause may be the toxin formed in the intestines by the widely distributed germ *Clostridium perfringens* (*Cl. welchii*) (*8*). A similar condition, known as pulpy kidney disease or milk colic, sometimes develops in sucking or weanling lambs pastured on a lush growth of rich forage (*2, 13*).

The prevention of enterotoxemia is essentially a matter of management. A sufficient interval should be allowed after placing lambs in the feed lot to permit their digestive organs to become accustomed to the new, rich feed. Different lots of lambs vary widely in their ability to consume feed; what one group will thrive on may be fatal to another. Hence, judgment, skill, and watchfulness are necessary in fattening operations. The ration should be graduated according to the size and condition of the animals being fed, beginning at first with feed consisting chiefly of hay or other roughage, with only a small amount of concentrates, the latter being gradually increased as the animals adapt themselves to the regime. The sheep should be graded according to size and condition, being penned for feeding in as nearly uniform lots as possible.

Once the animals reach the stage of full feed, they should be closely

---

[2] Italic numbers in parentheses refer to Literature Cited, p. 857.

watched. At this time, any disease in the lot will tend to cut down feed consumption by the sick lambs, leaving excessive amounts for the healthy individuals unless the ration is cut in proportion to the number of animals actually on feed. In flocks that develop milk colic on pasture, it is believed to be good practice to reduce the feed of the ewes and lambs by penning them at night and for a part of the day in a dry, clean lot without feed.

Sluggishness, reluctance to eat, and diarrhea are signs that lambs are going off feed. If the amount of grain is not reduced, considerable losses from death may follow. The animals may be found dead in the pens, a few or many each day, with or without having shown marked signs of abnormality. Sick sheep may be seen with the head elevated, staggering about the pen, running blindly into fences, or in convulsions. Constipation, which may appear early, is usually followed by diarrhea. At post mortem examination, large hemorrhages may be found in the abdominal cavity, along the intestines, in the diaphragm, or in the belly wall. The inside of the fourth stomach may be reddened. The kidneys and liver may be very friable, or easily torn. In animals that die after a brief illness, few significant abnormalities may be found.

Once lambs have been upset by overfeeding, great difficulty is usually experienced in getting them back into thrifty fattening condition.

While treatment of enterotoxemia is seldom successful and generally uneconomical, the veterinarian should be called to establish the diagnosis and for help in handling the flock in order that further losses may be avoided.

DISEASES OF THE RESPIRATORY SYSTEM

Respiratory diseases are relatively unimportant in sheep except in connection with shipping, as a result of which hemorrhagic septicemia, or so-called shipping fever, sometimes appears. (See the article on p. 526.) This is an infectious disease attributed at least in part to the germ *Pasteurella oviseptica*, which is a normal inhabitant of the respiratory passages and usually causes disease only under conditions adverse to the animal's resistance. Such conditions occur when sheep, especially lambs, are taken from grass pastures, shipped crowded together, and subjected to prolonged hunger and perhaps cold, frequently arriving at their destination weak and exhausted. They may be driven considerable distances, becoming overheated, and the feed they are given is usually strange. Young shed-dropped or farm lambs sometimes develop a form of pneumonia much like that of shipping fever.

In feed-lot lambs, shipping fever appears usually within the first few days of the feeding period. As many as half the animals in a shipment may become sick, and the death loss may be 10 percent or more in severe outbreaks (7).

Fever, depression, rapid breathing, sneezing, coughing, and discharge from the eyes and nose are common symptoms. In acute cases, death may result within 24 hours after the illness first appears, and there may be little of diagnostic significance at post mortem examination except perhaps numerous small to large hemorrhages under the skin or within the chest. Chronic cases usually develop into pneumonia, lasting from a few days to several weeks. If death does not intervene, there is a long period of convalescence. Diagnosis of either type of the disease usually depends upon bacteriological examinations.

Improved shipping conditions, including regular rest, feeding, and watering, and protection from severe weather and overcrowding tend to lessen the likelihood of hemorrhagic septicemia in sheep. The disease occurs irregularly, however, from season to season and year to year, and it may develop no matter how well the animals are handled.

Animals may be somewhat protected against the disease by vaccination with hemorrhagic septicemia bacterin, preferably administered some time before they are to be shipped. During years when the disease is prevalent, anti-hemorrhagic-septicemia serum may be given as a preventive. This has a quicker but less prolonged prophylactic effect than bacterin. The decision as to which if any biological product is to be used in each case should be left to the veterinarian familiar with all the circumstances.

Treatment of the disease is generally uneconomical, though serum may be used in selected cases with good results. Prompt isolation and good nursing of affected animals are advantageous.

Chronic progressive pneumonia, so-called lunger disease, is discussed elsewhere in the Yearbook (p. 927).

Exposure of sheep to cold after shearing or dipping may cause pneumonia. Other forms of pneumonia occur as a result of invasion of the lungs by various parasites or bacteria.

Nasal catarrh, or snuffles, is a common condition in sheep, especially those ranging on dry, sparsely vegetated land or traveling dusty trails. The ailment is generally negligible unless it becomes marked, as in pneumonia, severe cases of grub in the head, or specific local infection. Control and treatment under these conditions depend upon the nature of the cause.

DISEASES OF THE NERVOUS SYSTEM

Listerellosis (listeriosis), rabies, meningitis, enterotoxemia, paralysis, and gid infection (see p. 874) are included among diseases of the nervous system.

Listerellosis, or circling disease, in sheep consists essentially of an inflammation of the brain caused by the germ known as *Listerella monocytogenes*, or *Listeria*. The symptoms of the malady include nervous disorders, inflammation of the eye, and occasionally abortion. Dullness, fever, and strange, awkward movements, such as staggering, pushing the head into fences, and walking in circles, are observed. Paralysis, finally ending in death, follows in most cases.

It is not known how the disease is spread, and there are no proved means of prevention or treatment. Diagnosis depends upon laboratory examinations, since autopsy does not reveal characteristic changes in the body.

Rabies, which may affect any species of mammal, is discussed elsewhere in the Yearbook (p. 1109). It is referred to here to emphasize that when a nervous disease appears in goats or sheep, the possibility that rabies is the cause should be considered by the veterinarian. Small ruminants with rabies behave much like any other animal affected with the disease, and the symptoms commonly include those seen in other nervous diseases. Licking or gnawing at the site of the bite, stamping of the feet, and bleating are frequently observed. Some animals become belligerent before the final paralysis that ends in death. The prevention of rabies in sheep or goats is essentially the same as in the case of other animals.

Meningitis consists of an inflammation of the meninges, or membranes, which cover the brain within the cranial cavity. It generally accompanies encephalitis, or inflammation of the brain, to a greater or less extent, regardless of the cause of the latter. It is not a specific disease like cerebrospinal meningitis of man but may be caused by any of several micro-organisms. Pus-forming *Staphylococcus*, *Streptococcus*, and other organisms are responsible in some cases. These organisms frequently gain entrance to the body at the time of docking and castration or through the navel at birth and may become localized anywhere in the body. When they become established in the brain or spinal cord, symptoms of nervous disorder, including paralysis, may occur. Such cases are relatively infrequent and may be prevented almost entirely by proper technique in handling the animals during the operations mentioned. Determination of the exact cause of meningitis requires bacteriological study. Treatment is seldom practical.

Paralysis, or loss of the ability to move a part of the body, particularly the legs, rarely occurs except in the course of the diseases mentioned, although it is a common symptom of pregnancy disease and milk fever. Paralysis is sometimes attributed, however, to a toxin or other substance in certain ticks that feed upon sheep. Removal of the ticks usually leads to prompt recovery, as is also true in some cases of tularemia, or rabbit fever, which may be conveyed to sheep by infected ticks. Severe blows, falls, or other injuries sometimes cause fracture or dislocation of the vertebrae, leading to paralysis.

DISEASES OF THE SKIN

The commonest cause of abnormalities of the skin of sheep is scabies, or scab, discussed elsewhere in this Yearbook (p. 904). Other conditions that may affect the skin directly or indirectly include purulent dermatitis, ringworm, pox, contagious ecthyma, maggot infestation, filarial dermatosis, and actinobacillosis.

Purulent dermatitis, as here considered, consists in the invasion of the skin and underlying tissues by pus-forming micro-organisms. The organisms may be introduced by penetrating awns and other parts of grasses and other plants, such as foxtail, needlegrass, wild oats, and alfilaria, or through shearing cuts and other wounds. In severely affected animals, the abscesses formed as a result of the bacterial infection may occur deep in the underlying muscles or even in the abdominal cavity and may lead to pyemia, a form of general poisoning. Prevention consists in avoiding, or limiting as far as possible, objects on the pasture or in feed which may collect in the wool and are capable of penetrating the skin. Shear cuts and other wounds should be treated immediately with tincture of iodine or some other suitable antiseptic.

Ringworm is relatively rare in sheep. It may be due to various species of fungi that require laboratory study for identification. The disease should be distinguished from so-called lumpy wool due to *Actinomyces dermatonomus* (*3*), a funguslike organism that produces lumpy wool, as the name indicates, but little or no abnormality of the skin except as a secondary manifestation.

Sheep pox is caused by a filtrable virus resembling but not identical with that which causes smallpox in man.

Sheep pox is characterized by the formation of dark-red papules, which turn into blisterlike formations, or vesicles, chiefly on the bare or thinly wooled parts of the body. The vesicles break and become infected with pus-forming germs, which frequently cause death through septic infection. Fortunately, the disease has not become established in the United States.

Contagious ecthyma (p. 835), maggot infestation (p. 898), and filarial dermatosis (p. 890) are discussed alsewhere in the Yearbook.

Actinobacillosis (see also p. 549) is an infectious disease caused by the germ *Actinobacillus lignieresi*. As it has been observed in sheep, the infection enters the body through the punctures made by the awns or other parts of certain plants, such as needlegrass and pricklypear. Small pockets of pus form in the tissues beneath the skin, sometimes discharging their contents onto the skin and matting the wool in the regions affected, and sometimes leading to generalized lesions in the internal organs.

Diseases of the skin usually cause more or less itching, manifested by scratching or biting of the affected part. Attending this, there are more or less loss of wool and varying degrees of inflammation of the skin. The exact determination of the cause of the trouble usually requires the services of a veterinarian, who should be consulted as soon as the trouble is first noticed. It can then be determined whether the disease is contagious, and if so, its spread can be limited or entirely prevented.

DISEASES CONNECTED WITH REPRODUCTION

Abortion, the pregnancy toxemias, metritis, mastitis, prolapse of the genital organs, venereal infection, and orchitis are among the diseases connected with reproduction.

Abortion signifies the expulsion from the womb of either living or dead young before the normal time of birth. Damaged feeds, especially those that are moldy, are sometimes held responsible for abortion, and some cases are attributable to generalized infection, toxemia, injury, or undernourishment. Infectious abortion of sheep, unlike that of cattle, is rarely attributable to germs of the *Brucella* genus, being most often caused by *Vibrio fetus*, *Salmonella*, *Pasteurella*,

Listerella, or coliform organisms which infect the fetus and the fetal membranes. Goats, on the other hand, may suffer from infection with any of these organisms, including *Brucella.* With or without abortion, brucellosis in goats is more dangerous for man than brucellosis in any other animal species.

The interval between infection and abortion varies somewhat with the type of germ causing the trouble and may differ in individual outbreaks. Abortion early in the development of the fetus invariably means a dead lamb or kid. When it occurs later, near the normal time of birth, living young may be born, but they are usually so weak that they live only a few days.

Symptoms indicative of impending abortion may or may not be observed. The disease may develop slowly during the gestation period, finally resulting in depression and loss of appetite just before abortion takes place. There may be a rusty-colored discharge from the vulva, but usually there are no other symptoms. After abortion, an abnormally bloody discharge sometimes persists for a variable period. There may be serious losses due to septicemia, but generally the females return to apparent good health after a few days. The infection, depending on the type, often remains in the uterus, however, either preventing conception at the next breeding period or jeopardizing subsequent pregnancy.

No treatment is effective in preventing abortion once the infection has become established, but much may be done to prevent the spread of the disease within the band. Animals infected with *Brucella,* and sometimes the other types of organisms responsible for abortion, may be identified by means of agglutination tests. Animals so discovered should be so handled as to prevent exposure of other animals on the premises. This means isolation pending recovery or slaughter. Females showing symptoms of impending abortion and those that have aborted should be immediately isolated from the rest of the flock. The aborted fetus, membranes, and contaminated bedding should be completely burned. The quarters used by aborting animals should afterward be thoroughly cleaned and disinfected. Proper handling of the infected animals, including douching of the genital tract when this is advised by the veterinarian, may decrease the duration of infectivity. Those that have aborted should not be bred until no evidence of active infection remains. Many outbreaks of abortion in ewes caused by *Vibrio fetus* have been definitely associated with stagnant or filthy drinking water, through which the infection has been presumed to spread. Feed free from spoilage, as well as clean running water, should be supplied if possible.

Pregnancy toxemia includes two diseases, pregnancy disease and milk fever, which so closely resemble each other in their symptoms as to appear identical in many cases. Pregnancy disease, which is discussed elsewhere in the Yearbook (p. 923), occurs prior to lambing. Milk fever may occur just before, just after, or as long as 6 weeks after lambing. Milk fever, also called parturient paresis, occurs much more rarely than pregnancy disease. The symptoms of milk fever in ewes resemble those in cows, described elsewhere in the Yearbook (p. 533), where treatment is also discussed.

Metritis is defined as inflammation of the uterus. Caused by various types of infection, it accompanies and follows abortion or may develop after dystocia, or difficult parturition. Once it appears in a flock of lambing ewes, it may spread like wildfire unless great care is taken.

The symptoms include a brownish or blood-tinged, sometimes foul-smelling, discharge from the vulva. Depending on the severity of the infectious inflammation, there are varying degrees of fever and depression. The appetite is poor or is lost altogether. The back is often arched, and straining sometimes occurs. Death may follow from severe general intoxication, or septicemia. Less severe cases recover after a time, but fertility may be lost.

To prevent metritis, abortion should be controlled and lambing should be carried out under hygienic conditions. The sheds or barns for lambing are best used for this purpose only and should be thoroughly cleaned and disinfected after the conclusion of operations each season and left unoccupied thereafter. In mild weather, lambing on the range or in the pasture may be preferable to lambing indoors. Attendants of ewes with lamb, especially those assisting at lambing, should keep their persons and clothing meticulously clean.

Treatment, except for nursing, should be left to the veterinarian, as douching of the genital tract with medicinal agents is not without danger. General medication also should be given only by the veterinarian.

Mastitis, mammitis, or garget, signifying an inflammation of the udder, may be caused by one or more of several types of organisms (*Staphylococcus*, *Streptococcus*, *Pasteurella*-like, and colon-type organisms). The disease may occur during the lambing season or on the range when the lambs are 3 to 4 months old. It usually develops rapidly and is accompanied by fever, loss of appetite, systemic disturbances, and reddening, swelling, and tenderness of the udder. The milk secretion becomes thick, yellowish, and flaky and is sometimes stained with blood. Abscesses may form in the gland, or gangrene ("blue bag") may develop. Many severely affected animals die, especially if neglected. In those that recover, one or both sides of the udder often fail to function thereafter. When the disease occurs early in the nursing period, lambs whose mothers are affected become undernourished and are likely to die unless given special attention.

Field observations indicate that, like metritis and arthritis, the disease is promoted by insanitary conditions in sheds, corrals, or bed grounds. Older lambs may injure the udder by butting when nursing, making it more susceptible to infection. It is advisable to remove the affected ewes from the flock and hand-feed the lambs or place them with a foster mother. Sheds and corrals should be thoroughly cleaned and disinfected. On the range, bed grounds should be frequently changed. When the type of infection is definitely determined bacteriologically, bacterins or toxoids may aid in prevention.

In the early stages of the disease, the sick ewe may be given a saline cathartic (Epsom or Glauber's salts). The udder may be gently milked out several times a day by hand, and it may be bathed 3 or 4 times a day with a very warm solution of Epsom salts ($\frac{1}{2}$

pound in 1 quart of water) applied with cotton or cloths. Internal medication may be prescribed by the veterinarian. Drainage of abscesses or amputation of the udder may become necessary.

Mastitis in milk goats is somewhat different from the disease in ranch or range goats or sheep. Because of the relatively close confinement and the contact between animals, the disease may spread rapidly through the milking herd. Isolation of affected animals, strict hygiene in milking operations, and the other general principles of prevention and treatment of the disease in cattle (p. 518) are usually applicable.

Prolapse of the genital organs (eversion of the vagina or uterus) may occur before or after lambing. Excessively fat, closely confined females, those carrying twins or triplets, or those that are thin and undernourished are more likely to evert the uterus or vagina, usually the latter, than those in a normal, thrifty condition. Ewes or does that have had a difficult or delayed parturition or have been roughly treated in attempts to assist in delivery of young are prone to the condition.

The organs protrude from the vulva as a reddened, shining mass. If the condition is neglected, severe swelling, injury, and infection of the misplaced tissues inevitably develop. In such cases the condition is sooner or later complicated by retention of urine and feces and general intoxication. Delay in treatment until this stage is reached invariably results in the death of the animal.

The remedy is to replace the organs as soon as possible after their eversion is discovered. This usually requires the skill of a veterinarian. If one is not available, the parts may be gently bathed with warm physiological salt solution (a heaping teaspoonful of table salt to a quart of boiled water) and then sprinkled with cold boiled water or ordinary granulated sugar, either of which tends to shrink the congested tissues, thus aiding replacement. Return of the organs is sometimes facilitated by slowly bandaging them from behind forward, thus pressing out the blood and reducing the swelling. Replacement is effected by gentle folding and pressure along the course of the genital passage. Suturing (stitching) of the lips of the vulva or application of a trusslike bandage over the vulva may be required to keep the organs in place.

Venereal infection, as the term implies, is an infectious disease of the genital organs of ewes and rams believed to be spread principally by breeding. The condition, commonly referred to as foul sheath in rams, was for years considered to be a form of necrobacillosis, discussed later in this article, but a filtrable virus has lately been defined as the primary cause (15). Ulcers and scabs form on the penis and at the orifice or inside the sheath of the ram and on or about the lips of the vulva in the ewe. Uncomplicated cases recover in several days with few or no serious consequences, but when secondary infection occurs, severe swellings of the affected parts, with pus formation, ulceration, and even gangrene, are not uncommon. In males urination may be greatly restricted, and when this occurs a general septic infection and death may follow.

If begun early in the course of the disease, mild antiseptic treat-

ment is generally beneficial. Neglected or improperly treated animals
may be so seriously affected as to warrant destruction. Immediate
isolation and treatment of affected animals and thorough cleaning of
corrals and disinfection of barns and sheds are advocated for the control
of the disease.

Orchitis, or inflammation of the testicle, leads to more or less swelling and tenderness of the organ, with or without systemic disturbance,
and sometimes results in impotence or death.

The affected buck walks with a stiff, straddling gait. The testicle
becomes acutely inflamed or may be infiltrated with serum or pus.
Gangrene may develop.

In large bands of rams the condition arises from injuries caused by
fighting, or it may be due to excessive service or infection. Prevention
is implemented by sanitation, limiting the ewes for each ram to a
reasonable number, regulation of the diet, exercise for rams during the
interbreeding season, and finally the separation of fighting animals
and their grouping in small lots whenever practicable.

Treatment of orchitis in sheep or goats depends upon the character
and extent of the inflammation. Acute injuries may be remedied by
confinement, rest, laxative feed, and local applications of a saturated
solution of Epsom salts or cold or hot water. If pus forms, it may
become advisable to lance the organ, following with antiseptic treatment. In case of gangrene, castration may become necessary. Septicemia resulting from orchitis usually requires general medication.

Bacterins and other biological products may be applicable as preventives in flocks in which the type of infection has been definitely
determined.

DISEASES OF THE EYES

For practical purposes, diseases of the eyes of sheep are of two
classes—traumatic (that is, due to injury) and infectious.

Traumatic affections include wool blindness, entropion, and injuries
caused by foreign bodies. The first occurs in sheep with heavily wooled
faces. The wool grows over the eyes, obscuring the vision and sometimes injuring the eye tissues. The obvious remedies are to breed
sheep without this characteristic or to trim the wool around the eyes
periodically.

Entropion consists in an inversion of the eyelid over the eyeball,
in consequence of which the eyeball becomes inflamed. This condition
is suspected of being hereditary in nature, in which case it could be
avoided by careful selection of breeding animals. The remedy is surgery, involving removal of a part of the eyelid, then suturing the
organ, or—a more practical procedure—placing a stitch in the lid or
tying a fold of the lid with a ligature in such a way as to prevent
inversion.

Dust, plant particles, and other foreign substances cause inflammation when they become imbedded in the eye tissues. Healing can be
effected only after first removing the offending object.

Infectious keratitis, or pinkeye, is generally considered as an infectious disease that may spread rapidly from one animal to another
in a flock or may be carried from one flock to another. There is first

a watery discharge from the eye, attended by swelling, reddening, and tenderness of the lids. The conjunctiva (the membrane covering the front surfaces of the eyeball and the inside of the lids) is acutely inflamed, the blood vessels standing out clearly owing to congestion. The discharge later becomes purulent, and the lids are more or less stuck together. The cornea (clear portion of the eye) becomes opaque, appearing smoky or grayish, and at this stage the sheep is blind. This continues for a week or 10 days, when the eye usually clears up if it has been properly treated; otherwise the condition may progress to ulceration of the cornea, which tends to persist and usually results in total blindness. Some animals then die of thirst, hunger, or secondary infection.

To be distinguished from pinkeye is the condition in goats and sheep brought about by a diet low in vitamin A, in which, in addition to unthriftiness and urinary calculi, there may be symptoms of night blindness and sometimes opacity and ulceration of the eye (*9*).

Animals affected with infectious keratitis should be isolated from the rest of the flock in clean, darkened quarters, from which it is best to exclude flies if possible. Water and laxative, nutritious feed should be readily accessible. A solution or an ointment containing boric acid may be placed in the eyes twice or oftener each day. The same medication may or may not be suitable after removal of foreign bodies or an operation to correct entropion, depending on the nature of the case. In many cases of keratitis confinement and simple medication will suffice to forestall serious complications leading to permanent loss of sight, but it may be preferable to use stronger antiseptics, which should be prescribed by a veterinarian. Since the exact nature of the infectious agent that causes the disease is unknown, there are no specific biological agents for prevention or treatment, but bacterins are sometimes used in attempts to limit the severity of the disease.

OTHER INFECTIOUS DISEASES

The following infectious diseases deserve special consideration, in addition to those discussed directly or indirectly in this article or elsewhere in the Yearbook.

Arthritis, or inflammation of the joints, sometimes referred to as joint ill, occurs most commonly through infection of the navel stump at birth, or through wounds caused by castration, docking, shearing, or earmarking. According to available information, the disease is not common in goats. In lambs, streptococci, other pus-forming organisms, and *Erysipelothrix rhusiopathiae* (the cause of swine erysipelas), are the organisms usually involved.

The symptoms depend on the type of infection present, occurring within a week after birth or the operation or several weeks later. The joints, particularly the knee, hock, elbow, and stifle, are more or less swollen and painful. There may be mild to extreme lameness. Fever, with or without the formation of pus in the joints and abscesses in the internal organs, is a fairly regular symptom. Acutely affected lambs may die after a brief illness. In such cases loss of appetite, diarrhea, and progressive weakness are a part of the clinical picture. Most cases due to *Erysipelothrix rhusiopathiae* tend to become chronic. Recovery from the acute lameness is common, but in such instances more or less damage to the joints and general unthriftiness usually remain.

No treatment can be generally recommended, prevention being the mainstay in combating the disease. Three practices should be assiduously followed, especially on premises long used for sheep or other livestock: (1) Maintenance of sanitary conditions for lambing, (2) disinfection of the navel as soon as possible after birth, and (3) avoiding unclean instruments or insanitary methods in castration, docking, and earmarking, afterward turning the lambs out into fresh pasture whenever feasible.

An effective method of preventing infection through the navel is to hold a small, wide-mouthed bottle containing tincture of iodine over the stump of the cord, then turn the lamb over on its back with the bottle held in place, and allow the bottle to remain for a minute or two before releasing the lamb.

Black disease, or infectious necrotic hepatitis (*4, 10, 12*), is an acute malady affecting mature sheep in good condition. The disease is due to the germ *Clostridium novyi* type B (*Cl. oedematiens*) in the presence of liver flukes, and it may occur wherever flukes are present, which is usually on swampy, poorly drained land. Black disease is most prevalent in the late summer and early fall.

The onset of the disease is sudden and acute. The first evidence of the existence of the malady in a flock is usually the finding of dead sheep in the morning, although everything appeared to be in order the night before when the animals were penned or bedded down. The dead animals show no evidence of having struggled and appear as though they had died in their sleep. Bloody foam may come from the nose. If the flock is closely watched, stragglers may be observed lagging behind the rest of the flock or lying down instead of feeding. When aroused, such an animal will quickly start away, only to stop and stand quietly or lie down again after having rejoined the band. There may or may not be moderate fever and slightly increased respiration. Death may occur within an hour after these symptoms are first seen. Because of the difficulty of recognizing the disease from the symptoms alone, it is not known whether affected animals ever recover, but the mortality is probably very high and recovery rare.

At autopsy, if the animal has not been dead too long, a peculiar sweetish odor may be detected on opening the carcass. This will not be in evidence if post mortem decomposition and bloating have taken place. When affected animals are skinned, the inner surface of the pelt usually has a blackish appearance, from which the common name "black disease" arises. Since the discoloration is due to congestion of the skin, it is not necessarily characteristic of black disease only but may be observed in one form or another in other diseases. The lungs, though sometimes slightly congested, are usually essentially normal. The lung and peritoneal cavities and the heart sac usually contain considerable quantities of clear straw-colored or slightly blood-tinged fluid. Some of this may become clotted or congealed, forming jellylike masses. Small hemorrhages may be present on the inner surfaces of the heart. The liver is thickened, darkened, and friable and contains one to many areas of necrosis, grayish yellow in color and varying from one-fourth inch to an inch or more in diameter. Hemorrhages beneath the liver capsule and minute punctures of the capsule by young flukes may be found. Numerous very small flukes may be found in the liver tissue, but full-grown flukes are seldom present in this disease. The inner lining of the fourth stomach, or abomasum, is frequently slightly inflamed, being of a deep pink color. If examination of a sheep that has just died in a region where liver flukes abound discloses the lesions described, black disease may be strongly suspected. Effective post mortem examination of sheep can be made only if decomposition and bloating have not reached an advanced stage. If decomposition is marked, the changes due to disease may be somewhat, if not entirely, obscured. Post mortem examination of several dead animals is frequently desired by the veterinarian, and laboratory examination may be advisable.

Clostridium novyi apparently does not of itself produce black disease; initial damage to the liver by flukes is required before the organism increases and forms its death-dealing toxin. Hence, control of liver flukes is of primary importance in preventing the disease. Treatment of sheep with carbon tetrachloride or other fluke-killing drugs after the germ has grown and produced its toxin in the liver cannot be expected to cure the sheep. Such medication is rather to be considered as a part of the basic fluke-control program (see p. 892), through which black disease can be effectively prevented. Once infectious necrotic hepatitis becomes established in a flock through the agency of acute fluke infestation, there is little that can be done except to move the sheep to fluke-free land. Losses may then continue until the acute stages of the fluke invasion have passed. Other trouble, however, still threatens from chronic fluke infestation and pasture contamination.

Bacterin (anaculture), toxoid, and antitoxin, prepared in the laboratory from cultures of *Clostridium novyi*-type B, have been reported to be of value in the prevention of black disease (*14, 16*). These biological products have not been commonly adopted in this country, perhaps owing to the general use of fluke-control measures.

Caseous lymphadenitis, sometimes called pseudotuberculosis, is a widespread chronic infectious disease of sheep and goats caused by *Corynebacterium ovis* (Preisz-Nocard bacillus). The germ is a very resistant organism, capable of surviving for months in the dust of barns, shearing sheds, and corrals. Infection may take place through contaminated feed, inhalation of contaminated dust, or wounds (considered later).

The disease affects the body lymph nodes chiefly but may invade the lungs or other organs, depending upon the route by which the infection is acquired and the length of time the animal has been affected. Greenish-yellow or gray cheeselike, pasty, or sandlike pus is formed in the affected organs. In some cases the lesions resemble those of tuberculosis, actinomycosis, coccidioidomycosis, and other granulomatous diseases (characterized by tumorlike formations).

In the early stages of the infection, the animal appears not to be materially affected. Indeed, disturbance of general health does not often come before the time for discarding the animals as breeders. Then progressive loss of flesh and weakness, finally leading to death from exhaustion, may occur.

There is no practical method of treatment of the disease. On first thought it would appear to be an insignificant ailment, but considerable numbers of seriously affected sheep are condemned on account of it under meat-inspection regulations. Moreover, species other than sheep and goats are affected, including cattle, horses, rodents, and even certain wild animals.

Prevention of the disease is promoted by general sanitation and by special care when shearing, docking, castrating, or earmarking. (See wound infections, p. 854). Animals discharging pus from the abscesses of pseudotuberculosis should be isolated, care being taken to dispose of the discharges properly.

Dysentery consists in the frequent passage of liquid feces with varying amounts of blood and mucus owing to inflammation of the bowels. Aside from parasitic dysentery, the disease appears chiefly in three forms, paratyphoid dysentery, lamb dysentery, and Johne's disease, or paratuberculosis, each of which will be considered separately.

Paratyphoid dysentery (7) is comparatively rare, having been reported in this country in a few instances only, in lambs after shipment from the range to feed lots. It is caused by the germ *Salmonella aertrycke*, which is believed by some authorities to be a normal inhabitant of the bowel of some sheep, producing disease only when the animals have been long deprived of feed.

Affected animals are depressed and refuse feed; there is some fever, and the feces become watery and sometimes bloody. Death may come quickly after slight scouring, or profuse dysentery may develop, in which case the illness lasts longer. Losses in three reported outbreaks in the last decade ranged from 2 percent to about 7 percent (7).

In the opinion of some who have studied it, animals kept in good condition and fed regularly during transit should not develop serious cases of the disease. Accordingly, it is recommended that preparations be made to feed sheep at as frequent and regular intervals as possible during transit. If the disease develops, affected animals should be immediately segregated from the well ones. A laxative such as castor oil may be given, and this may be followed by intestinal medicaments and general stimulants. A light but nutritious diet should be provided during convalescence.

Lamb dysentery, sometimes called white scours, is a disease of the newborn that occurs within 48 hours or sometimes as long as a week after birth, the lambs meanwhile appearing normal. There is a very fluid, grayish diarrhea with an offensive odor, accompanied by great depression, and the lambs stop nursing. Many lambs die within 24 to 48 hours after the first symptoms appear, but those surviving this period may slowly recover. In severe outbreaks 20 to 40 percent of the lamb crop may die.

The disease is essentially filth-borne, and is attributed to several factors, including the micro-organisms known as *Clostridium welchii* and *Escherichia communior* (*5, 6*). Cold, wet, stormy weather during which lambing must take place in barns and sheds is conducive to the disease if the shelters have been allowed to become filthy. Such places must be frequently cleaned and freshly rebedded with clean bedding if danger of lamb dysentery is to be avoided. Some operators use elevated slatted floors with no bedding in lambing shelters. On warm sunny days, lambing may better be carried out on clean pasture or range. Tagging of the ewes—clipping the long wool from about the udder and the inside of the thighs to provide cleanly conditions for the nursing lamb—before lambing is recommended.

It is often impractical to treat lambs affected with lamb dysentery. Medicinal treatment is usually of no avail. In England anti-lamb-dysentery serum is sometimes used, but neither this nor the other biological products commonly used there with reported success have been generally adopted in the United States. Cultured milk, which consists of sterilized, skimmed cow's milk seeded with *Lactobacillus acidophilus*, has been used with reported success as a treatment by some investigators (*11*). Acidophilus milk can be properly prepared only in the laboratory, and its use is preferably, if not necessarily, undertaken with a veterinarian's supervision.

Johne's disease, or paratuberculosis, is a chronic disease caused by *Mycobacterium paratuberculosis*. This infection causes a chronic inflammation of the intestines, leading to dysentery and gradual weakening and loss of weight. The disease may be fatal in a few weeks or months, or it may be more prolonged.

Exact diagnosis is made through application of johnin, a biological product resembling tuberculin, or through finding the organisms in the feces or tissues in the laboratory.

As with cattle (p. 512), it is recommended that affected animals be slaughtered under veterinary supervision. Animals suspected of having Johne's disease should be isolated pending diagnosis. After their removal from the flock, pens, sheds, and troughs used by them should be thoroughly cleaned and disinfected. Contact between cattle and sheep should be prohibited. Repeated testing of the flock and the slaughter of reacting animals are usually necessary before the disease is eliminated.

Necrobacillosis consists in the invasion of the body by *Actinomyces necrophorus* (the necrosis bacillus). This organism is capable of producing disease in many species, including man. In sheep, it is of chief importance in sore mouth, venereal infection, navel infection, and foot rot. So far as is known, the organism is incapable of penetrating normal tissues, but once it has gained entrance through lesions caused by a virus or other infection, or through external accidental wounds, it frequently becomes established in the body. The effect is necrosis, or death, of the invaded tissues. What would ordinarily be a mild or inconsequential process without *Actinomyces necrophorus* becomes a serious disease.

Lambs thus infected through the navel or through sore mouth lesions frequently develop multiple necrotic and abscessed areas in the internal organs that lead to serious illness and in many instances to death. In the same way, secondary infection of lesions of venereal disease, caused primarily by a filtrable virus, leads to serious complications resulting in death or an extended convalescence.

Though not a very resistant organism in the ordinary sense, *Actinomyces necrophorus* appears to be able to survive for months in poorly drained, wet, filthy corrals and barns. Its elimination requires drainage, exposure to air and sunshine, and thorough cleaning and disinfection. These constitute the principles accepted as the basis for prevention of necrobacillosis.

The treatment of affected cases is often unsatisfactory. If the foci of infection are so located in the body as to permit exposure to the direct action of antiseptics, recovery may be effected. Otherwise little can be done aside from systemic nonspecific medication, which is generally unsuccessful.

Wound infections in the aggregate cause an enormous loss, which could be largely prevented. Castrating, docking, and earmarking involve surgical wounds, and wounds commonly occur when shearing is done too hurriedly or in a careless manner. The rupturing of the umbilical cord at birth, severing the lamb or kid from the blood supply of its dam, creates a wound that is particularly open to infection. Dog bites and other accidental wounds also provide entrance for disease-producing germs.

Many germs, such as *Staphylococcus*, *Streptoccoccus*, and other pus-producing organisms, may be considered as everywhere present. *Clostridium chauvoei*, the cause of blackleg in cattle and in sheep, persists, in spore form, for years in certain sections and on individual farms. Other germs of the genus *Clostridium*, such as *Cl. septicum*, the cause of malignant edema, *Cl. tetani*, the cause of tetanus, or lockjaw, and others that produce gas gangrene, are more or less widely distributed and are potential killers of sheep. All these and various other micro-organisms may cause trouble through wound infection.

The emphasis here is on the fact that wounds should be prevented as far as possible and accidental wounds should be properly cared for. Even castration can be performed without causing a wound in the external tissues by means of the so-called Burdizzo forceps, or emasculatome. This technique is preferred for that reason alone by many operators. The chief drawback is that it requires judgment and experience that not everyone has. Also, the emasculatome must be precisely constructed for uniform results. Ordinary castration, involving incision and the removal of the testicles, as well as docking and earmarking, should be considered as a surgical procedure requiring cleanliness and the use of sterile instruments. Docking may preferably be done with a hot iron. In all cases, lambs are much less likely to contract infection through operative wounds if, weather permitting, they are afterward turned out to pasture or range instead of being kept in a corral or barn. Shearing can be so humanely done that cuts and scratches are rare. When they occur, they should be immediately touched with tincture of iodine or some other suitable antiseptic. Shearers might well be required to clean and dip their clippers into 3-percent compound cresol solution or some other disinfectant before starting on another sheep. If dipping is planned after shearing, it is best to wait a few days to give wounds and scratches time to heal.

The symptoms that develop following wound infection depend upon the type of organism involved. Pus-forming organisms may become localized or may cause septicemia or pyemia (blood poisoning). Some germs of the genus *Clostridium* produce so-called gas gangrene infections that are usually fatal. Edema and gas are formed at the site of infection, and death results from toxemia. Tetanus, or lockjaw, results from the formation of toxin by the organism *Cl. tetani*. Symptoms may occur a few days after infection has taken place, but usually the interval is 1 to 2 weeks or longer. By then the wound may have healed externally. The symptoms consist of a stiff, stilted gait with bending of the neck and back to one side or upward or downward. The entire muscular system may become tense, giving the animal a saw-horse appearance.

As indicated, nearly all wound infections can be prevented by hygienic procedures, but on especially heavily infected premises where certain types of infection have previously caused trouble, prevention may be aided by the use of specific bacterins, vaccines, toxoids, or antitoxins. Intelligent use of these depends, of course, upon accurate diagnosis.

GOITER

This is a constitutional disease associated with enlargement of the thyroid glands, which are situated one on either side of the windpipe at its upper extremity near the angle of the jaw. Caused by lack of iodine, it is discussed in the article on Nutritional Diseases of Farm Animals, p. 332.

URINARY CALCULI (SAND OR GRAVEL)

Concretions (hard lumps) or deposits of mineral salts in the kidneys, ureters, bladder, or urethra sometimes cause considerable death loss. The calculi vary in size and consistency from small sandlike particles to large, rough or smooth rocklike or spongelike formations. The trouble is almost entirely confined to males. In the early stages of their development, these materials cause little or no trouble, but if the condition continues there are uneasiness and frequent urination. Later the animal stands and strains in an effort to urinate, and eventually the condition commonly referred to as water belly develops. The abdomen swells, owing to accumulated fluid in the cavity, the bladder is distended, urine dribbles from the prepuce, and dried salts appear in the wool about the opening. Without relief, death invariably follows.

The cause of the condition is not exactly known, though certain feeds, such as mangels, sugar beet pulp or tops, corn fodder, wheat bran, and linseed or cottonseed meal, especially when given in large amounts, are conducive to the trouble. There is experimental evidence to indicate that lack of vitamin A (*9*) and possibly infection of the urinary tract are responsible in some instances. In some cases, responsibility may be placed on the presence of large amounts of mineral salts in the water supply. Again, scarcity or lack of ready access to water may promote the accumulation of sand or gravel in the urinary tract.

The chemical composition of the concretions appears to depend partly upon the mineral constituents of the feed and water. Thus they may be comprised chiefly of phosphates, oxalates, or other ingredients which may be modified by internal medication or change of diet; but this or any other treatment is seldom practicable. In some instances in wethers or rams, in the beginning of the trouble, the small wormlike appendage (processus urethrae) at the end of the penis may be removed, thus permitting passage of the obstruction. Some cases may be relieved by passage of a catheter or sound to dislodge the stones. Finally, the special value of some animals may warrant a surgical operation for removal of the concretions from the urethra. Often, however, serious trouble from calculi does not develop until near the end of the fattening period, and the lambs may be continued on full feed without too serious loss for the short time remaining before they are finally finished.

STIFF LAMBS (WHITE-MUSCLE DISEASE)

The term "stiff lambs" is commonly applied by sheepmen to any condition causing lameness, paralysis, or a similar abnormality without distinction as to cause, such as arthritis, listerellosis, or tetanus. As here used, the term is given to a specific disease of unknown cause characterized by a peculiar degeneration of the muscles that occurs usually in lambs 3 to 10 weeks old. It is generally agreed that the disease is not infectious. Nutritional deficiencies and autointoxication have been suspected. The disease appears usually among winter or early spring lambs, which because of inclement weather and other conditions are often somewhat confined and restricted in diet. It seldom if ever occurs in lambs born and run on the range.

Although there is no known successful treatment, the trouble can be prevented to some extent by proper feeding and management, including provision for exercise and supplying feed for the ewes that satisfies nutritional requirements, especially as to minerals and vitamins. Diagnosis of the disease is best made through post mortem examination, which reveals characteristic white or grayish streaks in the muscles—those of the legs especially.

WOOL AND DIRT EATING

Young, nursing lambs sometimes eat wool, litter, soil, and other more or less indigestible substances that may lead to the formation of balls of wool or other material in the stomach. The foreign substances lead to indigestion, and, in many cases, to death, through stoppage of the exit from the stomach. Toxins are absorbed from the digestive tract, and the lambs show stupor, cease eating, and usually die within a few days.

In some cases the habit of eating indigestible substances such as wool may be attributed, at least in part, to close confinement and idleness, but field observations generally indicate that the basic cause of the trouble is a depraved appetite caused by lack of necessary minerals, especially phosphorus. The lambs thus instinctively nibble on anything at their disposal. To provide the needed substances, nutritious green pasture may be provided, and sometimes ground grain or bran may be placed in troughs in creeps readily accessible to the lambs.

Treatment is generally ineffectual, since intoxication due to stoppage of the digestive tract has usually progressed considerably before marked symptoms are observed. The indications are, however, that the trouble can be forestalled in most instances by feeding the ewes a well-balanced ration during gestation and the nursing period.

LITERATURE CITED

(1) BENNETTS, H. W.
    1932. INFECTIOUS ENTERO-TOXAEMIA (THE SO-CALLED BRAXYLIKE DISEASE) OF
        SHEEP IN WESTERN AUSTRALIA. Austral. Council Sci. & Indus. Res.
        Bul. 57, 72 pp., illus.
(2) BOUGHTON, I. B., and HARDY, W. T.
    1941. INFECTIOUS ENTERO-TOXEMIA (MILK COLIC) OF LAMBS AND KIDS. Tex.
        Agr. Expt. Sta. Bul. 598, 20 pp., illus.
(3) BULL, L. B.
    1929. DERMATOMYCOSIS OF THE SHEEP (LUMPY OR MATTED WOOL) DUE TO
        ACTINOMYCES DERMATONOMUS (N. SP.). Austral. Jour. Expt. Biol
        and Med. Sci. 6: [301]-314, illus.
(4) DODD, SYDNEY.
    1921. THE ETIOLOGY OF BLACK DISEASE. Jour. Compar. Path. and Ther. 34:
        1-26, illus.
(5) GAIGER, S. H., and DALLING, THOMAS.
    1923. BACILLARY DYSENTERY IN LAMBS. Jour. Compar. Path. and Ther.
        36: 120-125.
(6) MARSH, H., and TUNNICLIFF, E. A.
    1938. DYSENTERY OF NEW-BORN LAMBS. Mont. Agr. Expt. Sta. Bul. 361,
        42 pp.
(7) NEWSOM, I. E., and THORP, FRANK.
    1938. LAMB DISEASES IN COLORADO FEED LOTS. Colo. Agr. Expt. Sta. Bul.
        448, 42 pp., illus.
(8) —— and THORP, FRANK, JR.
    1938. THE TOXICITY OF INTESTINAL FILTRATES FROM LAMBS DEAD OF OVER-
        EATING. Amer. Vet. Med. Assoc. Jour. 93: 165-167.
(9) SCHMIDT, H.
    1941. VITAMIN A DEFICIENCIES IN RUMINANTS. Amer. Jour. Vet. Res.
        2: 373-389, illus.
(10) SCOTT, JOSEPH P., TURNER, A. W., and VAWTER, L. R.
    1934. GAS EDEMA DISEASES. 12th Internatl. Vet. Cong. Proc. 2: 168-187.
(11) SHAW, J. N., and MUTH, O. H.
    1937. THE USE OF ACIDOPHILUS MILK IN THE TREATMENT OF DYSENTERY OF
        YOUNG ANIMALS. Amer. Vet. Med. Assoc. Jour. 90: 171-175.
(12) —— MUTH, O. H., and SEGHETTI, L.
    1939. BLACK DISEASE. Oreg. Agr. Expt. Sta. Bul. 360, 18 pp., illus.
(13) —— MUTH, O. H., and SEGHETTI, L.
    1939. PULPY KIDNEY DISEASE IN OREGON LAMBS (INFECTIOUS ENTERO-TOX-
        EMIA). Oreg. Agr. Expt. Sta. Bul. 367, 17 pp., illus.

(14) TUNNICLIFF, E. A., and MARSH, H.
        1939. AN ALUM-PRECIPITATED TOXOID AS AN IMMUNIZING AGENT AGAINST
               INFECTIOUS NECROTIC HEPATITIS (BLACK DISEASE) IN SHEEP. Amer.
               Vet. Med. Assoc. Jour. 94: 98–110
(15) ———— and MATISHECK, PETER H.
        1941. A FILTERABLE VIRUS DEMONSTRATED TO BE THE INFECTIVE AGENT IN
               OVINE BALANO-POSTHITIS. Science 94: 283–284.
(16) TURNER, A. W.
        1930. BLACK DISEASE (INFECTIOUS NECROTIC HEPATITIS) OF SHEEP IN AUS-
               TRALIA. Austral. Council Sci. & Indus. Res. Bul. 46, 141 pp.,
               illus.

At the time this book went to press, the drugs
and other materials mentioned in various articles—chiefly as disinfectants, insecticides, and
anthelmintics—were still available for veterinary and medical use. Under war conditions,
however, it is possible that some of these materials may become scarce or unavailable. In
that case, the reader should obtain professional
advice from the Department of Agriculture, the
State experiment station, a local veterinarian,
or the county agent as to available substitutes.

Internal Parasites of Sheep and Goats

BY G. DIKMANS AND D. A. SHORB [1]

AS EVERY SHEEPMAN KNOWS, internal parasites are one of the greatest hazards in sheep production, and the problem of control is a difficult one. Here is a discussion of some 40 of these parasites, including life histories, symptoms of infestation, medicinal treatment, and preventive measures.

WHILE SHEEP, like other farm animals, suffer from various infectious and noninfectious diseases, the most serious losses, especially in farm flocks, are due to internal parasites. These losses result not so much from deaths from gross parasitism, although fatalities are not infrequent, as from loss of condition, unthriftiness, anemia, and other effects. Devastating and spectacular losses, such as were formerly caused among swine by hog cholera, among cattle by anthrax, and among horses by encephalomyelitis, seldom occur among sheep. Losses due to parasites are much less sensational, but they are constant, and especially in farm flocks they far exceed those due to bacterial diseases. They are difficult to evaluate, however, and do not as a rule receive the attention they deserve.

The principal internal parasites of sheep and goats are roundworms, tapeworms, flukes, and protozoa. Their scientific and common names and their locations in the host are given in table 1.

Another internal parasite of sheep, the sheep nasal fly, the grubs of which develop in the nasal passages and head sinuses, is discussed at the end of the article.

[1] G. Dikmans is Parasitologist and D. A. Shorb is Assistant Parasitologist, Zoological Division, Bureau of Animal Industry.

TABLE 1.—*Principal internal parasites of sheep and goats and their locations in the host animal*

Group and common name	Scientific name	Location in body of host animal
Nematodes, or roundworms:		
Gullet worms	*Gongylonema pulchrum* *G. verrucosum*	}Esophagus and rumen.
Twisted stomach worm	*Haemonchus contortus*	Abomasum, or fourth stomach.
Medium stomach worms	*Ostertagia circumcincta* *O. trifurcata*	} Do.
Small hairworm	*Trichostrongylus axei*	Do.
Hookworm	*Bunostomum trigonocephalum*	Small intestine.
Small hairworms	*Trichostrongylus colubriformis* *T. vitrinus* *T. capricola*	} Do.
(¹)	*Cooperia curticei* *C. oncophora* *C. pectinata* *C. punctata*	} Do.
Thread-necked strongyles	*Nematodirus filicollis* *N. spathiger* *N. abnormalis*	} Do.
(¹)	*Capillaria brevipes*	Do.
Whipworm	*Trichuris ovis*	Cecum and colon.
Nodular worm	*Oesophagostomum columbianum*	Do.
(¹)	*O. venulosum*	Do.
Large-mouthed bowel worm	*Chabertia ovina*	Do.
Thread lungworm	*Dictyocaulus filaria*	Trachea, bronchi.
Hair lungworm	*Muellerius capillaris*	Lungs.
(¹)	*Elaeophora schneideri*	Carotid and mesenteric arteries.
Eyeworm	*Thelazia californiensis*	Tear ducts.
Trematodes, or flukes:		
Common liver fluke	*Fasciola hepatica*	Liver.
Large American fluke	*Fascioloides magna*	Do.
Rumen flukes	*Cotylophoron cotylophorum* *Paramphistomum cervi*	}Rumen or paunch.
Mature cestodes, or tapeworms:		
Common tapeworms	*Moniezia expansa* *M. benedeni*	}Small intestine.
Fringed tapeworm	*Thysanosoma actinioides*	Bile ducts and small intestine.
Immature cestodes, or tapeworms (bladder worms):		
Thin or long-necked bladder worm.	*Cysticercus tenuicollis*	Omentum, mesentery, and liver.
Sheep measles	*C. ovis*	Heart and muscles.
Gid bladder worm	*Coenurus cerebralis,* or *Multiceps multiceps.*	Brain and spinal cord.
Hydatid, or echinococcus	*Echinococcus granulosus*	Liver and lungs.
Protozoa:		
Coccidia	*Eimeria* species	Small intestine.
Sarcosporidia	*Sarcocystis tenella*	Esophagus and voluntary muscles.
(¹)	*Globidium gilruthi*	Wall of fourth stomach and small intestine.

¹ No common name.

GEOGRAPHICAL DISTRIBUTION

While parasites may be found wherever sheep and goats are kept in the United States, they occur with the greatest frequency and are of greatest importance in the farm-flock area as distinguished from the western or range area. The farm-flock area lies roughly east of a line drawn from the western border of North Dakota to the Gulf of Mexico in the vicinity of Corpus Christi, exclusive of South Dakota. According to estimated figures of the Agricultural Marketing Service of the Department of Agriculture for 1940, there are in this area about 14,659,000 stock sheep and lambs, of which 7,255,000, or roughly 50 percent, are found in Ohio, Missouri, Iowa, Kentucky, and Michigan. Parasitism is worst under farm conditions because as a rule sheep in farm flocks remain concentrated on smaller areas for longer periods than under range conditions. The climatic conditions prevailing in this area are also more favorable for the development of worm eggs on pastures and the maintenance of pasture infection than are those prevailing in the range States.

In addition to the sheep in the farm-flock area, there are, according to Baker (*3*),[2] about 500,000 goats, the majority of them being located in southeastern Georgia, central Tennessee, and southern Missouri.

GENERAL FEATURES OF LIFE CYCLES

The life histories of all the common roundworms of sheep and goats, with the exception of *Muellerius capillaris*, *Elaeophora schneideri*, *Gongylonema pulchrum*, and *G. verrucosum*, which are discussed elsewhere in this article, are direct; that is, no intermediate hosts are required for their development. Tapeworms, flukes, and some of the parasitic protozoa, on the other hand, require intermediate hosts for the completion of their life cycles, details of which will be given separately under the discussions of the particular parasites.

Roundworms reproduce by means of eggs.. With the exception of those of lungworms, which hatch in the lungs (the larvae being discharged with the feces), the eggs of the roundworms parasitic in sheep and goats pass out in the droppings of infected animals. With a few exceptions, which will be noted in the discussion of the parasites to which they apply, the eggs develop on pasture into infective larvae in periods varying from a few days to a few weeks, depending upon conditions of temperature and moisture. In warm weather the eggs hatch in a few hours. If the temperature is below 40° F., the eggs remain dormant; if it is below freezing, the vitality of many of the eggs is eventually destroyed. Dryness also destroys many eggs, while moisture favors their development. The larvae as they hatch from the eggs are very susceptible to freezing and drying. In very warm weather they complete their development in 2 to 4 days, provided enough moisture is present. In cooler weather the time required for development is longer; at temperatures below 70° F., 10 days to several weeks may be necessary. Neither the eggs nor larvae in the early stages develop when ingested, or taken into the body, by sheep and goats; only when the larvae have reached the third stage do they become infective to their host. Hence this is known as the infective stage.

In the infective stage the larvae of many different species of these worms migrate to the stalks of grass or to other plants, becoming active whenever the air is saturated with moisture, as from rain, fog, or dew. When the air becomes dry and the moisture evaporates from the grass, the young worms cease their activity, and they resume their migrations only when the air again becomes laden with moisture. Unlike the eggs and the larvae in the early stages, larvae that have developed to the infective stage are able, as a rule, to survive long periods of freezing and dryness. They reach maturity and begin producing eggs about 2 to 6 weeks after they are taken up by their host.

---

[2] Italic numbers in parentheses refer to Literature Cited, p. 900.

SYMPTOMS OF WORM INFECTION

The general symptoms of worm infection are unthriftiness, loss of weight, diarrhea, anemia manifested by paleness of the visible mucous membranes of the eyes and mouth, development of potbelly, or enlargement of the abdomen, and often a soft swelling under the jaw, referred to as bottle jaw or poverty jaw. Since animals showing such symptoms are commonly infested with several species of parasites, it is impossible to determine from observation which species are responsible.

Experiments undertaken to determine the effects on sheep and goats of infections with single species of worm parasites have shown that animals infected only with the twisted stomach worm, *Haemonchus contortus*, show a marked anemia, similar to that produced by bleeding, caused by hemorrhage into the stomach. No diarrhea occurred. Experimental infection with small trichostrongyles, *Trichostrongylus* species (*1*), produced a marked, and in some cases prolonged, watery diarrhea. The infected animals appeared gaunt and depressed, showed evidence of abdominal pain, and refused to eat. Animals dying of this infection were emaciated, and the carcasses showed evidence of dehydration, or loss of water, resulting from the continuous diarrhea. There was little or no evidence of anemia. In Australia the diarrhea caused by infection with these small trichostrongyles is referred to as black scours because of the dark color of the feces passed by the infected animals. This black color, which was not observed in experimentally infected sheep and goats, may be due to the fact that the animals were on pasture or perhaps to blood in the feces resulting from a simultaneous infection with *H. contortus*.

Sheep experimentally infected with *Cooperia curticei*, another member of the group of worms commonly referred to as small intestinal trichostrongyles, did not show any serious clinical effects (*2*).

Symptoms shown by animals infected with hookworms, *Bunostomum trigonocephalum*, are similar to those generally found in hookworm infection in other animals.

While the twisted stomach worm, *Haemonchus contortus*, is the most common stomach worm of sheep and goats in the eastern half of the United States, the medium stomach worms, *Ostertagia* species, appear to be the most prevalent forms found in some areas in the western part of the country. The symptoms attributed to infection with these worms are the same as those attributed to infection with *H. contortus*, but they do not appear to develop as rapidly or to be quite so marked. Experimental infections with *Ostertagia circumcincta* (*51*) did not produce any marked clinical symptoms except in some animals to which enormous numbers of infective larvae had been administered.

Symptoms shown by animals infected with nodular worms are diarrhea, abdominal pain, and loss of flesh. These symptoms occur chiefly during the time that the larvae penetrate into and remain in the wall of the intestine.

Opinions differ as to the effect on sheep and goats of infection with the thread-necked strongyles, *Nematodirus* species. Such experimental evidence as is now available (*29*) appears to indicate that these worms cannot be considered as producing any noticeable symptoms in infected animals.

Experimental infections with *Chabertia ovina* (*13*, *28*) indicate that these worms may be responsible for symptoms of severe bloody diarrhea during their development to adult worms in the host. The effect of infection with adult worms has not been definitely determined.

PROTOZOA

A large number of protozoa have been reported as parasites of sheep and goats, but only a few of these are known to be harmful. They are all of minute size, too small to be·seen with the unaided eye.

COCCIDIA

A number of species (*7*) of coccidia, all belonging in the genus *Eimeria* but varying greatly in size and certain other characters of form and structure, have been reported as parasites of sheep and goats. They occur in the wall of the small intestine and cause a disease known as coccidiosis.

The resting, or spore, form of these parasites, which is the form usually found in microscopical examination of fecal specimens, is ellipsoidal or ovoid (football-shaped).

The life history of these parasites is very complicated. The resting, or spore, forms, known as oöcysts, pass out of the body with the feces. Under favorable conditions (*8*) four bodies known as sporocysts develop within the oöcyst. Within each sporocyst two sporozoites develop, so that at maturity the oöcyst contains eight sporozoites. This is the infective stage of the parasite. When taken up by a susceptible animal with feed or water, these sporozoites are liberated in the intestine and invade the intestinal wall. The preferred site in which the parasite undergoes its development is in the cells composing the inner lining of the small intestine. Here the parasites multiply, at first asexually and later sexually. At the beginning of an infection the asexual cycle is more prevalent, whereas later the sexual forms are more frequently found. The sexual reproduction results in the formation of oöcysts, which pass out of the body with the feces and, after maturing outside the body, become infective to a new host.

Little is known concerning the occurrence and actual importance of coccidial infection among farm sheep in the United States. Examinations made in 1937 by the Zoological Division of the Bureau of Animal Industry at Beltsville, Md., of over 100 miscellaneous adult ewes and lambs revealed that all of them were infected with coccidia, thus confirming similar observations made in other parts of the country and showing that healthy adult sheep are carriers of coccidia. During this study the course of coccidial infections was followed in 9 spring lambs by means of frequent fecal examinations from shortly after birth through the following several months. All 9 lambs acquired infection early, as shown by heavy oöcyst production beginning during the fifth and sixth weeks of life. In 5 of these animals that were followed until they were 7 months old, the infection remained relatively high for 6 to 8 weeks after the oöcysts first began to appear in the feces, then declined and remained at a low level during the summer months. These apparently heavy infections caused no noticeable inconvenience to the animals other than mild scouring during the first few days of heaviest oöcyst discharge.

It appears likely that as a result of the intimate relationship between young lambs and ewes, all normally reared lambs acquire coc-

Figure 1.—Sheep affected with coccidiosis.

cidial infection at an early age from oöcysts discharged by the adult carriers, but as a general rule thrifty, well-nourished lambs survive these early attacks without suffering any ill effects, and the infections do little or no harm to the great majority of the animals.

According to Thorp (*50*), severely affected animals (fig. 1) become dull and lethargic, lose their appetites, and suffer from diarrhea, the discharges often becoming bloody. The diarrhea may continue for several days, and in some animals for several weeks, causing weakness, loss of flesh, and death. Enteritis (inflammation) may be present in both the small and large intestines. The diagnosis rests on the demonstration of coccidia in the feces of affected animals.

The disease as it occurs in feed lots has been described by Thorp (*50*), Deem and Thorp (*15*), and Christensen (*9*). According to these authors virtually all of the lambs are discharging some coccidial oöcysts when they arrive at the feed lots. When the conditions are favorable, clinical symptoms of coccidiosis begin to manifest themselves about 2 weeks later. Deem and Thorp (*15*) reported that in a number of outbreaks most of the cases occurred between 2 and 3 weeks after the lambs were placed in the lots.

Christensen (*9*), studying an outbreak of this disease in a group of approximately 16,000 lambs, states that death losses from coccidiosis, together with widespread scouring and heavy oöcyst discharge in the feces, began 12 to 16 days after the lambs had been placed in the feed lots. Heavy death losses continued for about 2 weeks, after which they gradually subsided, but many animals continued to suffer from diarrhea for several weeks. During this outbreak 540 lambs, constituting 3.4 percent of the total number under observation, died as a result of coccidiosis, and 1,563 required special care and feeding because of emaciation resulting from excessive scouring.

Christensen demonstrated that in the particular case under consideration the source of infection was in the lambs themselves and not in the old, previously contaminated feed lots.

During this investigation Christensen noted that the corn silage that was used as part of the ration became heavily contaminated with sheep feces and that it was customary to replenish the supply in the feed troughs twice a day by adding fresh material to the uneaten portions of the previous feed. No attempt was made to clean out the troughs by removing unconsumed feed, and there was a gradual accumulation of uneaten silage beneath the fresh additions. Whole and fragmented fecal pellets containing coccidial oöcysts were found scattered throughout this silage in the feed troughs. Because of its high moisture content, the oöcysts found favorable conditions for sporulation, or spore production, in the silage.

Christensen concluded that in this case the contaminated corn silage was the principal source of the infective coccidia responsible for the enormously increased numbers of oöcysts found in the lambs 2 weeks after they were placed in the feed lots and for the severe clinical cases of coccidiosis in the group.

Coccidia occur in practically all lambs and sheep examined and under ordinary circumstances apparently cause little or no disturbance. The factors or combination of factors responsible for severe outbreaks of coccidiosis are not well known. The extent to which external factors, such as abrupt changes in feed or sudden marked changes in temperature, influence the development of coccidiosis by lowering the resistance of the animal is not known. Whether in outbreaks in feed lots the ingestion of increased numbers of oöcysts is the principal factor or whether the change of feed is a contributing factor of major importance remains to be determined.

There is no specific treatment for coccidiosis. Christensen (*9*), however, reports that the daily administration of small amounts of a combined copper sulfate and ferric sulfate solution over a period of 5 weeks from the beginning of confinement in feed lots significantly lowered the discharge of coccidial oöcysts in one group of healthy lambs as compared with that in another group not receiving such treatment. While this test suggests the possibility that there may be some benefit in the use of these chemicals as preventives, there is abundant evidence to indicate that in the actual treatment of the disease, these and other chemicals are of no value.

GLOBIDIUM GILRUTHI

Another protozoan parasite, *Globidium gilruthi*, occurs in the fourth stomach and small intestine of sheep. According to Wenyon (*55*) these parasites, which are probably related to sarcosporidia, occur as sickle-shaped spores enclosed in membranous cysts or sacs, in the wall of the fourth stomach and small intestine. These cysts appear as little white opalescent elevations of the mucous membrane. Within the mature cyst is a mass of spores. One end of the cyst is blunt and the other pointed.

The infection is not uncommon in sheep, but usually only a few cysts are present, and no clinical symptoms or disease condition referable to the infection can be noted. In some cases, however, the infection is heavy, and according to Marsh and Tunnicliff (*33*) such infections may cause a severe enteritis, or intestinal inflammation, manifested by pronounced diarrhea and accompanied by the usual depression and loss of weight. There is no fever, and no blood appears in the feces except where there is a hemorrhagic condition of the rectum.[3] Since nothing is known of the life history of the parasites, no recommendations for prevention or control can be made, and medicinal treatment has, so far as is known, not been attempted. It is possible that the administration of intestinal astringents such as those used by Christensen (*9*) in outbreaks of coccidiosis may have some beneficial effects.

FLUKES

Sheep and goats in the United States may be infested with one or more species of flukes, which are flat, leaflike parasites. Two kinds of flukes may occur in the liver, and two other kinds are found in the rumen, or paunch. Flukes reproduce by means of eggs, which pass out with the feces and hatch in water, releasing ciliated embryos—that is, embryos equipped with hairlike structures for moving around—known as miracidia. The miracidia penetrate certain species of snails and develop into cercariae (flukes in the larval stage), which leave the snails and encyst on vegetation. Encysted cercariae are ingested by sheep and goats in grazing and develop into mature flukes.

THE COMMON LIVER FLUKE

The common liver fluke, *Fasciola hepatica*, found in the liver, bile ducts, and gall bladder of sheep and goats is a flattened, leaflike,

---

[3] At post mortem examination of an animal dying from the infection, these authors found the small intestine studded along its entire length with small white cysts, some on the surface of the mucous membrane and others deeply embedded in it. The mucous membrane was hyperemic and had a somewhat furry appearance. In another case the infection was found to be greatest in the posterior portion of the small intestine, the cysts being less than 1 millimeter apart. Microscopic examination of affected areas of the small intestine showed large numbers of *Globidium* cysts, in different stages of development, in the mucosa, destruction of the epithelium of the villi, and infiltration of the tissue by large numbers of monocytes and lymphocytes.

brown worm, usually about an inch long. There is a sucker on a cone-shaped extension at the anterior, or front, end, and just behind this is a ventral sucker. Through the skin, or cuticula, the branching intestine and the uterus filled with eggs can be seen.

The cercaria, which develops within a snail (fig. 2), resembles a small fluke and is provided with a tail by means of which it swims about. It finally loses its tail and encysts, or becomes enclosed in a cyst. The encysted cercariae may float about on water or attach themselves to grass blades or other vegetation. When swallowed by

FIGURE 2.—Snails serve as intermediate hosts of the liver fluke, *Fasciola hepatica*. These snails were on the ground near a temporary pool in a herd pen in Texas. (Photograph by O. W. Olsen, Angleton, Tex.)

sheep or other suitable host animals, the larval flukes, on reaching the small intestine, bore through the wall to the body cavity. Here they wander over the surface of the viscera and walls of the body cavity, finally perforating the capsule of the liver and reaching the extremities of the biliary (bile) ducts. In the liver the young flukes grow to maturity in the larger bile ducts.

The distribution of the common liver fluke is world-wide wherever low, wet pastures and the suitable intermediate snail hosts occur. In the United States it is most prevalent on the west coast and in the Rocky Mountain States, the Southwest, and the Southeast.

The symptoms associated with liver fluke infection are, in a general

way, similar to those attributed to other worm infections—unthriftiness, anemia, etc. According to Clunies Ross and Gordon (*12*), in
acute cases resulting from massive invasion of the liver by large
numbers of young flukes, death may occur after an illness of only a
few days and without any symptoms that can be definitely attributed
to fluke infection. Sheep suffering from chronic fluke disease appear
languid and are easily fatigued when driven. When such animals
are examined the visible mucous membranes will be found to be
pale and anemic. As the disease progresses the gait becomes stiff,
the loss of condition becomes more marked, and dropsical (edematous) swellings develop under the jaw. According to Shaw and

Simms (*42*), these
swellings, commonly
called bottle jaw, occur
in sheep suffering from
infection with imma-
ture flukes as well as
in those affected with
chronic fluke disease.
These authors also re-
port that the distention
of the abdomen result-
ing from the accumula-
tion of fluid and com-
monly referred to as
potbelly (fig. 3) de-
velops during the early
stages of the infection
when parasites are pres-
ent in large numbers.
The condition later dis-
appears and is not pres-

FIGURE 3.—The sheep on the right shows the distention
of the abdomen known as potbelly, resulting from liver
fluke infestation. (Photograph by J. N. Shaw.)

ent when the parasites have developed to maturity.

The lesions found in the sheep at post mortem examination depend
upon the developmental stage of the fluke. If the infection is heavy,
there is considerable damage to the liver from penetration by the
immature flukes. This penetration leads to hemorrhage into the
abdominal cavity and an accumulation of fluid within it. Acute
inflammatory changes occur in the liver substance, and the liver becomes enlarged owing to engorgement with blood. As already noted,
infected animals may die as a result of massive invasion of the liver
by young flukes without showing any marked symptoms attributable
to fluke infection. After the flukes become mature in the bile ducts,
these ducts become greatly thickened as a result of continuous irritation. In advanced cases the ducts stand out prominently and, owing
to a deposit of calcium salts, become hard and gritty, as may be observed on cutting them.

THE LARGE LIVER FLUKE

The large American liver fluke, *Fascioloides magna*, is found in the
tissues of the liver, commonly in cysts which usually contain, in addi-

tion to the flukes, a quantity of dark-colored fluid and debris. The fluke may attain a' length of 7 centimeters (2¾ inches). The large liver fluke resembles an overgrown specimen of the common liver fluke except that the anterior, or front, sucker is not carried on a distinct cone. The life histories of the two are essentially the same. The same snails serve as intermediate hosts for both, and their development in the snail is the same.

So far as known, deer and sheep are the principal propagators of the large liver fluke. It appears to be indigenous to North America and is principally a parasite of deer, but specimens have been collected from sheep in Montana and Idaho.

According to Swales (*48, 49*), this fluke infects cattle as well as deer and sheep, but in cattle the parasites become encapsulated, or enclosed in a capsule, by the fibrous tissue formed around them through the reaction of the tissues. This prevents undue damage to the liver and the entrance of the eggs into the bile ducts, and it also precludes the continuance of the life cycle of the parasite. In deer a balance appears to have been established between host and parasite, the host reaction being adequate to prevent undue tissue damage but not to prevent reproduction. In sheep severe damage results from the almost unchecked migration of the parasite in the liver tissue. Sheep are the only hosts in which this parasite produces a severe clinical disease. Experimentally infected sheep became greatly emaciated and very weak, even though only a few flukes were found in the liver at post mortem examination.

The symptoms of infestation by the large liver fluke are similar to those associated with infection by the common liver fluke, and the control measures for the latter, discussed later, also apply to the large liver fluke. In addition, however, sheep should be prevented from grazing on snail-infested land occupied by deer.

THE RUMEN FLUKES

Two small flukes, *Paramphistomum cervi* and *Cotylophoron cotylophorum*, one-fifth to one-half inch in length, are found in the rumen, or paunch, usually near the opening into the reticulum, or honeycomb stomach.•

The bodies are pinkish when alive. They are convex on the back (dorsally) and slightly concave on the under side (ventrally). Shaped more or less like a cone, they are broad and blunt at the hind end and rather pointed at the front end.

The life history of one of these flukes, *Cotylophoron cotylophorum*, has been studied in detail (*5*) and found to be essentially the same as that of the common liver fluke, the same snails serving as intermediate hosts of both.

These flukes have been reported from sheep in Australia, South Africa (*32*), and India, but they occur most commonly in cattle. There is no record of their occurrence in sheep under natural conditions in the United States.

The adult parasites appear to be relatively harmless, and no definite lesions, or tissue injuries, have been ascribed to them. It has been reported, however, that in the immature stages they are definitely disease-producing. The symptoms described are very similar to those of roundworm infestation and the lesions occur chiefly in the small intestine.

Since snails act as intermediate hosts of these parasites, the methods of prevention later advocated in the case of the liver fluke may prove to be beneficial.

TAPEWORMS

Sheep and goats in the United States may harbor both adult and larval tapeworms. The adult tapeworm has a head provided with four suckers and a body consisting of a number of flat segments joined together to form a chain. Tapeworms produce eggs of microscopic size which pass out in the feces of the host animal, together with gravid segments (segments containing eggs), which, when dry, liberate more eggs. On being ingested by a suitable host the eggs develop into an intermediate stage—a larva known as a cysticercoid. Sheep and goats become infested by swallowing such larvae.

The larval tapeworms that occur in sheep and goats are commonly known as bladder worms; they are usually located in the tissues or cavities of the body. The bladder worm consists of a head and neck inverted in a membrane containing a clear fluid, the whole structure resembling a bladder. When a bladder worm is eaten by the final host, the head is extruded, or pushed out of the membrane, and passes to the small intestine of the host, where it develops into an adult worm by the growth of segments back of the head.

THE MONIEZIAS

Two species of tapeworms, *Moniezia expansa* and *M. benedeni*—long, flat, ribbonlike worms, which sometimes attain a length of several yards and a breadth of three-fourths of an inch—are known to occur in the small intestines of sheep and goats.

The eggs and segments containing eggs pass out with the feces onto the pasture. According to Stunkard (*47*) the eggs contained in the gravid segments are expelled as the segments dry. On the grass of the pasture the eggs are accessible to certain free-living mites known as oribatid mites and also as beetle mites, which serve as intermediate hosts of the tapeworms. The eggs contain six hooked embryos known as oncospheres. In the mite the oncospheres develop into cysticercoids, or tapeworm larvae, in 15 to 16 weeks.[4] Field experiments indicate that during the summer this development may be completed in 6 to 8 weeks.

Large numbers of different species of oribatid mites may occur on pastures, but only a few of these, all belonging in the genus *Galumna* and present on the grass during the cooler parts of the day and on warm, cloudy days, serve as intermediate hosts of the sheep tapeworm. During periods of intense sunlight and when strong,

---

[4] According to Krull (*31*), the mouth parts of the mites are not adapted to take in the entire tapeworm egg, and the mites therefore break the shell and ingest the oncosphere, which then develops into a cysticercoid in the body cavity.

drying winds prevail, the mites leave the grass and are found at the grass roots and in the soil. Saturation of the soil due to heavy or continued rains causes the mites to migrate onto the grass. They may be found throughout the year, but according to Krull (*31*) in the vicinity of Beltsville, Md., they are most abundant during April and May.

The tapeworms of sheep are cosmopolitan in distribution. They are commonly believed to be serious parasites of sheep, and various conditions, such as unthriftiness, loss of weight, anemia, and digestive disturbances manifested by diarrhea, have been attributed to tapeworm infection. The reasons for this belief are largely indirect but quite obvious. Tapeworm segments are often found singly or in strings of various lengths in the droppings of sheep running on pastures and showing clinical evidence of parasitic infection. On post mortem examination of such sheep, tapeworms are usually found in the small intestine, and the condition of the animals before death is naturally attributed to the tapeworms. The presence of other parasites, particularly small roundworms, is usually not taken into consideration.

Through experimental infection of lambs with tapeworms (*Moniezia expansa*) only, uncomplicated by roundworm infection such as is commonly found under natural conditions, Shorb (*43*, *44*) has shown that the effects of the former have been generally overrated. The principal effects observed were a slight intestinal disturbance, manifested by the passage of softened feces instead of the usual formed pellets, and a slight retardation of growth. The severity of the effects depends apparently on the age and size of the infected animal and the number of tapeworms present. Young, undersized lambs from 1 to 3 months of age are more seriously affected by a given number of tapeworms than well-grown, vigorous lambs about 6 months old, and in lambs of comparable ages and sizes those harboring the greater number of tapeworms showed the more marked effects.

Under natural conditions lambs become infected with tapeworms at an early age, and this infection, added to the roundworm infections usually acquired at the same time, may result in serious retardation of growth.

No recommendations as to prevention can be given until detailed information on the life history of the intermediate host has been obtained.

THE FRINGED TAPEWORM

Another tapeworm, which appears to be confined to range sheep, is known as the fringed tapeworm, *Thysanosoma actinioides*. It derives its common name from the fact that each of the segments has a fringe on its posterior, or rear, border, which distinguishes it from all other tapeworms. If the segments are put in water, the fringes float out and can be easily seen.

The fringed tapeworm is a parasite of western sheep and is found in the East only when sheep shipped from the West are slaughtered at eastern abattoirs.

On post mortem examination of infected animals the tapeworms are found in the small intestine, the bile ducts, the gall bladder, and sometimes the pancreatic duct. At times they may be numerous enough to apparently occlude, or close up, these ducts, and many serious pathological conditions and marked clinical symptoms, based largely on deductions from the post mortem findings, have been attributed to them. After examining a number of infected sheep and comparing their condition with that of similar uninfected sheep, however, Christensen (*10*) came to the conclusion that, at least so far as adult sheep are concerned, no serious effects can be ascribed to this tapeworm.

The life history of the fringed tapeworm is completely unknown, and until it has been ascertained and pure infections have been established, no definite statement concerning its effects on sheep are warranted.

At the present time the most serious loss resulting from infection is due to the fact that under Federal meat-inspection regulations, all sheep livers found on post mortem examination to be infected are condemned as unfit for human consumption.

BLADDER WORMS

The bladder worms found in sheep and goats, of which there are four kinds, are the larval or immature stages of tapeworms found in dogs and related carnivores. Their names and usual locations are given in table 1, page 860.

Sheep and goats become infected with these bladder worms by ingesting the eggs voided by dogs and related carnivores on pasture or range.

The Thin-Necked Bladder Worm

The thin-necked bladder worm, *Cysticercus tenuicollis*, has the appearance of a large sac filled with clear fluid. A white object, which is the head or neck, projects into it at one end. The bladder is usually about 1 inch in diameter and may attain a length of several inches. The bladder worm proper is surrounded by a cyst wall which is developed by the host animal as a protective measure against the parasite. When this cyst is broken, the parasite usually rolls out and is seen to be a thin-walled structure. By appropriate treatment the head and neck of the tapeworm may be pushed out and made to protrude from one end of the bladder.

When one of these bladder worms is ingested by a dog, the cyst wall is digested, and the tapeworm head and neck passes into the small intestine, where it develops into a mature tapeworm (*Taenia hydatigena*) by the growth of segments back of the neck. Egg-bearing segments develop in 10 to 12 weeks. When infested dogs run over pastures used by sheep and goats they may leave feces containing tapeworm eggs and segments on the pasture, and these eggs may be spread by rain onto the grass and into streams and puddles from which the animals drink. When sheep ingest the eggs the embryo escapes from its shell, makes its way to the liver, and begins to develop. In the course of time it escapes from the liver and becomes attached to the mesenteries or omenta (abdominal membranes). At first it is a bladder without a head, but later a head and neck develop, and the fully formed cysticercus is ready to infect any susceptible dog that eats it.

This parasite is quite generally distributed over the United States. It is most likely to be present where sheep are associated with dogs or where stray dogs commonly run over pastures and where animals are slaughtered on farms or at small country slaughterhouses at which little care is exercised in disposing of the viscera and of diseased portions of the carcasses.

Light infestations produce little damage, but severe ones may make an animal very sick and even cause death. In such cases the animal shows symptoms of dullness, weakness, loss of appetite, and fever. These symptoms are due to hemorrhage from the liver, caused by the wandering larvae, and the peritonitis, or inflammation of the abdominal lining, that results. The symptoms appearing in the early stages of the infestation are seldom associated with the invasion of tapeworm larvae.

On post mortem examination the bladder worms may be found in the liver or in the abdominal cavity attached to the mesenteries or omenta. No particular lesions are associated with light infestations. In animals dying of hemorrhage from the liver and peritonitis resulting from massive invasion, the liver surface shows a series of short ridges or serpentine markings running in all directions and most numerous near the thin edge. On cut sections the liver substance shows many burrows caused by the wandering tapeworm larvae.

Sheep Measles

Cysticercus ovis, the bladder worm responsible for "sheep measles," is most commonly found in the heart or diaphragm but occurs not infrequently in the muscles of mastication and the tongue and sometimes in other locations in the muscular system. It may occur in the lungs, the walls of the esophagus, and the wall of the stomach. This is a small oval bladder worm with the head and neck invaginated about midway between the ends instead of at one end as is the case of other bladder worms. The membrane of the bladder is very thin, with small mammillate projections. Sheep and goats become infected by swallowing the eggs produced by the adult tapeworm in the intestines of dogs and voided together with segments containing eggs, on pastures or elsewhere. After the eggs are swallowed, the shells are digested, and the embryos, armed with six hooks, penetrate through the wall of the intestine and reach the liver with the blood stream. They pass through the liver into the veins and thence to the heart. From the heart they pass by means of the general circulation to those parts of the body in which they are found at post mortem examination. They develop into mature bladder worms in about 2½ to 3 months.

This parasite is more or less generally distributed throughout the western part of the United States and may occur wherever sheep are attended by dogs, particularly where dogs have an opportunity to devour dead sheep. Ransom (*41*) recorded in 1912 that in that year 20,000 sheep carcasses were retained under Federal meat inspection at various abattoirs on account of infection with *Cysticercus ovis*.

No symptoms have been attributed to infection with these parasites, the infection usually being discovered only at the time of slaughter. Ransom records, however, that of six lambs experimentally infected with tapeworm eggs, five died in 13 to 23 days after the eggs had been fed them. The animals died approximately in the order of the size of the doses of tapeworm eggs given, those receiving the smallest doses surviving longest. Three of them received only the eggs contained in a single segment and the other two received 3 and 10 segments respectively. The sheep that survived received only one-half of a segment and was sick for a period corresponding to that during which the embryonic worms were invading the muscles. The nature of the symptoms was not described.

This bladder worm of sheep was formerly considered to be rare, and when it was found, it was confused with the bladder worm of swine, *Cysticercus cellulosae*, the larval form of *Taenia solium*, a tapeworm of man. (See Internal Parasites of Swine, p. 745.) In accordance with Federal meat inspection regulations governing the disposition of swine carcasses infected with *C. cellulosae*, carcasses and parts of carcasses of sheep found to be infected with muscle cysticerci were condemned as unfit for human consumption. Ransom (*41*) demonstrated that the muscle cysticerci found in sheep were the larvae of *T. ovis*, a tapeworm of dogs not transmissible to man, and he also showed that muscle cysticerci of sheep, instead of being rare, occurred in a large number of sheep slaughtered.

At the present time the parasite is important chiefly from the point of view of meat inspection. Heavily infected carcasses are condemned or rendered into inedible products. The infected portions of a lightly infected carcass are removed and condemned, and the remainder is passed for food. This disposition is made of infected material not because of any danger of human infection but because of the appearance of the meat.

The Gid Bladder Worm

The gid bladder worm, *Coenurus cerebralis*, occurs in the brain or spinal cord of infected animals as a large cyst, or bladder, attaining the size of a hen's egg or larger. It consists of a thin membrane containing a rather large amount of fluid. On the membrane there are a number of small white objects about the size of a grain of wheat, which project into the fluid. These are the tapeworm heads.

Sheep and goats acquire the infection in a manner similar to that described for the other bladder worms—by ingesting the tapeworm eggs voided by infected dogs or related carnivores on pasture or range. The embryos that emerge after the eggshells have been digested make their way through the wall of the intestine and are carried by the blood stream to various parts of the body, but only those that reach the brain or spinal cord are able to complete development, the others dying and degenerating before full larval development has been completed. Those that reach the central nervous system at first move about on or in the brain and spinal cord, forming curving channels. After a while the young worm comes to rest, and the bladder worm develops, completing its development in about 7 to 8 months.

At the time when the young worm gets to the brain there are usually slight symptoms of fever and restlessness, which are easily overlooked. If, as a result of severe infection, the sheep dies at this time, an examination of the brain will show a number of curving channels on its surface. If the infected animal does not die, the symptoms of this stage abate, and there is no further indication of the presence of the parasite until it has grown to the point where the heads form.

Infection with this parasite gives rise to certain characteristic symptoms (fig. 4), their occurrence and severity depending on the number of worms present. According to Neveu-Lemaire (*38*), animals harboring 10 to 12 or more parasites in the brain show, shortly after the beginning of the infection, symptoms of depression, somnolence, and loss of appetite and lose flesh rapidly. Disturbances of vision are noted, some animals becoming completely blind and running into objects in their path. The visual disturbances are accompanied by disturbances in locomotion. The

FIGURE 4.—A "giddy" sheep. (Photograph by M. C. Hall.)

animals stumble, fall down frequently, settle on the hindquarters or forequarters, and may lie down for whole days as if paralyzed. Death, resulting from acute encephalitis, or brain fever, follows in about a month. There is no evidence of turning or circling disease.

Animals infected with only a few parasites in many cases do not show these early symptoms; in others the symptoms occur, but they are less marked and disappear after about 8 to 10 days. For the next 4 to 6 months the animals show little evidence of infection. After that, disturbances in vision are noted, and they are accompanied by locomotor disturbances manifested by turning movements. The animals walk in circles either to the right or to the left, or they may pivot in one spot; others walk with the head high and with high knee action, or with the head low and a stumbling gait, the character of the movements depending on the location of the cysts in the brain. The animals refuse feed and water and become greatly emaciated. They may move about continuously or stop at times and gaze fixedly at nothing in particular. They are difficult or impossible to herd and tend to lag behind the flock or become lost. When the parasite is located in the spinal cord there is paralysis of the hindquarters, the rectum, and the bladder. At first the hind legs are brought up convulsively; later they drag, and the muscles atrophy.

In sheep that die in the early stages of a massive infection the aborted worms that have lodged at places unfavorable for their development may be detected by the presence in the muscles of sinuous channels, whitish or yellowish in color and enlarged at one end, where the aborted larvae may be found. Similar tracks, representing the wanderings of the worms, may be found on the brain in 2 to 4 weeks after it is invaded by the parasites. The pressure of the cysts causes,

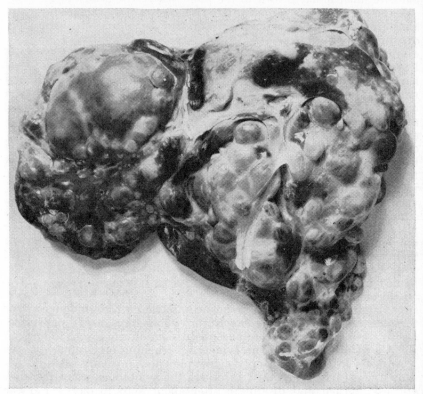

FIGURE 5.—Liver of sheep showing hydatid infestation.

atrophy, or wasting away, of the neighboring nervous tissue and the overlying bone. The bone becomes thin and may even be perforated.

The Hydatid

Hydatids (*Echinococcus granulosus*) occur most frequently in the liver (fig. 5) and the lungs, but they may be found in practically any organ or tissue. The cysts may vary from less than ¼ inch to more than 6 inches in diameter. They may be single or multiple, sterile or fertile. When located on the surface, the cysts form spherical protuberances. According to Mönnig (*35*) only 8 percent of hydatids in sheep are sterile. When sterile, they contain fluid only; when fertile, they contain minute objects resembling grains of sand attached to the cyst wall or lying unattached in the fluid. These grains are broad capsules, and each of them may contain a number of very small tapeworm heads.

While this tapeworm of dogs and related carnivores has a world-wide distribution, there is very little definite information on the frequency of its occurrence in dogs and its geographical distribution in the United States. Meat-inspection records covering the period 1930–38, inclusive, indicate that approximately 1,200 cattle livers were condemned each year for hydatid infestation. The locations of the meat-inspection establishments at which these livers were condemned indicate a wide distribution of the parasite throughout the United States.

The symptoms shown by animals affected with hydatids depend on the location of the parasites and their size. If the parasites are small or do not crowd important organs, few or no symptoms will be manifested. When the parasites are located in the heart or brain or some other vital organ, there may be marked symptoms or even death from pressure or from rupture of the cysts. As a rule infestations are not detected or diagnosed during life but are found only on post mortem examination.

ROUNDWORMS

Except in areas where liver flukes are prevalent, the roundworms are the most serious parasites of sheep and goats. Roundworm parasites occur in the respiratory tract, all parts of the digestive tract except the second and third stomachs, the circulatory system, and the eye and lachrymal (tear) ducts. The only roundworms occurring in the esophagus, or gullet, and the rumen, or paunch, are species of *Gongylonema*, which occur principally in the lining membranes of these organs and, so far as is known, have no marked harmful effects on their hosts.

Roundworm Parasites of the Abomasum, or Fourth Stomach

The Twisted Stomach Worm

The twisted stomach worm, *Haemonchus contortus*, is the most serious worm parasite of sheep and goats. It is from ¾ to 1½ inches long and about as thick as a pin. The females are larger than the males, and when alive, their bodies are marked with a spiral striping, which is responsible for the common designation, twisted stomach worm. On post mortem examination of animals that have died of stomach worm disease, these parasites are found, sometimes in enormous numbers, in the fourth stomach.

The general facts of the life histories of most of the common roundworms parasitic in the gastrointestinal tracts of sheep and goats have been given (p. 861). The life history of the stomach worm, *Haemonchus contortus*, as determined by Veglia (*52*), is here presented in detail for the purpose of illustration. Veglia's observations on the influence of temperature and moisture on the development of eggs and larvae of *H. contortus* are also noted.

The eggs are produced in the stomach and pass out with the feces. Under favorable conditions of temperature and moisture they hatch in a few hours, but unfavorable conditions may delay hatching for several days. In the course of the next few days the larvae that develop from the eggs molt twice and are transformed into third-stage, or infective, larvae. These third-stage larvae are enclosed in the skin of the second molt and are therefore also known as ensheathed larvae. They do not feed and are quite resistant to unfavorable climatic conditions. When the weather is warm and the grass is wet with rain or dew they climb up on grass blades, with which they are swallowed by host animals in grazing. Shortly after being ingested, they shed the skin of the second molt and reach the fourth stomach of the host animal, where, after another molt, they develop into the fourth larval stage. The fourth molt is completed between the ninth and tenth days after infection, and with the completion of this molt the worms reach the adult stage. They become mature in the course of 2 to 3 weeks. The period required for development, from the time the larvae are swallowed until the adult stage is reached, is variable, but it averages about 15 days. According to Veglia (*52*) eggs not uncommonly appear in the feces on the fifteenth day after infection, indicating that the adult stage was reached earlier. On the other hand oviposition (depositing of eggs) may be retarded for 10 days or more.

Larvae introduced into sheep by means of water reach the abomasum and there undergo the second molt. Larvae introduced with solid food start the second molt at once, that is, in the mouth. The larvae possess a distinct biotactism, or affinity, for the mucous membrane of the fourth stomach and do not remain in the rumen for any great length of time. After reaching the fourth stomach, they lodge between the minute epithelial processes of the mucous membrane without actually piercing it.

Veglia gives a detailed account of conditions affecting the development of the preparasitic, or free-living, stages of *Haemonchus contortus*. The results of his work on the factors of air, temperature, moisture, and light in relation to development and survival of eggs and larvae may be applied to field conditions as follows:

1. Constant warm dry weather, such as occurs during periods of drought, is unfavorable to the development of eggs and larvae of *Haemonchus contortus*.

2. Constant moist or cloudy warm weather is favorable to the development of the eggs and larvae.

3. Constant or prolonged cold wet weather delays development but does not prevent it, provided the moisture is not excessive.

4. Constant dry cold weather, especially if the temperature falls to freezing or below for long uninterrupted periods, kills both eggs and larvae.

5. No definite information can be given as to the effect of variable weather. A very high percentage of eggs and of freshly hatched

larvae are killed if during the first 2 days following their deposition on soil the air is dry and warm, provided the soil also is dry. If infected feces are deposited on dry soil, numerous eggs die, even if the first day is cloudy, whereas if the feces are dropped after a heavy rain, numerous eggs survive, especially in grass, even if the first day is sunny and warm.

6. The nature of the soil covering, that is, the pasture and the soil itself, are factors to be considered.

7. The great majority of the eggs passed by infected animals fail to reach maturity.

Various symptoms have been associated with stomach worm (*Haemonchus contortus*) infections, but experimental infection with this worm has demonstrated that the principal symptom is a severe anemia manifested by pallor of the skin and the visible mucous membranes (fig. 6). According to Clunies Ross and Gordon (*12*), l a m b s harboring considerable numbers of worms may exhibit l i t t l e obvious evidence of ill health provided f e e d conditions are satisfactory. Even in massive infections no obvious symptoms may be noted for some time, but when the symptoms develop they do so rapidly and are severe. Infected animals become weak, are

FIGURE 6.—Eye of a sheep, showing effects of severe experimental stomach worm infestation. (Photograph by J. S. Andrews.)

disinclined to move, and develop the characteristic swelling known as bottle jaw. In animals experimentally infected with the *H. contortus* worms, there was no evidence of diarrhea, a condition formerly commonly associated with such infection. This has also been noted by Clunies Ross and Gordon, who state that in the great majority of severe cases of stomach worm infection there is no diarrhea but on the contrary the feces are harder and drier than normal and greatly reduced in quantity. Lambing ewes, ewes with lambs at foot, and older animals may be severely affected, particularly late in the summer and in the fall when pasturage becomes short. Infected animals that show no marked evidence of stomach worm infection as long as they remain relatively quiet may die when driven for any distance. Fat lambs and even adult sheep may die suddenly when heavy infections are rapidly acquired. Such animals may literally bleed to death before they have had time to lose condition.

The lesions found in animals dying of stomach infection are those of severe anemia. The blood is thin and watery, and there is a gelatinous infiltration of the omenta and mesenteries. On examination the blood shows marked changes, the number of red cells being greatly reduced. The anemia found in stomach worm infection is due to hemorrhage. There is no evidence that the worms secrete any toxins that affect the sheep adversely (*12*). In experimentally infected animals blood appeared in the feces in 6 to 10 days after the animals were infected, several days before the worms had reached the egg-laying stage.

ROUNDWORM PARASITES OF THE FOURTH STOMACH AND SMALL INTESTINE

The Small Trichostrongyles

Sheep and goats are often infected with a number of smaller worms, collectively known as small trichostrongyles, and sometimes suffer severely as a result.

THE MEDIUM STOMACH WORMS, OR BROWN HAIR WORMS

The medium stomach worms, *Ostertagia circumcincta* and *O. trifurcata*, are found in the abomasum, or fourth stomach, generally at the end nearest the small intestine. They are small, brownish, hairlike worms about one-half inch long.

The life history of these worms is direct. The eggs are deposited by the female worms in the fourth stomach and pass out with the feces. Under favorable conditions of temperature and moisture they hatch in about a day and infective larvae develop in 5 to 6 days. The infective larvae are taken into the body during grazing, and after reaching the fourth stomach they penetrate into the wall of this organ. Further development to the adult stage takes place in about 15 days, and eggs are found in the manure of infested sheep about 18 days after experimental infection.

As a result of the penetration of the larvae the stomach wall becomes inflamed, dotted with small white elevated areas, and marked with minute hemorrhages. The white spots which contain the worms, increase in size and become nodular—knotlike or lumpy—as the worms grow. With maturity the worms emerge from these nodules, which recede and disappear.

Since under natural conditions infestation with *Ostertagia* is usually accompanied by infestation with the common stomach worm, *Haemonchus contortus*, as well as with other worms, it is rather difficult to describe any specific symptoms. Sheep primarily infested with *Ostertagia* species are said to show progressive loss of condition with intermittent diarrhea and a stunted appearance.

THE SMALL STOMACH AND INTESTINAL WORMS

Several species of small trichostrongyles (*Trichostrongylus axei*, *T. colubriformis*, *T. vitrinus*, and *T. capricola*) are found in the stomach and small intestine of sheep and goats. *T. axei* occurs for the most part in the fourth stomach, while the other three species are generally found in the small intestine, *T. capricola* occurring more frequently in goats than in sheep.

These trichostrongyles are small, hairlike worms about one-fourth to one-third of an inch long. . They are usually present in fairly large numbers, but because of their small size they are easily over-looked on post mortem examination. The easiest way to find them is to wash out the first 20 feet of the small intestine in a glass dish and then examine the washings against a dark background. Another method is to scrape the lining of the small intestine and examine the scrapings for the worms.

The life history of these small trichostrongyles is essentially similar to that of the common stomach worm, differing only in the resistance of the embryonated eggs (those containing embryos) to drying; they have been shown to be able to survive drying for 15 months under experimental conditions. This is of great importance since it enables the eggs to survive long periods of drought and resume their development as soon as sufficient moisture becomes available, thus continuing pasture infections that might otherwise be terminated by the dry weather.

FIGURE 7.—The thin goat on the right with soiled hindquarters is suffering from trichostrongylosis acquired on an infested pasture. (Photograph by O. J. Hummon.)

There are no noticeable gross lesions associated with trichostrongylosis (infection with trichostrongyles). It may be differentiated from haemonchosis (a disease due to infection with *Haemonchus contortus*) as follows: Trichostrongylosis is essentially a slow, protracted disease of young animals, especially lambs and yearlings, which appears shortly after weaning and continues through the summer and the next winter. It is marked by unthriftiness, pronounced diarrhea (fig. 7), progressive weakness, and loss of appetite. Anemia is not noticeable at first but becomes evident as the disease progresses; potbelly and bottle jaw are absent in pure infestations. Infection with stomach worms, on the other hand, is a rapidly fatal disease affecting all classes of animals, showing no noticeable stunting or consistent scours—that is, scouring may or may not be present, or it may be intermittent. Anemia appears early in the course of the disease, and potbelly and bottle jaw are commonly present.

Bone weakness, manifested by lameness and spontaneous fracture of the leg bones, especially the femur and the humerus (the upper bones of the hind and front legs), has been reported occasionally in sheep heavily infested with small trichostrongyles.

The Australian workers emphasize that the course of this disease is markedly influenced by the nutritional condition of the animal. Losses from trichostrongylosis occur during the dry summer months when the grass becomes scarce.

THE COOPERIAS

The species of *Cooperia* commonly found in the small intestine of sheep and goats are *C. curticei* and *C. oncophora; C. punctata* and *C. pectinata* have also been reported from sheep, although they occur more commonly in cattle. All of them are relatively small, hairlike worms about one-fourth to one-half inch long and of a brownish-red color when freshly collected.

The preparasitic stages of these nematodes are similar to those of *Haemonchus contortus* and of trichostrongyles. According to Andrews (*2*) the infective larvae lose their sheaths soon after being ingested and migrate into the crypts of the mucous membrane of the small intestine about 3 days after entering the host. They do not, however, penetrate into the mucous membrane. They undergo the third molt on the fourth day after entering the host, grow rapidly, and return to the lumen of the intestine on the fifth day. They pass through the fourth molt about the ninth day, and eggs may be found in the feces on the fifteenth day after infection.

Experimental infection with *Cooperia curticei* produced no marked symptoms or lesions in lambs receiving good care and an adequate amount of feed, although fatal infections in young goats by members of the genus *Cooperia* have been reported by Edgar (*18*). Andrews (*2*) reported that experimental infections with this worm decreased the ability of the infected animals to convert their feed into gain in weight, but no symptoms referable to the worm infection were noted and no lesions were found at post mortem examination.

The Sheep Hookworm

The sheep hookworm, *Bunostomum trigonocephalum*, is a relatively large white worm. The male is about half an inch and the female about three-fourths of an inch to an inch long. The worms are about one-half to three-fourths as thick as an ordinary pin.

The preparasitic, or free-living, stages of this worm are similar to those described for the other strongyle worms, except that the infective larvae, in addition to being able to enter the body by way of the mouth, are also able, according to Beller (*4*) and Ortlepp (*39, 40*), to penetrate the intact skin. Beller reported finding hookworm eggs in the feces of a sheep 17 days, and in those of a goat 15 days, after having applied infective larvae of *Bunostomum trigonocephalum* to the skin.

In 1939, on the basis of his investigations, Ortlepp (*40*) gave a detailed description of the life history of the sheep hookworm, which may be summarized as follows:[5] Under favorable conditions of temperature and moisture the eggs hatch in 24 hours, and the larvae reach the infective stage in 5 days. These larvae can infect sheep either through the mouth or through the skin. When applied to the skin, they penetrate it and are carried, presumably by the blood stream, to the lungs, which they reach in 6 days. They remain in this organ for about 5 days. During this time they grow, pass into the fourth stage, and are provided with a provisional mouth capsule. They molt and migrate from the lungs to the small intestine by way of the esophagus and stomach. They reach the small intestine as fourth-stage larvae about 11 days after infection. About 4 weeks after infection they reach the adult stage, and about 5 weeks later they reach maturity, the females at this time containing segmented eggs.

Ortlepp's experimental results are in agreement with field observations to the effect that mature hookworms do not occur in very young lambs.

While infections with this worm are usually complicated by the presence of stomach and other worms, it may be assumed that it does the same damage as other hookworms. This damage consists in the abstraction of blood from the host and the secretion of a hemolytic substance—one that destroys red corpuscles and prevents coagulation of the blood—which causes prolonged hemorrhage at the point of attachment when the worms move from one point to another. Animals infected with this worm manifest the characteristic anemia and edema generally resulting from hookworm infection and infection with other bloodsucking internal parasites.

The clinical symptoms of hookworm infection are identical for the most part with those of stomach worm infection, namely, anemia, edema, and unthriftiness. A clinical diagnosis that will differentiate one condition from the other is practically impossible.

The Thread-Necked Strongyles

The thread-necked strongyles, *Nematodirus spathiger*, *N. filicollis*, and *N. abnormalis*, are found in the small intestines of sheep.

The anterior portion of these worms is slenderer than the posterior, and the head and neck are thin and transversely striated, or marked with narrow circular bands. In *Nematodirus spathiger* the male is about three-fifths of an inch and the female about an inch long. These nematodes can be differentiated only by microscopic examination.

Their life history differs in some respects, according to Boulenger (*6*), from that of the other nematodes mentioned. The rather large eggs pass out with the feces, and an embryo develops in them. This embryo, instead of emerging from the shell and molting like the

---

[5] In a preliminary report (*39*) Ortlepp stated that he was able to infect 24 out of 27 sheep with *Bunostomum trigonocephalum* by placing infective larvae of this hookworm on the skin behind the ear. The worms, however, did not reach the egg-laying stage until 10 weeks after the larvae had been applied. In a sheep infected with hookworms in this way, Ortlepp found at post mortem examination, 8 weeks after infection, only adolescent hookworms, no female having reached the egg-producing stage.

larvae of most other strongyles, molts twice within the shell. Under the influence of alternate moistening and drying or of temperatures varying from 75° to 90° F., the infective larvae emerge from the shells and, like the larvae of stomach worms, crawl up on blades of grass and enter the body of the host animal with the feed.

According to available information, the distribution of these worms in the United States seems to be largely confined to the central and northern parts of the country.

No symptoms or lesions have been definitely attributed to these worms. Recently reported experiments (29) appear to show that these worms are not of any great importance as disease producers, at least so far as sheep are concerned, except perhaps when present in very large numbers. Sheep harboring up to 6,500 adult worms in the small intestine showed no clinical symptoms that could be attributed to infestation with *Nematodirus*, although on post mortem examination minute hemorrhages were found in the mucous membrane of the small intestine at the sites where the worms were found.

PARASITES OF THE CECUM AND COLON

The Whipworm

The whipworm *Trichuris ovis* is usually found attached to the wall of the cecum, or blind gut.

The body is made up of a thin anterior and a thick posterior portion. The anterior part may be compared to the lash of a whip and the posterior to the stock or handle; hence the name whipworm. The worms are white, and the eggs are brown and characteristically lemon-shaped.

So far as is known, this worm has a simple life history. An infective embryo develops in the shell, and sheep and goats are infected by swallowing infective eggs in grazing.

There are no well-defined clinical symptoms associated with whipworm infestation in sheep and goats, but it has been found that in man whipworm infection sets up a low-grade inflammation with distinct symptoms of discomfort and distress. In camels a severe whipworm infection has been found to cause a decided thickening of the wall of the cecum with an excessive secretion of mucus, and it is quite possible that in other animals heavily infected with whipworms similar pathological conditions may be produced. The anterior part of the worm is usually found deeply buried in the mucous membrane lining the cecum, or blind gut, and the most common lesions consist of inflamed and thickened areas surrounding the points of attachment.

The Nodular Worm

The adult nodular worm, *Oesophagostomum columbianum*, is found in the cecum and colon of sheep and goats. The larvae are found in nodules in the cecum and large intestine and in heavy infections may be distributed throughout the intestinal tract. The nodular worm, *O. columbianum*, is a fairly large, white worm, about five-eighths of an inch long. The head is usually bent, forming a hook with the rest of the body.

The free-living phase of the life history of this worm is similar to that of the other strongyles inhabiting the digestive tract of sheep. In lambs a considerable number of the larvae may leave the wall in 5 to 8 days, though some may remain much longer (*53*). In older sheep several months may be spent in the wall of the bowel. When the larvae return to the intestinal cavity they undergo their fourth and final molt and become adults. The first eggs are passed about 40 days after infection. According to Veglia (*54*), the adult worms may live for 21 months, but the majority probably die and pass out of the body in 9 to 12 months.

The chief symptom shown by infected animals during the time that the larvae are invading the wall of the bowel is diarrhea, the feces containing considerable quantities of mucus. According to South African workers, during this stage infected animals may show evidence of "rekziekte," or stretching disease, manifested by a characteristic position, with the legs, especially the hind legs, extended and the back hollowed. Clunies Ross and Gordon (*12*) report that in the more chronic stages due to adult worms, sheep show progressive weakness with intermittent characteristic diarrhea containing much mucus. The sheep lose weight, and there is some evidence of anemia.

The larvae cause local injury to the mucous membrane, but in initial infections of lambs in which the larvae remain in the wall of the intestine for only a short while, there is little evidence of nodule formation. In older sheep, a more severe local reaction follows the penetration of the wall of the intestine, and marked nodules develop. These nodules at first contain a mass of creamy, greenish material which gradually becomes first cheeselike and later hard and calcareous.

While the nodules, which may extend throughout the length of the intestine, are the most noticeable lesion, it has not been demonstrated that they are the principal cause of the harmful effects produced by infection with these parasites. It is true that interference with bowel function may result when nodules are large and very numerous, and complete impaction (stoppage due to a hardened mass of material) and intussusception (telescoping of one part over another) may occur when the lumen, or interior, of the bowel is excessively narrowed; but serious effects are reported (*12*, *54*) to have resulted from chronic infections in which the animals had survived the early stages and adult worms had developed. These effects apparently do not show up until some months after infection.

Nodular disease of sheep was first described in 1890 by Curtice, who at that time reported that it caused heavy economic losses both through its effect on the health of the sheep and because it rendered sheep intestines valueless for making sausage casings. While the disease is seldom fatal, it causes considerable loss of mutton and wool and an impairment of breeding stock. According to Curtice, sheep raising has had to be abandoned in certain areas on account of the nodular worm.

Theiler noted that in certain parts of South Africa two complications of nodular worm disease are found fairly often. One is an invagination of the ileum (infolding of the last section of the small intestine), called knopziekte or rekziekte, the symptoms being disinclination to move, standing in a stretching position with the back hollowed, and the presence of blood in the feces or stoppage of feces. The other is a septic (poisonous) infection of the peritoneal, or abdominal, cavity. Neither of these conditions is associated with nodular worm disease in the United States.

The Large-Mouthed Bowel Worm

The large-mouthed bowel worm, *Chabertia ovina*, is commonly found in the coiled portion of the colon of sheep and goats. The parasites are relatively large, creamy-white worms, up to three-fourths of an inch long. They are confined to the Temperate Zone; the records of the Bureau of Animal Industry, in fact, show no specimens collected south of Tennessee.

The development of eggs and larvae to the infective stage is similar to that of other strongyles and trichostrongyles.

According to Clunies Ross and Gordon (*12*), however, eggs and larvae are capable of development at low temperatures; mature larvae will develop even when eggs have been kept continuously at about 40° F. in the refrigerator. After ingestion, the infective larvae migrate to the large bowel, the skin of the second-stage larvae being shed immediately and the third molt taking place after some hours. The fourth-stage larvae have a prominent mouth capsule. The fourth molt is not undergone until nearly 2 months after infection, and the first eggs are not passed until 9 to 10 weeks after infection.

In experimental infections, diarrhea, often of an irregular character, usually develops about the fourth week, the feces containing much mucus and blood. The growth rate is slowed, and some animals may show extreme weakness and emaciation. As a rule, however, symptoms gradually disappear, and the animals recover after a period of 4 to 6 weeks.

The adult parasites are always associated with visible lesions, the wall of the colon being thickened and edematous or swollen, and the mucous membrane showing patchy congestion and even hemorrhage. According to Clunies Ross and Kauzal (*13*) developing worms may cause even more marked lesions, the colon being congested throughout its length. The immature worms are pinkish, owing to ingested blood. In heavy infections with immature worms there is a definite reduction in hemoglobin and red-cell count, and the white cells tend to increase. The immature worms appear to be more injurious than the adults, but the adults are probably not without effect on the host.

ROUNDWORM PARASITES OF THE RESPIRATORY TRACT

Lungworms

In the United States sheep and goats may be infected with two species of lungworms, the thread lungworm, *Dictyocaulus filaria*, and the hair lungworm, *Muellerius capillaris*. Other species of lungworms, belonging in the genus *Protostrongylus*, have been reported as parasites of sheep and goats in other parts of the world, but thus far nematodes of this genus have been found only in deer, mountain sheep, and rabbits in North America.

Thread lungworms are whitish worms up to 4 inches in length. They may be easily seen on opening the air passages of the lungs of infected animals.

The eggs, which already contain embryos when laid, hatch in the lungs. The larvae reach the pharynx, in the upper part of the throat, and may be expelled when the animal coughs or swallowed and passed out with the feces. They molt twice in the course of the next few days, the time varying with the temperature and moisture, and under ordinary circumstances reach the infective stage in about 10 days. According to Clunies Ross and Gordon the infective larvae are not very resistant to drying but are able to develop at relatively low temperatures, that is, about 40° F. After being swallowed by the sheep the larvae bore through the wall of the small intestine and, according to A. Hobmaier and M. Hobmaier (*24*), pass by way of the lymph stream into the lungs. In 2 to 5 days after infection they are found in large numbers in the mesenteric lymph nodes. Here they undergo the third molt, and the fourth-stage larvae then leave the glands and pass with the lymph stream to the heart and then with the blood to the lungs. They pass through the walls of the alveoli, or air cells, into the larger air passages. Adult male and female worms develop in the lungs about 18 days after infection, and eggs may be produced in 26 days but usually do not appear in less than 5 weeks.

The worms and their eggs and larvae set up an irritation, and the first symptom noted is a cough. While this may occur as early as the sixteenth day after infection (*25, 26, 27*), it usually starts about 30 days after infection and coincides with the development of adult worms in the lungs and the passage of larvae in the droppings. The cough is usually strong and harsh in light infections and may be very soft or even absent in heavy infections (*12*). In severe infections the breathing becomes rapid and shallow owing to the obstruction of the air passages. Heavily infected animals become weak and listless and lose condition rapidly, and death may occur about 2 months after infection. The effects produced by the adult worms, especially when they are numerous, appear to be largely mechanical. The masses of worms and eggs and the exudate, or discharge, produced by the irritated mucous membranes lead to complete blockage of the air passages and the consequent collapse of the lung tissue supplied by them. Large areas of the lungs may thus be rendered functionless, and in massive infections the principal cause of death appears to be suffocation from mechanical blocking of the air passages. The irritation of the small and large bronchial tubes by the worms may lead to bronchitis, which may spread to the lung tissues around the bronchial tubes and give rise to pneumonia. Secondary infection of the collapsed portions also may lead to pneumonia.

In light infections the lesions are usually confined to the lower parts of the lungs.

The hair lungworm, *Muellerius capillaris*, occurs in the small bronchial tubes and in the lung tissue. It is a small, very fine worm, seldom seen against the background of lung tissue in which it occurs. The eggs are unsegmented when laid but develop and hatch in the lungs. The larva has a characteristic undulating tail with a small spine on the upper side. Larvae either migrate to or are coughed up into the pharynx, where they are swallowed, and then pass out onto the pasture with the feces. They can survive considerable periods of dryness and freezing temperatures in spite of the fact that they have no protective sheath. It has been shown experimentally by the Hobmaiers (*23*) that these larvae can penetrate and develop to infective larvae in land snails. It is assumed that sheep become infected by ingesting the snails in grazing. After being liberated, the infective larvae reach the lungs in the same manner as the larvae of the thread lungworm, *Dictyocaulus filaria.*

No specific symptoms are attributed to infection with these worms. The presence of the worms and their larvae is indicated by raised, grayish areas on the surface of the lungs. These areas are usually rounded and vary in size from ¼ to 1 inch in diameter. On being cut through, they are seen to be greenish gray owing to the accumulation of eosinophiles (certain white blood corpuscles). At times definite pneumonic changes are associated with these lesions.

ROUNDWORM PARASITES OF THE EYES OF SHEEP

Small roundworms, about one-third to four-fifths of an inch in length, may occur in the ducts of the tear glands, between the eye and the lids, or under the nictitating membrane—the so-called third eyelid—of domestic and wild ruminants. These worms belong in the genus *Thelazia*, and one species, *Thelazia californiensis*, has recently been reported as occurring in the eyes of sheep and deer in California.

These worms normally occur in the ducts of the tear glands, but they may escape from their usual location and be found on the surface of the eyeball beneath the lids, under the nictitating membrane, or even in the eyeball. They are white, slender, and tapering at both ends. The males are one-third to one-half and the females one-half to three-fourths of an inch in length. Nothing is known of the life history of the worms, but in view of the fact that a closely related eye worm of chickens requires an insect intermediate host in its life cycle and that putting larvae of *Thelazia callipaeda*, an eye worm of the dog, directly into the eye of a dog failed to produce an infection (*19*), it is assumed that the life history of the eye worm of sheep also is indirect and that an intermediate host is required in its life cycle.

According to Stewart (*46*) excessive watering of the eyes, or lachrymation, engorgement of the blood vessels of the membranes and of the eyeball, and small areas of hemorrhage on the membranes and under surface of the lids were observed in infected sheep in California. The author notes, however, that some of these symptoms may have been due to infectious keratitis, or inflammation of the cornea, with which some animals in the flocks examined were affected. In other animals from which these worms have been reported, it has been found that they cause irritation of the conjunctiva, profuse lachrymation, sensitiveness to light, and cloudiness, followed later by definite opacity, of the cornea. As a result of invasion by pus-producing organisms the cornea may become ulcerated, and this in turn may lead to an inflammation of the iris and other structures of the eye. If the worms are not removed, the eyelids and the nictitating membrane may become swollen, and, owing to the drying of the purulent, or puslike, discharge exuding between the eyelids, the lids stick together. Mechanical injuries due to loss of sight and the fixation of the nictitating membrane, which is unable to function because of its swollen condition, may aggravate the primary difficulty.

The presence of these eye worms may be suspected when one or more animals in a flock show signs of sensitiveness to light with profuse watering of the eyes, or lachrymation. The parasites are most easily found in animals showing the earliest stages of the clinical manifestations, namely, lachrymation with slight opacity of the cornea and little, if any, purulent discharge. The septic, or poisoning, processes due to secondary infection appear to kill off the nematodes, or at least to confine them to the depths of the tear ducts. The worms are not always seen in a cursory examination of the eye, because of their unusual habitat. It is necessary, therefore, to examine the parts thoroughly by exposing the under surface of the nictitating membrane and the eyelids, when the worms can be detected by their active wriggling movements in the lachrymal secretion. They appear to be washed up with the tears from the lachrymal duct, as any manipulation or application of dressings that tends to increase the lachrymal secretions facilitates the recovery of specimens from infected animals. The instillation into the eye of a few drops of a 1-percent solution of cocaine or other suitable local anesthetic facilitates the examination of the eye. According to Stewart (*46*) this procedure also causes the worms to crawl out of the inner cornea of the eye and makes it easier to remove them.

Until the life history of these worms has been worked out, no preventive or control measures can be recommended.

The treatment consists in the mechanical removal of the worms from the eye. After the worms have been removed the eyes should be treated as in cases of inflammation due to other causes.

ROUNDWORM PARASITES OF THE CIRCULATORY SYSTEM

The roundworm, *Elaeophora schneideri*, has been found in the arteries (carotid, mesenteric, and iliac) of sheep. It is a slender white worm. The male is about 60 millimeters (2.5 inches) and the female 110 to 120 millimeters (4.5 to 5 inches) long, tapering at both ends.

These roundworms, or nematodes, have been found in sheep in Catron County, N. Mex., and in deer in Utah. Lesions similar to those caused by the microfilariae, the larvae of these nematodes, have been noted in sheep in Arizona and Colorado.

The life history of the worms is not definitely known, but since they are filarids and all filarids require an intermediate host in their life cycles, it is assumed that some arthropod (insect or insectlike animal) acts as their intermediate host.

The adult worms produce no known symptoms in infected animals, but Kemper (*30*) reports that the microfilariae cause a dermatitis, or skin inflammation, usually involving the skin in the region of the poll (fig. 8) and in a few cases extending forward over the face to the nostrils and lips. Lesions sometimes occur also on the foot used to scratch the head and on the abdomen where the affected

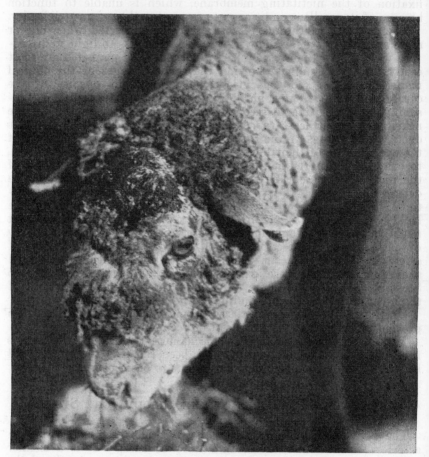

FIGURE 8.—Head of a sheep, showing lesions caused by microfilariae of *Elaeophora schneideri*. (From Kemper.)

foot has come in repeated contact with the skin, perhaps while the sheep was lying down. The lesions are primarily those of a chronic dermatitis with excessive growth of tissue and the formation of numerous small abscesses. The extent of scratching and rubbing, apparently a result of intense itching, more or less determines the ultimate size of the lesion.

THE CONTROL OF INTERNAL PARASITES OF SHEEP AND GOATS

As previously noted, the internal parasites of sheep and goats include protozoa, flukes, tapeworms, and roundworms. Control depends on effective anthelmintic medication—the use of effective worm medicines—and a thorough knowledge of the life histories of the parasites. There are two phases in the life histories of all of these parasites. One, the reproductive phase, is spent within the body of the sheep, and the other is spent either free in the natural environment of the sheep or in some intermediate host. The intermediate hosts do not serve merely as mechanical carriers, since a definite part of the life history of the parasites is completed within them. A knowledge of the life cycles of the intermediate hosts is generally necessary before effective control measures can be formulated for the parasites that require such hosts.

CONTROL OF THE PROTOZOAN PARASITES

The protozoan parasites of sheep that are known to be of importance in this country are various species of coccidia and *Globidium gilruthi*. They are all microscopic parasites too small to be seen with the naked eye. Seven different species of coccidia have been recently reported by Christensen (7) as parasites of sheep in this country. Whether there is any difference among these species in their effect on sheep is not definitely known at present.

As already pointed out, there is no specific medicinal treatment for coccidiosis. Affected animals should be removed from the flock and isolated, and the exposed but healthy individuals should then be allowed to run over a large acreage to lessen the chances of infection. All straw, litter, or other material soiled by the discharges of affected animals should be burned or disposed of in such a manner as not to form a source of infection for other animals. The premises occupied by infected animals should be thoroughly cleaned and disinfected before being used for healthy animals. In the cases described by Christensen (9), referred to earlier in this article, it is obvious that either some method of feeding should be devised which will prevent the contamination of the feed with sheep feces, or the unconsumed portions of feed should be removed from the feed troughs and the troughs thoroughly cleaned before fresh supplies are placed in them. The extent to which such measures can be applied will depend on the stockman's interest and on circumstances. Practical methods of using copper sulfate and ferric sulfate mixtures as a means of lowering the level of infection remain to be devised. If, as suggested by Christensen, these substances can be used in powdered form in the feed or in solution in the drinking water and be so distributed as to insure each animal's receiving the required amount, sufficient protection may be afforded to obviate serious outbreaks of the disease.

CONTROL OF FLUKES

In common with all other flukes, the flukes of sheep and goats require a snail intermediate host for the completion of their life cycles. It is obvious, therefore, that the control of these parasites in sheep and goats depends on the control of the snails. A thorough knowledge of the environment, distribution, etc., of the intermediate hosts is necessary to accomplish this control.

The most effective medicinal treatment of sheep and goats for liver fluke infection is the administration of carbon tetrachloride. For convenience in administration, this drug can be incorporated in a suitable vehicle, such as liquid paraffin or raw linseed oil. Carbon tetrachloride, however, is effective only against the adult parasites in the bile ducts. Immature flukes which may be present in the liver tissues or which have only recently arrived in the bile ducts are not affected by the treatment, and it should therefore be repeated at intervals to remove the flukes as they mature. Although the carbon tetrachloride treatment is normally safe for sheep, it may, at times, according to Clunies Ross and Gordon (*12*), be followed by heavy losses 3 to 4 days after the drug has been administered. Affected animals show evidence of acute abdominal pain, and at post mortem examination acute inflammation of the fourth stomach and intestine are noted. Scattered hemorrhages are found in the mesenteries and pleura—the membrane lining the thorax and covering the lung. These authors also report that some sheep lose their wool 2 to 3 weeks after treatment.

While the reasons for this occasional toxicity of carbon tetrachloride for sheep are not well known, certain general precautions should be observed: Only reliable preparations of carbon tetrachloride, free from phosgene and sulfur impurities, should be used; when liquid paraffin is used as a vehicle in the administration of the drug, it should be of a high medicinal quality; where the drug has not previously been employed, a trial group of sheep should be treated a few days ahead of the whole flock; abrupt changes of feed prior to treatment should be avoided; feeding of concentrates should be discontinued at least a week before treatment; sheep should never be drenched in cold, inclement weather; if there is any indication of mineral deficiency, sheep should be given access to mineral supplements containing a mixture of steamed bonemeal and salt and ground limestone or dicalcium phosphate and salt (*12*).

The destruction of the snails [6] which are the hosts of the intermediate stages of the fluke is the most important control measure. This may be accomplished by drainage of wet areas where snails propagate, by the use of copper sulfate (bluestone, blue vitriol) for their destruction, or by a combination of the two. Since snails require a certain amount of water in which to live and propagate, drainage is the preferred method. Complete drainage so changes the environment as to make it impossible for snails to survive. If the drainage ditches are kept open and clean, the drained area will

---

[6] For details see: JAY, ROBERT. CONTROL OF LIVER FLUKES AND FLUKE DISEASE OF SHEEP, GOATS, AND CATTLE. U. S. Bur. Anim. Indus. Cir., 6 pp., illus. 1938. (Revised.) [Processed.]

remain unfavorable for snails and will require no other attention. If the ditches become infested, treating the banks with copper sulfate will destroy the snails. Drainage is not always possible, however, because of the cost or engineering difficulties; though in figuring the cost of any drainage project, the increased value of the land and of the improved forage that can be produced should always be considered. Wherever drainage is either impractical or impossible the treatment of snail-infested areas with copper sulfate should be considered.

Copper sulfate has proved to be very effective for killing snails. While this chemical, diluted 1 part to 1,500,000 parts of water, will kill them overnight, the thorough distribution of such small amounts is difficult to accomplish, and it is usually applied in much greater concentrations.

Copper sulfate kills the snails, the miracidia, and the free-swimming cercariae. It does not injure the fluke eggs or the encysted cercariae; hence, to prevent infestation, the snails should be destroyed before the water and grasses become infected. As used in dilutions for killing snails, copper sulfate is not injurious to grasses or flowering plants and will not poison livestock. It will, however, kill the lower forms of plant life, such as the algae and mosses, and it may kill fish.

The method of application varies with the movement and distribution of the infested waters. In a stream originating on a stockman's land and with the water confined within definite banks, sacks containing large crystals of copper sulfate may be placed in the headwaters. To reach the snails on the banks, dams may be thrown across the stream at various places, depending on the fall of the stream, to raise the treated water to cover the snails. Overflow lands, stagnant backwaters, marshes, pools, and similar wet places are best treated by broadcasting powdered copper sulfate. The water troughs, and especially the puddles around the troughs, should not be overlooked. It is more economical to use the powdered than the crystalline copper sulfate for treating these places. The chemical may be mixed with a carrier such as sand or land plaster in the proportion of 1 part of the copper sulfate to 4 to 8 parts of the carrier, depending on the volume of water to be treated. The land plaster has the advantage of marking the treated area. The airplane has been found to be practical in spreading copper sulfate over large swampy areas, but when applied in this way the copper sulfate and carrier mixture must be fine enough to be applied as a dust.

To estimate the amount of copper sulfate needed to treat the water in a stream, it is necessary to know the flow in cubic feet per second. To determine this, select a uniform section of the stream about 50 feet long, measure the width and the average depth of the flowing water, and multiply them to get the area of the cross section in square feet. Mark off 50 feet, throw a chip in the water at the upper end, and ascertain the number of seconds required for the chip to float the 50 feet. Divide this by 50 to obtain the velocity in feet per second. The number of square feet of cross section multiplied by the velocity in feet per second equals the approximate flow in cubic feet per second.

For example: A stream 6 feet wide has an average depth of 6 inches; the area of cross section equals 6 times 0.5, or 3 square feet. If it takes a chip 25 seconds to float 50 feet, the rate of flow is 2 feet per second. Multiply the cross section (3 square feet) by the velocity (2 feet per second) and the result is a flow of 6 cubic feet per second. For a 24-hour treatment at a dilution of 1 to 500,000 parts of water, 12 pounds of copper sulfate are required for each cubic foot per second of flow. Therefore, the amount of copper sulfate required for this stream would be 6 times 12, or 72 pounds.

Where the amount of copper sulfate required to treat the water in a lake would be excessive or where the lake is used as a fish preserve, the copper sulfate may be broadcast along the banks and on the water a few feet out from the bank.

A few days after treating the water it is well to make a careful investigation of the effect on the snails. Usually one treatment at the right time is enough for a year, but if live snails are found after an application of copper sulfate, the waters should have another application. When once a range is infested, it is necessary to repeat the copper-sulfate treatment once a year until all snails are killed. The best time to treat is when the greatest number of snails can be reached; usually this is after the spring rains.

Often a combination of drainage and the use of copper sulfate will bring about the desired results. Where complete drainage is either impractical or impossible, partial drainage may prove to be of value in reducing the size of the wet area. The remaining undrained portion can then be treated with copper sulfate. The methods used will depend entirely on local conditions.

Control of Roundworms

Except in the areas where liver flukes occur, the roundworms are the most important parasites of sheep and goats. With the exception of *Elaeophora schneideri*, a threadworm found in the blood vessels of sheep, *Gongylonema pulchrum* and *G. verrucosum* (the gullet worms), and *Muellerius capillaris*, one of the lungworms, the life histories of all the roundworm parasites of sheep are direct, no intermediate hosts being required.

The only known effective method of attacking the parasites in the parasitic phase of their existence consists in anthelmintic medication. Many drugs have been tried and recommended as anthelmintics, but, for all practical purposes, there are at the present time only three drugs and one combination of drugs available for effective treatment: Phenothiazine, copper sulfate, tetrachlorethylene, and a combination of copper sulfate and nicotine solution.

Phenothiazine has a very high degree of efficacy when used in the treatment of sheep for large stomach worms, *Haemonchus contortus;* hookworms, *Bunostomum trigonocephalum;* nodular worms, *Oesophagostomum columbianum;* and large-mouthed bowel worms, *Chabertia ovina.* It has given satisfactory results when used in treating sheep for the small trichostrongyles, *Ostertagia, Trichostrongylus,* and *Cooperia* species (fig. 9, *A* and *B*). It appears to be ineffective, however, in the treatment of sheep for the removal of thread-necked strongyles, *Nematodirus* species; whipworms, *Trichuris* species; and lungworms and tapeworms.

Copper sulfate alone is effective against the common twisted stomach worm, *Haemonchus contortus*, but it is not very effective against the other worms found in the stomach and small intestines. Copper sulfate and nicotine solution, commonly referred to as Cu-Nic, is as effective against the common stomach worm as copper sulfate alone and is more effective than copper sulfate alone against the other worms found in the stomach and against some of the worms in the small intestine. Tetrachlorethylene appears to be effective against

FIGURE 9.—*A*, Bottle jaw in a sheep suffering from general gastrointestinal parasitism; *B*, the same sheep 19 days after treatment with phenothiazine. (From Habermann and Hunt.)

stomach and intestinal worms, and it is apparently more effective against the small trichostrongyles than either copper sulfate or a mixture of copper sulfate and nicotine solution. The thread-necked strongyles, *Nematodirus* species, are only slightly affected by treatment. However, so far as is known at present, these parasites do not produce any serious disturbance in sheep in spite of the fact that they may be present in large numbers. The nodular worm, *Oesophagostomum columbianum*, and the large intestinal worm, *Chabertia ovina*, are not amenable to treatment with either Cu-Nic or tetrachlorethylene. South African workers, however, report good results from a treatment consisting of a mixture of copper arsenate, 2 parts; calcium hydroxide, or slaked lime, 3 parts; and copper tartrate, 5 parts. The dose of this mixture is 1 gram (15 grains) for lambs 3 to 6 months old; 1.8 grams (27 grains) for lambs 6 to 18 months old; and 2.5 grams (37.5 grains) for animals over 18 months old. Two doses are given on consecutive days, and each treatment is preceded by the administration of 2.5 cc. of a 10-percent solution of copper sulfate. The treatment is administered as follows:

The sheep's mouth is opened wide and the copper sulfate solution is poured alongside the tongue so that it runs down into the throat; then before the sheep's mouth is closed, the proper dose of the copper arsenate, lime, and copper tartrate mixture, which is made up in the form of a powder, is placed on the back of the tongue. The treatment is repeated the next day. Sheep should not be given grain or be permitted access to a salt lick for 2 days before and 1 day after the treatment. If the pasture is dry, green feed should be furnished for a few hours before dosing. Sheep must not be kept from feed and water before treatment. After treatment they may graze immediately but should have no water for 1 to 2 hours.

Suckling lambs should not be treated unless this is necessary. If treatment is necessary the lambs should not be permitted access to water from 4 hours before to 4 hours after the treatment. Weak lambs should receive only one dose, and weak sheep and those that are small for their ages should get a smaller dose on the second day.

From this brief review it is quite clear that from the viewpoint of anthelmintic treatment it does not make any great difference with what particular roundworms the sheep are infected. Two things are necessary: (1) An accurate diagnosis of worm infection should be made, and (2) anthelmintic treatment should be given as and when necessary.

The prevention of infection with gastrointestinal roundworms depends upon a thorough knowledge of the preparasitic, or free-living, stages of these parasites—the egg and the first, second, and third (infective) larval stages. As already noted in connection with roundworms in general and *Haemonchus contortus* in particular, the development and survival of these stages depend on conditions of temperature, moisture, soil, sunlight, etc.

Reports of some recent observations on the longevity of infective larvae of various species of parasitic roundworms indicate that the major portion of these larvae died within a few weeks after they were placed on grass plots outdoors and that only a comparatively small number survived for as long as 4 months. Other reports show that the infective larvae of some species may survive much longer. There is a marked difference in the ability of the eggs and infective larvae of the various species to withstand unfavorable environmental conditions, and much more detailed information is necessary before general recommendations for the prevention of parasitic infection applicable to various parts of the United States can be made. Present indications, however, are that the majority of the infective larvae die in periods of 6 to 12 weeks, but since infective larvae develop under favorable conditions in 4 to 10 days after the eggs reach the pasture, it is clear that pasture rotation alone at intervals of 6 weeks and over cannot be relied on to control parasites.

There is no completely satisfactory medicinal treatment for the removal of lungworms from sheep and goats. The intratracheal injection of various drugs and combinations of drugs, the inhalation of chloroform and sulfur fumes, and the administration of certain volatile compounds that are excreted through the lungs, have been recommended by various authors. Clunies Ross and Gordon state that in Australia the intratracheal injection of a mixture of 1 part creosote, 1 part chloroform, 2 parts turpentine, and 4 parts olive oil, in doses of 4 milliliters (1 dram) for lambs, is recommended. In other countries intratracheal injections of pyrethrin in olive oil and Lugol's solution of iodine in glycerin are advocated, but Mönnig (*36*) reports that intratracheal injections with the latter two substances are of little value.

The development from eggs to infective larvae can take place through quite a wide range of temperature, and the results of cultural experiments indicate that lungworm larvae are well adapted to temperate climates. Although the infective larvae are quite resistant to unfavorable environmental conditions, the eggs and the first- and second-stage larvae are destroyed by drying, and it is a common observation that lungworm infections by *Dictyocaulus filaria* are intimately connected with low-lying, wet pastures. The use of such areas as pastures, wherever the topography permits of a choice, should therefore be avoided. This applies also, of course, to the prevention of infection with other worm parasites. Removal of lungworm-infected animals from infected pastures to dry lots to avoid constant reinfection is also to be recommended wherever it is practicable.

As previously noted, the gullet worms *Gongylonema pulchrum* and *G. verrucosum*, the hair lungworm *Muellerius capillaris*, and *Elaeophora schneideri*, a roundworm found in the blood vessels of sheep and deer, require intermediate hosts in their life cycles.

There is no medicinal treatment for the removal of either gullet worms or hair lungworms. Kemper (*30*) reports that the administration of fuadin was of benefit in the case of sheep infected with *Elaeophora schneideri*. The administration of 88 cubic centimeters or more of fuadin intramuscularly in doses of 4 cubic centimeters daily was followed by complete healing of the skin lesions caused by the microfilariae of this parasite.

The tapeworms *Moniezia expansa*, *M. benedeni*, and *Thysanosoma actinioides* also require intermediate hosts in their life cycles. The combination of copper sulfate and nicotine solution has been reported as effective for the removal of tapeworms (*Moniezia* spp.) from sheep (*20*), but there is no effective medicinal treatment for the removal of the fringed tapeworm, *Thysanosoma actinioides*.

The prevention of infection with bladder worms obviously consists in the proper disposal of all infected sheep carcasses and parts of carcasses, the elimination of stray dogs, and the examination and proper anthelmintic treatment, whenever necessary, of all dogs that can come in contact with sheep or wander over the pastures on which the sheep graze.

Where sheep are housed during the winter months it is a good practice to treat them once every month in order to reduce the infection to a minimum. When such sheep and their lambs are placed on pasture in the spring, most of the pasture infection will have been eliminated; and, with only a few parasites in the old sheep, it will take some time for a pasture infection to build up to a point where it becomes dangerous. Frequent rotation of pasture, with the sheep not returning to any one pasture in less than 3 months, will be a material aid in controlling infection.

The well-known recommendation for early lambing is based on the known influence of climatic conditions on pasture infection. Low temperatures retard development of eggs and larvae, and temperatures sufficiently low and prolonged will kill them. Lambs dropped early in the season and well cared for will either be ready for market before the favorable season for parasitic development arrives, or if they are retained for flock replacements, they will be in a better condition to withstand parasitic infection than lambs dropped later in the season and going on pasture when the weather favors development of parasites.

One of the most beneficial results of pasture rotation lies in the improved grazing furnished by the pasture as a result of rest and the consequent improved feeding conditions for the animals. While more information is needed concerning the relation of nutrition to parasitic disease, common observation and such experimental evidence as is available indicate very clearly that the nutritional state of the animal has a decided influence on its susceptibility to parasitic attacks. Clunies Ross and Gordon (*11*) found that resistance to stomach worm infection in older sheep was broken down when the sheep were kept for a considerable time on a diet low in protein and minerals.

THE SHEEP NASAL FLY

The condition in sheep commonly referred to as grub-in-the-head is due to the larvae or grubs of the sheep nasal fly, *Oestrus ovis*, also called the sheep gadfly and the head maggot fly. This fly is somewhat larger than the common horsefly, dull yellow or brownish in color, and hairy (*22*).

The flies are active during the warm part of the day and rest in warm corners and crevices during the cooler parts. They are viviparous—that is, they bear living young instead of eggs—and deposit their larvae around the nostrils of sheep. In attempting to deposit the larvae, the flies cause great annoyance to the sheep. The animals stop feeding, become restless, press their noses against the ground or against other sheep, and huddle together under buildings, rock ledges, and shade trees along fences.

After being deposited, the minute larvae migrate into the nasal passages. They remain on the nasal mucous membranes for varying periods of time before migrating to the frontal sinuses, where they complete their development as larvae. The mature larvae then leave the sinuses, return to the nasal passages, and drop to the ground, where they burrow into the soil and pupate. The period of pupation may last from approximately 3 weeks to 2 months, depending on soil temperature and moisture. At the end of this period the adult flies emerge from the pupal cases, crawl to the surface, and become active.

According to Mitchell and Cobbett (*34*), larvae deposited in the nostrils of spring lambs early in the season may complete their development in 2½ to 3½ months. Since such larvae may pupate in 12 to 72 hours after reaching maturity and the period of pupation may last from 17 to 57 days, a full life cycle may be completed in 3 to 5½ months. In New Mexico the flies are active during the late spring, summer, and early fall, and many larvae develop to maturity and are expelled in 25 to 35 days. Many do not develop during the season in which they are deposited, but remain in the nasal chambers throughout the late fall and the winter and do not migrate to the frontal sinuses until the next spring. Cobbett (*14*) expresses the opinion that the flies overwinter in the nasal cavities of sheep as first-stage larvae.

As the larvae crawl about on the nasal mucous membrane they set up an irritation that results in an increased flow of mucus from the nose, resembling that accompanying a cold in the head. This discharge is thin and clear at first, but as a result of bacterial infection, it soon thickens and becomes discolored, presenting the condition commonly called snotty nose, the most generally recognized symptom of grub infestation. Other symptoms shown by affected animals are frequent sneezing and difficulty in breathing. The eyes become inflamed, and the head is carried low. The animals grate their teeth and lose their appetite, or at least there is interference with feeding.

According to Mitchell and Cobbett (*34*), post mortem examination of the heads of infested sheep shows little pathological change in the tissues affected by live larvae other than increased mucous secretion, even when the head cavities contain many larvae. Only when dead larvae were encountered in the frontal sinus was there evidence of inflammation of the affected tissues, with discoloration and thickening of the mucous membrane and the presence of a thick, discolored secretion.

Many attempts have been made to treat or to prevent grub infestation of sheep. They may be summarized as follows: (1) Attempts to kill the grubs in the frontal sinuses of the head by injecting materials through perforations in the frontal bones; (2) attempts to kill the grubs by injecting materials into the nasal cavities; (3) attempts to remove the grubs by introducing irritants into the nasal passages for the purpose of causing the animal to sneeze and expel the grubs. Efforts to prevent infestation have been largely confined to placing repellents on the nasal openings. Critical examination has shown that the repellents employed thus far are of little or no value.

Stewart (*45*), Du Toit (*16*), and Du Toit and Clark (*17*) report having obtained satisfactory results in treating sheep for grub infestation by injecting various preparations into the frontal sinuses through openings made in the frontal bones. They described the technique of the operation and reported that they observed no deleterious effects from the treatment. They also noted that in sheep slaughtered a few days after the treatment had been given, no dead larvae were found in the sinuses, apparently demonstrating that the treatment completely eliminated grubs from the head. Gildow and Hickman (*21*), Du Toit (*16*), and Mönnig and Du Toit (*37*) have described a treatment that consists in the introduction of larvicides into the nasal cavities. The animals to be treated were restrained on their backs with the heads held at an angle of 45 degrees with the ground.

Cobbett (*14*) recently reported having obtained satisfactory results from the injection under pressure into the nasal cavities of a 3-percent solution of a saponified cresol preparation known as saponated solution of cresol. The chief difference between this treatment and those previously described consists in the fact that Cobbett's treatment is mainly directed toward killing the small larvae in the nasal cavities before they reach the sinuses, whereas the purpose of the other treatment is to kill the larvae in the frontal sinuses.

Cobbett reports that irrigation of the nasal mucous membranes of sheep with this solution caused no injury to the animals treated. Some sneezing and coughing occurred immediately after the treatment, but these and the subsequent nasal discharge were of short duration. Occasionally an animal held its breath immediately after treatment and fell to the ground, but such animals recovered promptly when assisted to their feet. The author calls attention to the fact that this treatment is effective as a control measure only in areas where the temperature during the winter months is sufficiently low to kill the adult flies and prevent any adult-fly activity.

LITERATURE CITED

(1) ANDREWS, JOHN S.
  1939. EXPERIMENTAL TRICHOSTRONGYLOSIS IN SHEEP AND GOATS. Jour. Agr. Res. 58 : 761–770, illus.
(2) ————
  1939. LIFE HISTORY OF THE NEMATODE COOPERIA CURTICEI, AND DEVELOPMENT OF RESISTANCE IN SHEEP. Jour. Agr. Res. 58 : 771–785, illus.
(3) BAKER, O. E.
  1939. A GRAPHIC SUMMARY OF FARM ANIMALS AND ANIMAL PRODUCTS. U. S. Dept. Agr. Misc. Pub. 269, 88 pp., illus.
(4) BELLER, K.
  1928. INFEKTIONSWEGE UND ENTWICKLUNG DES HAKENWURMS VOM SCHAFE (BUNOSTOMUM TRIGONOCEPHALUM RUD. 1808). Ztschr. f. Infektionskrank., Parasitäre Krank. u. Hyg. der Haustiere 32 : [232]–251, illus.
(5) BENNETT, HARRY JACKSON.
  1936. THE LIFE HISTORY OF COTYLOPHORON COTYLOPHORUM, A TREMATODE FROM RUMINANTS. Ill. Biol. Monog., (n. s.) v. 14, No. 4. 119 pp., illus.
(6) BOULENGER, CHARLES L.
  1915. THE LIFE-HISTORY OF NEMATODIRUS FILICOLLIS RUD., A NEMATODE PARASITE OF THE SHEEP'S INTESTINE. Parasitology 8 : [133]–155, illus.
(7) CHRISTENSEN, J. F.
  1938. SPECIES DIFFERENTIATION IN THE COCCIDIA FROM THE DOMESTIC SHEEP. Jour. Parasitol. 24 : 453–467, illus.
(8) ————
  1939. SPORULATION AND VIABILITY OF OÖCYSTS OF EIMERIA ARLOINGI FROM THE DOMESTIC SHEEP. Jour. Agr. Res. 59 : 527–534.
(9) ————
  1940. THE SOURCE AND AVAILABILITY OF INFECTIVE OÖCYSTS IN AN OUTBREAK OF COCCIDIOSIS IN LAMBS IN NEBRASKA FEEDLOTS. Amer. Jour. Vet. Res. 1 : 27–35.
(10) CHRISTENSEN, REED O.
  1931. AN ANALYSIS OF REPUTED PATHOGENICITY OF THYSANOSOMA ACTINIOIDES IN ADULT SHEEP. Jour. Agr. Res. 42 : 245–249, illus.
(11) CLUNIES ROSS, I., and GORDON, H. McL.
  .1933. NUTRITIONAL FACTORS AFFECTING RESISTANCE TO HÆMONCHOSIS. Austral. Vet. Jour. 9 (3) : 100–107, illus.

(12) CLUNIES ROSS, I., and GORDON, H. McL.
    1936. THE INTERNAL PARASITES AND PARASITIC DISEASES OF SHEEP; THEIR TREATMENT AND CONTROL. 238 pp., illus. Sydney, Australia.
(13) ——— and KAUZAL, G.
    1933. PRELIMINARY NOTE ON THE PATHOGENIC IMPORTANCE OF CHABERTIA OVINA (FABRICIUS, 1788). Austral. Vet. Jour. 9: 215–218.
(14) COBBETT, N. G.
    1940. AN EFFECTIVE TREATMENT FOR THE CONTROL OF THE SHEEP HEAD GRUB, OESTRUS OVIS, IN AREAS WHERE THE WINTERS ARE COLD. Amer. Vet. Med. Assoc. Jour. 97: 565–570.
(15) DEEM, A. W., and THORP, FRANK, Jr.
    1939. VARIATION IN NUMBERS OF COCCIDIA IN LAMBS DURING THE FEEDING SEASON. Vet. Med. 34: 46–47, illus.
(16) DU TOIT, R.
    1938. THE EXTERNAL PARASITES OF SHEEP. Farming in South Africa 13: 403–404, 407, illus.
(17) ——— and CLARK, R.
    1935. THE SHEEP NASAL FLY. A METHOD OF TREATMENT FOR SHEEP INFECTED WITH LARVAE OF OESTRUS OVIS. South African Vet. Med. Assoc. Jour. 6 (1): 25–32, illus.
(18) EDGAR, GRAHAME.
    1936. FATAL EFFECT OF HEAVY INFESTATION WITH COOPERIA CURTICEI (RAILLIET, 1893) IN GOATS. Austral. Vet. Jour. 12 (2): 58–61.
(19) FAUST, ERNEST CARROLL.
    1928. STUDIES ON THELAZIA CALLIPAEDA RAILLIET AND HENRY, 1910. Jour. Parasitol. 15: [75]–86.
(20) FREEBORN, STANLEY B., and BERRY, LESTER J.
    1934. OBSERVATIONS ON THE SHEEP TAPEWORM, MONIEZIA EXPANSA, IN CALIFORNIA. Amer. Vet. Med. Assoc. Jour. 85: 611–616, illus.
(21) GILDOW, E. M., and HICKMAN, C. W.
    1931. A NEW TREATMENT FOR OESTRUS OVIS LARVAE IN THE HEAD OF SHEEP. Amer. Vet. Med. Assoc. Jour. 79: 210–216, illus.
(22) HERMS, WILLIAM B.
    1923. MEDICAL AND VETERINARY ENTOMOLOGY. Ed. 2, 462 pp. illus. New York.
(23) HOBMAIER, ADELE, and HOBMAIER, MICHAEL.
    1929. UEBER DIE ENTWICKLUNG DES LUNGENWURMES SYNTHETOCAULUS CAPILLARIS IN NACKT-, WEG- UND SCHNIRKELSCHNECKEN. München. Tierärztl. Wchnschr., 80: [497]–500, illus.
(24) ——— and HOBMAIER, MICHAEL.
    1929. DIE ENTWICKLUNG DES LUNGENWURMES DES SCHAFES, DICTYOCAULUS FILARIA RUD., AUSSERHALB UND INNERHALB DES TIERKÖRPERS. München. Tierärztl. Wchnschr. 80: [621]–625, illus.
(25) KAUZAL, G.
    1932. NOTE ON THE TREATMENT OF LUNG WORM, DICTYOCAULUS FILARIA (RUD., 1809), INFESTATION OF SHEEP. Austral. Vet. Jour. 8: 25–28.
(26) ———
    1933. OBSERVATIONS ON THE BIONOMICS OF DICTYOCAULUS FILARIA, WITH A NOTE ON THE CLINICAL MANIFESTATIONS IN ARTIFICIAL INFECTIONS IN SHEEP. Austral. Vet. Jour. 9: 20–26, illus.
(27) ———
    1934. OBSERVATIONS ON THE DEVELOPMENT OF RESISTANCE TO DICTYOCAULUS FILARIA. Austral. Vet. Jour. 10: 100–111, illus.
(28) ———
    1936. FURTHER STUDIES ON THE PATHOGENIC IMPORTANCE OF CHABERTIA OVINA. Austral. Vet. Jour. 12: 107–110.
(29) ———
    1937. A PRELIMINARY STUDY OF THE PATHOGENIC EFFECT OF NEMATODIRUS SPP. IN SHEEP. Austral. Vet. Jour. 13: 120–123.
(30) KEMPER, H. E.
    1938 FILARIAL DERMATOSIS OF SHEEP. North Amer. Vet. 19 (9): 36–41, illus.

(31) KRULL, WENDELL H.
      1939. OBSERVATIONS ON THE DISTRIBUTION AND ECOLOGY OF THE ORIBATID
            MITES. Wash. Acad. Sci. Jour. 29: 519–528.
(32) LE ROUX, P. L.
      1930. A PRELIMINARY COMMUNICATION ON THE LIFE CYCLE OF COTYLOPHORON
            COTYLOPHORUM AND ITS PATHOGENICITY FOR SHEEP AND CATTLE.
            Union So. Africa Dept. Agr. Rpt. Dir. Vet. Serv. and Anim.
            Indus. 16: 243–253, illus.
(33) MARSH, H., and TUNNICLIFF, E. A.
      1941. ENTERITIS IN SHEEP CAUSED BY INFECTION WITH THE PROTOZOAN PARA-
            SITE GLOBIDIUM GILRUTHI. Amer. Jour. Vet. Res. 2: 174–177, illus.
(34) MITCHELL, W. C., and COBBETT, N. G.
      1933. FIELD INVESTIGATIONS RELATIVE TO CONTROL OF OESTRUS OVIS. Amer.
            Vet. Med. Assoc. Jour. 83: 247–254, illus.
(35) MÖNNIG, H. O.
      1938. VETERINARY HELMINTHOLOGY AND ENTOMOLOGY. THE DISEASES OF
            DOMESTICATED ANIMALS CAUSED BY HELMINTH AND ARTHROPOD PARA-
            SITES. Ed. 2, 409 pp. London.
(36) ————
      1940. TREATMENT AGAINST LUNGWORMS (DICTYOCAULUS FILARIA) IN SHEEP.
            Onderstepoort Jour. Vet. Sci. and Anim. Indus. 14: 111–114.
(37) ———— and DU TOIT, R.
      1939. THE SHEEP NASAL WORM. Farming in South Africa 14: 242, 251,
            illus.
(38) NEVEU-LEMAIRE, M.
      1936. TRAITÉ D'HELMINTHOLOGIE MÉDICALE ET VÉTÉRINAIRE. 1514 pp., illus.
            Paris.
(39) ORTLEPP, R. J.
      1937. OBSERVATIONS ON THE MORPHOLOGY AND LIFE-HISTORY OF GAIGERIA
            PACHYS CELLS RAILL. AND HENRY, 1910 : A HOOKWORM PARASITE OF
            SHEEP AND GOATS. Onderstepoort Jour. Vet. Sci. and Anim.
            Indus. 8: 183–212, illus.
(40) ————
      1939. OBSERVATIONS ON THE LIFE-HISTORY OF BUNOSTOMUM TRIGONO-
            CEPHALUM, A HOOKWORM OF SHEEP AND GOATS. Onderstepoort Jour.
            Vet. Sci. and Anim. Indus. 12: 305–318, illus.
(41) RANSOM, B. H.
      1913. CYSTICERCUS OVIS, THE CAUSE OF TAPEWORM CYSTS IN MUTTON. Jour.
            Agr. Res. 1: 15–58, illus.
(42) SHAW, J. N., and SIMMS, B. T.
      1930. STUDIES IN FASCIOLIASIS IN OREGON SHEEP AND GOATS. Oreg. Agr.
            Expt. Sta. Bul. 266, 24 pp., illus.
(43) SHORB, D. A.
      1939. PRELIMINARY OBSERVATIONS ON THE EFFECT ON SHEEP OF PURE IN-
            FESTATION WITH THE TAPEWORM, MONIEZIA EXPANSA. Helminthol.
            Soc. Wash. Proc. 6: 77–79, illus.
(44) ————
      1940. A NOTE ON THE EFFECT OF TAPEWORM INFESTATION ON THE CONDITION
            OF SHEEP. Vet. Med. 35: 180–181, illus.
(45) STEWART, J. R.
      1932. TREATMENT FOR OESTRUS OVIS. Amer. Vet. Med. Assoc. Jour. 80: 108.
(46) STEWART, M. A.
      1940. OVINE THELAZIASIS. Amer. Vet. Med. Assoc. Jour. 96: 486–489.
(47) STUNKARD, HORACE W.
      1938. THE DEVELOPMENT OF MONIEZIA EXPANSA IN THE INTERMEDIATE HOST.
            Parasitology 30: 491–501, illus.
(48) SWALES, W. E.
      1935. THE LIFE CYCLE OF FASCIOLOIDES MAGNA (BASSI, 1875), THE LARGE
            LIVER FLUKE OF RUMINANTS, IN CANADA, WITH OBSERVATIONS ON
            THE BIONOMICS OF THE LARVAL STAGES AND THE INTERMEDIATE HOSTS,
            PATHOLOGY OF FASCIOLOIDIASIS MAGNA, AND CONTROL MEASURES.
            Canad. Jour. Res. 12: 177–215, illus.

(49) SWALES, W. E.
    1936. FURTHER STUDIES ON FASCIOLOIDES MAGNA (BASSI, 1875), WARD, 1917, AS A PARASITE OF RUMINANTS. Canad. Jour. Res. Sect. D, Zool. Sci. 14: [83]-95, illus.

(50) THORP, FRANK, Jr.
    1938. SOME FEEDLOT DISEASES OF LAMBS. Vet. Med. 33(10) : 442-444, illus.

(51) THRELKELD, W. L., and DOWNING, T. O.
    1936. A REPORT ON EXPERIMENTAL INFECTIONS OF OVIS ARIES WITH THE INFECTIVE LARVAE OF OSTERTAGIA CIRCUMCINCTA. Jour. Parasitol. 22: [187]-201, illus.

(52) VEGLIA, FRANK.
    1915. THE ANATOMY AND LIFE-HISTORY OF HÆMONCHUS CONTORTUS (RUD.). Union So. Africa Dept. Agr. Rpts. Dir. Vet. Res. 3 and 4: [347]-500, illus.

(53) ————
    1924. PRELIMINARY NOTES ON THE LIFE-HISTORY OF OESOPHAGOSTOMUM COLUMBIANUM. Union So. Africa Dept. Agr. Rpts. Dir. Vet. Ed. and Res. 9 and 10 (1923) : [811]-823, illus.

(54) ————
    1928. OESOPHAGOSTOMIASIS IN SHEEP (PRELIMINARY NOTE). Dept. Agr. Rpts. Dir. Vet. Ed. and Res. 13 and 14: [755]-797, illus.

(55) WENYON, C. M.
    1926. PROTOZOOLOGY. A MANUAL FOR MEDICAL MEN, VETERINARIANS AND ZOOLOGISTS. 2 v., 1563 pp., illus. London.

Sheep Scab and Its Control

BY A. W. MILLER [1]

SCAB, which affects the skin and is caused by mange mites, can be bad enough on any animal. It is especially serious in the case of sheep because it directly damages the wool; hence the strict Federal quarantines long ago clamped on infected areas. These, and official dipping operations, have been very effective, and sheep scab is now mostly found in farming, not range, areas. Here is what you should do if scab occurs in your flock.

SHEEP SCAB, or scabies, has been known for many centuries; in fact, it is referred to in Leviticus 22:22, which forbids the use of scabbed sheep in sacrifices.

A half century ago the disease was the greatest draw-back to the sheep industry in the Western States, and it caused heavy losses to feeders in the Corn Belt States also. In fact, sheep scabies was so widespread as to deter many ranchers from engaging in the sheep business, and farmers refused to buy undipped range sheep for feeding purposes. So prevalent was the disease that in 1896 England prohibited the importation of live sheep from the United States.

The parasitic mites that cause scab in sheep are of four species— psoroptic, sarcoptic, chorioptic, and demodectic. Each kind of mite has distinctive habits, with the result that the nature and location of the lesions, or tissue injuries, are more or less characteristic. The psoroptic mites live on the surface of the skin, usually on the withers, back, sides, and rump. The sarcoptic mites burrow into the skin, usually on the head and face or other parts where there is little or no wool. The chorioptic mites live on the surface of the skin, and the lesions they cause are usually found on the legs. The demodectic mites, the smallest in the group, are found in the hair follicles and the glands of the skin, where they cause pimples or nodules.

---

[1] A. W. Miller is Chief, Interstate Inspection Division, Bureau of Animal Industry.

904

PSOROPTIC, COMMON, OR BODY SCAB

The form of sheep scabies of the greatest economic importance to the sheep industry in the United States is the psoroptic, or common, scab. A highly contagious skin disease readily transmitted from sheep to sheep, it usually spreads rapidly after it is introduced into a flock. The irritation and other effects of the disease make the animals unthrifty and cause loss of weight, a decrease in wool production, and in some instances the death of a large number of affected animals, especially where weather conditions are severe and adequate

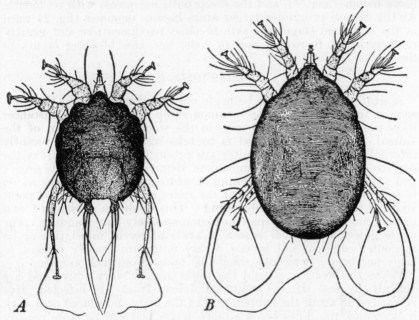

FIGURE 1.—The psoroptic mites that cause common sheep scab, viewed from above: *A*, Male; *B*, female. Greatly enlarged.

feed is not available. This form of the disease, however, is rather easily cured by appropriate treatment.

The mites (*Psoroptes equi* var. *ovis*) that cause common scab are white or yellowish and visible to the unaided eye (fig. 1, *A* and *B*). Their entire life cycle is passed on the body of the host. Each female may deposit 15 to 24 eggs, which usually hatch after 4 to 7 days' incubation. The young mites reach maturity and mate, and females deposit eggs within 10 to 12 days after hatching. These stages in the life history have an important bearing on the interval which should elapse between treatments.

The mites of common, or body, scab prick the skin of the animal to obtain food and probably introduce a poisonous saliva into the wound by this action. As the mites multiply and more wounds are made in the skin, there is itching, inflammation, and exudation of serum.

This serum, mixed with particles of dirt and other material, soon hardens and forms scabs. At first only a small pimple can be seen, but as the mites multiply they seek the healthier parts around the edges of the diseased area, and the lesion becomes larger. The affected areas of the skin become hardened and thickened, as may be observed by pinching up a portion and comparing it with the surrounding healthy skin. Infected sheep become restless, scratch themselves, and rub against fences and other members of the flock. The itching becomes more intense when the sheep are warm.

The wool is disturbed; at first slender tags come loose, then the fleece becomes matted, and the sheep pulls out pieces with its mouth. As the disease progresses larger areas become denuded (fig. 2) until in the advanced stages the skin becomes parchmentlike and greatly thickened and furrowed, and in some instances bleeding occurs in the cracks.

DIAGNOSIS

A definite diagnosis can be made only by demonstrating the presence of the mite that causes common sheep scab. In some instances it is possible to detect the mite in the wool or on the skin of the animal, but the best method is to take scrapings from a recently infected area. When the mites are producing active irritation the surface of the skin in the immediate vicinity of the lesion is greasy and appears bright and glistening or white and glossy. If the lesion is dull and dry it indicates that the mites are inactive at that point and that they will be difficult to find. This condition is usually found in the center of a scabby patch of comparatively long standing. The white glossy appearance is seen in areas of recent infestation or on the outer edges of old lesions, where mites are usually present in large numbers. Scrapings should be taken from such areas.

When the weather is cold the mites are not very active and are difficult to see. If the material taken from an infected area is warmed to about the temperature of the body and placed on a dark background, the mites become more active and can be more readily seen as they move about. A low-power hand lens is a great aid in demonstrating the presence of the mites.

TRANSMISSIBILITY

As already noted, common sheep scab is exceedingly contagious among sheep, but it is not transmissible to other animals except goats. Infected sheep are practically the only source from which sheep scab spreads. Experiments show that clean sheep seldom contract scab from so-called infectious premises. As a precautionary measure, however, such premises should not be used for clean sheep for 30 days after they have been occupied by scabby sheep. Freshly dipped sheep do not become infected from infectious premises, and flocks may safely be held on such premises between the first and second dippings. It is a good sanitary practice, however, to avoid old bed grounds, and small enclosures that have been occupied by scabby sheep should be thoroughly cleaned and disinfected. Sheep scab is transmissible at any season of the year, though during hot, dry weather it often remains dormant, seeming to have been cured. With the advent of cold, rainy weather, however, it again manifests itself.

TREATMENT

Contrary to the previous opinion that internal medication with sulfur or other medicinal agents would cure the disease, the only effective treatment for common scab is the external application of some medicinal agent that will kill the scab mites. This is best accomplished by dipping, but when dipping is impracticable because of cold weather or for any other reason, isolation of the visibly affected a n i m a l s and hand dressing of the scabs are advisable. Hand dressing consists in soaking the affected parts with warm dip. In dipping flocks in which the disease is in the advanced stage, animals with hard scabs should be separated from the others just prior to dipping, the scabs soaked with warm dip, and the crusts broken up by rubbing with a stiff brush or stick.

Two dippings are necessary to cure common scab. The first dipping

FIGURE 2.—Stages in the development of sheep scab. *A*, First stage of scab, showing the wool on the shoulder disturbed by biting and scratching; *B*, first break in the fleece; *C*, an advanced case of sheep scab.

kills the mites but does not destroy all the eggs. The unkilled eggs hatch and form a new generation of mites, which must be destroyed by a second dipping before they have had time to lay eggs. The proper interval between the first and second dippings is 10 to 12 days, but in an emergency it may be extended to a maximum of 14 days.

Many medicinal agents have been used for dips. Some have been found to be useless; others have given satisfactory results in some instances but at other times failed to effect a cure. Workers engaged in sheep scabies eradication realized that a method must be found that would make it possible to maintain dips at a uniform strength throughout the entire dipping operation. After years of experimentation, tests for keeping lime-and-sulfur and nicotine dips uniform were developed. Under existing regulations of the Department of Agriculture, no dip can be used in official dipping of sheep for scabies unless the strength of the bath prepared from it can be satisfactorily determined in the field by a practical, portable testing outfit and unless dipping in a bath of definite strength under actual field conditions will effectually eradicate scabies infection without injury to the animals.

The only dips now permitted in official dipping are those made from lime-sulfur or nicotine. The liquid should be used at a temperature of 95° to 105° F. and must at all times be maintained at a strength of not less than 2 percent of "sulfide sulfur," if it is a lime-sulfur dip, and at not less than 0.05 percent of nicotine, if it is a nicotine dip.

SARCOPTIC, OR HEAD, SCAB

Sarcoptic scab is not common in the United States. It is difficult to eradicate, but it can be cured. Thorough soaking of the affected parts with warm lime-and-sulfur dip every 5 or 6 days for a month or 6 weeks will usually be effective.

CHORIOPTIC, OR FOOT, SCAB

The form of sheep scabies commonly known as foot scab is caused by a mite (*Chorioptes bovis* var. *ovis*) that closely resembles the psoroptic mite of common sheep scab. The visible lesions usually occur first around the feet but in severe cases may spread to the legs, thighs, and udder, and they are most pronounced during cold weather. The disease is distinguished from common scab by the location of the lesions. This form of sheep scab can be effectively combated with the treatment recommended for common scab. During very cold weather, wading tanks filled with dip may be used instead of dipping vats.

DEMODECTIC, OR FOLLICULAR, SCAB

Demodectic scab is not common in sheep in the United States, but cases have been reported in milk goats. The mite (*Demodex canis* var. *ovis*) that causes this form of scab is not visible to the unaided eye. It is wormlike in form and infests the hair follicles and the sebaceous glands, which lubricate the skin. When present in large numbers the mites cause swellings or nodules that extend deeply into the skin.

No effective method is known for the treatment of flocks infected with demodectic mange. Individual animals that are affected should be removed from the flock and treated or destroyed. Treatment consists in opening all the nodules, removing the contents, and syringing the pockets out with a 2-percent solution of coal-tar-creosote dip.

DIPPING SHEEP

The method universally practiced in the United States to combat sheep scab is to dip infected and exposed flocks. As already noted, two or more dippings are necessary to effect a cure. All the sheep in a flock should be dipped regardless of the number infected.

In dipping sheep it is most important that close attention be given to numerous details. Sheep should not be dipped immediately after shearing, and great care should be exercised not to dip in a lime-and-sulfur solution any sheep that have unhealed wounds from shear cuts or other causes. Animals with such wounds when dipped in this kind of solution usually develop blood poisoning, the mortality from which is very high. Every possible effort should be made to handle the sheep quietly and to avoid rough treatment of any kind.

Ewes and lambs should be dipped separately as there is great danger of drowning the younger animals if they are dipped together. As ewes recognize their lambs by smell and not by sight, the two groups should be turned together after dipping in order that each mother may have an opportunity to find her lamb.

Several hours before the sheep are to be dipped they should be given a moderate amount of feed and water, but care should be taken to see that they are not too full when dipped. As far as possible, dipping operations should not be undertaken on days when the weather is extremely cold and stormy. If it is necessary in an emergency to dip sheep during winter weather, the operation should be completed early in the day in order that the animals may have time to dry off and be fed before night.

The quantity of dip in the vat should be sufficient to submerge the sheep completely, and the liquid should be maintained at a temperature of 95° to 105° F. An accurate thermometer should be provided and the temperature checked frequently. The sheep should be kept in the dipping vat long enough for the wool to become fairly well saturated; in the case of infected sheep this will not be less than 2 minutes. In well-advanced cases the hard scabs should be broken up and soaked with the dipping fluid, but in dressing such areas care should be taken not to cause the wounds to bleed, as the blood may protect the mites from the effects of the dip.

While being put in the vat, the animals should be carefully watched by men with dipping forks stationed along the file of sheep to see that the dipping is properly done and to prevent accidents (fig. 3). As soon as the dip becomes dirty it should be changed regardless of the number of sheep that have been dipped in it. When lime-and-sulfur dip is used, the solution should be changed after it is 10 days old. Only dips permitted by the Department of Agriculture should be used in the treatment of sheep against scabies. As already noted, it is essential that the dip be maintained at the required strength at all times. By frequent testing of the solution with the field tests available for lime-and-sulfur and nicotine dips it is possible to determine when it is necessary to add fresh dip to maintain the required strength.

FIGURE 3.—Dipping sheep to control scab. The dipping forks (poles with hooks) are used to control the movement of sheep through the dipping vat and also to force their heads under the surface momentarily to make sure that all the scab mites are reached by the dip.

CONDUCT OF CONTROL WORK

In June 1897 the Department of Agriculture issued an order governing the transportation of sheep affected with scabies, and Federal inspectors were placed at the principal feeding points of all the railroads leading to market centers to inspect and supervise the shipping of sheep. In 1899 an order was issued requiring that all sheep shipped from stockyards to other States for feeding purposes be dipped, and in July of that year another order forbade any sheep affected with scabies to be shipped interstate that had not been dipped in a mixture approved by the Department.

The following year inspectors were stationed at a number of points in the Western range States, and various livestock sanitary officials issued dipping orders. This plan was more satisfactory to the sheep growers and transportation companies than the previous one, but still the desired results were not accomplished. Accordingly, on June 1, 1905, a Federal quarantine was placed on all the territory west of the eastern border of North Dakota, South Dakota, Kansas, Oklahoma, and Texas, an area of more than 1,700,000 square miles.

Under cooperative arrangements with the livestock sanitary officials of the several States, systematic inspections by State and Federal employees were made of all sheep in infected localities, and all flocks found to be infected or exposed were dipped under official supervision. This work was supplemented by rigid inspection of sheep arriving at public stockyards and appropriate treatment or other disposition of those classed as infected or exposed. When this work was inaugurated 90 percent of all the bands of sheep in some States were infected with scabies. Progress toward the eradication of the disease continued, and from time to time the quarantine on various areas was lifted. At the present time only small areas in two States are under Federal quarantine for this disease. So successful has the eradication work been that most of the range States in which the sheep industry is important have been entirely free from the disease for several years. The remaining infection is largely confined to a few farming States where numerous auction markets and the almost exclusive use of trucks for transportation have made the eradication problem a difficult one.

Control work is conducted at present under cooperative agreement between the United States Bureau of Animal Industry and the livestock sanitary officials of the various States. The agreements specify in some detail the part that each of these cooperative agencies shall take in the work of eradication. Generally both parties to an agreement furnish trained men to make inspections and supervise the dipping of infected and exposed flocks.

In recent years the States with few exceptions have handled the quarantine of flocks and areas infected with sheep scab so effectively that it has not been necessary to impose Federal quarantines. The situation in several of the farming States has been rather serious during recent years, however. The indiscriminate movement of sheep through auction markets in these States and their uncontrolled transportation by trucks have presented a difficult problem, but it is being gradually solved by the enforcement of State regulations at the auction markets and by the active cooperation of Federal and State inspectors in locating centers of infection and enforcing appropriate control measures when diseased flocks are found.

Flock owners who plan to dip sheep of their own accord are strongly advised to have the work supervised by a veterinarian or other properly trained and equipped person who is experienced in dealing with sheep scab and prepared to test the strength of the dip. Flock owners are reminded also that for their own protection and that of the community they should report the appearance of sheep scab promptly to the nearest veterinarian, State livestock official, or representative of the Bureau of Animal Industry. These professional workers are prepared to take suitable action to eradicate the infection.

Sheep Ticks

BY MARION IMES AND O. G. BABCOCK [1]

THE SHEEP TICK, which is not a tick at all but a fly, can do a good deal of damage to fleeces, besides causing a serious set-back in lambs. A number of substances, used as dips according to the directions in this article, will control these parasites.

THE SHEEP TICK or ked (*Melophagus ovinus*) is not a true tick but a wingless parasitic fly that lives in the fleece of sheep. The adult female is about one-quarter of an inch long and the male is slightly smaller (fig. 1, *A* and *B*). The ticks are brown, have six legs, and are plainly visible to the unaided eye.

Sheep ticks are widely distributed, occurring in practically all parts of the United States where sheep are kept, and affecting primarily the coarse-wool and medium-wool breeds, and sometimes Angora goats. The fine-wool breeds of sheep are usually not affected to any great extent; the parasites apparently are not adapted to thrive in their tight, greasy fleeces.

In obtaining their food, sheep ticks puncture the skin and suck blood and lymph from the host animal. They do not remain attached in one place like true ticks but move about in the fleece, making a new puncture each time they feed. Hence when sheep are grossly infested many punctures are made in the skin, and the resulting intense itching and irritation cause the animals to become restless so that they do not eat well or gain weight normally. To relieve the itching, infested sheep rub, bite, and scratch themselves, with the result that the fleeces are disarranged, tufts of wool are pulled out, and some of the wool fibers are broken or damaged. Since losses in body weight and damage to fleeces reduce the value of sheep, it is profitable to the flock owner to control or eradicate sheep ticks.

---

[1] Marion Imes is Senior Veterinarian, Zoological Division, Bureau of Animal Industry, and O. G. Babcock is Associate Entomologist, Division of Insects Affecting Man and Animals, Bureau of Entomology and Plant Quarantine.

LIFE HISTORY

The four stages in the life cycle of the sheep tick are the egg, the larva, the pupa, and the adult or sexually mature parasite. The egg is not laid but is retained in the body of the female, where it develops into a larva in about 7 days. At the time of birth the larva is covered with a soft white membrane, which turns brown and becomes a hard shell or puparium in about 12 hours (fig. 2). The puparium is attached to the wool fibers of the sheep by a gluelike substance that is soluble in water.

The pupal stage of the insect is passed in the shell, or puparium. These shell-covered pupae are commonly called eggs. In 19 to 24 days from the time it is deposited, the shell of the pupa is broken open at one end and the young tick emerges to become active in the fleece. The duration of the pupal stage, usually called the period of incubation, is influenced by the weather. During warm weather the average period of incubation on the host is about 19 days, while during cold weather it is 24 days or longer.

After emerging from the puparium the young tick develops rapidly and reaches sexual maturity in 3 or 4 days. The female usually deposits its first pupa within 8 to 10 days after mating. From the practical standpoint the two important stages in the life cycle may be summarized as follows:

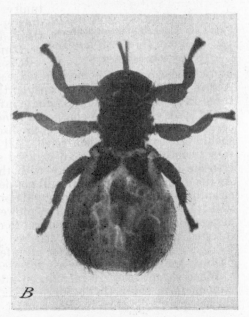

FIGURE 1.—*A*, An engorged female sheep tick, under side (×10). *B*, A mature male sheep tick, upper side (×10).

When about 14 days old the female tick deposits its first pupa; from this pupa a young tick emerges in about 19 to 24 days.

HABITS AND SPREAD

Each female sheep tick produces an average of 12 to 15 pupae during its lifetime, one being deposited about every 7 or 8 days. The pupae are attached to the wool fibers from ½ to 1 inch from the skin. Thus when the sheep are shorn the majority of the pupae and some of the ticks are removed with the fleece. As freshly shorn sheep offer little protection for the ticks, they usually migrate in large numbers to the unshorn lambs during the shearing season. When lambs become heavily infested they receive a setback at an important period in their development, which causes considerable financial loss to the owner.

FIGURE 2.—Sheep tick pupa (×10). Pupae are attached to the wool fibers; because of their hard shells they are commonly called eggs.

When separated from their host, adult sheep ticks live only about 4 days. Dislodged pupae, however, may retain their vitality during warm weather and emerge as active young ticks in due time, when they attach themselves to sheep at the first opportunity. Pupae dislodged from sheep during cold weather do not complete their development, as freezing temperatures kill them.

It is evident that premises occupied by ticky sheep may become infested, especially during warm weather. A safe basis of practice is to consider that buildings, corrals, and pastures occupied by ticky sheep remain infested during warm weather for about 60 days after the sheep are removed. Before infested stables, corrals, or other small enclosures are used for clean sheep, the premises should be cleaned and disinfected. All litter should be removed down to a smooth surface, then all exposed surfaces sprayed with coal-tar creosote diluted in accordance with the directions on the container. As the disinfectant probably will not destroy the vitality of the pupae, cleaning should be done thoroughly so that pupae will be removed with the litter, which should be plowed under, burned, or otherwise destroyed. Since it is not practical to clean and disinfect large areas, infected pastures should not be used for clean sheep during warm weather. About 2 months after all infested sheep have been removed, pastures may be considered safe for use.

When sheep ticks are introduced into a flock they spread rapidly. Among farm sheep this occurs especially during cold weather when the sheep usually come in close contact with one another, but it occurs at all seasons among range sheep which are usually closely herded, crowded into corrals, and in close contact on the bed grounds.

DETECTING TICKS ON SHEEP

When sheep are heavily infested with sheep ticks they bite and scratch themselves and rub against any available object, including other members of the flock. These efforts to relieve the intense itching caused by the ticks disturb and damage the wool, giving the fleece a ragged appearance.

Sheep ticks may sometimes be seen crawling over the tips of the wool fibers during warm weather, but usually they remain deep in the fleece, especially during cold weather. Their favorite locations on the animal are the neck, breast, shoulders, belly, and thighs, where the fleece is thin and the skin tender. In examining sheep for ticks the wool over these regions should be parted. If ticks are present, they and the pupae can be easily seen.

The first symptoms of tick infestation are similar to those of scabies, lice, wildfire, and other conditions that cause intense itching. Finding ticks on sheep, therefore, does not exclude other possible causes of itching and irritation, and the examination should be thorough to assure that other causes have not been overlooked.

ERADICATION OR CONTROL BY DIPPING

The only known practical method of eradicating sheep ticks is to dip the infested sheep in a liquid that will kill the parasites. Killing the adult ticks by dipping is a simple matter, but the pupae, which are more resistant to dips, may complete their development and produce a new crop of ticks. To complete the eradication it is necessary to kill the newly hatched ticks before they are old enough to deposit pupae. This may be done either by dipping the sheep again after an interval of 24 to 28 days or by using a dip that will remain active in the fleece long enough to destroy the young ticks after they emerge from the shell.

Fall dipping is good insurance against the ravages of ticks during the winter when the weather is too cold for dipping. If the lambs become heavily infested shortly after shearing, which often occurs, the flock should be dipped as soon as the shear cuts heal.

In dipping sheep for ticks, the depth of the dip in the vat should be 40 to 48 inches or deep enough to swim the tallest animal.[2] All members of the flock, regardless of the number showing infestation, should be dipped, as well as all animals of other species running with the flock. The animals should be held in the dip about 1 minute, or long enough to saturate the fleece. The head of each animal should be submerged, or ducked, twice for an instant. It is not necessary to heat dips used for sheep ticks, but the temperature of the liquid should not be low enough to chill the animals.

[2] IMES, MARION. THE SHEEP TICK AND ITS ERADICATION BY DIPPING. U. S. Dept. Agr. Farmers' Bul. 798, 22 pp., illus. 1917. (Revised, 1932 and 1940.)

77434°—51——59

The three kinds of dips commonly used when sheep are dipped twice for sheep ticks are nicotine, coal-tar creosote, and cresol. These dips are concentrated liquids sold under various trade names, and directions for diluting and using them are supplied with each package or container. They are effective in eradicating sheep ticks when used in fairly soft water.

There are also three classes or kinds of dips used for eradicating sheep ticks at one dipping, namely, fused-bentonite-sulfur-cube, arsenic-sulfur-rotenone, and home-made derris or cube dip. The first two are proprietary products sold under different trade names. When used according to the instructions furnished by the manufacturers with each package, they are effective in eradicating sheep ticks. In using products containing arsenic it should be remembered that it is a poison, and proper precaution should be taken to avoid injury to men and animals.

Derris powder, the pulverized roots of a shrub that grows in the Tropics of the Old World, and cube powder, made from the roots of plants found in South America, are among the effective insecticides that have come into general use during recent years. One of the active ingredients of both these powders is rotenone, and they are about equally effective as remedies for external parasites of animals. Powders commercially classed as containing 5 percent of rotenone are generally used.

In making home-made derris or cube dip, either derris powder or cube powder may be used. To prepare derris or cube dip fill the dipping vat with water to the dip line and add the powder in the proportion of 1 pound to each 100 gallons of water. Mix the powder with a small quantity of water to form a thin paste and distribute it over the surface of the water in the vat. When the contents of the vat are well stirred so the paste is uniformly mixed with the water, the dip is ready for use. Freshly prepared dip should always be used, since old dip which has stood in the vat for several days is no longer suitable.

At the time this book went to press, the drugs and other materials mentioned in various articles—chiefly as disinfectants, insecticides, and anthelmintics—were still available for veterinary and medical use. Under war conditions, however, it is possible that some of these materials may become scarce or unavailable. In that case, the reader should' obtain professional advice from the Department of Agriculture, the State experiment station, a local veterinarian, or the county agent as to available substitutes.

Goat Lice

BY O. G. BABCOCK AND EMORY C. CUSHING [1]

TWO KINDS of blue lice, two kinds of red lice, and a large yellow louse attack goats. Although they are the worst external parasite the goat keeper has to contend with, he can get rid of them with very little trouble if he will follow the directions given here.

LICE are the most widespread and probably the most important external parasites of goats of all breeds in the United States. Yet the control of these pests is not difficult, and there would seem to be little reason for goat raisers throughout the country to sustain the losses that are at present caused by these parasites year after year.

SPECIES, LIFE HISTORY, AND SPREAD OF GOAT LICE

Goats are commonly infested with five species of lice, two of which (*Linognathus stenopsis* and *L. africanus*), called blue lice, feed by puncturing the skin and sucking blood. The other three have mouth parts fitted for chewing and feed on the hair, scales from the skin, and extraneous matter on the skin surface. Of these three species, one (*Bovicola penicillata*) is commonly referred to as the large yellow or hairy louse and the other two (*B. limbatus* and *B. caprae*) as red lice.

The different species of goat lice have much the same breeding habits, and their life cycles are similar. Ordinarily, goat lice spend their entire lives on the bodies of goats; they mate, lay their eggs, and develop without leaving the host. Sometimes other animals such as sheep, dogs, and burros that are in close association with infested flocks may act as temporary carriers of goat lice, but they are not subject to true infestations.

---

[1] O. G. Babcock is Associate Entomologist and Emory C. Cushing is Senior Entomologist, Division of Insects Affecting Man and Animals, Bureau of Entomology and Plant Quarantine.

The nits, or eggs of the lice, are laid in the fleece and are attached firmly to the hair close to the skin. Quite often an egg is cemented to more than one fiber, which accounts for the matting of the hair frequently seen in heavily infested animals. The eggs hatch in 7 to 14 days, depending on the temperature of the air.

After hatching, the immature louse must shed its skin twice before reaching the adult stage. The first molt occurs 2 to 10 days after hatching and the second 3 to 13 days after the first. As many as 15 days after the second molt are sometimes required for the young

FIGURE 1.—Goat heavily infested with lice.

lice to become sexually mature. The entire life cycle of goat lice from the time the eggs are laid until full maturity is reached ranges in length from 14 to 75 days.

Infestations of goat lice are easily detected, although newly hatched lice are almost transparent and it is difficult to see them. The adults can readily be seen with the unaided eye, however, and the fact that in ordinary infestations all stages are present on the goat at the same time makes detection easy. During the summer months the number of lice on the animals is greatly reduced, but it increases rapidly through the fall and winter.

Lice do not remain attached in one place as do true ticks but move about over the body of the animal, feeding at frequent intervals and causing a constant and extreme itching and irritation of the skin.

Because of the annoyance occasioned by both sucking and biting lice, the infested animals are restless and do not feed well; hence they lose weight, become unthrifty, and show signs of low vitality (fig. 1). The mohair becomes ragged and broken from scratching, biting, and rubbing. The fibers are weakened, lack luster, and become matted, tangled, and discolored. In some sections of the country where goat raising and mohair production have been highly developed, ranchmen recognize that in heavily infested flocks the quality and quantity of mohair are greatly reduced, the actual loss amounting to as much as one-half pound of mohair per animal. Moreover, infested animals are apt to scratch themselves on sharp objects, such as pointed broken boards, protruding nails in corrals, and wire fences, with the result that the skin is often broken, making wounds that are susceptible to screwworm infestation, which may cause further losses.

Kids and the old, weak, unthrifty animals of the flock are usually the most heavily infested.

When introduced into a clean herd, goat lice spread rapidly from one animal to another, especially during cold weather or when the animals are confined in close contact with one another. The spread of the infestation is due chiefly to the direct contact of lousy animals with uninfested ones. It is possible, however, for an infestation to start among clean goats that are confined on premises previously occupied by lousy animals, owing to the fact that under favorable conditions some adult lice may live apart from a host for periods of 3 to 18 days, particularly in warm weather. The nits attached to dislodged hair may continue to hatch for several days, and the young lice may live for 3 or 4 days.

CONTROL AND ERADICATION

Goat lice are probably more easily eliminated, usually at less expense in money and labor, than any other group of insect parasites of domestic animals. Several insecticides that are cheap and readily available are effective in killing these insects.

The blue, or sucking, lice are harder to kill and inflict greater injury than the biting lice, but both can be eradicated by proper control practices.

Perhaps the simplest method, and the only effective one for eradicating the lice, is to dip the goats in a water solution or suspension of the louse-killing material. Since it is not advisable to use this treatment in cold weather, when the lice become much more numerous, the owner should not wait until winter to begin control treatments. When infestations become so heavy during the winter that treatments are imperative, if only a few animals are involved, they may be hand-dusted with an insecticide to keep the parasites in check. Although this cannot be depended upon to kill all the lice, it will greatly reduce their number and prevent severe injury to the goats. Spraying is sometimes resorted to, but, like hand dusting, it is not completely effective.

The best time to dip Angora goats is 1 month to 6 weeks after they are sheared, provided this permits the dipping to be done before cold weather. .If Angoras are treated too short a time before shearing, the insecticides may lower the quality of the fleece by removing some of the natural oil. Furthermore, animals dipped when they have a heavy fleece carry out more dip, which increases the cost of the treatment. A month to 6 weeks after shearing, the fleece is heavy enough to retain a sufficient amount of the insecticide to kill the lice, but it does not retain excessive amounts of the dip.

Goats of breeds other than Angora may be treated at any time when weather conditions are favorable.

None of the insecticides now recommended is effective in killing louse eggs, and since these may continue to hatch for 10 or 12 days, it is necessary to follow the first dipping with a second one in 11 to 16 days. Usually two dippings are sufficient to eradicate all the lice in a flock, provided every animal is found and treated. When lice make their appearance in a flock it is always advisable to treat every animal. The dipped animals should then be turned into pastures that have not been occupied by goats for the previous 4 to 6 weeks.

INSECTICIDES FOR KILLING GOAT LICE

Several materials are useful for treating goats infested with lice. All of them have certain disadvantages, but they are about equally effective in eradicating the parasites. Finely ground sulfur, 98 percent of which will pass through a sieve having 325 meshes to the inch, is one of the simplest. Since the sulfur particles are not wetted by contact with water, it is necessary to combine the material with a so-called wetting agent, which permits the mixing of the sulfur with water and holds the particles in suspension so that they become enmeshed in the hair of the animal when it is dipped. Commercial companies now supply, at reasonable prices, wettable sulfur—that is, sulfur with a wetting agent added—already prepared, and it is advisable for goat raisers to purchase sulfur in this form rather than attempt to prepare the mixture themselves. All wettable sulfurs do not combine well in hard water, especially those containing relatively large amounts of alkali and gypsum, but the use of certain wetting agents will largely overcome this difficulty. Goat raisers in the United States who have not had previous experience with the use of sulfur in their present localities should request the advice of the United States Department of Agriculture regarding the proper material to use.

Wettable sulfur kills lice slowly, requiring from 7 to 10 days to effect a complete kill. It is not known definitely how sulfur kills the lice, but the available evidence indicates that a gas, hydrogen sulfide, is given off as a result of the contact of the sulfur with the animal, and that this gas destroys the insects. In preparation for dipping, the sulfur is mixed with water at the rate of 10 pounds per 100 gallons. A mixture of wettable sulfur and one of the powdered insecticidal plant materials, cube or derris, containing at least 4 to 5 percent rotenone is somewhat more efficient in killing lice than sulfur alone. Fifty pounds of wettable sulfur plus 10 pounds of either cube or derris powder per 1,000 gallons of water makes an efficient dip. The same combination in these proportions of sulfur and cube or derris is a good dust for hand treating infested goats; or sulfur, cube, or derris may be used alone. An ounce or two per animal is sufficient for one treatment.

Prepared arsenical dips which are available on the market and are recommended by the Government for use in dipping cattle to remove the cattle fever tick are also suitable for the control of goat lice. The instructions on the label of the container should be followed closely in diluting and using ready-prepared arsenical dips. Since they are poisonous to animals when taken internally, care should be taken that the animals do not drink any of the dip. The vat should not be emptied where the liquid will soil pasture or feed, and the freshly treated animals should be held in a drain pen or a suitable inclosure where the dip dripping from them cannot form pools. Men working around the vat should be careful not to get their clothing wet with the arsenical solution, and should wash their hands frequently to prevent possible absorption of the arsenic.

When used with soft water, coal-tar-creosote dips, sold under various trade names, are effective for the control of goat lice. In hard water the ingredients often separate, and injury to the animals and the fleeces results.

Treating Infested Goats

Where only a small number of animals are to be treated, a large washtub or a small galvanized-iron tank will suffice, but when several hundred animals are to be dipped, it is more convenient and economical to construct a special vat. The round vat shown in figure 2 has proved the most economical for the dipping of goats alone. If it is necessary to dip horses, cattle, and other large animals also, it is advisable to construct a rectangular vat. Specifications for these vats may be obtained from the United States Department of Agriculture.

The animals should not be dipped if there is likely to be a cold wave before they become thoroughly dry. Dipping in excessively hot weather also should be avoided. The animals should not be driven any distance just before or very soon after dipping. Care in throwing them into the vat will help to avoid injuries and reduce the possibility of strangling. In fact, quiet, careful handling is essential to get the best results and to prevent losses.

The animal should be kept in the dip approximately 1 minute. When it comes to the surface after the first immersion, it should be allowed to get its breath, then its head should be ducked beneath the surface momentarily, and it should receive another ducking before leaving the vat.

The dipping fluid in the vat should always be 40 to 60 inches deep. In estimating the amount of dip required to treat a flock, allow at least 2 quarts for each freshly sheared goat and about 1 gallon for each full-fleeced animal.

FIGURE 2.—A round vat for dipping goats.

FURTHER STUDIES ON THE CONTROL OF GOAT LICE

Dips now recommended for the control of goat lice are sometimes toxic to the animals and none of them destroy the eggs. Research is being carried on to find a nonpoisonous insecticide that will kill all lice and eggs in a single application. Such a dip would eliminate much of the time and labor required in using present remedies that must be applied two or three times a season to effect control. Results of recent experiments encourage the belief that such an insecticide will soon be found.

Pregnancy Disease of Sheep

BY M. S. SHAHAN [1]

NINETY PERCENT of the ewes affected by pregnancy disease die within 1 to 10 days. Although the cause of the disease is not known, it is very probably due to poor nutrition and lack of exercise during pregnancy. Hence it is largely preventable by the methods here suggested.

THE UNOBSTRUCTED DEVELOPMENT of pregnancy disease in a flock or band of pregnant ewes often leads to disastrous losses. Frequently as many as one-fourth of the group develop the disease and 9 of every 10 sick animals die, most of the lambs being lost as well as the mothers.

Although the disease is also known as preparturient paralysis, acidosis of pregnant ewes, lambing paralysis, pregnancy ketosis, pregnancy toxemia, and old ewe disease, the term "pregnancy disease" is at present generally preferred because of the primary association of the condition with pregnancy and the lack of complete scientific evidence as to its exact character. Apparently its distribution is worldwide, and no part of the United States is free from it so far as is known. The ailment is primarily one of pregnant ewes, especially those carrying twins or triplets, though occasionally those with only one lamb in the uterus are affected. Usually the ewes are in the fourth or the fifth (last) month of pregnancy when the disease occurs. The occasional occurrence of a similar disease in rams, wethers, and nonpregnant ewes has been reported (1; 4, pp. 52 and 53).[2] Other species of animals are not known to be affected.

Ewes from 3 to 6 years old appear to be more commonly affected than younger or older ewes. The condition is more common in small farm flocks than in large bands on the range. There is no generally accepted evidence that one breed is more likely to develop the disease than others, although the breeds or strains that normally produce a

[1] M. S. Shahan is Veterinarian, Pathological Division, Bureau of Animal Industry.
[2] Italic numbers in parentheses refer to Literature Cited, p. 926.

923

considerable proportion of twins and triplets may be more frequently affected, other things being equal, than breeds or strains producing single lambs predominantly.

The ailment has been observed in well-nourished as well as in poorly nourished ewes. Because of ignorance, lack of adequate facilities, or protracted inclement weather, pregnant ewes may be so closely confined that they do not get enough exercise. Often, for the same or other reasons, they are poorly or unwisely fed. Either of these conditions appears to be especially conducive to pregnancy disease.

CAUSE OF PREGNANCY DISEASE

Pregnancy, poor feeding, and lack of exercise appear to be the chief factors causing the disease. No evidence that infection plays a part has been found. Although it has been very difficult for those studying the disease to produce it experimentally, the prevailing opinion is that it is of metabolic origin (*2, 6, 7, 8, 9*), that is, it is associated with the processes by which the animal body transforms feedstuffs into tissue elements and converts complex substances in the feed into simpler ones in the production of energy.

Pregnancy in any case is a critical period for the ewe. In addition to preserving and nourishing her own body, including the fleece, through the feed she consumes, the pregnant ewe is furnishing food for the development of the unborn lamb. If there is more than one fetus, the need for minerals, proteins, carbohydrates, and the other food elements is correspondingly increased.

With the growth and development of the fetus, the tax on the mother increases. The eliminative processes, functioning to rid the body of waste materials, are often greatly impaired in the later stages of pregnancy. The accumulation of waste products, which may assume the nature of poisons or toxins, seriously affects her well-being, and consequently that of the unborn offspring. In cases of pregnancy disease, a definite acidosis, or reduction in the alkali reserves of the body, develops. This is believed to result primarily from impaired metabolism of carbohydrates and fats.

Before the development of definite, clear-cut, outward symptoms of the disease in affected ewes, primary evidences may be detectable in the blood or urine by analysis in the laboratory. These evidences consist essentially of an increase in the ketone bodies (complex acids derived from fat metabolism) and a decrease in the normal blood sugar. With the progress of the disease, these changes become more marked. The relationships of other factors in pregnancy disease have as yet not been proved.

SYMPTOMS AND POST MORTEM FINDINGS

The death of one or more ewes in a flock just before lambing time justifies suspicion of pregnancy disease. The first sign of the disease (*3, 5, 6*) may be the lagging of one or more of the ewes when the flock is being driven. An affected ewe nearly always grinds her teeth, appears dull and weak, urinates frequently, and trembles when exercised. Later, she refuses feed, drinks little water, urinates less and less often, breathes rapidly, becomes stupid or highly nervous, appears to be blind, and finally loses the power to stand, going down in a few hours or after 1 or 2 days. Animals affected with pregnancy disease often lie on the sternum (breast) with the head turned around to the side of the body, much like a cow with parturient paresis, or milk fever. They may lie in this position or flat on the side for days. Usually there is no fever. The disease lasts from 1 to 10 days, and death results in more than 90 percent of the cases. If lambing should occur, however, especially during the early stages of the disease, recovery usually follows. The lambs are likely to be weak and usually die, either from the toxic effect of the disease or because the amount of milk given by the ewe is not sufficient to sustain life.

Ewes that die of pregnancy disease almost invariably are carrying more than one fetus in the uterus. Usually the carcass contains little fat, but sometimes there is a normal or even more than normal amount, which frequently has a dull, mottled appearance. The most striking changes observed in post mortem examination are in the liver, which appears to be thickened and is of a light yellowish-brown color. Microscopically it is found to be affected by severe fatty degeneration, and chemically there is a decrease in glycogen (a form of body sugar). The kidneys also are usually pale and softened.

PREVENTION AND TREATMENT

The prevention of pregnancy disease, as of most diseases, is much more practical and economical than treatment. Fortunately, enough is known about the disease to prevent it in most cases. Of first importance is the feeding of proper rations. The principles of good feeding are outlined in A Handbook for Better Feeding of Livestock (*10*), as well as in more detailed form in the 1939 Yearbook of Agriculture, Food and Life (*11*). Throughout pregnancy, ewes that are not on good green pasture should receive a liberal allowance of clean, bright legume hay. In addition, especially during the last month or two of pregnancy, they should receive good, sound grain daily, beginning with one-fourth of a pound a day during the eighth to the sixth week before lambing, and the amount should be gradually increased to 1 pound during the fourth to the second weeks. Ewes in good condition may not require more than half a pound daily during the latter period, and very fat ewes may need little or nothing more than good pasture or a liberal supply of legume hay. With the grain ration, small quantities of molasses, pure dextrose, corn sirup, or brown sugar may be given. A constant supply of salt is necessary, and regular hours of feeding are desirable. Abrupt changes in the kind or amount of feed should not be made.

A moderate amount of exercise is essential. Ewes in good condition should have more than those that are weak and thin, but in all cases the animals should be taken some distance, at least a quarter of a mile if possible, from the bedding ground or shed for feeding. If it is impossible to provide exercise in this way because of deep snow or other conditions, some other method should be used. Rapid, forced driving, however, is not desirable, especially for thin ewes.

Treatment of advanced cases of pregnancy disease is rarely successful. Sometimes, however, recovery may be effected by the injection of certain sugar solutions into the blood stream, and such other appropriate treatments may be given as are believed by the veterinarian to be advisable. Certain glandular products have been tried experimentally, but there is not yet conclusive proof of their efficacy. Cases detected in the earliest stages by tests of the blood or urine for ketone bodies may recover if given corn syrup or some other form of dextrose, either on the feed, by stomach tube, or by injection into the blood stream.

LITERATURE CITED

(1) BRUCE, E. A.
    1919. STERCOREMIA OF SHEEP. Amer. Vet. Med. Assoc. Jour. 55 (n. s. 8):
        553–558.
(2) CAMERON, H. S., and GOSS, H.
    1940. PREPARTURIENT PARESIS IN EWES. Amer. Vet. Med. Assoc. Jour. 96:
        165–169, illus.
(3) ELDER, CECIL, and UREN, A. W.
    1940. PREGNANCY DISEASE OF SHEEP. Mo. Agr. Expt. Sta. Bul. 412, 16 pp.,
        illus.
(4) KENTUCKY AGRICULTURAL EXPERIMENT STATION.
    1922. REPORT OF THE DIRECTOR. Ky. Agr. Expt. Sta. Ann. Rpt. 35, pt. 1,
        [61] pp.
(5) MARSH, HADLEIGH.
    1929. SOME OBSCURE DISEASES OF SHEEP. Amer. Vet. Med. Assoc. Jour. 74:
        724–735.
(6) RODERICK, LEE M., and HARSHFIELD, G. S.
    1932. PREGNANCY DISEASE OF SHEEP. N. Dak. Agr. Expt. Sta. Tech. Bul. 261,
        31 pp., illus.
(7) —— HARSHFIELD, G. S., and HAWN, M. C.
    1937. THE PATHOGENESIS OF KETOSIS: PREGNANCY DISEASE OF SHEEP. Amer.
        Vet. Med. Assoc. Jour 90: 41–50.
(8) SAMPSON, J., GONZAGA, A. C., and HAYDEN, C. E.
    1933. THE KETONES OF THE BLOOD AND URINE OF THE COW AND EWE IN
        HEALTH AND DISEASE. Cornell Vet. 23: 184–207.
(9) —— and HAYDEN, C. E.
    1936. PHYSIOLOGICAL ASPECTS OF KETOSIS IN COWS AND EWES WITH SPECIAL
        REFERENCE TO CARBOHYDRATE METABOLISM. Cornell Vet. 26:
        183–199. illus.
(10) SHEETS, E. W., and JACKSON, WILLIAM, compilers.
    [1924.] A HANDBOOK FOR BETTER FEEDING OF LIVESTOCK. U. S. Dept. Agr.
        Misc. Cir. 12, 48 pp.
(11) UNITED STATES DEPARTMENT OF AGRICULTURE.
    1939. FOOD AND LIFE. U. S. Dept. Agr. Yearbook 1939, 1165 pp., illus.

Lunger Disease of Sheep

BY G. T. CREECH [1]

THE AUTHOR tells what little is known about a fatal
pneumonia that carries off range sheep in the Northwest
and cannot yet be prevented or cured.

A CHRONIC FATAL DISEASE has been known to exist among the sheep
of Montana, Oregon, and other Northwestern States for a considerable
time, the most prominent symptom of which is difficult or labored
breathing. Since this indicates that the lungs are affected, the disease
is commonly referred to by herdsmen and sheep owners as lunger
disease, and the affected animals are usually called lungers.

Marsh (4),[2] in Montana, who was among the first to make studies
of this disease, found it to be of the nature of a chronic progressive
pneumonia. He reported his findings in 1922. Later, rather extensive studies were also made by Creech and Gochenour (3), of the
Bureau of Animal Industry.

A disease very similar in character, known as jagziekte, which has
been recognized among the sheep of South Africa for many years,
has been reported by Cowdry (1) and others. Because of the striking
similarity of the lesions, or tissue injuries, of jagziekte in South Africa
and chronic progressive pneumonia in Montana, Cowdry and Marsh
(2) made joint comparative studies of the two diseases and concluded
that they were probably identical.

Chronic progressive pneumonia is unquestionably of considerable
economic importance. Marsh (4) estimated that the rate of loss from
the disease among Montana sheep ranges from 2 to 10 percent, varying
somewhat in different herds. The mortality among the animals
affected is generally believed to be 100 percent. Observations have
indicated that the losses are greater among older animals, but sheep of
all ages appear to be susceptible.

Several theories as to the cause of this type of chronic pneumonia
and jagziekte in sheep have been presented by different investigators.
In his bacteriological studies of chronic progressive pneumonia, Marsh
(5) frequently isolated a diphtheroid (a micro-organism closely re-

[1] G. T. Creech is Senior Veterinarian, Pathological Division, Bureau of Animal Industry.
[2] Italic numbers in parentheses refer to Literature Cited, p. 929.

sembling the diphtheria bacillus) and considered it a causative factor
either associated with or secondary to certain other possible predisposing factors. Robertson (*7*), who was one of the earlier investigators of jagziekte in South African sheep, believed the causative
factor in that disease was a protozoan. Mitchell (*6*) pointed to a
specific virus as the cause of jagziekte. Cowdry and Marsh (*2*), in
their later studies of the two diseases, reached the conclusion that although these chronic pneumonias, in which the lung lesions are particularly characteristic, may be due primarily to a specific cause, the
disease complex as a whole is such as might be caused by a variety of
predisposing and exciting factors operating over a period of time. In
the investigations of the disease made in the Bureau of Animal Industry (*3*), extensive bacteriological studies of the lungs of affected
sheep and various animal inoculations, or exposure tests, failed to reveal anything in the nature of a specific causative factor.

Since the disease occurs largely in range sheep, it seems rather probable that there may be certain predisposing environmental conditions,
such as the methods of handling the sheep or irritation of the lung
tissue by dust, which may make the animals more susceptible.

SYMPTOMS AND CONTROL MEASURES

Because of the insidious nature of chronic progressive pneumonia
of sheep, it is not known how long the animals may be affected before
the first clinical symptoms can be observed. The first noticeable symptom is labored breathing after exercise. As the disease progresses,
there are more rapid respiration, dilated nostrils, and flank breathing
or pumping, even while the animal is at rest. More or less coughing
and some nasal discharge have been observed in some cases. In the
late stages the affected sheep show marked weakness and emaciation,
and breathing becomes still more difficult. The disease eventually terminates in death.

No treatment for the disease is known. While there is no definite
evidence to indicate that the disease is of an infectious or contagious
nature, or that it may be transmitted from animal to animal, it would
nevertheless seem advisable when the disease appears to separate the
affected sheep from the healthy ones and, if practicable, to move the
herd to an entirely new environment. The problem of controlling the
disease by treatment or preventive measures will remain difficult of
solution until more specific information is available about its cause.

A technical description of the conditions found on post mortem
examination of sheep that have died of the disease follows.

TECHNICAL DESCRIPTION OF POST MORTEM
FINDINGS

The gross lesions found on autopsy are confined largely to the thoracic cavity. When the cavity is opened the lungs do not collapse but
fill the entire cavity, and usually more or less fluid is found. Frequently extensive pleuritic adhesions are seen, and as a result of these
fibrous proliferations the lung surface may show a constricted, or

lobulated, appearance. In advanced cases there is extensive solidification of the lung tissue, which on cross sectioning has a characteristic pale or grayish appearance, with prominence of the lung lobules. In some cases a puslike material may be forced out of the bronchi and bronchioles, and occasionally bronchial concretions are observed. The associated bronchial and mediastinal lymph glands are swollen and moist, or edematous, in appearance.

The usual histological picture is that of a chronic catarrhal pneumonia. The walls of the alveoli show infiltrations of lymphocytes and large mononuclear cells. The cellular exudate in the alveoli consists of large mononuclear cells and leucocytes occasionally mixed with red cells. The large mononuclear cells in the lumen of the alveoli are frequently swollen and vacuolated.

Scattered through the affected lung tissue frequently are accumulations of lymphocytes, or lymphoid nodules, which have been referred to as tuberclelike nodules. Such nodules are seen in the peribronchial and also in the interalveolar tissue. In the consolidated portions of the lung tissue most of the alveoli are filled either with the cellular exudate or with mucous plugs. In some cases many of the alveoli and bronchioles are filled with polymorphonuclear leucocytes.

Epithelial proliferations of the alveoli and bronchioles, which are considered characteristic of progressive pneumonia, are observed in many cases of the disease. As the disease progresses, fibrous changes in the areas involved gradually increase, and in some cases practically complete fibrosis of a considerable portion of the lung tissue may be observed in the later stages.

LITERATURE CITED

(1) Cowdry, E. V.
  1925. studies of the etiology of jagziekte. i. the primary lesions. Jour. Expt. Med. 42: 323–333, illus.
(2) ——— and Marsh, Hadleigh.
  1927. comparative pathology of south african jagziekte and montana progressive pneumonia of sheep. Jour. Expt. Med. 45: 571–585, illus.
(3) Creech, G. T., and Gochenour, W. S.
  1936. chronic progressive pneumonia of sheep, with particular reference to its etiology and transmission. Jour. Agr. Res. 52: 667–679, illus.
(4) Marsh, Hadleigh.
  1923. progressive pneumonia in sheep. Amer. Vet. Med. Assoc. Jour. 62: 458–473.
(5) ———
  1923. the bacteriology of progressive pneumonia of sheep. Amer. Vet. Med. Assoc. Jour. 64: 304–317.
(6) Mitchell, D. T.
  1915. investigations into jagziekte, or chronic catarrhal-pneumonia of sheep. Union So. Africa Dept. Agr. Dir. Res. Rpts. 3 and 4: [585]–614.
(7) Robertson, Wm.
  1904. jagziekte or chronic catarrhal pneumonia (sheep). Jour. Compar. Path. and Ther. 17: 221–224.

At the time this book went to press, the drugs
and other materials mentioned in various articles—chiefly as disinfectants, insecticides, and
anthelmintics—were still available for veterinary and medical use. Under war conditions,
however, it is possible that some of these materials may become scarce or unavailable. In
that case, the reader should obtain professional
advice from the Department of Agriculture, the
State experiment station, a local veterinarian,
or the county agent as to available substitutes.

Pullorum Disease

BY HUBERT BUNYEA [1]

HERE is the story of one of the most insidious and devastating of all poultry diseases and how it is being successfully combated by a determined drive on a national scale.

DURING THE EARLY DAYS of the present century a new poultry disease was causing much confusion. First called a fatal chick septicemia and later bacillary white diarrhea, it is now known as pullorum disease. Among the causes to which it was attributed were chilling, overheating, poor care, coccidiosis, and bacteria of indefinite types. The incubator also came in for a share of the blame. The origin of the disease was shrouded in mystery, probably because it was masked by the multitude of conditions with which it was confused. The first step toward its control came in 1900 and 1901 when Rettger [2] announced the discovery of the causative organism, *Salmonella pullorum*. Since Rettger's memorable contribution, pullorum disease has been made the subject of an enormous amount of scientific research, as attested by the 400 to 500 references to it in technical literature.

ECONOMIC IMPORTANCE

The disease is important from an economic standpoint because it injures the productivity of hens and lowers the livability of chicks. From the medical standpoint as well as the economic, it is important because the infection in the ovary, to which pullorum disease is usually confined in hens, is transmitted to some of the eggs and to the chicks hatched from these eggs. The resulting mortality among chicks is

---

[1] Hubert Bunyea is Veterinarian, Pathological Division, Bureau of Animal Industry.
[2] RETTGER, LEO F. SEPTICÆMIA AMONG YOUNG CHICKENS and SEPTICÆMIA IN YOUNG) CHICKENS N. Y. Med. Jour. 71 : 803–805, illus., and 73 : 267–268, illus. 1900 and 1901.

at times enormous. The damage is increased by the fact that chicks from healthy hens may also acquire the disease by contact with infected chicks in incubators and brooders, as well as under hens. Infected chicks are constantly voiding enormous numbers of the germs in their droppings, thereby spreading the infection.

The chicks from infected eggs may die in the shell or a short time after hatching. Some diseased chicks may survive for only 2 or 3 weeks, whereas others live to maturity and perpetuate the disease by harboring the germ in their egg organs and infecting their eggs and chicks.

Although definite statistics on the annual losses to the poultry industry in the United States from pullorum disease are not available, it is known that the disease exists in every part of the country and probably in every locality where appreciable numbers of poultry are kept. It would be impossible to estimate the cost of the disease to the industry through the death of baby chicks alone, not to mention diminished egg production in hens and pullets, reduced hatchability of eggs, and occasionally the death of hens due to generalized pullorum infection.

CAUSE, OCCURRENCE, AND SYMPTOMS

The disease is caused by the toxin-forming germ *Salmonella pullorum.* Although this germ is easily destroyed, it has been known to

FIGURE 1.—Chicks sick and dead from pullorum disease. The sick ones show such symptoms as drowsiness, depression, and drooping wings.

remain alive in soil or manure in sheltered places for many days, or even for months. The primary seat of infection is the ovary of the infected hen. Although the disease is commonly transmitted from the hen to the chick by means of the egg, not every egg laid by an infected, or carrier, hen contains the germ. Infected eggs, if hatched, are likely to produce infected chicks.

Besides occurring in chickens, pullorum disease within recent years has come to have increased importance as an infection of turkeys. It has also been observed in a few instances in ducks, sparrows, European bullfinches, pigeons, quail, geese, pheasants, bittern, peafowl,

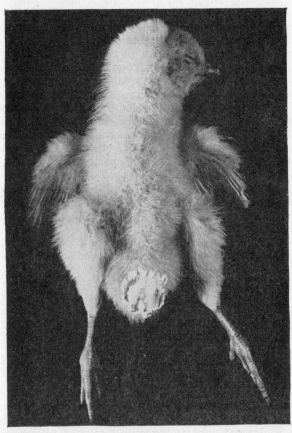

FIGURE 2.—Chick dead from pullorum disease, showing occlusion of vent with mucilaginous excreta characteristic of this disease.

goldfinches, greenfinches, green canaries, turtledoves, guinea fowl, and rabbits. Human beings and other mammals are not known to be affected.

In hens and pullets, pullorum disease is as a rule localized in the egg-making organs and produces no outward symptoms. It may, therefore, exist unsuspected in a breeder flock. In chicks the symptoms of the disease and the deaths it causes are sometimes wrongly attributed to some other cause, such as fungus pneumonia (aspergillosis), ceiling, and overheating. The description of its principal characteristics which follows furnishes some means of recognizing the presence of the disease. It is not to be assumed, however, that a definite diagnosis can be made by the symptoms alone. In order to diagnose the disease beyond question, clinical observations must be confirmed in most cases by bacteriological proof.

Pullorum disease is observed in chicks from the time of hatching until they are about 3 weeks old or older. The chicks may die suddenly after showing slight symptoms for a short time. Generally, however, they first seem disposed to huddle together or to remain too much of the time under the hen or the hover. They soon appear drowsy and indifferent to their surroundings. They stand with closed eyes and ruffled plumage, listlessly picking at their feed from time to time but apparently not eating it (fig. 1). Their droppings may be whitish, foamy, and sticky but are sometimes brownish in color; the name "bacillary white diarrhea" is in some cases an inaccurate description. Sometimes the excreta stick to the down around the vent and accumulate until they completely cover and plug the opening (fig. 2). This condition, known as "pasting up behind," unless soon relieved, will quickly cause the death of chicks. When attempting to void excrement, the sick chicks utter shrill cries of pain. Labored abdominal breathing signals the approach of death, which may come quickly or after a period of extreme prostration. The death rate in infected broods may range from 50 to 80 percent or even higher.

In baby chicks infected in the egg, symptoms and death may occur immediately after hatching or in a day or so. Chicks that contract the disease after hatching show symptoms in 6 to 8 days, or even later. Deaths may occur from the time of hatching until about 3 weeks later, when the brood may be practically exterminated.

Not all pullorum-infected chicks die young; if this were the case, the disease would be self-limiting. Unfortunately, many infected chicks survive to maturity and harbor the infection in their egg-making organs, and as a result many of their chicks die and the disease is perpetuated in at least some of those that survive. Some pullorum-infected embryos die in the shell.

POST MORTEM FINDINGS

In hens and pullets the outstanding change brought about by the disease is that seen in the ovary on post mortem examination or when the carcass is dressed. In an advanced case of pullorum infection, the partly or wholly developed yolks are angular in outline (fig. 3), shrunken, hard, and of an abnormal brownish or greenish color. Yolks containing dark fluid are sometimes seen. The presence of the germ in diseased ova can be demonstrated readily by laboratory methods. In incipient cases, the infection may exist in ovaries of apparently normal appearance.

In a chick dead from pullorum disease, the presence of noticeable changes depends somewhat on the age of the chick. Chicks 1 to 5 days old often fail to show visible internal evidences of the disease. Chicks dying at 6 days of age and upwards often have small spots of destroyed tissue, like whitish deposits, in the lungs, in the muscles of the heart, and occasionally on the outer surface of the intestines.

Early writers ascribed importance to pneumonia, ocher-colored livers, and unabsorbed yolks as evidences of the disease in chicks, but later research has shown that these symptoms occur irrespective of pullorum infection. On the other hand, the absence of any pathological changes observable on autopsy does not exclude the possibility that the disease is present. Only by bacteriological examination of the dead chick can the presence or absence of pullorum infection be definitely determined. The germs sometimes inhabit practically every organ in the chick's body, but they are most frequently sought for and recovered from the heart blood, liver. lungs, and unabsorbed portions of yolk.

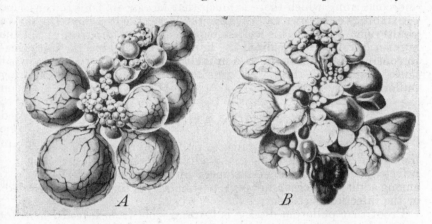

FIGURE 3.—*A*, Normal ovary of fowl; *B*, ovary affected with *Salmonella pullorum*. (After Rettger.)

The technique of demonstrating the presence of this infection in fowls of any age requires highly specialized training, as well as the use of equipment and materials not generally available outside a laboratory. It is usually possible to obtain an expert bacteriological examination of suspected cases of pullorum disease at any of the various State agricultural experiment stations.

DISSEMINATION IN INCUBATORS OR BROODERS

Pullorum disease has existed for many years in the United States, but its economic importance increased with the recent tremendous development of the hatching industry. Medical science has shown that pullorum disease is capable of spreading from infected to healthy chicks in all the various types of incubators in common use when some of the eggs hatched are from infected parent stock. The shells of infected eggs and the fluff or down which the newly hatched chicks shed may also contain the infection; hence, it often happens that the hatching of pullorum-infected eggs in an incubator results in wide-spread transmission of the disease to other chicks hatched from, uninfected eggs in the same incubator. Infected chicks will also spread the disease to healthy chicks in a brooder house. Pullorum-infected eggs will produce diseased chicks under a hen just as in an incubator;

and the disease may also spread to the healthy chicks of the brood. In the hatchery chick, however, the danger of acquiring the disease is multiplied by the fact that the eggs for hatching are frequently assembled from a number of flocks, and if one or more of these flocks harbor the disease agent, the entire output of the incubator is exposed to infection.

Through the hatchery, from which chicks are distributed over a wide territory, the disease may be disseminated over large areas and may cause enormous losses to the poultry industry. The hatcheryman therefore has a responsibility, which he has not been slow to recognize and concerning which there is much that he can do, both to conserve the stability of his own enterprise and to serve the best interests of the poultrymen on whom his success depends. Many progressive hatcherymen have already realized the importance of taking the initiative in controlling pullorum disease in their communities by requiring the flocks that supply them with eggs to be tested for the presence of pullorum disease carriers.

TRANSMISSION AMONG ADULTS

It is well known that resistance to pullorum infection increases with the age of the chick and that many adult fowls remain healthy among infected ones. Occasional instances of transmission of the disease among adult fowls occur, however, particularly if the birds are crowded or the infection is concentrated.

Proof that pullorum disease is transmissible from infected hens to normal hens or pullets was obtained in an experiment conducted by the United States Department of Agriculture. Twelve pullets free from pullorum disease were allowed to mingle for 7 months with 35 hens which were shown to be infected with the disease by their reaction to the agglutination test, described later. The two groups were then separated and mated to nonreactor cockerels. During the following 2 months the hens were trap-nested, and their eggs were saved for hatching. Bacteriological examinations of the dead embryos, the baby chicks that died within 2 weeks after hatching, and the exposed pullets showed that half the exposed pullets acquired the disease from the infected hens. Similar examination confirmed the presence of the disease in the 35 originally infected hens. Such evidence shows that under conditions of concentrated infection, pullorum disease is transmissible from infected to normal hens irrespective of the influence of the male birds.

CONTROL MEASURES

Since the invention of the mammoth incubator in recent years, poultry production has advanced to a high position in agriculture, and the hatchery industry has assumed gigantic proportions. This development has intensified the problem of pullorum disease control, one of the most serious confronting the hatchery industry. It is obvious, however, that the control of pullorum disease is not primarily an incubator problem but one of flock hygiene and that its solution in the main depends not on special appliances or procedures in the hatching of eggs or the brooding of chicks but rather on the successful diagnosis of the disease in carrier adults, so that such adults may be eliminated or excluded from breeding flocks.

No known medicinal treatment or method of vaccination is of value in the prevention or cure of pullorum disease in chicks or hens. Indeed, the very nature of the disease renders treatment both futile and undesirable. Flocks harboring the infection should not be used for breeding purposes. The fact that the cycle of infection (fig. 4)

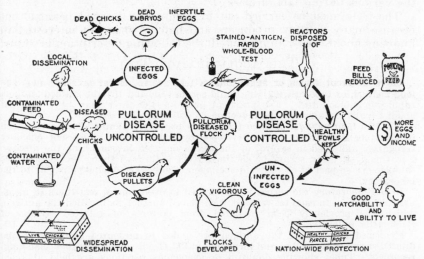

FIGURE 4.—Comparison of injurious effects of uncontrolled pullorum disease with benefits resulting from the application of the agglutination test and the disposal of reactors.

includes the diseased hen, the infected egg, the surviving infected baby chick, and the diseased pullet indicates that it is not advisable to save for breeders any chicks that have recovered from an attack of pullorum disease. Hens that harbor the infection in their ovaries are likely to lay infected eggs from which diseased chicks will be hatched. The only practicable means of controlling pullorum disease, therefore, is to detect the carrier hens and eliminate them from the breeding flock.

DIAGNOSIS

The clinical diagnosis of the carrier state in pullorum control is made difficult by reason of the fact, already noted, that the infection is usually localized in the ovary of the hen or pullet and betrays no outward evidence of its presence. In fact, the pullorum-infected hen is frequently one of the healthiest looking birds in the flock.

Two methods of detecting pullorum disease carriers have been developed, namely, the agglutination test and the intradermic, or wattle, test. Since its adaptation to diagnosis of this disease in 1913, the agglutination test has been almost universally accepted as the most satisfactory method available for the diagnosis of the infection in fowls of breeding age. Repeated comparative experimental tests have demonstrated its superiority to the intradermic test. Like most other diagnostic tests, however, it is admittedly not infallible. It has been employed in various parts of the country with such variations in technique and interpretation as to make errors inevitable in some instances. Improvement in this respect has gradually followed the standardization of test methods; and uniformity of equipment, technique, and interpretation of results is little by little being achieved in the various testing laboratories.

The tests must be carried out by technically trained persons, but because many poultry producers and hatcherymen are interested in knowing about the techniques used, the following description is given:

THE AGGLUTINATION TEST

Three different forms of agglutination test are in use at present: (1) The long method, or tube test, (2) the rapid serum test, and (3) the stained-antigen, rapid whole-blood test. For practical purposes the three may be considered about equally reliable for the detection of pullorum disease.

(1) *The long method, or tube test.* This test for pullorum disease has been in use since 1913, when it was developed by Jones.[3] It is at present officially recognized and used in several of the States engaged in combating the disease. For this test, clear serum is obtained from each fowl to be tested, and the samples are so packed as to avoid spoilage and breakage during shipment to the laboratory.

In the laboratory the serum is distributed in one or more test tubes in measured amounts. In each test tube is then placed another fluid called the antigen, which has previously been prepared from cultures of selected strains of *Salmonella pullorum.*

Measured amounts of the antigen are added to measured amounts of the diluted serum in test tubes and incubated at 37° C. Readings are then made and recorded. Tubes showing doubtful or suspicious reactions are held at room temperature for an additional 24 hours, after which the final reading is made.

Positive agglutination (fig. 5, *A*) involves the complete clearing of the fluid and the clumping of the hitherto suspended matter in the bottom of the tube. A doubtful reaction (Fig. 5, *B*) should always be reported as suspicious, and the fowl should be retested or removed from the flock. Results are negative (fig. 5, *C*) when there is no clearing and no separation of the suspended matter.

Some diagnostic laboratories modify this procedure in various ways. The test has been found to be rather expensive, and in many of the States no facilities are available for its application. The tube test was adopted in 1932 by the United States Live Stock Sanitary Association as a standard method.[4]

With a view to reducing the cost of poultry testing to the flock owner and thus placing the test within the reach of a larger part of the industry, research workers have within recent years developed rapid agglutination-test methods.

(2) *The rapid serum test.* This method of testing fowls for pullorum disease was originally described by Runnells and his associates[5] in 1927. The undiluted clear serum of the fowl to be tested is mixed with a highly concentrated antigen on a pane of glass ruled in 1-inch squares which forms the top of a box, black on the inside and illuminated by a frosted incandescent bulb within. Two squares on the glass are used for each sample of clear serum to be tested.

[3] JONES, F. S. THE VALUE OF THE MACROSCOPIC AGGLUTINATION TEST IN DETECTING FOWLS THAT ARE HARBORING BACTERIUM PULLORUM. N. Y. State Vet. Col. Rept. 1911–12, pp. 149–158. 1913. See also Jour. Med. Res. 27: 481–495. 1913.
[4] The standard tube agglutination test. REPORT OF THE CONFERENCE OF OFFICIAL RESEARCH WORKERS IN ANIMAL DISEASES. II. SEROLOGICAL DIAGNOSIS OF PULLORUM DISEASE (CARRIER CONDITION) IN MATURING AND IN ADULT BREEDING STOCK. Amer. Vet. Med. Assoc. Jour. 82: 488–490. 1933.
[5] RUNNELLS, R. A., COON, C. J., FARLEY, H., and THORP, F. AN APPLICATION OF THE RAPID-METHOD AGGLUTINATION TEST TO THE DIAGNOSIS OF BACILLARY WHITE DIARRHEA INFECTION. Amer. Vet. Med. Assoc. Jour. 70: 660–662. 1927.

Amounts of the serum used are 0.02 cubic centimenter and 0.01 cubic centimeter, respectively, and 0.02 cubic centimeter of antigen is used in each case. The two substances are mixed with a toothpick. The reaction may occur immediately or may require several minutes. A positive reaction consists in the formation of visible clumps of the bacteria suspended in the antigen and a clearing of the intervening fluid. A negative test remains uniformly cloudy without the formation of clumps. Because it requires clear serum for testing, this method is essentially a laboratory procedure, but under certain circumstances it may be made adaptable to field use.

(3) *The stained-antigen, rapid whole-blood test.* This test, which was developed by workers in the Bureau of Animal Industry,[6] is somewhat similar in its technique to the rapid serum test. Outstanding features of the rapid whole-blood test are the following:

(a) The use of a single drop of fresh whole blood immediately after it is obtained from the fowl.

(b) The use of a stained antigen, which makes reacting samples easily detectable over a white background without artificial illumination.

(c) The fact that the presence or absence of pullorum infection is immediately diagnosed in one handling of the fowl, and reactors are disposed of at the time of the test, which eliminates the necessity of rehandling or banding the fowls.

The antigen for the rapid whole-blood test is stained with an aqueous solution of crystal violet.

In applying this test a drop of blood is secured by pricking the wing vein with a sharp-pointed instrument, or in any other convenient manner. The drop of blood is picked up by the aid of a

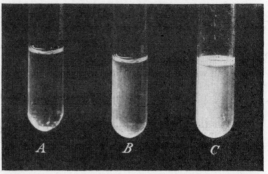

FIGURE 5.—Tube agglutination-test reactions for pullorum disease: *A*, positive reaction; *B*, suspicious or doubtful reaction; *C*, negative reaction.

loop of fine wire. A drop of stained antigen is placed on a white glass plate. A loopful of blood is taken up from the wing vein. The blood is then stirred into the antigen and the mixture spread to a diameter of about 1 inch. The loop is then rinsed in clean water and dried by touching it to a piece of clean blotting paper if necessary.

The glass plate is rocked from side to side a few times to mix the antigen and blood thoroughly and to facilitate agglutination. The reaction is usually visible in 5 seconds to 2 minutes. Slight reactions which require more than 2 minutes should be disregarded.

Various degrees of reaction are observed in this as in other agglutination tests (fig. 6). The greater the agglutinating power of the blood, the more rapid the clumping and the larger the clumps. A positive reaction (fig 6, *A*) consists in a clumping of the antigen in well-developed flocculi (separated particles) surrounded by clear spaces. This reaction is easily distinguished against a white background. A somewhat weaker reaction (fig. 6, *B*) consists of small but still clearly visible clumps of antigen surrounded by spaces only partly clear. The interpretation of these partial or suspicious reactions should be the same as that of similarly incomplete tube-method agglutination reactions. Between this point and a negative reaction (fig. 6, *D*) there sometimes occurs a very fine granulation barely visible to the naked eye (fig. 6, *C*); this should be disregarded in making a diagnosis. In a nonreactor the smear remains homogeneous. The very fine, marginal flocculation (separation of particles) which may occur just before the sample dries up is also regarded as negative.

⁶ SCHAFFER, J. M., MacDONALD, A. D., HALL, W. J., and BUNYEA, H. A STAINED ANTIGEN FOR THE RAPID WHOLE BLOOD TEST FOR PULLORUM DISEASE. Amer. Vet. Med. Assoc. Jour. 79 : 236–240. 1931.

A white glass plate has proved most satisfactory for this work. The use of the plate enables the tester to have a number of successive test mixtures under observation without delaying the work to wait for results before proceeding to the next bird. As a result of long experience in testing with this antigen, it has been decided to regard as definitely positive only those reactions

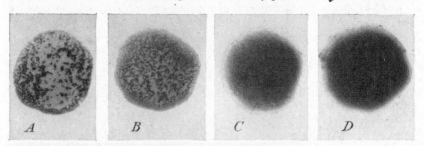

FIGURE 6.—Reactions to the stained-antigen, rapid whole-blood test: *A*, a positive reaction; *B*, a doubtful or suspicious reaction; *C*, a false, or pin-point reaction; *D*, a negative reaction.

that appear within 1 minute after mixing the antigen and blood, while those appearing within 2 minutes are regarded as suspicious.

THE INTRADERMIC TEST

This method, which was described by Ward and Gallagher [7] in 1917, consists in injecting into the dermis, or skin, of the wattle a small amount of a diagnostic agent prepared from a broth culture of *Salmonella pullorum*. The product is prepared by incubating a broth culture of *S. pullorum* for about a month, after which it is preserved by the addition of 0.5 percent of phenol and held for several weeks before use.

In applying the test, the fluid is injected slightly above the lower border of the wattle. In reacting cases an edematous, or watery swelling, of the injected wattle appears after approximately 24 hours. Although the results reported by Ward and Gallagher were in some measure discordant with the results of the agglutination test and the autopsy findings, these authors believed that the intradermic test had showed sufficient promise to warrant further extensive trial in the field in comparison with the agglutination test.

A number of investigators have at different times pursued more advanced comparative researches with this method of testing fowls for pullorum disease. None, however, have thus far been successful in developing the test to a degree of accuracy comparable to that of the agglutination-test methods.

PULLORUM DISEASE IN TURKEYS

The problem of controlling pullorum disease in turkeys has several aspects that make it different from the control problem in chickens.

The first is the behavior of the disease in turkeys. The scientific evidence now available indicates that turkey poults are very susceptible and suffer a high mortality when exposed to the disease. Such outbreaks in poults have in many instances been attributed to the fact that they were hatched in the same incubator or brooded in the same quarters with pullorum-diseased chicks. Other out-

[7] WARD, A. R., and GALLAGHER, B. A. AN INTRADERMAL TEST FOR BACTERIUM PULLORUM INFECTION IN FOWLS. U. S. Dept. Agr. Dept. Bull. 517, 15 pp. 1917.

breaks have been traced directly to pullorum infection harbored in the ovaries of breeding turkey hens.

The adult turkey may not ordinarily be a natural host for *Salmonella pullorum*. The germ has been found, however, at autopsy in turkeys that reacted to the agglutination test for pullorum disease, as well as in eggs from reacting turkeys. In a number of outbreaks of pullorum disease in turkey poults it has been found that the condition was not transmitted through the eggs from infected dams. Adult turkeys that have reacted to the test tend to become either partly or completely negative to it within a year or less, suggesting that the turkey is an unfavorable host for the infection and is therefore able to overcome it as the chicken cannot.

The stained-antigen, rapid whole-blood test was developed for the testing of chickens for pullorum disease, but within recent years the method has been used to some extent in testing adult turkeys also for this disease. The stained antigen for chickens has not been found altogether satisfactory for turkeys, however, and experiments are under way in the Bureau of Animal Industry looking to the development of a suitable stained antigen for testing turkeys. At present, the tube-agglutination test is probably the most satisfactory method.

The operation of a general blood-testing program for pullorum disease control in turkeys is beset with complicating considerations. Other germs, of both disease-producing and harmless species, are able to cause the turkey's blood to react to the pullorum disease agglutination test. The injection of certain bacterins (vaccines prepared from bacteria) may cause the bird to give a false pullorum disease reaction for as long as 1 or 2 months; hence, the pullorum disease test is very difficult to interpret in turkeys. Where evidence exists that an occasional breeding flock has become accidentally infected, however, some investigators advise that the flock be tested and the reactors removed before eggs are saved for hatching. Such incidents may largely be averted by hatching turkey eggs separately from chicken eggs in properly disinfected incubators and by brooding poults entirely apart from chicks. It seems advisable from the standpoint of a Nation-wide program of control of pullorum disease in turkeys to place the emphasis on the importance of separate hatching and separate brooding.

PULLORUM CONTROL UNDER THE NATIONAL POULTRY IMPROVEMENT PLAN

The losses from pullorum disease were so great that the need for organized efforts to control it was early recognized. By 1925 a number of the States had inaugurated programs to that end. Although much good was accomplished, it soon became apparent that the diversity of terminology and of methods would eventually lead to chaos. Leaders in the movement began to think about a properly coordinated, nationally sponsored program in which the terminology would be uniform and the objectives and procedures could be intelligently guided into definite, constructive, and mutually advantageous channels.

Numerous State, regional, and national conferences were held by members of the industry at key points, and as a result the National Poultry Improvement Plan was inaugurated July 1, 1935. The plan is administered by official State agencies in each of the voluntarily participating States in cooperation with the Bureau of Animal Industry. The aim is in part to establish a workable pullorum-control program in each State. Each State agency is responsible not only for carrying out the breeding stages of the plan but also for the systematic testing of participating flocks for pullorum disease.

Although the application of the pullorum control and eradication phase of the plan has heretofore been optional with the individual States, beginning September 1, 1943, all flocks in the plan must be officially tested for pullorum disease.

The three agglutination-test methods described are given equal recognition in the pullorum-control plan. All pullorum testing under the plan is performed by individuals properly trained and authorized by the official State agency.

The testing is done by a livestock sanitary authority, an official of the State college of agriculture, or a similarly authorized State employee. In the U. S. Pullorum-Tested and U. S. Pullorum-Controlled classes, special provisions enable the work to be done by a pullorum-testing agent who has been officially trained and authorized to do this work.

There are four pullorum-control and eradication classes: U. S. Pullorum-Tested, U. S. Pullorum-Controlled, U. S. Pullorum-Passed, and U. S. Pullorum-Clean. Tolerance of pullorum reactors in the U. S. Pullorum-Tested class in the 1941–42 testing year is required to be less than 9 percent, and this percentage is to decrease 1 percent a year until it is less than 5 percent, which will occur in the fall of 1945. Reactors must have been removed from the premises before hatching eggs may be saved. All birds over 5 months of age to be used as breeders must be tested.

In the U. S. Pullorum-Controlled class the number of reactors tolerated in the last test must be fewer than 2 percent of the flock. The test must be made within 12 months immediately preceding the date of sale of hatching eggs or chicks from such flock. All chickens over 5 months of age to be used as breeders must be tested.

In the U. S. Pullorum-Passed and the U. S. Pullorum-Clean classes, no reactors may be found in any test. In the U. S. Pullorum-Passed class, all birds 5 months of age or older must be tested within the testing year immediately preceding the date of sale of hatching eggs or chicks. In the U. S. Pullorum-Clean class, no reactors may be found in either of two consecutive tests not less than 6 months apart, the last test being made within the testing year immediately preceding the date of sale of hatching eggs or chicks. In this class all chickens over 5 months of age to be used as breeders must be tested.

The participation of the States in the various pullorum-control classes has increased each year since the inauguration of the plan, beginning with 30 States in 1935–36 and reaching a total of 44 in 1940–41. The number of birds officially tested in accordance with the provisions of the plan increased from 2,058,782 during the first year to 10,527,946 birds during the sixth year, 1940–41. During the year ended June 30, 1941, approximately three-fourths of the birds were in the U. S. Pullorum-Tested class.

Although definite chick-mortality statistics are not available, reports from the industry all over the country indicate that the hatchability of eggs is gradually improving and mortality among chicks is steadily decreasing as a result of the pullorum-control phase of the National Poultry Improvement Plan.

An individual poultryman or hatcheryman who desires to have the benefit of the pullorum test for his breeding flock or flocks may do one of several things: (1) He may become a participant in the National Poultry Improvement Plan by complying with the preliminary requirements in his State. The application for participation should be made to the official State agency of the National Poultry Improvement Plan, whose exact name and post-office address may be obtained from county agricultural agents, State agricultural extension services, State departments of agriculture, or the Bureau of Animal Industry at Washington, D. C. (2) Individuals who do not care to participate in the National Poultry Improvement Plan may have their flocks tested privately by applying to their State veterinarian or to the agricultural experiment station, which is affiliated with their State agricultural college. In many States, practicing veterinarians may be called upon for such service.

It is not advisable for persons not properly trained in the use of pullorum antigen to undertake to perform the test on their own hens or those of other persons.

Fowl Paralysis
and Other Forms of the
Avian Leukosis Complex

BY C. A. BRANDLY, NELSON F. WATERS,
AND W. J. HALL [1]

FOWL PARALYSIS is one form of a very damaging
disease complex that probably costs poultrymen in the
United States as much as all other diseases put together.
No one knows what causes it, how it spreads, or how to
control it. This article tells about a concerted drive
to discover more facts, with a view to reducing a tremendous annual loss.

The disease called fowl paralysis, together with several other allied
conditions classed together as the avian leukosis complex,[2] causes a
tremendous loss to the poultry industry. The paralysis form of
this disease complex was first recognized in the United States along
the eastern coast about 1920.

During the last 20 years the avian leukosis complex has spread
rapidly until few flocks of chickens in the United States have escaped
its ravages. Its yearly toll in this country is believed to exceed that
of any other poultry disease and it also causes great damage in other
countries of the world where the production of poultry is conducted

---

[1] C. A. Brandly is Senior Pathologist and Nelson F. Waters is Senior Geneticist, Regional
Poultry Research Laboratory, East Lansing, Mich., and W. J. Hall is Veterinarian, Beltsville Research Center, Beltsville, Md., Bureau of Animal Industry.

[2] In the avian leukosis complex may be included in addition to so-called fowl paralysis,
or range paralysis, also termed neurolymphomatosis, other forms of lymphomatosis; ocular
lymphomatosis, or iritis; visceral lymphomatosis, or big-liver disease; lymphocytoma,
myelocytoma, and leukotic tumors; osteopetrosis, or marble bone; and the leukoses—erythroleukosis, erythrosis, myeloleukosis, erythromyeloblastic or erythroblastic, and granuloblastic
leukosis, etc. These diseases or expressions of disease show differences in various features;
yet marked similarities exist among certain of their characteristics. These resemblances
are taken as a basis for a common group or name, although the knowledge of the relationship which one type or form of disease may have to another within the complex is quite
limited.

on a considerable scale. Although chickens from a few weeks old to a year of age or older may become affected, the disease usually does not appear to a great extent in flocks until after the expense of rearing has been incurred. It is partly for this reason that the disease exacts such a great financial toll. The control of the avian leukosis complex consequently is of major interest to all concerned with the poultry industry.

With the aim of finding some means to reduce losses from this disease, investigations are being actively carried out by various State and Federal workers.

TYPES AND SYMPTOMS

One of the most obvious symptoms of the avian leukosis complex is a paralyzed condition in one or more parts of a bird's body. This led early workers to call the disease fowl paralysis. Later examinations and study revealed a great variety of apparently closely related disease manifestations. Practically all the tissues, organs, and other parts of the body have been found to be involved. The numerous expressions of disease make it desirable to use the more inclusive term "avian-leukosis complex," of which paralysis, or nerve involvement, is only one type or manifestation.

The various types of the leukosis complex may be classified as (1) nerve (neural), (2) eye (ocular), (3) internal-organ (visceral), (4) bone, and (5) blood (leukosis). It should be emphasized that a bird may be affected by one or all these types at the same time. In addition, other unrelated diseases may also be present. These facts greatly complicate the already difficult task of determining the true nature of the disease or diseases present.

The various types described in the following paragraphs may be found in both males and females, and some may exist in a bird for long periods without producing any noticeable effect.

Nerve Type (Neural Lymphomatosis)

The nerve type of the disease is most familiar to the poultryman, Figure 1 shows a typical position of the legs (spraddling), which is considered characteristic. One or both legs or wings may be affected, with a resulting partial or complete paralysis of these parts. Examination of the nerves of the diseased part with the unaided eye may show great enlargement and a slight yellowish discoloration, but often the use of a microscope is necessary to detect the disease changes. The nerves of other parts of the body may also be affected, resulting in so-called sour crop, wry neck, and a general incoordination of the entire body. Partial or complete paralysis of the viscera occurs in many cases. Breathing through the mouth or difficult respiration may be observed when the vagus nerve, which serves the lungs and stomach, is involved. The length of time an affected bird may survive depends on the extent, location, and function of the nerve or nerves affected. Partially paralyzed birds have been known to live many months in individual pens with access to feed and water.

Other diseases of the fowl that produce similar or identical symptoms of paralysis may be confused with the nerve type of the avian leukosis complex. Among these are certain of the nutritional diseases, including several vitamin deficiencies, and infectious diseases, such as epidemic tremor, or avian encephalomyelitis. The fact that several other diseases may show all the gross symptoms and changes

FIGURE 1.—Typical spraddling position of the legs in neurolymphomatosis, the nerve form of fowl paralysis.

of the nerve type of the avian leukosis complex indicates the need for careful diagnosis and makes it evident that the term "fowl paralysis" refers to a symptom of disease and not a disease. A final differentiation between so-called fowl paralysis, or neurolymphomatosis, and paralysis resulting from other causes often requires microscopic and various additional laboratory examinations and procedures.

EYE TYPE (OCULAR LYMPHOMATOSIS)

The eye type is quite common and is frequently manifested in the bird by loss of color in the iris and development of gray eyes and "fishy," or bulging, eyeballs (fig. 2). Changes in the size and shape of the pupil are also commonly seen in ocular lymphomatosis. In some cases the nerves leading to the eyes are affected, with partial or complete blindness as the usual result. There is a considerable amount of variability in the time when eye disorders are manifested. They may first be observed as early as the fourth month of age, but the majority of cases occur between the fourth and twelfth months. New cases may appear, however, even after the birds are a year or more old. It should be remembered that though the iris of the eye of the adult fowl is normally pigmented, during the first few months after hatching the eye is gray or unpigmented. Thus the lack of pigment during the early period should not be confused with loss of pigment resulting from the eye type of the leukosis complex. Since the eye changes usually develop slowly, an affected hen may remain in production until almost complete blindness interferes with its obtaining feed and water.

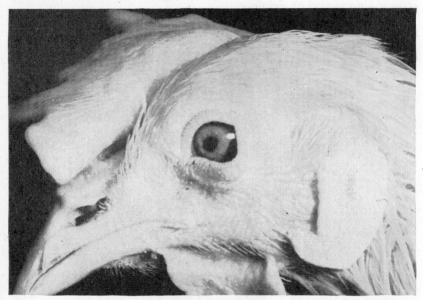

FIGURE 2.—Gray coloration of the iris and distortion of the pupil, called pearly eye and iritis, seen in ocular lymphomatosis, the eye type of fowl paralysis.

INTERNAL-ORGAN, OR VISCERAL, TYPE (VISCERAL LYMPHOMATOSIS)

Laboratory examinations indicate that all the internal organs of the bird are affected by the avian leukosis complex. The liver, lungs, heart, spleen, ovary, testicles, kidneys, intestines, skin, and in fact every tissue or organ may show disease manifestations that are part of this complex (fig. 3). All of these organs may not, however, be affected at the same time. The disease may be seen in birds from a few weeks to several years of age.

On examination the various internal organs of diseased birds frequently show gross tumorlike masses, though in some cases these "tumors" may be seen only with the aid of a microscope. An infiltration of young or immature blood cells into the liver may cause a general enlargement of this organ without a nodular, or spotted, effect. The liver may increase to several times its normal size. Livers weighing more than a pound have been found in affected birds weighing less than 4 pounds. This condition is frequently called big-liver disease. The external symptoms shown by a bird vary according to the location and extent of the disease condition. For example, when the liver is seriously affected the blood circulation and digestive system do not function normally, and the bird generally loses flesh, becoming weak and nonproductive. As in other forms of the leukosis complex and in other diseases, a diarrhea often develops either as a direct consequence or as a result of complications. Death may occur either before serious external symptoms are observed or after a long period of sickness.

Various unrelated diseases may cause symptoms identical with those shown by birds affected by the visceral type of the leukosis

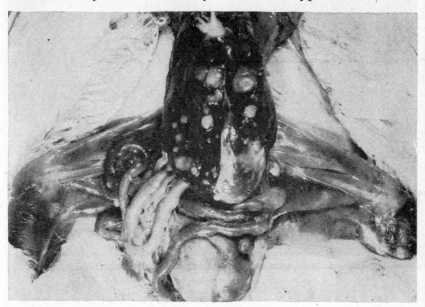

FIGURE 3.—Lymphoid tumors in the liver and intestines of a chicken, a result of visceral lymphomatosis.

complex. The lesions, or tissue injuries, of tuberculosis may be so similar that frequently differentiation can be made only by laboratory examinations. The fact that other forms of the leukosis complex, the nerve type, for example, may be seen in a flock suggests but does not prove that the organ, or visceral, type is present also.

BONE TYPE (OSTEOPETROSIS)

A bone condition (*25, 27*)[3] in which the long bones (leg and wing) are thickened and enlarged without any increase in length taking place has been found to be associated with the avian leukosis complex (fig. 4). The walls of the bone become thickened and very hard, and the amount of space normally occupied by the bone marrow is greatly diminished. In advanced cases the bone deformity of the shanks is readily noticed, and affected birds have a stilted

[3] Italic numbers in parentheses refer to Literature Cited, p. 960

or jerky gait. The scientific name of this bone condition is osteo-petrosis (literally, hardening of the bone).

FIGURE 4.—Marble bone—such enlargement of the shanks and other bones in fowls is caused by osteopetrotic lymphomatosis.

BLOOD TYPES (LEUKOSIS)

In one type of the avian leukosis complex the blood and blood-forming organs and tissues, especially the bone marrow (where blood cells are made), are affected. The blood is the direct means for carrying oxygen and nourishment to the different body tissues as well as for removing waste. Consequently, when the blood shows evidence of disease, there is a general disturbance of the body functions.

Affected birds become anemic—thin, weak, and pale. The wattles, comb, and skin may become intensely yellow. The blood is often pale and watery. In the late stages of the disease the bird is fre-quently too weak to stand, and this extreme weakness and inactivity are sometimes mistaken for paralysis.

Unlike the other types of this complex, which seldom show pro-gressive changes in the blood cells, the blood types are largely limited to alterations developing within the blood-vessel system. Alterations of the blood or blood circulation may occur which quickly endanger the life of the bird. Frequently great numbers of immature blood cells collect in the smaller blood vessels of the various organs and cause an enlargement which may resemble that in other forms of the leukosis complex. Parts of the bone marrow may be swollen and may vary in color from dark to white or chalky.

OTHER TUMORS

Various tumors, or neoplasms, of poultry are found in flocks affected with the avian leukosis complex. The tumors are often localized in muscle tissue or are attached to some part of the viscera. Little is known of their origin, and though they are frequently classed under the avian leukosis complex, there is some doubt that they are actually connected with it.

CAUSE OF THE AVIAN LEUKOSIS COMPLEX

The cause of the avian leukosis complex with all its various manifestations is not definitely known, even though a great deal of work has been done both by workers concerned with the disease because of its great economic importance to the poultry industry and by those interested in it for the information it might yield on the problem of leukemic diseases in man and other mammals. Most authorities have expressed the opinion that it is caused by a virus or a viruslike agent. The fact that the various types of the avian leukosis complex have been transmitted from bird to bird by various means under suitable conditions strongly suggest that it is of an infectious nature and may spread readily.

Present knowledge would eliminate improper nutrition as a direct cause of the avian leukosis complex. Parasites, such as coccidia and tapeworms, do not cause the disease, although they produce injury that may favor entrance of the leukosis complex agent into the body. Claims that bacteria or their products will induce the disease have not been confirmed. Neither can an unfavorable environment, with faulty ventilation or poor housing, be held responsible.

HOW IS THE DISEASE TRANSMITTED?

To the poultryman probably the most pressing question pertaining to the avian leukosis complex is that of the method of transmission, or spread, of this disease or group of diseases from bird to bird and flock to flock. Effective control measures must await further knowledge of the ways and means by which the disease is spread. Experimental work has shown that it is not difficult to transmit various forms, or types, of the disease by inoculating young birds artificially with blood or material from the organs of diseased birds. It is exceedingly difficult, however, to be sure how the disease is spread under farm and commercial conditions. Under field conditions transmission of the avian leukosis complex would appear to occur in various ways. The observation that the disease seems to have been introduced into clean flocks by hatching eggs or baby chicks from affected sources points to spread through the eggs, possibly in a manner similar to that in which pullorum disease spreads. The fact that the offspring of hens showing various forms of the disease complex sometimes develop the condition at an early age would also favor this possibility.

The fact that the avian leukosis complex has first appeared in a flock after the introduction of birds from flocks where the disease was present suggests spread by contact. Some investigators report transmission of the disease by means of feed contaminated with droppings of affected birds, whereas other workers obtained negative results in similar experiments. In general, however, the common eye, nerve, and visceral forms appear to spread more readily under ordinary conditions than the blood, or leukotic, forms. On the other hand, the leukotic forms seem to be more easily transmitted by artificial means, as, for example, by injection of the blood or organs of diseased birds (*50*).

Resistance to the avian leukosis complex increases rapidly with age, so that .special precautions against exposure during the first several months after hatching are justified. Worms, coccidia, and other parasites may lower the vitality of the birds and produce injury through which the disease agent may enter the body tissues. Transmission by mites and ticks has been suggested, and different experiments have yielded both positive and negative results.

Recent observations on the avian leukosis disease complex, as well as on leukotic diseases in other animals, also emphasize the important influence which natural or inherited differences in susceptibility may have on the spread of various infectious and parasitic diseases. Some individuals of a family, or entire families, or even strains of birds develop disease after apparently very mild exposure, whereas others do not become affected even when severely exposed. That such resistance may be greatly lowered by unfavorable conditions of housing, handling, or feeding must, however, be fully recognized.

WHAT IS KNOWN ABOUT CONTROL MEASURES

Despite the economic importance of the avian leukosis complex and the fact that it has been recognized and studied to some extent for over 20 years, adequate means of control are not known. This situation may be attributed in part to the insidious nature of the disease and in part to the lack of funds, facilities, and personnel to study the many aspects of the problem.

The poultry raiser, therefore, cannot at present rely on any definite practical control measures as a protection against serious and recurring losses from the avian leukosis complex. There are, however, two methods, namely, sanitation and breeding, either or both of which hold some promise of being effective.

IMPORTANCE OF SANITATION

Sanitation and hygiene are the keystones of successful management of poultry flocks. Better management is sorely needed on the vast majority of farms where poultry are kept. Poultry will be more thrifty, and consequently more profitable, if they are fed a complete diet and housed and yarded in clean, sanitary quarters.

Furthermore, where clean quarters are provided, there will be less chance of exposure to disease agents. Poultry raisers who foster disease through continued neglect and mismanagement not only jeopardize their own interests but maintain a menace to the flocks of those who have adopted sanitary practices.

Sanitation assumes a major role in the transfer of stock from farm to farm and from State to State. The enormous exchange in breeding stock, hatching eggs, baby chicks, and live market poultry provides an excellent opportunity for dissemination of disease. Specific management recommendations, though admittedly inadequate in controlling the avian leukosis complex, suggest the adoption of quarantine measures and a minimum exchange of poultry stock.

Distributors of poultry, in any form, must realize that they are handling an animal that is susceptible to a large number of diseases, many of which are infectious and highly contagious. They must see the problem of disease dissemination as it now exists and by united effort attempt to solve it.

Breeding Methods Offer Promise

Careful breeding procedures hold some promise of eventually reducing the incidence of the avian leukosis complex. This may come about in two ways, by mating birds that have the proper hereditary resistant factors and by selecting parents that will not indirectly or by way of the egg transmit the disease to their progeny. Both of these possibilities are supported by sufficient evidence to warrant exhaustive study. Roberts and Card (*47*), reporting on data obtained over a 10-year period on more than 29,000 birds, present evidence that heredity is an important factor in resistance and susceptibility to pullorum disease. Lambert and Knox (*31*) have demonstrated that five generations of selective breeding decreased the mortality from fowl typhoid from 85 to 10 percent. Gildow et al. (*18, 19*) reported a reduction of fowl paralysis at the Idaho Experiment Station flock by selective breeding. Marble (*37*) gives data indicating a 50-percent decrease in mortality over a 5-year period when selective breeding was practiced.

Asmundson and Biely (*2*) indicated that there are inherited differences in susceptibility and resistance to fowl paralysis. Patterson and associates (*45*) stated that decided strain differences were found in birds susceptible or resistant to paralysis. These experiments and many others (*3, 10, 11, 32, 36, 57*) with both fowls and mammals indicate that resistance or susceptibility to disease has a genetic basis. It should be emphasized, however, that the absence of disease manifestations does not necessarily indicate genetic resistance, since individual birds or all progeny of certain parents may not have been exposed at all. Such conclusions are warranted only when an adequate number of inoculated controls are available for comparison. It is entirely possible, also, that acquired immunity may account for the failure of many individuals to show manifestations of the disease.

That the egg is a means of pullorum disease transmission has been fully established, and the possibility that the avian leukosis complex may be transmitted in a like manner should not be overlooked. It is recommended that breeding flocks be closed to unrelated birds. The closing of flocks to outside breeding should be practiced more widely than it is. Whenever unproved birds are introduced into a flock, there is great danger of bringing in not only the avian leukosis complex but many other diseases. From a strictly genetic standpoint, uniformity for almost any character will be difficult to attain if birds from new sources are consistently introduced into the breeding pens. The average breeder is reluctant to return to the same source for breeding stock year after year because of the prevalent belief that new blood must be introduced frequently to obtain the best results. This is certainly a misconception on the part of any breeder when large numbers of birds are involved. Marble (*37*) demonstrated the possibility of reducing losses from disease by using proved blood lines and closing the flocks to outside breeding. Many of the most successful breeders in the United States have maintained closed flocks for years with no loss in either reproductive ability or general health.

The use of older birds for breeding purposes would appear to have some advantage in that they have at least proved their ability to live for a long time. This procedure would be of little value, however, if the hen were a carrier able to transmit the disease to her progeny. Possibly the better recommendation would be to use hens from families showing high viability, or livability, or from hens that have produced progeny showing high viability.

No Treatment Known

Specific agents or measures for the prevention or treatment of the avian leukosis complex are not known. No feed, vaccine, drug, combination of drugs, or other agent has been found to be of value for the control of this group of diseases. The claim that wheat-germ oil would prevent and cure the nerve type of the leukosis complex has not been confirmed by investigations carried out at a number of experiment stations. Consequently, any claims for direct or specific benefits from medicinal, biological, or other agents or products against the avian leukosis complex must be regarded with extreme caution.

HISTORY AND OCCURRENCE

A form of transmissible avian leukosis was described by Ellermann and Bang (*7*) as early as 1908. In 1907 Marek (*38*), in Austria, first described a disease in chickens which he called polyneuritis and which is now known as neural lymphomatosis or neurolymphomatosis— the so-called fowl paralysis. The same disease was apparently first described in America by Kaupp in 1921 (*28*). It was subsequently reported from Holland by Van der Walle and Winkler-Junius in 1924 (*55*); from England by Galloway in 1929 (*16*); from Germany by Seifried in 1930 (*49*); and from Japan by Emoto and Miyamoto in 1930 (*8*). Today there is evidence that the avian leukosis complex is widespread throughout the world and that the disease is a serious problem in all areas where the practices of the modern poultry industry (large-scale hatching and distribution) are followed.

Chickens are most commonly and seriously affected by the avian leukosis complex. The disease has been reported also in turkeys, guinea fowl, pheasants, and various ornamental birds. Transmission from one species to another seems to occur rarely, if ever. The first 2 to 3 months of life appear to be the period of greatest susceptibility, although exposure to artificial inoculation indicates marked variation in susceptibility among older stock. Great variations, from several days to many months, are observed in the period of incubation (the time from exposure until symptoms or disease changes appear) as well as in the course or duration of the disease, even in the relatively rapidly developing leukoses. In some flocks only a few birds may show signs of the disease, whereas in other flocks a high proportion become affected. Few of the visibly affected individuals recover.

Differences in susceptibility, as determined by the number of affected birds and the time of development of the avian leukosis complex, have been observed among breeds as well as within strains and among families of a breed.

That there are significant sex differences in susceptibility to the avian leukosis complex has not been fully demonstrated.

SCIENTIFIC INVESTIGATIONS

Scientific study and research dealing with the avian leukosis complex began with the finding of so-called Marek's disease or fowl paralysis in 1907 (*38*) and of a transmissible leukosis by Ellermann and Bang in 1908 (*7*). As already pointed out, the leukosis complex in its various forms was recognized as a major enemy of poultry in various countries before 1930. The malady has attracted the interest and enlisted the energies of many research workers, both abroad and in this country. Progress in the attack on the perplexing problem has, however, been slow and somewhat discouraging.

Observations on various aspects of the problem made by workers in Europe, the United States, and Canada, and other countries have been largely in agreement. The earlier investigations of the avian leukosis complex in this country were directed chiefly toward study of the nature of the disease and its transmission or spread. Schmeisser (*48*) in 1915 reported artificial transmission of a case of myeloid leukosis to about half the chickens inoculated. May, Tittsler, and Goodner (*39*) gave a preliminary report of field and laboratory findings in so-called fowl paralysis. Doyle (*4, 5*), in spite of negative transmission experiments, suggested the infectious nature of the disease, as well as a relationship between the nerve and eye types. He indicated that the disease was spread by the introduction of stock and through the egg. Pappenheimer and coworkers (*42, 43, 44*) in extensive studies clarified various features of so-called fowl paralysis. They proposed the term "neurolymphomatosis gallinarum" and recognized an apparent relationship between lymphomatosis lesions in the nerves and in other tissues. The disease was transmitted by injection with diseased nerves. No relation was found between paralysis and infestation with coccidia and intestinal worms. Patterson and associates (*45*) presented evidence of the spread of the avian leukosis complex by means of manure and contaminated litter. Work at other stations (Ohio (*29*), Idaho (*18, 19*), South Carolina (*1*), Illinois (*54*), and Connecticut (*26*)) tended to confirm this observation. Ratcliffe and Stubbs (*46*) failed to transmit leukosis by mosquitoes and mites. Johnson (*24*) concluded that mites could carry the disease from affected to healthy birds and that it might be mechanically transmitted during the process of vaccination against fowl pox.

The work of Furth (*12, 13, 14*), Furth and Breedis (*15*), Stubbs (*51*), and Stubbs and Furth (*52, 53*), dealing with various manifestations of the disease grouped as the avian leukosis complex, indicated differences among strains of the agent or agents causing leukosis, as well as between the agents responsible for leukosis and lymphomatosis. This view was supported by the findings of Feldman and Olson (*9, 10*), Olson (*40, 41*), Fenstermacher (*11*), and Jungherr (*25, 26, 27*). The Iowa workers (Patterson and associates (*45*), Lee and associates (*33, 34*)), as well as Johnson (*22, 23*), hold the view that all manifestations of the avian leukosis complex are associated with a common causative agent. Wilcke and coworkers (*58*) found that cod-liver oil, yeast, green feed, iodine, and various ratios and amounts of calcium and phosphorus had no effect on the incidence or course of the disease.

Observations on the influence of heredity on susceptibility and resistance to the avian leukosis complex have already been alluded to. This phase of the problem is now receiving much attention.

The recent work of Durant and McDougle (*6*) suggests the importance of egg transmission and the almost continuous infectivity of the blood of chicks from clinically affected dams. Lee reported in 1940 [4] that affected hens apparently are much more likely to transmit the disease through the egg than are diseased males. Gibbs (*17*), Kirschbaum and Stern (*30*), Hall and associates (*20*), and Brandly and Cottral [5] were able to induce manifestations of the avian leukosis complex by inoculating incubating chick embryos or their membranes with the blood, tissues, and extracts of diseased birds.

Though the findings of these and other investigations have added materially to the information on the disease or diseases designated as the avian leukosis complex, it is clear that much additional information is desirable and necessary. Some of the lack of agreement in work and opinions may be ascribed to difficulties peculiar to the study of diseases with long incubation or developmental periods, irregular manifestations, and undetermined causes. Likewise, studies with hosts or birds of unknown genetic background magnify the difficulties. These problems obviously demand a more comprehensive and coordinated program supported by proper facilities and suitable personnel if they are to be successfully attacked.

---

[4] In a paper presented at seventy-sixth annual meeting of the American Veterinary Medical Association
[5] Unpublished data, 1940

A Coordinated Program of Research Begun

In view of the seriousness of the poultry-disease situation as represented by the avian leukosis complex and various other conditions, recommendations were drawn up during 1937 in a conference of 25 directors of experiment stations in the North Central and Northeastern States. The Secretary of the United States Department of Agriculture was subsequently petitioned to establish a regional laboratory for the improvement of viability in poultry. The Regional Poultry Research Laboratory was approved and was established at East Lansing, Mich., March 25, 1938. Its work is done in close and active cooperation with that in each of the 25 North Central and Northeastern States and that of the Animal Disease Station, Beltsville, Md., where investigation of this disease has been carried on for several years. In this research program, experiment station workers and the Regional Poultry Research Laboratory staff are collaborating in the investigation of various ways and means for the control of the avian leukosis complex. Such collaboration will eliminate needless duplication of effort and at the same time provide the laboratory with active and advisory assistance.

Of the 31 State experiment stations in the United States which have undertaken studies of the avian leukosis complex, 21 are in the group of States designated as the major region of the Regional Poultry Research Laboratory program. Besides these experiment stations, numerous other institutions in various States are investigating the avian leukosis complex particularly as it relates to leukemia and similar conditions found in other species, including man.

At the present time, 10 States within the major region have cooperative projects with the Laboratory. These States are conducting work either in combination or separately on various phases of pathology, breeding, and nutrition.

Investigations Under Way

The work project of the regional program has four aspects: Genetic and physiologic, management, nutritional, and pathologic. Because there are neither funds nor facilities available to undertake at the start all the phases of the research that need attention, the genetics and physiology and the pathology (the study of the nature of the disease itself) will receive first attention.

The Genetic Approach

A genetic approach to this problem calls for the formation of families inherently resistant or susceptible to fowl leukosis and possessing to a marked degree characters of general economic value (*56*). Though susceptible families would be of little economc importance, their genetic value would be great, for without such lines the mode of inheritance of resistance and the influence of the environment would be difficult to determine. In addition, susceptible noncarrier stocks are necessary for pathologic studies, including epizoology (the study of the disease as an epidemic among animals), immunization, and various nongenetic control methods.

Careful consideration was given to the selection of birds to be used for experimental purposes at the Regional Laboratory. A survey of breeding stock in the United States indicated that it was possible to obtain from widely separated geographic regions many strains of Single Comb White Leghorns about the viability and production of which much was known. The White Leghorn was therefore selected as the most suitable material for the research on fowl paralysis.

In the spring of 1939, more than 1,000 hatching eggs were introduced from each of 10 different White Leghorn flocks. Upon hatching, the chicks were divided into two groups. One group, unexposed to the avian leukosis complex, used as a control, was confined in strictly quarantine houses on the west, or control, side of the plant. The other group was subdivided into an inoculated group and a noninoculated, pen-contact group, which was confined in the same pens with the inoculated chicks and quarantined in similar houses on the east, or infection, side or unit of the plant. All the chicks, except those from one flock which were subsequently discarded, were of known ancestry. This fact permitted a distribution of chicks from the same dam to both control and inoculated groups. The inoculated birds were to provide an estimate of the resistance or susceptibility of their unexposed sibs (sisters and brothers).

Only birds from the noninoculated control units were to be used for breeding purposes. It was decided to close the entire flock to all outside breeding and to attempt a breeding program which would as quickly as possible segregate the birds with the greatest number of desirable characters and those with the fewest. In a breeding experiment with a closed flock, no inherited trait can be incorporated into a group of birds, except for possible mutations unless the genes exist in the original foundation stock. This emphasizes the importance of starting with suitable material.

One of the main objectives of the breeding program is to segregate birds resistant or susceptible to fowl paralysis as quickly as possible while sacrificing valuable economic characters as little as possible. On the basis of incomplete family performance, therefore, birds of the original 1939 population within families showing the most resistance and those within families showing the most susceptibility were mated to obtain a 1940 population. The chicks hatched in 1940 were divided into inoculated and control groups as in the case of the 1939 population.

Pathology Phase

The pathology program includes studies planned or under way on methods of diagnosis, both before and after the appearance of symptoms; possible means of detecting carriers; means of transmission, including the role that parasites, bacteria, and other agents may play; the nature, properties, and tissue distribution of the causative agent or agents; embryo and chick susceptibility; the mechanism of acquired immunity; and the development and improvement of experimental methods and procedures for the study of the avian leukosis complex.

The initial study at the Laboratory was projected jointly toward a study of the susceptibility and resistance of the 10 strains of chickens on the one hand, and on the other, of the properties of several strains or causative agents of the avian leukosis complex.

Extensive examination of all the birds that developed disease during the course of the experimental work was recognized as necessary in order to make accurate diagnoses. The data collected from the examinations indicate the nature and distribution of the lesions. The value of such information from the practical as well as the experimental standpoint is apparent.

The fact that a very high percentage of birds less than 3 weeks of age (approximately 1,700) inoculated in April and May 1939 with lymphomatosis material from two different sources developed the disease is not particularly significant. Under the conditions that prevailed, however, the occurrence of the disease among each of the 10 strains of the uninoculated, or control, population would tend to incriminate egg transmission of the avian leukosis complex as important. In this connection it is pointed out that only hatching eggs representing the 10 different strains were brought onto the Laboratory premises. Live poultry and other birds as well as animals and human beings, from the outside were excluded. Furthermore, all buildings were under quarantine, and strict sanitary precautions were followed. The caretakers were limited to the separate units and required to change clothing and footwear before going from one unit to another, and other rigid quarantine measures were observed. Complete confinement of all birds has been practiced since the beginning of the experiment. Despite all these precautions, cases of the avian leukosis complex began to appear among birds in the west or control unit of the Laboratory as early as 40 days after the first hatching of eggs from the original 10 strains of White Leghorns. The disease did not appear any earlier in the birds in the east or infection unit, even though approximately two-thirds of the latter stock were inoculated at an early age with the blood of birds showing disease changes characteristic of some form of the avian leukosis complex. Furthermore, the mortality from the avian leukosis complex among the 1939 population was not significantly less in the birds in the control unit than in the birds reared in contact with the inoculated stock.

The results obtained, under strict quarantine and sanitary measures, may be regarded as satisfactory despite the appearance of the avian leukosis complex among the control birds, because no other diseases or parasites, with the exception of sporadic cases of coccidiosis, have been found on the premises. The first outbreak of coccidiosis, in several houses and among both controls and inoculated birds, occurred in November 1939, 8 months after the work was started. The manner in which coccidiosis first appeared suggests contamination by way of feed or litter, or both.

In serial-passage [6] experiments, the inoculation of different groups of chicks with lymphomatotic material from widely separated sources

---

[6] Serial passage is passage of the disease from bird to bird by artificial inoculation of a healthy chick with tissues from an individual affected with the disease.

has consistently reproduced both nerve and visceral types of the disease. One of these strains of inoculum has associated with it the bone changes termed "osteopetrosis." The bone changes have been seen in about half the chicks inoculated with that particular strain, or agent. Furthermore, when the material was inoculated into incubating eggs, the resulting chicks showed about the same percentage of bone changes as the birds inoculated after hatching. Osteopetrosis has not been seen in uninoculated birds kept continuously in the same pens with affected individuals for long periods. Another of the strains of material used for inoculation in the serial-passage work has induced a high percentage of blood, or leukosis, cases. In the serial-passage experiments with strains showing osteopetrosis and leukosis, respectively, the nerve and visceral forms of the disease were also manifested. This might be accepted as proof of the capacity of a particular strain to induce all manifestations and types of the disease complex if it were not for the development of similar numbers of cases of nerve and visceral types of the disease in uninjected control birds.

These observations do not clarify the question whether all types of disease classed within the avian leukosis complex are due to one causative agent or whether each type or a combination of types is caused by a separate and distinct agent. The observations on the source, or strain, of the material used for inoculation do, however, emphasize clearly that progress on this entire problem will depend to a large extent on securing disease-free stock for experimental purposes. In order to identify the agent or agents causing the avian leukosis complex and to measure the resistance or susceptibility of birds, there must be reasonable assurance that the disease has not been introduced either by way of the egg or by any other means. This phase of the problem, therefore, is being studied intensively.

Other Phases of the Investigation

Many other phases of the problem presented by the avian leukosis complex have been outlined as a part of the long-time laboratory program. Some work that has been outlined cannot be undertaken at present because of lack of facilities and personnel. Other parts of the program must await the results of investigations under way in other branches of science before they can be approached properly and to the best advantage.

Poultry management factors that demand study and clarification include (1) the value of sanitary procedures and (2) the time required for the infection present in contaminated areas and premises to die out.

Nutritional aspects of the problem to be studied embrace the effect of diet on the incidence of the avian-leukosis complex in stock of known genetic background.

LITERATURE CITED

(1) ANDERSON, G. W., RINGROSE, R. C., and MORGAN, C. L.
1937. A STUDY OF SO-CALLED FOWL PARALYSIS. S. C. Agr. Expt. Sta. Ann. Rpt. 50: 73.

(2) ASMUNDSON, V. S., and BIELY, JACOB.
1932. INHERITANCE OF RESISTANCE TO FOWL PARALYSIS (NEUROLYMPHOMATOSIS GALLINARUM). I. DIFFERENCES IN SUSCEPTIBILITY. Canad. Jour. Res. 6: 171–176.

(3) BIELY, JACOB, PALMER, ELVIRA, and ASMUNDSON, V. S.
1932. INHERITANCE OF RESISTANCE TO FOWL PARALYSIS (NEUROLYMPHOMATOSIS GALLINARUM). II. ON A SIGNIFICANT DIFFERENCE IN THE INCIDENCE OF FOWL PARALYSIS IN TWO GROUPS OF CHICKS. Canad. Jour. Res. 6: 374–380, illus.

(4) DOYLE, L. P.
1926. NEURITIS IN CHICKENS. Amer. Vet. Med. Assoc. Jour. 68: 622–630, illus.

(5) ——
1928. NEURITIS OR PARALYSIS IN CHICKENS. Amer. Vet. Med. Assoc. Jour. 72: 585–587.

(6) DURANT, A. J., and McDOUGLE, H. C.
1939. STUDIES ON THE ORIGIN AND TRANSMISSION OF FOWL PARALYSIS (NEUROLYMPHOMATOSIS) BY BLOOD INOCULATION. Mo. Agr. Expt. Sta. Res. Bul. 304, 23 pp., illus.

(7) ELLERMANN, V., and BANG, O.
1908. EXPERIMENTELLE LEUKÄMIE BEI HUHNERN. Centbl. f. Bakt. [etc.] Originale (I) 46: 595–609, illus.

(8) EMOTO, O., and MIYAMOTO, K.
1930. STUDIES ON THE FOWL PARALYSIS. Jap. Soc. Vet. Sci. Jour. 9: 309–325, illus.

(9) FELDMAN, WILLIAM H., and OLSON, CARL, JR.
1933. THE PATHOLOGY OF SPONTANEOUS LEUKOSIS OF CHICKENS. Amer. Vet. Med. Assoc. Jour. 82: 875–900, illus.

(10) —— and OLSON, CARL, JR.
1934. LEUKOSIS OF THE COMMON CHICKEN. Amer. Vet. Med. Assoc. Jour. 84: 488–498.

(11) FENSTERMACHER, R.
1936. LYMPHOCYTOMA AND FOWL PARALYSIS. Amer. Vet. Med. Assoc. Jour. 88: 600–613.

(12) FURTH, J.
1931. ERYTHROLEUKOSIS AND THE ANEMIAS OF THE FOWL. Arch. Path. 12: 1–30, illus.

(13) ——
1933 LYMPHOMATOSIS, MYELOMATOSIS, AND ENDOTHELIONA OF CHICKENS CAUSED BY A FILTERABLE AGENT. I. TRANSMISSION EXPERIMENTS. Jour. Expt. Med. 58: 253–275.

(14) ——
1936. THE RELATION OF LEUKOSIS TO SARCOMA OF CHICKENS. II. MIXED OSTEOCHONDROSARCOMA AND LYMPHOMATOSIS (STRAIN 12). Jour. Expt. Med. 63: 127–143, illus. III. SARCOMATA OF STRAINS 11 AND 15 AND THEIR RELATION TO LEUKOSIS. Jour. Expt. Med. 63: 145–155, illus.

(15) —— and BREEDIS, CHARLES.
1935. LYMPHOMATOSIS IN RELATION TO FOWL PARALYSIS. Arch. Path. 20: 379–428, illus.

(16) GALLOWAY, A. I.
1929. DISCUSSION ON ENCEPHALO-MYELITIS OF MAN AND ANIMALS. Joint Discuss. No. 8, Roy. Soc. Med. Proc. 22: 1167–1171.

(17) GIBBS, CHARLES S.
1936. OBSERVATIONS AND EXPERIMENTS WITH NEUROLYMPHOMATOSIS AND THE LEUKOTIC DISEASES. Mass. Agr. Expt. Sta. Bull. 337, 31 pp., illus.

(18) GILDOW, E. M., WILLIAMS, J. K., and LAMPMAN, C. E.
1936. THE TRANSMISSION OF FOWL PARALYSIS (LYMPHOMATOSIS). Poultry Sci. 15: 244–248.
(19) ——— WILLIAMS, J. K., and LAMPMAN, C. E.
1940. THE TRANSMISSION OF AND RESISTANCE TO FOWL PARALYSIS (LYMPHOMATOSIS). Idaho. Agr. Expt. Sta. Bul. 235, 22 pp., illus.
(20) HALL, W. J., BEAN, C. W., and POLLARD, MORRIS.
1940. PRELIMINARY REPORT ON THE PROPAGATION OF THE FOWL-LEUCOSIS VIRUS ON CHICK EMBRYOS BY INTRAVENOUS INOCULATION. Amer. Vet. Med. Assoc. Jour. 97: 247.
(21) HAMILTON, C. M., and SAWYER, C. E.
1939. TRANSMISSION OF ERYTHROLEUKOSIS IN YOUNG CHICKENS. Poultry Sci. 18: 388–393.
(22) JOHNSON, E. P.
1932. A STUDY OF LYMPHOMATOSIS OF FOWLS (FOWL PARALYSIS). Va. Agr. Expt. Sta. Tech. Bull. 44, 22 pp., illus.
(23) ———
1934. THE ETIOLOGY AND HISTOGENESIS OF LEUCOSIS AND LYMPHOMATOSIS OF FOWLS. Va. Agr. Expt. Sta. Tech. Bul. 56, 32 pp., illus.
(24) ———
1937. TRANSMISSION OF FOWL LEUKOSIS. Poultry Sci. 16: 255–260.
(25) JUNGHERR, ERWIN.
1935. THE ETIOLOGIC AND DIAGNOSTIC ASPECTS OF THE FOWL PARALYSIS PROBLEM. Amer. Vet. Med. Assoc. Jour. 86: 424–432, illus.
(26) ———
1937. STUDIES ON FOWL PARALYSIS. 2. TRANSMISSION EXPERIMENTS. Conn. (Storrs) Agr. Expt. Sta. Bul. 218, 47 pp., illus.
(27) ——— and LANDAUER, W.
1938. STUDIES ON FOWL PARALYSIS. 3. A CONDITION RESEMBLING OSTEOPETROSIS (MARBLE BONE) IN THE COMMON FOWL. Conn. (Storrs) Agr. Expt. Sta. Bul. 222, 34 pp., illus.
(28) KAUPP, B. F.
1921. PARALYSIS OF THE DOMESTIC FOWL. Amer. Assoc. Instr. and Invest. Poultry Husb. Jour. 7: 25–31, illus.
(29) KENNARD, D. C., and CHAMBERLIN, V. D.
1934. PULLET MORTALITY. Ohio Agr. Expt. Sta. Bimo. Bul. 19ˑ (169): 137–142, illus.
(30) KIRSCHBAUM, ARTHUR, and STERN, KURT G.
1940. LEUKEMIA IN THE FOWL FOLLOWING INOCULATION OF NON-CELLULAR AGENT OBTAINED BY ULTRACENTRIFUGATION OF LEUKEMIC BONE MARROW EXTRACT AND PLASMA. Anat. Rec. 76, Sup. 2 (Abstracts of papers), p. 37.
(31) LAMBERT, W. V., and KNOX, C. W.
1932. SELECTION FOR RESISTANCE TO FOWL-TYPHOID IN THE CHICKEN WITH REFERENCE TO ITS INHERITANCE. Iowa Agr. Expt. Sta. Res. Bul. 153: 261–295, illus.
(32) LAMPMAN, C. E.
1937. FLOCKS ESTABLISH RESISTANCE TO FOWL PARALYSIS. Idaho Agr. Expt. Sta. Ann. Rpt. 1936 (Bul. 221): 43–44.
(33) LEE, C. D., WILCKE, H. L., MURRAY, CHAS., and HENDERSON, E. W.
1937. FOWL LEUCOSIS. Amer. Vet. Med. Assoc. Jour. 91: 146–162.
(34) ——— WILCKE, H. L., MURRAY, CHAS., and HENDERSON, E. W.
1937. FOWL LEUKOSIS. Jour. Infect. Dis. 61: [1]–20.
(35) McCLARY, C. F., and UPP, CHAS. W.
1939. IS PARALYSIS OF FOWLS, AS MANIFESTED BY IRITIS, TRANSMITTED THROUGH THE EGG? Poultry Sci. 18: 210–219, illus.
(36) MADSEN, D. E.
1937. THE EFFECT OF IRITIS OF BREEDING HENS ON THEIR PROGENY. Poultry Sci. 16: 393–397.
(37) MARBLE, D. R.
1939. BREEDING POULTRY FOR VIABILITY. Pa. Agr. Expt. Sta. Bul. 377, 38 pp., illus.

(38) MAREK, J.
 1907. MULTIPLE NERVENENTZÜNDUNG (POLYNEURITIS) BEI HÜHNERN. Deut. Tierärztl. Wchnsch. 15: [417]–421, illus.
(39) MAY, HENRY G., TITTSLER, RALPH P., and GOODNER, KENNETH.
 1925. FIELD OBSERVATIONS AND LABORATORY FINDINGS IN PARALYSIS OF THE DOMESTIC FOWL. R. I. Expt. Sta. Bul. 202, 18 pp., illus.
(40) OLSON, CARL, JR.
 1936. A STUDY OF TRANSMISSIBLE FOWL LEUKOSIS. Amer. Vet. Med. Assoc.
(41) —— Jour. 89: 681–705, illus.
 1940. TRANSMISSIBLE FOWL LEUKOSIS. A REVIEW OF THE LITERATURE. Mass. Agr. Expt. Sta. Bul. 370, 48 pp.
(42) PAPPENHEIMER, ALVIN M., DUNN, LESLIE C., and CONE, VERNON.
 1926. A STUDY OF FOWL PARALYSIS (NEUROLYMPHOMATOSIS GALLINARUM). Conn. (Storrs) Agr. Expt. Sta. Bul. 143, pp. 183–290, illus.
(43) —— DUNN, LESLIE C., and CONE, VERNON.
 1929. STUDIES ON FOWL PARALYSIS (NEUROLYMPHOMATOSIS GALLINARUM). I. CLINICAL FEATURES AND PATHOLOGY. Jour. Expt. Med. 49: 63–86, illus.
(44) —— DUNN, LESLIE C., and SEIDLIN, S. M.
 1929. STUDIES ON FOWL PARALYSIS (NEUROLYMPHOMATOSIS GALLINARUM). II. TRANSMISSION EXPERIMENTS. Jour. Expt. Med. 49: 87–102.
(45) PATTERSON, F. D., WILCKE, H. L., MURRAY, CHAS., and HENDERSON, E. W.
 1932. SO-CALLED RANGE PARALYSIS OF CHICKENS. Amer. Vet. Med. Assoc. Jour. 81: 747–767, illus.
(46) RATCLIFFE, HERBERT L., and STUBBS, E. L.
 1935. ATTEMPTS TO TRANSMIT CHICKEN LEUKOSIS BY MOSQUITOES AND BY MITES. Jour. Infect. Dis. 56: [301]–304.
(47) ROBERTS, ELMER, and CARD, L. E.
 1935. INHERITANCE OF RESISTANCE TO BACTERIAL INFECTION IN ANIMALS. Ill. Agr. Expt. Sta. Bul. 419: 465–493, illus.
(48) SCHMEISSER, HARRY C.
 1915. SPONTANEOUS AND EXPERIMENTAL LEUKEMIA OF THE FOWL. Jour. Expt. Med. 22: 820–838.
(49) SEIFRIED, OSKAR.
 1930. INFEKTIÖSE PARALYSE BEI HÜHNERN. Arch. f. Wiss. u. Prakt. Tier-heilk. 62: [209]–222, illus.
(50) STUBBS, E. L.
 1933. THE RELATION OF AGE, BREED, AND SPECIES TO SUSCEPTIBILITY TO TRANSMISSIBLE LEUCOSIS OF CHICKENS. Jour. Amer. Vet. Med. Assoc. 82: 232–242.
(51) ——
 1938. FOWL LEUKOSIS. Amer. Vet. Med. Assoc. Jour. 92: 73–82.
(52) —— and FURTH, J.
 1931. TRANSMISSION EXPERIMENTS WITH LEUCOSIS OF FOWLS. Jour. Expt. Med. 53: 269–276.
(53) —— and FURTH, J.
 1935. THE RELATION OF LEUKOSIS TO SARCOMA OF CHICKENS. I. SARCOMA AND ERYTHROLEUKOSIS (STRAIN 13). Jour. Expt. Med. 61: 593–615, illus.
(54) THORP, FRANK, JR., and GRAHAM, ROBERT.
 1936. TRANSMISSION STUDIES IN LEUCEMIA. Vet. Med. 31: 82–85, illus.
(55) WALLE, N. VAN DER, and WINKLER-JUNIUS, E.
 1924. DE NEURITIS-EPIZOÖTIE BIJ KIPPEN TE BARNEVELD IN 1921. Tijdschr. v. Vergelijk. Geneesk. 10: 34–50, illus. [In Dutch. English summary, pp. 46–47.]
(56) WATERS, NELSON F., and BYWATERS, JAMES H.
 1941. THE PROPOSED BREEDING PROGRAM OF THE REGIONAL POULTRY RESEARCH LABORATORY. Poultry Sci. 20: 221–223.
(57) WILCKE, H. L., LEE, C. D., and MURRAY, CHARLES.
 1938. SUSCEPTIBILITY AND RESISTANCE OF SOME STRAINS OF CHICKENS TO FOWL LEUCOSIS. Poultry Sci. 17: 58–66, illus.
(58) —— PATTERSON, F. D., HENDERSON, E. W., and MURRAY, CHARLES.
 1933. THE EFFECT OF THE RATION UPON THE INCIDENCE OF SO-CALLED RANGE PARALYSIS. Poultry Sci. 12: 226–232.

Respiratory Diseases of Chickens and Turkeys

BY W. J. HALL [1]

EVERY YEAR poultry producers incur heavy losses from respiratory diseases in their flocks. Here is a careful account of the causes, symptoms, diagnosis, treatment, and prevention of these maladies.

SEVERAL RESPIRATORY DISEASES of fowls cause major losses to the poultry industry throughout the country. These losses, which usually occur in the fall or winter, after the expense of rearing the chickens has been incurred and when replacement is difficult and costly, can be prevented only by constant vigilance and attention to management and traffic in fowls. In come cases and under certain circumstances, preventive vaccination may be helpful.

The most important diseases affecting the respiratory tract of chickens are infectious laryngotracheitis, infectious bronchitis, and infectious coryza. Other diseases that may produce respiratory symptoms are fowl pox, pullorum disease, aspergillosis, fowl paralysis, gapes, and occasionally infestation by air-sac mites. In fowl pox, hollow casts or linings of cheeselike pus may form an obstruction in the larynx to the free interchange of air. In pullorum disease and in aspergillosis abscesses may be so numerous as to interfere seriously with the oxygenation of the blood. Gapeworms sometimes collect in such numbers as to restrict breathing. In some cases of fowl paralysis the nerve supply to the respiratory apparatus is damaged, causing difficulty in breathing. Gasping, or gapes, is the common symptom in all the disease conditions that interfere with breathing.

INFECTIOUS LARYNGOTRACHEITIS

Infectious laryngotracheitis has been variously called infectious bronchitis, infectious tracheitis, tracheolaryngitis, chicken "flu," and

---

[1] W. J. Hall is Veterinarian, Animal Disease Station, Bureau of Animal Industry.

77434°—51——62

Canadian "flu." The name "infectious laryngotracheitis," suggested in 1930, has finally been generally adopted as being the most suitable.

The disease is found in all parts of the United States and in Canada, England, Germany, Hawaii, and Australia. Chickens of all ages, from baby chicks to mature fowls, are affected.

Respiratory diseases resembling laryngotracheitis were noted by poultry feeders at the beginning of the century. The mortality was comparatively low in these outbreaks. The affected birds were known as wheezers or callers, and removing them from the flock was effective in preventing serious losses. It was not until about 1920, however, that the disease was described by poultry pathologists.

In 1930 and 1931 the causative agent was definitely established as a filtrable virus [2] (*1, 3, 14, 15*).[3] The virus is quickly destroyed by disinfectants such as 3-percent solution of liquor cresolis compositis, 1-percent lye solution, or 5-percent carbolic acid, as well as by 7 hours of exposure to direct sunlight. Under favorable conditions it may survive on contaminated premises as long as 3 months. In dead birds the virus does not survive the decomposition of the carcass (*27*).

The mucous membrane lining the respiratory tract of the fowl is the principal tissue affected. In the acute form of the disease the mucous membrane of the larynx and trachea is the site of the principal tissue changes. In the milder subacute or chronic form the mucous membrane of the conjunctivae (the lining of the eyelids) and of the nasal and ocular sinuses may also become affected. The secretions of the respiratory tract are the richest source of virus. It has also been reported in the spleens and livers of infected birds (*2*).

The disease comes on suddenly. In the acute form the course is usually rapid, the affected bird recovering or dying within a week or less. In less virulent (subacute) outbreaks the disease may be localized in the eyes and adjacent sinuses, and the course may be prolonged to 2 or 3 weeks. The incubation period (the time between exposure to the disease and the appearance of symptoms) in the acute form has been stated to be 3 to 10 days and in natural outbreaks 7 to 12 days (*20, 21*).

A tentative diagnosis of the disease may be made by noting the principal symptoms and lesions (tissue changes), but in order to make a positive diagnosis differentiating the condition from others that resemble it, cross-immunity tests may be necessary.

The outstanding symptom of laryngotracheitis is gasping. On inhaling, the head is extended upward with mouth wide open (fig. 1, *A*), and on expiration the head is retracted on the breast, with the mouth closed (fig. 1, *B*). This series of motions is repeated with each breath. The gasping is interrupted occasionally by coughing, followed by shaking of the head in an endeavor to rid the nose and mouth of the mucus, blood, and pus brought up in coughing. Respiration is usually accompanied by a variety of noises, rattling, wheezing, and sometimes loud cries. The breathing noises are caused by partial obstructions of the respiratory passages with exudates, or discharges, of blood-stained mucus and pus.

---

[2] A filtrable virus is a disease-producing agent so small that it will pass through fine porcelain bacteria-retaining filters, and it is invisible even with the aid of a microscope.
[3] Italic numbers in parentheses refer to Literature Cited, p. 975.

Laryngotracheitis is usually mild in young chicks and may be wrongly diagnosed as a cold.

Cross-immunity tests cannot safely be carried out on the farm. If laboratory service cannot be secured to conduct such tests, a tentative diagnosis may be made by careful observations of the following principal characteristics of laryngotracheitis: Sudden onset and rapid spread; rapid course—nearly all deaths occur within a week and are due to suffocation; g a s p i n g respiration; coughing up blood-stained exudate; and the confinement of the lesions in early cases to the larynx and trachea, which contains a variable amount of mucus, pus, and blood.

A c r o s s-immunity test may be conducted as follows: Tracheal exudate is collected from a bird ill with suspected laryngotracheitis by inserting a sterile cotton swab into the trachea. The exudate on the swab is then immediately transferred to the trachea of a normal susceptible bird (one that has never been exposed to any respiratory disease). In the same manner a bird that has been immunized to infectious laryngotracheitis by cloacal vaccina-

FIGURE 1.—A hen with a severe case of laryngotracheitis, showing *A*, attitude during inspiration, *B*, attitude during expiration. (Courtesy of the Division of Veterinary Science, California Agricultural Experiment Station.)

tion (described later) is inoculated. If the susceptible bird develops the disease while the immune bird remains well, there is strong evidence that the disease is laryngotracheitis. If both birds develop a respiratory disease as a result of the inoculation of the unknown agent, the disease is not infectious laryngotracheities but may be infectious bronchitis, which is caused by a filtrable virus that is distinct from the standpoint of immunity, from the virus of laryngotracheities.

The principal tissue changes in a typical acute outbreak are located in the larynx and trachea, as the name of the disease indicates. Severe inflammation of the mucous membrane lining these organs produces a great increase in the amounts of mucous discharge, which becomes blood-stained from capillary hemorrhages and later is thickened and yellowish. As the discharge dries on the walls of the trachea and larynx it may form a hollow cast, or false membrane. As more mucus dries within this cast the opening is gradually narrowed until breathing becomes difficult or impossible, and death results from suffocation. In other cases, suffocation is caused by the formation of a cheesy pus in the larynx.

In mild cases such complications may ensue as swelling and exudation in the nasal passages, eyelids, and adjacent sinuses, which are clinically indistinguishable from the so-called roup, or coryza. In other cases the disease may terminate in pneumonia or bronchitis.

Losses from this disease are due not only to a relatively high mortality but also to a marked drop in egg production and a greatly increased number of unthrifty birds. The death losses vary from few or none in young chicks in warm weather up to 70 percent in heavy birds in high production in cold weather. One survey showed that losses from the drop in egg production following an outbreak may amount to one-fourth the loss from mortality.

The most important method of spread is the carrier bird. A bird that recovers from the disease is immune but becomes a carrier for life. Although such a bird may appear healthy, the exudate from its respiratory tract is highly virulent to susceptible birds. If carrier birds are retained in a flock, each new crop of chicks may be infected and the disease thus perpetuated. It may also be spread from flock to flock by means of contaminated crates and probably also by contaminated clothing of caretakers, feed bags, and utensils.

The part played by wild birds and vermin in disseminating the disease has not been definitely established, but they should be excluded from contact with poultry as much as possible.

That the virus of laryngotracheitis is not transmitted by or through the egg is fairly well established (*5*).

Various chemicals and disinfectants have been recommended for the treatment of laryngotracheitis by spraying, vaporization, and administration in the feed and drinking water, but controlled experimental tests have shown that they are of little value in the cure of this disease.

The best methods of prevention are sanitation and vaccination.

Visitors should be excluded from the poultry quarters as much as possible.

Traffic in birds should be reduced to a minimum.

Shipping crates should be disinfected before being returned to poultry quarters.

In 1932 Hudson and Beaudette (*18*) discovered that application of the virus of laryngotracheitis to the mucous membrane of the cloaca (vent) and bursa Fabricius (a gland opening into the cloaca) produced only a local reaction lasting about 10 days and characterized by swelling and redness and the formation of a small amount of pus at the site of vaccination. After recovery, the bird was immune to the disease. This technique proved to be a satisfactory method of vaccination (*4*).

Laryngotracheitis vaccine is prepared from the tracheal exudate, or discharge, of infected fowls. This material, consisting of mucus, blood, pus, and cast-off cells from the mucous membrane, is dried under vacuum, ground to a fine powder, and then mixed with a measured amount of 50-percent glycerin immediately before use. A more recent method of producing the vaccine is the propagation of the virus on developing chick embryos, in which the virus may be grown free of bacteria.

The vaccine is applied to the mucous membrane of the cloaca by means of several vigorous strokes of a stiff bristle brush until redness or a slight hemorrhage is produced. After 5 days the bird is examined for a vaccination reaction, or take, evidenced by swelling and redness of the mucous membrane of the cloaca (fig. 2). If no take is apparent the bird must be revaccinated, as such birds, except an occasional one that possesses natural immunity, may otherwise develop the disease in the trachea. Birds successfully vaccinated are immune for life. For the first 10 or 12 days after vaccination, virus may be eliminated in the droppings, and during that time a vaccinated bird is a potential source of danger to birds in the flock that were not successfully vaccinated. After that period, however, the vaccinated bird is not only immune but does not become a virus carrier, as does one that has recovered from a natural attack of the disease.

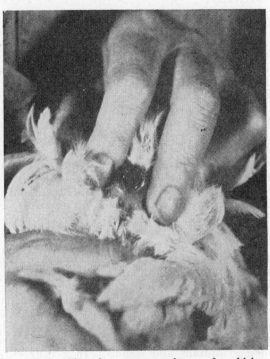

FIGURE 2.—Cloacal mucous membrane of a chicken, swollen and red as the result of vaccination for laryngo-tracheitis. This reaction indicates a take, which is followed by immunity. (Courtesy of the Division of Veterinary Science, California Agricultural Experiment Station.)

Vaccination against laryngotracheitis is usually recommended only under the following circumstances: (1) When the disease is prevalent in the immediate neighborhood and when it occurs from year to year in the pullets owing to the presence in the flock of carriers from previous outbreaks; (2) when birds, usually males, are brought into the flock from outside sources where exposure was probable; and (3) in outbreaks in large flocks where the disease is confined to one pen. In the last case, the birds in the other pens may be saved by vaccination if it is done promptly.

Where the disease was present the year before, chicks should be vaccinated when 2 to 3 months old. At that age they may be vaccinated at the same time against pox.

Where no laryngotracheitis exists in the neighborhood and there is little if any chance of exposure of the flock to the disease, vaccination should not be practiced, since after the vaccine, which is a live virus, is introduced into a flock, annual vaccination may be necessary in order to protect each new crop of pullets from possible carriers.

INFECTIOUS BRONCHITIS

Infectious bronchitis is a respiratory disease primarily of young chicks. It is immunologically distinct—that is, infection with one disease does not create immunity against the other—from infectious laryngotracheitis and infectious coryza. It is sometimes called gasping disease of chicks.

First described in 1931 (*25*) and again in 1933, it was said to be widespread in the Middle West at that time (*6*). It was seen mostly in hatchery-produced chicks and was thought to be spread from hatcheries. In 1939 the disease was reported as becoming more common, and it is now said to be one of the most frequently observed respiratory diseases in Rhode Island (*10*).

Those who investigated the disease were able to reproduce it by inoculation of filtered tracheal exudates from sick birds into the trachea of susceptible birds. The causative agent is now generally regarded as a filtrable virus.

Various investigators have reported that chicks were susceptible to the disease as early as the fourth day and as late as the sixth month of age. As in infectious laryngotracheitis, an attack of infectious bronchitis leaves the survivor solidly immune to subsequent exposure to the virus by either natural or artificial means.

It is difficult to make a positive diagnosis distinguishing between infectious bronchitis, infectious laryngotracheitis, and infectious coryza, since all three of these respiratory diseases may produce common symptoms and lesions. In a differential diagnosis, the symptoms, lesions, course of the disease, causative agent, morbidity, and mortality must all be taken into account. Frequently, cross-immunity tests and bacteriological examination must be made before there can be a positive diagnosis.

The symptoms of bronchitis may include some of those seen in laryngotracheitis and in coryza, such as gasping or mouth breathing, coughing, breathing noises (rales, mucous click), swelling of the nasal sinuses, nasal discharge, watering of the eyes, and swelling under the mandible.

The lesions in uncomplicated bronchitis are located in the lungs, whereas in uncomplicated laryngotracheitis the principal tissue changes are found in the larynx and trachea. The lungs are congested and red. The large and small bronchial tubes contain mucopus which later may become cheesy and form solid yellow plugs or casts that exclude the air and produce difficult, gasping breathing. Occasionally unusual cases may be seen in which blood-stained mucopus is present throughout the trachea, as in infectious laryngotracheitis.

The course of the disease has been variously reported to run from 3 or 4 to as many as 8 days, with losses of infected chicks ranging from 10 to over 90 percent.

It has been suggested that the infection may be carried through the egg or by carrier hens, as well as by the excretions of sick birds. It seems probable that the virus may survive in recovered birds for an undetermined period and thus infect younger susceptible chickens.

As in infectious laryngotracheitis, prevention seems to offer the best method of control. On account of the sudden onset and rapid course of the disease in very young chicks, as well as its sporadic nature, preventive vaccination does not seem to be feasible. When attempts were made to immunize chickens against infectious bronchitis by cloacal vaccination as used for laryngotracheitis, it was found that the virus was carried from the cloaca to the lungs, where the disease developed before immunity could be established as a result of the vaccination.

The disease is spread by infected chicks. Hence, when chicks are purchased they should be carefully inspected for evidence of respiratory infection.

It has been reported that the respiratory distress in young chicks may be ameliorated if it is treated in the early stages by vaporizing the chicks with such volatile oils as menthol, eucalyptol, and guaiacol.

After the removal of infected chicks, the brooder house and all utensils should be thoroughly cleaned and disinfected before being restocked with healthy chicks.

It is further recommended that careful attention be paid to heating, ventilation, and sanitation in the brooder house, since neglect of these points may predispose the chicks to respiratory disease. The brooder house should be well ventilated without drafts. It should not be allowed to become too hot, dry, and dusty. Overcrowding and insanitary conditions are to be avoided.

INFECTIOUS FOWL CORYZA

Infectious coryza in fowls is an acute inflammatory and contagious disease of the upper air passages. Older names and synonyms are catarrhal roup, cold, rhinitis, and sinusitis. Catarrhal diseases of the mucous membranes of the nose, eyes, and adjacent sinuses of the fowl were formerly called roup, regardless of the causative agent. Roup, therefore, came to have a very broad meaning, but as the causes of the various catarrhal diseases of the head become known, this term has disappeared from the literature on the subject.

In addition to the nasal passages and adjacent sinuses, the mucous membranes of the eye (conjunctival sac) and the sinuses under the eye frequently become involved.

Beginning in 1932, several investigators reported isolating a bacillus (*Hemophilus gallinarum*) from chickens that were suffering with coryza and reproducing the disease by inoculating the germs into susceptible chickens (*8, 9, 13, 23, 26*). At least two distinct types of coryza are now recognized which are different from a causal as well as a clinical standpoint. The type caused by the germ *H. gallinarum* has a rapid onset and relatively short duration, whereas a second type, the causative agent of which has not been determined with certainty, takes 9 to 27 days to develop and lasts 2 months or longer.

In California two types of coryza have been reported, a mild type with only a nasal discharge and a severe type with complications. In the former, the course was short, and the losses were negligible. The most common complication was an edematous swelling of the face, which in males sometimes extended to the wattles. Other complications were inflammation of the sinuses, conjunctivae, trachea, and bronchial tubes and air-sac infection. When the lower respiratory tract was involved there were coughing and gasping. When complications

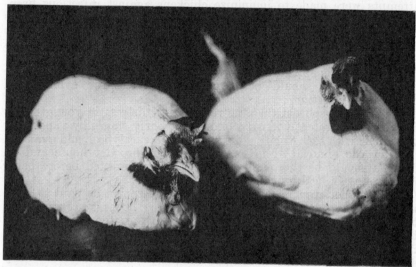

FIGURE 3.—Results of a natural infection with infectious fowl coryza. Left, severe swelling of the head; right, slight facial swelling and conjunctivitis. (Courtesy of the Division of Veterinary Science, California Agricultural Experiment Station.)

were present the course of the disease was prolonged from several weeks to several months. The mortality varied from a few cases to more than 50 percent of a flock.

A coryza caused by the fowl cholera bacillus, *Pasteurella avicida*, has been reported (*19, 24*). It was found that when fowl cholera has been prevalent in a flock for some time the cholera bacillus loses virulence and tends to become localized in different parts of the body. The reaction to this local infection varies with the individual; some develop sinusitis, or ocular roup, whereas others become healthy carriers. It is thought the latter may cause the annual occurrence of colds among susceptible pullets each year.

When there is only a simple discharge from the nose, coryza is easy to diagnose, but when complications intervene, such as swelling of the face and wattles and gasping or coughing, diagnosis becomes a problem. Coryza must then be differentiated from cholera infection, infectious laryngotracheitis, and infectious bronchitis. A differential diagnosis can be made with certainty only by means of a bacteriological examination and cross-immunity tests, which are carried out as already described for laryngotracheitis.

Infectious coryza begins with a watery exudate from the nose and often from the eyes as well. In a short time the exudate, which usually has a very offensive odor, becomes thick and sticky. As it dries around the nostrils and eyelids, the latter tend to stick together. In some cases exudate accumulates in the nasal sinuses and those under the eyes in large, cheesy masses which exert pressure on the eye, closing it (fig. 3) and sometimes destroying the sight. There may be a watery (edematous) swelling of the entire face and wattles (fig. 4).

In an outbreak in Rhode Island, an elevation of body temperature at the onset was reported. The d i s e a s e spread rapidly, with a high mortality which was ascribed to the presence of some toxic principle. The principal symptoms were a discharge from the nasal passages and sinusitis. There was also considerable involvement of the eyes, with reddening, swelling, watering, and sensitiveness to light. The larynx, trachea, or bronchial tube were little

FIGURE 4.—Swelling of the entire face and wattles produced by injection of a culture of *Hemophilus gallinarum*, the causative agent of infectious fowl coryza, into the wattles. (Courtesy of the Division of Veterinary Science, California Agricultural Experiment Station.)

affected. Sick birds lost their appetites and rapidly became emaciated. On the other hand, it has also been reported that birds artificially infected by injection of the coryza bacillus did not appear ill, and few died, but growth was retarded and egg production was depressed; in about 10 percent of the cases there were secondary manifestations such as tracheal involvement, with noisy breathing and gasping.

Recently it has been found that sulfathiazole administered at the rate of approximately 4 grams per pound of feed, or 1 percent, is effective in the treatment of the acute type of coryza caused by *Hemophilus gallinarum* but its effect on other types of coryza has not been fully determined (*10a*).

The means by which the disease is spread from flock to flock under natural conditions are not known. It appears probable that recovered birds may become carriers, as in infectious laryngotracheitis and infectious bronchitis. It has been demonstrated that as long as 46 days after recovery fowls may be carriers of the causative agent of the disease, but that cages and feed and water vessels contaminated by a virulent exudate from infected chickens did not remain infective to susceptible chickens for more than 24 hours. The disease is readily transmitted by placing infected chickens in the same pen with susceptible chickens.

In contrast to the solid, lasting immunity induced by an attack of infectious laryngotracheitis and infectious bronchitis, the immunity of birds that have recovered from an attack of infectious coryza has been reported to be temporary.

It is recommended that careful attention should be paid to housing and to the nutrition of the pullets when they go into the laying house. Drafts, insufficient ventilation, overcrowding, dampness, and insanitary conditions should be avoided so as not to lower the natural resistance of the birds.

The yearly occurrence of colds among pullets in California (7) has been attributed to the carrying over of the causative agent by fowls that recovered from an attack during the previous year. Recommendations for control include the complete segregation of pullets from flocks held over from the previous year by (1) depopulation—disposal of all old flocks—and cleaning and disinfecting the quarters occupied by these flocks before bringing in a new stock of pullets; and (2) segregation—the old stock to be removed to houses as far from the pullet quarters as possible so that there is no contact between the two groups.

NONINFECTIOUS CORYZAS

Coryzalike symptoms—a nasal discharge and swelling of the sinuses or chalky deposits in the conjunctival sac—may also be caused by vitamin A deficiency, sometimes referred to as nutritional roup, or by mechanical irritation by foreign particles, and these conditions may be confused with infectious coryza.

In the noninfectious coryza caused by vitamin A deficiency there is usually a thin, watery discharge from the nostrils, followed by a grayish-white, cheesy deposit in the conjunctival sac, and sometimes in the nasal cleft, in the mouth, and on the pharynx and gullet, where the deposit occurs as white, pinhead-size nodules. Post mortem examination sometimes reveals white, chalky deposits in the heart sac, on the surface of the liver, and in the kidneys.

Nutritional coryza may be cured by increasing the proportion in the diet of vitamin-A-rich supplements such as green feed, yellow corn, cod-liver oil, alfalfa leaf meal, and carrots.

Occasionally sporadic cases of noninfectious coryza may occur as the result of irritation of the mucous membranes of the nasal sinuses and eyelids by foreign particles such as dust, grain, litter, and disinfectant chemicals. The irritation may set up inflammation of the mucous membranes, which is followed by a discharge of mucus and pus. This type of nonspecific coryza is infrequent. The symptoms may be indistinguishable from those of infectious coryza, but only an occasional bird is affected, and the disease does not spread.

SINUSITIS (ROUP, SWELLHEAD) IN TURKEYS

A form of coryza in turkeys is characterized by swelling of the sinuses under the eyes. From a causative standpoint two types are described, one infectious and one nutritional, but the causative agent in the so-called infectious type has not yet been found.

The first symptom of the infectious type of the disease is a thin, watery discharge from the nostrils, which soon becomes thick and adhesive. The bird shakes it head and wipes its face on its feathers in an effort to dislodge the discharge. This is followed by bulging or swelling of the face just below and in front of the eye due to the filling of the sinus with an exudate that resembles thin egg albumen. The swelling may appear on one or both sides of the face and in some cases it obstructs vision so that the bird is unable to eat.

In outbreaks in Utah it was found that the swellings varied in size from a slight enlargement to one the size of a hen's egg. It was also reported that sinusitis in turkeys differs from that in chickens in that the exudate consists of a yellowish mucus which remains liquid, whereas in the chicken it becomes cheesy. Only in cases of long standing do the contents of the sinuses in the turkeys become caseous, or cheesy. Although early spontaneous recovery sometimes occurs, the infectious type of the disease usually persists in a flock for weeks or months. The course is more prolonged in those cases in which the exudate becomes firm and cheesy.

In addition to the symptoms and lesions described for the infectious type, the nutritional type, caused by an insufficient amount of vitamin A in the diet, has been reported to show a whitish exudate in the eye in over 80 percent of the cases; pustules in the mouth and esophagus in over 30 percent and in the crop in 60 percent; a catarrhal or cheesy exudate in the bursa of Fabricius in nearly 70 percent; white deposits of urates in the kidneys and body cavities in a few cases; and occasionally a cheesy plug in the larynx or a tubular cast in the trachea.

In all the outbreaks described, losses to the grower were said to be heavy, not so much from mortality as from loss of flesh and unsalability of the birds. In California (*11*) the mortality was low, but the morbidity (percentage of sick birds) was from 10 to 90 percent of the flock. The disease occurs widely in New South Wales (*16*), Australia, where it causes heavy losses and considerable mortality. It occurs most frequently in birds 3 to 5 months of age, but it may also affect birds a few weeks old, and among the latter the mortality is said to be heavy.

In making a diagnosis it should be determined whether the disease is of the infectious or nutritional type. The nutritional type of sinusitis may be prevented by providing the birds with a sufficient amount of vitamin A in the diet through the use of green feed, yellow corn, alfalfa leaf meal, or cod-liver oil. It has been shown that turkey poults require nearly twice as much vitamin-A-rich supplements to maintain health as do chicks (*17*).

A diet containing adequate amounts of vitamin A is also desirable to build up resistance to the so-called infectious sinusitis. Overcrowding, insanitary conditions, and exposure to drafts and storms should be avoided.

Infectious sinusitis in turkeys can be successfully treated by evacuating the sinus and injecting argyrol or silver nitrate. Some investigators report that silver nitrate is preferable for turkeys, and others have reported that a 15-percent solution of fresh argyrol was ineffective when injected into the infraorbital sinuses of fowls affected with coryza (*12*).

The procedure used in California for the treatment of sinusitis in turkeys is as follows: The swollen sinus is emptied by inserting a hypodermic needle of large (12 or 15) gage, attached to a glass syringe (Luer type) into the lower portion of the sinus and then slowly withdrawing the plunger, thus drawing the mucus into the syringe. Care should be taken not to damage the wall of the sinus or the mucous membrane in inserting the syringe or withdrawing the exudate so as not to clog the needle by sucking in the mucous membrane. After withdrawal of the exudate from the swollen sinus, the syringe may be detached from the needle, which is left in the sinus. Another syringe containing 15-percent fresh argyrol, or 4-percent silver nitrate is attached to the needle, and about 1 cubic centimeter is injected into the sinus. The sinus may then be gently massaged before withdrawal of the needle. Care should be observed not to inject the medicine into the tissues surrounding the sinus, as this may cause severe inflammation and sloughing. With this treatment the swelling subsides in 2 or 3 days and in the majority of cases recovery is complete in about 2 weeks. A few cases require a second treatment.

In Utah two techniques have been used. In one, an incision about three-eighths of an inch in length was made over the sinus with a sharp, pointed knife, and the exudate was forced out through the incision by massage. Through the opening 15 to 20 drops of medicinal solution (20-percent argyrol or 4-percent silver nitrate) was instilled by means of a medicine dropper. In cases where bleeding was severe the sinus was packed with cotton. In the other technique, a 10- to 20–cubic centimeter hypodermic syringe, fitted with a 16–gage needle 1½ inches long, was used to empty the sinus. Another syringe fitted with a smaller needle (18–gage) was used to inject 1 cubic centimeter of the medicine into the sinus, through the hole made by the larger needle. The syringe technique was preferred to the knife technique (*22*).

Good results were obtained in Australia in the treatment of sinusitis in turkeys by the use of 2- to 5-percent silver nitrate. It is said that new cases respond best to treatment, whereas long-standing cases in which the sinus contents are cheeselike are refractory.

In still another treatment technique the contents of the sinus were evacuated through the orifice leading into the nasal cavity by gentle massage of the swollen sinus, after which 1 to 2 cubic centimeters of fresh 15-percent argyrol was injected (*28*).

An attack of the disease is said to confer immunity to a second attack, but successful immunization of turkeys by subcutaneous injection of the exudate or by application of the exudate to the mucous membrane of the cloaca has not been reported.

LITERATURE CITED

(1) BEACH, J. R.
   1930. THE VIRUS OF LARYNGOTRACHEITIS OF FOWLS. Science 72 : 633–634.
(2) ———
   1931. A BACTERIOLOGICAL STUDY OF INFECTIOUS LARYNGOTRACHEITIS OF CHICKENS. Jour. Expt. Med. 54 : 801–808.
(3) BEAUDETTE, F. R.
   1930. BRONCHITIS IN POULTRY. N. J. Agr. 12 (5) : 3, 4.
(4) ——— and HUDSON, C. B.
   1933. EXPERIMENTS ON IMMUNIZATION AGAINST LARYNGOTRACHEITIS IN FOWLS. Amer. Vet. Med. Assoc. Jour. 82 : 460–476.
(5) BRANDLY, C. A.
   1934. SOME STUDIES OF INFECTIOUS LARYNGOTRACHEITIS. Amer. Vet. Med. Assoc. Jour. 84 : 588–595.
(6) BUSHNELL, L. D., and BRANDLY, C. A.
   1933. LARYNGOTRACHEITIS IN CHICKS. Poultry Sci. 12 : 55–60.
(7) BUSIC, W. H., and BEACH, J. R.
   1934. HANDLING COLDS ON POULTRY FARMS. Pacific Rural Press 128 : 368.
(8) DE-BLIECK, L.
   1932. A HÆMOGLOBINOPHILIC BACTERIUM AS THE CAUSE OF CONTAGIOUS CATARRH OF THE FOWL. (CORYZA INFECTIOSA GALLINARUM). Vet. Jour. 88 : 9–13.
(9) DELAPLANE, J. P., ERWIN, L. E., and STUART, H. O.
   1934. A HEMOPHILIC BACILLUS AS THE CAUSE OF AN INFECTIOUS RHINITIS. R. I. Agr. Expt. Sta. Bul. 244, 12 pp., illus.
(10) ——— and STUART, H. O.
   1939. STUDIES OF INFECTIOUS BRONCHITIS. R. I. Expt. Sta. Bul. 273, 15 pp.
(10a) ——— and STUART, H. O.
   1941. THE CHEMOTHERAPEUTIC VALUE OF SULFATHIAZOLE IN PREVENTING AND TREATING INFECTIOUS CORYZA (HEMOPHILUS GALLINARUM INFECTION) IN CHICKENS. Am. Vet. Med. Assoc. Jour. 99 (772) : 41–42.
(11) DICKINSON, E. M., and HINSHAW, W. R.
   1938. TREATMENT OF INFECTIOUS SINUSITIS OF TURKEYS WITH ARGYROL AND SILVER NITRATE. Amer. Vet. Med. Assoc. Jour. 93 : 151–156, illus.
(12) ——— and BEACH, J. R.
   1938. TREATMENT OF FOWL CORYZA OF CHICKENS WITH ARGYROL. Amer. Vet. Med. Assoc. Jour. 93 : 108.
(13) ELIOT, CALISTA P., and LEWIS, MARGARET R.
   1934. A HEMOPHILIC BACTERIUM AS A CAUSE OF INFECTIOUS CORYZA IN THE FOWL. Amer. Vet. Med. Assoc. Jour. 84 : 878–888.
(14) GIBBS, CHARLES S.
   1931. INFECTIOUS TRACHITIS. Mass. Agr. Expt. Sta. Bul. 273, pp. [25]–55, illus.
(15) GRAHAM, ROBERT, THORP, FRANK, JR., and JAMES, W. A.
   1931. A FILTERABLE VIRUS-LIKE AGENT IN AVIAN LARYNGOTRACHEITIS. Amer. Vet. Med. Assoc. Jour. 78 : 506.
(16) HART, L.
   1940. SINUSITIS IN TURKEYS. Austral. Vet. Jour. 16 : 163–168, illus.
(17) HINSHAW, W. R., and LLOYD, W. E.
   1934. VITAMIN-A DEFICIENCY IN TURKEYS. Hilgardia 8 : 281–304, illus.
(18) HUDSON, C. B., and BEAUDETTE, F. R.
   1932. INFECTION OF THE CLOACA WITH THE VIRUS OF INFECTIOUS BRONCHITIS. Science 76 : 34.
(19) HUGHES, THOMAS P., and PRITCHETT, IDA W.
   1930. THE EPIDEMIOLOGY OF FOWL CHOLERA. III. PORTAL OF ENTRY OF P. AVICIDA; REACTION OF THE HOST. Jour. Expt. Med. 51 : 239–248, illus.
(20) HUNGERFORD, T. G.
   1938. INFECTIOUS LARYNGOTRACHEITIS. Agr. Gaz. N. S. · Wales 49 : 628–632, illus.
(21) KERNOHAN, GEORGE.
   1931. INFECTIOUS LARYNGOTRACHEITIS OF FOWLS. Amer. Vet. Med. Assoc. Jour. 78 : 196–202.

(22) MADSEN, D. E.
    1938. SINUSITIS OF TURKEYS. Utah Agr. Expt. Sta. Bul. 280, 12 pp., illus.
(23) NELSON, JOHN B.
    1932. ETIOLOGY OF AN UNCOMPLICATED CORYZA IN THE DOMESTIC FOWL. Soc. Exp. Biol. and Med. Proc. 30: 306–307.
(24) PRITCHETT, IDA W., BEAUDETTE, F. R., and HUGHES, T. P.
    1930. THE EPIDEMIOLOGY OF FOWL CHOLERA. IV. FIELD OBSERVATIONS OF THE "SPONTANEOUS" DISEASE. Jour. Expt. Med. 51: 249–258.
(25) SCHALK, A. F., and HAWN, M .C.
    1931. AN APPARENTLY NEW RESPIRATORY DISEASE OF BABY CHICKS. Amer. Vet. Med. Assoc. Jour. 78: 413–422.
(26) SCHALM, O. W., and BEACH, J. R.
    1934. THE ETIOLOGY OF A RESPIRATORY DISEASE OF CHICKENS. Science 79: 416–417.
(27) —— and BEACH, J. R.
    1935. THE RESISTANCE OF THE VIRUS OF INFECTIOUS LARYNGOTRACHEITIS TO CERTAIN PHYSICAL AND CHEMICAL FACTORS. Jour. Infect. Dis. 56: [210]–223.
(28) TYZZER, E. E.
    1926. THE INJECTION OF ARGYROL FOR THE TREATMENT OF SINUSITIS IN TURKEYS. Cornell Vet. 16: 221–224.

At the time this book went to press, the drugs and other materials mentioned in various articles—chiefly as disinfectants, insecticides, and anthelmintics—were still available for veterinary and medical use. Under war conditions, however, it is possible that some of these materials may become scarce or unavailable. In that case, the reader should obtain professional advice from the Department of Agriculture, the State experiment station, a local veterinarian, or the county agent as to available substitutes.

Fowl Pox (Diphtheria)

BY HUBERT BUNYEA [1]

THE SKIN FORM of fowl pox is a comparatively mild disease, but it has a diphtheritic form that can be extremely serious. Fortunately, it is one of the diseases for which successful vaccination methods have been developed.

FOWL POX is a disease complex consisting of lesions, or tissue injuries, of the skin (pox) and of the mucous membranes (diphtheria). It affects many species of domestic fowls and free-flying wild birds.

It is now known that fowl pox is caused by an invisible disease-producing agency. From time to time many agents, including bacteria and protozoa of various kinds, have been believed to produce the disease. In an old book on poultry diseases [2] the origin of diphtheria is attributed mainly to "improper care, and sudden changes of weather and variations of temperature," and the author adds that "it is also occasioned by improper and damp coops and roosts." About the beginning of the present century, however, it was discovered that infectious material from pox-infected fowls was capable of retaining its disease-producing power even after it had passed through filters too fine to permit the passage of bacteria. Such an infective agent is known as a filtrable virus.

Two types or strains of the virus are known to be infectious for avian species. The more common and more important strain causes natural outbreaks in chickens and other barnyard fowl, including turkeys, guinea fowl, pheasants, ducks, geese, and other species. Of less importance is pigeon pox virus, which, as its name implies, produces the disease in pigeons. Other species are relatively resistant to pigeon pox virus, but it has produced mild lesions experimentally in chickens, particularly when inoculated into feather follicles, a fact that is the basis for immunization of chickens with this type of the virus, as discussed later. Pigeons are quite resistant to the other type.

---

[1] Hubert Bunyea is Veterinarian, Pathological Division, Bureau of Animal Industry.
[2] LEWIS, W. M. THE PEOPLE'S PRACTICAL POULTRY BOOK. Ed. 7, 223 pp., illus. New York. 1876.

The virus of fowl pox, or chicken pox, is very resistant to desiccation, or drying. Infectious matter from the diseased birds may therefore be scattered around the premises and will remain in a dried condition for many months, during which time it may come into contact with susceptible birds and bring about a new outbreak. Such an outbreak usually begins with the occurrence of the typical pox lesions on the face parts of the fowls. The virus may gain entrance where the comb or wattle has been wounded, possibly during fights with other birds. Certain species of mosquitoes may spread the disease by carrying the infection from a diseased fowl to a susceptible one. A mosquito may be infectious for as long as 27 days after feeding on an infected fowl.

It is probable that the disease is transmitted only through damaged or broken skin or mucous membranes. Wounds too small to be observed may afford an entrance for the virus into the skin.

Fowl pox virus is not infectious for human beings or any species of mammal; so-called chicken pox (varicella) in human beings is an entirely distinct disease. Fowls and free-flying birds of any age are susceptible to fowl pox. Usually, however, very young and very old birds are not affected, probably because the young birds are more sheltered from exposure and the old birds have in many cases survived a previous outbreak and developed immunity. Fowls of any breed and practically all species are susceptible to the disease. Large-combed and large-wattled birds seem to acquire the pox lesions more often, probably because of the greater surface of these parts exposed to skin wounds. The diphtheria manifestations affect all breeds equally.

SYMPTOMS

The cutaneous (pox) lesions are usually the first to appear, the membranous (diphtheria) lesions occurring later. The infection gains a foothold in the flock through the pox lesions, but in the diphtheritic form it may persist longer and do greater damage. Fowl pox may appear at any season, though as a rule it is more likely to occur in the fall or winter.

The pox manifestations, known as fowl pox, bird pox, chicken pox, sorehead, dry pox, avian molluscum, or contagious epithelioma, occur as wartlike nodules (fig. 1) on the unfeathered parts of the body such as the comb, wattles, eyelids, and vent. The diphtheritic manifestations, known as avian diphtheria, diphtheritic roup, wet pox or canker, occur as a deposit on the mucous membranes of the eyes, mouth, or respiratory region, and are sometimes accompanied by coughing and gasping. Both types of lesion frequently occur in a single outbreak of the disease.

For many years the two manifestations were regarded as entirely distinct diseases due to different infective agents. Within comparatively recent times, however, it has been clearly demonstrated that the two disease manifestations have a common origin. Virus collected from pox lesions has been shown by inoculation to be infective for the membranes of the eye, mouth, and air passages, whereas virus collected from diphtheria lesions, when rubbed into scarified (scraped) areas on the comb, wattles, or other parts of a fowl's body, has been shown to be capable of producing typical pox lesions.

In the cutaneous, or pox, manifestation of the infection, the lesions appear 3 to 4 days after exposure, in the form of minute grayish pimples or blisters, usually on the unfeathered parts of the fowl's body. The blisters contain a straw-colored fluid which is very virulent. In the course of several days they begin to enlarge and run together. Meanwhile the skin around the blisters takes on an angry.

FIGURE 1.—Pox lesions on comb, wattle, eyelid, and mouth parts of a chicken.

red appearance. After 10 to 14 days, the blisters may begin to darken and form dry, hard scabs resembling warts, which may cling to the skin for another week or two or even longer. Finally the scabs loosen and drop off, revealing new and possibly scarred skin beneath.

In the diphtheritic form the disease has no definite course, but may persist for weeks or possibly months before it is terminated by death or recovery. Yellowish or whitish cheesy patches form on the mucous membrane of the tongue, mouth, esophagus, and larynx. The patches of membranelike material found in some cases within the trachea may cause gaping and labored breathing, which may be mistaken for symptoms of infectious laryngotracheitis. The patches are very tough and adherent. If forcibly removed, they leave the true membrane in a bleeding and ulcerous condition. Similar deposits may occur in the sinuses of the eye, preceded by watering and inflammation. The eyelids eventually become swollen and tend to stick together. This type of diphtheria is sometimes incorrectly alluded to as diphtheritic roup.

The presence of the cheesy membranous deposits in the mouth, eyes, and air passages interferes seriously with the bird's vision and respiration and tends to interfere with its eating. As a result, progressive emaciation sets in, and egg production definitely and sometimes permanently stops. Weakness, starvation, and in many cases suffocation precede death. Recovery may occur in mild cases of diphtheria, imparting prolonged immunity, as does recovery from the cutaneous or pox manifestations of the disease.

MORTALITY AND ECONOMIC IMPORTANCE

The cutaneous pox manifestations are usually mild and after a fairly definite period terminate in an uneventful recovery. The diphtheritic type of infection, however, may cause more or less mortality among the birds, the rate being influenced by the age of the birds and general health conditions in the flock. Other things being equal, the death rate is highest among pullets in egg production. However, complication with other diseases of a debilitating nature, poor nutrition, bad housing conditions, severe weather, or even a moderately heavy parasitic infestation will increase the losses.

No authentic statistics on the economic loss to the poultry industry occasioned by this disease are available. It has been estimated that uncontrolled outbreaks may cost poultry keepers $30 to $70 per hundred birds. Losses are chargeable to such items, in addition to mortality, as the time, work, and equipment used in isolating and treating sick birds; the loss of vitality of sick birds; the suppression of egg production in affected birds—many do not return to production for a number of months, and some never regain normal production; the decreased reproductive power in breeding stock; and the predisposition of affected birds to other diseases.

TREATMENT AND CONTROL

In severe outbreaks medicinal treatment is usually of little or no value. Birds lightly affected, if of more than ordinary value, may be removed from the flock and placed under quarantine in comfortable quarters. The false membrane should be removed from the mouth or larynx so that the bird may eat and breathe more easily. Tincture of iodine, argyrol, or iodoform powder should be applied to the underlying ulcers to promote healing. The drinking water should be made antiseptic by the addition of one-third of a dram (one-third teaspoonful) of potassium permanganate crystals per gallon. Strict sanitation should be observed in the quarantine house, and the attendant, if possible, should refrain from visiting the quarters of the healthy flock. Changing clothes and disinfecting the footwear should be done faithfully after working in the quarantine house.

No special control measures can be recommended for fowl pox. General hygienic precautions should be adopted. Affected birds should be segregated and, if in a serious condition, may as well be slaughtered, since the likelihood of their becoming profitable is remote. The premises from which sick birds have been removed for quarantine or slaughter should be thoroughly cleansed and disinfected. A good disinfectant for this purpose may be made by dissolving 1 pound of commercial lye (containing 94 percent of sodium hydroxide) and 2½ pounds of water-slaked lime in 5½ gallons of water. Unless kept tightly covered, this solution will deteriorate on standing. It is injurious to painted or varnished surfaces, aluminum utensils, and some fabrics, but it is relatively harmless to the equipment usually found around chicken houses.

Precautions should be taken against introducing the disease in pox-free flocks or areas. So far as possible, wild birds should be excluded from contact with the flock and prevented from visiting premises used for poultry. Visitors who own poultry that may be harboring the infection should not be permitted access to the flock, or, if this is unavoidable, they should be provided with a pair of clean rubbers. Hucksters, peddlers, feed dealers, and other itinerant persons are potential transmitters of infection, as they frequently visit many poultry establishments in a day, and they should by all means be excluded from the poultry houses. Veterinarians and officials engaged in various lines of poultry work may be expected to take what precautions are necessary to avoid transmitting infections from place to place in the discharge of their duties.

VACCINATION

If the outbreak is light and of recent origin, vaccination of the healthy birds may be resorted to after removal of the affected ones. After the disease has been present for several weeks or months, however, vaccination is of doubtful value. Birds that remain healthy for that long may be presumed to be resistant; it is always possible that they may have acquired unseen pox lesions and have thereby developed immunity. The fact that fowls that recover from the disease possess a solid immunity to further attack for a considerable length of time has been the basis for much of the experimental work that has led to the present methods of vaccination of poultry for the prevention of fowl pox.

As early as 1910, investigators reported favorable results from the injection into the veins of pox-scab material ground in a physiological salt solution (one that is like the body fluids). Later workers announced the production of immunity in fowls injected twice at 5-day intervals with a saline suspension of pox scabs and diphtheritic membrane that had been filtered and heated for an hour at 55° C.

(131° F.). These methods, however, failed to gain wide acceptance owing to the lack of uniformly satisfactory results.

Within the last 22 years a definitely successful procedure has been developed for the immunization of chickens against pox. The basic agent employed is the living virus of chicken pox or of pigeon pox.

FIGURE 2.—Pigeon pox vaccination lesion on the breast of a pigeon.

Instead of these materials being injected under the skin or into the veins, they are applied by superficial stabs into the skin or to four or six follicles from which the feathers have been plucked. Except in the stab, or stick, method the vaccine is usually vigorously applied with a bristle brush to the prepared area. A successful vaccination is followed by the development of a typical pox lesion at the point of vaccination. Pigeon pox vaccine is applied only to the feather follicles; 12 to 20 feathers are plucked and the follicles are inoculated (fig. 2). In employing the stab method, any clean, sterile, sharp-pointed instrument may be used that will penetrate the skin and convey a minute amount of the virus to the inoculated area. A popular method is to bind two sewing-machine needles to the end of a wooden handle about the thickness of a lead pencil, leaving exposed only the eyes of the needles. When this instrument, after being disinfected, is dipped into the vaccine suspension, sufficient vaccine is picked up in the eyes of the needles to inoculate the skin on both sides of the wing. The needles are then thrust through the web of one wing. This method is economical, efficient, and speedy. Other parts of the skin, such as the thigh, may be inoculated if preferred.

The vaccine is a standardized powder consisting of material that came originally from pox scabs, thoroughly dried and finely pulverized. Under proper conditions, the powder will retain its potency for a long time. For immediate use it is usually mixed with a sterilized fluid consisting of equal parts of glycerine and physiological salt solution. This fluid suspension of the vaccine is very short-lived. It should be kept from exposure to extreme temperatures, excessive sunlight, or atmospheric contamination, and any part remaining unused at the end of the day should be destroyed by burning or disinfection.

Within the last decade it has been discovered that certain viruses, including those of fowl pox and pigeon pox, can be propagated on the embryonic tissue in incubated eggs of chickens. This method of propagation, which eliminates the necessity of constantly collecting virus from actual cases, has therefore come into use for the production of virus vaccines. It is more economical than methods previously employed for preparing fowl pox and pigeon pox vaccines, and, when properly produced, such vaccine has been found to be as potent as that made from pox scabs.

The question is sometimes asked, "if a natural outbreak of fowl pox will produce immunity, why go to the bother of vaccinating?" The reasons may be summed up about as follows:

1. To prevent the possible losses that might result if the disease were allowed to run its course. Vaccination is likely to be considerably cheaper than natural immunity.

2. To speed up the production of immunity.

3. To have some control over the time of occurrence of the disease (vaccination is an artificial production of the disease). Without vaccination, a natural outbreak might occur at a most inconvenient time and might take a long time to go through a flock.

4. To be sure that the lesions have time to heal completely before egg production begins. (Vaccination as well as a natural outbreak immediately prior to or during egg production is likely to depress productivity.)

5. To control the size and location of the lesions. Occasionally the disease spreads from the vaccinated area to other parts of the body, and it may even break out in the diphtheritic form. As a rule, however, the lesion remains confined to the vaccinated area and does not appreciably enlarge.

Birds that have been vaccinated within a year with fowl pox vaccine or that have recovered from the disease within that period may be presumed to be immune. Pigeon pox vaccine imparts only temporary immunity of a relatively low degree. Birds previously vaccinated with the pigeon pox vaccine only and all susceptible adults, yearlings, or pullets should be vaccinated with fowl pox vaccine. Baby chicks should be safeguarded from all contact with the disease, as it is not considered profitable to attempt to immunize them. Other species on the premises, especially turkeys, guineas, and pheasants, should be vaccinated.

The program of vaccination should not be unduly prolonged but should be completed as rapidly as is compatible with efficient work.

If the work is carried over several days, freshly mixed vaccine should be used each day, and birds not yet vaccinated should be kept completely isolated for their own protection. If any adult birds cannot be included, they too must be completely isolated from any contact with the vaccinated birds or their attendants. When pigeon pox vaccine is used, there is little or no danger of the disease spreading among chickens.

Birds to be shipped or to be entered in egglaying contests or exhibitions may be vaccinated with pigeon pox vaccine in order to impart a temporary immunity without undue disturbance of productivity. This vaccine may also be safely employed in protecting a flock approaching the laying season or when the disease has broken out during a period of egg production. Following the cessation of production, however, it would be well to revaccinate the birds with fowl pox vaccine in order to insure a prolonged immunity.

Birds that are weakened by a heavy parasitic infestation or the effects of some other disease condition should not be subjected to vaccination with fowl pox vaccine. Poorly feathered, undernourished, undersized birds or crowded or otherwise poorly housed flocks are not fit subjects for vaccination.

In areas where it is known that the disease does not exist, vaccination is not necessary or desirable. In the first place, the fowls are in no danger of acquiring the disease, and, secondly, the vaccine itself, being the active principle of the disease, may introduce it into the flock and necessitate a continuous vaccination program.

Vaccination at various ages and various times of the year has been recommended. It is possible to vaccinate baby chicks, but it has been shown that this temporarily interferes with gains in weight, and complications with pullorum disease, coccidiosis, and other infections are likely to cause a high mortality from vaccination in young birds.

The practice usually recommended is to vaccinate the pullets with fowl pox vaccine well before the expected onset of egg production. If possible, vaccination should be performed at least 2 months in advance to permit the flock to recuperate fully from the artificially induced disease before beginning to lay. Vaccination between the ages of 12 to 16 weeks usually allows for such an interval.

Contest or exhibition birds should be immunized in time to recover fully before leaving the premises.

Although pigeon pox vaccine may be used without any appreciable disturbance of the bird's health or productivity, it has the disadvantage, as already noted, of giving only temporary and sometimes partial immunity.

Immunity established with fowl pox vaccine, on the other hand, may endure for 1 or 2 years or even for the life of the bird. The lesions caused by this type of vaccination, however, are likely to be severe and may spread to other parts of the body. They usually appear 4 to 9 days after vaccination. Failure of lesions to appear may indicate that the vaccine is impotent or that the bird is already immune. Egg production may be indefinitely postponed by vaccination, or, if it has started, it may be stopped abruptly. The vaccinated birds may be droopy and depressed for a number of days or weeks. Appetite is likely to be impaired. Heavily parasitized or debilitated birds will succumb. Should the artificially induced disease break over into the diphtheritic form, more or less mortality and chronic diphtheria will probably result. However, in the vast majority of flocks, vaccination is not accompanied by these serious after effects, and immunity is established in an interval of 2 to 4 weeks.

PRACTICAL SUGGESTIONS FOR VACCINATION

It is desirable to have one or more assistants in catching and handling the fowls that are to be vaccinated. Adequate help and properly coordinated teamwork play a large part in expediting the work.

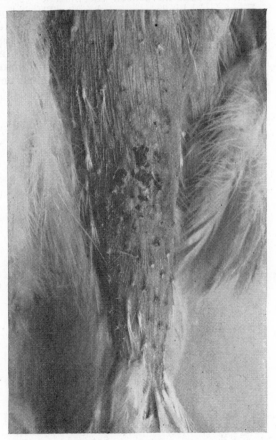

In follicular vaccination, the operator plucks from the thigh of the bird the necessary number of feathers (fig. 3). The same leg or wing should always be vaccinated to facilitate the checking of takes (positive vaccination reactions) later. The flock should be examined for takes in 7 to 10 days. A take is indicated by a typical pox vaccination lesion at the site of inoculation. Birds showing no take should be revaccinated at once with fresh vaccine. A predominating number of no takes suggests either that the flock possesses a certain amount of immunity or that the vaccine used was low or lacking in potency. A history of convalescence from a previous outbreak of fowl pox would go far to explain the occurrence of no takes following vaccination.

FIGURE 3.—Follicular vaccination on the thigh of a chicken, showing inoculated and uninoculated (denuded) follicles.

The powdered vaccine should be mixed with the fluid furnished in the package and nothing else. Under no circumstances should additional water or other fluids be added in order to make it go farther or for any other reason. During operations the mixture should be kept from the rays of the sun and from intense heat or freezing, and it should be kept covered when not in use, to prevent contamination. It should be used the same day it is mixed. If operations are to be interrupted or suspended for as long as 1 hour or more, the mixed vaccine should be placed in a refrigerator. It should not be used the day after it has been mixed.

In large establishments the work of vaccination may require several days, and vaccinated birds should be kept separate from those not yet vaccinated. Systematic procedure will insure that all birds come up for vaccination and that susceptible birds do not come in contact with those that have been vaccinated.

Vaccinated birds are sick birds. They should be made as comfortable as possible, kept dry, and be properly fed and watered.

Some operators prefer to vaccinate at night when the fowls are on the roosts. They are quiet then and may be handled with a minimum of disturbance. Adequate illumination must be provided for night vaccination, but the roosts must be shielded from the light in order not to disturb the rest of the flock.

Psittacosis

BY K. F. MEYER

PSITTACOSIS, a virus disease spread by birds of the parrot family, causes an insidious ailment in human beings that is often hard to distinguish from influenza or pneumonia. Various restrictive measures against birds of the parrot family have been applied in this country in an effort to reduce or wipe out the disease. Recent research discloses the startling fact that the virus may be harbored by other birds, entirely unrelated to parrots—including pigeons and chickens.

IT IS GENERALLY BELIEVED that psittacosis is primarily a disease of parrots, parrakeets, or other birds of the parrot family (psittacine birds) which occasionally spread their infection to other cage birds, such as canaries and finches. That these avian maladies may cause serious pneumonias, not typical of ordinary pneumonia, in human beings is well known. It was recognized in 1931 [2] that the breeding establishments and aviaries for the raising of parrakeets (*Melopsittacus undulatus* (Shaw)) in California harbored apparently healthy birds that were spreading the disease through their droppings. In fact, it was soon realized not only that imported psittacine birds from South America and Australia may be dangerous pets but that the local breeders in the West and in Florida, Texas, and even Canada are the disseminators of sickness.

Until a few months ago, however, it was not suspected that barnyards and pigeon lofts may be sheltering bearers of disease and even death. The unexpected discovery that the disease can exist in such places puts psittacosis in the ranks of diseases of interest and importance to the poultry farmer. Although the available facts are as

[1] K. F. Meyer is Director of the Hooper Foundation, University of California, San Francisco.
[2] MEYER, K. F., and EDDIE, B. LATENT PSITTACOSIS INFECTIONS IN SHELL PARRAKEETS. Soc. Expt. Biol. and Med. Proc. 30: 484–488. 1933.

yet meager, they clearly indicate the magnitude of the problem and the complexity of the control measures that may ultimately be required to prevent serious losses and to protect man from this menace.

With the discovery by Haagen and Mauer [3] that psittacosis affects the Arctic fulmar (*Fulmarus glacialis glacialis* L.), or petrel, on the Faroe Islands and the proved susceptibility of the domestic fowl to the germ,[4] it was anticipated that sooner or later infections of other avian species might be encountered. This has happened; but before the observations are recorded it may be advisable to outline briefly the facts about psittacosis known by the end of 1940.

THE HUMAN DISEASE

The term "psittacosis," from the Greek word for parrot, was suggested in 1895 by Morange to designate a peculiar contagious disease of man which had been noted among members of households exposed to sick birds from foreign countries, primarily parrots. In view of the later findings, described in this article, that the disease is more widespread among birds than was at first realized, the name "ornithosis" might be a suitable designation.

The malady became known through localized outbreaks of severe pneumonia in Switzerland in 1879 and in Paris in 1892. These epidemics stopped after a series of orders prohibiting importations of parrots had been issued. Occasionally single or group infections were reported from England and the United States, but generally the disease ranked as a medical curiosity. From being a rare and obscure infection, psittacosis became a malady of world-wide interest in 1929–30, when shipments of sick parrots imported from South America into Europe and the United States caused disease in 750 to 800 human beings. The subsequent endemic distribution of psittacosis of parrakeets in the United States, Canada, and Germany, which was responsible for an additional 600 recorded human cases, has offered an opportunity to many investigators for a thorough study of the avian as well as the human disease, from the standpoint of its cause as well as its epidemic spread.

It is now firmly established that psittacosis is an infection caused by a filtrable bacterium, known as *Microbacterium multiforme psittacosis*, consisting of a protoplasmic cell which can be microscopically demonstrated and cultivated. The hypothesis originally advanced by Nocard that the disease is a *Salmonella* infection has been entirely abandoned.

Household outbreaks follow a typical pattern. An unusual type of pneumonia suddenly develops in a member of a family into which a parrot or a pair of parrakeets, more rarely canaries or finches, have recently been introduced as cage pets. In rapid succession, additional cases occur among the relatives and even guests or visitors. The responsible birds may or may not be visibly sick. Usually

[3] HAAGEN, E., and MAUER, G. UEBER EINE AUF DEN MENSCHEN ÜBERTRAGBARE VIRUS KRANKHEIT DIE STURMVÖGELN UND IHRE BEZIEHNING ZUR PSITTAKOSE. Zentbl. f. Bakt. [etc.]. Originale (I) 143 : 81–88. 1938.
[4] MEYER, K. F. PSITTACOSIS. 12th Internatl. Vet. Cong. Proc. 3 : 182–205, illus. 1935.

people of middle age are quite susceptible, whereas children rarely contract the malady.

Human beings suffering from psittacosis or ornithosis complain suddenly of general malaise, chills, headache, restlessness, insomnia, nosebleed, and a nonproductive cough (without phlegm). The temperature rises rapidly and after a period of continued elevation begins to fall during the second week. As a rule the signs of a peculiar pneumonia appear early in the X-ray picture but it is difficult to distinguish the changes in the lung tissues from those observed in typical influenza. Despite the inflammation in the lung the breathing rate is only slightly increased, usually no chest pain is noted, and the number of white blood corpuscles does not increase as in typical pneumonia. The patient is unable to raise much sputum. Since these signs are not distinct enough for diagnosis, an examination of the sputum and a blood test are the diagnostic aids commonly used. Convalescence is slow and tedious. The mortality rate, given as 20 percent, is probably too high, since mild, unreported cases are undoubtedly frequent. The younger the individual the greater is the likelihood that the infection will be mild and atypical—like grippe. There is no specific treatment, though serum from recovered patients may reduce the mortality rate.

Occupational liability among persons engaged in the breeding and trading of psittacine birds is high. Laboratory workers, physicians, and sanitary inspectors also frequently contract the disease during the execution of their professional duties. Furthermore, it is important to emphasize that the sputum of patients is sometimes highly infectious, and thus transmission from one human being to another is by no means infrequent.

The infection may be passed from bird to man in one of two ways: (1) Inhalation of dust contaminated with infective particles from dried fecal droppings, urine, feathers, etc., and droplets from the nasal secretions of sick or healthy birds, or (2) by direct contact through bites, though this is rare. The high infectivity of the psittacosis virus, which resembles that of smallpox or measles, is reflected in the histories in which fleeting exposure occurred in a pet shop where diseased birds had been kept. Since air currents may disseminate the virus, actual contact with diseased psittacine birds is not necessary.

Without any definite history of exposure to tropical birds or parrakeets, it is difficult to differentiate psittacosis from influenza or some of the virus pneumonias without laboratory aid. The sputum, if it is raised by the patient in sufficient amounts, may be tested by injecting a suspension of the excretion into the peritoneum, or lining of the abdominal cavity, of white mice. These rodents are extremely susceptible to psittacosis and usually succumb to the infection in 5 to 14 days. In recent years the blood test (complement-fixation test) with specially prepared reagents has proved of great value in the early diagnosis of human infections; moreover, it is useful in discovering the existence of psittacosis in aviaries.

THE DISEASE IN TROPICAL BIRDS AND FINCHES

.The .recognition that avian psittacosis of undetermined origin but as a natural disease is common among the cockatoos, lorikeets, cockateels, and rosellas of the Australian bush, probably serving as a population regulator, and the discovery that shell parrakeets bred and raised in the United States, Canada, and Europe and parrots from Panama and Mexico may act as sources of infection are important contributions resulting from the researches conducted since 1931. Particularly far reaching, however, is the finding that apparently healthy birds may harbor the virus and disseminate it. The incidence of these unrecognized latent infections in aviaries and breeding establishments may range from 10 to 90 percent.

With the aid of the so-called mouse-inoculation test or the blood-serum test, it is now practical to detect these carriers. The suspected large birds are bled from the wing vein; the smaller birds are killed, portions of the liver, spleen, and kidneys carefully ground up, and suspensions of the organs inoculated into white mice or Java rice-birds. When the psittacosis virus is present in the tissues of the suspected birds, the experimental animals acquire the infection and frequently die, providing significant autopsy and microscopic findings. It is important to remember that the clinical manifestations of psittacosis in parrots, parrakeets, canaries, or finches are by no means characteristic, and without laboratory tests the identity of the illness cannot be determined.

In many of the importations, the mortality among the parrots has been very high, whereas in the breeding establishments housing parrakeets under fairly sanitary conditions rarely more than 5 to 10 percent succumb to acute psittacosis. It is well known, however, that many of the pen mates of sick birds carry the infective agent, and, when brought under adverse environmental conditions, such as crowding. malnutrition, and lack of sunlight, these chronically infected birds may suffer relapses. At autopsy, emaciation, an enlarged saffron-colored liver studded with wedge-shaped pale areas of destroyed tissue (infarcts), and a spleen tumor are usually observed. Preparations made from the tissues reveal colonies and clusters of the elementary bodies in large numbers.

Young birds are more susceptible than older ones; the young ones contract the infection in the nests, and whether they are visibly sick or not they may spread the infection for many months and thus maintain the disease indefinitely in breeding establishments or pet shops. The virus-carrying excreta may soil the food and water; hence it is not surprising that contaminated birdseed from pet shops may occasionally cause new infections in cage birds not directly exposed to diseased parrakeets or parrots.

Public health officials are principally concerned with the elimination of infected psittacine birds from the retail trade in pet shops. Some degree of protection has been obtained. by such restrictive measures as an embargo on imported birds, quarantines for not less than 6 months, and isolation. The recent outbreaks of psittacosis in zoological gardens, however, amply attest to the inadequacy of these precautionary measures. Certain States, including Connecticut, New York, and Oregon, maintain a permanent quarantine against psittacine birds.

Since the commercial aviaries engaged in the breeding and raising of shell parrakeets are the principal distributors of diseased birds and the sources of severe outbreaks (epizootics) among canaries and finches in pet shops, California has attempted to free the bird industry from psittacosis in that State. Anyone engaged in selling, trading, or bartering shell parrakeets must obtain a certificate of registration (California Senate Bill 516, 1933). According to regulations, the aviaries must furnish 10 to 20 percent of the birds for two laboratory tests before they may be certified and the birds released for sale. The parrakeets are killed and their viscera tested for virus through inoculation of mice. Aviaries found to harbor birds with the psittacosis virus are quarantined, and the owners are advised to destroy their stocks. The birds of a certified aviary wear a leg band with a code number assigned to them by the California State Department of Public Health. For interstate shipment, the United States Public Health Service requires a certificate issued by the State of origin. These control measures have progressively reduced the incidence of latent infections in California. In 1934, 47, or 23.9 percent, of 196 aviaries were found to harbor latent psittacosis, while in 1941, of 124 establishments only 7, or 5.6 percent, were infected. It is believed that annual retests and a more rigid supervision of dishonest breeders will in time eradicate the infected stocks in California.

PSITTACOSIS IN PIGEONS AND CHICKENS

The investigation of a fatal case of human psittacosis in California disclosed the important fact that the patient had frequently watched the return of some racing pigeons owned by his son. A blood-serum examination of the 30 pigeons involved was made, and 20 gave strong reactions indicative of a present or past infection with the psittacosis virus. The organs of the entire pigeon flock were tested on mice, and a virus similar to that of psittacosis was ultimately isolated from one of the pigeons.

While these studies were in progress, the father of another boy who owned a flock of racing pigeons outside Los Angeles contracted psittacosis. In this case, also, a psittacosis virus was demonstrated as being present in the kidneys of an old, emaciated, and definitely sick female pigeon in the loft.

In New York, a mother and daughter picked up a sick pigeon; both contracted a disease that was diagnosed as psittacosis at the Rockefeller Hospital. Of 30 pigeons obtained through the courtesy of the New York City Health Department, at least 20 gave positive serum reactions.

A group of pigeons obtained from a dealer in the San Francisco Bay area were held in crowded cages in a damp room. Over a period of a month, 8 birds died. On post mortem examination they showed lesions of emaciation, fibrinous pericarditis (inflammation of the membrane around the heart), and peritonitis (inflammation of the membrane lining the abdominal cavity), spleen tumor, and enlarged and engorged livers occasionally studded with small necroses. Since the culture yielded *Salmonella typhimurium* Castellani and Chalmers, the true cause of these deaths was at first not recognized. In view of the observations previously made, an examination of the exudates, or discharges, was instituted, and *Microbacterium multiforme psittacosis* was found. The virus was isolated from two of the dead pigeons, and serum tests made on the remaining birds indicated that the flock had been heavily exposed to the virus.

The wide distribution in the United States of latent psittacosis in pigeons is further attested by the studies of Pinkerton and Swank,[5] who recovered from the inflamed heart covering of pigeons held on a thiamin-deficient diet a bacterium indistinguishable from *Microbacterium multiforme psittacosis*. It is amply supported by serum tests which have been recently made on birds from lofts located in various sections of California, South Carolina, and Iowa. Between 10 and 50 percent of the tests have produced positive reactions. Although the data are limited, they indicate the widespread existence of a psittacosis infection that possesses a highly adapted parasitism for pigeons. It must be reserved for future studies to determine its spread in the pigeon lofts, its relation to pigeon typhoid, its method of escape from the body, and, in consequence, its potential danger to man. In all probability, it is the direct handling of a sick pigeon that entails a certain risk. Methods of control that may be needed to protect the pigeon-breeding industry will have to be worked out in the future.

Once more in connection with the investigation of a human case of psittacosis, attention was called to the possibility that the high mortality of the chickens on a farm in New Jersey had some definite relationship to the case. Investigations led to the isolation of the psittacosis virus from two chickens from this poultry ranch. The disease agent resembles that found in pigeons in a great many ways. How the infection was brought to the poultry-raising establishment is not known. It is not unlikely that doves or pigeons may have introduced it. As early as 1933, Meyer and Eddie observed the transmission of psittacosis to chickens held in a pen with psittacosis-infected parrakeets. The innate susceptibility of the fowl to psittacosis was thus recognized; in the light of the information presented, it must be looked upon as a potentially important poultry disease in the future. From both an economic and a public health point of view, it is imperative that these apparently new infections should receive prompt and detailed investigation.

[5] PINKERTON, H., and SWANK, R. L. RECOVERY OF VIRUS MORPHOLOGICALLY IDENTICAL WITH PSITTACOSIS FROM THIAMIN-DEFICIENT PIGEONS. Soc. Expt. Biol. and Med. 45: 704–706. 1940.

Miscellaneous Diseases of Poultry

BY HUBERT BUNYEA [1]

THIS ARTICLE discusses various diseases and injuries to which poultry are subject, including paratyphoid infection; fowl typhoid; fowl cholera; thrush; aspergillosis; favus; epidemic tremor; avian tuberculosis; poisoning; and bumblefoot, sod disease, and other forms of lameness. The author ends with a set of general recommendations for keeping poultry healthy.

PARATYPHOID INFECTION

FOWLS are susceptible to numerous infections attributable to some member of the paratyphoid group of organisms, of the genus *Salmonella*. Among the principal avian paratyphoid infections are those caused by *S. anatum* in ducks and by *S. aertrycke* in chickens, ducklings, pigeons, and other species (typhimurium). *S. enteritidis* infection of chicks and ducks is prevalent in Europe but not common in the United States.

Paratyphoid infection is characterized by inflammation of the intestines (enteritis), lack of appetite (inappetence), unthriftiness, and diarrhea. The mortality rate is variable. This is essentially a disease of young birds. In adult birds it seldom occurs in acute form, but it may occur with low-grade symptoms, either sporadically or as an epizootic (corresponding to an epidemic of a human disease). In pigeons it is characterized by symptoms of inflammation of the lining of the stomach and intestines (gastroenteritis) and by the formation of abscesses around the joints (periarticular abscesses), especially the wing joints (paratyphoid arthritis), which interfere

[1] Hubert Bunyea is Veterinarian, Pathological Division, Bureau of Animal Industry.

seriously with flying. The abscesses tend to recover without surgical treatment, and flying may be resumed.

The frequency with which the *Salmonella* organism is recovered from ovaries indicates that the infection is probably in some instances transmitted through the egg. Infection may also occur in other organs of the body and be disseminated in the droppings.

Paratyphoid infections are difficult to control. The use of blood tests similar to the test successfully used for diagnosis and control of pullorum disease has not been found practical. The use of hygienic measures in the hatching and rearing of the young is of paramount importance in controlling the disease. Sometimes, however, it is extremely difficult to apply such measures; in pigeon husbandry, for example, the squabs must be fed and reared by the adult pigeons. If it is noted that certain adult birds are particularly unsuccessful in rearing their young on account of paratyphoid infection, such birds should not be used for breeding, or, if they are especially valuable, their eggs might be hatched and the squabs reared by healthy foster parents.

Eggs and poultry affected by paratyphoid infections should not be used as food. In Europe food poisoning has occurred in numerous instances from meringues, mayonnaise, custards, and other articles containing uncooked or partially cooked duck eggs. In the United States one or two instances of such poisoning have served to emphasize the advisability of thoroughly cooking duck eggs originating from flocks known to be or suspected of being affected with paratyphoid infections. The flesh of squabs harboring paratyphoid infection, if incompletely cooked, may also be the cause of food poisoning of human beings.

FOWL TYPHOID

Fowl typhoid occurs sporadically in almost every part of the United States. It attacks chickens, turkeys, pigeons, and other domestic species. Being a form of bacteriemic infection [2] caused by *Shigella gallinarum*, it somewhat resembles fowl cholera in its symptoms and course. Mortality is not so high as in fowl cholera, however, and in general the condition is not of major importance, particularly in chickens. The decline of the disease among chickens probably results, at least in part, from the fact that typhoid carriers are detected by the blood test for pullorum disease and are removed along with the pullorum carriers. Typhoid in turkeys is increasing in importance.

In the absence of a remedy or a dependable vaccine for typhoid, the condition must be controlled largely through the application of sanitary measures. No reliable statistics are available concerning mortality among poultry due to various causes, but this disease is not now an important factor in poultry raising.

[2] A bacteriemic infection is one characterized by the presence of living bacteria in the blood stream.

FOWL CHOLERA

Fowl cholera is an infectious disease caused by the organism *Pasteurella avicida*. It affects all domesticated fowl but is most serious in chickens. It is manifested by intestinal disturbances, depression, and a high mortality. The disease assumes both the acute and chronic forms. Chronic cases may become carriers and perpetuate the infection from season to season. Outside the body of the carrier, the infection is easily destroyed by sanitary measures and by the natural elements. In the absence of any dependable means of immunizing susceptible birds or curing sick ones, sanitation has been the principal defense against fowl cholera for many years. A whole-blood agglutination test has recently been developed which detects fowl cholera carriers, thus making it possible to remove the source of perpetuation of the infection. It is thought that the application of this test during a chronic outbreak or at the subsidence of an acute outbreak will permit the detection of the carrier birds and that their removal will break the cycle of the infection in the flock. The test has not yet gained wide acceptance, however, and has had only limited trials.

Fowl cholera is not limited in its occurrence to any particular geographical location. It is probably most prevalent in the Middle West, and it is a serious problem at poultry-fattening plants and among feeder poultry in transit by railroad to eastern markets but not in the industry generally. No figures are available as to the losses caused by this disease.

MYCOSIS

Mycosis is a disease caused by fungus growths. Fungi attack the skin, respiratory tract, and digestive tract of chickens. The most serious type of mycosis is that which affects the digestive tract. Known as thrush or moniliasis and caused by the fungus *Saccharomyces albicans*, it affects chickens, pigeons, turkeys, and geese. Gray or white patches form on the mucous membranes of the gastric tract and sometimes enlarge and run together. A discharge runs from the mouth. Loss of appetite, weakness, and emaciation ensue and there is a progressive diarrhea, with green droppings. Mortality runs high in the affected birds, and production is curtailed in those that survive.

Medicinal treatment in the form of mild antiseptics may be applied to visible lesions, but the disease, if deep-seated, is beyond the reach of drugs. Clean houses, clean drinking fountains, feed that is free from molds, and dry litter all aid in the prevention or control of the disease. It is not of major economic importance and probably does not occur to any great extent in well-managed establishments.

Preparatory to medicinal treatment, the accessible thrush deposits in the mouth and larynx of the affected bird should be removed with forceps, after which the ulcers should be painted with a mixture of 4 parts of glycerin and 1 part of tincture of iodine. Thrush of the crop may be treated by washing out the crop with a 2-percent solution of boric acid, using a fountain syringe.

Mycosis of the Air Passages (Aspergillosis)

Mycosis of the air passages may occur in any species of fowl but is particularly prevalent among waterfowl and zoo birds. It is caused by the green mold *Aspergillus fumigatus* and sometimes by the black mold *A. niger*.

The disease assumes the form of chronic progressive dyspnea (labored breathing) attended with unthriftiness and emaciation. Mucous rales—a gurgling sound in the breathing—occur when the bird exhales. These and the usual mouth-breathing (gasping) symptoms may be mistaken for evidences of avian diphtheria, laryngotracheitis, bronchitis, or coryza. Aspergillosis, however, may be differentiated at autopsy by the appearance of white or dirty-yellowish nodules (small lumps) in the trachea, lungs, or air sacs. In advanced cases these lesions may coalesce into elevated dirty deposits consisting of mold growths in the air passages. Aspergillosis in brooder chicks (brooder pneumonia) may be confused with pullorum disease, which sometimes affects the lungs of baby chicks, producing dyspneic and pneumonic manifestations. Aspergillosis of young chicks is rapidly and invariably fatal. In older birds the condition assumes the more chronic form, but there are no recoveries. Medicinal treatment or vaccination is of no known value in combating the condition. The only procedure that can be recommended as having any prospect of controlling aspergillosis is the practice of strict sanitation. Moldy feeds and moldy litter must be removed; floors, nests, dropping boards, and feed and water containers should be cleaned and disinfected; and clean litter and unspoiled feed should be provided.

Feed bags that have become damp and moldy are a possible source of the disease and should be destroyed. Feed should be purchased in new bags and stored in such a way that molds and dampness cannot occur. The feeding of wet mashes necessitates scrupulous care in the daily cleansing of the feed receptacles. Left-over wet mash should be discarded beyond the reach of the flock.

The sick birds should be segregated or, better still, destroyed so they cannot spread the infection. Those that die should be burned or otherwise disposed of properly.

Mycosis of the Skin (Favus, White Comb, Avian Mycotic Dermatitis)

Favus is caused by the fungus *Lophophyton gallinae*, which is readily transmitted from bird to bird and is also said to be infectious to human beings. It is manifested by the formation of grayish-white growths or crusts on the unfeathered head parts of the affected bird. If it spreads to the feathered part, the feathers break off, and the disease becomes increasingly difficult to· control. Birds so affected had better be destroyed. When only the unfeathered parts of the body are affected, the daily application of tincture of iodine to the lesions has been recommended. Greater success has been reported, however, from applying formalized petrolatum, which is prepared by adding 5 percent (by weight) of commercial formalin to melted petrolatum and shaking these together in a tightly closed container until the petrolatum has congealed. One application of formalized petrolatum is said to have effected a cure in nearly all cases treated. **Rubber gloves should be worn during its preparation and administration.**

INFECTIOUS AVIAN ENCEPHALOMYELITIS

Infectious avian encephalomyelitis (epidemic tremor) occurs in chicks 1 to 2 days up to 2 to 3 weeks old. Fifty percent or more of the chicks in a flock may be affected. Many are likely to recover, but others may continue to manifest some tremor symptoms for a time.

The practice usually recommended is to finish surviving chicks quickly for early marketing as broilers or fryers. Under favorable living conditions, the recovered and slowly convalescing birds may mature and may become normally productive of eggs and healthy chicks. They may, however, turn out to be carriers of the infection, which they may transmit to their offspring.

The disease does not usually affect every hatch but may disappear during the hatching season only to return unexpectedly, recurring sporadically from to time with varying degrees of severity.

The disease is disseminated through contact among the brood. It may also be spread through contact in the incubator, and there is some scientific evidence to indicate that infection may be handed down from parent to offspring through the egg. In this way epidemic tremor may be broadcast to remote areas through the dispersal of an infected or exposed hatch of chicks. Fortunately some strains of chickens appear to possess more resistance to the disease than others.

AVIAN TUBERCULOSIS

Tuberculosis is a chronic infectious disease which affects practically all species of domesticated birds and many species of wild birds in captivity. It is manifested by the formation of nodules in various organs, such as the liver, spleen, kidneys, and heart muscle, and along the mesentery and intestinal tract. The seriousness of the tuberculosis problem in connection with poultry, the distribution of the disease, the use of the tuberculin test, and the preventive measures are discussed in the article on Tuberculosis, page 246. It is necessary here to add only a few points to that discussion.

The clinical diagnosis of avian tuberculosis is difficult because many of the symptoms, such as emaciation, dejection, articular lameness of legs or wings, paleness, and diarrhea, are common to other conditions. However, the occurrence of numerous cases showing one or more of such symptoms, along with a history of occasional mortality in the flock, strongly suggests tuberculosis infection. An early symptom is emaciation of the breast muscles, and this progresses to the point where no flesh separates the skin and bone. The bird continues to eat well, and the temperature remains normal until the approach of death, when it becomes subnormal. Autopsies of such birds show an almost complete absence of body or visceral fat.

The lameness occurring in an advanced stage of the disease is occasioned by purulent swellings of the affected articulations, or joints. These swellings may rupture and exude a cheesy pus. The head parts are strikingly pale, withered, and dry. Listlessness and weakness are progressive. A greenish or yellowish diarrhea develops and aggravates the weakened condition of the birds. The feathers assume a ruffled, unkempt appearance as a result of the bird's weakness and neglect in preening itself.

Tuberculous lesions found in the carcass include large or small tumorlike masses within the liver, spleen, kidney, ovaries, peritoneum, intestinal tract, joints, and elsewhere. The occurrence of such lesions is not, however, conclusive as a diagnosis of tuberculosis. The final proof is the microscopic demonstration of the presence of the organism of the disease.

The tuberculin test is, in general, reliable and it is useful within certain limits. The cost of the test and the labor of applying it, although moderate, must be taken into consideration, especially when planning to test flocks of no more than average value. Whether or not the tuberculin test is applied, it is important to obtain a diagnosis when the disease is suspected.

Since avian tuberculosis is not amenable to medicinal treatment, the only method of control is the slaughter of all reactors to tuberculin or all clinically suspicious cases of the disease. Where the infection appears to have taken a firm hold, it is frequently desirable to destroy the entire flock; although, if the birds are of exceptional breeding value, it may be advisable in rare cases to preserve them long enough to obtain a few hatching eggs to perpetuate the strain. Such eggs must be hatched and the resulting chicks reared under the most hygienic conditions.

After an outbreak of tuberculosis, strict sanitary measures, including disinfection, should be taken, as discussed in another part of this article, page 1009. Only after the premises have been completely freed of the infection will it be safe to introduce new stock from healthy sources.

The practice of disposing of all birds when they are about 16 or 18 months of age tends to reduce to a minimum the chances of having dangerous cases of tuberculosis on the place, since it is known that as a rule the disease develops very slowly in the growing bird.

COMMON FORMS OF POISONING OF POULTRY

LIMBER-NECK (BOTULISM)

The toxic disease known as limber-neck, or botulism, of chickens is characterized primarily by the dysphagia (difficult swallowing) caused by paralysis of the pharynx, lack of appetite, and a paralysis of the neck muscles which makes it impossible for the bird to raise or control its head.

Botulism is caused by eating feed or other material which has been contaminated with the organism *Clostridium botulinum* and on which this germ has multiplied and elaborated its toxic byproducts. Decomposed flesh and the maggots of flies which have bred on it are considered probable sources of botulinus poisoning. Ducks frequenting the western marshlands have died in great numbers from botulism. (See Diseases of Wildlife and Their Relation to Domestic Livestock, p. 1225.)

Early symptoms of botulism include lassitude, drowsiness, and leg weakness. The fowl first loses the ability to stand on its feet and then the power to hold up its head. It finally assumes a posture of extreme prostration from which it cannot be aroused. The feathers become loose and are easily shed if the bird is handled. The severity of the symptoms depends on the amount of the toxin swallowed. The paralysis may affect the eyes to the extent of preventing the contraction of the pupils, and may also cause a relaxation of the bowels, resulting in diarrhea.

The course of the disease is fairly rapid, death usually occurring a few hours after the appearance of symptoms.

By the time symptoms are noted, it is usually too late for effective treatment. Birds exposed to the toxin but not yet affected may be given a drench of Epsom salts solution, 1 pound of Epsom salts being used for each 100 birds treated, or about 1 teaspoonful of the crystals, dissolved in water, for each bird. The solution may be introduced into the crop by means of a funnel or fountain syringe to insure complete dosage and prompt action. Botulinus antitoxin, types A and C, may be given intraperitoneally—injected into the lining of the abdomen. (Type B botulinus toxin does not affect poultry.) The cost of the treatment is prohibitive, however, except for birds of unusual value.

The crops of affected or exposed birds may be emptied and flushed out with fluids or evacuated by surgical incision if the value of the birds justifies such procedure.

When an outbreak of limber-neck occurs, an effort should be made to locate the cause. Decomposed flesh, dead animals and fowls, etc., which may be accessible to poultry, should be burned or buried. Spoiled canned goods used as feed are a prolific source of limber-neck among poultry.

CHEMICAL POISONING

Poultry are susceptible to chemical poisoning, but they exhibit a tolerance for relatively large doses of some poisonous substances. It is not wise, however, to leave rat poisons containing arsenic, phosphorus, barium carbonate, or other poisonous substances within reach of poultry, or to allow poultry access to orchards, cabbage patches, or other farm areas that have recently been sprayed or dusted with arsenical preparations.

Arsenic is sometimes employed for poisoning locusts or grasshoppers. Poultry eating a number of such poisoned insects or a quantity of the bait may be poisoned by the arsenic. Chickens sometimes gain access to poison bait containing strychnin intended for poisoning crows or hawks, with disastrous results.

Kamala and nicotine sulfate, sometimes used for ridding poultry of parasites, are dangerous unless used in accordance with directions. Kamala may cause a serious bowel disturbance, with a resultant loss of egg production as well as a decrease in egg weight. Small doses of a well-diluted solution of nicotine sulfate have proved fatal to young chickens.

Other toxic material frequently left within reach of poultry includes fish brine, ice-cream salt, calcium carbide slack from acetylene gas tanks, and similar substances. Spent fireworks are dangerous around poultry premises. Instances are on record of children detonating "devil-chasers" in the driveway of the farm home and leaving them there, with the result that early the next morning pullets picked up the sharp gravel from the fireworks in the driveway and within a short time died of phosphorus poisoning.

Satisfactory treatments of poultry for the various kinds of chemical poisoning mentioned are not known.

Rose Chafer Poisoning

Rose chafers are found in great numbers on grapevines, rose bushes, and other shrubbery during the spring. Young chickens eat these beetles readily and are fatally poisoned by a relatively small number of them. Some birds may recover from a slight attack of the poisoning. Drowsiness and weakness are the first symptoms, followed by prostration and convulsions. The head is thrown back, and the bird utters shrill cries.

No treatment is effective after the poison has begun to act. Birds that have been exposed to the danger may be given Epsom salts or castor oil to hasten the elimination of any beetles swallowed. Young chicks should be restrained from visiting areas infested with rose chafers.

LAMENESS IN POULTRY

Poultry may acquire leg lameness and sometimes wing lameness from a variety of causes, environmental, nutritional, infectious, and parasitic.

Lameness Due to Environmental Conditions
Injuries

Young chicks sometimes get their feet or hock joints caught in the meshes of wire-cloth battery-brooder floors. As a precaution against such accidents it is well to use wire cloth of sufficiently close mesh so that the legs or feet of chicks are not likely to become ensnared.

Fowls of any age living where the winters are cold may freeze their toes and feet. If sufficiently frost-bitten, the toes will become swollen and sore, then gangrenous, and finally drop off, leaving the foot tender and crippled. There is no cure for seriously frosted feet. The obvious preventive measure is to confine the fowls to comfortable living quarters with warm, dry floors and plenty of litter.

Bumblefoot

Bumblefoot is a swelling of the feet of poultry caused by an accumulation of a cheesy exudate, or discharge. Various explanations have been offered for its occurrence. It has long been believed that injury caused by jumping from high roosts to hard floors was responsible for this condition, but its occurrence where roosts are low and floors are well bedded with litter throws doubt upon that theory. It is probable that, through briar wounds and otherwise, infection gains entry into the tissues of the foot and sets up the production of pus in the underlying tissues, causing the bird great pain as well as lameness.

Staphylococcus aureus, the yellow-pus organism, has frequently been isolated from bumblefoot lesions and is considered the probable cause in some cases. An acid-fast organism resembling *Mycobacterium tuberculosis avium* has been demonstrated microscopically to be present in this condition, but its significance as a causative factor has not been established.

The treatment of bumblefoot should include all possible provisions for relieving the suffering of the affected birds. Low roosts and well-bedded floors are helpful. The abscesses may be evacuated by removing the scabs from the pad of the foot and the between-the-toes spaces and extracting the cheesy pus by pressure and the use of forceps. In advanced cases it may be necessary to lance the foot to remove the pus completely. The cavity may then be irrigated with some mild but effective antiseptic, such as 5-percent phenol or full-strength hydrogen peroxide solution, after which the cavity may be packed with pads of cotton soaked in a similar solution and bandaged with gauze and adhesive tape to keep the wound clean. The treatment should be repeated at 2- to 3-day intervals until evidence of healing appears.

A type of bumblefoot caused by a deficiency of vitamin A has been described.

Sod Disease

Sod disease is a vesicular dermatitis (an inflammation of the skin characterized by small swellings filled with fluid) of young chicks and occasionally older fowls ranging in early summer on unbroken prairie land. Blisters and swelling of the feet, culminating in scabs, eventually cause lameness. Parts of or even whole toes may slough off. Recovered birds may develop misshapen toes. The eyelids may stick together, and the birds may be unable to find their feed.

The disease is economically important not only because of rather high mortality in young birds but also because of the permanent disability caused by chronic foot trouble in recovered cases.

No cause or cure for the disease is known, but it can be easily prevented by excluding the birds from unplowed prairie land.

LAMENESS DUE TO FAULTY NUTRITION

Nutritional diseases of poultry are discussed in detail in another part of this report. The types of lameness that may be classified as of nutritional origin include articular gout, polyneuritis, rickets, slipped tendon (perosis), nutritional encephalomalacia, and nutritional paralysis and curled-toe disease.

One of the forms of gout consists of swollen and painful joints of the legs or wings caused by the depositing of urates in the articular regions, rendering movement difficult and increasing the danger of starvation. Although the cause of gout is not clear in all cases, it is believed at times to be due to a prolonged feeding of high protein rations. Lack of exercise and factors affecting the proper function of the kidneys are also possibly involved in the origin and development of gout.

The swollen joints, if opened at autopsy, are found to contain a yellowish exudate consisting of waste matter from the kidneys. Similar chalky deposits may be found in the kidneys, which are usually pale and swollen. The surface of the heart, liver, spleen, and mesentery may also present a pearly, chalklike appearance due to urate deposits (salts of uric acid), and may reveal a marked absence of visceral fat.

From the dietetic standpoint, the occurrence of gout in a flock suggests the advisability of a reduction of protein to a level of not more than 10 percent of the total ration and an increase in the proportion of bulky green feeds. The entire flock may be put on a saline purge consisting in the administration of a solution containing one-third of· a teaspoonful of Epsom salts crystals per hen. The painful swellings in the vicinity of articulations may be lanced and the urates evacuated, after which the incision may be dressed with a healing ointment such as zinc oxide ointment and bandaged to keep out contamination.

LAMENESS DUE TO INFECTIONS

The principal form of lameness due to infection is fowl paralysis. The disease is discussed at length elsewhere in this book (p. 944).

Paratyphoid arthritis occurring specifically in pigeons infected with *Salmonella typhimurium* is discussed in connection with paratyphoid infections.

Lameness from Fowl Cholera

Like avian tuberculosis, fowl cholera tends to form localized foci of infection. Common locations are in the articular regions of the legs or wings.

Outbreaks of the chronic form of fowl cholera may be characterized by a number of cases of lameness in the flock. An examination of the lame birds may disclose a soft or doughy lump on the joint of the affected member. The abscess will be found to be filled with pus as a result of localization of the cholera infection at that point. The presence of the active infection in these lesions may be demonstrated by laboratory procedures.

No treatment for lameness from fowl cholera infection can be recommended. Birds so affected are a menace and should be destroyed.

Staphylococcic Arthritis

In addition to being a cause of bumblefoot, the pus-producing organism *Staphylococcus aureus*, through infection of the joints, causes a number of other conditions resulting in lameness of the feet, legs, or wings of various species of birds.

Staphylococcic arthritis occurs in chickens, ducks, geese, turkeys, pigeons, pheasants, and possibly other species. The common symptoms in all species are lameness and swelling of the affected joints. Autopsy findings may vary from local abscesses to the erosion of articular surfaces of the bones and pus in the tendon sheaths and bones. Mortality is relatively high.

Treatment is palliative, giving relief only, and consists in providing comfortable housing conditions, with feed and water easily accessible to the sick birds. Separation of the affected individuals contributes to their comfort and may help to check the spread of the disease. Sanitation about the premises, including cleanliness of feed and water supply, should not be overlooked. No medicinal treatment can be recommended.

LAMENESS FROM PARASITIC INFESTATION

Chickens, turkeys, pheasants, partridges, and caged birds are susceptible to infestation by a parasitic itch mite (*Cnemidocoptes mutans*), which causes the condition known as scaly leg, discussed in the article on Poultry Mites, page 1058.

KEEPING POULTRY HEALTHY

Proper location of the poultry house will do much toward keeping a flock healthy. The poultry quarters should be on light, preferably sandy, well-drained soil and should be provided with some trees or shelters for shade. The house should face opposite the direction from which storms ordinarily come.

Clean, comfortable, well-ventilated and spacious poultry houses, abundant and nourishing feeds, and clean water in clean receptacles help keep fowls in good physical condition; when these things are provided, no medicine is needed to keep poultry well and productive. Without such provisions, no medicinal treatment will insure the maintenance of health.

In brooder houses, young fowls require some warmth under the hovers, but only enough not to become chilled. Too much heat is probably as unfavorable as too little. Ventilation is essential, when coal or oil heat is used, since chicks in poorly ventilated brooder houses may be killed by an accumulation of carbon monoxide gas. The floor space should not be crowded, and as the chicks grow they should from time to time be given additional room. By degrees, depending on the advance of milder weather and the state of development of the birds, artificial heat should be gradually diminished.

Feed hoppers and water fountains of a size and shape to provide space for fowls of any age should be supplied; otherwise, some birds will monopolize the privileges, and others, perhaps small and unthrifty to start with, will be crowded out.

Growing stock may be reared to maturity on open range provided sufficient area is available so that the houses or range shelters may be moved at frequent intervals. Sufficient ground around the shelter may be enclosed so that the birds may range for a week or more. Grass sod makes an excellent range for young poultry, but the location should be changed before the sod is bare or the ground polluted. As the birds grow, additional space becomes necessary, and this can be provided by taking out the males at about 8 weeks of age.

When the breeders are taken off the range, weaklings and unthrifty birds should be rigidly culled out. The laying houses, including floors, dropping boards, and nests, should be in good condition and thoroughly cleaned and disinfected, aired out, and thoroughly dried, and the floors should be covered with clean litter for the new occupants. Provision should be made for correct ventilation. Feed and water receptacles should be clean and in good working condition. Large laying flocks had best be divided into smaller breeding units, not only from the standpoint of matings and as good husbandry practice, but also as an aid to proper hygiene. Pullets off the range should be housed separately from old hens. Under no circumstances should birds of different species be housed together.

The windows of laying houses should be covered with mesh wire to keep out free-flying birds. Fly screening is even better, since flies and mosquitoes are carriers of poultry-disease infections. The doors also should be screened. Poultry hucksters, feed and remedy salesmen, and other transients should be positively excluded from poultry houses and their vicinity. In disease-ridden localities it is good policy to refrain from showing neighbors or visitors around poultry premises or, if this cannot be tactfully avoided, to provide them with clean overshoes. Where poultry diseases exist in one part of the establishment or in neighboring flocks, it is suggested that at the door of the poultry houses cocomats be set in shallow concrete depressions and be kept soaked with a diluted cresol compound solution, carbolic acid, or stock dip. Persons entering the houses may thus easily wipe and disinfect the soles of their footwear at one operation. The lye solutions recommended elsewhere in this article for disinfecting purposes might be injurious to shoes.

New birds purchased for breeding or show purposes, as well as birds returning from poultry exhibitions or egg-laying contests, should be kept under quarantine for observation for a period of 2 to 4 weeks before being placed with the flock. Should there be evidence of disease during this period, competent advice should be sought concerning the disposal of such birds or others exposed to them.

The occurrence of infectious disease in a flock calls for prompt and decisive action. The sick birds should be carefully separated from the healthy ones, and if possible the healthy birds should be moved to clean comfortable quarters. If this is not practicable, the sick ones must be taken out and the place promptly cleaned and disinfected as thoroughly as possible, the healthy birds during this time being temporarily moved out to a place where no diseased poultry have been. After each room is cleaned and disinfected, new dry litter should be placed on the floor, and then the flock may be readmitted. The healthy birds should be closely observed for the possible appearance of new cases of disease.

The advisability of keeping the sick birds in separate quarters for medicinal treatment is very doubtful. It is usually better to destroy them, since sick chickens seldom respond to treatment and may only be a means of perpetuating infection on the premises. The carcasses of fowls that die from disease should be autopsied, if at all, by a competent diagnostician. In any event such carcasses should be completely burned or buried deep in the ground.

Preparatory to disinfecting poultry houses, all nesting, litter, manure, and other contaminated material and movable equipment should be removed. Dust and cobwebs should be swept from the ceilings, window sills, and ledges. Beginning with the ceiling and taking in all surfaces, the entire room from top to bottom should be thoroughly sprayed with a suitable germicidal solution. Numerous disinfecting substances are satisfactory for this operation.[3] For general purposes a satisfactory solution may be prepared by dissolving 1 pound of commercial lye containing 94 percent of sodium hydroxide and 2½ pounds of water-slaked lime in 5½ gallons of water. It should be strained through a fine wire screen to remove particles of lime which might otherwise clog the sprayer. Any type of sprayer may be used to apply the disinfectant, but one that generates enough air pressure to drive the solution with considerable force onto the surface to be disinfected is especially effective. All surfaces should be thoroughly wet with the solution, which should also be forced into all cracks and corners. The white residue on the surface that has received the treatment will indicate spots that have been missed. The unused solution should be tightly covered to prevent deterioration. The ground around the poultry house may be disinfected with the same solution, using ½ to 1 gallon for each square yard to be disinfected. The yard must, however, be thoroughly cleaned of trash and refuse beforehand.

Because of the caustic nature of lye solutions, the following precautions should be observed: **The operator should protect his person and clothing by wearing rubber boots, coat, hat, and gloves. He should also protect his eyes with goggles.** Lye solutions should not be used on painted surfaces or fabric curtains. The spray apparatus should be thoroughly flushed out with clean water after use to avoid damage to leather or fabric gaskets, fabric-lined hose, etc.

A single exception is made to the recommendation of lye solution as a disinfectant. It has been found that it does not destroy the germs of tuberculosis. To combat that infection, the usual preparatory measures are taken, after which the premises and utensils are thoroughly sprayed with a material such as compound solution of creosol or a permitted saponified creosol solution in 3-percent dilution, or carbolic acid in 5-percent dilution. Some other germicides also are known to be effective against *Mycobacterium tuberculosis avium*.

---

[3] The reader is referred to Farmers' Bulletin 926, Some Common Disinfectants, and Farmers' Bulletin 954, The Disinfection of Stables, as well as to Disinfection and Disinfectants, in this Yearbook, p. 179.

A final suggestion concerning the prevention of diseases in poultry: It is a good idea to provide for a competent periodic inspection service on the health of the flock, including expert advice on the hygiene of the surroundings. Such service cannot be satisfactorily given by itinerant "poultry specialists," who probably have no reliable recommendation and all too frequently have something to sell. The local veterinarian, on the other hand, has qualified himself for the task of controlling poultry diseases and may be looked to with confidence to make clinical examinations, apply diagnostic tests, administer vaccines and remedies, and suggest sanitary measures calculated to cope with whatever disease problem may confront the poultryman. The staffs of many State agricultural experiment stations are also in a position to render similar services. Poultrymen would save themselves considerable financial and other losses if they would obtain competent diagnosis and advice on disease problems instead of giving undue heed to the advice of unqualified strangers or even to that of well-meaning but uninformed neighbors.

Internal Parasites of Poultry

BY EVERETT E. WEHR
AND JOHN F. CHRISTENSEN [1]

A THOROUGH ACCOUNT of the principal parasites of poultry in the United States, including practical measures for preventing some of the heavy annual losses from this source.

JAMES E. RICE, formerly head of the Poultry Husbandry Department of Cornell University, who has been called the father of poultry husbandry in the United States, once made the statement that there was no way to save the poultry industry except through a scientific approach to the control of poultry diseases. The significance of this statement becomes apparent with the realization that losses from poultry diseases in the United States have been estimated by Government authorities to be approximately 100 million dollars annually.

That the presence of disease has been responsible for the curtailment of poultry raising in many areas cannot be questioned. A few years ago poultrymen in many sections of the United States were forced to abandon the raising of turkeys because of the prevalence of blackhead, caused by a protozoan parasite. Only a drastic change in poultry-husbandry practices made turkey production again a profitable enterprise in these areas.

Farmers are losing 18.8 percent of their poultry because of disease, or 1 out of every 5 birds, according to C. M. Ferguson of the University of Ohio. This is a tremendous loss, since statistics indicate that chickens are kept on 85 percent of the farms in the United States at the present time.

Internal parasitism is usually more insidious, and therefore not so noticeable as specific diseases, many of which are deadly in their effects and spectacular in nature, but parasites constitute a real menace to successful poultry raising. Unlike bacterial diseases, the majority

[1] Everett E. Wehr is Zoologist and John F. Christensen is Associate Protozoologist, Zoological Division, Bureau of Animal Industry.

of the parasitic diseases do not result in early fatalities. The protozoan diseases, blackhead and coccidiosis, are exceptions, since the destruction of the intestinal mucous membrane in the former and of the
liver tissue in the latter are attended by a high rate of mortality.

Poultry raisers are demanding more and better control measures
for both parasites and diseases. Though only a few satisfactory
drugs for the removal of poultry parasites have been found, practical
and reliable control measures are not lacking. Sanitation, when
properly carried out, has proved to be one of the most effective and
practical means of reducing parasitism in poultry flocks.

Since measures for the control of internal parasites in poultry are
largely preventive and apply to almost the whole group of parasites,
they will be discussed first in this article. The little that can be done
in the way of curative treatment will also be included in the first part
of the article. Descriptions of the large numbers of poultry parasites
and the injuries they cause will follow the section on control.

CONTROL OF POULTRY PARASITES

Many species of parasites must spend a part of their developmental
cycle outside the body of the host or they cannot continue to exist.
In the case of poultry parasites, with few exceptions, the stage away
from the bird is spent in the feces. Some of the protozoan parasites,
however, spend this developmental stage in the blood stream, and
these parasites are therefore not eliminated through any of the body
openings of the host. Their escape from the body depends on their
being removed by bloodsucking insects.

In their infective stages, parasites are introduced into susceptible
hosts in a number of ways: (1) By means of contaminated litter and
soil. (2) By means of contaminated food and water. (3) By means
of carriers; birds that have had a light infection or have survived
a more severe one may carry the organisms within their intestinal
tracts for long periods of time and spread the parasites in their discharges. (4) By intermediate hosts; insects such as flies, mosquitoes,
and beetles, or other low forms of animal life such as snails and slugs,
in which a part of the development of the parasite takes place, are
eaten by susceptible hosts, and as a result infection is set up. (5) By
mechanical means; animals and human beings may carry infective
material on their feet and thus spread the parasites from one pen to
another—attendants have been known to carry infective material
from an infected pen to a sanitary one; contaminated chicken coops
and other equipment may be a source of infection when carelessly
moved from place to place or used for healthy birds.

PREVENTION VERSUS CURE

The old adage that an ounce of prevention is worth a pound of cure
is just as applicable to poultry parasites as it is to human diseases.
After a disease has once gained a foothold in a flock, far more time
and money are usually spent in getting rid of the disease than would

have been necessary to keep the premises free of it. In addition, the mortality may be high before the disease is finally checked.

Preventive measures include sanitation, disinfection, hygiene, and management.

SANITATION AND HYGIENE

Sanitation means establishing an environment in which the possibility of infection with disease-producing organisms is reduced to a minimum.

The first essential is the proper selection of the poultry site. The soil should be of a sandy or gravelly nature in order to provide for good drainage. To take advantage of natural drainage, the site should preferably be located on a gentle slope. If the lay of the land or the nature of the soil renders natural drainage impossible, artificial drainage must be resorted to. Since moisture is essential to the development of most parasites in their free-living stages, the presence of surface water, which the birds are apt to drink, must be regarded as unhealthful. Pools of water in the poultry yards should be immediately filled in or drained.

Poultry houses or shelters are essential for the protection of the birds against inclement weather, including rain, storms, and extremes of temperature. The excreta, or body wastes, of the birds which collect in the houses or shelters must be properly handled, or they may serve as a source of infection with parasites and other diseases. Irrespective of the type of poultry house built, it is of the utmost importance that it possess certain features of design and arrangement to facilitate cleaning and to keep the birds well and strong. The floors and walls should be constructed of material that is impervious to moisture and easy to clean and will exclude vermin of all types. Floors of dirt or wood are seriously objectionable because they are difficult to clean and disinfect; concrete floors are much more desirable. The roosts and nests should be simply constructed so that they may be taken apart easily for cleaning and disinfecting. (See Farmers' Bulletin 1070 (*10*).)[2] The house should be so constructed as to insure the entrance of an abundance of direct sunlight, which is important to the health of the fowls as well as destructive to bacteria and certain parasites.

The hygienic condition of poultry yards is of tremendous importance to the health of the birds. It is not so convenient to collect and dispose of body wastes in the poultry runs as in the houses. For this reason, the small overcrowded poultry runs too frequently observed are apt to receive a larger amount of wastes than the ground can adequately take care of. When a disease is once introduced in such a place, it quickly becomes epizootic, that is, like an epidemic among human beings, and soon all the birds have contracted it. This condition exists on many farms in the United States, and because of the prevalence of disease under such conditions, the individual farm flock rarely pays for itself.

---

[2] Italic numbers in parentheses refer to Literature Cited, p. 1037.

PERMANENT QUARTERS OR ROTATION

Keeping birds on the same ground year after year will ultimately cause the soil to become a more or less continual hotbed of infection if parasitized or diseased birds are present in the flock. The eggs of parasites are known to live in the soil from year to year, and contaminated soil serves as an important source of infection for the intermediate hosts of poultry parasites.

What is the remedy for such a situation? The course that a poultryman may choose depends very largely on the size of the flock, the available space for rearing the birds, the amount of money that can be allotted for poultry equipment, and the type of soil. If only a small area of land is available, it may be best to raise the birds in confinement. This system has the advantage that the birds may occupy the same quarters year after year. In order to provide adequate sunlight, a small wire-covered sun porch may be constructed in front of the house, or there may be a small fenced-in yard covered with cinders or other porous material.

Where a considerable area of land is available for poultry raising, the practice of rotating the fowls has been followed with reasonably good success. This system consists of using enclosed poultry yards which are occupied by the birds intermittently in order to prevent excessive contamination. The four-yard system is the one most widely advocated and is probably the one best suited for general farm practice. A plot of land—the acreage depends on the number of birds to be raised, figuring about 650 to 800 birds per acre—is fenced and cross fenced so as to have four equal-sized pens. The shelter or house is located in the center of the plot and built with a door opening directly into each pen. The birds are placed in lot No. 1, kept there for a month or two, and then moved into lot No. 2. The practice of moving the birds at regular intervals from one pen to another is continued until all four pens have been occupied, when the birds are again placed in pen No. 1. Immediately following the removal of the birds from one of the pens, the ground should be prepared and planted to some green crop or left idle to undergo self-sterilization. In the latter case the contaminated soil is left undisturbed so that the sun, wind, and cold can act directly on the parasites present in it. Some poultrymen plant the lots to a permanent crop, such as alfalfa. Such a crop furnishes abundant green feed for the growing birds, and this makes it less likely that they will pick up contaminated material from the soil. The house and adjacent grounds should be cleaned at least once a week, and oftener if necessary.

MANURE DISPOSAL

Every poultry owner is faced with the problem of disposing of the body wastes from his birds in a sanitary manner. To allow the excreta to accumulate in large quantities either in the house or in the yard is to bring into operation the law of nature that no species of animal can exist for very long in intimate contact with its own body wastes without endangering its health through the contraction of disease. Wild birds and animals are not restricted in their range as are the species raised in more or less confinement, hence wild creatures are less apt to pick up infections from their excretions.

Under present conditions in the poultry industry it is often necessary to raise several thousand birds together, and proper steps must be taken to remove the body wastes at frequent intervals and to dispose of them in a sanitary manner if mortality from disease is to be kept at a low level. The body wastes from farm flocks can readily be disposed of by having them hauled to the fields and spread thinly over the land for use as fertilizer. Poultry manure, when properly handled, is an excellent fertilizer for garden and field crops. The body wastes from flocks raised in back yards or in communities where poultry raising is intensively practiced cannot be so easily disposed of as on the farm and must be taken care of in some other way. In some heavily populated areas, poultry raisers have been known to store the manure from their flocks in one or more centrally located storage sheds and sell it. Poultry manure usually retails for a very good price.

To properly preserve the fertilizing value of poultry manure, it must be stored in a suitable screened-in shed with a cement floor and a roof to keep out rain and snow. Manure stored in this manner is also protected from flying and crawling insects and other forms of animal life that may serve as carriers or intermediate hosts of poultry parasites. Just what effect the storage of poultry manure in piles has on the livability of the eggs of poultry parasites and of coccidial oöcysts has not been definitely determined.

DIFFERENT TYPES OF POULTRY SHOULD BE RAISED SEPARATELY

It has been demonstrated repeatedly that in order to prevent the spread of parasitic and other poultry diseases the different types of poultry should be raised separately and in small flocks. Observations have shown that turkeys serve as carriers of gapeworms and transmit gapeworm disease to little chicks, while older chickens are almost entirely resistant to gapeworm infection under range conditions. On the other hand, Tyzzer (*46*) shows that chickens carry the organisms of blackhead in their intestinal tracts, and young turkeys may contract the disease by exposure to infected chickens or to areas infected by them and usually die in large numbers from the disease. Only in exceptional cases do the chickens show symptoms of the disease, and infected chickens usually recover and remain carriers of the organisms for an indefinite period.

It is also dangerous for chickens to associate with pigeons. Levine (*34*) was successful in producing severe experimental infections in chickens with the pigeon capillarid, *Capillaria columbae*. Wehr (*52a*) has reported that chickens heavily infected with *C. columbae* showed symptoms of emaciation, diarrhea, and listlessness and that such an infection usually resulted in death.

What To Do In Case of An Outbreak

In case of an outbreak of a poultry disease, an early diagnosis is essential in order that the proper control measures may be employed. Unfortunately, in many places the services of a poultry-disease diagnostician or a competent veterinarian are not available. In such cases, the State agricultural experiment station should be consulted immediately as to the advisability of shipping birds to its poultry department or veterinary science department for a diagnosis. Should it be necessary to ship sick birds to a distant diagnostic laboratory, it may be several days before a reply is received. In the meantime, losses may continue, and the disease, if acute in character, may gain such a foothold that control measures, when finally applied, will be of little use. Since it is urgent that the disease be checked as soon as possible after its appearance, it is suggested that the following first-aid measures be put into effect immediately in an attempt to control it before it reaches epizootic proportions.

The first requirement in bringing an outbreak of disease under control is to remove all visibly sick birds from the flock, confine them in a room or house separate from the healthy birds, and burn the carcasses of any birds that have died. The healthy birds should if possible be moved to a clean house and clean grounds, but if this is impossible, the body wastes that have accumulated in the house should be disposed of in a sanitary manner, and the house and all its equipment should be thoroughly cleaned and disinfected with some suitable disinfectant, such as hot water or hot lye solution (see the article on Disinfection and Disinfectants, p. 179). As soon as the house and equipment have been cleaned and disinfected, the healthy birds should be put back in the house and confined there until the symptoms have subsided in the sick birds. During this period of confinement, the healthy birds should be watched carefully, and any of them that become sick should be removed immediately and placed with the sick birds. The houses occupied by both the healthy and sick birds should be thoroughly cleaned daily, preferably dry-cleaned, and the litter burned. In case of diarrhea, a mild laxative should be given to all the birds. For flock treatment, 1 pound of Epsom salts dissolved in about 2 gallons of water will make enough medicated liquid for 100 birds. The birds should be kept warm and be disturbed as little as possible, and crowding should be avoided. The feed should be placed in sanitary hoppers and the watering devices protected with wire frames, so that the birds will have less chance to contaminate the drinking water. If the same person must tend both the sick and the healthy birds, the sick birds should be attended to last in order to prevent the mechanical transfer of the causative agent of the disease to the healthy birds. The attendant should be provided with a pair of rubbers for use in each pen and a pan of disinfectant (a weak lysol solution) for dipping the soles of the shoes or rubbers before and after entering the pen or house. Visitors who have been handling poultry elsewhere should not enter the poultry house or yard.

MEDICINAL AGENTS AND THEIR USE

While anthelmintic (worm-expelling) treatment has proved to be applicable to many kinds of livestock and has served to reduce parasitism in them to the point where it apparently does little or no harm, the use of medicinal agents in the control of poultry parasites has not met with any great success. Despite the large amount of experimental work done on the control of poultry parasites by means of medication, effective and practical drugs for the control of such economically important diseases as coccidiosis, blackhead, and tapeworms are still lacking. Although some progress has been made in the treatment of other parasitic diseases of poultry, satisfactory drugs for the control of many of the roundworms are also lacking.

To be satisfactory, a drug designed for the removal of parasites from poultry must be inexpensive, relatively easy to administer, highly effective, and relatively nontoxic. The value of the individual bird is ordinarily so low that the cost of administering drugs to fowls, unless mass treatment can be resorted to, is in most cases prohibitive.

FIGURE 1.—Equipment for and method of administering barium antimonyl tartrate to chickens infected with gapeworms.

Effective drugs have been discovered for the removal of the gapeworm, the large roundworm, and the cecum worm, and the treatment will be discussed briefly.

Hall and Shillinger (*17*), and others, have reported that carbon tetrachloride is an effective drug for the removal of the large intestinal roundworm, *Ascaridia galli.* Ackert and Graham (*3*) found carbon tetrachloride highly efficacious in removing the large intestinal roundworm from young chickens with apparently no ill effects.

For the control of the cecum worm, Hall and Shillinger (*17*) recommend rectal injections of a mixture of oil of chenopodium and olive or cottonseed oil. McCulloch and Nicholson (*37*) stated that phenothiazine, given in either single or repeated doses, was very effective for the removal of cecum worms from chickens. Roberts (*40*) reported that phenothiazine was effective for the removal of the cecum worm but not of the large intestinal roundworm.

Wehr, Harwood, and Schaffer (*53*) found that barium antimonyl tartrate given as an inhalant successfully removed a large percentage of the gapeworms (*Syngamus trachea*) from chicks, turkey poults, and grown turkeys. For treatment, the infected birds are confined in a tight container into which the powder is introduced through an opening near the top by means of a dust gun (fig. 1). The worms in the trachea are killed by the dust inhaled by the birds.

It has been demonstrated that trichomoniasis (infection with trichomonads) of the lower digestive tract of poultry can be successfully treated by means of heat therapy. Olsen and Allen (*38*) successfully treated a number of turkeys infected with *Trichomonas gallinarum* by placing them in a thermostatically controlled cabinet for periods ranging from 1 to 2 hours. The internal body temperature of the birds was raised from 2° to 6° above the normal temperature of 106.5° F. by maintaining an air temperature of approximately 104° F., and a relative humidity of 60 to 70 percent within the treatment box. These investigators found that three treatments at intervals of every other day were sufficient to check the disease, but in advanced cases it was sometimes necessary to administer as many as six treatments. As soon as the body temperature returned to normal, the birds were removed from the cabinet and placed in wire-bottomed cages. Forced feeding of liquid mash was resorted to when the birds refused to eat voluntarily.

Occasionally a bird failed to respond to the heat treatment. Those that did respond usually began to eat voluntarily, gained in weight, and behaved like normal, active birds after the second or third treatment. Several adult turkey hens were treated and later laid several clutches of eggs.

A few of the treated birds were killed at different stages of recovery following treatment, and post mortem examinations disclosed that many of the liver lesions (tissue injuries) had almost completely disappeared and others were in the process of healing. Cultures made from partly healed lesions showed no trichomonads. A relatively large percentage of the untreated birds died from trichomoniasis.

No satisfactory treatment for trichomoniasis of the upper digestive tract has been developed.

THE PROTOZOAN PARASITES OF POULTRY

The protozoan parasites of poultry that are significant as disease producers and therefore of concern to poultrymen belong to two major groups, the flagellates and the Sporozoa. The flagellates include actively moving protozoa equipped with from one to many whiplike hairs, or flagella, which are used to propel the organism through the fluids in which they live. The Sporozoa, or spore-forming organisms, are almost exclusively parasitic and are characterized by the absence of definite organs for movement and by their peculiar, often complex life histories.

A species of the flagellated organisms scientifically designated as *Hexamita meleagridis* is suspected of playing an important role in the production of a severe intestinal infection in young turkeys known as infectious catarrhal enteritis (inflammation of the intes· tines). The part played by another flagellate, *Histomonas meleagridis*, in the production of so-called "blackhead" disease, or enterohepatitis (literally, inflammation of the intestines and the liver), of turkeys is well known. At least two species of flagellates of the genus *Trichomonas* are associated with intestinal disturbances of young turkeys, one producing caseating necrotic lesions (injuries characterized by the presence of cheesy matter and dead tissue) in the crop and esophagus, or gullet, and the other responsible for large cecal (blindgut) and liver lesions similar in character to those of blackhead; these conditions have been designated as trichomoniasis of the upper digestive tract and of the lower digestive tract, respectively.

The most important sporozoan parasites of poultry are the coccidia, which are of such tremendous economic importance as the cause of coccidiosis in chickens that they are discussed in a separate article in this Yearbook (p. 1041). Two other sporozoan parasites that are arousing considerable attention and are believed to be responsible for malarialike diseases of young ducks and turkeys are identified by most investigators as species of *Leucocytozoon*.

With the exception of the coccidia, the protozoan parasites of poultry have their greatest significance, from the disease standpoint, in turkeys. Other domestic birds such as chickens, ducks, geese, guinea fowl, and pigeons frequently harbor similar or identical parasites, a few of which appear to be pathogenic, or disease-producing, to their hosts, while most are tolerated with little or no inconvenience. In the following discussion of specific diseases known or believed to be caused by protozoan parasites, primary emphasis is placed on turkeys, the host birds in which these disorders reach their largest proportions. The general principles of protozoan parasitism and parasite control, however, apply equally to other poultry.

Infectious Catarrhal Enteritis of Turkeys

Infectious catarrhal enteritis (hexamitiasis) of turkeys, associated with *Hexamita meleagridis*,[3] is becoming increasingly important in the United States. This disease has been known to exist in California for some time. It is apparently increasing in occurrence and severity with the expansion in turkey production, the increased crowding of birds on ranches probably affording greater opportunities for turkeys to acquire the infection. The technical name "infectious catarrhal enteritis" indicates that the disease is a contagious in-

---

[3] Among other designations, the disease has been described recently as a "trichomoniasis," but Hinshaw, McNeil, and Kofoid (21) presented convincing field and experimental evidence which definitely eliminated *Trichomonas* as the causative agent and implicated another protozoan parasite, a species of *Hexamita*. Hinshaw and McNeil (20) gave the specific name *meleagridis* to the *Hexamita* which they stated was "the causative agent of infectious catarrhal enteritis" in turkeys. In view of this recent information, there seems to be justification for designating the infection as hexamitiasis. The present discussion of the disease is based on the work of these investigators.

testinal inflammation characterized by abnormally heavy secretion from the mucous glands of the affected intestine.

Hexamitiasis is primarily an acute infection of the upper part of the small intestine of turkey poults between the ages of 1 and 12 weeks, with the greatest death loss occurring at 3 to 5 weeks of age. The symptoms of an acute outbreak are not very specific, being in general similar to those of other acute intestinal diseases. Sick poults are listless and droopy, walk with a stilted gait, and often have a watery or foamy diarrhea. The birds may continue to eat but fail to digest and assimilate food normally, with rapid loss of flesh as a consequence. In individual birds, the acute infection runs a short course of 1 to 6 days after symptoms appear, but in large flocks the peak of mortality during an outbreak occurs in 7 to 10 days after the first sick birds are observed. Most birds that survive acute infections fail to recover from the emaciation and remain stunted. Mortality from acute outbreaks on California ranches has been reported to vary from 20 to 90 percent. Subacute infections sometimes occur, characterized by listlessness and loss of weight in affected birds. The majority of the birds that survive acute infections, as well as those with subacute infections, become carriers and are potential sources of infection to young birds.

The chief sign of the disease seen on post mortem examination of birds that have died from acute hexamitiasis is catarrhal inflammation of the upper part of the small intestine. The intestinal contents are thin and abnormally watery. The intestinal walls have lost tone and may be thin and flabby, with local distended areas having an inflamed mucous membrane. *Hexamita meleagridis* may be consistently demonstrated under the microscope in scrapings from the affected intestinal wall and occurs in particularly large numbers in the inflamed distended areas. In severe cases the flagellates may occur throughout the entire small intestine. The enormous numbers of *Hexamita meleagridis* found in poults with enteritis have not been observed in healthy birds.

Hexamita meleagridis is a microscopic, spindle-shaped, flagellated protozoan measuring on the average about one twenty-five hundredth of an inch in length. It is readily distinguished in structure and movements from the trichomonads, which are often found associated with it in the cecal discharges of the same bird, by the absence of an undulating membrane along the edge of the body, by the absence of an axostyle, or "tail," at the hind end, and by the fact that the *Hexamita* organism moves rapidly in a fairly straight line rather than jerkily. This parasite reproduces by simple longitudinal splitting, each organism dividing frequently to form two individuals. In both diseased and carrier birds living flagellates are continually discharged in the droppings. Susceptible poults may acquire the infection by swallowing feed or soil contaminated with droppings containing the parasites.

Both field and experimental evidence point to *Hexamita meleagridis* as the sole or principal cause of catarrhal enteritis of turkey poults.

It has been definitely shown by investigators in California that the adult turkey is the primary source of infection. The causative agent of the disease has been transmitted to quail and from quail to turkeys. Field evidence indicates that quail may serve as an important carrier of the infection in some regions.

HISTOMONIASIS, OR SO-CALLED "BLACKHEAD" INFECTION

Histomoniasis, or enterohepatitis, is an acute, highly fatal disease of turkeys attributed to infection with the protozoan parasite *Histomonas meleagridis*. Though the acute infection in chickens is usually mild and transitory, chickens have an important part in the complete picture of histomoniasis because they are established as carriers following primary infection and thus serve as a source of infection for susceptible turkeys. Since the principal sites of infection in diseased turkeys are the walls of the ceca and the liver, the disease is technically termed "infectious enterohepatitis," which indicates that it is a contagious infection involving the intestine and liver. Under farm conditions, histomoniasis probably includes most of the so-called blackhead of turkeys. Dark discoloration of the head is not a constant symptom of the disease, however, and may be produced by disorders of the circulatory system due to other causes. It is therefore probably more appropriate to designate the disease as histomoniasis. The unfortunate nonspecific term blackhead might well be eliminated from the veterinary vocabulary. Although the technical name may seem difficult to laymen, usage would soon give it the same currency as such names as "coccidiosis" and "trichomoniasis."

Histomoniasis has forced the abandonment of turkey raising in many parts of this country. Application of the principles unearthed in recent researches, however, particularly those of Tyzzer and his associates, has again made turkey production a successful enterprise in these areas. Tyzzer's report (*45*) on histomoniasis summarized the detailed information on the modes of infection of susceptible birds and the form, structure, and life history of the parasite that is the basis of the present conception of the disease.

Turkeys are susceptible to histomoniasis at any age up to maturity. The disease develops within 2 to 3 weeks after the susceptible birds acquire infective organisms by ingesting feed or soil contaminated with droppings from infected birds. The course of the disease is rapid, death usually occurring soon after the development of symptoms. Sick birds are weak, listless, and droopy, and usually have a sulfur-colored diarrhea. Dark discoloration of the head, as already noted, is not a constant symptom. Death may sometimes occur without visible symptoms. Histomoniasis in older birds is less acute than in young poults, the illness usually being more prolonged and the mortality lower. The great majority of the younger birds that develop the disease die, the mortality often being 100 percent.

On post mortem examination, birds dying from histomoniasis show greatly enlarged ceca, or blind pouches, that contain cheesy masses of tissue debris often infiltrated with blood. The cecal walls are thickened and congested and show large, ulcerlike lesions. The liver also usually appears somewhat enlarged and is blotched with characteristic, slightly sunken, reddish-gray lesions of various sizes. Thin sections from the cecal walls, when mounted on slides and stained appropriately for examination under the microscope, show *Histomonas* organisms among the surface cells lining the walls. The living parasites may often be recovered from the characteristic liver lesions and demonstrated under the microscope.

The histomonads are peculiar flagellated protozoa with certain amoeboid, or amoebalike, tendencies. As they occur in the cecal contents of carrier birds, they are normally more or less rounded bodies that usually show amoeboid movements of the protoplasm (that is, they are capable of pushing out temporary arms of protoplasm from their surfaces) as well as rhythmic rotatory movements produced by the beating of a single locomotor whip, or flagellum. They measure on an average about one two-thousandth of an inch in length, although individuals may be considerably larger and possess as many as four flagella.

Immediately upon establishment in the ceca of a susceptible host bird, the histomonads multiply rapidly, invade the mucous membrane of the cecal walls, and become rounded tissue forms. Invasion of tissues is usually brief in the chicken, which recovers with only slight inconvenience, though deaths from histomoniasis among chickens have been known, and typical cecal and liver lesions have been seen at autopsy. The histomonads usually persist in the cecal contents indefinitely, and the chicken is established as a carrier of the infection. In the more susceptible turkey, invasion of tissues is so energetic that the histomonads gain access to the blood stream and are carried to the liver, where the characteristic lesions are produced. The infected birds usually die from severe cecal and liver infection (enterohepatitis). The few turkeys able to survive the acute infection also become carriers. Both chickens and turkeys with acute or carrier infections are sources of infection to new susceptible hosts, discharging living histomonads regularly in their droppings. When shed from infected birds, the histomonads are either free in the feces or housed in some manner not yet clearly understood within the eggs of the cecal worm, *Heterakis gallinae*, which are also eliminated in the feces after being produced by the adult worms in the ceca of the host birds. New hosts acquire the infection by swallowing feed or soil contaminated with droppings containing the parasites, either free or within the eggs of the cecal worm.

LEUCOCYTOZOAN DISEASE OF DUCKS AND TURKEYS

Turkey poults under 12 weeks of age and ducklings 10 days to a few weeks old are most susceptible to leucocytozoan disease. The general symptoms are common to both kinds of host birds, and therefore the infections in the two need not be differentiated. In the young birds the disease strikes suddenly, with acute symptoms lasting only 2 or 3 days. Sick birds first lose appetite, become droopy, and have a tendency to sit down from weakness or exhaustion. They seem to be thirsty and drink large amounts of water. Their breathing becomes heavy, and they may crawl instead of walking. In the later stages of severe infections, the birds are excitable and when disturbed may fall over, lapse into a coma during which the breathing is labored, and die. Some very sick birds die after only a few minor convulsions. Blood removed from the vein of a bird sick with this condition shows greatly enlarged spindle-shaped cells, somewhat larger than the normal red blood cells, which contain the parasitic organisms. The most characteristic lesion at autopsy is an enlarged and blackened spleen. The birds that recover from acute infections may either remain permanently stunted or show no serious effects, but most become carriers of the infection. Mortality from the acute disease is reported to range from 0 to 100 percent in ducklings and from 10 to 50 percent in turkeys.

It was originally believed that the parasites invaded the white cells, or leucocytes, of the blood of infected birds, and for this reason they were named *Leucocytozoon*. Some later investigators believed, however, that the red corpuscles rather than the leucocytes were the host cells. This question is still not settled definitely. Whatever these host cells may prove to be, they are greatly altered by parasitism with the leucocytozoa. The parasitized host cells become elongated to 4 or 5 times their normal length, with ends tapered to points. The full-grown parasites, usually one to each host cell, are elongated oval or bean-shaped structures that almost completely fill the parasitized cells exclusive of the tapered ends. The ultimate result of this parasitism is the destruction of the host cells, with anemia as a consequence. It has been suggested that the cause of the respiratory difficulties observed in birds with advanced, severe leucocytozoan disease may be due to mechanical blocking of the small capillaries of the lungs with these large parasites.

The large parasites inside the cells of the circulating blood of the host birds represent only a stage of the life history of *Leucocytozoon*. They develop further only when ingested by certain species of *Simulium*, or common blackflies, that feed on the blood of the infected birds. In the engorged blackflies, the leucocytozoa pass through a definite cycle of development, and within a few days small infective forms known as sporozoites are present in the salivary glands. Some of these sporozoites are expelled into the blood stream of susceptible young birds on which the blackflies feed. In ducks, the sporozoites are said to penetrate the surface cells lining the small capillaries of the lungs, liver, and spleen and to undergo generations of multiplication there that result in the production of enormous numbers of parasites. Eventually these products of multiplication are liberated into the blood stream and invade cells of the circulating blood, where they may be detected by means of stained blood smears. The entire life history has been determined to require only 2 to 3 days in the blackflies and 9 or 10 days in the host birds.[4]

TRICHOMONIASIS OF THE UPPER DIGESTIVE TRACT OF TURKEYS

Trichomoniasis (that is, infection with trichomonads) of the upper digestive tract is characterized by the presence of peculiar cheesy

[4] Further details of research are given in citations 23, 24, 39, 42, and 43.

lesions of dead tissue piled up to as high as approximately two-tenths of an inch above the surface of the mucous membranes of the esophagus and crop. The entire upper digestive tract is studded with small grayish-white nodules, or lumps, resembling the pustules found in nutritional roup. The mucous membrane is entirely destroyed, and an examination of the cheesy lesions or retained fluid of the upper digestive tract discloses countless numbers of flagellates. The lesions usually end abruptly at the zone dividing the esophagus from the proventriculus, or true stomach, indicating perhaps that the gastric juice of the true stomach may be detrimental to the survival of these organisms.

Sick birds are characterized by a depressed appearance, loss of appetite, sagging wings, emaciation, and drooling at the mouth. The droppings are usually of the consistency of water and contain large numbers of the flagellated parasites. Young birds may die as soon as 1 day after the appearance of symptoms, but older birds may linger for several weeks. In older birds the region surrounding the crop usually appears depressed and sometimes pendulous. Although certain other diseases may produce similar symptoms, birds that make repeated attempts to swallow, extend the head and neck, and retain the crop fluid should be suspected of trichomoniasis. Often diagnosis can be confirmed by inspection of the mouths of sick birds, since the lesions frequently occupy visible portions of the upper digestive tract. Ordinarily mortality is slight, but it has been reported to range as high as 73 percent in mature flocks to 87 percent in young flocks.

Individuals of *Trichomonas gallinae* are roughly egg-shaped flagellates measuring on an average one twenty-five hundredth of an inch in length. They are extremely active trichomonads capable of rapid forward spiral locomotion produced by the beating of the flagella at the front end and movements of the protoplasmic flange, or undulating membrane, extending along the edge of the body. It is generally believed that these upper-digestive-tract trichomonads are distinct from those inhabiting the ceca and lower intestine of turkeys. They differ in certain aspects of structure and behavior, in their respective sites of localization within the digestive tracts of the host birds, and apparently in their disease-producing capabilities. As with the other protozoan infections of turkeys, a certain percentage of the adult birds become carriers of the trichomonads and thus serve as sources of infection to susceptible birds. Presumably infection of new hosts occurs through ingestion of contaminated feed, soil, or drinking water with living trichomonads discharged from infected birds either in the droppings or in the discharges from the mouth.[5]

Trichomoniasis of the Lower Digestive Tract of Turkeys

Turkeys are victims of another disease, which was believed by Allen (7) to be due to *Trichomonas gallinarum*, a flagellate commonly found in the ceca and lower intestine of chickens, turkeys, guinea fowl, and probably other domestic fowls. Infection with these para-

---

[5] See citations *14, 19, 29, 32, 33, 43, 44,* and *49* for further details of research.

sites is common in healthy chickens and turkeys, but disease symptoms develop with much greater frequency and severity in the latter. According to Allen (*8*) the infection resembles histomoniasis in producing lesions in the ceca and liver of turkeys, but these lesions are characteristically different from those of histomoniasis. The disease may be designated tentatively as "trichomoniasis of the lower digestive tract" to distinguish it from *T. gallinae* infection of the esophagus and crop.

Birds experimentally infected with *Trichomonas gallinarum* sometimes develop the acute type of infection, characterized by diarrhea and occasional mortality in the young turkeys a few days after inoculation, but more often they develop a chronic type of the disease, the symptoms of which do not appear for several weeks after infection. Under certain conditions not yet fully understood, these trichomonads may produce an enterohepatitis, with lesions distinct from those of histomoniasis. Liver lesions have not been observed in experimentally or naturally infected birds under 3 months of age. The turkeys that develop the disease gradually and progressively lose their thrifty condition, become droopy, often have intermittent attacks of diarrhea characterized by pale-yellow droppings, and usually die. The slow, chronic development of the disease is sharply contrasted with the acuteness of histomoniasis. The importance of this type of trichomoniasis has not been fully determined. The insidious, chronic nature of the infection, its tendency to produce isolated losses rather than mass mortality, and the possible confusion of the specific lesions with those of histomoniasis have probably permitted the disease to go undetected. The studies of Allen indicate that it may prove to be of considerable importance.

The cecal and liver lesions are the most obvious changes to be observed at post mortem examination of birds dead of the disease. The liver lesions are the most clearly defined, being irregular, granular, often slightly elevated areas of cheesy appearance, quite distinct from the rounded, nongranular, noticeably depressed lesions of histomoniasis. Similar lesions are present on the cecal walls, and often one or both ceca contain cores of cheesy, dead material infiltrated with blood. In naturally infected turkeys, the lesions may occur separately or together with those of histomoniasis, and there appears to be basis for the belief that in the past the lesions of the two distinct diseases have often been collectively diagnosed as blackhead lesions. In the interest of accurate diagnosis and proper evaluation of their relative importance the two infections should be carefully differentiated.

Allen (*7*) expressed the opinion that the common cecal trichomonads of turkeys are identical with *Trichomonas gallinarum*, described previously from the chicken. These trichomonads are on an average considerably smaller but much more active than the histomonads, which may often occur in the same cecal contents from infected birds. They vary from nearly spherical to distinctly pear-shaped, and their average length is approximately one thirty-five hundredth of an inch. They are typical trichomonads, each individual possessing several whips, or flagella, and an undulating membrane along the edge of the body. The combined movements of these flagella and the undulating membrane give a jerky type of locomotion with little forward progression, characteristically different from the rapid forward movements of *T. gallinae.*

As known at present, the life history of *Trichomonas gallinarum* is apparently simple. The trichomonads in the cecal contents of the host birds feed by absorption from the fluids in the lumen, or cavity, of the ceca, and each individual periodically reproduces by asexual splitting to form two trichomonads. Infected birds regularly shed living trichomonads in the cecal droppings. No resistant, or cyst, forms have been observed in the course of the life history; and if no cysts are formed, it is evident that young birds must pick up living trichomonads very soon after they are discharged from infected birds, since these flagellates are extremely susceptible to drying and changes in temperature. Once ingested by susceptible birds in feed, soil, or drinking water, the parasites must survive the passage through the alimentary tract in order to become established in the lower intestine and ceca of the new host birds.

METAZOAN PARASITES OF POULTRY

TREMATODES

Flukes, or trematodes, are small, flattened, unsegmented worms which as adults are parasites of both invertebrates and vertebrates. Most flukes are internal parasites, usually inhabiting the intestinal tract, lung, liver, or some other internal organ. A few, however, have been classified as external parasites, since they are found in the skin and similar locations.

At least three species of flukes have been reported as parasitizing poultry in the United States, but none of them is of any great economic importance. One species, *Collyriclum faba,* is an external parasite that occurs in the skin of domestic and wild birds. The other two species, *Prosthogonimus macrorchis* and *Psilostomum ondatrae,* are internal parasites, the former occurring in the bursa Fabricii (a glandular sac), and the egg-forming organs and the latter in the proventriculus.

The cystic or skin fluke, *Collyriclum faba,* has been reported from the domestic fowl in Minnesota, and it has also been found in wild birds in Massachusetts, Maryland, Minnesota, Wisconsin, New Jersey, New York, and Michigan.

These flukes produce small, hard, cystlike structures, usually in the region of the vent. However, they have also been found in the skin just in front of the anus, in the chest region, over the lower surface of the abdomen and breast, around the beak on both the external and the internal surfaces, on the neck, and on the crop.

The smooth, shiny, grayish-white cysts are one-twelfth to two-fifths inch (2 to 10 mm.) in diameter and contain two approximately hemispherical flukes, in contact along their flattened surfaces. A dark-brown or almost black substance exudes from the opened cyst, which contains the minute eggs of the parasite.

The life history of the fluke is not completely known. It is believed that some snail is its first intermediate host, and evidence points very definitely to nymphs of dragonflies as the second intermediate host. The eggs escape from the cysts through an opening in the cyst wall and are scattered wherever the bird goes. Masses of degenerating and decaying cysts have been noted on chickens which, when they are removed or have dropped off, apparently serve to disseminate the disease, since the dead areas contain myriads of eggs. When brought into contact with water, the eggs hatch and apparently continue their development in a snail. The prevalence of this parasite in sparrows, crows, nuthatches, and other land birds, however, suggests that some land invertebrate may serve as the first intermediate host. Because of its prevalence in the English sparrow, it is thought that this bird may serve as an important disseminator of the disease.

The effects of the parasite on the fowl, aside from the possible slight injury to the general health of the bird and a disfigurement of the skin, which lowers the market value, are not noteworthy.

Proventriculitis (inflammation of the true stomach) in chickens may be due to a small fluke, *Psilostomum ondatrae*, commonly found in muskrats and water birds. The life history of this fluke is not known. The only report of the parasite's occurring in domestic fowl in the United States is from Colorado. Twenty-nine deaths in a flock of 42 White Leghorns 8 weeks old and 8 deaths in a flock of Plymouth Rock pullets were attributed to infection with the parasite. Infected birds develop inappetence (lack of appetite) and lethargy and gradually waste away. After several days of sickness, death results, apparently from starvation. Post mortem findings are an enlarged and ulcerated proventriculus, a deep reddening around the openings of the glands, and, in severe cases of infection, a grayish exudate, or discharge, on the surface of the glandular stomach. The flukes apparently do not burrow into the proventriculus but produce the irritation by their presence on the surface of the mucous membrane.

A small, reddish-colored fluke, nearly one-fourth of an inch long, occurs in the bursa Fabricii and oviduct of the domestic chicken and duck in the Great Lakes region. This parasite has been reported by Kotlan and Chandler (*30*) from the oviduct of a wing-pinioned duck in Michigan. Although believed by some investigators to be identical with *Prosthogonimus pellucidus*, a species of fluke occurring in a similar location in the domestic chicken and duck in Europe, this fluke has been described by Macy (*35*) as a new species, *P. macrorchis*.

Owing to its location within the reproductive organs, *Prosthogonimus macrorchis* may be responsible for serious losses, due to reduced or complete stoppage of egg production among laying hens. The symptoms shown by infected fowls are dullness, loss of weight, and a greatly decreased egg production. Controlled experiments have shown that uninfected birds laid nearly 10 times as many eggs as the infected hens. In the oviduct, the parasites are responsible for acute inflammation and the formation of abnormal eggs. The irritation resulting from the presence of these flukes in the oviduct causes a reversal of the peristaltic movements, which results in broken yolks, albumen, bacteria, and parasitic material entering the abdominal cavity and giving rise to acute peritonitis, or inflammation of the abdominal lining. Kotlan and Chandler (*30*) described the pathological changes resulting from the presence of these worms as—

heavy emaciation and anemia; fibrinous peritonitis, with a large amount of sticky, yellow exudate, containing large masses of egg-yolk and albumen material; a number of red-colored, live flukes were found in the exudate. The ovary showed a number of diseased, collapsed ovules, containing grayish-yellow, egg-yolk-like material mixed with fibrin and pus. Some of the ovules were apparently ruptured. The oviduct was greatly distended, its serous coverings showing a more or less pronounced reddish discoloration. The lumen of the oviduct contained a large amount of albumen material forming ovoid clots of about one to two centimeters in diameter; the mucosa was covered with a sticky exudate consisting in the main of albumen, blood and fibrin.

The life cycle of the parasite involves two intermediate hosts, snails and dragonflies. Macy (*36*) found that the snail *Amnicola limosa porata*, which is common in the lakes of Michigan, Wisconsin, Minnesota and other Northern States, served as the first intermediate host. He succeeded in infecting dragonfly nymphs by placing a number of cercariae of *Prosthogonimus macrorchis* (the form of the organism found in snails) in Syracuse watch glasses containing the young dragonflies.

Kotlan and Chandler (*31*) demonstrated experimentally that chickens can become infected with the adult flukes by feeding them dragonfly nymphs containing cysts of *Prosthogonimus* species. It is believed that ducks are the normal hosts of *P. macrorchis* and the domestic hen is the abnormal host, as the latter loses its infection in 3 to 5 weeks. The rate of growth of the adult fluke is relatively slow in ducks and chicks, but more rapid in the oviduct of the hen. The fluke develops only in the oviducts of laying hens and has been occasionally found in hen's eggs.

CESTODES

Tapeworms, or cestodes, are flattened or ribbon-shaped worms composed cf numerous segments or divisions. The head, neck, and a small number of the front segments are usually much narrower than the remaining portion of the worm, which grows from the neck backwards, so that the segments farthest removed from the head are the oldest from the standpoint of development. The terminal segments of the fully developed tapeworm may be filled with eggs; these are known as gravid segments and are the ones usually found in the droppings of infected birds.

Several species of tapeworms inhabit the small intestines of fowls. Each species usually shows some preference for a certain part of the small intestine to which to attach itself and develop. If tapeworms are present in large numbers, however, specimens may be found attached to portions of the intestine other than the one normally preferred.

So far as has been ascertained by experimentation, all poultry tapeworms pass the earlier part of their development in one of the lower animals. These so-called intermediate hosts include houseflies, snails, slugs, ants, earthworms, grasshoppers, sandhoppers, and others.

Intermediate hosts become infected with young tapeworms by swallowing the gravid, or egg-bearing, segments which have been passed in the droppings of infected birds. Within the body cavity of the intermediate host, the bladder worm, or young tapeworm, has the appearance of a sac filled with liquid in the center of which is seen the head of the adult tapeworm. The head contains four cup-shaped cavities, or suckers, and a number of hooks surround the front end.

When a susceptible bird host swallows an intermediate host containing these bladder worms, they attach themselves to the intestinal wall and begin to develop segments, which appear first just back of the head in the so-called neck or growing region.

The nodular tapeworm, *Raillietina echinobothrida*, produces nodules or tuberclelike bodies in the subserous and muscular coats of the walls of the posterior (hind) portion of the small intestines of chickens and other fowls. These lesions closely resemble those of avian tuberculosis, and it is important that a careful examination be made before a positive diagnosis is given. The diagnosis should not be difficult, since nodules in the wall of the small intestine in the absence of tapeworms may be considered as being due to the tubercle bacillus and not to the nodular tapeworm. The tapeworm may be quite small and may be overlooked in a hurried or cursory examination. In case of doubt, the affected intestine should be opened and washed carefully in a stream of water. The washed intestine is then placed in a dish of water deep enough to cover it; if tapeworms are present, they will be seen hanging to the mucous membrane. This discovery, in the absence of lesions in the liver or other organs, would warrant the diagnosis of tapeworm disease.

Jones and Horsfall (*26, 27*) showed that the ants *Tetramorium caespitum* and *Pheidole vinelandica* naturally harbored bladder worms of this tapeworm and also those of another closely related species, *Raillietina tetragona*. When these two bladder worms were fed to young chickens, the latter became infected with the adults of the cestodes. Joyeux and Baer (*28*) reported finding bladder worms of *R. echinobothrida* in naturally infected ants, *Tetramorium semilaeve*, in the region of Marseilles, France.

The proliferating, or branching, tapeworm, *Hymenolepis cantaniana*, occurs in the small intestines of chickens, quail, pheasants, turkeys, and peafowl.

Alicata and Jones (*6*) found that the small dung beetle, *Ataenius cognatus*, served as an intermediate host of this tapeworm. As found in the infected beetle, the young tapeworm consists of numerous branches with a few terminal buds which represent completely developed bladder worms. From 2 to 3 weeks are required for the bladder worm to develop into the adult tapeworm in the avian host.

The broad-headed tapeworm, *Raillietina cesticillus*, attaches itself by preference to the anterior (front) and middle portions of the small intestine of the chicken, guinea fowl, and turkey. This tapeworm is probably one of the most common cestodes of domestic fowls in the United States. It may be readily distinguished from other species of tapeworms infecting poultry by the broadly developed head which carries a double row of 400 to 500 delicate, hammer-shaped hooks; the suckers are weakly developed and devoid of spines.

Several species of beetles belonging to the families Scarabaeidae, Tenebrionidae, and Carabidae have been shown experimentally to serve as intermediate hosts for *Raillietina cesticillus*. The meal beetles, *Tribolium castaneum* and *T. confusum*, which are commonly found infesting poultry feeds, have been shown recently to serve in this capacity.

Ackert and Reid (*4*) demonstrated experimentally that chickens 2½ to 5 months of age are more resistant to infection with this species of tapeworm than younger birds and that a reduction in the blood sugar and hemoglobin contents of the blood resulted from such infections. Harwood and Luttermoser (*18*) reported that the growth of Rhode Island Red and White Leghorn chicks was retarded by infections with the tapeworm.

The minute tapeworm *Davainea proglottina* usually inhabits the duodenal region (the first part of the small intestine) of the chicken, turkey, and occasionally other birds. In heavy infections, individual tapeworms may be found as far back as the yolk stalk. This tapeworm has been reported from widely separated areas in the United States, but most often from the Eastern States. It is one of the smallest tapeworms found infecting poultry. A fully developed specimen measures about one-fiftieth to three twenty-fifths of an inch in length and is composed of two to five segments which gradually increase in length and breadth as the worm matures; the last segment may be larger than all the rest of the parasite. Because of its small size, this tapeworm is frequently overlooked.

The life cycle of *Davainea proglottina* was first demonstrated experimentally by Grassi and Rovelli (*15*) who showed that the common garden slug, also called the gray field slug, *Agriolimax agrestis*, could be successfully infected with the bladder worms of this tapeworm. In addition to this slug, many other species of slugs and two species of snails, *Polygyra thyroides* and *Zonitoides arboreus*, have been incriminated experimentally as intermediate hosts of the tapeworm. The gray field slug is very common in those sections from which *D. proglottina* has been reported and probably plays a very important role in the perpetuation of the disease wherever it and the parasite occur together.

This species has been considered by a number of investigators to be one of the obviously dangerous tapeworms infecting poultry. Heavily infected birds are said to become lethargic and waste away. On post mortem examination, the intestinal mucous membrane appears thickened, which may be due to hemorrhages, and the intestine contains a large quantity of mucus, which tends to be fetid. Leg weakness has been attributed to infections with this tapeworm, but its true relationship to this condition is still unknown.

Domesticated fowls are hosts of a number of other species of tapeworms. *Hymenolepis carioca* is a very common cestode of poultry in the United States. It is a small tapeworm measuring 1⅕ to 3⅛ inches long, threadlike, and very fragile; the segments break off easily when handled. It sometimes occurs in large numbers in chickens and turkeys, but it has very little, if any, effect on the growth rate of young chicks. This species of tapeworm utilizes the dung beetles, *Onthophagus hecate*, *Aphodius granarius*, *Choeridium histeroides*, and others as intermediate hosts.

Metroliasthes lucida, a common cestode of turkeys, measures as much as 8 inches (20 cm.) in length. It lacks a rostellum (beak), and the suckers are devoid of spines. Jones (*25*) found that the eggs of this tapeworm would develop to the bladder worm stage in grasshoppers.

Amoebotaenia sphenoides is principally a parasite of chickens. This tapeworm measures only from one-twelfth to one-sixth inch (2 to 4 mm.) long; the head has a single row of 14 hooks and is followed by a short neck. The 18 to 20 segments that follow the neck gradually increase in size up to the fourteenth and then gradually decrease. It has been demonstrated that a species of earthworm, *Ocnerodrilus africanus*, served as an intermediate host of this tapeworm. More recently, the earthworms *Helodrilus foetidus*, *Pheretina pequana*, and *Allolobrophora chloritica* have been assigned to this role. Chickens in Texas, Kansas, and Michigan have been reported as being infected with this species of tapeworm.

Under normal conditions this parasite probably causes very little damage to fowls.

Choanotaenia infundibulum, a cestode parasite of the duodenum, or forward part of the small intestine, of chickens, turkeys, and several species of wild game birds, is frequently met with in chickens and turkeys in the United States. Houseflies, grasshoppers, and several species of beetles have been reported as intermediate hosts of this tapeworm.

NEMATODES

Roundworms, or nematodes, are usually elongated, cylindrical, unsegmented worms which vary from only a small fraction of an inch to several inches in length. They likewise differ greatly in habitat, having been found in poultry in almost every organ.

On the basis of their life histories, the roundworms of poultry may be divided into two general groups: (1) Those transmitted directly from bird host to bird host and (2) those requiring an insect or some other lower animal for their complete development.

The first type of life cycle is considered the simplest, for its completion involves merely the swallowing by a host animal of the embryonated roundworm eggs (those containing embryos, which are infective) with the food and water or bits of soil. The embryo roundworm hatches in the intestinal tract, and direct development to the adult stage usually takes place there. Soon after hatching, the young of many of the species of roundworms of poultry penetrate into the mucosa, or lining of the intestinal tract, and usually spend a number of days there before reentering the intestinal cavity. In the case of the gapeworm, the young worms leave the alimentary tract and wander through various organs of the body before settling down permanently in the trachea, or windpipe.

In addition to the roundworms that pass part of their development in insects or some other form of animal life, thus requiring a true intermediate host, a third group is recognized in which the infective stage is transmitted either directly, through the medium of contaminated food and water, or indirectly, by swallowing some insect or other animal in the body of which the infective stage has encysted. The gapeworm of poultry is an example of the latter group.

CROP WORMS

Domestic fowls are susceptible to infection with at least three species of crop worms, namely, *Capillaria annulata*, *C. contorta*, and *Gongylonema ingluvicola*. The first two species are commonly known

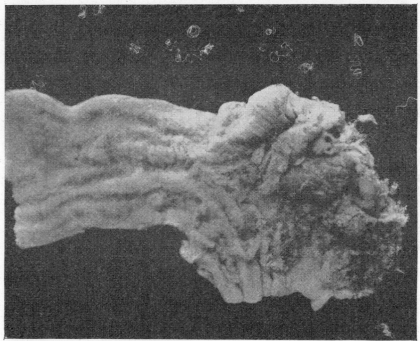

FIGURE 2.—Crop and esophagus of a bird heavily infested with the crop worm, *Capillaria annulata*

as capillarid worms, threadworms, or hairworms, while the last has been called the gullet worm.

These crop worms are long and slender, varying in length from half an inch to 2 or more inches. They bury themselves in the mucous membrane of the crop and esophagus, or gullet, in tortuous burrows, from which it is often difficult to remove them whole (fig. 2). In heavy infections, these worms may be found in the undilated portion of the esophagus as well as the dilated portion or crop.[6]

The life histories of the two threadworms are known, but that of the gullet worm is yet to be discovered. The transmission of *Capillaria contorta* was found to be direct by Cram (*12*). At about the same time (1936) Wehr (*50*) discovered that *Capillaria annulata* required the earthworm as an intermediate host.

The chief injury produced by the crop worms is a thickening of the wall and an enlargement of the glands of the crop and esophagus. In heavy infections the crop wall is greatly thickened, highly inflamed, and congested, and the mucous membrane is loose and torn.

STOMACH WORMS

The proventriculus, or true stomach, is the site of infection by two parasitic roundworms, *Dispharynx spiralis* and *Tetrameres americana*.

The spiral stomach worm, *Dispharynx spiralis*, has been observed in the proventriculus of the chicken, turkey, guinea fowl, pigeon, and a few wild gallinaceous birds (the same order to which domestic poultry belong). In certain sections of the United States, particularly California and Texas, pigeons have been found to be very heavily infected with this parasitic roundworm.

The adult worms are short and thick and usually are curved or rolled in the form of a spiral; the hind end of the male is very tightly coiled. At the site of infection, the nematodes are usually found with their heads buried deeply in the wall of the proventriculus. Tumors are usually formed at the site of the attachment of the worms, and in heavy infections the wall of the glandular, or true, stomach becomes enormously and uniformly thickened as well as ulcerated.

Cram demonstrated experimentally that the pill bug serves as the intermediate host of the spiral stomach worm. Whether it is the principal intermediate host for the spread of the parasite under natural conditions is not known.

The globular roundworm, *Tetrameres americana*, is strikingly different in appearance from most roundworms. The male worm is very small and in general resembles other nematodes, but the female is globular and bright red. The two sexes likewise differ in their location within the stomach. The female worms, apparently when quite young, enter the tubular glands (Lieberkühn's glands) of the stomach wall, leaving only the hind part of the body, including the vulva, protruding into the stomach cavity. The male lives free in

---

[6] Wehr (*51*) observed that each of these three species of roundworms, when viewed in their normal position in the mucosa of the esophagus, displayed a different body contour. This discovery afforded a reasonably accurate method of identifying the worms at the site of the infection without resorting to a detailed microscopic examination of each worm. All three species assume a twisted position in the mucosa, but in the case of the gullet worm the perspective is one of a series of folds, approximately uniform in size and shape, following one another in close succession and usually extending in a straight course. In the two species of *Capillaria*, the body shape consists of a series of irregularly shaped folds. However, *Capillaria annulata* may be readily distinguished from *Capillaria contorta* by its much smaller size. In case of doubt the particular worm may be removed from its burrow and examined microscopically for the presence of a cuticular swelling directly back of the head which identifies it as *Capillaria annulata*.

the cavity of the stomach and apparently enters Lieberkühn's glands only for a short time to mate with the female.

Infective larvae of *Tetrameres americana* have been recovered from the body cavities of the grasshoppers *Melanoplus femur-rubrum* and *M. differentialis* 42 days after experimental infection. Chickens to which infected grasshoppers were fed later became infected with the adults of this stomach worm. Barber (*9*) stated that *T. americana* was the cause of a serious catarrhal condition in chickens in Guam. In heavy infections the walls of the proventriculus become so swollen that the cavity is almost obliterated.

Gizzard Worms

Of the parasitic roundworms occurring underneath the thick, horny lining of the gizzard of poultry, only two species are of economic importance. These worms burrow through the horny lining of the gizzard and bury themselves, sometimes deeply, in the muscles beneath. The gizzard worm of chickens and turkeys, *Cheilospirura hamulosa*, selects the anterior and posterior (front and back) portions of the gizzard, regions in which the horny covering is thin and soft, while the gizzard worm of ducks and geese, *Amidostomum anseris*, may be found generally throughout this organ.

In life these worms are reddish in color, indicating perhaps that they are bloodsuckers. The damage they cause to the gizzard may be so severe that this organ cannot function properly; thus they interfere with the digestion of the bird.

Cheilospirura hamulosa requires an intermediate host for its complete development. Several species of grasshoppers and numerous beetles, including the common meal beetle, *Tribolium castaneum*, have been found experimentally to serve in this capacity.

In lightly infected birds the lining of the gizzard may show a slight ulcerative condition, which may involve the muscular tissue as well. Soft nodules inclosing the nematodes are sometimes found in the muscular portion of the gizzard, especially in the thinner parts. In heavy infections a large part of the posterior portion of the gizzard may become enlarged and frequently loses its natural shape. The symptoms vary with the degree of infection. Mild infections are scarcely detectable, whereas severe ones are said to produce anemia and emaciation.

Amidostomum anseris frequently occurs underneath the horny lining of the gizzard of ducks and geese, sometimes in large numbers. Cram (*11*) reported a severe outbreak of this disease among a flock of geese in New York. The owner of the flock reported a large number of deaths as a result of the outbreak.

The life history of this nematode is direct. The eggs are voided in the droppings and readily hatch in the presence of moisture. The newly hatched larvae reach the infective stage within a few days; when picked up by a susceptible host, the infective larvae develop to the adult stage in the gizzard.

Young infected birds show symptoms of dullness, loss of appetite, and emaciation. The clinical symptoms are largely the result of the improper functioning of the diseased gizzard. On post mortem examination, the inner surfaces of the gizzard, in cases of heavy infections, appear necrotic, or characterized by dead tissue; the heavy lining is loosened or sloughed in places and appears dark brown or black at the site of infection.

LARGE INTESTINAL ROUNDWORMS

One of the commonest and perhaps the most frequently seen of the parasitic roundworms of poultry is the large intestinal roundworm of chickens, *Ascaridia galli.* This parasite is very common wherever chickens are raised. It has occasionally been found in turkeys, and its occurrence in ducks and geese has been reported. Similar worms, *Ascaridia columbae* and *Ascaridia numidae,* are frequently found in considerable numbers in the intestines of pigeons and guinea fowl, respectively.

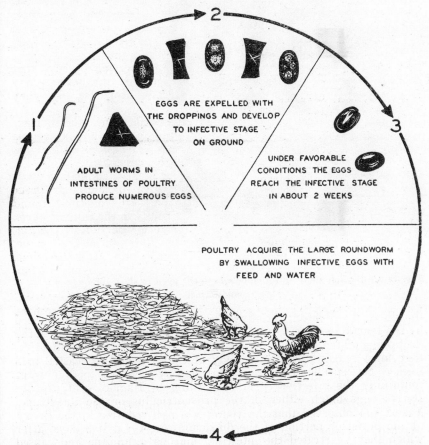

EGGS ARE EXPELLED WITH THE DROPPINGS AND DEVELOP TO INFECTIVE STAGE ON GROUND

ADULT WORMS IN INTESTINES OF POULTRY PRODUCE NUMEROUS EGGS

UNDER FAVORABLE CONDITIONS THE EGGS REACH THE INFECTIVE STAGE IN ABOUT 2 WEEKS

POULTRY ACQUIRE THE LARGE ROUNDWORM BY SWALLOWING INFECTIVE EGGS WITH FEED AND WATER

FIGURE 3.—Life-history chart of the large roundworm of the chicken, *Ascaridia galli.*

The mature worms of the three species named range in length from 1½ to 4 inches. The chicken worm is the longest and slenderest, averaging in thickness about the size of the lead of an ordinary pencil. Specimens of this ascarid have been removed on a number of occasions from broken eggs. The worms had presumably wandered up the oviduct from the intestine via the cloaca and were later incorporated in the developing egg.

The life histories of two of these ascarids have been worked out and found to be similar. Since the life history of *Ascaridia galli* (fig. 3) has been more fully discussed in the scientific literature than

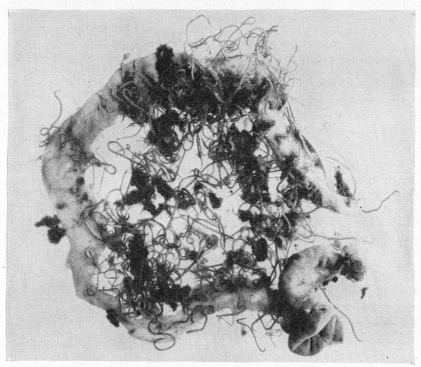

FIGURE 4.—Portion of the intestine of a bird, slit open to show the large number of roundworms.

the others, it will be only briefly reviewed here. The eggs are deposited by the female in the cavity of the intestinal tract and pass out in the droppings of the infected bird. Before these eggs become infective, they must remain outside the body of the bird host at least 2 to 3 weeks. Susceptible birds become infected by ingesting food or water containing the infective eggs. According to Itagaki (*22*), the infective eggs hatch either in the proventriculus or the duodenum. Ackert (*1*) observed that the young worms lived free in the cavity of the posterior portion of the duodenum for the first 9 days, after which they penetrated the intestinal mucous membrane and caused hemorrhages (fig. 4). By the seventeenth or eighteenth day, the young worms have left the mucous membrane and thereafter are to be found free in the cavity of the duodenum. Maturity is reached in about 50 days.

Chickens 3 to 4 months of age or older are quite resistant to parasitism with *Ascaridia galli.* Ackert, Edgar, and Frick (*2*) stated that a relationship existed between the number of duodenal goblet cells (goblet-shaped cells on the membrane) and the mucin (the principal protoplasm in mucus) which these cells secreted and the development of the natural resistance of the growing chickens to this nematode. Since more goblet cells per area were found in the epithelial, or surface, lining of the duodenum of chickens 4 months old than in younger birds, the authors concluded that these cells were in some way responsible for the greater resistance developed by the older birds. The age at which the peak of the goblet-cell formation occurred was found to correspond very closely to the development of the maximum resistance of the chicken to the growth of the nematodes.

Animal proteins in the form of milk and meat have been shown to be important dietary supplements in the development of resistance of chickens to *Ascaridia galli*, and a diet wholly of plant origin was not found to be conducive to resistance to helminth (worm) invasion. Ackert and his coworkers have shown that foods high in vitamins A and B increase the fowl's resistance to this nematode and that the lack of the vitamin B complex definitely favors parasitism.

Birds heavily infected with *Ascaridia galli* have been found to suffer from loss of blood, reduced blood-sugar content, increased urates, shrunken thymus glands, and retarded growth, and mortality among them greatly increased. Droopiness, emaciation, and diarrhea are symptoms of a heavily parasitized condition. Death sometimes results if treatment is not given.

SMALL INTESTINAL ROUNDWORMS

Several species of hairworms, or capillarids (*Capillaria* species), occur in the small intestines and ceca of domestic fowls. Since these worms are small and hairlike in appearance and from one-half to three-fourths of an inch long, they may be easily overlooked on a casual examination of the opened intestine at autopsy. It is, therefore, necessary to resort to the microscope to make sure of their presence in case of light infections.

One species, *Capillaria columbae*, has commonly been observed in the intestines of pigeons and less commonly in the intestines of the mourning dove, chicken, and turkey. Uninfected birds become infected with this roundworm by swallowing the embryonated egg with the food and water.

Birds heavily infected with this hairworm show symptoms of emaciation, listlessness, and diarrhea. Such birds spend much of their time in a huddled position on the ground. Their feathers are ruffled and soiled around the vent, and the skin and visible mucous membranes are more or less pale. Food and water are taken sparingly. Death may occur as a result of heavy infections.

Levine (*34*) reported that the intestines of chickens heavily infected with *Capillaria columbae* under experimental conditions showed a moderate thickening of the mucous membrane, which contained "reddish areas varying from pinhead hemorrhagic spots to diffuse hyperemia [excess of blood] of large portions of the mucosa." The writer has observed that the intestines of heavily infected pigeons showed extensive destruction of the mucous membrane, which was frequently completely sloughed off and contained a large quantity of fluid.

The roundworm *Ornithostrongylus quadriradiatus* may be the cause of serious intestinal disturbances in pigeons. Turtledoves and mourning doves have also been reported as hosts. The eggs of this roundworm are voided in the droppings and hatch within 19 to 24 hours. Three to four days more are required for the young larvae to become infective. When the infective larvae are swallowed by a pigeon or other susceptible host, they mature in the small intestines, and the female worms begin to deposit eggs 5 or 6 days after the larvae are ingested.

Cuvillier (*13*) reported that heavily parasitized birds become droopy and have ruffled feathers, with head and neck retracted. The birds remain squatting on the ground; if disturbed, they try to move but usually tip forward on the breast and head. Food is taken sparingly and is frequently regurgitated, along with bile-stained fluid. The birds usually drink an excessive amount of water. There is a pronounced greenish diarrhea, and the birds lose weight rapidly. Death is preceded by prostration and difficult, rapid breathing. The intestines of fatally infected birds are markedly haemorrhagic and have a green mucoid content, with masses of cast-off membrane tissue.

The cecum worm of poultry, *Heterakis gallinae*, occurs commonly in the ceca of chickens, turkeys, and possibly other domestic fowls. This worm attains a length of three-tenths to one-half inch. The life history is direct. The embryonated eggs hatch in the upper part of the intestine, and at the end of 24 hours the majority of the young worms have reached the ceca.

The chief economic importance of the cecum worm lies in its role as a carrier of the causative agent of blackhead. Graybill and Smith (*16*) discovered that blackhead can be produced by feeding large numbers of embryonated eggs of *Heterakis gallinae* removed from blackhead-infected birds. They offered the tentative hypothesis that the worms lowered the resistance of the host to the causative parasites already present in the ceca. Tyzzer and Fabyan (*47*), however, presented evidence which indicated that the protozoan parasite is incorporated in the worm egg, but they were unable to demonstrate its presence there.

Two other species of cecum worms, *Heterakis beramporia* and *H. eisolonche*, produce nodules in the ceca of chickens and pheasants, respectively.

Studies by Alicata (*5*) in Hawaii have shown that various insects, such as beetles and earwigs, serve experimentally as intermediate hosts of *Subulura brumpti*, a common pinworm of the ceca of chickens in the Hawaiian Islands.

An extremely small roundworm, *Strongyloides avium*, has been found in the ceca and small intestine of chickens in Louisiana and Puerto Rico. The walls of the ceca and small intestine of infected birds may be greatly thickened, and a bloody diarrhea may be present. If infected chicks survive the acute stage, they may, when fully grown, show no ill effects from the parasite, even though it is present. Young chickens may die as a result of a heavy infection, but if the infection is very light little or no clinical effect has been noted.

The life history of this nematode is direct. The eggs pass out of the fowl's body in the droppings. They hatch within 18 to 24 hours, and the young worms develop in the soil into adult males and females, which shortly give rise to other young. These feed, molt, and in turn either develop into adult males and females or transform to another type of larvae known as infective larvae. When these infective larvae are swallowed by a susceptible host, infection results. Unlike most species of nematodes, the parasitic cycle of *Strongyloides avium* consists of females only.

THE EYE WORM

The eye worm of poultry, *Oxyspirura mansoni* is found only in Florida and Louisiana. The white worms are found beneath the nictitating membrane, or third eyelid, sometimes in large numbers.

Studies by Sanders (*41*) in Florida showed that the cockroach *Leucophala surinamensis* is the intermediate host of the chicken eye worm. The eggs of the female worms are washed down the tear ducts, swallowed, and pass to the exterior in the droppings. The cockroach ingests the eggs or newly hatched larvae, and the latter develop to the infective stage in the body cavity of the insect. When the cockroach is subsequently eaten by a chicken or other susceptible host, the infective larva is freed in the crop and passes up the esophagus to the mouth, and then through the nasolachrymal duct (the tear duct) to the eye. Affected birds show signs of uneasiness and scratch at the eyes, which exhibit an acute inflammation accompanied by an abundant secretion of tears. The nictitating membrane is swollen, projects slightly beyond the eyelids at the corners of the eye, and is kept in continual motion as if to remove some foreign body from the eye. The eyelids sometimes become stuck together, and a white cheesy matter collects beneath them. Occasionally severe ophthalmia (inflammation of the eye) develops, and the eyeball may be destroyed if treatment of some sort is not resorted to. When this stage is reached the worms are no longer to be found in the eye. Severely affected birds eat very little, decline in strength, become anemic, and may die within a few weeks.

GAPEWORMS

Gapeworm infection, commonly known as gapes, is caused by roundworms that live in the windpipe. These worms, *Syngamus trachea*, are sometimes called red worms because of their red color or forked worms because the males and females so firmly adhere to one another that they appear like the letter Y. The male worm attains a length of about one-fifth of an inch, while the female reaches a length of nearly 1 inch.

This parasite has a direct life history. Eggs are coughed up from the windpipe and swallowed by the bird. They pass out in the droppings and develop, and some of them hatch. Fowls become infected by swallowing either the infective eggs or the young roundworms that hatch from them. Earthworms may swallow the infective eggs or the young roundworms and are then a source of infection to fowls that swallow them.

The worms clog the windpipe of young poultry, causing them to sneeze, cough, and gape for air (fig. 5). An extensive irritation of the mucous lining of the windpipe results from the bloodsucking activities of the gapeworms, and coughing is apparently caused by

FIGURE 5.—Young chickens infected with gapeworms. The chicken on the right is gaping as a result of obstruction of the trachea by the worms.

this irritation. Similar symptoms result from bronchitis and laryngotracheitis, but if gapeworms are responsible they can be readily found by destroying a sick bird and slitting open the windpipe. The red, Y-shaped worms, if present, are usually found in the lower half of the windpipe.

Lesions or nodules are usually found at the point of attachment of the male worms only. Hence, it is believed that the male worm usually remains permanently attached to the tracheal wall, while the female worm loosens her hold from time to time and selects a new feeding place. Nodule formation occurs frequently in the tracheas of infected turkeys but is rarely seen in infected chicks because the latter rarely remain infected long enough for it to take place.

Affected birds become weak and emaciated and spend much of their time huddled on the floor with the eyes closed and the head drawn back against the body. The head is regularly thrown forward and upward and the mouth is opened wide to draw in air, or the head may be given a convulsive shake in an attempt to loosen the obstruction in the windpipe so that normal breathing may be resumed. Sudden death is due primarily to suffocation caused by the mechanical obstruction of the windpipe by the rapidly growing worms and the accumulation of secreted mucus.

Wehr (*52*) observed that young turkey poults usually develop gapeworm symptoms in approximately 7 or 8 days, whereas young chickens do not ordinarily show symptoms of gaping and coughing until 10 to 14 days after experimental infection. The turkey poults likewise begin to die from gapeworm infections sooner than young chickens. Characteristic gapeworm symptoms of coughing and gaping have not been observed in guinea fowl and ducks. Young pheasants, however, suffer from the disease to an extent comparable to that of young chicks and turkey poults. Older birds, unless heavily infected, usually show only mild symptoms or none at all. Chickens more than 10 weeks of age seldom harbor gapeworms under natural conditions. It has been reported, however, that in Ceylon gapeworms occur commonly in fowls of all ages, even up to 3 years. The role played by wild birds in the spread of gapeworm disease is still questionable.

LITERATURE CITED

(1) ACKERT, JAMES E.
   1931. THE MORPHOLOGY AND LIFE HISTORY OF THE FOWL NEMATODE ASCARIDIA LINEATA (SCHNEIDER). Parasitology 23: 360–379, illus.
(2) —— EDGAR, S. A., and FRICK, L. P.
   1939. GOBLET CELLS AND AGE RESISTANCE OF ANIMALS TO PARASITISM. Amer. Micros. Soc. Trans. 58: 81–89.
(3) —— and GRAHAM, G. L.
   1935. THE EFFICACY OF CARBON TETRACHLORIDE IN ROUNDWORM CONTROL. Poultry Sci. 14: 228–231, illus.
(4) —— and REID, W. M.
   1937. AGE RESISTANCE OF CHICKENS TO THE CESTODE RAILLIETINA CESTICILLUS (MOLIN). (Abstract) Jour. Parasitol, 23: 558.
(5) ALICATA, JOSEPH E.
   1939. PRELIMINARY NOTE ON THE LIFE HISTORY OF SUBULURA BRUMPTI, A COMMON CECAL NEMATODE OF POULTRY IN HAWAII. (Research note) Jour. Parasitol. 25: 179–180, illus.
(6) —— and JONES, MYRNA F.
   1933. THE DUNG BEETLE, ATAENIUS COGNATUS, AS THE INTERMEDIATE HOST OF HYMENOLEPIS CANTANIANA. (Abstract of paper) Jour. Parasitol. 19: 244, illus.
(7) ALLEN, ENA A.
   1940. A REDESCRIPTION OF TRICHOMONAS GALLINARUM MARTIN AND ROBERTSON, 1911, FROM THE CHICKEN AND TURKEY. Helminthol. Soc. Wash. Proc. 7: 65–68, illus.
(8) ——
   1941. MACROSCOPIC DIFFERENTIATION OF LESIONS OF. HISTOMONIASIS AND TRICHOMONIASIS IN TURKEYS. Amer. Jour. Vet. Res. 2: 214–217, illus.
(9) [BARBER, L. B.]
   1916. LIVE STOCK DISEASE INVESTIGATIONS. Guam Agr. Expt. Sta. Rpt. 1915: 25–41, illus.
(10) BISHOPP, F. C.
   1927. THE FOWL TICK AND HOW PREMISES MAY BE FREED FROM IT. U. S. Dept. Agr. Farmers' Bul. 1070, 14 pp., illus. (Revised.)

(11) CRAM, ELOISE B.
　　1926. A PARASITIC NEMATODE AS THE CAUSE OF LOSSES AMONG DEMESTIC GEESE.
　　　　North Amer. Vet. 7: 27–29, illus.
(12) ———
　　1936. SPECIES OF CAPILIARIA PARASITIC IN THE UPPER DIGESTIVE TRACT OF
　　　　BIRDS. U. S. Dept. Agr. Tech. Bull. 516, 28 pp., illus.
(13) CUVILLIER, EUGENIA.
　　1937. THE NEMATODE, ORNITHOSTRONGYLUS QUADRIRADIATUS, A PARASITE OF
　　　　THE DOMESTICATED PIGEON. U. S. Dept Agr. Tech. Bull. 569,
　　　　36 pp., illus.
(14) GIERKE, A. G.
　　1933. TRICHOMONIASIS OF THE UPPER DIGESTIVE TRACT OF CHICKENS. Calif.
　　　　Dept. Agr., Monthly Bul. 22: 205–208, illus.
(15) GRASSI, [B.], and ROVELLI, [G.]
　　1888. DÉVELOPPEMENT EXPÉRIMENTAL DU TÆNIA PROGLOTTINA DAV. (Revue)
　　　　Rec. de Méd. Vét. 65: 675–676.
(16) GRAYBILL, H. W., and SMITH, THEOBALD.
　　1920. PRODUCTION OF FATAL BLACKHEAD IN TURKEYS BY FEEDING EMBRYONATED
　　　　EGGS OF HETERAKIS PAPILLOSA. Jour. Expt. Med. 31: 647–655.
(17) HALL, MAURICE C., and SHILLINGER, JACOB E.
　　1923. MISCELLANEOUS TESTS OF CARBON TETRACHLORIDE AS AN ANTHELMINTIC.
　　　　Jour. Agr. Res. 23: 163–192.
(18) HARWOOD, PAUL D., and LUTTERMOSER, GEORGE W.
　　1938. THE INFLUENCE OF INFECTIONS WITH THE TAPEWORM, RAILLIETINA
　　　　CESTICILLUS, ON THE GROWTH OF CHICKENS. Helminthol. Soc.
　　　　Wash. Proc. 5: 60–62.
(19) HAWN, M. C.
　　1937. TRICHOMONIASIS OF TURKEYS. Jour. Infect. Dis. 61: [184]–197.
(20) HINSHAW, W. R., and MCNEIL, E.
　　1941. CARRIERS OF HEXAMITA MELEAGRIDIS. Amer. Jour. Vet. Res. 2: 453–458.
(21) ——— MCNEIL, E., and KOFOID, C. A.
　　1938. THE RELATIONSHIP OF HEXAMITA SP. TO AN ENTERITIS OF TURKEY
　　　　POULTS. Cornell Vet. 28: 281–293.
(22) ITAGAKI, SHIRO.
　　1927. ON THE LIFE HISTORY OF THE CHICKEN NEMATODE, ASCARIDIA PER-
　　　　SPICILLUM. 3d World's Poultry Cong. Proc., pp. 339–344, illus.
(23) JOHNSON, E. P.
　　1939. A METHOD OF RAISING TURKEYS IN CONFINEMENT TO PREVENT PARASITIC
　　　　DISEASES. Va. Agr. Expt. Sta. Bul. 323, 16 pp.
(24) ——— UNDERHILL, G. W., COX, J. A., and THRELKELD, W. L.
　　1938. A BLOOD PROTOZOON OF TURKEYS TRANSMITTED BY SIMUDIUM NIGRO-
　　　　PARVUM (TWINN). Amer. Jour. Hyg. 27: 649–665, illus.
(25) JONES, MYRNA F.
　　1936. METROLIASTHES LUCIDA, A CESTODE OF GALLIFORM BIRDS, IN ARTHRO-
　　　　POD AND AVIAN HOSTS. Helminthol. Soc. Wash. Proc. 3: 26–30,
　　　　illus.
(26) ——— and HORSFALL, M. W.
　　1935. ANTS AS INTERMEDIATE HOSTS FOR TWO SPECIES OF RAILLIETINA
　　　　PARASITIC IN CHICKENS. Jour. Parasitol. 27: 442–443.
(27) ——— and HORSFALL, MARGERY W.
　　1936. THE LIFE HISTORY OF A POULTRY CESTODE. Science 83: 303–304.
(28) JOYEUX, CHARLES, and BAER, JEAN GEORGES.
　　1937. RECHERCHES SUR L'ÉVOLUTION DES CESTODES DE GALLINACÉS. [Paris]
　　　　Acad. des Sci. Compt. Rend. 205: 751–753.
(29) JUNGHERR, ERWIN.
　　1927. TWO INTERESTING TURKEY DISEASES. Amer. Vet. Med. Assoc. Jour.
　　　　71: 636–640, illus.
(30) KOTLAN, A., and CHANDLER, W. L.
　　1925. A NEWLY RECOGNIZED FLUKE DISEASE (PROSTHOGONIMIASIS) OF FOWLS
　　　　IN THE UNITED STATES. Amer. Vet. Med. Assoc. Jour. 67: 756–
　　　　763, illus.
(31) ——— and CHANDLER, W. L.
　　1927. ON THE ROLE PLAYED BY DRAGONFLIES IN THE TRANSFER OF PROSTHO-
　　　　GONIMUS. Amer. Vet. Med. Assoc. Jour. 70: 520–524.

(32) LEVINE, NORMAN D., BOLEY, L. E., and HESTER, H. R.
1941. EXPERIMENTAL TRANSMISSION OF TRICHOMONAS GALLINAE FROM THE
CHICKEN TO OTHER BIRDS. Amer. Jour. Hyg., Sect. C, 33 : 23–32.
(33) ——— and BRANDLY, C. A.
1939. A PATHOGENIC TRICHOMONAS FROM THE UPPER DIGESTIVE TRACT OF
CHICKENS. Amer. Vet. Med. Assoc. Jour. 95 : 77–78, illus.
(34) LEVINE, P. P.
1938. INFECTION OF THE CHICKEN WITH CAPILLARIA COLUMBAE (RUD.). Jour.
Parasitol. 24 : [45]–52.
(35) MACY, RALPH W.
1934. PROSTHOGONIMUS MACRORCHIS N. SP., THE COMMON OVIDUCT FLUKE OF
DOMESTIC FOWLS IN THE NORTHERN UNITED STATES. Amer. Micros.
Soc. Trans. 53 : 30–34, illus.
(36) ———
1934. STUDIES ON THE TAXONOMY, MORPHOLOGY, AND BIOLOGY OF PROSTHO-
GONIMUS MACRORCHIS MACY, A COMMON OVIDUCT FLUKE OF DOMESTIC
FOWLS IN NORTH AMERICA. Minn. Agr. Expt. Sta. Tech. Bul. 98,
71 pp., illus.
(37) McCULLOCH, ERNEST C., and NICHOLSON, LYLE G.
1940. PHENOTHIAZINE FOR THE REMOVAL OF HETERAKIS GALLINAE FROM
CHICKENS. Vet. Med. 35 : 398–400, illus.
(38) OLSEN, MARLOW W., and ALLEN, ENA A.
1940. TREATMENT OF CECAL AND LIVER TRICHOMONIASIS IN TURKEYS BY
FEVER THERAPY. (Preliminary paper) Soc. Expt. Biol. and Med.
Proc. 45 : 875–876.
(39) O'ROKE, EARL C.
1934. A MALARIA-LIKE DISEASE OF DUCKS CAUSED BY LEUCOCYTOZOON ANATIS
WICKWARE. Mich. Univ. School Forestry and Conserv. Bul. 4,
44 pp., illus.
(40) ROBERTS, F. H. S.
1940. A PRELIMINARY NOTE ON THE EFFICIENCY OF PHENOTHIAZINE AGAINST
SOME POULTRY HELMINTHS. Austral. Vet. Jour. 16 : 172–174.
(41) SANDERS, D. A.
1928. MANSON'S EYEWORM OF POULTRY. Amer. Vet. Med. Assoc. Jour. 72 :
568–584, illus.
(42) SKIDMORE, LOUIS V.
1932. LEUCOCYTOZOON SMITHI INFECTION IN TURKEYS AND ITS TRANSMISSION
BY SIMULIUM OCCIDENTALE TOWNSEND. Zentbl. f. Bakt. [etc.]
Originale (I) 125 : 329–335, illus.
(43) STABLER, ROBERT M.
1938. THE SIMILARITY BETWEEN THE FLAGELLATE OF TURKEY TRICHOMONI-
ASIS AND T. COLUMBAE IN THE PIGEON. Amer. Vet. Med. Assoc.
Jour. 93 : 33–34, illus.
(44) ———
1938. TRICHOMONAS GALLINAE RIVOLTA (1878) THE CORRECT NAME FOR THE
FLAGELLATE IN THE MOUTH, CROP AND LIVER OF THE PIGEON. (Research note) Jour. Parasitol. 24 : 553–554.
(45) TYZZER, ERNEST EDWARD.
1927. ENTERO-HEPATITIS IN TURKEYS AND ITS TRANSMISSION THROUGH THE
AGENCY OF HETERAKIS VESICULARIS. 3d World's Poultry Cong.
Proc., pp. 286–290, illus.
(46) ———
1934. STUDIES ON HISTOMONIASIS, OR "BLACKHEAD" INFECTION, IN THE
CHICKEN AND TURKEY. Amer. Acad. Arts and Sci. Proc. 69 :
[189]–264, illus.
(47) ——— and FABYAN, M.
1920. FURTHER STUDIES ON "BLACKHEAD" IN TURKEYS, WITH SPECIAL REFER-
ENCE TO TRANSMISSION BY INOCULATION. Jour. Infect. Dis. 27 :
[207]–239, illus.
(48) UNDERHILL, G. W.
1939. TWO SIMULIIDS FOUND FEEDING ON TURKEYS IN VIRGINIA. Jour. Econ.
Ent. 32.: 765–768.

(49) VOLKMAR, FRITZ.
    1930. TRICHOMONAS DIVERSA N. SP. AND ITS ASSOCIATION WITH A DISEASE
        OF TURKEYS. Jour. Parasitol. 17: [85]–89, illus.
(50) WEHR, EVERETT E.
    1936. EARTHWORMS AS TRANSMITTERS OF CAPILLARIA ANNULATA, THE "CROP-
        WORM" OF CHICKENS. North Amer. Vet. (8) : 18–20, illus.
(51) ——
    1937. RELATIVE ABUNDANCE OF CROP WORMS IN TURKEYS: MACROSCOPIC DIF-
        FERENTIATION OF SPECIES. Vet. Med. 32: 230–233, illus.
(52) ——
    1939. THE GAPEWORM AS A MENACE TO POULTRY PRODUCTION. 7th World's
        Poultry Cong. Proc., pp. 267–270.
(52a) ——
    1939. STUDIES ON THE DEVELOPMENT OF THE PIGEON CAPILLARID, CAPILLARIA
        COLUMBAE. U. S. Dept. Agr. Tech. Bul. 679, 19 pp., illus.
(53) —— HARWOOD, PAUL D., and SCHAFFER, JACOB M.
    1939. BARIUM ANTIMONYL TARTRATE AS A REMEDY FOR THE REMOVAL OF
        GAPEWORMS FROM CHICKENS. Poultry Sci. 18: 63–65.

At the time this book went to press, the drugs
and other materials mentioned in various articles—chiefly as disinfectants, insecticides, and
anthelmintics—were still available for veterinary and medical use. Under war conditions,
however, it is possible that some of these materials may become scarce or unavailable. In
that case, the reader should obtain professional
advice from the Department of Agriculture, the
State experiment station, a local veterinarian,
or the county agent as to available substitutes.

Coccidiosis
of the Chicken

BY JOHN F. CHRISTENSEN
AND ENA A. ALLEN [1]

AN ACCOUNT of the life history, symptoms of infection, and methods of control of a group of internal parasites that are among the most serious enemies of poultry production.

"IT IS PROBABLE that coccidia cause greater economic loss among domesticated animals of the temperate zone than any other group of protozoa." Thus Becker [2] aptly indicated the importance of coccidiosis, the specific disease caused by these protozoan parasites. It may be added that the coccidia probably cause greater economic loss among chickens alone than among all other domesticated animals combined, despite the fact that coccidiosis occurs frequently in severe outbreaks among other domesticated fowl, cattle, and sheep and occasionally among goats, pigs and dogs. Because of the preponderant significance of the disease in chickens, this article is confined to a description of the coccidia and coccidiosis of these birds. However, the life histories of the parasites, the nature of the disease, and the principles of control are essentially similar for all domesticated and semidomesticated fowl, and the information given therefore applies in general also to coccidiosis of the duck, goose, guinea fowl, pheasant, pigeon, quail, and turkey, all of which harbor characteristic kinds or species of coccidia.

THE LIFE HISTORY OF A POULTRY COCCIDIUM

The coccidia belong to a group of Protozoa known as Sporozoa, so designated because they produce sporelike infective bodies at

[1] John F. Christensen and Ena A. Allen are Associate Protozoologists, Zoological Division, Bureau of Animal Industry.
[2] BECKER, ELERY R. COCCIDIA AND COCCIDIOSIS OF DOMESTICATED, GAME AND LABORATORY ANIMALS AND OF MAN. 147 pp., illus. Ames, Iowa. 1934.

1041

some stage in their life histories. Resistant cysts—enclosed, egglike forms—of these parasites are discharged from their hosts in the feces or droppings and must pass through a process of development called sporulation in the outside environment before being infective to other animals. With the exception of *Tyzzeria* of the duck, the coccidia of the chicken, and all other barnyard fowls belong to the genus *Eimeria*, the life histories of all species of which are in general similar.

The life history may be said to begin with the discharge of the microscopic, egglike, resistant forms known as oöcysts in the droppings of infected birds. Under conditions of optimum moisture, moderate temperature, and ample oxygen supply, these eliminated oöcysts sporulate within a few days. This process consists in division of the protoplasm within each oöcyst shell into four elongated bodies, each in turn secreting its own shell, within which the protoplasm again divides to form two comma-shaped or sausage-shaped sporozoites. Each sporulated oöcyst thus contains eight sporozoites, which are infective agents capable of giving rise to coccidial infection when swallowed by susceptible birds.

Sporulated oöcysts may be ingested by susceptible birds soon after development is complete, or they may lie dormant for months in litter or soil, if temperature and moisture are favorable, before being picked up by new hosts. Once eaten by a susceptible bird, the oöcysts are in some way activated in the intestine of the host so that the sporozoites are released into the intestinal canal. The liberated sporozoites are capable of slow flexing movements, and when they come in contact with the intestinal wall in certain regions of the alimentary tract they penetrate cell membranes and enter the living protoplasm.

Inside the host cells the sporozoites lose their ability to move around, and they grow at the expense of the parasitized cells. After a definite period of growth the protoplasm of each parasite divides into many small, elongated bodies known as merozoites, which are expelled from the tissue by rupture of the cell membranes. These merozoites also possess limited powers of locomotion and immediately parasitize other cells. Again there is growth and multiplication, with the production of additional swarms of merozoites. After two or more generations of such asexual reproduction, some of the merozoites become sexually differentiated after entering new cells. The female parasites are large, rounded, and inactive. The male parasite produces by segmentation vast numbers of extremely small, actively moving bodies each capable of activating or fertilizing a single female parasite. After fertilization and secretion of a resistant shell, the female parasites are extruded, or pushed out, from the damaged host tissue into the alimentary stream and discharged from the host birds in the droppings, being then designated as oöcysts.

CECAL COCCIDIOSIS

There are two distinct types of coccidiosis of the chicken, depending upon the site of localization and multiplication of the parasites in the digestive tracts of the infected birds. In cecal coccidiosis, the coccidia invade the mucous membrane of the ceca, or blind guts, of chicks (fig. 1), producing as a result of rapid multiplication and extensive destruction of tissue an acute and often highly fatal disease characterized by severe cecal hemorrhage. In the intestinal disease, the parasites become localized largely in the small intestine and give rise to a serious but usually less acute infection of older, maturing birds sometimes characterized by extreme wasting of flesh and slow, insidious development.

Cecal coccidiosis is primarily a disease of chicks 3 to 5 weeks old, although infection may occur in birds of any

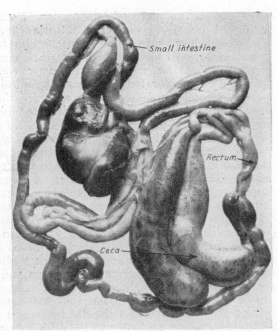

FIGURE 1.—Viscera of a chicken that died from an infection of *Eimeria tenella*. Note ceca distended with blood.

age. The disease usually strikes rather suddenly, producing illness or death in a considerable number of chicks at about the same time. In severe infections, many birds may die suddenly without showing visible symptoms, but they usually have pale combs and some blood on the feathers surrounding the vent, and when the birds are opened for examination, the ceca are found to be bulging with blood. Other birds have a ruffled, droopy appearance (fig. 2), lose appetite, fall off rapidly in weight, have a subnormal temperature, show pale skin and mucous membranes as a result of cecal hemmor-

FIGURE 2.—Chicken suffering from an attack of cecal coccidiosis.

rhage, and discharge bloody droppings. Some of these sick birds die during the first few days of illness, while others linger for several days to a week or more before finally succumbing to emaciation or wasting of flesh and loss of blood. With good care, many sick chicks gradually overcome the pallor, regain flesh, and recover.

Tyzzer [3] demonstrated that cecal coccidiosis is caused by a single species of coccidium, *Eimeria tenella*. The information he obtained from study with experimentally infected birds provided the basis for a complete understanding of the natural disease. On the fourth day after inoculation with heavy doses of sporulated oöcysts of *E. tenella*, birds show symptoms of severe cecal coccidiosis, and when they are killed for examination, bleeding from the cecal walls has begun. The greatest number of deaths occur on the fifth and sixth days of infection, when cecal hemorrhage reaches its peak, the birds show pale skin and mucous membranes from loss of blood, and the droppings contain blood. Chicks that die during the period of greatest hemorrhage have ceca bulging with fluid blood (fig. 1). When death occurs later in the infection, the blood and tissue debris in the ceca have formed clotted or cheesy cores, while the cecal walls appear thickened and mottled from hemorrhage and the tissues and organs are pale from loss of blood. It was demonstrated that the widespread leakage of blood from the cecal mucous membrane during the infection results from the destruction of tissue by the maturing second generation parasites and the liberation of enormous numbers of second generation merozoites.

INTESTINAL COCCIDIOSIS

Although usually less acute and spectacular in its onset than the cecal infection, intestinal coccidiosis causes a tremendous economic loss to poultry farmers by making heavy inroads on flocks of maturing chickens at a time when considerable cash outlay is represented. Of the six well-established species of coccidia that become localized in the small intestine of chickens, *Eimeria necatrix* is the one responsible for severe clinical intestinal coccidiosis, although other species have been demonstrated by experimental infections to produce less severe clinical symptoms. Thus, *E. acervulina* may produce coccidiosis of long duration characterized by extreme emaciation, and *E. maxima* causes thickening of the intestinal wall and produces a slight hemorrhage from the damaged mucous membrane in very heavy infections.

This type of coccidiosis is primarily a disease of maturing birds and frequently appears soon after pullets are confined to laying houses. The infection is first recognized in only a few birds of a flock, but additional individuals develop symptoms from day to day until considerable numbers are affected. The symptoms are in general similar to those noted for chicks with cecal coccidiosis, consisting in droopiness, a ruffled appearance, loss of appetite, increasing

[3] TYZZER, ERNEST EDWARD. COCCIDIOSIS IN GALLINACEOUS BIRDS. Amer. Jour. Hyg. 10 : 269–383, illus. 1929.

emaciation and weakness, and pallor resulting from intestinal hemorrhage. Death from the disease may occur during the early stages of the attack, but usually only after several days to 2 or 3 weeks of illness. Many sick birds gradually regain their appetite and strength and recover from the attack.

As Tyzzer had done previously for *Eimeria tenella*, Tyzzer, Theiler, and Jones [4] worked out the intricate details of the life history of *E. necatrix* and the course of experimental infection in the chicken in

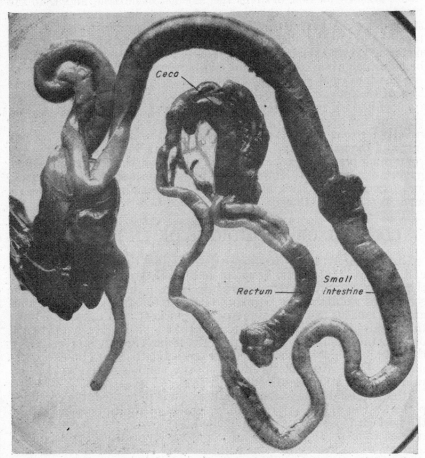

FIGURE 3.—Viscera of a chicken that died from an infection of *Eimeria necatrix*. Note that the entire small intestine as well as the ceca is affected.

order to obtain the information essential for an accurate conception of the natural disease. They demonstrated that susceptible chickens experimentally infected with large single dosages of sporulated oöcysts of *E. necatrix* show the first symptoms of coccidiosis at the

[4] TYZZER, ERNEST E., THEILER, HANS, and JONES, E. ELIZABETH. COCCIDIOSIS IN GALLINACEOUS BIRDS. II. A COMPARATIVE STUDY OF SPECIES OF EIMERIA OF THE CHICKEN. Amer. Jour. Hyg. 15 : 319–393, illus. 1932.

end of 4 days of infection. The heaviest death losses occur on the sixth and seventh days of infection as a result of the destruction of tissue and the bleeding produced by the action of the parasites in the intestinal mucous membrane. The unopened small intestine of birds that die at the height of infection appears heavily peppered with small opaque spots and hemorrhagic blotches and streaks, especially in the middle portion (fig. 3). Microscopic study reveals that these opaque spots or lesions are large colonies of maturing second-generation parasites located deep in the mucous membrane and that the bleeding commences at the centers of these lesions in the tissue destroyed by the parasites. The affected intestine is congested with blood and is flabby, distended, and easily ruptured; it is filled with material varying from a clear, jellylike, yellowish exudate to clotted blood, which often forms a solid, fibrinous cylinder completely blocking the intestinal canal. During the sixth day, the muscular function of the intestine is usually completely lost as a result of obstruction with these masses of clotted tissue, exudate, and blood. Birds that survive the seventh day of these heavy experimental infections usually recover. Within a day or two the intestine resumes functioning, and the recovering chickens begin discharging watery droppings containing blood, mucus, and occasional cylindrical masses of clotted material. Gradually the droppings become normal, appetite returns, and paleness disappears, but the birds may remain extremely emaciated from malnutrition.

CONTROL OF COCCIDIOSIS OF THE CHICKEN

Unfortunately, losses from coccidiosis do not cease with the deaths and sickness that result from an outbreak. According to Tyzzer, the damage resulting from severe infections to the ceca and intestine sometimes results in the permanent loss of function of considerable areas of mucous membrane in recovered chickens, and this contributes to the chronic unthriftiness of many of these birds. Such fowls not only mature more slowly but produce fewer eggs during maturity than similar chickens that have had no early attack of clinical coccidiosis.[5] These after effects of the disease emphasize the wisdom of prevention as a means of control.

It is well established [6] that if reinfection is prevented, the coccidial parasites run fairly rapid, definite courses of multiplication within the host birds and are soon eliminated as oöcysts; that birds surviving severe or continued mild infections are subsequently resistant or immune to severe reinfections with the same species of coccidia; and that such immune adult birds are healthy carriers of coccidia and thus possible sources of infection to young stock. Prevention is based on these facts, which at once suggest that the supply of infective oöcysts should be kept as low as possible by application of rigid sanitation and that young susceptible birds should be kept strictly isolated from adult fowls.

[5] MAYHEW, ROY L. STUDIES ON COCCIDIOSIS. VI. EFFECT OF EARLY ATTACK ON EGG PRODUCTION. Poultry Sci. 13 : 148–154, illus. 1934.
[6] JOHNSON, W. T. COCCIDIOSIS OF THE CHICKEN. Oreg. Agr. Expt. Sta. Bul. 238, 16 pp., illus. 1928. See also the citation in footnote 3.

Floors, walls, windows, and equipment of brooder houses should be cleaned thoroughly with soap and hot water before the birds are admitted. After that the floors should be thoroughly dry-cleaned with a scuffle hoe and a stiff broom at least twice weekly until the birds are 10 or 12 weeks old, then weekly until they are transferred to laying houses. Dry cleaning prevents the accumulation of moisture, which favors the sporulation of oöcysts. Fresh, clean litter should be put in after each cleaning. If chicks are kept in cages, cleaning should be done daily, if possible. Feeding and watering equipment should be cleaned frequently and should be designed to prevent accumulations of moisture on floors or contamination of feed and drinking water with infective material.

If there is enough land available, it is wise to use movable brooder houses that can be transferred occasionally to new ground. Stationary brooder houses should be located on well-drained, preferably sandy soil, which provides the quick-drying terrain least favorable for oöcyst development. It has been recommended that stationary brooder houses be provided with sloping concrete runs, which can be covered lightly with sand and cleaned thoroughly at the same time the houses are cleaned. During the period of confinement to laying houses special care must be taken to prevent conditions that would favor the development of intestinal coccidiosis among the pullets. The laying houses should be cleaned thoroughly before occupancy and frequently thereafter, in order that accumulations of moisture and litter, which favor oöcyst development, may be avoided. The same attention to sanitation should be given to the feeding and watering equipment for these older birds as to those for the brooding stock. If considerable range is available, clean ground should be provided for each group of pullets. At all times, the feeding, watering, and cleaning equipment for young and adult stock should be kept separated in order to prevent any significant transfer of infective material to susceptible birds. Though strict application of these sanitary measures in the handling of young birds cannot be expected to eliminate coccidial infection completely, it should permit successful rearing.

Even when excellent care is provided, outbreaks of coccidiosis occur occasionally among young birds, and at these times there is a demand for an immediate remedy. It is the general opinion among qualified authorities on poultry coccidiosis that there is little value in medicinal treatment of sick birds during an outbreak and that effort is applied more profitably in proper management. Early diagnosis and prompt adjustments in the feeding and care of birds are important. It is wise to segregate sick chickens, provide warm quarters, avoid overcrowding, supply appetizing, easily digested, nutritious feed, and redouble efforts at sanitation in order to remove oöcysts, which are shed in the droppings of sick birds in enormous numbers. Meticulous attention to all details of good feeding and care of sick birds may be expected to minimize losses during an outbreak, but treatment "can be recommended only as a means of making the best of an already bad situation, not as a routine preventive." [7]

[7] See reference in footnote 6.

Poultry Lice and Their Control

BY F. C. BISHOPP [1]

SEVERAL different kinds of biting and chewing lice infest poultry, each having its preferred location on certain parts of the body. Young birds especially can be seriously affected or even killed by severe attacks. The delousing procedure described in this article can easily be applied on any farm.

POULTRYMEN realize that it is essential to control poultry lice, particularly in the case of chickens. These parasites are also a problem to those who raise turkeys, ducks, geese, guineas, and pigeons or grow wild birds, such as quail and grouse, in captivity. Losses due to poultry lice throughout the United States run high in the millions of dollars each year as the result of death, especially among young fowls, retarded development, reduced egg production, interference with incubation, and damage to plumage. Probably the losses are heaviest among farm and backyard flocks kept as a side line rather than among commercial flocks, which are given special attention. Enough is known about lice and their control to make these losses totally unnecessary.

All lice infesting poultry and birds are of the biting and chewing, not the bloodsucking, kind. Some persons confuse lice with mites. The latter suck blood, differ from lice in their habits, and are controlled by different methods.

In general, each species of poultry lice is confined to a particular kind of poultry, but some pass readily from one kind of fowl to another, especially when the birds are closely associated. In this country, chickens are rather commonly infested with seven species of lice, turkeys with three, ducks and geese with three, pigeons with three, and guinea fowl and peafowl with two or three each.

---

[1] F. C. Bishopp is Assistant Chief of the Bureau of Entomology and Plant Quarantine.

1048

DEVELOPMENT AND HABITS OF POULTRY LICE

All species of poultry lice have certain habits in common. All of them live continuously on feathered hosts and soon die if removed from them. The eggs are attached to the feathers, and the young lice closely resemble the adults except in color and size. All poultry lice have strong chewing jaws, flattened bodies, legs fitted for clinging to feathers, and a remarkable ability to move about and hide among the feathers.

They differ, however, in their preferred locations on the body and the feathers, and these preferences have given rise to the common names applied to the various species.

The length of the incubation and development periods of several of the species have not been determined, but they are believed not to vary widely. In general it may be said that the incubation period ranges from 4 to 7 days, and the development of the lice from hatching to the adult stage requires 17 to 21 days. As the lice grow, the skins are shed two or three times. Mating takes place on the fowl, and egg laying begins 2 or 3 days after the lice mature. The number of eggs deposited has not been accurately determined but appears to range from 50 to 300.

CHICKEN LICE

THE HEAD LOUSE

As the name "head louse" suggests, this species (*Lipeurus heterographus*) is found mainly on the head, although it occurs occasionally on the neck and elsewhere. It is usually located close to the skin in the down or at the base of the feathers on the top and back of the head and beneath the bill. In fact, the head of the louse is often found so close to the skin that poultrymen think it is actually attached to the skin or is sucking blood. Although it does not suck blood, it is very irritating and ranks first among the lice as a pest of young chickens and turkeys, which often become infested within a few hours after hatching by lice from the mother. In cases of heavy infestation the chicks soon become droopy and weak and may die before they are a month old. When the chickens become fairly well feathered, head lice decrease in numbers, but they may increase again when the fowls reach maturity.

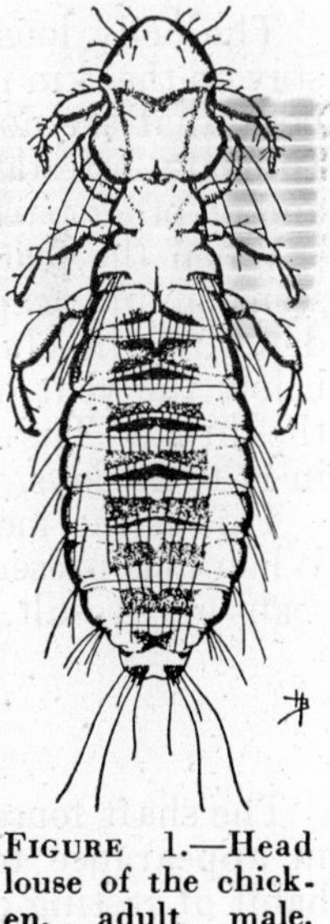

This louse (fig. 1) is oblong, grayish, and about one-tenth of an inch in length. The pearly white eggs (fig. 2) are attached singly to the down or at the base of the small feathers on the head. They hatch in 4 or 5 days into minute, pale, translucent lice, resembling the adults in shape.

FIGURE 1.—Head louse of the chicken, adult male. Greatly enlarged.

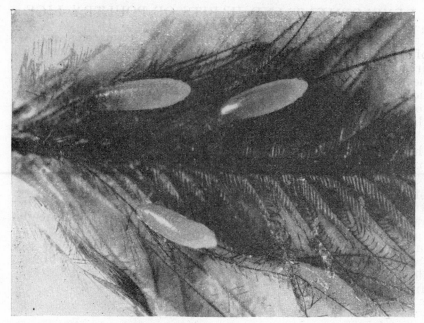

FIGURE 2.—Eggs of the head louse of the chicken.   Greatly enlarged.

THE BODY LOUSE

The body louse (*Menacanthus stramineus*) of chickens prefers to stay on the skin rather than on the feathers, and it chooses parts of the body that are not densely feathered, such as the area below the vent. In heavy infestations it may be found on the breast, under the wings, and on other parts of the body, including even the head.

When the feathers are parted, the straw-colored body lice may be seen running rapidly on the skin in search of cover.   The eggs are deposited in clusters near the base of small feathers, particularly below the vent or, in young fowls, frequently on the head or along the throat.   The eggs hatch in about a week, and the lice reach maturity in 17 to 20 days.

This is the most important of the lice that infest grown chickens. When it is present in large numbers, the skin is greatly irritated, and scabs may result, especially below the vent.

THE SHAFT LOUSE

The shaft louse, or small body louse (*Menopon gallinae*), is similar in appearance to the body louse but somewhat smaller.   It has a habit of resting on the shafts of the body feathers of chickens, where it may be seen running rapidly toward the body when the feathers are suddenly parted.   Sometimes as many as a dozen lice may be seen scurrying downward along a feather shaft.

Since the shaft louse apparently feeds only on parts of the feathers, it is much less important than its relative, the body louse. It is found in limited numbers on turkeys, guinea fowl, and ducks kept in close association with chickens. It does not stay on young birds until they become well feathered.

OTHER KINDS OF CHICKEN LICE

Four other kinds of lice are found rather commonly on chickens, but they are usually less abundant and important than those just discussed. The wing louse (*Lipeurus caponis*), a slender gray species resembling the head louse, to which it is related, is the most widely distributed and is found in the greatest numbers. It is sluggish and is usually seen resting between the barbules of the wing and tail feathers, or occasionally on the neck hackles and feathers of the back.

The fluff louse (*Goniocotes hologaster*), which is found, as the common name implies, on the fluff of the body feathers, is small, rather broad, yellow in color, and inactive. As it stays mostly in the fluff, it causes little irritation or other injury.

The large chicken louse (*Goniocotes gigas*) is a robust, dark, smoky-gray species of striking appearance. It is seldom abundant or of much importance.

The brown chicken louse (*Goniodes dissimilis*), occurring mainly in the Southern States, is large and reddish brown in color. It seldom occurs in large enough numbers to cause serious damage.

TURKEY LICE

The slender turkey louse (*Lipeurus gallipavonis*) and the large turkey louse (*Goniodes meleagridis*) are found on both wild and domesticated turkeys and may cause serious annoyance, although as a rule they are not very abundant. Poults hatched by chickens are often infested with the common body louse and the head louse, which pass to them from the foster mother. The combined attacks of these lice may retard growth and reduce the vigor of young turkeys. Head lice have been reported to have caused heavy mortality among newly hatched poults.

LICE OF GEESE, DUCKS, PIGEONS, AND OTHER POULTRY

Geese and ducks are seldom noticeably affected by lice. Three of four species are occasionally found on these fowls, and when the young are hatched by hens they are often attacked by the head louse of chickens.

Pigeons are subject to the attacks of six species of lice. Some of these are to be found on the birds in practically every pigeon loft, but they seldom become sufficiently abundant to cause marked ill effects. Carrier pigeons and show birds frequently have damaged feathers, and some owners attribute this to lice, particularly the large body louse (fig. 3). The damage in such cases adversely affects the appearance of the birds and probably also their speed and endurance in flight.

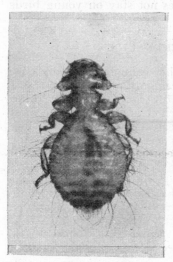

FIGURE 3.—The large body louse of pigeons. Enlarged.

CONTROL MEASURES

Since all bird lice live continuously and breed on the plumage and bodies of their hosts, little attention need be paid in control operations to the houses, litter, and yards. In eradicating lice all poultry on the premises should be regarded as lousy if any of them have lice.

In general it is advisable to delouse a flock in the fall when the surplus stock is disposed of so that the number of fowls to be treated is reduced. This assures their entering the winter free from lice. If no infested fowls are added to the flock, it will be free from the pests the following spring, which is especially desirable where hens are used for hatching and brooding.

Fortunately control procedures have been developed that are highly effective and thoroughly practical.

SODIUM FLUORIDE VERSUS LICE

Methods of eradicating poultry lice through the use of sodium fluoride as a powder or a dip were first described in 1917.[2] A single treatment will destroy all species of lice, including all eggs, without injury to the fowls.

Commercial sodium fluoride is recommended for this purpose. It is a white powder which should contain 90 to 98 percent sodium fluoride. The material is generally available and usually retails at 30 to 60 cents a pound. **Since sodium flouride is poisonous to human beings and animals when taken internally, care should be exercised in storing the powder, so that it will not be mistaken for something else, and in disposing of solutions of it.**

To insure treatment of all louse carriers the fowls should be shut up at night and a search made for any that do not roost in the poultry house.

DUSTING

The lice are found on various parts of the body, and it is essential that the sodium fluoride be placed on the infested areas. With this method it is necessary for two people to work together, one holding the fowl and the other applying the insecticide. The powder may be applied with a shaker can held in one hand while with the other the

---

[2] BISHOPP, F. C., and WOOD, H. P. MITES AND LICE ON POULTRY. U. S. Dept. Agr. Farmers' Bul. 801, 27 pp., illus. 1917. (Revised, 1939.)

feathers are raised so the powder will reach the skin. It is best to hold the birds over a shallow pan to catch the surplus powder. It is also economical to dilute the powder by adding 2 parts of some fine material, such as flour, road dust, or sulfur, to 1 part of sodium fluoride.

The so-called pinch method is preferable to the use of a shaker. It involves less waste and less dust floating in the air, and only one operator is required. The fowl is held in one hand by grasping the base of the wings over the back, and the powder, kept in a pan near at hand, is applied by placing a small pinch among the feathers next to the skin. About 11 pinches are applied to the fowl, 2 along the back, 1 on the neck, 1 on the head, 1 on the breast, 1 below the vent, 1 on each thigh, 1 on the tail, and 1 on each wing when spread.

Since sodium fluoride is irritating to the nose and throat, the operator should wear a respirator or a piece of wet cloth over his nose and mouth. The fowls should be released in the open air as fast as they are treated.

Young chickens and other fowls are likely to be injured if they are hovered closely by the mother after she has been treated. It is therefore highly advisable to delouse hens before the young hatch. If this has not been done, the young should not be treated until they are a week old, and then only two very small pinches of the powder should be applied to each, one distributed on the back, neck, and head and the other on the under side, including the throat.

Grown turkeys should receive about 15 pinches of the powder and pigeons 5. Because of the close feathers of the latter, however, dipping is more effective.

Dipping

Some poultry raisers maintain that fowls should not be dipped. Extensive experience, however, has shown that when more than 35 fowls are to be treated, dipping in sodium fluoride solution is highly effective, economical, convenient, and without ill effects on the poultry. The only precautions necessary are that the birds should be handled carefully, that the work should be done on a mild sunny day or in a warm poultry house, and that the operation should be completed at least an hour before sundown. Fowls dipped in the solution are not thoroughly wet, and the feathers dry in an hour or two.

The procedure is simple. Tepid water is measured into a tub, and a rounded tablespoonful of sodium fluoride is added for each gallon. The solution should be within 6 or 8 inches of the top of the tub, which is then placed on a box at a convenient height for dipping. The fowls are held in one hand by the wings over the back and lowered into the solution, with the head left out above it. The feathers are then raised beneath the solution with the other hand to allow penetration, the head is ducked, and the fowl is lifted out, allowed to drain a few seconds, and liberated. The actual dipping of a fowl requires only 20 to 30 seconds.

To completely rid pigeons of lice it is necessary to add 1 ounce of laundry soap to the dip to obtain a complete wetting of the feathers.[3]

[3] Wood, H. P. THE ERADICATION OF LICE ON PIGEONS. U. S. Dept. Agr. Dept. Cir. 213, 4 pp. 1922.

COST OF TREATMENT

One pound of sodium fluoride applied by the pinch method will treat about 100 hens. When a considerable number of fowls are to be treated, less than half that amount is required for dipping. Figuring the powder at 40 cents a pound and the labor at 30 cents an hour, the cost for treating 100 fowls amounts to $1.65 by the pinch method and $1 by the dipping method. This is very reasonable when it is considered that one treatment means the complete eradication of all lice from the premises, provided all the fowls are treated.

OTHER REMEDIES

Nicotine sulfate applied to the roosts under proper conditions is reasonably effective in eradicating lice. The pure (40-percent) material is applied with a brush to the upper side of the roosts about half an hour before the fowls go to roost. The fumes penetrate the feathers, and the lice continue to die and drop out during several nights following the application. This method works best in reasonably tight chicken houses and during warm weather. It cannot be depended on to eradicate lice completely, however, as it does not reach all of them, especially those on the head, and usually some of the fowls do not roost on the treated perches.

Sodium fluosilicate, a compound related to sodium fluoride, is a satisfactory substitute when used as a dip in the same way as the latter. The material is usually too coarse for very effective use as a dust.

Fine sulfur applied freely as a dust has been found satisfactory as a control for poultry lice. In order to destroy all the parasites in a single treatment, the treatment must be very thorough.

Many other materials and mixtures will destroy poultry lice, but everything considered, none is equal to sodium fluoride. Dust baths are useful in holding down louse infestations, but some fowls do not use such baths, and elimination of lice is never accomplished by this means.

Some remedies offered for sale and even widely used have little or no value in louse control. Among these should be mentioned materials sold for putting in the water or feed of poultry. Most of these are sulfur compounds. Such internal medication has been found to be valueless for the control of external parasites.

Poultry Mites

BY F. C. BISHOPP [1]

GOOD POULTRY HUSBANDRY requires keeping the birds free of mites as far as possible, since these pests can do considerable damage. The remedies are simple and fairly easy to apply.

ALL CLASSES of poultry are subject to the attack of mites, some of which are bloodsuckers, while others burrow in the skin or live on or in the feathers and still others occur in the air passage and in the lungs, liver, and other internal organs.

The total loss chargeable to poultry mites is large, since these parasites cause retarded growth, reduced egg production, poor condition, lowered vitality, damaged plumage, and even death. Much of the injury, consisting of constant irritation and loss of blood, is not apparent. A large percentage of the chickens, turkeys, and other poultry throughout the country are more or less constantly infested with one or several kinds of mites. Some of the more important forms will be briefly discussed in this article, and methods of combating them will be outlined.

THE CHICKEN MITE

Most poultry raisers are familiar with the common chicken mite (*Dermanyssus gallinae*). This pest is present in all parts of the country and affects all kinds of poultry. It is a bloodsucker and, when present in large numbers, saps the vitality of the birds, the loss of blood and the irritation caused being sufficient to make the fowls anaemic, weak, and restless. Egg production is seriously reduced, the eggs are spotted with mite excrement, and setting hens are disturbed and may be driven off the nests so that the eggs do not hatch. Hens have been known to die from mite attacks while sitting on the nest, and stock on feed fail to fatten. In addition, these mites may become annoying pests of human beings, especially persons who take

[1] F. C. Bishopp is Assistant Chief of the Bureau of Entomology and Plant Quarantine.

care of poultry, and livestock in buildings adjacent to poultry houses are also attacked.

The chicken mites are night raiders; for the most part they remain hidden away in cracks and crevices during the day. Hens on nests may be attacked during the day, however, and on very heavily infested premises some mites are to be found among the feathers of the fowls during the day.

In all its active stages the mite sucks the blood of fowls, which is necessary to its development and reproduction. Usually the mites become engorged in a few minutes after inserting their beaks. They may bite the fowls on any part of the body. After feeding, the mites crawl off the host and seek a hiding place around the roosts or nests. When numerous, they may spread to the walls, floor, and ceiling of the poultry house. About a day after feeding, the adult female mites deposit 3 to 7 pearly white eggs in the crack where they are hiding. As many as 8 clutches of eggs are deposited by each female, with a blood meal preceding each.

The eggs hatch in about 2 days, and the young six-legged mite molts its skin without feeding and gains another pair of legs. The mite then feeds and molts its skin 1 or 2 days later. This process is repeated once more, and the mite is then mature. Since the cycle from egg to adult requires only about a week, multiplication can be very rapid under favorable conditions. During cold weather, development is slowed down and the life span is extended. An infested poultry house will remain infested 4 or 5 months after it is vacated, and even longer in winter.

The chicken mite will feed freely on pigeons, canaries, and wild birds such as sparrows. Wild birds are undoubtedly responsible for the spread of mites in some cases, but such things as infested baskets and crates, and even human carriers, are of much greater importance.

Since chicken mites hide during the daytime in cracks around the roosting and nesting places of the fowls, they may be eliminated by properly treating these places and without paying any attention to the fowls. The major difficulty is to reach the hidden mites. This requires thorough application of an effective and very penetrating insecticide.

The control methods recommended for the chicken mite are also effective against the fowl tick and the bedbug.

The first step is to remove unnecessary boards, boxes, and trash from the poultry house and yard. Next, remove and burn litter and nest material. Then apply one of the carbolineums (high-grade anthracene oil), crude petroleum, or creosote oil. If the house is very heavily infested, the entire interior, including the roof, should be sprayed. If the infestation is light, applying the material to the roosts, roost supports, nests, and adjacent areas on the walls usually suffices.

General spray applications are best made with a bucket pump, knapsack sprayer, or barrel pump. A high pressure must be maintained, and the spray material should be driven into all cracks. For light infestations a hand sprayer may be used, or the material may be applied with a brush.

The materials recommended have considerable penetrating power and persist well, so that if the application is thorough a single treatment will usually clear up the infestation. Occasionally a second application 3 or 4 weeks after the first is necessary, and this may be made with a brush.

Since these materials stain and are somewhat caustic, care should be taken not to get them on the clothing, face, or body, or on the fowls. The spraying should be done early in the day so the material will have time to soak in before the fowls go to roost. It is advisable to clean out infestations before hens are set and to treat brooders and colony houses before they are used for young stock.

There are a number of other materials, such as kerosene-pyrethrum and nicotine sulfate, which if thoroughly and persistently used will clean up an infestation, but in the long run the materials first mentioned are usually more effective and cheaper. Whitewash is of some value in reducing mite infestations by sealing the mites in the cracks, but it will not accomplish complete control.

THE FEATHER MITE

The feather mite (*Liponyssus sylviarum*) is an occasional but serious pest of chickens. Heavy infestations result in lowered condition of the birds and reduced egg production as well as a scabby condition of the skin and discoloration of the plumage. This mite remains on the fowls constantly and hence is more irritating to them than the common chicken mite.

Since the feather mite is found on a number of species of free-flying birds, including robins, swallows, and sparrows, it seems almost certain that many of the infestations on poultry farms come from the contacts of these birds with the chickens.

FIGURE 1.—Feather mites on a chicken feather.

The mite closely resembles the common chicken mite, but it is slightly smaller and somewhat more active. It can be differentiated from other mites by the fact that it is present in numbers on fowls in the daytime and causes a dirty appearance of the feathers (fig. 1). It prefers the areas below the vent and around the tail, but in heavy infestations it occurs on the back and other parts and may also be seen running about on the eggs in the nests.

The female lays its eggs among the feathers, where the young mites hatch and complete their development without leaving the fowl.

Since the feather mite remains on the fowls most of the time, it is necessary to treat the fowls with an insecticide rather than to treat the roosts, as in the case of the chicken mite.

In view of the seriousness of the pest and the fact that it is not generally distributed among poultry, it should be completely eradicated before it spreads any further. In numerous instances eradication has been accomplished by the following procedure:

Dip every well-feathered fowl in a tub nearly filled with water to which 2 ounces of fine sulfur (98 percent passing a 325-mesh sieve) and 1 ounce of soap have been added for each gallon. Hold the fowl by the wings over the back and dip it, taking care to wet all the feathers thoroughly, and duck the head also. Since this treatment makes all the feathers wet, it is necessary to do the work on a warm sunny day or in a heated building so that the birds will not be chilled while drying.

If the outbreak occurs during the winter, complete destruction of all the mites on the fowls may be accomplished by dusting them thoroughly and freely with fine sulfur.

While the fowls are being treated, the nest material and litter should be removed and burned and the nest boxes, walls, and floors sprayed as recommended for control of the chicken mite.

Nests of English sparrows around the buildings should be pulled down and burned, and these birds should be prevented from nesting about the premises.

Applying nicotine sulfate to the perches shortly before the fowls go to roost, as is sometimes done for controlling lice (p. 1054), has been found by Cleveland [2] to eliminate an infestation of these mites when it is done under favorable conditions. This treatment is especially useful during cold weather when dipping cannot be carried out.

THE SCALY-LEG MITE

The scaly-leg mite (*Cnemidocoptes mutans*) commonly afflicts chickens throughout the country. In many instances it does not cause serious injury, but when nothing is done to check it an attack may result in deformity of the feet and legs and even actual loss of the tips of the toes.

The parasite is one of the itch mites, living beneath the scales of the shanks and feet and also attacking the comb, wattles, and neck.

[2] Cleveland, C. R. control of poultry lice and mites. Ind. Univ. Ext. Bul. 109, 8 pp., illus. 1922.

At first the only manifestation of the trouble is the irritation shown by the fowls, but later the scales begin to thicken and rise, and soon the feet and legs become unsightly.

The mites spread principally when the fowls are in close contact with each other, either in crates or on the roost. Occasionally a few fowls in a flock may be badly infested without the others showing material injury; nevertheless it is well to treat fowls as soon as there is evidence of an infestation.

Painting the roosts and nests with one of the carbolineums for the control of the common poultry mite will do much to reduce the spread of the scaly-leg mite. If only a few fowls show infestations they may be culled out and disposed of, or the legs may be dipped in crude petroleum (fig. 2). Care should be taken not to permit the oil to get on the feathers and not to immerse the legs above the hock. One application is usually sufficient, but if most of the scales have

FIGURE 2.—Dipping the legs of a chicken in crude petroleum to control the scaly-leg mite.

not dropped off after a month, a second treatment should be given. Sometimes it is necessary to dip the legs of all the fowls in a flock. This should certainly be done if there is evidence of widespread infestation among them.

THE DEPLUMING MITE

Another mite, *Cnemidocoptes gallinae*, related to the scaly-leg mite, frequently causes severe irritation by burrowing in the skin near the base of the feathers; as a result, the feathers are often pulled or broken by the fowls. The mite, called the depluming mite, is very small, scarcely visible to the unaided eye, and it is usually found in the follicles at the base of the feathers, particularly on the back and sides.

At times the mites leave their burrows and crawl about, and this enables them to spread when chickens are in close contact.

The depluming mite can be completely eliminated from the flock by thoroughly dipping every chicken on the premises in a sulfur bath. To accomplish this a tub should be nearly filled with tepid water, 2 ounces of fine sulfur (98 percent passing a 325-mesh sieve) and ½ ounce of laundry soap being added for each gallon. The fowls should be submerged and the feathers raised so as to wet them thoroughly. The head of each bird should be ducked quickly two or three times.

If lice are also present on the birds, it is advisable to add ¾ ounce (1 heaping tablespoonful) of sodium fluoride to each gallon of water.

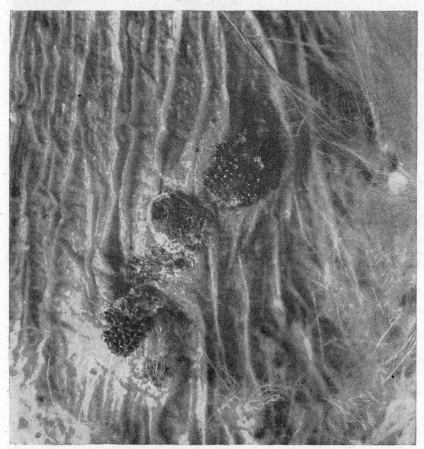

FIGURE 3.—Masses of chiggers on the skin of a chicken and the sores caused by them. Greatly enlarged.

Since the soapy water thoroughly wets the feathers, this treatment should be applied only on warm sunny days or in a heated building.

CHIGGERS (RED BUGS OR HARVEST MITES)

Chiggers (*Eutrombicula alfreddugèsi*) attack human beings and also infest chickens. Normally these small reddish mites feed upon wild animals, birds, snakes, and lizards. The adult chiggers are the brilliant red, velvety mites that are sometimes seen crawling on the ground. The mite is parasitic only in its first stage of development. It does not penetrate the skin, as is commonly believed, but attaches itself in much the same manner as does the tick. After a few days it becomes engorged and drops off, if it is not dislodged by scratching. During the period of attachment it injects a poisonous secretion that sets up a violent local irritation and itching. On fowls, chiggers are inclined to attach themselves in groups, mainly on the wings, breast, and neck. Injury to grown fowls is not very apparent except for the local lesions where the chiggers are or have been attached. Young chickens, however, are very susceptible to chigger infestations and soon become droopy, refuse to eat, and frequently die in a short time (fig. 3).

Chiggers are most abundant in the Southern States, especially on heavy soils. They usually appear some time after warm weather begins and are active until frost.

Since chigger injury to young turkeys and chickens is severe, where these parasites are abundant it is advisable to hatch the chicks early and, in case of late hatches, to keep the chicks out of the grass and weeds. Keeping vegetation closely cut in the poultry yards is helpful, and infestations may also be reduced by dusting the chicken ranges with sulfur at the rate of about 50 pounds per acre.

Dusting the chicks lightly with sulfur also aids in protecting them. The lesions on grown chickens should be touched lightly with carbolated vaseline or sulfur ointment.

The Fowl Tick

BY F. C. BISHOPP [1]

MANY POULTRY RAISERS have burned down a chicken house badly infested with fowl ticks because they thought there was no other way to get rid of this tough and dangerous pest. It can be controlled, however, by following the directions given in this article.

ONE of the most serious handicaps to poultry raising in the Southwestern States is the fowl tick, or blue bug (*Argas mineatus*). It is a persistent bloodsucker, and its presence in a poultry house in considerable numbers results in weakened stock, fewer eggs, and emaciation and not infrequently death of some of the fowls. A form of paralysis associated with this tick also affects many fowls, some of which die.

The tick was first found in southern Texas; it probably occurred in southern New Mexico, Arizona, and California many years ago. More recently it has become established in Florida, and it has spread northward in the Southwestern States so that it is now found in about two-thirds of California and Arizona, and the southwestern half of Oklahoma. Isolated infestations have occurred in Louisiana, Mississippi, Alabama, Nevada, and Utah.

There is abundant opportunity for the tick to be shipped about the country because of its habit of remaining attached to fowls for several days and of hiding in crates and other places. If it were not for the adverse effect of cold and damp climates, it would no doubt by now have spread over the entire country.

LIFE HISTORY AND HABITS

The fowl tick is extremely hardy. It can withstand many insecticides, and specimens have lived shut up in a small box without food for more than 3 years. In all its stages of development, the tick feeds exclusively on blood. Although it may occasionally bite

---

[1] F. C. Bishopp is Assistant Chief, Bureau of Entomology and Plant Quarantine.

domestic animals and human beings, it much prefers to feed on birds, including poultry. Chickens and turkeys are most affected, but ducks, geese, and other domestic fowls, as well as some wild birds such as turkeys, quail, hawks, and vultures are also attacked.

The tick is oval and very flat and has a leathery skin, so that it can easily hide in cracks. Its habits are also admirably adapted to those of the poultry on which it feeds. The hungry ticks become active at night and crawl about, seeking the fowls on the roost. The adults and those in the second, or nymphal, stages crawl onto the sleeping fowls and insert their beaks, drawing blood rapidly. Before day breaks they have returned to their hiding places in cracks about the roosts, walls, and nests.

Mating takes place in the hiding places, and a few days after feeding the female lays a batch of 50 to 100 brownish eggs (fig. 1). Another blood meal is taken a few weeks later, and a second clutch of eggs is deposited. This process may be repeated as many as 8 times and a total of 900 eggs may be deposited. During warm weather the eggs hatch in 10 or 12 days, but in cool weather the period may be as long as 3 months.

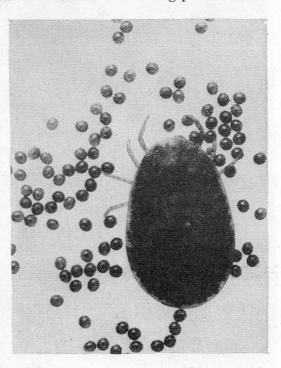

FIGURE 1.—Female fowl tick with eggs. Greatly enlarged.

The young seed ticks that hatch from the eggs are grayish in color and have six legs. After a few nights they crawl about actively in search of a fowl. When one is encountered they crawl upon it and attach themselves to various parts of the body, particularly where the feathers are sparse (fig. 2). Over a period of 3 to 10 days the seed ticks enlarge considerably and become dark reddish blue. They leave the fowls at night and crawl about in search of cracks or crevices, or even rough places on the roosts in which to hide. During a period of 4 to 9 days spent in these hiding places, the seed ticks shed their skins, acquire another pair of legs, and increase somewhat in size, although they remain very flat. A blood meal is taken in a few days, and then a second molt occurs, followed by another feeding and a molt to the adult stage. While hiding, the ticks move about to some extent, even when not hungry. They void a dark-colored excrement that dries on the wood and readily shows their presence.

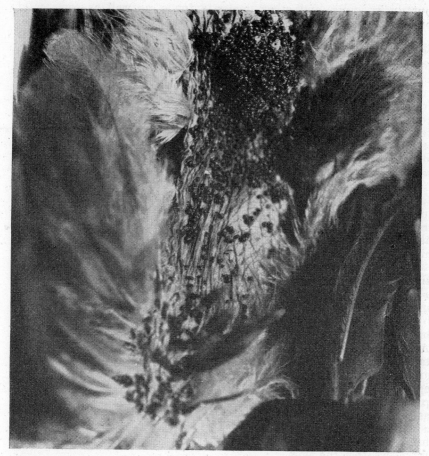

FIGURE 2.—The fowl tick. A mass of seed ticks (first stage) attached beneath wing of a chicken.

METHODS OF CONTROL

The great resistance of the fowl tick to insecticides makes it inadvisable to attempt to destroy the seed ticks on the fowls. Moreover, most of the ticks present at any one time are to be found in the cracks and crevices around the roosts and roost supports, in the nest boxes, and on adjacent walls. In old and heavy infestations the ticks are established throughout the poultry house, including the roof, and not infrequently they are in barns and other outbuildings and in trees frequented by poultry.

To destroy these tough and well-hidden parasites a strong and penetrating material is required. Pure carbolineums, chemically

houses, and they are often abundant in crates, both of wood and metal, in which poultry are shipped or in which they are held and fed at markets. As many as 2,500 well-grown, well-fed bedbugs were removed from the cracks of two wooden crates taken at random from one poultry market, no count being made of the multitude of eggs and very young bedbugs present. As infestations progress, the cracks may become filled with egg-shells, molted skins, and dead insects, all fused into a more or less solid mass by bedbug excrement. Figure 1 is a photograph of such a crack filled with bedbugs, and it shows the surrounding wood stained with many black specks. These specks, which are the most easily observable evidence of bedbug infestation, are the dried remains of the insects' semiliquid excrement. Log houses, used for poultry on farms in many parts of the country, are especially subject to infestation by bedbugs, the cracks and the holes made by wood-boring insects in the logs making excellent retreats for the insects and giving protection

FIGURE 2.—Bedbugs, mostly well-fed, shown, greatly enlarged, in a spindle hole in a wooden crate three-eighths of an inch in diameter by eleven-sixteenths inch deep.

not only against adverse weather but also against insecticides.

A mature, well-grown bedbug[2] is a wingless brown insect between one-fourth and three-eighths of an inch long. It is paper-thin when starved, but when engorged with blood it assumes the shape of the bugs shown in figure 2. It has a strong, characteristic odor.

[2] BACK, E. A. BEDBUGS. U. S. Dept. Agr. Leaflet 146, 8 pp., illus. 1937.

.Bedbugs are sucking insects. Their mouth parts are modified to form an elongated sharp beak, or proboscis, which can be thrust into the skin and through which blood can be drawn. It takes 3 to 5 minutes for a well-grown bedbug to become engorged with blood if its feeding is unmolested. Once filled to capacity, the bug withdraws its beak and quickly crawls to its hiding place, where it remains for several days digesting its meal. When hunger finally reasserts itself, the bedbug seeks a host for another meal.

Bedbugs normally feed at night or in subdued light. They are not known to carry any disease of poultry, but when allowed to become very abundant in henhouses or in crates in which chickens are held for fattening, they take so much blood that the chickens do not fatten, egg laying is reduced, and setting hens may become weak or even die. When bedbugs become abundant in pigeon lofts, the effect on young squabs may be disastrous. According to Levi[3] the squabs from 1 to 3 days old become very anemic and, if the attack continues, die about the fourth day. The older squabs and adult birds also become pale. The latter are restless, and brooding is interfered with. The presence of bedbugs in poultry establishments is also a menace to the homes of people working in such places, as stray bedbugs are apt to be carried about on clothing and may establish infestations in furniture or bedding.

The mature female bedbug, under favorable conditions, lives from 6 to 10 months and may lay as many as 541 eggs, although 200 eggs is probably a fair average. The eggs are pearly white and about one-thirty-second of an inch long. They are deposited singly or in clusters in the crevices where bedbugs congregate. No eggs are laid when the temperature is lower than 50° F., and very few between 50° and 60°: maximum egg laying occurs only when the temperature is above 70° and when the female has ample opportunity to feed. Starved females soon stop laying eggs. At 70° F. or above, eggs hatch in 6 to 17 days, but at lower temperatures they may require 28 days.

The newly hatched, translucent, nearly colorless young bedbug feeds at the first opportunity. During growth it resembles the parent. It molts, or sheds its skin, five times before reaching maturity. The cast skins are white and fluffy. Development from hatching to the adult stage requires 4 to 6 weeks during warm summer weather or in heated rooms. There may be three or four generations or even more in a year, depending on circumstances. In unheated poultry houses the bedbug overwinters mostly in the adult form. The older bedbugs commonly go 2 weeks to 2 months without food. Because bedbugs can subsist on the blood of mice and rats as well as that of poultry, human beings, and domestic animals, the insect has been credited with living without food for periods of well over a year. It is a mystery to many poultry dealers how bedbugs can live over the winter in chicken crates used only during the summer and fall months, but usually the period of disuse is well within the capacity of the insects to exist under starvation conditions.

---

[3] LEVI, WENDELL MITCHELL. THE PIGEON. 512 pp., illus. Columbia, S. C. 1941.

THE MEXICAN CHICKEN BUG AND RELATED FORMS

The Mexican chicken bug, or coruco (*Haematosiphon inodora*), is an important enemy of poultry in the semiarid and arid Southwest. It is particularly abundant in adobe chicken houses, and for this reason it is called the adobe bug locally. The chicken bug resembles the bedbug, and its habits are similar, but it does not have characteristic bedbug odor.

Several species of bugs related to the bedbug and chicken bug are commonly associated with bats and swallows. Although swallows are frequently accused of bringing bugs into poultry establishments, this is probably an unusual occurrence, as the kind of bug found in swallows' nests is rarely found in poultry houses.

CONTROL METHODS

Control of bedbugs and chicken bugs in poultry establishments requires vigilance and persistent effort. Often these pests are overlooked until they are so numerous and widespread in the plant or about the farm buildings that it is difficult to eliminate them.

The bugs and their eggs are not difficult to kill when they can be reached with insecticidal sprays. Every effort should be made, therefore, to eliminate hiding places. Unnecessary boards and trash should be removed, and when it is practicable cracks and holes should be filled with plaster, putty, or other materials. Roosts, nests, feeding batteries, and other equipment should be simple in construction and easily moved for examination and treatment.

Bugs can be killed with fumigants, such as sulfur (3 pounds burned per 1,000 cubic feet), but most poultry houses are not built tightly enough to hold the gas sufficiently long to give good results. In general, spraying with creosote oil or one of the carbolineums, as advised for the control of the fowl tick (p. 1065), is satisfactory for the treatment of infested buildings and equipment. Usually two sprayings will eliminate an infestation from a chicken house built of wood. In the case of feeding establishments where the pests are continually reintroduced, it is good practice to spray all crates once a month. Kerosene or pyrethrum-kerosene fly sprays may be employed where the staining caused by creosotes would be objectionable. In any event, the sprays must be thoroughly driven into cracks and crevices.

Pigeon lofts may be treated in the same way, but eggs and squabs may be injured by being returned to treated nests even when new nesting material is supplied. Levi (see footnote 3, p. 1070, for reference) has successfully used live steam in his large commercial pigeon plant. The steam is forced into the lofts and the temperature held at 125° F. or higher for 1 or 2 hours. The building is closed as tightly as possible with tar paper and canvas before being steamed.

The Pigeon Fly

BY F. C. BISHOPP [1]

THIS PERSISTENT ENEMY of pigeons and their
close relatives is not only a bloodsucker but a carrier of
pigeon malaria. It can be effectively controlled by the
simple methods here outlined.

THE PIGEON FLY (*Pseudolynchia canariensis*) is of sufficient importance as a parasite to warrant the attention of those who raise
pigeons as messengers in the military service, for food, for the study
of diseases or of genetics, or simply as a hobby.

These peculiar, bloodsucking flies feed only upon pigeons or closely
related birds and breed in association with them. The flies attack
squabs soon after the latter hatch and live and move about with
ease among the closely set feathers of the adult pigeons. The loss of
blood and the irritation caused by the flies are distinctly injurious
to both squabs and adult birds. The flies also transmit the organism
Haemoproteus columbae, which causes pigeon malaria, serving as its
intermediate host.

THE INSECT AND ITS HABITS

The pigeon fly is slightly smaller than the common housefly, flat,
and brownish. It has a rounded abdomen, rather long wings, and
a stout beak (fig. 1). Its flight is quick and erratic and it does not
usually leave the birds and take wing unless it is considerably disturbed. When driven off the host, it usually alights on some nearby
object, especially a moving object, and in buildings it often goes
toward the light at windows or open doors.

On grown pigeons the flies may be found on any part of the body.
They crawl rapidly from place to place on or among the feathers,
often moving backwards or sideways. Squabs often become heavily
infested especially when they are partly feathered, the flies usually
congregating at the base of the feathers of the tail and wings.

Both male and female flies suck blood. They leave no marked

[1] F. C. Bishopp is Assistant Chief, Bureau of Entomology and Plant Quarantine.

evidence of their bites on pigeons but evidently annoy them a great deal. They frequently bite human beings, especially where squabs are dressed for market, and are often very annoying to the workers. The points of attack may continue to show signs of irritation for 4 or 5 days.

The flies are active on the pigeons throughout the winter in the warmer parts of the country, though their numbers diminish markedly toward spring. The insect has the peculiar habit of retaining its larvae until they have pupated. The fly gives birth to the ovoid pupae one at a time. The pupae are about one-eighth of an inch long, at first pale yellowish in color but soon turning brownish, and within about 3 hours becoming shiny black (fig. 2). They are usually deposited while the flies are on the pigeons and may hang temporarily in the feathers, though they soon drop off among the nest material, where they usually fall through to the bottom of the nest boxes.

FIGURE 1.—The pigeon fly as seen from above. Enlarged about 6 times.

At an average temperature of 73° F. the pupal stage lasts 25 days during hot weather to 31 days or longer in cold weather.

The fly emerges by pushing open the front end of the hard pupa case, which splits along a definite line running around the case about one-third of its length from the head end. The fly is pale and soft at first, but it soon hardens, turns brown, and is ready to take a meal of blood.

METHODS OF CONTROL

Pigeons should be kept in confinement, and the loft should be so arranged as to make it easy to clean the nests and floors. Probably the simplest and most effective single step in the control of pigeon flies is to clean out the nests thoroughly every 25 days. The pupae are so smooth and round that, as already indicated, they usually drop to the bottom of the nest boxes. This makes it possible to pick up the nest, brush the dirt and pupae off the bottom of the box, and return the nest with little disturbance. Since the pupae roll freely, nest cleaning should proceed from the top downward, and care should be taken to brush the pupae out of the cracks. It is well to spread a piece of canvas on the floor beneath the boxes before cleaning to catch any pupae that may drop to the floor. The trash may then be burned or, if used for fertilizer, stored in a screened pit or bin, preferably one in which there is a conical fly trap to catch the flies that emerge. Most of the pupae will be destroyed if the material is scattered on a field and promptly plowed under to a depth of 4 or 5 inches.

The pupae are rather resistant to insecticides, but they may be killed by being wetted thoroughly with a high-grade pyrethrum-kerosene fly spray.

A number of insecticides have been found to be effective in killing the flies on the birds. The main difficulty is to reach the insects and yet not burn the skin or stain the feathers of the pigeons. One of the most easily applied and effective treatments for squabs is fresh pyrethrum powder. From one to three pinches, depending on the size of the squab, dusted in the feather tufts, will kill all flies present. Grown pigeons are harder to treat and on them the powder is less effective, especially when the birds are flying about. Derris or cube powder, containing 3 to 5 percent rotenone, is nearly as effective as pyrethrum and should be used in the same way.

FIGURE 2.—Pupae of the pigeon fly. Enlarged about 6 times.

Kerosene extract of pyrethrum, prepared and sold as high-grade fly spray, is very effective in killing the flies either free in handling and killing rooms or on the birds. The material is applied lightly on the birds in a fine spray as the feathers are lifted. This must be done very carefully, however, since an excessive amount, especially on squabs, will burn the skin and make the eyes sore.

Many lofts are free of pigeon flies, and care should be taken to treat any new stock brought into a clean loft and to check closely on birds sent to races and shows. Special care should be taken to keep racing pigeons free from these flies and other parasites, which distinctly handicap the performance of the birds.

Cold weather apparently kills the pigeon flies in many lofts in the North, and when this occurs an effort should be made to keep them fly-free during the summer, when the parasite can breed rather rapidly.

The control measures used against the pigeon fly are very helpful in keeping down other insect enemies of the pigeon.

Nutritional Diseases of Poultry

BY HARRY W. TITUS [1]

THIS ARTICLE discusses 16 well-defined nutritional diseases, a group of less-well-defined diseases, and the effect of nutritional deficiencies on growth and reproduction. The material is especially significant because a good deal of rather precise work has been done in this field with poultry.

A FAIRLY LARGE NUMBER of different elements and compounds are required for the normal nutrition of poultry. If one or more of them are not present in the diet in adequate quantity, or if certain ones are present in an unsuitable ratio, there is a disturbance of nutrition, or of the functioning of the body, which may be referred to as a nutritional disease. Other nutritional diseases may result from harmful elements or compounds in the diet.

Knowledge in the field of nutritional diseases of poultry is in a state of active change. That which is believed to be true today may be disproved tomorrow, or, as perhaps more often happens, may prove to be only part of the truth. In several instances an abnormal condition that was originally thought to be the result of a single nutritional deficiency has been found to result from a multiple deficiency. A good example is polyneuritis in the chicken. At one time the cause of this condition was believed to be a deficiency of vitamin B_1, and this vitamin was—and still is—referred to as the antineuritic vitamin and was given the name "aneurin." It is now known that the condition originally described as polyneuritis gallinarum was produced by diets deficient in vitamins A, E, and G and pantothenic acid as well as in vitamin B_1. Moreover, it has been shown that a deficiency of vitamin B_1 alone does not produce nerve degeneration in the chicken, although it does have other serious effects on the nerves.

[1] Harry W. Titus is Senior Biological Chemist, in Charge of Poultry Nutrition Investigations, Animal Nutrition Division, Bureau of Animal Industry.

VITAMIN A DEFICIENCY

If day-old chicks are placed on a diet markedly deficient in vitamin A, their rate of growth falls below normal after about 2 weeks and then declines rapidly. The first characteristic symptoms, other than the decrease in rate of growth, are droopiness, a staggering gait, and a ruffled appearance of the feathers. These symptoms may appear as early as the end of the third week. Some of the chicks die before the

FIGURE 1.—Effects of vitamin A deficiency in an advanced stage. Note the swelling around the eye and the cheesy exudate under the lids. (Courtesy of J. R. Beach, Division of Veterinary Science, California Agricultural Experiment Station, Berkeley, Calif.)

end of the fourth week, and most of the others before they are 5 weeks old. Growth usually ceases several days before death occurs. In many of the chicks that survive for more than a week after the first characteristic symptoms appear, the eyes become inflamed and there is a discharge from the nostrils; in some there are a swelling around the eyes and an accumulation of sticky exudate beneath the lids.

With a diet partially deficient in vitamin A, the first symptoms may not appear until the chicks are 5 or 6 weeks old. In this case, a larger proportion of the chicks eventually have inflamed eyes and an accumulation of white cheesy material under the lids (fig. 1).

In mature chickens the symptoms develop much more slowly than in growing chicks, but the inflammation of the eyes becomes strikingly more pronounced. Ofter there are a white membranous film over the nictitating membrane, or third eyelid, and a cheesy exudate or discharge, in the conjunctival sacs. There may also be a sticky discharge, either clear or turbid, from the nostrils.

The symptoms of vitamin A deficiency in the turkey poult are in general similar to those in the chick, but according to Hinshaw and Lloyd (*21*)[2] the disease is much more acute in poults. These authors described the symptoms in poults that had received little or no vitamin A from the time of hatching as "those of an acute-infectio-contagious disease except that fever was absent." In chicks that were fed the same diet as the poults and kept in the same pen there was a marked nervousness, which the poults did not exhibit.

FINDINGS AFTER DEATH [3]

An examination of chickens and turkeys that die as a result of vitamin A deficiency reveals lesions, or tissue changes, in many parts of the body, their location

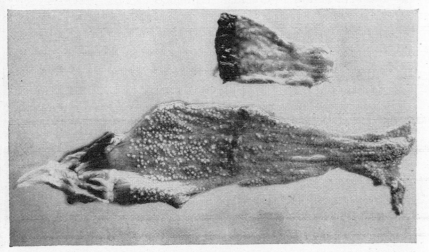

FIGURE 2.—Pustulelike lesions in the esophagus caused by vitamin A deficiency. (Courtesy of L. D. Bushnell, Bacteriology Department, Kansas Agricultural Experiment Station.)

and severity depending to some extent on the age of the bird, the degree of the deficiency, and the length of time between the appearance of the first symptoms and death.

In mature birds lesions resembling pustules are almost invariably found in the mouth, pharynx, and esophagus (fig. 2); in young growing birds these are seen much less frequently. Usually there are white or grayish-white deposits of urates in the kidneys and ureters, which occur more frequently in the chick than in the poult. Sometimes there are deposits of urates on the surface of the heart, liver, and spleen. Hinshaw and Lloyd (*21*) have reported that they found white, flaky, uratelike deposits between thickened folds of the bursa Fabricii in most of the poults and chicks they examined, and Heywang and Morgan (*20*) have confirmed their findings in the case of the chick.

[2] Italic numbers in parentheses refer to Literature Cited, p. 1105.
[3] In this article, material on post mortem findings and also material on diseases that seldom or never occur in ordinary poultry production but are of great interest from the experimental standpoint are set in smaller type.

In general, there is a keratinization, or hornlike hardening, of the epithelial cells of the olfactory, respiratory, upper alimentary, and urinary tracts. In severe cases, especially if the birds are mature, virtually every organ in the body may be affected. Also, there are degenerative changes in both the central and peripheral nervous systems, and these explain the staggering gait, which is one of the first symptoms of vitamin A deficiency in chickens, and the extreme lack of muscular coordination in advanced cases.

FUNCTION OF VITAMIN A AND PREVENTION OF DEFICIENCIES

Histological examinations—that is, examinations of the minute structure—of the tissues of chickens that have been fed a diet deficient in vitamin A indicate that one of the functions—if not the primary function—of vitamin A is the proper nourishment and repair of all the epithelial structures, extremal and internal, in the body. In extreme vitamin A deficiency in the chicken the uric acid content of the blood may increase to eight or nine times its normal value. The accumulation of uric acid in the blood and the previously mentioned occurrence of deposits of uric acid in the ureters, the kidneys, and elsewhere are probably results of failure of repair of epithelial structures, especially those of the kidneys.

Studies made with other animals have shown that vitamin A is necessary for the normal functioning of the eyes. Apparently, however, it plays no detectable role in the absorption and metabolism of fats, carbohydrates, and proteins.

Vitamin A has been referred to as the anti-infective vitamin, but repeated attempts to show that it affects the mechanisms that give the body immunity against infections have failed. When the diet is deficient in vitamin A, however, the epithelium, or surface layer, of the mucous membranes is damaged, and as a result the entry of bacteria is made easier. Thus, although vitamin A is of no value in making an animal immune to infectious diseases, it is of value in maintaining the "first line of defense," the epithelial structures.

As has been pointed out by Barger and Card (2), a partial deficiency of vitamin A in diets for poultry is more common than is generally supposed. They state that it is especially likely to occur in regions where the summers are hot and dry and there is a resulting shortage of green forage. Partial vitamin A deficiency is often an aftermath of drought. A partial vitamin A deficiency is also possible when flocks are closely confined unless an adequate supply is included in the feed.

The obvious method of preventing the development of vitamin-A-deficiency disease in poultry is to supply an adequate quantity of this vitamin in the feed. The minimum vitamin A requirement of the growing chick is about 675 to 775 International units per pound of feed; that of the growing poult is about 2½ times as much. An adequate supply, as distinguished from the minimum, is about 1,450 International units per pound of feed for the chick and about 3,650 per pound of feed for the poult. The vitamin A in mixed feeds, however, is not very stable, and for this reason it is a good practice to formulate the diets of chicks and poults so that they will contain 3,000 and 7,500 International units per pound of feed, respectively. The feed of chickens kept for egg production should contain approximately 3,150

International units per pound. The feed of breeding stock—chickens or turkeys—should contain about 4,720 units per pound.

The approximate vitamin A contents of some of the richer sources of this vitamin used in feeding poultry are as follows:

	International units per pound
Fortified cod-liver oil	1, 360, 770
Fortified sardine oil	1, 360, 770
Cod-liver oil	385, 550
Sardine oil	52, 000
Alfalfa-leaf meal, dehydrated	95, 000
Alfalfa-leaf meal	32, 000
Alfalfa meal	13, 000
Corn-gluten meal	6, 800
Yellow corn	3, 180

VITAMIN B₁ DEFICIENCY

The symptoms of vitamin B₁ deficiency are similar in chickens and turkeys and are essentially the same at different ages. A diet containing little or no vitamin B₁ but otherwise adequate causes a prompt decrease in appetite, followed soon by a steady decline in live weight. After 7 to 10 days there is progressive development of general paralysis. The extensor muscles of the legs are the first

FIGURE 3.—Head retraction is a characteristic symptom of vitamin B₁ deficiency in the late stage. (Courtesy of L. C. Norris, Nutrition Division, Department of Poultry Husbandry, Cornell University.)

to become affected, but soon the paralysis extends to the wings and neck and, finally, to all the muscles. In the early stages of paralysis the bird swallows feed or water with great difficulty; in the later stages the body temperature falls, and the head is raised and drawn back. Death follows, usually within 1 or 2 days after the typical symptom of head retraction appears (fig. 3).

When the diet is only partially deficient in vitamin B₁, 30 days or more may elapse before the symptoms of paralysis appear. In the ability of chickens and other birds to survive on diets that are only partially deficient in vitamin B₁ there are marked individual differences. In adult and nearly grown birds there is a loss of about 20 percent of the initial live weight before death occurs.

The first symptom in pigeons is a partial loss of the ability to walk. The next symptom is uncontrolled movement of the head. Finally, head retraction occurs, and the legs are drawn up close to the body; often the bird turns somersaults. As in the chicken, death follows soon after head retraction occurs.

FINDINGS AFTER DEATH

With few exceptions, the diets that have been used in studying vitamin B₁ deficiency have not contained adequate quantities of some of the other vitamins, especially vitamin A and those that commonly occur with vitamin B₁ in natural products. As a matter of fact, the diets that were used in the first studies of vitamin B₁ deficiency in the chicken and pigeon were also markedly deficient in vitamin A. Many of the earlier descriptions of the findings after death from what was considered to be vitamin B₁ deficiency were for this reason in reality descriptions of the results of a multiple deficiency.

For many years it was believed that a deficiency of vitamin B₁ caused extensive degeneration of the peripheral nervous system. Engel and Phillips (*11*) have shown, however, that there is no nerve degeneration in either the rat or the chick when the vitamin-B₁-deficient diet contains a fully adequate supply of vitamin A and vitamin G. Moreover, there is evidence that the withholding of feed produces in the chicken and other animals many of the changes that are observed when a diet deficient in vitamin B₁ is fed.

At the time this is being written there is not available to the writer a good description of the post mortem findings in birds that have died as a result of an uncomplicated vitamin B₁ deficiency.

FUNCTION OF VITAMIN B₁ AND PREVENTION OF DEFICIENCIES

According to the evidence now available, vitamin B₁ is required for the proper metabolism of carbohydrates.[4]

Nitzescu and Ioanid (*39*) found that if hens are deprived of vitamin B₁ the sugar content of their blood decreases and remains below normal for 10 to 14 days, then rises rapidly in the next few days to more than twice normal. If vitamin B₁ is injected, the sugar content of the blood returns to normal. They found also that injections of vitamin B₁ produce appreciable decreases in the sugar content of the blood of normal hens.

The animal has relatively little capacity for storing vitamin B₁, and for this reason, when there is a multiple deficiency of this and other vitamins, the symptoms of vitamin B₁ deficiency tend to appear first. That these symptoms, paralysis and head retraction—the first except cessation of growth—are the result of vitamin B₁ deficiency may be shown conclusively by causing them to disappear in a short time—often less than 2 hours—by the administration of synthetic crystalline vitamin B₁. That these symptoms can thus be made to disappear is evidence that they are not the result of nerve degeneration.

Vitamin B₁ deficiency in poultry is rarely observed under practical conditions. It can be produced by feeding a diet that consists wholly of polished rice or degerminated grain or specially formulated diets.

In practical poultry production no special precautions need be taken to prevent vitamin B₁ deficiency. The minimum vitamin B₁ requirement of poultry is about 90 to 135 International units per pound of feed. An adequate supply is about 180 International units per pound of feed. Most diets for poultry contain two to three times this quantity.

---

[4] More specifically, soon after vitamin B₁ is absorbed from the intestinal tract, it is converted into cocarboxylase, which functions as a coenzyme in the metabolism of pyruvic acid. When the diet does not contain enough vitamin B₁, pyruvic acid accumulates in various tissues of the body and exerts a toxic effect on the nervous system.

The approximate vitamin B₁ contents of some of its richer sources in feeding poultry are as follows:

	International units per pound
Yeast, brewers', dried	4,500
Soybean meal	1,600
Oats	1,200
Wheat middlings, standard	1,000
Wheat bran	840
Wheat	680
Skim milk, dried	500
Buttermilk, dried	450
Barley	400
Corn	400

VITAMIN B₆ DEFICIENCY

Very little is known about the vitamin B₆ requirements of poultry or the symptoms of vitamin B₆ deficiency. In 1939 Jukes (*23*) reported that the symptoms in chicks consist of slow growth, depressed appetite, and inefficient utilization of feed, followed in some cases by spasmodic convulsions and death, but in 1940 he reported (*24*) that the diet that he had used in studying vitamin B₆ deficiency was deficient even when supplemented with the vitamin. More recently, Hegsted, Oleson, Elvehjem, and Hart (*19*) reported that the only symptoms of vitamin B₆ deficiency that they had observed in growing chicks were lack of growth and extreme weakness.

Vitamin B₆ is widely distributed in nature, and for this reason a deficiency does not occur among poultry that are fed practical diets but would be produced only by special, highly simplified diets. Yeast, wheat germ, and egg yolk are some of the best sources of B₆ vitamin; other good sources are kidney, liver, fish meal, dried skim milk, dried buttermilk, alfalfa products, and rice polishings; all the grains appear to be fairly good sources.

VITAMIN D DEFICIENCY AND RICKETS

Abnormal development of the bones of growing chickens, turkeys, and other kinds of poultry may result from a number of dietary causes, among which are (1) a deficiency of one or more of the following substances: Vitamin D, calcium, phosphorus, manganese, and choline; (2) a marked unbalance of calcium and phosphorus; and (3) the presence of certain substances that make the vitamin D or the phosphorus unavailable. The discussion here is restricted to those conditions in which the absorption and metabolism of vitamin D, calcium, and phosphorus are directly involved. The condition that results from a deficiency of manganese or choline or both is discussed later.

Some writers—for example, McGowan and Emslie (*34*)—distinguish between rickets and another condition of the bones, osteoporosis, on the ground that the former is the result of a deficiency of phosphorus and the latter of a deficiency of calcium. The distinction is warranted because the changes that occur in the bones are not the same in the two conditions. However, both may be prevented or cured by including sufficient vitamin D in the diet, unless the deficiency of phosphorus or calcium is very marked.

At the time of hatching, the chick is essentially osteoporotic, that is, its bones have a much lower calcium-phosphorus ratio than they do later on; hence it requires an immediate supply of calcium in its diet. If the diet is deficient in calcium or if that which is present is unavailable as a result of a deficiency of vitamin D, the osteoporotic condition becomes more pronounced. If there is an adequate supply of calcium but a deficiency of phosphorus or vitamin D or both, rickets develops.

Rickets may be produced on diets that contain adequate quantities of vitamin D, calcium, and phosphorus if the diets also contain large quantities of certain inorganic compounds, such as soluble salts of iron, lead, and beryllium. This is because iron, lead, and beryllium form insoluble compounds with the phosphorus and make it unavailable. Excessive quantities of calcium in the diet of growing chicks may also make much of the phosphorus unavailable as a result of the formation of the relatively insoluble calcium phosphate. A diet deficient in vitamin D is therefore more rachitogenic (rickets-causing) if it contains an excessive quantity of calcium than if it contains a much smaller but adequate quantity.

A condition called sulfur rickets may result from the inclusion in the diet of 2 percent or more of sulfur for the control of coccidiosis. If the particles of sulfur are very small (for example, colloidal), less than 2 percent may cause this condition. Why sulfur has this effect is not known, but there are reasons for believing that it interferes with the absorption of vitamin D. The condition is relieved but not entirely eliminated by doubling or trebling the vitamin D content of the diet. Sunshine appears to be more effective than, vitamin D in preventing sulfur rickets.

The rickety and osteoporotic conditions encountered in the practical production of poultry are most frequently caused by a deficiency of vitamin D rather than by a deficiency of calcium or phosphorus or the presence in the diet of large quantities of soluble salts of iron, beryllium, or lead.

If a vitamin-D-deficient diet is fed, beginning with the first feeding, the first symptoms usually make their appearance in the poult toward the end of the third week and in the chick about a week later. Usually most of the poults die within 5 weeks and a large proportion of the chicks within 8 weeks.

In the adult chicken the first symptom of vitamin D deficiency is a thinning of the shells of its eggs. If the deficiency is marked, there is a fairly prompt decrease in both egg production and hatchability. After a time the breast bones become distinctly less rigid. Adult chickens, however, can live for months on a diet that supplies practically no vitamin D.

The first symptoms of vitamin D deficiency in the growing chicken and turkey are a tendency to rest frequently in a squatting position, a disinclination to walk, and a lame, stiff-legged gait. These symptoms are readily distinguishable from those of vitamin A deficiency in that in vitamin D deficiency the chick or poult at first is alert rather than droopy and walks with a lame rather than a staggerng gait. Other symptoms, in the usual order of their occurrence, are retardation of growth, enlargement of the hock joints, beading at the ends of the ribs, and marked softening of the beak (fig. 4). As in many other

FIGURE 4.—Vitamin D deficiency in a young chicken. Note the crossed beak, which is soft and rubbery, and the inability to stand.

nutritional diseases of poultry, the feathers soon acquire a ruffled appearance.

GROSS CHANGES AND CHEMICAL FINDINGS

In the chick and poult, vitamin D deficiency produces marked changes in the bones and the parathyroid and thyroid glands and variable changes in the calcium and phosphorus content of the blood. The bones may be soft or only moderately so, but in any case their ash (mineral) content is much less than normal, and in some instances the ash content of the tibia (drumstick bones) may be as little as 27 percent on a moisture-and-fat-free basis. (The normal ash value for the tibiae of young chicks is about 46 percent.) The epiphyses, or growing ends, of the long bones are usually enlarged. The parathyroid becomes enlarged, sometimes to eight times its normal size, as a result of an increase in both the size of the cells and the number of epithelial cells. At most there is no great change in the size of the thyroid, but there is an appreciable increase in the number of cells.

The changes in the calcium and phosphorus content of the blood depend on the calcium and phosphorus content of the diet. If the diet has a high calcium content, the calcium content of the blood may be approximately normal and the phosphorus content low. In such a case the bones may be somewhat rarefied rather than soft. If there is a deficiency of both calcium and phosphorus in the diet, the blood may contain less than the normal quantities of these elements. When there is a deficiency of phosphorus, the bones tend to be soft and may be bent.

In adult chickens a deficiency of vitamin D eventually produces changes in the parathyroid similar to those produced in chicks. The bones tend to become rarefied (osteoporotic) rather than soft.

FUNCTION OF VITAMIN D AND PREVENTION OF DEFICIENCIES

It must be concluded that vitamin D is required for the normal metabolism of calcium and phosphorus in the chicken, but the exact manner in which it performs its function is not known. A diet deficient in vitamin D does not produce rickets in rats if it contains suitable quantities of calcium and phosphorus, but rickets is always produced in chickens by a deficiency of vitamin D, even when the diet contains calcium and phosphorus in suitable quantities. There is good evidence that in the rat vitamin D regulates the absorption of calcium and phosphorus from the intestine, and it is highly probable that it performs the same function in the chicken.

Before the discovery of the importance of vitamin D in the nutrition of poultry, it was not possible to raise poultry in strict confinement; that is, without access to sunshine. Even under normal conditions, rickets was likely to occur in poultry whenever there were long periods of cloudy or rainy weather during the brooding season. It is now a common practice to include at least some vitamin D in the diet of poultry whether they have access to sunshine or not. Even so, rickets is occasionally encountered as a result of using an inferior grade of cod-liver oil or other source of vitamin D.

Laying flocks are frequently housed in quarters into which little or no sunshine penetrates, and many such flocks suffer from the effects of vitamin D deficiency. Even when laying flocks are allowed to range the year round, they may get too little sunshine during the late fall, winter, and early spring. It is advisable, therefore, to include some vitamin D in the diet of all laying stock, whether or not they are allowed to range.

The usual sources of vitamin D, other than sunshine, are cod-liver oil, sardine oil, certain other fish oils, and "D"-activated animal sterol. Vitamin D deficiency is readily prevented or cured by a suitable quantity of any one of those materials. The minimum vitamin D requirement of the growing chick is about 60 to 90 A. O. A. C. chick units [5] per pound of feed; that of the growing poult is about 2 to 3½ times as much. An adequate supply for the chick is about 180 A. O. A. C. chick units per pound of feed and for the poult about 360 units. The duckling apparently requires about as much vitamin D as the poult.

Chickens that are being kept for the eggs they produce should receive about 360 A. O. A. C. chick units of vitamin D per pound of feed, and breeding stock—both chickens and turkeys—about 540 units.

Cod-liver oil that is sold as such in interstate commerce is required by law to contain not less than 85 United States Pharmacopoeia units of vitamin D per gram, or about 38,560 U. S. P. units per pound. In the case of cod-liver oil 1 U. S. P. unit of vitamin D is equal to 1 A. O. A. C. chick unit. The fortified cod-liver oil and sardine oils now on the market are usually guaranteed to contain about 181,600 A. O. A. C. chick units per pound. Other oils and other products used as sources of vitamin D in feeding poultry are usually

---

[5] The standard unit of the Association of Official Agricultural Chemists.

sold on the basis of a guaranteed number of A. O. A. C. chick units per gram or per pound.

VITAMIN E DEFICIENCY

By feeding a diet high in fat but markedly deficient in vitamin E to chicks, ducklings, and poults, Pappenheimer, Goettsch, and Jungherr (*41*) produced nutritional encephalomalacia (crazy-chick disease) in the chicks, nutritional myopathy (a disease of the muscles) in the ducklings, and nutritional myopathy of the gizzard in the poults. They were able to prevent or at least greatly reduce the incidence of the encephalomalacia in the chicks by including various vegetable oils in their diet. They completely prevented the development of encephalomalacia by administering small quantities of alpha-tocopherol (vitamin E) by mouth. In a single experiment with ducklings the nutritional myopathy was prevented by substituting 5 percent of hydrogenated cottonseed oil for an equal weight of lard in the diet. In the case of poults the administration by mouth of 0.34 cubic centimeter of wheat-germ oil per head per day in gelatin capsules greatly reduced the incidence of the gizzard condition but did not eliminate it completely.

Symptoms of Nutritional Encephalomalacia in the Chick

When a diet such as that used by Pappenheimer and associates (*41*) is fed to day-old chicks, the encephalomalacia may occur as early as the seventh and as late as the fifty-sixth day, but the highest incidence is between the fifteenth and thirtieth days after hatching. The average age at which the disease occurs is about 5 weeks. In older chicks the average number of days before the onset of the disease depends on the age at which the deficient diet is first fed; the older the chicks are, up to 8 weeks of age, the more quickly they are affected. The disease rarely occurs among chicks more than 8 weeks old.

The symptoms of nutritional encephalomalacia are described very well by its popular name, "crazy-chick disease." When the chicks attempt to walk, they often fall forward, backward, or to one side and then wheel in circles. In advanced cases there is frequently complete prostration, with the legs extended, the head sometimes retracted, and tremors of both head and legs (fig. 5).

Figure 5.—A chicken prostrated by nutritional encephalomalacia, or crazy-chick disease, in an advanced stage. The retracted head is also a result of vitamin E deficiency. (Courtesy of Erwin Jungherr, Department of Animal Disease, Storrs Agricultural Experiment Station, Storrs, Conn.)

Extensive lesions are usually found in the brains of chicks that have died of nutritional encephalomalacia. The cerebellum (the hind part of the brain) is most commonly affected; but in somewhat more than 25 percent of all cases lesions are found also in the cerebral hemispheres, and in about 12 percent of all cases in the medulla. In some cases four-fifths of the cerebellum may be affected, and in others the lesions may be so small that they cannot be detected with the unaided eye. The affected tissues change from pink to greenish yellow and in the healing stage to a rusty brown. For a rather complete description of the microscopic changes that take place in the brain, the reader is referred to Pappenheimer, Goettsch, and Jungherr's monograph (*41*).

Symptoms of Nutritional Myopathy, or Muscle Disease

The symptoms of nutritional myopathy in ducklings appear quite suddenly, usually in the second or third week. In the early stages the ducklings walk awkwardly, with their feet turned in and sometimes overlapping. Often they are found sprawled out and unable to rise. Sometimes there are coarse tremors. Only the skeletal muscles show pathologic changes; the muscles are pale in color—a light creamy yellow rather than dark red. There are widespread hyaline necrosis and some edema, or watery swelling.

When the Pappenheimer-Goettsch diet is fed to young poults, there are no specific outward indications that anything is wrong, but on post mortem examination, lesions or tissue changes are found in the muscular wall of the gizzard. Histologically, the changes in the muscles of the gizzard are hyaline necrosis and fibrosis.

Other Conditions Attributable to a Deficiency of Vitamin E

By feeding special diets to chicks, Dam and Glavind (*9*) produced a condition, which they called alimentary (nutritional) exudative diathesis, that could be cured by adding synthetic vitamin E (d,l alpha-tocopherol) to the diets. The condition was characterized by an accumulation of large quantities of transparent fluid in the subcutaneous tissues. The accumulations were found in various parts of the body but most frequently in the breast and abdomen. The fluid had the same composition as blood plasma and clotted readily. In addition to the accumulations of fluid, hyperemia (excess of blood), slight hemorrhage, and accumulation of white blood corpuscles in connective tissues were observed.

Bird and Culton (*3*) have described a generalized edema which they produced in young chicks by feeding a diet of dried skim milk, dextrinized cornstarch, cod-liver oil, and mineral salts. This diet is deficient in vitamin E and in other nutritional factors, but Bird and Culton were able to prevent the development of the edema by administering d,l alpha-tocopherol.

Hammond, at the Beltsville Research Center, Beltsville, Md., produced crazy-chick disease by feeding diets that contained 3 percent or more of cod-liver oil to day-old chicks. Mild cases were cured within a few days by administering synthetic vitamin E. This condition was essentially the same as the crazy-chick disease sometimes observed in commercial flocks, and the brain lesions were like those found by Pappenheimer, Goettsch, and Jungherr (*41*) in nutritional encephalomalacia.

Occurrence and Prevention of Vitamin E Deficiency

Crazy-chick disease, or nutritional encephalomalacia, occurs occasionally in commercial flocks that are fed typical feed mixtures for poultry. In such cases it has been often found that the feed mixture was prepared several months before it was used, strongly suggesting that the vitamin E originally in the feed was destroyed or inactivated before the feed was used.

Much can be done to avoid the destruction or inactivation of the vitamin E in feed mixtures by not using excessive quantities of cod-liver oil or other fats and oils and by feeding all mixtures within a short time after they are prepared.

Very few quantitative data are available on the vitamin E content of feedstuffs, and little is known about the quantitative requirements of poultry for vitamin E. It is known, however, that good sources of vitamin E include wheat-germ meal, alfalfa, alfalfa meal, alfalfa-leaf meal, wheat middlings, wheat shorts, wheat bran, and all unground grains and seeds.

When nutritional encephalomalacia occurs in a flock, it can be checked, and the individual cases that do not become acute can be cured, by adding to the diet 1 to 2 percent of corn oil, soybean oil, peanut oil, wheat-germ oil, or cottonseed oil for a few weeks. Experience has shown that the addition to the diet of more than 2 percent of such oils is often much less effective than the addition of 1 percent.

VITAMIN G DEFICIENCY

The characteristic symptom of vitamin G deficiency in the chick is a condition referred to as curled-toe paralysis, but, according to Norris, Wilgus, Ringrose, and others (*40*) and Stokstad and Manning (*48*), this condition does not occur if the diet is so extremely deficient in vitamin G that the chick dies. If a small quantity of vitamin G is added to an extremely deficient diet, the paralysis occurs, while if a sufficiently large quantity is added the paralysis is prevented. Three degrees of severity of curled-toe paralysis in chicks have been described by Stokstad and Manning (*48*). The first degree is characterized by a tendency to rest on the hocks and a slight curling of the toes, the second by marked weakness of the legs and a distinct curling of the toes of one or both feet, and the third by toes that are completely curled inward or under and a weakened condition of the legs that compels the chicks to walk on their hocks.

Other symptoms of vitamin G deficiency in the chick are a marked decrease in the rate of growth or even complete failure to grow, diarrhea after 8 or 10 days, and a high mortality rate after about 3 weeks. According to Lepkovsky and Jukes (*31*) the growth of the feathers appears not to be impaired. These workers have reported that, as a matter of fact, the main wing feathers appear to become disproportionately long.

The symptoms of vitamin G deficiency in the poult were found by Lepkovsky and Jukes (*31*) to be different from those in the chick. According to these workers, a dermatitis, or skin inflammation (fig. 6), appears in young poults after about 8 days, and the vent becomes

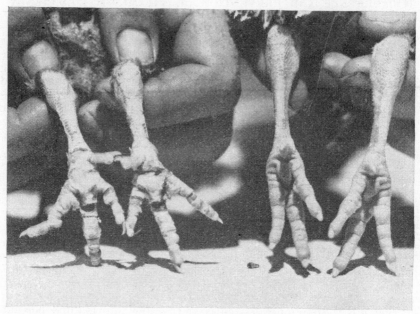

FIGURE 6.—Vitamin G deficiency in a turkey poult. Note the swelling, scaling, and fissuring in the feet of the poult at the left, produced by feeding a diet deficient in vitamin G. The poult whose normal feet are shown at the right received the same diet with the addition of a vitamin G concentrate made from whey. (Courtesy of Thomas H. Jukes, Division of Poultry Husbandry, California Agricultural Experiment Station, Davis, Calif.)

encrusted, inflamed, and excoriated, or stripped of skin. Growth slows up and ceases completely by about the seventeenth day, and deaths begin to occur about the twenty-first day.

FINDINGS AFTER DEATH

According to Phillips and Engel (*42*) a deficiency of vitamin G in the diet of the chick produces specific changes in the main peripheral nerve trunks. In acute cases there are hypertrophy (increase in cell size) of the nerve trunks and a readily observable change in their appearance. Degenerative changes also appear in the myelin of the nerves. Phillips and Engel also found congestion and premature atrophy (wasting) of the lobes of the thymus. The kidney, thyroid and suprarenal glands, brain, and brain stem appeared not to be affected.

FUNCTION OF VITAMIN G AND PREVENTION OF DEFICIENCIES

It is know that vitamin G is an essential component of certain enzyme systems and that it has some functions in the oxidation processes of the cell. Just what happens when these enzyme systems fail is not definitely known, but the evidence available indicates that the growing chick requires vitamin G for the normal functioning and maintenance of the nervous system, particularly the main peripheral nerve trunks.

Relatively few of the feedstuffs used for poultry contain enough vitamin G to meet the minimum requirement of the chick or poult during the first few weeks of life; hence if the ingredients of the diet of the young chick or poult are not selected so as to include one or more of the richer sources of vitamin G, the diet is likely to be deficient in this vitamin. In the case of chicks and poults that are closely confined this is especially true unless green feeds or other good sources of vitamin G, such as dried skim milk, dried buttermilk, and alfalfa-leaf meal are supplied.

The minimum vitamin G requirement of the growing chick and poult varies with their age. During the first week it is about 1,300 micrograms per pound of feed for the chick and about 1,600 micrograms for the poult. The duckling's requirement is about the same as that of the chick. An adequate supply of vitamin G for the first 4 or 5 weeks for all three species is about 1,670 micrograms per pound of feed.

The vitamin G requirement of the adult chicken, turkey, or duck is relatively low, but it increases somewhat with the onset of egg production. Chickens being kept for the eggs they produce probably require only 600 to 800 micrograms of vitamin G per pound of feed, but the feed of breeding stock—chickens or turkeys—should contain about 1,250 micrograms per pound to maintain a high hatchability.

The approximate vitamin G contents of some of the richer sources of this vitamin used in feeding poultry are as follows:

Micrograms per pound

Yeast, brewers', dried	16,000
Dried buttermilk (sweet cream)	12,000
Dried whey	10,000
Dried buttermilk	9,000
Dried skim milk	9,000
Alfalfa-leaf meal, dehydrated	8,000
Alfalfa-leaf meal	7,000
Alfalfa meal	5,000
Fish meal, whitefish	4,200
Fish meal, sardine	3,200
Meat scrap	3,000
Soybean meal	1,500

VITAMIN K DEFICIENCY

Apparently vitamin K is necessary for the formation of prothrombin, which in turn is necessary for the normal clotting of blood.

If very young chicks are fed a diet deficient in vitamin K, the time required for their blood to clot begins to increase after 5 to 10 days and becomes greatly increased after 7 to 12 days. After about a week on such a diet, hemorrhages often occur in any part of the body, spontaneously or as the result of an injury or bruise. The only external symptoms of vitamin K deficiency are the resulting accumulations of blood under the skin.

Chicks on a vitamin-K-deficient diet become anemic after a time as a result of the hemorrhages. Examination after death often reveals accumulations of blood in various parts of the body, and there are invariably erosions of the gizzard lining (*1*).

The symptoms of vitamin K deficiency may be produced quite easily in young chicks in the laboratory, but they are seldom if ever observed when the chicks are raised in the usual manner. The age at which the vitamin-K-deficient diet is first fed influences the development of the resulting deficiency disease. The younger the chicks, the more susceptible they are; the deficient diet does not cause the disease after the chicks are a few weeks old. Hemorrhages may be produced within 12 to 20 days in adult chickens, however, by tying off the bile ducts, indicating that bile is necessary for the absorption of vitamin K.

Vitamin K has been found in such diverse materials as dried alfalfa, fish meal, and rice bran that had been moistened and allowed to stand at room temperature for a few days, kale, tomatoes, hempseed meal, and hog-liver fat. In corn, wheat, or rice there appears to be little or no vitamin K. In any case, it may be pointed out that in compounding practical diets for poultry it is not necessary to take special precautions to insure an adequate supply of vitamin K.

PANTOTHENIC ACID DEFICIENCY [6]

SYMPTOMS

The symptoms of pantothenic acid deficiency in the chick, according to Ringrose, Norris, and Heuser (*46*), are as follows: Growth

is retarded, and the feathers become ragged in appearance. Within 12 to 14 days the margins of the eyelids become granulated, and frequently a viscous exudate, which causes the eyelids to stick firmly together, is formed. Crusty scabs appear at the corners of the mouth (fig. 7), and the skin on the bottoms of the feet often becomes thickened and cornified. At first there is no loss of down or feathers, but after about 18 weeks complete loss of feathers in limited areas on the head and neck may occur.

The symptoms of pantothenic acid deficiency and egg-white injury (see the next section) are very similar, but according to Jukes [7] the two conditions may be distinguished from

FIGURE 7.—Pantothenic-acid deficiency. Note the lesions at the corner of the mouth and on the eyelids, which are stuck together.

[6] The nutritional factor now called pantothenic acid has been referred to at various times as the chick antipellagra factor, the filtrate factor, the chick antidermatitis or antidermatosis factor, and the antidermatosis vitamin.

[7] Personal communication from T. H. Jukes, University of California, Davis, Calif.

each other as follows: In egg-white injury the first symptom is a roughening of the skin below the lower mandible, whereas the dermatitis, or inflammation of the skin, observed in pantothenic acid deficiency appears first at the corners of the mouth and is seldom seen below the mandible. In egg-white injury the feet become involved at the same time as the mouth, whereas dermatitis of the feet is rarely seen in pantothenic acid deficiency and then only in the later stages—usually about 2 or 3 weeks after dermatitis has appeared at the corners of the mouth.

The characteristic dermatitis produced in chicks by feeding diets deficient in pantothenic acid has not been found in adult chickens fed similar diets.

FINDINGS AFTER DEATH

Ringrose, Norris, and Heuser (*46*) reported that on post mortem examination of the affected chicks a puslike substance was frequently observed in the mouth and an opaque, grayish-white exudate in the proventriculus. The entire intestinal tract was found to be almost entirely devoid of feed residues, and the small intestine lacked normal tone and was atrophic (wasted). The liver frequently had an abnormal color that varied from a faint yellow to a deep dirty yellow. The spleen appeared to be small and atrophic and the kidneys inflamed or hemorrhagic.

Phillips and Engel (*43*) found lesions in the spinal cord of chicks that had received a diet deficient in pantothenic acid. The lesions were characterized by a myelin degeneration (degeneration of the sheath) of the myelinated fibers. Such degenerating fibers were found in all segments of the spinal cord down to the lumbar region. Involution (degeneration) of the thymus and liver damage also were found.

The manner in which pantothenic acid functions in the chicken is not known, but the observations of Phillips and Engel show that it is necessary for the maintenance of a normal spinal cord in the growing chick.

OCCURRENCE AND PREVENTION OF PANTOTHENIC ACID DEFICIENCY

Most of the feedstuffs ordinarily fed to poultry are fairly good sources of pantothenic acid, but diets composed largely of the cereal grains, wheat middlings, and meat scrap or fish meal may contain less of this factor than is required by the growing chick. It should also be noted that the kiln-drying of corn tends to destroy much of the pantothenic acid originally present.

Cases of dermatosis (a general name for any skin disease) have been observed among growing chicks that were being raised under practical conditions and presumably were receiving an adequate diet. Undoubtedly there are causes of dermatosis other than a deficiency of pantothenic acid, and it is possible that some of them are nutritional in nature. In the turkey, for example, a dermatosis may be produced by feeding a diet deficient in vitamin G.

The minimum pantothenic acid requirement of the chicken is set tentatively at about 5 milligrams per pound of feed. An adequate supply is about 6 milligrams per pound of feed, but apparently the diet of breeding stock should contain about 7 milligrams per pound of feed in order to insure good hatchability.

The approximate pantothenic acid contents of the richer sources of this vitamin, or vitaminlike factor, that are used in feeding poultry are:

	Milligrams per pound
Yeast, brewers', dried	95
Cane molasses	6 to 38
Peanut meal	25
Dried whey	25
Dried buttermilk	19
Alfalfa-leaf meal, dehydrated	19
Dried skim milk	16
Alfalfa-leaf meal	13
Wheat bran	11
Rice bran	11
Soybean meal	6

EGG-WHITE INJURY

A condition in chicks that resembles pantothenic-acid-deficiency disease may be produced by feeding diets in which all or a rather large proportion of the animal protein is derived from egg white or from whole egg. It is called egg-white injury. Even as little as 5 percent of dried egg white or an equivalent quantity of liquid egg white in such diets produces a dermatitis at the corners of the mouth and on the bottoms of the feet.

Egg-white injury does not appear if 5 to 10 times as much egg yolk as egg white is also included in the diet. It may be prevented also by including relatively large quantities of dried skim milk, or about as much dried liver as egg white, or about half as much cooked pig kidney as egg white. If the egg white is cooked before it is dried, it does not produce the dermatitis.

The first symptoms of egg-white injury is the development of a dermatitis almost simultaneously at the corners of the mouth, below the lower mandible, and on the bottoms of the feet. According to Jukes, however, roughening of the skin below the lower mandible is usually the first symptom to appear and is particularly noticeable where the skin joins the mandible. Later the eyes may be stuck shut, and fissures appear in the skin on the bottoms of the feet. If the chicks survive long enough, the fissures become numerous and rather deep.

The precise cause of egg-white injury is not known, but it appears to result from a deficiency of biotin (vitamin H—one of the group of B vitamins). Apparently the egg white, if not denatured by cooking or otherwise, combines with and inactivates the biotin unless a rather large quantity is present in the diet.

MANGANESE AND CHOLINE DEFICIENCIES[8]

SYMPTOMS OF PEROSIS

If young chicks are fed a diet deficient in manganese, symptoms of perosis will develop within 2 to 10 weeks, depending on the severity of the deficiency, the breed and strain of chicken, the composition of the diet, and the age at which the diet is first fed. If the deficient diet is fed from the first feeding; that is, when the chicks are 1 or 2 days old, the symptoms generally develop between the ages of 3 and 6 weeks, but if it is not fed until the chicks are 10 weeks old, the usual symptoms may not appear.

The first readily noticeable symptom is a tendency on the part of some of the chicks to rest for long periods in a squatting posi-

---

[8] This disease has been referred to at various times as hock disease, slipped tendon, and deforming leg weakness.

tion. If the tibiotarsal joints (hocks) in these chicks are carefully examined, a slight puffiness may be observed. Within a few days the joints become slightly enlarged, and frequently the skin covering them has a bluish-green cast. Apparently this is a critical stage, because in some cases, especially among the more resistant breeds or strains, the chicks frequently recover to such an extent that no readily noticeable permanent deformity results.

As the joints become further enlarged, they tend to become flattened, and the metatarsi (shank bones) and tibiae exhibit a slight bending and also often undergo a rotational twisting. As the condition continues to develop, the bones become more and more bent until gross deformity results. Frequently the articular, or joint, cartilage at the lower end of the tibia slips from its normal position, and this in turn causes the main tendons to slip from their condyles (the knucklelike ends of bones). Sometimes the curvature of a tibia is so great at its lower end that the tendons slip even though the articular cartilage has not been displaced. These changes may take place in either one or in both legs; when they take place in both legs the chicken is forced to walk on its hocks.

The symptoms of perosis in young poults and ducklings are similar to those observed in young chicks, but in the poult the next higher joint in the leg frequently becomes affected. Perosis has been found also in various wild birds, including pheasants, grouse, quail, and sparrows.

OTHER EFFECTS OF A DEFICIENCY OF MANGANESE

If adult chickens are fed a diet deficient in manganese, no observable changes in their leg joints and bones occur, but the shells of their eggs tend to become thinner and less resistant to breakage. If the deficiency is sufficiently great, egg production is decreased, and the eggs that are produced do not hatch well. The hatchability is reduced as a result of an increase in the embryonic mortality that occurs after the tenth day of incubation. According to Lyons and Insko (*33*) this embryonic mortality reaches its peak on the twentieth and twenty-first days of incubation, and the embryos that die after the tenth day are chondrodystrophic and characterized by very short, thickened legs, short wings, "parrot beak," a globular contour of the head, protruding abdomen, and, in the most severe cases, retarded development of the down and poor growth.

If the deficiency of manganese in the diet of laying hens is marked but not extreme, a few of the eggs may hatch. The resulting chicks may have very short leg bones, and in some cases the bones may be deformed as in chicks that develop perosis after hatching. Caskey and Norris (*8*) raised some of the short-legged chicks on diets that contained an adequate quantity of manganese and found that this condition of the legs persisted during a period much longer than that required for the attainment of maturity.

Chemical Findings and General Condition of the Bones in Perosis

The early work of Hall and King (*14*) indicated that chicks with slipped tendons had less bone phosphatase than normal chicks. Later Wiese, Johnson, Elvehjem, and Hart (*52*) observed that both the blood and bone phosphatase and the ester phosphorus of the blood are decreased in manganese deficiency in the chick.

Although the majority of workers who have studied perosis in the chicken have reported that there is no material difference in the ash content of the leg bones in perotic and normal chicks, Caskey, Gallup, and Norris (*7*) found that the leg bones of perotic chicks contained somewhat less ash than those of normal chicks.

Caskey, Gallup, and Norris found also that a deficiency of manganese in the diet of chicks results in a significant thickening and shortening of the bones of the legs, wings, and spinal column. In rickets, as in perosis, the leg bones may become thickened and shortened, but the shafts are poorly calcified and tough, whereas in perosis they are well calcified and relatively brittle. In osteoporosis the shafts are of normal length and much thinner than in rickets or perosis and are somewhat more springy than in perosis. In all three conditions the upper end of the tibia becomes enlarged, but it has a bulbous shape in rickets, a conical shape in perosis, and an approximately normal shape in osteoporosis.

The Combined Action (Synergism) of Manganese and Choline

Soon after it was reported by Wilgus, Norris, and Heuser (*54*) that manganese plays an important role in preventing perosis in growing chickens, several workers observed that the addition of manganese to the diet was not in every case completely effective. In most instances no perosis occurred, but in a few instances.2 to 5 percent of the chicks developed relatively mild cases. Later it was found that the addition of manganese was less effective in preventing perosis in turkeys than in chickens.

Thus the matter stood until Jukes (*25, 26*) reported that choline, a widely distributed substance found in most animal and plant tissues, is effective in preventing perosis in both poults and chicks if the diet contains manganese. Workers in several institutions soon confirmed Jukes' finding that the diet must contain adequate quantities of both manganese and choline if complete protection against perosis is to be obtained.

The manner in which manganese and choline function in the development of a normal skeleton is not yet known.

Occurrence and Prevention of Perosis

Perosis was seldom observed before the more intensive methods of raising poultry came into use. With development of out-of-season production of broilers it became a serious problem. In general, it occurred frequently whenever chickens and turkeys were raised without access to the soil. The reason is now apparent: only about 10 percent of the individual ingredients of mixed feeds for poultry contain enough manganese to furnish an adequate supply of this element, and often these feedstuffs account for only 40 percent or less of the usual feed mixtures, but when poultry have access to the soil they

ordinarily are able to obtain enough additional manganese to meet their requirement.

Corn and milk are extremely poor sources of manganese, and diets composed largely of these two ingredients are likely to cause perosis, unless additional manganese is added. On the other hand, wheat bran, wheat middlings, and rice bran are relatively rich sources, and perosis is not likely to occur on diets that contain 20 percent or more of the first two or 10 percent of the third of these feedstuffs. In any case, it is good insurance against perosis to include a small quantity of manganese sulfate in the diet.

Most research workers in poultry nutrition agree that, for adequate protection against perosis, the diet of chickens should contain about 50 parts per million of manganese. Turkeys apparently require more manganese than chickens, but 50 to 60 parts per million will ordinarily meet their requirements, provided their diet also includes a sufficient quantity of choline.

Inasmuch as most diets for poultry are likely to contain at least 20 parts per million of manganese, adequate protection against perosis generally will be obtained if about 30 parts per million are added. This quantity of manganese may be supplied easily through the use of a mixture of 100 parts, by weight, of common salt and 1.7 parts of pure anhydrous manganous sulfate, or about 2.2 parts of so-called technical grade anhydrous manganous sulfate. About 0.5 percent of this mixture should be included in all-mash diets and 1 percent in mashes with which an approximately equal quantity of grain is to be fed.

Nearly all the feedstuffs commonly used in feeding poultry contain some choline, so that typical diets for poultry are not likely to be deficient in this substance. One of the better sources of choline among feedstuffs is soybean meal, and for this reason, the inclusion of 5 to 10 percent of this feedstuff in diets for poultry, especially for turkeys, will tend to insure against a deficiency of choline.

IRON AND COPPER DEFICIENCIES AND ANEMIA

Anemia rarely if ever occurs among chickens on practical diets, but it has been demonstrated (*10, 16*) that it can be produced in young chicks by feeding a diet extremely deficient in iron or copper or both. The workers cited produced anemia in young chicks by feeding a diet of cow's milk, polished rice, calcium carbonate, and salt and a similar diet in which the rice was replaced by corn.

When the rice-containing diet was fed, the hemoglobin content of the blood fell from 8 grams per 100 cubic centimeters to 4 grams per 100 cubic centimeters within 12 to 15 days. The anemia was prevented by adding a small quantity of a soluble salt of iron to the diet. However, if the rice was first treated to remove the small quantity of copper it contained, it was necessary to add salts of both iron and copper to obtain normal hemoglobin formation.

When the corn-containing diet was fed, anemia developed during the early growing period but gradually disappeared as the chicks became older. As in the case of the rice-containing diet, the addition of iron prevented the occurrence of anemia.

As was found by Hogan and Parrott (*22*), anemia can also be produced in young chicks by feeding special, simplified diets that presumably have an adequate content of iron and copper. In such instances the anemia is the result of a deficiency of some as yet unknown nutritional factor.

Although anemia of nutritional origin occurs extremely rarely in chickens, it has been observed in developing embryos in eggs from hens that had received more or less typical diets for poultry. Anemic embryos are encountered most frequently in the fall and winter, when the parent stock does not receive much sunshine. The exact cause of this anemia in embryos is not known, but probably the cause is a deficiency of iron or copper or both. At least there is evidence that if chickens do not receive sunshine or do not have some cod-liver oil in their diet, the transfer of iron and copper to their eggs is appreciably reduced.

The available evidence on the subject indicates that under ordinary, practical conditions it is unnecessary to add compounds of iron and copper to the diets of poultry to prevent anemia. As a matter of fact, the addition of large quantities of iron compounds may produce rickets by making the phosphorus unavailable.

IODINE DEFICIENCY AND GOITER

Only a few cases of goiter, or enlarged thyroid (fig. 8), in chickens have been observed and reported in this country, but Welch (*51*) has stated that it is very common in Montana, and Kernkamp (*28*) has reported two cases in Minnesota Goiter in the chicken

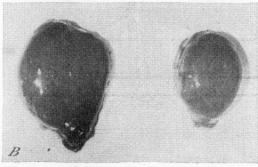

probably is more common in certain sections of this country than is generally realized. Undoubtedly the reason that only a few cases have been reported is that the enlarged thyroids are concealed by the feathers and are not readily detected. Moreover, goiter does not appear to affect the health of chickens seriously or to be a cause of heavy mortality.

Goiter has been produced experimentally in chickens by Gassner and Wilgus (*13*). They fed diets of extremely low iodine content (25 parts per billion) to laying hens and found enlarged thyroid glands in the chicks that hatched from their eggs.

FIGURE 8.—*A*, normal, and *B*, enlarged thyroid glands of chickens. The enlarged thyroid was removed from a chicken that had been fed a diet deficient in iodine. (Courtesy of H. S. Wilgus, Colorado Agricultural Experiment Station, Fort Collins, Colo.)

Wilgus and associates (*53*) were able to produce goiter in young growing chicks by feeding them a simplified diet of low iodine content in which the sole protein supplement was soybeans. However, when they added sufficient iodine to this diet the thyroid glands were normal in size and structure.

Such experiments have provided definite evidence that the chicken requires a small quantity of iodine, but neither the minimum nor

the optimum amount is known. Mitchell and McClure (*37*) estimated that the daily iodine requirement of a 5-pound chicken is 4.5 to 9 micrograms (a microgram is one-millionth of a gram, or slightly less than one twenty-eight millionth of an ounce).

Most American workers who have studied the effect of adding small quantities of iodine to the diet of chickens have reported that no beneficial results were obtained, which suggests that typical diets for poultry are not likely to be deficient in iodine. Nevertheless, the use of so-called iodized salt in diets for poultry—especially in sections of the country where goiter is encountered in other farm animals—may be a worth-while means of insuring against a possible deficiency of iodine.

GIZZARD EROSION

Several different kinds of gizzard erosion are found in poultry, and the meager evidence now available suggests that they are the result of different causes or combinations of causes. The kind most frequently encountered is preceded by hemorrhages from the glandular layer of the gizzard, which originate from the capillaries in the submucosa. A second kind, which is less common, is characterized by a softening and a pronounced thickening of the lining of the gizzard. In a third kind, which is of still less frequent occurrence and has been observed chiefly in turkeys, the lining softens and separates completely from the glandular layer. The last kind of erosion is distinctly different from the first but resembles the second in that there is a softening of the lining.

Little or nothing is known about the development of the second and third kinds of gizzard erosion, but the histological studies of Lansing, Miller, and Titus (*30*) have yielded some information regarding the development of the first kind, which is discussed in the following paragraphs.

According to these authors the erosions are formed in the following way: At one or more places in the glandular layer of the gizzard there is a seepage of blood into the secretion from which the lining is formed, and the lining is thus weakened in these places and loses some of its coherence. Reddish-brown stains in the lining, varying in size from a mere speck to several square centimeters, are evidence of such seepage. If the passage of blood into the secretion stops at this stage, the subsequent secretion yields a normal layer of lining under the affected area. After a short time threadlike, shallow fissures appear on the attrition surface of the lining in such places.

Sometimes the initial seepage of blood is followed by a pronounced hemorrhage, and blood clots form between the weakened lining and the glandular layer. If the seepage continues for some time before the hemorrhage occurs, a fairly thick but deeply stained lining may be found over the blood clot; but if the hemorrhage follows promptly after the initial seepage, only a thin lining or no lining at all is found over the site of the hemorrhage. In either case, the affected portion of the lining now lacks the backing, or support, of the glandular layer and soon cracks or sloughs off. The final result is the formation of deeply fissured areas, holes in the lining, or both.

Apparently, when the hemorrhages are large the secreting activity of the glands is markedly reduced or even stopped. In any case, new lining is not formed and large eroded areas appear.

If at any stage in the development of gizzard erosions a suitable diet is fed, the hemorrhages stop, and after 2 or 3 weeks a lining of normal appearance may be formed.

Gizzard erosion has been found in all sections of the country and presumably in all breeds of chickens. Its incidence is greatest in very young chicks and decreases with increasing age.

Apparently gizzard erosion has no appreciable effect on the rate of growth or the health of chickens. In any case, its occurrence in very young chicks is not a cause for concern. If it is found in chicks older than 4 weeks, however, the diet fed is probably not entirely satisfactory.

Various feedstuffs and other materials have been reported to be of value in clearing up gizzard erosion. Among those reputed to be of special value are dried ox bile, cholic acid, kale, hempseed meal, alfalfa products, wheat bran, wheat middlings, oats, soybean meal, pig liver and kidney, lung tissue, cartilage, and chondroitin. Of these materials the most effective are dried ox bile and cholic acid.

The diverse nature of the materials just mentioned strongly suggests that gizzard erosion may result from a deficiency of more than one nutritional factor and that the deficiency may be single or multiple. This suggestion is strengthened by the fact that although dried ox bile has been very effective in the experiments of all workers who have tested it, some workers have failed to get a response from cartilage and chondroitin, and others have obtained very little if any response from alfalfa.

FEATHER PICKING AND CANNIBALISM

Cannibalism is a term used by some poultrymen in referring to the habit sometimes developed by chickens, turkeys, other poultry, and game birds of picking one another's feathers, toes, beaks, heads, combs, backs, vents, and other parts of the body. Some poultrymen, however, restrict the use of this term to cases in which blood is drawn. Inasmuch as there are instances in which only the feathers are picked, or pulled, it seems desirable to make a distinction between feather picking and cannibalism.

Often the only result of feather picking is that some of the birds lose many of their feathers, but cannibalism nearly always leads to heavy losses through death. In flocks of pullets just starting to lay, cannibalism generally follows a case of prolapsus of the oviduct; in such cases a number of birds may become disemboweled, and rather heavy losses may result. Cannibalism among chicks often appears first in the form of toe picking, back picking, or wing picking; once established, it spreads rapidly through the flock.

Although there is evidence that feather picking and cannibalism are the result, in part, of unsatisfactory diets, there are often other contributing causes, such as overcrowding and overheating— especially in the case of chicks in battery brooders. The exact nature of the nutritional deficiency or deficiencies involved is not known, but it has been found that feather picking and cannibalism are less likely to occur if the diet contains about 20 percent of barley or oats or about 30 percent of bran and middlings.

Carver (6) has reported that feather picking and cannibalism may be controlled by using ruby-colored lights in place of ordinary lights in

battery brooders and brooder houses. Miller and Bearse (*35*) have reported that if oats are fed as the sole grain in diets for growing and laying pullets, cannibalism is significantly reduced. They found that the effective part of the oats was the hulls. Their findings and those of other workers indicate that feather picking and cannibalism are likely to appear if diets of very low crude-fiber content are fed.

One of the most effective methods of stopping feather picking and cannibalism is to increase the salt content of the diet for 2 or 3 days. If an all-mash diet is being fed, add 2 percent of salt, but if both mash and grain are being fed, add 4 percent of salt to the mash. Usually the feather picking or cannibalism stops within a few hours, but in some cases 2 or 3 days may be required. It should be noted that the salt treatment is recommended as a curative rather than a preventive measure; that is, it is not recommended that more than 0.5 to 0.7 percent of added salt be included regularly in all-mash diets or that more than 1 to 1.2 percent be included in mashes with which grain is fed.

Among poultrymen there is a fairly common belief that salt is poisonous to poultry, and for that reason they may be somewhat reluctant to use the salt treatment. Salt is poisonous to all animals if consumed in large single doses; Mitchell, Card, and Carman (*36*) have reported, however, that a daily intake of 6 to 8 grams (about 0.2 to 0.3 ounce) of salt mixed in the feed appears to have no harmful effect on chickens 9 weeks or more of age. They found that the minimum lethal dose for chickens weighing 3 to 5 pounds is equivalent to about 0.4 percent of their live weight. When the salt treatment is used, the largest quantity of salt likely to be consumed by an adult bird in a day is about 5 grams; that likely to be consumed by a growing bird is usually much less. It is thus clear that there is no danger of so-called salt poisoning when the salt treatment is used.

If the salt treatment is not effective after 2 or 3 days, it may be necessary to trim or sear back to the quick the upper mandible of the beaks of all the birds. The trimming may be done with a sharp knife, the searing with a hot soldering iron. When carefully done, the operation is painless. Ordinarily, only about three-sixteenths of an inch of the tip of the beak is removed; the proper amount can be judged readily by the appearance of the beak substance.

FLUORINE POISONING

Although the tolerance of chickens for fluorine is greater than that of cattle and swine, the continued ingestion of diets containing appreciable quantities may depress the rate of growth and the egg production. Fluorine is distributed almost universally in plants and feedstuffs, as well as in animal tissues, but the quantity present is usually very small. Danger of fluorine toxicosis, or poisoning, in chickens exists only when the drinking water contains about 2 parts per million or more of fluorine or when rock phosphate or phosphatic limestone is included in the diet. Apparently the only observable effects of fluorine toxicosis are those it has on growth and egg production.

Most of the available information about the effects of fluorine on chickens has been obtained from experiments conducted at the Wisconsin and Ohio experiment stations.

Experiments by Halpin and Lamb (*15*) at the Wisconsin station showed that the inclusion in the diet of chicks of 1 percent of rock phosphate that contained about 3.5 percent of fluorine had no harmful effect, but the inclusion of 2 percent depressed the growth to some extent, and the inclusion of 3 percent had a more marked effect. Only the highest of the three levels of rock phosphate in the diet of pullets tended to decrease egg production.

At the Ohio experiment station the studies of Kick, Bethke, and Record (*29*) showed that chicks can tolerate a larger quantity of fluorine in the form of calcium fluoride than in the form of sodium fluoride; the fluorine in rock phosphate also was more toxic than that in the calcium fluoride. They concluded that when the diet of chicks contains more than 0.036 percent of fluorine, from either sodium fluoride or rock phosphate, feed consumption and growth are decreased in proportion to the fluorine content of the diet. However, according to Hauck, Steenbock, Lowe, and Halpin (*17*) diets that contain as much as 0.068 percent of fluorine in the form of sodium fluoride may be fed to chicks without affecting their growth. In any case it is apparently not advisable to include rock phosphate or phosphatic limestone in diets for poultry.

SELENIUM POISONING

Practically all our knowledge of selenium toxicosis in poultry has resulted from studies conducted at the South Dakota Agricultural Experiment Station. It should be pointed out, however, that South Dakota is not the only State in which selenium toxicosis may be encountered. According to Moxon (*38*) selenium has been found in the soils and vegetation of at least 11 of the States in the Great Plains and the Rocky Mountains, and it is probably present in the soils of other States in these regions.

Poley, Moxon, and Franke (*45*) found that if laying chickens were fed diets that contained grain in which the selenium content was about 15 parts per million, feed consumption decreased appreciably, the chickens lost weight, and after about a week none of their eggs would hatch. Tully and Franke (*49*) observed that if chicks were fed a diet that contained 65 percent of the toxic grain their growth was definitely inhibited and their feathers became ruffled. The egg production of the pullets raised on such diets was both delayed and reduced.

In later studies Poley and Moxon (*44*) found that if the diet of laying chickens contained only 2½ parts per million of selenium, hatchability was not appreciably affected; if the diet contained about 5 parts per million of selenium, however, the hatchability was reduced somewhat; and if it contained 10 parts per million the hatchability soon decreased to zero. The decrease in hatchability was attributed to abnormal development of the embryos, most of which died before the twenty-first day of incubation. The most prominent deformity among the abnormal embryos was the lack of a full-sized upper beak. Other abnormalities were the absence of eyes, feet, and wings, wiry down, and edema of the head and neck.

OTHER DISEASES OF NUTRITIONAL ORIGIN

Several poultry-nutrition workers, while studying the effects of feeding simplified diets, have encountered various abnormal conditions in poultry that apparently could not have been caused by a deficiency of any known nutritional factor. However, the very fact that simplified diets were being fed suggests that the abnormal conditions were of nutritional origin. One such condition, the anemia described by Hogan and Parrott (*22*), has been mentioned in a preceding section; others are enteritis (intestinal inflammation), paralysis, arthritis, dermatosis, and fatty liver; undoubtedly there are still others.

Certain abnormal conditions, such as enteritis, dermatosis, and fatty liver have been observed even when supposedly adequate diets were being fed. As more is learned about the nutritional requirements of poultry and the nutritive properties of feedstuffs, it is probable that the causes of these abnormal conditions will be found.

ENTERITIS

Enteritis, or inflammation of the intestine—chiefly the small intestine—is frequently observed in chickens that are being raised without access to the soil and green growing plants. On autopsy, the intestine is often found to be filled with bits of shavings, straw, or other material that had been used as litter; sometimes large quantities of grit are also found. A somewhat similar but more severe condition, called ulcerative enteritis, causes heavy losses among quail, pheasants, grouse, and wild turkeys that are being raised in captivity.

Attempts to demonstrate that such conditions are caused by a microorganism or other causative agent have failed. It has been suggested that in game birds the immediate cause is a diet of high fiber content, but enteritis is frequently encountered among both chickens and quail fed diets of comparatively low fiber content.

PARALYSIS

As has been pointed out in preceding sections, a deficiency of vitamin E in the diet of the young growing chicken produces lesions in the brain, of pantothenic acid in the spinal cord, of vitamin G in the main peripheral nerve trunks, of vitamin A in the central and peripheral nervous systems. Moreover, a dietary deficiency of vitamin B_1 produces a toxicosis, or poisoning, of the nervous system. Accordingly, a deficiency of one or more of these vitamins may produce paralysis or a similar condition.

Paralysis of nutritional origin has been observed, however, when adequate quantities of all five of the vitamins just mentioned were supplied. For example, Jukes and Babcock (*27*) have described a paralysis that could be prevented by supplementing the diet with alfalfa meal or a water extract of alfalfa, and Bird and Oleson (*4*) have described a condition, in which there is incoordination of the leg muscles, which they attribute to a deficiency of vitamin B_4. According to Hegsted, Oleson, Elvehjem, and Hart (*19*) the latter condition is not prevented by alfalfa or vitamin E but is prevented by relatively large quantities of dried brain, cartilage, wheat middlings, yellow corn, or wheat.

ARTHRITIS

In 1935 Van der Hoorn, Branion, and Graham (*50*) described a deformity of the legs of chickens that resulted from feeding simplified diets that contained highly purified casein. They tentatively called the condition arthritis. Later Branion and his associates (*5*) concluded that this condition is probably the result of a deficiency of one or more inorganic elements. Still later other workers (*19*) suggested that the "paralysis" (see the preceding discussion of paralysis) that they had encountered in the chicken might be the same as the "arthritis" reported by Van der Hoorn, Branion, and Graham (*50*).

According to the latter authors, the first symptom of this arthritis appeared when the chicks were about 3 weeks old. At first the chicks were merely less active than usual, but within a few days they showed very little inclination to walk, and when they did walk their gait was decidedly stilted, and there was practically no flexion of the tibiotarsal (hock) joints. At this stage the capsule of the joint was swollen and somewhat congested, and there was a slight excess of fluid in the cavity. Gradually the symptoms became more pronounced until the chicks refused to walk. Often the leg bones became deformed as in perosis, but the investigators concluded that their "arthritis" was not perosis.

DERMATOSIS

From time to time a dermatosis similar to that produced by a deficiency of pantothenic acid or to that which results from the feeding of egg white is observed among growing chickens that are receiving supposedly adequate diets. This condition often disappears if a complete change of diet is made, but it is not cured by adding rich sources of pantothenic acid to the original diet.

Hegsted and associates (*18*) have reported such a condition occurring among chicks that were fed a purified diet in which there was an adequate supply of pantothenic acid. In many respects the symptoms were the same as those of egg-white injury, and complete cures were obtained by injecting a potent preparation of vitamin H (biotin). Hegsted and associates concluded that it is possible that all proteins have the effect of egg white to some extent but that the effect would be evidence only when purified diets low in the protective factor are fed.

FATTY LIVER

When growing chickens are fed certain simplified diets, their livers often have an abnormal yellow color and show evidence of fatty degeneration. Lepkovsky, Taylor, Jukes, and Almquist (*32*) have reported that a deficiency of vitamin G (riboflavin) causes fatty liver in chicks, and Engel and Phillips (*12*) have reported that when vitamin B_1 is administered to chicks that have been on a diet deficient in this vitamin a similar condition develops. However, Hegsted, Oleson, Elvehjem, and Hart (*19*) have described a fatty degeneration of the liver that could not be attributed to either of the causes just mentioned.

The available evidence indicates that fatty liver in chickens may be the result of a number of causes and not a single, specific nutritional deficiency. When fatty liver is found, however, it may be concluded that the diet is unsatisfactory, as a result either of one or more deficiencies or of an imbalance of certain nutritional factors.

EFFECT OF NUTRITIONAL DEFICIENCIES ON GROWTH AND REPRODUCTION

Although an animal's capacity to grow is an inherited character, the growth it makes depends on its nutrition. The dependence of

FIGURE 9.—Many nutritional deficiencies retard growth. Both these chickens are 114 days old. The one at the left received an ordinary mixed diet; the one at the right received a diet deficient in vitamin G. (Courtesy of Thomas H. Jukes, Division of Poultry Husbandry, California Agricultural Experiment Station, Davis, Calif.)

growth on nutrition is so great that when an adequate diet is fed the relationship between live weight and feed consumption may be expressed with a high degree of accuracy by a mathematical equation. When an inadequate diet is fed, the animal's growth is usually retarded and irregular. Often a retardation of growth is the first indication that the diet is deficient.

A fairly large number of nutritive factors are required for normal growth. Among those that play especially prominent roles in maintaining growth in poultry are vitamins A, B_1, B_6, D, and G (fig. 9), pantothenic acid, glucuronic acid, choline, several of the amino acids, and many of the inorganic elements. Apparently, there are other vitamins or vitaminlike factors that affect growth, but very little is yet known about them.

Obviously, a retardation of growth merely indicates that the diet is inadequate. Only when other symptoms appear, or when information about the diet that is being fed is fairly complete, is it possible to identify the deficiency. The symptoms of a number of nutritional deficiencies have already been described.

Egg production sometimes continues even though a deficient diet is fed. Likewise the fertility of the eggs appears not to be greatly affected by dietary deficiencies unless they are acute and prolonged enough to affect the health of the birds, especially that of the males. The hatchability of the eggs is readily decreased by a number of dietary deficiencies. However, as a matter of fact, the first and frequently the only indication that the diet of adult birds is deficient in one or more nutritive factors is a low hatchability of the eggs.

Among the nutritional factors known to be required for 'the production of hatchable eggs are vitamins A, D, E, and G, pantothenic acid, protein of good quality, calcium, and manganese. To this list may be added the "alcohol-precipitate factor" of Schumacher and Heuser (*47*). Undoubtedly, other factors are required, and as more work is done they will be discovered and described.

Nutritional deficiencies are not the only causes of poor hatchability. As was mentioned in the discussion of selenium poisoning, if the diet of the dams contains as much as 10 parts per million of selenium none of their eggs will hatch. Moreover, the inclusion of excessively large quantities of calcium or phosphorus in the diet also decreases hatchability.

Just how a deficiency of vitamin A in the diet of the dams affects the development of the embryos in their eggs is not known, but the ultimate effect—a decreased hatchability—may be easily demonstrated.

When the diet of the dams is deficient in vitamin D, the embryos in their eggs are unable to obtain enough calcium and phosphorus, and the embryonic mortality reaches a peak on the eighteenth or nineteenth day of incubation. An excessive intake of vitamin D (5 or 6 times the normal requirement) also decreases the hatchability of the eggs.

A vitamin E deficiency in the diet of the dams is manifested by a marked increase in the embryonic death rate between the third and fifth days of incubation.

When there is a deficiency of vitamin G or of protein of good quality, a marked increase in the so-called second-week embryonic mortality occurs.

A deficiency of pantothenic acid in the diet reduces the hatchability of the eggs, but no characteristic peak of embryonic mortality has been reported.

A deficiency of calcium in the diet seems to have an effect similar to that of a deficiency of vitamin D. An excess of either calcium or phosphorus causes an increase in embryonic mortality during the last 3 days of the incubation period.

The effect on the embryos of feeding diets deficient in manganese to chickens has been previously discussed.

LITERATURE CITED

(1) ALMQUIST, H. J., and STOKSTAD, E. L. R.
   1935. HEMORRHAGIC CHICK DISEASE OF DIETARY ORIGIN. Jour. Biol. Chem. 111: 105–113.

(2) BARGER, EDGAR HUGH, and CARD, LESLIE ELLSWORTH.
   1938. DISEASES AND PARASITES OF POULTRY. Ed. 2, 386 pp., illus. Philadelphia.

(3) BIRD, H. R., and CULTON, THOS. G.
   1940. GENERALIZED EDEMA IN CHICKS PREVENTED BY D, L-ALPHA TOCOPHEROL. Soc. Expt. Biol. and Med. Proc. 44 (2): 543–547, illus.

(4) ———— and OLESON, J. J.
   1938. VITAMIN A DEFICIENCY IN CHICKS FED PURIFIED RATIONS CONTAINING COD LIVER OIL. Soc. Expt. Biol. and Med. Proc. 38: 870–871.

(5) BRANION, H. D., MARTIN, R. L., ROBERTSON, E. B., and others.
   1938. THE VARIATION IN THE NUTRITIVE VALUE OF CASEIN. Poultry Sci. 17: 301–316.

(6) CARVER, J. S.
   1931. THE CONTROL OF CANNIBALISM IN BATTERY BROODERS AND FATTENING BATTERIES. Poultry Sci. 10: 275–277.

(7) CASKEY, C. D., GALLUP, W. D., and NORRIS, L. C.
   1939. THE NEED FOR MANGANESE IN THE BONE DEVELOPMENT OF THE CHICK. Jour. Nutr. 17: 407–417, illus.

(8) ———— and NORRIS, L. C.
   1940. MICROMELIA IN ADULT FOWL CAUSED BY MANGANESE DEFICIENCY DURING EMBRYONIC DEVELOPMENT. Soc. Expt. Biol. and Med. Proc. 44: 332–335, illus.

(9) DAM, HENRIK, and GLAVIND, JOHANNES.
   1940. VITAMIN E UND KAPILLARPERMEABILITÄT. Naturwissenschaften 28: 207.

(10) ELVEHJEM, C. A., and HART, E. B.
   1929. THE RELATION OF IRON AND COPPER TO HEMOGLOBIN SYNTHESIS IN THE CHICK. Jour. Biol. Chem. 84: 131–141.

(11) ENGEL, R. W., and PHILLIPS, P. H.
   1938. THE LACK OF NERVE DEGENERATION IN UNCOMPLICATED VITAMIN B_1 DEFICIENCY IN THE CHICK AND THE RAT. Jour. Nutr. 16: 585–596.

(12) ———— and PHILLIPS, P. H.
   1939. FATTY LIVERS AS A RESULT OF THIAMIN ADMINISTRATION IN VITAMIN B_1 DEFICIENCY OF THE RAT AND THE CHICK. Jour. Nutr. 18 (4): 329–338, illus.

(13) GASSNER, F. X., and WILGUS, H. S.
   1940. CONGENITAL GOITER IN CHICKS. (Abstract of paper) Poutry Sci. 19: 349.

(14) HALL, G. E., and KING, EARL J.
   1931. CALCIUM AND PHOSPHORUS METABOLISM IN THE CHICKEN. II. "RANGE PARALYSIS." Poultry Sci. 10: 259–268, illus.

(15) HALPIN, J. G., and LAMB, ALVIN R.
   1932. THE EFFECT OF GROUND PHOSPHATE ROCK FED AT VARIOUS LEVELS ON THE GROWTH OF CHICKS AND ON EGG PRODUCTION. Poultry Sci. 11: 5–13.

(16) HART, E. B., ELVEHJEM, C. A., KEMMERER, A. R., and HALPIN, J. G.
   1930. DOES THE PRACTICAL CHICK RATION NEED IRON AND COPPER ADDITIONS TO INSURE NORMAL HEMOGLOBIN BUILDING? Poultry Sci. 9: 92–101.

(17) HAUCK, HAZEL M., STEENBOCK, H., LOWE, JAMES T., and HALPIN, J. G.
    1933. EFFECT OF FLUORINE ON GROWTH, CALCIFICATION AND PARATHYROIDS IN
        THE CHICKEN. Poultry Sci. 12: 242–249, illus.
(18) HEGSTED, D. MARK, OLESON, J. J., MILLS, R. C., and others.
    1940. STUDIES ON A DERMATITIS IN CHICKS DISTINCT FROM PANTOTHENIC
        ACID DEFICIENCY. Jour. Nutr. 20: 599–606, illus.
(19) —— OLESON, J. J., ELVEHJEM, C. A., and HART, E. B.
    1940. THE ESSENTIAL NATURE OF A NEW GROWTH FACTOR AND VITAMIN B₆
        FOR CHICKS. Poultry Sci. 19: 167–176.
(20) HEYWANG, BURT W., and MORGAN, RUDOLPH B.
    1937. OBSERVATIONS ON SOME SYMPTOMS OF VITAMIN A DEFICIENCY IN
        CHICKS. Poultry Sci. 16: 388–392, illus.
(21) HINSHAW, W. R., and LLOYD, W. E.
    1934. VITAMIN-A DEFIENCY IN TURKEYS. Hilgardia 8: 281–304, illus.
(22) HOGAN, ALBERT G., and PARROTT, ERNEST M.
    1940. ANEMIA IN CHICKS CAUSED BY A VITAMIN DEFICIENCY. Jour. Biol.
        Chem. 132: 507–517, illus.
(23) JUKES, THOMAS H.
    1939. VITAMIN B₆ DEFICIENCY IN CHICKS. Soc. Expt. Biol. and Med. Proc.
        42: 180–182, illus.
(24) ——
    1940. EFFECT OF YEAST EXTRACT AND OTHER SUPPLEMENTS ON THE GROWTH
        OF CHICKS FED SIMPLIFIED DIETS. Jour. Biol. Chem. 133: 631–632.
(25) ——
    1940. PREVENTION OF PEROSIS BY CHOLINE. Jour. Biol. Chem. 134: 789–790.
(26) ——
    1940. EFFECT OF CHOLINE AND OTHER SUPPLEMENTS ON PEROSIS. Jour. Nutr.
        20: 445–458, illus.
(27) —— and BABCOCK, SIDNEY H., JR.
    1938. EXPERIMENTS WITH A FACTOR PROMOTING GROWTH AND PREVENTING
        PARALYSIS IN CHICKS ON A SIMPLIFIED DIET. Jour. Biol. Chem.
        125: 169–181, illus.
(28) KERNKAMP, H. C. H.
    1925. GOITER IN POULTRY. Amer. Vet. Med. Assoc. Jour. 67: 223–228, illus.
(29) KICK, C. H., BETHKE, R. M., and RECORD, P. R.
    1933. EFFECT OF FLUORINE ON THE NUTRITION OF THE CHICK. Poultry Sci.
        12: 382–387.
(30) LANSING, ALBERT I., MILLER, DAVID, and TITUS, HARRY W.
    1939. THE FORMATION OF EROSIONS OF THE GIZZARD LINING IN THE YOUNG
        CHICK. Poultry Sci. 18: 475–480, illus.
(31) LEPKOVSKY, SAMUEL, and JUKES, THOMAS H.
    1936. THE RESPONSE OF RATS, CHICKS, AND TURKEY POULTS TO CRYSTALLINE
        VITAMIN G (FLAVIN). Jour. Nutr. 12: 515–526, illus.
(32) —— TAYLOR, L. W., JUKES, T. H., and ALMQUIST, H. J.
    1938. THE EFFECT OF RIBOFLAVIN AND THE FILTRATE FACTOR ON EGG PRODUC-
        TION AND HATCHABILITY. Hilgardia 11: 559–591, illus.
(33) LYONS, MALCOLM, and INSKO, W. M., JR.
    1937. CHONDRODYSTROPHY IN THE CHICK EMBRYO PRODUCED BY MANGANESE
        DEFICIENCY IN THE DIET OF THE HEN. Ky. Agr. Expt. Sta. Bul.
        371: 61–75, illus.
(34) MCGOWAN, JOHN POOL, and EMSLIE, ARTHUR RAYMOND GORDON.
    1934. RICKETS IN CHICKENS, WITH SPECIAL REFERENCE TO ITS NATURE AND
        PATHOGENESIS. Biochem. Jour. 28: [1503]–1512, illus.
(35) MILLER, M. WAYNE, and BEARSE, GORDON E.
    1937. THE CANNIBALISM PREVENTING PROPERTIES OF OATS. Poultry Sci.
        16: 314–321.
(36) MITCHELL, H. H., CARD, L. E., and CARMAN, G. G.
    1926. THE TOXICITY OF SALT FOR CHICKENS. Ill. Agr. Expt. Sta. Bul.
        279: 133–156, illus.
(37) —— and MCCLURE, F. J.
    1937. MINERAL NUTRITION OF FARM ANIMALS. Natl. Res. Council Bul. 99,
        135 pp.

(38) Moxon, Alvin L.
   1937. ALKALI DISEASE OR SELENIUM POISONING. S. Dak. Agr. Expt. Sta. Bul. 311, 91 pp., illus.
(39) Nitzescu, I. I., and Ioanid, V.
   1940. LA GLYCÉMIE CHEZ LES POULES EN AVITAMINOSE B₁. Soc. de Biol. [Paris] Compt. Rend. 133 : 490–491, illus.
(40) Norris, L. C., Wilgus, H. S., Jr., Ringrose, A. T., and others.
   1936. THE VITAMIN-G REQUIREMENT OF POULTRY. N. Y. (Cornell) Agr. Expt. Sta. Bul. 660, 20 pp., illus.
(41) Pappenheimer, Alwin M., Goettsch, Marianne, and Jungherr, Erwin.
   1939. NUTRITIONAL ENCEPHALOMALACIA IN CHICKS AND CERTAIN RELATED DISORDERS OF DOMESTIC BIRDS. Conn. (Storrs) Expt. Sta. Bul. 229, 121 pp., illus.
(42) Phillips, Paul H., and Engel, R. W.
   1938. THE HISTOPATHOLOGY OF NEUROMALACIA AND "CURLED TOE" PARALYSIS IN THE CHICK FED LOW RIBOFLAVIN DIETS. Jour. Nutr. 16 : 451–463, illus.
(43) ——— and Engel, R. W.
   1939. SOME HISTOPATHOLOGIC OBSERVATIONS ON CHICKS DEFICIENT IN THE CHICK ANTIDERMATITIS FACTOR OR PANTOTHENIC ACID. Jour. Nutr. 18 : 227–232, illus.
(44) Poley, W. E., and Moxon, A. L.
   1938. TOLERANCE LEVELS OF SELENIFEROUS GRAINS IN LAYING RATIONS. Poultry Sci. 17 : 72–76, illus.
(45) ——— Moxon, A. L., and Franke, K. W.
   1937. FURTHER STUDIES OF THE EFFECTS OF SELENIUM POISONING ON HATCHABILITY. Poultry Sci. 16 : 219–225, illus.
(46) Ringrose, A. T., Norris, L. C., and Heuser, G. F.
   1931. THE OCCURRENCE OF A PELLAGRA-LIKE SYNDROME IN CHICKS. Poultry Sci. 10 : 166–177, illus.
(47) Schumacher, A. E., and Heuser, G. F.
   1940. SOME PROPERTIES OF THE ALCOHOL-PRECIPITATE FACTOR WITH FURTHER RESULTS OF ITS EFFECTS ON CHICKS AND HENS. Poultry Sci. 19 : 315–320.
(48) Stokstad, E. L. R., and Manning, P. D. V.
   1938. THE EFFECT OF RIBOFLAVIN ON THE INCIDENCE OF CURLED TOE PARALYSIS IN CHICKS. Jour. Nutr. 16 : 279–283.
(49) Tully, W. C., and Franke, K. W.
   1935. A NEW TOXICANT OCCURRING NATURALLY IN CERTAIN SAMPLES OF PLANT FOODSTUFFS. VI. A STUDY OF THE EFFECT OF AFFECTED GRAINS ON GROWING CHICKS. Poultry Sci. 14 : 280–284, illus.
(50) Van der Hoorn, R., Branion, H. D., and Graham, W. R., Jr.
   1935. STUDIES IN THE NUTRITION OF THE CHICK. II. EFFECT OF PURIFICATION OF CASEIN IN SIMPLIFIED DIET. Poultry Sci. 14 : 285–290, illus.
(51) Welch, Howard.
   1928. GOITER IN FARM ANIMALS. Mont. Agr. Expt. Sta. Bul. 214, 26 pp., illus.
(52) Wiese, A. C., Johnson, B. C., Elvehjem, C. A., and Hart, E. B.
   1938. PHOSPHORUS METABOLISM OF CHICKS AFFLICTED WITH PEROSIS. Science 88 : 383–384.
(53) Wilgus, H. S., Gassner, F. X., Patton, A. R., and Gustavson, R. G.
   1940. THE GOITROGENICITY OF SOYBEANS. (Abstract of paper) Poultry Sci. 19 : 366.
(54) Wilgus, H. S., Jr., Norris, L. C., and Heuser, G. F.
   1936. THE RÔLE OF CERTAIN INORGANIC ELEMENTS IN THE CAUSE AND PREVENTION OF PEROSIS. Science 84 : 252–253.

At the time this book went to press, the drugs
and other materials mentioned in various articles—chiefly as disinfectants, insecticides, and
anthelmintics—were still available for veterinary and medical use. Under war conditions,
however, it is possible that some of these materials may become scarce or unavailable. In
that case, the reader should obtain professional
advice from the Department of Agriculture, the
State experiment station, a local veterinarian,
or the county agent as to available substitutes.

PART 8

Common Diseases and Parasites of Dogs and Cats

Rabies and Its Control

BY H. W. SCHOENING [1]

RABIES is an outstanding example of a dangerous disease which could be controlled or eventually eradicated in this country but which is not under control because of failure to impose and thoroughly carry out uniform regulations. Here is an account of the disease and the control measures it demands.

THROUGH ITS VETERINARY SERVICES, Federal, State, and private, the United States has been outstanding among the countries of the world in controlling and eradicating animal diseases and, generally speaking, has attained a freedom from infectious animal diseases second to none. There is one animal disease that is far too prevalent in this country, however, and that disease is rabies. The irony of the situation lies in the fact that rabies is controllable and even eradicable if present knowledge were applied. Outstanding livestock sanitarians and scientists visiting this country from abroad have from time to time expressed amazement at the prevalence of rabies in the United States—a country in which such great strides have been made in the control or eradication of foot-and-mouth disease, tuberculosis, brucellosis, and other contagious diseases of animals.

Before entering into a discussion of the reasons for the prevalence of rabies in this country it would be well to discuss the known facts concerning the disease and methods for its control.

NATURE AND CHARACTERISTICS OF RABIES

Rabies or hydrophobia is ages old; it was described several centuries before the beginning of the Christian era as a dread disease.

[1] H. W. Schoening is Chief, Pathological Division, Bureau of Animal Industry.

Only in modern times, however, through the brilliant work of Pasteur and others following him, has exact information become available on the cause, transmission, and control of rabies.

The disease is primarily one of the dog, although a wide variety of species are susceptible to infection, including man. Rabies has been reported in the cat, cow, horse, mule, sheep, goat, hog, wolf, fox, coyote, hyena, skunk, monkey, deer, antelope, camel, bear, elk, polecat, bat, squirrel, hare, rabbit, rat, mouse, jackal, badger, marmot, woodchuck, porcupine, weasel, hedgehog, gopher, raccoon, owl, hawk, chicken, pigeon, and stork. It is definitely recognized, however, that the chief disseminator of rabies is the dog and that when rabies is once controlled in this species it will cease to be of any great importance from an economic or public health standpoint. It should be recognized, however, that once the disease becomes established in a wild species, a serious situation develops, and strenuous efforts must be made to control it in the species affected.

The disease is caused by a filtrable virus—a type of infective agent sometimes called an ultramicroscopic virus, capable of passing through certain filters that retain ordinary bacteria and not rendered visible by any of our present-day microscopes. The infective agent is found in the saliva of affected animals, and under natural conditions, as it exists in dogs, the disease is produced by the bite of a rabid animal or by contact with the saliva of a rabid animal. The bite makes a wound in which the virus in the saliva is deposited.

The period of incubation, that is, the time between exposure to infection and the first appearance of symptoms of the disease, is variable. It may be as short as 2 weeks or as long as many months. The majority of cases, however, develop within a 3-month period.

Every animal or person bitten does not necessarily develop the disease, and the percentage of fatalities has been variously estimated. According to Hogyes, the proportion of persons who contract the disease after being bitten by rabid dogs and not treated is conservatively estimated at 15 percent. The percentage is considerably higher in man following bites by the wolf. From 35 to 45 percent of the dogs, 40 percent of the horses, 36 percent of the hogs, and 25 to 30 percent of the cattle bitten by rabid animals contract the disease, making a general average of about 35 percent for these animals. Whether an individual animal contracts the disease depends in part on the location and size of the wound, the amount of hemorrhage produced, and various other conditions. In general, the nearer the bite to the central nervous system and the deeper the wound, the greater is the danger of infection. In cases in which the hemorrhage resulting from the bite is profuse, there is a possibility that the virus will be washed out of the wound. Also, exact information is not available on whether the virus of rabies is constantly present in the saliva of a rabid animal. It may be variable in both quantity and virulence.

After being deposited in the wound, the virus remains latent for an extremely variable period of time, which depends on the size and depth of the wound as well as its location and the amount of virulent saliva introduced. Experiments have proved that the virus follows the course of the nerves to the spinal cord and along the latter to the brain before the symptoms appear. Gerlach, who collected statistics from a large number of cases, found the period between the bite and the appearance of the first symptom to vary from 14 to 285 days.

RABIES IN DOGS
SYMPTOMS

In dogs the first symptom of rabies may be a change in behavior. The animal may become restless, somewhat nervous, and excitable. This condition may subside, to reappear within a short time. The dog's disposition may change; a friendly dog may become irritable and snappy, whereas an ordinarily less amiable animal may become friendly. Later the animal may have a tendency to wander, and may disappear for a day or two, returning exhausted and considerably emaciated. The dog may seek dark corners and hide. At times a characteristic change in the bark, or "change in voice," is noted, which might best be described as a different tone.

Later the animal develops partial paralysis, staggers, and has difficulty in drinking, although it may make efforts to lap water. It staggers around until complete paralysis sets in and the symptoms finally terminate in death. Since the virus attacks the brain and spinal cord and sets up degenerative changes, the various symptoms noted—excitability, convulsions, and paralysis—can be correlated with changes in the central nervous system. The inability to swallow results from paralysis of the muscles of the throat.

Although the term "hydrophobia" means fear of water, its application to the disease in dogs appears to be a misnomer, since affected dogs show no fear of water. The use of the term probably has its origin in the fact that dogs and human beings affected with the disease have been observed to develop convulsions through their unsuccessful efforts to drink. Even the mere thought of drinking on the part of human beings has been responsible for convulsions, and a dread of water or drinking becomes established in many patients.

In the furious form of the disease, the animal is aggressive, will snap at various objects that are placed before it, and will attack dogs, people, or any object. When confined in a cage, it may attack the bars with such vigor that it may break some of its teeth.

In this form of the disease, the dog's tendency to roam, its restlessness, and its inclination to bite, particularly anything moving, lead to the dissemination of the disease over a wide area. It should be remembered that rabies may manifest itself in a number of forms and that the symptoms described are those of a typical case. Many animals affected with rabies do not exhibit these symptoms. The symptoms may be more or less masked and perhaps be manifested eventually only by paralysis.

In the dumb form of rabies, paralytic symptoms are the outstanding feature. The dog is not vicious, has no tendency to bite or roam, and is not excitable; in fact, it may be the opposite. The outstanding clinical feature of so-called dumb rabies is paralysis of the lower jaw, or "dropped jaw." The animal's mouth stays open from about an inch to 3 or 4 inches. It can be closed with the hands, but the dog has lost the power to close its own jaw. Many times this is mistakenly thought to be due to a bone in the throat, and many persons have exposed themselves to the virus of rabies by examining the mouth and throat for the presence of a bone. Usually a dog with a bone stuck in its mouth or throat will continually make efforts with its paws or otherwise to remove the object, whereas in dumb rabies the animal makes no motion about the head with its paws. An animal with a dropped jaw should be viewed with suspicion, and no examination should be made of the throat; such an animal should be taken immediately to a veterinarian for a diagnosis.

In addition to the dropped jaw, in the dumb form of rabies the animal shows evidence of paralysis of the hindquarters and forequarters within a few days. It eventually becomes completely paralyzed and dies.

The course of the disease in both the furious and the dumb forms is usually short, the animal dying within 3 to 7 days.

TRANSMISSION

As already noted, the virus of rabies is found in the saliva of the rabid dog. The presence, quantity, and virulence of the virus in the saliva may vary considerably in different animals and even in the same animal during the course of the disease. After death the virus is found in the brain and spinal cord. Evidence has been presented to show that the virus of rabies may be present in the animal some days before clinical symptoms are apparent. It has been demonstrated that the bite of a dog may be infectious at least 3 days before the dog manifests symptoms of rabies, and in one case in the Pasteur Institute at Athens, Greece, infection was found to be present in the saliva 8 days before the dog showed signs of the disease. Exact information is not available on the regularity with which the virus appears in the saliva before animals show evidence of the disease, nor is there exact information on the persistence of the virus in the saliva of animals showing clinical symptoms.

For a dog to transmit rabies through a bite, it must itself be affected with the disease. Bites of dogs not affected with rabies cannot result in the transmission of rabies. The bite of a normal dog can be disregarded from the standpoint of the possibility of its producing rabies and need only be treated as any other injury would be.

DIAGNOSIS

It is of great importance to establish definitely the presence or absence of rabies infection in dogs that have bitten people, so that proper measures can be taken. Since the diagnosis of the disease can be based on both clinical and laboratory examinations, it is essential that the dog be kept under observation by a qualified veterinarian. Since rabies is a fatal disease and an affected animal will shortly die, the brain can then be subjected to laboratory examination for the presence of specific changes, which are indicated by the presence of Negri bodies in certain portions. This valuable laboratory diagnostic procedure was developed through the work of an Italian scientist named Negri, who first called attention to the presence of these bodies in the brain of rabid dogs. Although the bodies are specific in the diagnosis of rabies, they may in certain cases be few in number, particularly if the animals have been destroyed in the early stages of the disease. For this reason it is advisable to allow the disease to progress to its termination or to a well-advanced stage so that the laboratory diagnosis can be conclusive.

Since it has been reported that the virus of rabies may be in the saliva of a rabid dog 8 days before the animal shows any clinical evidence of the disease, it is important that dogs suspected of having rabies or dogs that have bitten people be held in strict quarantine in suitable strong, tight quarters for a period of 2 weeks in order that a correct diagnosis may be made. It is essential that the quarters in which the animal is confined be well-made and escape-proof, since animals developing rabies will make extraordinary efforts to gain their freedom. If a rabid dog is not properly housed, it may work its way out and disappear, to die some days later at a distant point without ever being identified; and this would make the handling of a case of a person bitten by the dog more difficult. The fact that the dog has escaped would in itself be some indication that it might have been rabid, but in the absence of proof, an uncertain situation develops.

RABIES IN CATTLE

Both furious and dumb rabies are met with in cattle, the former being the more common. A sharp distinction cannot always be drawn between the two, however, as the furious type usually merges into the dumb owing to the paralysis that always appears before death. The typical cases of dumb rabies are those in which the paralysis occurs at the beginning of the attack and remains until the death of the animal. The disease first manifests itself by loss of appetite, stopping of the secretion of milk, great restlessness, anxiety, manifestations of fear, and a change in disposition. This preliminary stage is followed in a day or two by the stage of excitation or madness, which is indicated by increasing restlessness, loud bellowing with a peculiar change in the sound of the voice, violent butting with the head and pawing the ground, and an insane tendency to attack other animals, although the desire to bite is not so marked in cattle as in dogs. About the fourth day the animal usually becomes quieter, and the walk is stiff, unsteady, and swaying, showing that the final paralysis is coming on. Loss of flesh is very rapid, and even during the short course of the disease the animal becomes extremely emaciated. The temperature is never elevated but usually remains about normal or even subnormal. Finally, there is complete paralysis of the hindquarters, the animal is unable to rise and, except for irregular convulsive movements, lies in a comatose condition, and dies usually in 4 to 6 days after the appearance of the first symptoms.

RABIES IN CATS

When the disease attacks cats, they generally hide under the furniture or in some dark corner, and there they may die unobserved in a day or two. As a rule, however, the disease in cats implies danger for human beings. The rabid cat becomes very bellicose; from the dark corner where it has hidden it will suddenly attack animals or persons, especially children, jumping up to the face and inflicting severe wounds with its teeth and claws. In the violence of this attack it frequently bites itself. The rabid cat nearly loses its voice, being able only to mew hoarsely. Later it loses its appetite, has difficulty in swallowing, becomes emaciated, and succumbs within several days with symptoms of paralysis.

RABIES IN WILDLIFE

As has been previously stated, rabies may appear in wildlife, since a wide variety of wild animals, already listed, are susceptible. In certain parts of the country the appearance of the disease among wildlife has caused considerable loss of livestock, as well as presenting a human health hazard.

In 1915, according to the United States Biological Survey, epizootics, or severe outbreaks, among wild animals, especially coyotes, appeared in Oregon, California, Nevada, and Idaho. In one feed lot alone, a single rabid coyote bit and caused the loss of 27 steers. There were further outbreaks in 1921 to 1928, and more or less serious outbreaks have been reported since that time. Outbreaks of rabies in foxes occurred in Maine in 1934 and in Massachusetts in 1935.

More recently, in 1940, a serious outbreak of rabies among foxes occurred in several of the Southern States, the worst center of infection being in Georgia, although adjoining areas in South Carolina and Alabama reported infection in foxes. Just where the infection originated is not known, but of 291 fox heads examined in Georgia up to December 1940, 88, or 30.2 percent, were found to be affected with rabies. At least 90 head of livestock were reported to have developed the disease from exposure to rabid foxes, and it is probable that the total far exceeds that number. In addition, the Georgia Department of Public Health furnished antirabic treatment to 17 persons bitten by or exposed to rabid foxes.

The problem of the control of rabies in wildlife has aspects different from those in the control of rabies in dogs. As the first step, it is necessary to reduce the number of wild animals in the area, particularly the affected species, by trapping, poisoning, and other means. Effective cooperation between Federal, State, and local agencies and the public at large is an essential feature of control of the disease.

POST MORTEM APPEARANCE

In rabies no constant or definite lesions are observed on post mortem examination. In fact the alterations are slight, variable, and almost absent at times, so that, unless there is a definite history of characteristic symptoms, a positive diagnosis cannot be made without recourse to microscopic examination or animal inoculations with material from the brain of the suspected animal. The most suggestive indication of rabies is the presence in the stomach of unusual bodies, such as stones, wood, earth, cloth, iron, and feathers. Frequently the stomach is empty of food but distended with material of this character. Its mucous membrane is frequently inflamed, and at times a marked reddening of the folds of the stomach, with or without erosions, is noticed. There may also be inflammation of the covering of the brain and spinal cord as well as of the mucous lining of the mouth, throat, and respiratory tract. The feet of rabid dogs may present sores and bruises, denoting extensive travel during the period of roving. The heart and the surrounding membrane (pericardium) are often inflamed, but these and similar lesions are more frequently due to the condition of the animal before dying than to any specific alteration. The carcass undergoes rapid decomposition.

TRANSMISSION BY MILK AND MEAT

From the reports in the literature it appears that in a few instances rabies virus has been found in the milk or udder tissue of lactating animals. This subject has been investigated by a number of workers in different parts of the world at various times. The great majority have failed to find the virus of rabies in the milk or in udder tissue. In 1934 the Bureau of Animal Industry conducted some experimental work on this point, since it is important to know whether milk can carry the infection.

The virus of rabies was inoculated into the tongues of two milking cows on different occasions. Samples of milk were taken from these animals during the course of the disease at frequent intervals. In addition, milk from the cistern and udder tissues of the animals was collected at death, and samples were inoculated into the brains of rabbits. All these inoculations resulted negatively. A calf and four pigs were fed the milk taken daily from the two cows from the time of exposure to the virus to the time of death from rabies. The mucous membrane of the mouth of two of the pigs and the calf was scarified frequently, producing minute wounds in the mouth parts, but in no case did these animals show any harmful effects from the consumption of this milk. In further tests, rabies virus in the form of a brain emulsion was added to milk and then fed to 4 hogs. Abrasions were produced mechanically on the mucous surfaces of the mouths of these animals. In no case did the animals show any evidence of rabies. It appears, therefore, from the information available, that although the virus of rabies may at times be found in milk, the chances of such a happening are remote, and from a practical standpoint there would appear to be little danger in the consumption of milk from even a rabid animal. Milk secretion is usually considerably diminished at the clinical appearance of the disease, with the result that in most cases none of the animal's milk has been consumed after symptoms have appeared. However, the milk from a rabid or suspected cow naturally should be condemned as unfit for consumption.

The same position should be taken with regard to the meat or meat food products of a rabid or suspected animal. The disposition of farm animals that have been exposed to the bites of a rabid dog but do not show signs of the disease also presents a practical sanitary police problem. The International Rabies Conference held in Paris in 1927 under the auspices of the Health Committee of the League of Nations made the following recommendation on this point: "Animals bitten by rabid animals, whether treated or not after the bite, should not be butchered between the eighth day and, at the very least, the end of the third month following the bite." [2] Since this may be a problem of considerable importance in areas where rabies exists, the recommendations quoted form a basis for methods of procedure.

PREVALENCE OF RABIES IN THE UNITED STATES

Exact information on the prevalence of rabies in the United States is difficult to obtain. The Bureau of Animal Industry collected the available information on the incidence of rabies in the various States in 1938 and 1939 through a questionnaire submitted to the various State livestock sanitary officials and State health officers. It is very probable that there were more cases of the disease in the United States than were reported by the officials with whom contacts were made. Table 1 gives the number of cases of rabies by States in the various species in the calendar years 1938 and 1939.

TABLE 1.—*Cases of rabies reported in the United States, by States, during 1938 and 1939*

State and year	Dogs	Cattle	Horses	Sheep	Swine	Cats	Goats	Miscellaneous [1]	Man	Total
Alabama:	*Number*	*Number*	*Number*	*Number*	*Number*	*Number*	*Number*	*Number*	*Number*	*Number*
1938	(²)	(²)	(²)	(²)	(²)	(²)	(²)	(²)	2	2
1939	221	5	0	0	0	15	0	0	3	244
Arizona:										
1938	(³)	(³)	(³)	(³)	(³)	(³)	(³)	(³)	1	1
1939	9	0	0	0	0	0	0	0	0	9
Arkansas:										
1938	256	40	3	80	0	0	0	0	2	381
1939	233	11	2	1	0	9	0	0	0	256
California:										
1938	1,576	50	3	56	4	30	6	6	4	1,735
1939	828	17	1	1	2	38	2	10	1	900
Colorado:										
1938	2	0	0	0	0	0	0	0	0	2
1939	2	0	0	0	0	0	0	0	0	2
Connecticut:										
1938	40	0	0	0	0	2	0	0	0	42
1939	11	0	0	0	0	1	0	0	0	12
Delaware:										
1938	3	0	0	0	0	0	0	0	0	3
1939	12	0	1	0	0	0	0	0	0	13
District of Columbia:										
1938	2	0	0	0	0	0	0	0	0	2
1939	0	0	0	0	0	0	0	0	0	0

See footnotes at end of table.

[2] RESOLUTIONS ADOPTED BY THE CONFERENCE. League of Nations Health Organ., Internatl. Rabies Conf. Rpts., pp. 7–11. 1927.

TABLE 1.—*Cases of rabies reported in the United States, by States, during 1938 and 1939*—Continued

State and year	Dogs	Cattle	Horses	Sheep	Swine	Cats	Goats	Miscellaneous [1]	Man	Total
Florida:	*Number*	*Number*	*Number*	*Number*	*Number*	*Number*	*Number*	*Number*	*Number*	*Number*
1938	311	11	0	0	0	11	0	0	3	336
1939	14	0	0	0	0	3	0	0	0	17
Georgia:										
1938	543	13	3	0	2	41	1	1	2	606
1939	434	19	0	0	1	25	0	2	1	482
Idaho:										
1938	0	0	0	0	0	0	0	0	0	0
1939	3	0	0	0	0	0	0	0	0	3
Illinois:										
1938	645	37	1	0	2	0	0	0	5	690
1939	266	0	0	0	0	0	0	54	2	322
Indiana:										
1938	505	63	3	6	16	21	0	2	0	616
1939	329	39	1	3	13	22	2	11	2	422
Iowa:										
1938	8	3	1	0	0	1	0	5	0	18
1939	11	8	7	0	4	4	0	15	0	49
Kansas:										
1938	52	3	0	0	0	1	0	2	0	58
1939	31	7	0	0	0	7	0	6	0	51
Kentucky:										
1938	63	4	1	0	4	4	0	5	0	81
1939	73	1	0	1	0	3	0	0	1	79
Louisiana:										
1938	130	16	0	0	0	18	0	0	0	164
1939	185	18	2	0	0	7	0	35	2	249
Maine:										
1938	1	0	0	0	0	0	0	0	0	1
1939	1	0	0	0	0	0	0	0	0	1
Maryland:										
1938	15	2	1	0	0	0	0	0	0	18
1939	1	0	0	0	0	0	0	0	0	1
Massachusetts:										
1938	59	1	0	0	0	0	0	0	0	60
1939	39	0	0	0	0	1	0	0	0	40
Michigan:										
1938	317	37	6	21	3	4	0	1	4	393
1939	548	43	5	4	7	11	0	0	5	623
Minnesota:										
1938	137	4	1	0	5	1	0	0	0	148
1939	16	6	1	0	4	3	1	0	0	31
Mississippi:										
1938	250	(4)	(4)	(4)	(4)	(4)	(4)	(4)	3	253
1939	131	12	2	1	0	10	0	0	0	156
Missouri:										
1938	(5)	(5)	(5)	(5)	(5)	(5)	(5)	(5)	(5)	0
1939	47	0	0	0	0	0	0	0	0	47
Montana:										
1938	0	0	0	0	0	0	0	0	0	0
1939	0	0	0	0	0	0	0	0	0	0
Nebraska:										
1938	0	0	0	0	0	0	0	0	0	0
1939	0	0	0	0	0	0	0	0	0	0
Nevada:										
1938	0	0	0	0	0	0	0	0	0	0
1939	0	0	0	0	0	0	0	0	0	0
New Hampshire:										
1938	6	0	0	0	0	0	0	0	0	6
1939	0	0	0	0	0	0	0	0	0	0
New Jersey:										
1938	563	3	0	0	0	5	2	0	2	575
1939	679	11	0	0	0	0	0	0	2	692
New Mexico:										
1938	100	2	0	0	0	0	1	0	0	103
1939	87	3	0	0	0	1	1	0	0	92
New York State:										
1938	75	0	0	0	0	0	0	0	0	75
1939	153	1	0	0	0	0	0	0	0	154
New York City:										
1938	86	0	0	0	0	3	0	0	1	90
1939	58	0	0	0	0	0	0	0	0	58
North Carolina:										
1938	253	12	2	0	0	0	0	0	1	268
1939	235	9	0	0	0	8	1	10	1	264

See footnotes at end of table.

TABLE 1.—*Cases of rabies reported in the United States, by States, during 1938 and 1939*—Continued

State and year	Dogs	Cattle	Horses	Sheep	Swine	Cats	Goats	Miscellaneous [1]	Man	Total
North Dakota:	Number	Number	Number	Number	Number	Number	Number	Number	Number	Number
1938	1	0	0	0	0	0	0	0	0	1
1939	0	0	0	0	0	0	0	0	0	0
Ohio:										
1938	(5)	(5)	(5)	(5)	(5)	(5)	(5)	(4)	3	3
1939	271	15	1	2	0	8	0	8	0	305
Oklahoma:										
1938	233	(4)	(4)	(4)	(4)	(4)	(4)	(4)	1	234
1939	168	21	1	1	3	15	1	6	1	217
Oregon:										
1938	9	10	0	0	0	0	0	0	0	19
1939	29	9	0	0	0	1	1	0	0	40
Pennsylvania:										
1938	493	3	0	0	1	9	0	0	4	510
1939	420	4	4	0	0	5	0	0	2	435
Rhode Island:										
1938	33	0	0	0	0	0	0	0	0	33
1939	17	2	1	0	0	1	0	0	0	21
South Carolina:										
1938	348	0	0	0	0	0	0	0	2	350
1939	295	3	0	0	1	10	0	4	4	317
South Dakota:										
1938	1	0	0	0	0	0	0	0	0	1
1939	0	0	0	0	0	0	0	0	0	0
Tennessee:										
1938	182	15	0	0	0	12	0	0	4	213
1939	237	9	0	2	1	11	0	4	2	266
Texas:										
1938	484	46	5	0	1	32	1	0	0	569
1939	782	55	4	0	0	38	0	4	0	883
Utah:										
1938	0	0	0	0	0	0	0	0	0	0
1939	0	0	0	0	0	0	0	0	0	0
Vermont:										
1938	0	0	0	0	0	0	0	0	0	0
1939	3	2	0	0	0	0	0	0	0	5
Virginia:										
1938	68	(4)	(4)	(4)	(4)	(4)	(4)	(4)	(4)	68
1939	40	3	1	0	0	0	0	0	0	44
Washington:										
1938	355	13	0	0	2	4	0	0	1	375
1939	310	17	0	1	2	5	1	0	1	337
West Virginia:										
1938	231	7	0	1	1	7	0	0	2	249
1939	130	4	0	0	0	5	0	0	0	139
Wisconsin:										
1938	16	18	2	0	1	1	0	22	0	60
1939	24	4	0	0	0	2	0	3	0	33
Wyoming:										
1938	0	0	0	0	0	0	0	0	0	0
1939	3	0	0	0	0	0	0	0	0	3
Totals:										
1938	8,452	413	32	164	42	207	11	44	47	9,412
1939	7,386	358	[6] 36	17	38	269	10	172	30	8,314

[1] Includes coyote, deer, bobcat, fox, squirrel, skunk, wolf, burro, gopher, raccoon, monkey, and civet cat.
[2] No repor t received on rabies in animals.
[3] Present, but reliable statement cannot be made.
[4] Not separated as to type.
[5] Present, but no statistics available.
[6] Includes 4 mules.

RABIES IN OTHER COUNTRIES

After the first World War, rabies became widespread, chiefly in central Europe. Owing to strict sanitary regulations, the incidence of the disease has been greatly reduced. Northern countries, including Great Britain, Denmark, Sweden, and Norway, have been free from

rabies for the last decade. The disease has not appeared recently in the Netherlands, Belgium, and Switzerland, but it is still present to a limited extent in Germany and Austria. In the southern and eastern countries of Europe it is of frequent occurrence, although its incidence has been reduced under that following the last war. In certain South American countries the disease is seen in cattle and horses as a result of infection by the vampire bat. Rabies is reported in Asia, Japan, and parts of Africa, but Australia has remained free from it.

CONTROL MEASURES

The control of rabies in the United States at the present time lies within the authority of the States. In many instances this authority is divided between the State livestock sanitary service and the State department of health. The laws and regulations governing the control of rabies in the various States are reasonably satisfactory and are based on modern knowledge of the disease. The subject is well covered in the report of the Committee on Rabies of the United States Live Stock Sanitary Association for 1939,[3] from which the following is taken.

No matter how thorough the regulations are which are promulgated for the control of the disease, the regulations in themselves will be of no avail unless the proper machinery is set up for their enforcement. This, the committee believes, is the weak link, generally speaking, in the present method of control of rabies in this country.

The recognized measures for the control of rabies in dogs include:

(1) The proper disposition of rabid and suspected rabid dogs and the definite diagnosis of the disease in these animals.

(2) The destruction of the definitely known bitten dogs and the strict quarantining or destruction of contact dogs for at least a 6-month period.

(3) Strict licensing of all dogs.

(4) The impounding and disposal of stray dogs.

(5) Strict general quarantine measures over a sufficiently wide area.

(6) Muzzling of all dogs in certain areas.

(7) To these may be added the use of rabies vaccines.

Not any one of these measures can accomplish the desired end. Except for item 7, the use of rabies vaccines, all the measures must be used in combination. Their successful use will depend on how thoroughly they are applied.

The officials in this country charged with the control of livestock diseases have been successful in eradicating one of the most contagious diseases known, namely, foot-and-mouth disease. This disease has appeared in this country on a number of occasions, involving at times considerable territory, but has always been successfully eradicated. The methods used in the eradication of this disease, if applied to rabies, would result in the control and possibly the eventual eradication of the disease. It is felt that the incidence of the disease at least would be reduced to such a point that it would no longer be an economic or public health problem.

In order to follow out such measures in the control of rabies, it is essential that sufficient machinery and funds be available. It is not the purpose of this committee at this time to make any recommendations as to what this machinery should be but it is merely intended to bring out the points necessary to accomplish the desired end. After reviewing the questionnaires from the various States, the committee believes that there are not at the present time, in any State where rabies exists to any appreciable extent, sufficient funds and machinery to carry out a proper control program.

---

[3] UNITED STATES LIVE STOCK SANITARY ASSOCIATION. REPORT OF THE COMMITTEE ON RABIES. 43d Ann. Meeting U. S. Live Stock Sanit. Assoc. Proc., pp. 151–161. 1939.

THE PROPHYLACTIC VACCINATION OF DOGS AGAINST RABIES

Prophylactic vaccination of dogs in communities where outbreaks of rabies exist is predicated on the reduction of the susceptibility of dogs in that area to the disease. If rabies vaccines, for example, are only a certain percent effective, it could be assumed that, depending on the number of dogs vaccinated, the number of susceptible dogs would be decreased by that percent. The fewer the susceptible animals, the fewer the number of animals that would become infected and the less chance the disease has for spreading.

The magnitude of a rabies-control program in this country is realized by the committee. Rabies has flourished in many parts of the country for years, and we may be faced with factors and problems which have not been apparent in other countries where the disease has appeared only for a short time and then has been eradicated. Rabies vaccines may well play an important role in a well-regulated control program. As an example of the probable value of the use of vaccines in controlling rabies, a recent article comes to attention from Hungary concerning a report on rabies which has been in evidence in that country for many years in spite of vigorous measures for its control. It has been only in the past few years when compulsory prophylactic vaccination was instituted in certain areas that the disease has been reduced to a minimum. In this case, of course, vaccination was only an added means of control, the other sanitary police measures being vigorously pursued at the same time.

The committee states emphatically that the use of rabies vaccines alone, no matter how effective, cannot control the disease, but that such vaccines can be used to advantage in some communities and under certain conditions in conjunction with other standard measures. The State-wide compulsory vaccination of dogs is not considered advisable as practiced at the present time. Its compulsory use in restricted communities should be approached with caution and only on a sound basis of administration.

In the report of the same committee for 1940 [4] the following information concerning the control of rabies is given:

It is realized that it is not possible at this time and in the present stage of rabies control in the various States to prescribe hard and fast regulations, since local conditions, with particular reference to the presence or absence of rabies, may make it advisable to modify certain of the regulations. The following proposed regulations, therefore, should be considered in this light:

(1) All dogs shall be licensed annually. The fee shall be at least $1 for a male, $1 for a spayed female, and $2 for an unspayed female.

(2) The license tag issued when the dog is licensed must be affixed to the collar of the dog and worn at all times when the animal is on public property.

(3) All unlicensed dogs or dogs not wearing license tags shall be either humanely destroyed or impounded and disposed of as follows: Animals shall be kept 48 hours (or 72 or 96 hours) and if not claimed within that time shall be humanely destroyed. If an animal is claimed by its owner and has not been licensed, such a dog may be returned to the owner upon the payment of a license fee and a collection and maintenance charge of $2. A licensed dog claimed shall be returned to the owner upon payment of $1 collection charge. (In this connection it may be advisable to assess a penalty against the owner of the dog for violation of the dog regulations. It is also well to consider the possibility of rabies being spread through the return of impounded dogs to their owners and through the practice of selling dogs from the pound. Serious consideration should be given to these points, but they probably can best be handled as local conditions warrant.)

(4) A sufficient full-time personnel shall be available to properly control stray dogs and unlicensed dogs as provided above.

(5) In the event that rabies is reported or suspected in a dog, it shall be the duty of the official in charge to have definitely determined whether or not the animal is rabid. In the event that rabies is established, a thorough inquiry should be made immediately insofar as possible into the movements of the rabid dog so that all dogs known to have been bitten by or exposed to the rabid dog may be destroyed or kept in quarantine or otherwise treated as hereinafter provided.

A quarantine of at least 60 days shall be placed over an area covering the possible movements of the said rabid dog. This quarantine shall provide that all dogs be kept on the premises of the owner, or, when upon public property, shall be held on a leash not over 6 feet long in the hands of a competent person.

Dogs not definitely known to have been bitten but which have had contact with a rabid dog may be kept in strict quarantine on the premises of the owner for a period of not less than 6 months. Such an animal in addition may be given a series of vaccination treatments by a qualified veterinarian. In this event the quarantine period may be reduced to 2 months. Dogs may not be removed from the quarantined area without specific permission from the constituted authority.

(6) Funds: There shall be ample funds available for immediate use at all times for the proper carrying out of these regulations. These funds shall be consistent with the size of the community. In addition to this, there shall be set aside a sum of money for the specific purpose of controlling outbreaks of rabies as they might occur. This money shall be available at all times and shall not be used for any other purpose than controlling such outbreaks. This money might come from regularly appropriated State funds labeled for this specific purpose or from dog-tax revenues or from any source that seems consistent with procedures in the State. In any event, it shall be available at all times in sufficient amounts to meet any expected need.

(7) Personnel: Since rabies is an animal disease, the veterinary profession shall be represented in the personnel concerned with the control of the disease. The control of rabies in a State shall be fixed in an authority with power to work in any section of the State and to call for such local cooperation as may be feasible or desirable. In outbreaks in communities, due notice of such outbreak and quarantines that might be imposed shall be given publicity and in all possible ways brought to the attention of the public at large and the dog owner in particular.

(8) Vaccination: When thought advisable or desirable, prophylactic vaccination of dogs may be encouraged or advocated on a voluntary basis. Vaccinated dogs, however, shall not enjoy any special privileges because of such vaccination, since vaccination is considered to be only an adjunct in any program for the control of rabies.

(9) The authority in the State charged with the control of rabies shall notify the authorities in the several States of outbreaks of rabies and their location as they occur, together with the date or dates the quarantine is lifted. All transportation companies in a State shall be notified of outbreaks of rabies and the quarantine regulations imposed governing such outbreaks.

VACCINATION OF DOGS AGAINST RABIES

Vaccination against rabies dates back to the work of Pasteur, and the method for persons exposed to the disease (the Pasteur treatment) has been in use many years, but its use is limited to human beings. It consists of a number of daily injections of a specially prepared vaccine. In recent years several modifications of Pasteur's vaccine have been in use, and good results have been reported. These methods have also been applied for years to dogs and other animals following exposure to the disease.

In 1921 the single-injection prophylactic vaccination (the one-shot method) against rabies was described by two Japanese investigators, Umeno and Doi, and was introduced into this country by Eichhorn and Lyon in 1922. This type of vaccination has for its purpose the development of immunity in dogs previous to exposure to rabies infection. Although measures are available for the control of rabies without the use of vaccination, in many communities in the past, owing to lack of funds and of cooperation of dog owners and others, these measures have not been carried out as vigorously as they should have been, and the disease under these conditions has been brought under control only after considerable time. In recent years, in order to improve their methods of control, many authorities have enlisted prophylactic vaccination as an adjunct.

Since its introduction in the United States, the prophylactic vaccination of dogs has had extensive use. The vaccines prepared in this country are killed vaccines, the killing agent being either phenol or chloroform. Considerable experimental work has been done with these vaccines, both in dogs and more recently in other animals in the laboratory. Although there has at times been some disagreement in results, particularly with laboratory animals, the results of tests on dogs indicate that this method of vaccination has definite value. It should be remembered, however, as noted in the committee report, that the immunity produced by vaccination in dogs is relative and differs in different dogs. Occasional reactions from the vaccine itself have been observed, chiefly paralysis, which has been for the most part transitory but has caused a few deaths. No generally satisfactory explanation as to the cause of these adverse reactions has been advanced. Many thousands, perhaps millions, of dogs have been vaccinated with no untoward effect from the vaccine itself, and there is no doubt that vaccination has in many instances been unjustly accused of causing trouble for which it was in no way responsible. Since there is a possibility of a negative phase following vaccination (a period in which an animal might be sensitive to infection preceding the establishment of immunity), it is desirable to confine treated dogs in such a manner as to avoid the possibility of exposure for 2 to 3 weeks.

Much experimental work on rabies has been done in recent years, and laboratory methods for the evaluation of rabies vaccine have been made available. By their use it is now possible to produce more uniformly potent rabies vaccines than were available in the past. On the basis of the recent experimental work, the Bureau of Animal Industry now requires that all rabies vaccines prepared by licensed establishments must pass the standards of a test devised by the National Institute of Health.

NEED FOR PUBLIC INTEREST

Table 1 shows that there were at least 9,412 cases of rabies in domestic animals and man in 1938 and 8,314 in 1939. Since the disease once contracted is fatal, much anxiety is caused to persons exposed to rabid or suspected animals. Local treatment of wounds and the necessity of taking antirabies treatment, which is expensive, make the presence of rabies in a community a heavy expense. The number of persons who have to take the antirabies treatment in this country runs into the thousands annually. In addition to the public-health aspect of the disease, losses of livestock from rabies run into considerable figures annually. As an example of this, the statement is made in a circular issued by one of the Southern States that in 1936 reports from county agents in 105 counties of the State show that the value of livestock lost from rabies was $65,000 in that State.

It may be noted from table 1 that rabies does not exist or is of little importance in some States, whereas in many others it is prevalent. In many parts of the country where the disease prevails, misunderstanding concerning its nature and the efforts made to control it has resulted in dissension which has hampered control measures. Probably, however, one of the most important reasons for the prevalence of rabies in many sections is the lack of funds to carry out the control measures properly.

It is time for the public at large to realize that rabies should be brought under control, with the goal of eventual eradication from the country, and to lend whole-hearted support to control efforts in each community. Once the disease has been eradicated from this country, its reappearance could be prevented by a 6-months quarantine of all dogs imported into the United States from countries where rabies is prevalent.

Distemper of Dogs

BY C. D. STEIN [1]

ONE of the most common and frequently fatal diseases of young dogs, distemper still causes many deaths every year, though it can now be largely prevented by vaccination.

CANINE DISTEMPER is an acute, highly contagious, febrile disease caused by a filtrable virus and affecting principally young dogs. The disease is characterized by a catarrhal inflammation of all the mucous membranes of the body, which is frequently accompanied by nervous symptoms and pustular eruptions of the skin. It has its human counterpart in the form of influenza, which, though not identical with distemper, is very similar in many respects.

This insidious disease, which has been referred to by some writers as the "scourge of dogdom," is one of the most common and fatal diseases affecting dogs and has probably been the subject of more discussion and investigation than any other canine malady.

It will be readily appreciated from the foregoing that distemper is a very serious and complicated disease, requiring expert attention; hence, when a dog is suspected of having it, a veterinarian should be consulted immediately. However, persons who have some knowledge of the general characteristics and methods of prevention and control of the disease are in a position to reduce to a minimum the danger that their dogs will acquire it and to safeguard affected dogs, at least to some extent, from its ravages and after effects. The purpose of this discussion is to furnish such information rather than to outline a thorough course of treatment for distemper.

Distemper is known in all countries where there are dogs and occurs in all parts of the United States at all seasons of the year, but it appears to be more prevalent during the winter and the cold damp weather of early spring and late autumn. While young dogs of all breeds are susceptible, it appears to be more common in highly bred animals than in mongrels. Puppies with weak constitutions, and pampered, overfed, underexercised pet dogs kept in overheated

---

[1] C. D. Stein is Veterinarian, Pathological Division, Bureau of Animal Industry.

quarters appear to contract the infection more readily and suffer more from the disease than hardy animals properly fed and living in a natural environment.

While distemper is, as stated, primarily a disease of young dogs, affecting principally animals between the ages of 2 months and 1 year, typical cases are occasionally observed in mature dogs. The disease rarely occurs in unweaned pups, since some degree of protection is passed on to a nursing litter through the milk of the bitch.

According to Kirk [2] distemper is most prevalent during the process of dentition, occurring most commonly in puppies 6 weeks to 9 months old, but cases have been observed in pups as young as 10 to 14 days old and in rare instances in very old dogs.

Few species of animals other than dogs are susceptible to the disease. Cats, rabbits, guinea pigs, rats, and human beings are not susceptible. The ferret is extremely susceptible and is used as a laboratory animal by research workers in studying the disease. Reports indicate that distemper may occur in minks, weasels, foxes, wolves, wild dogs, lynxes, and raccoons in captivity.

Devitalizing influences which decrease the resistance of puppies, such as rickets, parasitic infestation, insanitary, poorly ventilated kennels, lack of exercise, and an unbalanced diet, are factors predisposing to distemper.

CAUSE AND TRANSMISSION

The primary causative agent was first demonstrated to be a filtrable virus by Carré [3] in 1905. Laidlaw and Dunkin,[4] during their classical researches on this disease in 1926 to 1928, proved conclusively that the primary causative factor in simple, uncomplicated distemper was a filterable virus. This finding has since been confirmed by a number of investigators in this country.

From a clinical standpoint, however, the disease may be divided into a primary filterable virus stage and a secondary stage complicated by invasion of bacterial organisms. Two distinct factors, therefore, play a part in canine distemper: (1) The specific filtrable virus, which produces the early symptoms, and (2) the bacterial organisms, such as *Alcaligenes bronchisepticus* and others referred to as secondary invaders, which produce serious complicating conditions usually associated with the disease. In this respect, distemper in dogs is analogous to influenza in horses, swine, and human beings, in which a specific virus plays the primary and bacterial organisms a secondary role.

The virus is readily destroyed by heat and by most of the common disinfectants in a few hours, but it resists drying and low temperatures for several days. At temperatures below freezing it can survive for months.

[2] KIRK, HAMILTON. CANINE DISTEMPER, ITS COMPLICATIONS, SEQUELÆ, AND TREATMENT. 226 pp., illus. London. 1922.
[3] CARRÉ, H. SUR LA MALADIE DES JEUNES CHIENS. [Paris] Acad. des Sci. Compt. Rend. 140 : 689-690. 1905.
[4] LAIDLAW, P. P., and DUNKIN, G. W. A REPORT UPON THE CAUSE AND PREVENTION OF DOG DISTEMPER. Vet. Jour. 84 : 600-637, illus. 1928.

Although it is often impossible to ascertain the source of infection in outbreaks of distemper in individual dogs or kennels, it is known that the infection may spread from affected to susceptible animals either by direct or indirect contact. Where large numbers of dogs are assembled, as in dog pounds, shows, pet shops, or boarding kennels, the infection is apt to exist and be spread to susceptible dogs. According to Laidlaw and Dunkin, distemper is highly infectious in the early stages, even before clinical symptoms are noticeable. They further reported that the virus was uniformly found in the nasal secretion and blood early in the disease but not always late in the attack. There was also evidence that infection might be carried short distances in the air in confined places.

Pyle [5] regards droplet infection as the principal factor in natural transmission. In transmission experiments with ferrets he was unable to demonstrate that the infection was air-borne. In further experiments with dogs he obtained evidence to indicate that animals that had recovered from distemper or those immunized with live virus were not virus carriers.

SYMPTOMS AND DIAGNOSIS

The period of incubation in distemper (that is, the length of time between exposure to infection and the appearance of the first symptoms), is very variable. Laidlaw and Dunkin reported that under experimental conditions the incubation period tends to be constant at 4 days, with a minimum of 3 days and a maximum of 6. Pyle regards 4 or 5 days as the average period of incubation. Regenos [6] considers the incubation period from natural exposure to range from 4 to 10 days or longer, with an average of about a week. He further reports that the average course of the disease, whether it ends in recovery or death, is 29 days, while seriously complicated cases may run a course of 4 to 12 weeks. Dailey,[7] in reporting on observations made on more than 3,600 cases in 1 year, states that in natural exposure the incubation period is about 7 days and that the disease runs a course of about 4 weeks, barring complications.

The symptoms in an established case of distemper depends to a large extent on the form the disease takes and are therefore very variable.

The early symptoms, as a rule, are of so mild a nature that they are recognized by careful observers only. These first symptoms may be a rise in the body temperature and watery discharges from the eyes and nose. The appetite may be somewhat impaired, and the general disposition becomes more or less sluggish. In about a week's time the symptoms become well marked, a discharge of mucus and pus from eyes and nose appears, and complications of a more or less serious nature, such as broncho-pneumonia, hemorrhagic inflammation of the gastrointestinal tract, and disturbances of the brain and

[5] PYLE, NORMAN J. CANINE DISTEMPER AND ITS BIOLOGICAL THERAPY. Vet. Med. 29: 116–119. 1934.
[6] REGENOS, S. H. CANINE DISTEMPER AND ITS CONTROL. Amer. Vet. Med. Assoc. Jour. 86: 84–95. 1935.
[7] DAILEY, HUGH F. CANINE DISTEMPER. Pa. Univ. School Vet. Med., Vet. Ext. Quart. 29 (29): 1–7. 1929.

spinal cord, frequently set in. During the early stages of the disease, the body temperature may suddenly rise from the normal 101° F. to 103° or 105°. Shivering, dryness of the nostrils and a slight dry cough, increased thirst, a drowsy expression of the eyes, and a desire to sleep may be observed. Later diarrhea, pneumonia, convulsions, paralysis, or chorea (a nervous disorder) may develop. An inflammation of the membranes of the eyes may sometimes occur, which in turn may permanently damage the eyesight through ulceration or opacity of the cornea. Extreme weakness and a great loss of body weight occur in the advanced stages.

The changes in the body tissues resulting from canine distemper, like the clinical symptoms, are variable. In acute uncomplicated cases, enlargement of the spleen and abdominal lymph glands and the presence of a few scattered pin-point hemorrhages may constitute the only lesions, or tissue alterations. Subacute and chronic cases usually cause marked alterations in the respiratory and gastrointestinal tracts due to bacterial infection with secondary invaders. Hemorrhagic areas, congestion, edema (watery swelling), or pneumonia may be observed in the lungs, whereas a catarrhal or hemorrhagic enteritis, or intestinal inflammation, and exudates in the abdominal cavity may also be found.

On account of its obscure nature and great similarity to other catarrhal affections of bacterial origin, the diagnosis of distemper is sometimes difficult, especially in the early stages. In young dogs with a history of exposure to the disease, however, an elevation of body temperature, together with shivering, sneezing, partial loss of appetite, a slight eye and nasal discharge, sluggishness, and diarrhea, is very suggestive of distemper.

TREATMENT AND PREVENTION

Good nursing and proper care are important in promoting the recovery of sick dogs. Like similar febrile diseases due to filtrable viruses, distemper runs a definite course regardless of any medicinal treatment that may be administered. Therefore, nostrums advanced as so-called quick cures for distemper have no value.

The treatment of distemper is largely concerned with alleviating the symptoms and is usually attended with considerable difficulty. No drug or combination of drugs is known at this time that has a specific action in this disease. Homologous anti-canine-distemper serum, a biological product prepared from the blood of immune dogs that have been hyperimmunized against the disease, is of value in lessening the severity of an attack if administered subcutaneously or intravenously (under the skin or into the veins) during the early stages of the disease. Dogs affected with distemper should be provided with clean, warm, dry, well-ventilated quarters and should be given only small quantities of such easily digested, nourishing foods as milk, raw eggs, raw beef, and beef broth. Affected animals should be kept quiet and can be kept clean by daily grooming with brush and comb. The eyes and nose should be kept free from accumulated discharges. The eyes may be bathed with a weak boric acid solution to allay irritation, and petrolatum may be applied to the edges of the nostrils to prevent cracking and irritation of the skin. Under no circumstances should an affected animal be permitted to get wet or chilled, nor should drugs be administered unless prescribed by a veterinarian. When the animal begins to show signs of improvement it must not be given an undue quantity of food at one meal, since overeating may cause a relapse or even death. The convalescing dog should be allowed to exercise only very moderately.

Diseases of the nervous system frequently occur during or after an attack of distemper. Chorea, a disease characterized by a persistent twitching of certain muscles or groups of muscles, is one of the most common of these affections. No specific treatment can be recommended to cure chorea. There is a tendency for the twitching to become progressively worse and terminate in paralysis of one or more groups of muscles. A nutritious diet of fresh meat, milk, and eggs, regular evacuation of the bowels and bladder, and clean, warm, dry, and comfortable surroundings free from annoyance may assist in the recovery of mild cases. The treatment of the after effects of distemper, like that of the disease itself, should be under the supervision of a qualified veterinarian.

Much progress has been made in recent years in immunization against canine distemper, but in spite of the great advances made in the control of the disease, it still takes a heavy annual death toll among unvaccinated dogs and causes considerable financial losses to owners and breeders.

There are two recognized standard methods of distemper prophylaxis, or prevention: (1) The vaccine-virus, or Laidlaw-Dunkin method, which consists in the administration of vaccine followed by living virus, and (2) the serum-virus method, which consists in the administration of anti-canine-distemper serum and living virus. The different methods of vaccination now in use in this country are all modifications of one or the other of these basic forms of immunization. The Department of Agriculture has conducted no tests to determine the relative merits of the different methods of immunization, but reports from the field indicate that, when properly applied, any one is an effective means of controlling the disease.

It is generally believed that puppies should not be immunized against distemper until they are at least 3 months old. Some investigators who have done considerable research on this problem are of the opinion that when puppies under 4 to 6 months of age are vaccinated, complete immunity is not produced. When danger of infection is imminent, however, puppies 6 to 8 weeks old may be protected by the administration of vaccine or anti-canine-distemper serum and revaccinated at 4 to 6 months of age by one of the standard methods of immunization, which should include the administration of living virus. The dog to be vaccinated should be free from parasites and rickets and in a state of general good health.

The vaccination of dogs against distemper should be undertaken only by a qualified veterinarian, as proper immunization involves not only an understanding of the principles of immunity but the consideration of a number of other factors.

In the control of distemper it is important that affected animals be promptly isolated, as close contact between infected and susceptible dogs during an outbreak results in a rapid passage of the disease to the latter.

Inasmuch as distemper is caused by a specific contagion that is known to remain alive and active outside the animal body, it is essential that after an outbreak the premises be thoroughly disinfected before susceptible animals are brought in. For this purpose, a 5-percent solution of phenol, a 2-percent formaldehyde solution, a 2-percent lye solution, or a 3-percent compound solution of cresol, U.S.P. (see the article on Disinfection and Disinfectants, p. 179) may be used.

To eradicate completely the contagion of distemper from the premises, it is essential that all objects that have come in contact with affected dogs, as well as the quarters occupied by them, be thoroughly cleaned and disinfected. All litter or old bedding should be burned. The infective agent is destroyed in a short time when exposed to direct sunlight. It would be advisable to allow several weeks to elapse even after a thorough cleansing and disinfection of the premises before bringing in a new puppy, unless the puppy has previously been immunized against distemper.

At the time this book went to press, the drugs and other materials mentioned in various articles—chiefly as disinfectants, insecticides, and anthelmintics—were still available for veterinary and medical use. Under war conditions, however, it is possible that some of these materials may become scarce or unavailable. In that case, the reader should obtain professional advice from the Department of Agriculture, the State experiment station, a local veterinarian, or the county agent as to available substitutes.

Feline Enteritis

BY C. D. STEIN [1]

IN its disastrous effects on young animals and its high
mortality rate, feline enteritis is the counterpart of
distemper of dogs. Here is a description of the disease
and an account of such control measures as are available.

FELINE ENTERITIS is an acute, specific, infectious, highly contagious
disease of cats, usually young cats, commonly known as infectious
gastroenteritis and feline distemper.[2] It is also referred to as croupous enteritis, epizootic enteritis, malignant panleucopenia, infectious
feline agranulocytosis, and feline typhus. The disease, which is
world-wide in distribution, occurs in all parts of the United States in
cats of all breeds and at all seasons, but it appears to be most prevalent during the cold damp weather of early spring and late autumn.
It is considered to be the most serious disease encountered in cats
and takes its greatest death toll among kittens and young cats. It
often occurs as an epizootic (corresponding to an epidemic among
human beings) affecting and rapidly decimating the entire young cat
population in certain districts. The occurrence of the disease has
recently been reported by Torres (11) in wild as well as domestic cats
in Brazil.

Feline enteritis is characterized principally by its sudden onset,
highly contagious nature, rapid and violent course, profound alterations in the blood, and frequent fatal termination, and by its predilection for young cats. Although the symptoms are variable, those
most characteristic are high fever, loss of appetite, enteritis (acute
inflammation of the intestinal tract), a marked decrease of white
blood cells, rapid loss of flesh, great depression, diarrhea, vomiting,
and sometimes a discharge from the eyes and nose. Affected cats
manifest extreme soreness of the abdomen and may assume a peculiar

[1] C. D. Stein is Veterinarian, Pathological Division, Bureau of Animal Industry.
[2] The term, "feline distemper" is also used to designate a mild infectious disease of
young cats, characterized by catarrhal inflammation of the mucous membranes, known as
feline influenza. Kirk (5)[3] and Salsbery (10) consider feline distemper to be an entirely
distinct disease. Hindle and Findlay (4), on the other hand, describe an infectious disease
of cats due to a filtrable virus with symptoms similar to feline infectious enteritis as feline
distemper.
[3] Italic numbers in parentheses refer to Literature Cited, p. 1133.

characteristic position, lying flat on the abdomen with head lowered, forelegs spread laterally, and hind legs stretched out. Roughening of the coat, complete loss of appetite, sudden elevation of temperature, and depression are usually the first symptoms observed. These may be followed by severe diarrhea, the stool sometimes being streaked with blood, vomiting, extreme weakness, marked emaciation, complete exhaustion, and death.

The incubation period, that is, the time between exposure to the infection and the appearance of the first symptoms, is 5 to 6 days under experimental conditions and 6 to 8 days or longer in natural infection. The course of the disease is usually very rapid, affected animals sometimes dying in 24 to 48 hours, and in especially acute cases, particularly in kittens, it is often so rapid that death may occur before any well-marked symptoms develop. Cases of this type, particularly when several cats in the same neighborhood are similarly affected, are frequently mistaken by the owners for poisoning. The mortality is high, often exceeding 80 percent.

As a rule definite lesions, or tissue alterations, mainly in the intestinal tract, are observed on post mortem examination, though in some cases such lesions may be slight or lacking. Inflammation of the small and large intestines is usually present, varying in intensity from simple congestion to a well-marked hemorrhagic enteritis involving all or a portion of the intestinal tract. The mesenteric lymph glands (in the intestinal region) may be congested and show an infiltration of blood due to hemorrhages. Moderate congestion of the liver, spleen, and kidneys may also be observed in some cases.

Devitalizing influences that decrease the resistance of kittens, such as rickets, parasitic infestation (particularly hookworms), insanitary, poorly ventilated quarters, and undernourishment, are predisposing factors to feline infectious enteritis.

The causative agent is a filtrable virus. Verge and Cristoforoni (*13*) in 1928 were the first to establish this fact, and others have confirmed the finding.[4]

A highly infectious and acute disease of young cats, due to a filtrable virus, characterized by marked changes in the blood, with clinical symptoms of enteritis, and considered to be identical with feline enteritis, has been described under different names by various investigators,[5] all of whom have pointed out that in addition to enteritis, leucopenia (a decrease in the white blood cells) is a more or less constant finding of considerable diagnostic importance in this disease.

As already noted, the disease frequently occurs as an epizootic and is so highly contagious that it spreads rapidly when once established. Natural infection may occur by direct contact of healthy with diseased cats or by exposure to contaminated quarters, bedding, utensils, or other articles that have been in contact with infected cats. Macchiavello and Bezerra Coutinho (*9*) were the first workers to present

---

[4] Hindle and Findley (*4*) in 1932, Urban (*12*) in 1933, Leasure, Lienhardt, and Taberner (*8*) in 1934, and Salsbery (*10*) in 1938.

[5] By Macchiavello and Bezerra Countinho (*9*) as infectious adenomyeloenterosis; by Lawrence and Syverton (*6*) as spontaneous agranulocytosis; by Lawrence, Syverton, Shaw, and Smith (*7*) as infectious agranulocytosis; by Hammon and Enders (*2, 3*) as malignant panleucopenia; and by Torres (*11*) as feline gastroenteritis.

evidence that fleas may harbor the virus, and recently Torres (*11*) reported evidence definitely indicating that fleas may play an important role in the spread of the disease.

According to Leasure, Lienhardt, and Taberner (*8*), who made an extensive study of this disease, the virus is found in the urine, feces, and blood and remains alive for a considerable length of time. They reported that virus kept under refrigeration at 42° F. and also virus kept at room temperature (50° to 85° F.) remained virulent for 91 days.

The successful immunization of cats against this disease under experimental conditions, either by the use of tissue vaccine treated with formalin (formalized) prepared from the organs of infected cats or by the simultaneous injection of feline infectious enteritis virus and homologous hyperimmune antiserum (prepared with material from cats), has been reported.[6] As a result of studies on immunization against malignant panleucopenia (now considered identical with feline infectious enteritis), Enders and Hammon (*1*) reported evidence to indicate that resistance to the disease in susceptible cats can be induced by the injection of formalized suspensions of organs from infected cats. They also reported that the serum of cats that have recovered from the infection, as well as that of animals immunized against the disease, will protect susceptible cats for a limited time against subsequent exposure. Biological products (vaccines, antisera, and bacterins) are commercially available for use in the treatment and prevention of the disease. While the Department of Agriculture has carried on no experiments to determine the relative merits of these products, reports from the practicing veterinarians indicate that these biologics may have some value if properly applied.

From the field of small-animal practice it has been reported that: (1) Improvement is often noted in sick cats following the administration of repeated large doses of homologous feline enteritis serum and that the administration of such serum is the best prophylactic (preventive) measure for healthy cats during an epidemic of the disease. (2) If treatment with serum is commenced in the early stages of the disease before the temperature begins to drop, a large percentage of cases can be saved. For best results, treatment with a combination of homologous feline enteritis antiserum injected into the abdominal cavity and mixed antibacterial feline serum injected under the skin is recommended. (3) Complete protection of young kittens against the disease during hospital exposure can be assured by prophylactic doses of 2 to 3 cubic centimeters of serum obtained from immune adult cats that have been exposed to the disease.

No specific medicinal treatment is known for this disease. Affected cats should be isolated and placed in warm, dry quarters. If animals show an inclination to take nourishment, a diet of broth, milk, and raw eggs should be supplied. The administration of biologics and drugs for the treatment and relief of affected cats should be undertaken only by a qualified veterinarian.

In controlling outbreaks of the disease, immediate isolation of sick animals from healthy ones and a prompt and thorough cleaning and

---

[6] By Urbain (*12*), Leasure, Lienhardt, and Taberner (*8*), and Salsbery (*10*).

disinfection of premises are of first importance. To prevent new cats brought into the house from acquiring infectious enteritis after an outbreak, it is necessary to eradicate the infection, from the premises. To accomplish this, it is essential that all objects that have come in contact with diseased cats, as well as the quarters occupied by them, be thoroughly cleaned and disinfected. All litter and bedding should be burned. A period of at least 2 to 3 months should elapse before restocking with healthy cats.

Since it has been definitely shown that fleas may transmit the disease from infected to susceptible cats, necessary steps should also be taken to eliminate flea infestation, both in the house and on cats.

LITERATURE CITED

(1) ENDERS, JOHN F., and HAMMON, WILLIAM D.
   1940. ACTIVE AND PASSIVE IMMUNIZATION AGAINST THE VIRUS OF MALIGNANT PANLEUCOPENIA OF CATS. Soc. Expt. Biol. and Med. Proc. 43: 194–200.
(2) HAMMON, WILLIAM D., and ENDERS, JOHN F.
   1939. A VIRUS DISEASE OF CATS, PRINCIPALLY CHARACTERIZED BY ALEUCOCYTOSIS, ENTERIC LESIONS AND THE PRESENCE OF INTRANUCLEAR INCLUSION BODIES. Jour. Expt. Med. 69: 327–352, illus.
(3) —— and ENDERS, JOHN F.
   1939. FURTHER STUDIES ON THE BLOOD AND THE HEMATOPOIETIC TISSUES IN MALIGNANT PANLEUCOPENIA OF CATS. Jour. Expt. Med. 70: 557–564, illus.
(4) HINDLE, E., and FINDLAY, G. M.
   1932. STUDIES ON FELINE DISTEMPER. Jour. Compar. Path. and Ther. 45: 11–26.
(5) KIRK, HAMILTON.
   1933. FELINE DISTEMPER VERSUS SPECIFIC FELINE INFECTIOUS ENTERITIS. Vet. Rec. 45: [147]–149.
(6) LAWRENCE, JOHN S., and SYVERTON, JEROME T.
   1938. SPONTANEOUS AGRANULOCYTOSIS IN THE CAT. Soc. Expt. Biol. and Med. Proc. 38: 914–918, illus.
(7) —— SYVERTON, JEROME T., SHAW, JOHN S., and SMITH, FRANK P.
   1940. INFECTIOUS FELINE AGRANULOCYTOSIS. Amer. Jour. Path. 16: 333–354, illus.
(8) LEASURE, E. E., LIENHARDT, H. F., and TABERNER, F. R.
   1934. FELINE INFECTIOUS ENTERITIS. North Amer. Vet. 15 (7): 30–44, illus.
(9) MACCHIAVELLO, ATILIO, and COUTINHO, ALUZIO BEZERRA.
   1940. EPIZOOTIAS FELINAS DO NORDESTE DO BRASIL ADENO-MYELOENTEROSE ESPECIPIA POR VIRUS FILTRAVEL. [FELINE DISEASES IN THE NORTHEAST OF BRAZIL.] Brasil Med. 54: [113]–118.
(10) SALSBERY, C. E.
   1939. INFECTIOUS GASTROENTERITIS OF CATS. Amer. Vet. Med. Assoc. Jour. 95: 195–200.
(11) TORRES, SYLVIO.
   1941. INFECTIOUS FELINE GASTROENTERITIS IN WILD CATS. North Amer. Vet. 22: 297–299.
(12) URBAIN, ACH.
   1933. CONTRIBUTION À L'ÉTUDE DE LA GASTRO-ENTÉRITE INFECTIEUSE DES CHATS. Ann de l'Inst. Pasteur 51: 202–214.
(13) VERGE, J., and CRISTOFORONI, N.
   1928. LA GASTRO-ENTÉRITE INFECTIEUSE DES CHATS: EST-ELLE DUE A UN VIRUS FILTRABLE? Soc. de Biol. [Paris] Compt. Rend. 99: 312–314.

Miscellaneous Diseases of Dogs and Cats

BY C. D. STEIN [1]

CONDENSED FACTS and suggestions concerning a host of conditions about which the pet owner should have some knowledge.

KEEPING PET ANIMALS WELL depends largely on giving them intelligent care. Hence proper and regular feeding, sufficient and regular exercise, hygienic surroundings, warm, dry, well-ventilated sleeping quarters, provision for regular evacuation of the bowels and bladder, freedom from parasitic infestation, and regular and proper grooming are extremely important. Observance of these recognized common-sense methods of management, together with an elementary knowledge of the causes and characteristics of the common ailments, will materially assist pet owners in maintaining their animals in good condition and safeguarding them against many of the common maladies.

The home treatment of ailments of pet animals with so-called "sure-cure" remedies is frequently dangerous, since many diseases are of a serious nature and require expert attention. It is therefore suggested that, when possible, treatment should be under the supervision of a veterinarian specializing in diseases of small pet animals.

ABNORMAL GROWTHS

Abnormal growths in dogs and cats may be due to the formation of abscesses, cysts, or tumors, to the enlargement of superficial glands, or to hernias.

An abscess is an enlargement due to an accumulation of pus enclosed in a capsule and may occur on any part of the body. It frequently follows injuries such as scratches, bites, and puncture wounds which permit pus-producing micro-organisms to enter the tissues.

[1] C. D. Stein is Veterinarian, Pathological Division, Bureau of Animal Industry.

1134

Pain in the area of the abscess, caused by pressure on the tissues, and a rise in body temperature may occur. Treatment consists in the use of hot applications to bring the abscess to a head, an incision with a sterile knife at the lowest point for drainage, and the application of mild antiseptics.

A cyst is a fluctuating tumorlike enlargement due to the accumulation and distention of tissue cavities with a fluid or semifluid substance.

There are a number of different types of cysts, but the most common in the dog and cat is the blood cyst of the ear (haematoma), which follows an injury. Cysts of other types may occur in the skin on different parts of the body, on the eyelids, in the ovaries, and in the uterus. Since surgical interference is indicated in most types of cysts, the diagnosis and treatment of this condition should be left to a veterinarian.

Tumors are enlargements due to tissue growth of a morbid nature. They may appear in any part of the body and occur for the most part in aged animals—for example, tumors of the mammary gland in old female dogs and skin tumors in old cats. Tumors are of two types—malignant tumors, which develop rapidly and may spread progressively to other tissues in the body and destroy them; and nonmalignant tumors, which grow slowly and are usually well encapsulated, or enclosed in a surrounding membrane. Nonmalignant tumors occasionally become malignant, but as a rule they remain localized, though they may grow to a large size and interfere with the functions of the parts affected. Early diagnosis and surgical removal of tumors are important, and for this reason a veterinarian should be consulted immediately if their presence is suspected.

Mumps (parotitis), is an enlargement and inflammation of the salivary glands due to injury or infection. The affection manifests itself by a rapidly developing swelling of the glands and surrounding tissues of the ear. The head and neck may become enlarged, swallowing may be difficult, fever develops, and abscesses may form in the affected glands. Affected dogs should be isolated, and treatment should be under the supervision of a veterinarian.

Goiter is an enlargement of the thyroid gland and appears as a swelling on both sides of the trachea (windpipe) in the lower part of the neck. In some cases the glands become greatly enlarged, making breathing difficult. Daily applications of tincture of iodine externally for 4 or 5 days are sometimes beneficial. Good results have also been reported from administering thyroid extract.

Hodgkins disease (lymphadenoma) is marked by enlargement of the lymphatic glands in various parts of the body. The cause of the disease is not definitely known, and no satisfactory treatment has been discovered.

Rupture (hernia) may be described as a saclike enlargement in the abdominal wall produced by the protrusion of abdominal organs (principally the intestines) through a small opening in the wall into the surrounding tissues. There are several different types of rupture that take their name from the structures affected. Umbilical, abdominal, scrotal, and inguinal (groin) ruptures are the most common in the cat and dog. Hereditary or acquired defects in the abdominal wall and increased abdominal pressure are the direct causes of rupture. Enlargements in the region of the abdomen caused by abscesses and tumors may be mistaken for rupture. Diagnosis and treatment should be left to a veterinarian.

ANAL GLAND INFECTION

The anal glands in the dog, located in each side of the rectum near its terminal point, normally secrete a grayish-brown substance with a fetid odor. The opening in the glands sometimes becomes clogged, especially in old dogs, resulting in sensitive swellings on both sides of the rectum at the margin of the anus. Affected animals show evidences of pain on defecation, drag themselves on the floor, and lick and bite at the rectum. In mild cases the condition can be relieved by squeezing out the glands by pressing them between the thumb and forefinger. In cases of long standing, the formation of pus, accompanied by an abscess, often occurs, requiring surgical treatment.

ASCITES (DROPSY)

Ascites is characterized by the collection of fluid in the abdominal cavity, which causes it to become enlarged and pendulous. It is usually the result of disease conditions affecting the heart, liver, or kidneys, and is most often seen in old dogs. Treatment is not very satisfactory. The condition can be relieved by puncturing and draining off fluid, but the trouble tends to recur. Treatment should be under the supervision of a veterinarian.

AILMENTS OF AGED DOGS

Instances are on record which show that in exceptional cases, dogs may live 20 years or longer. The average life of dogs, however, is generally considered to be from 10 to 12 years. Old or aging dogs are subject to a number of afflictions, such as asthma, ascites, diseases of the heart, liver, and kidneys, cataracts, deafness, arthritis, and toxemia, or general poisoning of the system.

In the aged dog, little can be done to cure these conditions, but good care, comfortable quarters, a pleasant environment, and nourishing, easily digested food, together with persistent treatment for the relief of chronic ailments, will materially assist in prolonging the life of the animal.

BLACKTONGUE

Blacktongue is sometimes mistaken for or referred to as canine typhus, Stuttgart disease, or hemorrhagic gastroenteritis (inflammation of the stomach and intestines). It is an acute, often fatal disease characterized by a severe stomatitis, or inflammation of the mouth, and gastroenteritis.

The disease may affect young dogs but is most common in middle age or old. age. It is considered to be a nutritional disease. (See Nutritional Diseases of Dogs and Cats, p. 1212.) Experimental evidence indicates that a diet deficient in nicotinic acid and perhaps other B vitamins is probably the cause.

The first symptom usually observed in affected animals is inflammation of the membranes of the mouth, accompanied by drooling. In a short time the inflamed areas on the lips, gums, and tongue ulcerate and slough away, and the tongue may assume a bluish-black color, which gives the disease its name. The mouth has a characteristic putrid odor. Loss of appetite, frequent vomiting, a bloody, fetid diarrhea, a rapid loss of weight due to loss of water from the tissues (dehydration), and great weakness are manifested during the rapid course of the disease.

Dietary treatment is of first importance in its prevention and cure. If it has not progressed too far, the disease will usually respond to treatment with pure dried yeast, ½ to 1 ounce, depending on the size of the dog, given two or three times daily, plus well-balanced rations. In addition to dried yeast, fresh meat, fresh milk, canned salmon, and liver are highly effective in the prevention and treatment of blacktongue, while fresh eggs, tomato juice, and whole-wheat products furnish protection to a somewhat less extent.

DIGESTIVE DISORDERS

Diseases of the digestive tract, usually due to improper feeding, are among the most common ailments of dogs and cats.

Vomiting, diarrhea, and constipation are the common symptoms in ordinary digestive disorders, but they may also occur in a number of specific diseases. Mild attacks of vomiting and diarrhea, and constipation when it has not lasted too long, may frequently be cleared up by the removal from the digestive tract of irritant substances, or hardened fecal matter in the case of constipation, through the administration of suitable purgatives such as mineral oil, milk of magnesia, or castor oil, or the use of enemas. Affected animals should be placed on a diet of nourishing, easily digested foods, such as boiled skimmed milk, egg yolks, gruels, meat broth free from excessive fat, ground fresh lean beef, and small amounts of gelatin. The addition of small amounts of limewater, boiled rice, or barley and cheese to the diet may help to check mild cases of diarrhea, and the administration of bismuth subnitrate is also of value.

Perverted appetite in pet animals, that is, the eating of dirt, fecal matter, and other indigestible materials, may be due to a deficiency of certain minerals in the diet or to a deficiency of vitamins, to parasitic infestation, or to habit. Grass eating is also a habit acquired by some dogs and is observed when there are digestive disorders or thirst, and in sultry weather. Animals showing signs of a depraved appetite should be kept in clean quarters, fed a balanced ration containing meat and milk, and given plenty of exercise. Small amounts of limewater, calcium lactate, cod-liver oil, and yeast in the diet are also of value.

Pet animals, especially dogs, are apt to swallow sharp objects such as pins, needles, tacks, fishhooks, and other things which may lodge in the tongue, esophagus, stomach, or intestines. Bones from chicken, fish, chops, or steaks may also become lodged in the throat and choke the animal. A foreign body produces irritation and inflammation at the point of lodgment; its exact location should be determined, and it should be removed by a veterinarian.

Concretions of hair, known as hair balls, sometimes form in the intestines of cats owing to continual swallowing of hair. Hair balls sometimes become quite large, producing digestive disturbances and at times fecal impaction. Daily grooming of long-haired cats and of short-haired ones during shedding will help to prevent this trouble.

A common trouble of both dogs and cats is due directly to the consumption of indigestible material which obstructs the intestine. The symptoms include loss of appetite, vomiting, distention and rigidity of the abdomen, and constipation. Intestinal irrigation and the administration of mineral oil for removal of the foreign material, followed by a liquid diet, is the usual treatment.

Gastroenteritis, an inflammation of the mucous membrane (lining) of the stomach and intestines, is a common malady in pet animals, especially dogs.

There are two types, a catarrhal and a hemorrhagic form.

The catarrhal form may run an acute or chronic course and is due principally to improper feeding. Other causative factors are swallowing decomposed food, indigestible material, and chemical poisons, as well as parasitic infestation and bacterial infection. Affected animals may show a decrease in appetite, increased thirst, tenderness and pain in the region of the stomach, general uneasiness, and some stiffness in moving about and may vomit frequently. In severe cases, diarrhea may develop. If not corrected, repeated attacks of acute catarrhal gastritis may develop into the chronic form.

Since faulty feeding is usually the cause of this condition, the treatment is principally dietetic. In mild cases, food should be withheld for a day or two, and purgatives such as milk of magnesia or castor oil should be administered to eliminate irritants from the digestive tract. The diet should consist of small quantities of easily digested foods such as milk, eggs, beef extract, gelatin, and later ground fresh lean beef. Chronic cases in which there is frequent vomiting may require irrigation of the stomach with a weak solution of sodium bicarbonate, together with other special treatment by a veterinarian. (For information on the relation of intestinal parasites to digestive disorders, see the article on Internal Parasites of Dogs and Cats, p. 1150.)

Hemorrhagic gastroenteritis is an acute inflammation of the lining of the stomach and intestines with a discharge of blood (hemorrhage) into the intestinal tract. The causes are the same as those given for the catarrhal form. Hemorrhagic gastroenteritis may also occur as one of the principal symptoms in different types of poisoning and in a number of specific diseases of the dog such as blacktongue, distemper, and infectious leptospirosis, as well as in infectious feline enteritis of cats.

The symptoms observed in affected animals are loss of appetite, vomiting, increased thirst, foul breath, abdominal pain, bloody diarrhea, rapid loss of flesh, dehydration, and extreme weakness.

Since this is a serious disease that usually runs a rapid course, the diagnosis and treatment should be left to a veterinarian.

EAR DISEASES

The two most common ear affections in the dog and cat are otorrhea (canker) and haematoma.

The two types of ear canker are: (1) External canker, characterized by ulceration of the concha (lobe) and edges of the external ear, and (2) internal canker, which may be of parasitic or nonparasitic origin, characterized by inflammation and infection of the ear canal. Frequent shaking of the head and scratching the ear with the paws are indicative of ear affections.

Dogs with long ears, such as hounds and setters, are most frequently affected with external canker, which is caused by injuries to the ear such as cuts, scratches, and bites, which later become infected. The constant shaking of the head and scratching of the ear, together with fly bites, increase the irritation and tend to prevent healing. When of long standing, the condition is often resistant to treatment. Cleaning the affected part with soap and water to remove dried crusts, daily application of an antiseptic dusting powder, and protection of the ears against further injury or irritation from fly bites will assist in clearing up mild cases. (See discussion on dermatitis in article on Nonparasitic Skin Diseases of Dogs and Cats, p. 1197.)

In internal canker the ear canal shows inflammation and the formation of pus and produces a profuse brownish-colored putrid discharge. The condition may be caused by the irritation produced by mange mites or by the accumulation of ear secretions, dirt, and hair, or it may occur as a complication in eczema, distemper, and other diseases.

Daily cleansing of the ear canal with sterile cotton swabs dipped in ether or alcohol, followed by the application of a few drops of 2-percent carbolic acid in sweet oil or glycerin will help to clear up mild cases if treatment is commenced during the early inflammatory stages of the disease before pus has begun to form. Cases of long standing, however, are usually difficult to cure, requiring persistent and painstaking attention over a long period of time; and even then the results are sometimes unsatisfactory. Treatment of these cases should be under the supervision of a veterinarian. (For information on mange mites and their relation to the cause of ear canker, see the article on Mange of Dogs, p. 1175.)

Haematoma of the ear is common in dogs, especially those with long, floppy ears, but occurs less frequently in cats. It appears as a sensitive swelling between the skin and the cartilage of the ear. Haematoma usually develops suddenly and is the result of injuries which rupture small blood vessels, permitting the escape of blood and serum into the tissue spaces between the skin and the cartilage. Treatment is surgical and consists in drawing off the excess fluid, followed by suturing (stitching) and the application of antiseptics.

ECLAMPSIA

Eclampsia is a nervous affection occurring in the nursing bitch and characterized by convulsions. The cause is not definitely known, but the condition is believed by some observers to be associated with a calcium deficiency.[2] It is occasionally observed in pregnant bitches just prior to whelping but most often occurs a few days to several weeks after parturition.

The attacks appear suddenly. The symptoms are first panting, excitement, and restlessness, soon followed by convulsive spasms; the animal falls on its side and may kick violently. The muscles become tense, breathing is rapid, the pulse is accelerated, mucous membranes are congested, and there is an increased flow of saliva. The animal remains conscious during an attack. The duration and severity of an attack vary, but affected animals should receive immediate treatment.

Intravenous injection of calcium gluconate is the most satisfactory treatment and should be administered by a veterinarian. Administration of sedatives, such as morphine and nembutal, is of value in controlling an acute attack. The affected bitch should be placed in warm, quiet quarters and not allowed to nurse her puppies during the attack or for some time after recovery.

EYE DISEASES

The eyes of pet animals, like those of human beings, are subject to many diseases; only the most common ailments will be dealt with in this discussion.

Conjunctivitis, an inflammation of the membranes lining the eyelids, may be caused by irritants, injuries, and infections, or it may be a symptom of certain febrile diseases such as distemper. It manifests itself first by congestion of the membrane and watering of the eyes (lachrymation), followed by formation and discharge of mucus and finally of pus. Frequent washing of the eyes with warm boric acid solution, the application of cold compresses two or three times a day, and placing a drop or two of freshly prepared argyrol (5- to 10-percent solution) or zinc sulfate (1-percent solution) in the eyes will usually clear up this trouble. The application of borated petrolatum to the edges of the eyelids will prevent their being stuck together by the accumulated discharge.

Keratitis is an inflammation of the cornea—the normally transparent covering of the front of the eyeball—due to wounds, the presence of foreign bodies or irritants, or the spread of inflammation from other structures of the eye. It may be mild or serious. The symptoms are lachrymation, photophobia (extreme sensitiveness to light), and clouding of the cornea, indicated by the appearance of a bluish-white film.

The treatment for mild cases is the same as that suggested for conjunctivitis, that is, washing the eyes four or five times daily with warm mild antiseptics, such as boric acid. Severe cases require professional attention.

Suppurative keratitis (ulceration of the cornea) is more or less common in dogs, the ulcers varying in size from pin-point depressions to large, deep, circular or irregular areas. The ulceration may be caused by infection entering through slight wounds, scratches, bites, or other injuries, or it may occur in purulent conjunctivitis and in such

[2] For a brief discussion of eclampsia as a nutritional disease, see p. 1206.

infectious diseases as distemper. Inflammation, lachrymation, photo-phobia, and pus formation are more or less constant symptoms. The healed ulcers frequently leave scars, and this occasionally leads to perforation of the cornea and a permanent opacity. Successful treatment requires professional attention. Flushing out the eye with mild antiseptics, such as 2-percent boric acid, is beneficial and tends to prevent further spread of the ulcer.

Cataract is a disease in which opacity occurs in the lens of the eye and its capsule. Senile cataract is common in aged dogs and cats, but cataract also results from injury and sometimes develops from an attack of distemper. It runs a chronic course, usually ending in loss of vision. Treatment is surgical, but it is frequently unsuccessful and is therefore seldom carried out.

Glaucoma is a disease characterized by marked hardness of the eye-ball due to increased tension within the eye. It usually develops slowly, without evidence of inflammation, and causes gradual loss of vision. Treatment is surgical to relieve intraocular pressure but is usually unsatisfactory.

Entropion, an inversion, or turning in, of the eyelids against the cornea, producing inflammation and sometimes ulceration, is common in certain breeds of dogs such as Chows, Spaniels, and Bull Dogs. Ectropion, a turning out of the eyelids, exposing the membranes of the lower lids particularly and causing them to become congested and inflamed with a copious flow of tears, occurs mostly in Setters, Blood-hounds, and Saint Bernards. Application of mild antiseptics will assist in relieving the inflammation of the lids in both these conditions, but surgical procedure is usually necessary to correct the trouble.

FITS (CONVULSIONS OR NERVOUS SPASMS)

Common fits, or convulsions, may occur in cats and dogs of all ages but are more common in dogs, especially puppies during teething. A fit is not a disease in itself but merely a symptom of some other disorder, usually of an irritating nature. Violent exercise, nervous excitement, teething in young puppies, indigestion, foreign bodies in the stomach or intestines, parasitic infestation (worms in the intestines or mange mites in the ears) are some of the common causes of fits. They may also occur during the onset of distemper and sometimes appear to be of a hereditary nature (epileptic fits).

Attacks usually occur suddenly; muscular movements become un-controllable and there is a rigidity affecting all the muscles and champing of the jaws, with the appearance of frothy saliva about the mouth. The animal may finally fall on its side, kick violently, and lose consciousness. After a few minutes, it rises to its feet with a staggering gait and appears to be in a state of bewilderment. When symptoms of a coming seizure are noticed, or during convulsions, the animal should be moved to a quiet, dark room and left alone until it recovers. As a protection against bites and scratches during an attack, a cat or dog should be handled only with heavy gloves or wrapped in a blanket.

After recovery, food should be withheld for a day, and a mild laxa-tive should be given to clear out intestinal irritants. To prevent further attacks, attempts should be made to determine the source of the trouble.

ICTERUS (JAUNDICE OR YELLOWS)

Icterus is a condition characterized by a yellowish discoloration of the skin and the visible mucous membranes, indicative of diseases of the liver interfering with the normal flow of bile.

The two principal types of icterus in the dog are: (1) A simple or catarrhal form due to obstruction of the bile ducts and occurring in diseases of the liver and in gastric disorders; and (2) an infectious hemolytic form, known as infectious canine leptospirosis, or sometimes as canine typhus, which is considered to be identical with Weil's disease (infectious jaundice) of human beings.

Infectious canine leptospirosis, while not very prevalent in the United States, has been reported from a number of different localities. The disease occurs in all breeds of dogs but rarely in animals under 8 or 9 months of age. It spreads rapidly and is often fatal. The causative factor is either of two spirochaetes, *Leptospira canicola* or *L. icterohemorrhagiae*, both of which are believed to be carried by rats. There is some evidence that the disease may be transmitted from dogs to man.

Symptoms in affected animals are a high temperature, vomiting, bleeding of the gums, loss of appetite, gastroenteritis, bloody diarrhea, and frequently jaundice and great depression.

Treatment of this disease is not very satisfactory. Recently, however, antileptospiral serum and vaccine have been used experimentally with very good results. As control measures, steps should be taken to exterminate rats in areas where the disease is known to exist, and the premises where infected dogs have been kept should be cleaned and disinfected.

METRITIS

Metritis is an acute or chronic inflammation of the uterus (womb) in the bitch and the female cat, caused by retention of the fetal membranes, infection introduced at the time of parturition, wounds of the mucous membranes of the vagina and uterus, or injuries. Cold, damp kennels are also conducive to the disease. In animals affected with acute metritis there are swelling and congestion of the vulva and vagina with a brownish or blood-stained fetid discharge from the vagina. Other symptoms are fever, loss of appetite, vomiting, and tenderness in the region of the uterus.

Treatment in mild cases consists in irrigation of the uterus with mild antiseptics. In severe cases, surgical treatment is often necessary to effect a cure.

Chronic metritis (pyometra), characterized by the collection of pus in the uterus, occurs more frequently in dogs than in cats and, like the acute form, appears after parturition. It is due to the same causes as the acute form. The principal symptom is the continuous discharge of grayish-red fetid pus from the vulva. Other symptoms are enlargement of the abdomen, emaciation, weakness, and a rough coat.

Treatment is surgical and consists in the removal of the uterus and ovaries.

POSTERIOR PARALYSIS

Although paralysis of the jaw, forelegs, and groups of muscles in other parts of the body occasionally occurs in the dog, the most common form of paralysis is that of the hind limbs. It may be caused by infectious diseases such as distemper, obscure nervous diseases, injuries to the back, abnormal growths that cause pressure on the spine, intestinal obstructions resulting in autointoxication, heavy infestation by certain types of ticks (tick paralysis), and senility. Weakness or lameness, particularly in puppies, is sometimes mistaken for paralysis.

When paralysis is caused by a toxic infection resulting from obstinate constipation, the condition can frequently be corrected by the use of enemas to clean out the intestinal tract, together with other treatment prescribed by a veterinarian.

A nutritious diet, regular evacuation of the bowels and bladder, and clean, dry, comfortable sleeping quarters, together with massage of the affected parts and the application of hot packs, may relieve mild cases or assist in recovery.

In cases of posterior paralysis following distemper, and especially in cases in which the spinal cord has been severed or extensively damaged (as by an accident), treatment is usually of little or no value.

URINARY CALCULI

The formation of calculi, or urinary stones, in the kidney is rare in small animals, but their occurrence in the bladder and urethra is common, especially in the dog.

Calculi vary in size, shape, and composition. In size they range from that of a grain of sand to that of a pea or larger. In shape they may be round and smooth or rough and irregular. They may consist of more or less hard concretions of salts, such as phosphates, oxalates, or urates, or of soft, waxy formations of nitrogenous material, when they are known as cystine stones.

The formation of the concretions (calculi) in the bladder may be due to a general systemic disturbance, to local inflammatory diseases of the urinary tract which produce an excess of salts in the urine, or to food or water rich in salts of various kinds.

The symptoms produced by bladder stones depend to some extent on their type, number, and size. Large, hard calculi produce the most pronounced symptoms. Urination may be difficult, and there may be small amounts of blood in the urine after severe straining, and constant dribbling of urine. Pus may also appear in the urine, there may be tenderness and pain in the region of the bladder, and the animal may move stiffly and stand with an arched back. In severe cases, general depression with loss of appetite and symptoms of uremic poisoning (chills, trembling, extreme weakness, and stupor) may develop.

Calculi in the urethra result from the stones that are formed in the bladder and lodge in the urethra. They are more common in the male than in the female dog. Affected animals make frequent attempts to urinate; there is evidence of pain and sometimes complete stoppage of urine, with a greatly distended bladder. Symptoms of calculi in the bladder may also be evident.

Treatment for urinary calculi is surgical.

RESPIRATORY AFFECTIONS

Inflammatory conditions of the different parts of the respiratory tract frequently occur in dogs and cats. The most common disorders are colds (inflammation of the mucous membrane of the nose and sinuses), laryngitis, bronchitis, pleurisy, and pneumonia.

Pleurisy and pneumonia may occur as complications in certain infectious diseases such as distemper in the dog, or they may be the direct result of injury, but for the most part inflammation of the different parts of the respiratory tract in pet animals is due principally to some type of direct infection. The inhalation of irritating substances such as dust and gases, sudden changes of temperature, exposure to rain and to cold damp winds, and cold damp sleeping quarters are all conducive to respiratory diseases.

In ordinary colds there is congestion of the mucous membranes of the nasal passages and head, with sneezing, coughing, and discharge from the eyes or nose.

An easily digested, nutritious diet, regular evacuation of the bowels and bladder, clean, dry, warm sleeping quarters, and the use of boric acid eye washes may materially assist in recovery from colds and other affections of the respiratory tract.

The treatment of serious respiratory diseases such as pneumonia and pleurisy, which are accompanied by symptoms of chilling, fever, difficult breathing, and weakness, should be under the supervision of a veterinarian.

RANULA (SALIVARY CYST)

Ranula is a cystlike formation on the floor of the mouth under the side of the tongue. It usually appears in the form of an oval enlargement that may sometimes attain the size of a hen's egg. The condition is caused by an occlusion, or stopping up, of the salivary ducts. The affected animal has difficulty in controlling the movements of the tongue and in eating and drinking. Treatment is surgical. Temporary relief may be afforded by puncturing the cyst with a sterile, sharp instrument and forcing out the contents, but surgical removal of the cyst wall is necessary in most instances to effect a cure.

WARTS (PAPILLOMATA)

Warts are small nodular growths occurring on the skin and mucous membranes in different parts of the body. They are of two types: Hard warts characterized by round, smooth, horny elevations, which occur especially on the eyelids, neck, head, and back of old cats and dogs; and soft warts characterized by a flat, rough, cauliflowerlike appearance, which occur principally in the mouth and on the genital organs of young dogs.

The appearance of large numbers of warts on dogs, especially in the mouth or on the genital organs in young animals, is not uncommon. The condition is considered to be contagious and is referred to as infectious buccal papillomata. Dogs affected with this type of wart should be isolated to prevent the spread of the disease to other animals. Buccal warts usually appear suddenly; they may persist for some time and disappear spontaneously without any treatment. Their presence in large numbers may interfere with eating and cause excessive salivation. In some cases applications of dilute vinegar to the warts will relieve the condition.

Intravenous administration of arsenical compounds is also of value in clearing up warts. Treatment for large warts is surgical and consists in their removal, followed by cauterization with silver nitrate.

POISONING

Dogs and cats are poisoned mostly by accident, but occasionally they are deliberately fed poisoned material.

In a case of suspected poisoning, the animal should receive expert veterinary attention as soon as possible, since the immediate administration of specific antidotes, sedatives, and hypodermic injections to induce vomiting, as well as the use of the stomach pump and enemas for elimination of the poison from the digestive tract, is necessary to save its life.

In applying first-aid measures, an attempt should be made to remove the poison from the digestive tract by inducing vomiting (if it has not already occurred) through the administration of warm mustard water or salt water, and by the use of enemas or castor oil to produce bowel movements. Animals should be kept warm, and the antidotes suggested below for each type of poisoning should be administered:

Arsenic and phosphorus poisoning occur mostly from eating food containing rat or insect poison.

In arsenic poisoning the symptoms are similar to those of gastroenteritis. There may be loss of appetite, intense thirst, signs of abdominal pain, vomiting, bloody diarrhea, general depression, rapid shallow breathing, and complete collapse. Limewater, whites of raw eggs, or milk with raw white of egg may be given to allay intestinal irritation. A solution prepared from iron sulfate and magnesium oxide is the recognized antidote. Hypodermic injections of apomorphine are also beneficial in the early stages to induce vomiting.

Phosphorus poisoning usually develops slowly, sometimes requiring several days. The symptoms commonly observed are great restlessness, colicky pains, vomiting of material of a greenish-brown color, swelling of the tongue, icterus (yellow discoloration of the visible mucous membranes), and general weakness.

For first-aid treatment administer 2 or 3 teaspoonfuls of milk of magnesia. Feed barley soup or oatmeal gruel, which may absorb some of the phosphorus. *Never* give castor oil or other purgative oils in phosphorus poisoning.

Recognized antidotes are copper sulfate, 1 part to 50 parts of water, or 0.1 percent solution of potassium permanganate.

Lead poisoning in dogs or cats results from licking paints or drinking water or eating food from old paint cans. It occurs either in an acute form, characterized by acute gastroenteritis, colic, labored breathing, trembling, general weakness, and coma, or in a chronic form from taking small quantities of the poison over a long period, characterized by bluish discoloration at the margin of the gums.

Strong solutions of coffee are beneficial as a stimulant. As an antidote, Epsom salts or Glauber salts, 2 teaspoonfuls to a glass of warm water, should be given. Raw white of egg and milk may also be given to allay intestinal irritation.

Strychnine poisoning in dogs is often caused by the administration of cathartic tablets containing small amounts of the drug and intended for human beings. An amount harmless to a man may produce poisoning in dogs because of their great susceptibility to strychnine.

Symptoms of strychnine poisoning, principally convulsions, develop rapidly, their severity depending largely on the quantity of the drug consumed. Spasmodic twitchings of the muscles of the limbs are first noted, followed by rigidity of the muscles and inability to stand. The eyes protrude, the jaw becomes locked, and the head and tail are drawn upwards. Death usually occurs after repeated convulsions. Prompt treatment is highly important and consists principally in the administration of a quick-acting emetic such as apomorphine given as a hypodermic to induce vomiting, and sedatives such as morphine, chloral, or ether to relieve spasms.

Phenol (carbolic acid) poisoning is usually caused by licking ointments or surgical dressings containing coal-tar products such as phenol, lysol, and creolin that have been applied to the skin. Cats are particularly susceptible to coal-tar products, and for this reason ointments, salves, and dusting powder containing them should under no circumstances be used on cats. Neither should soaps containing coal-tar products, such as lysol, creosote, creolin, or tar and carbolic acid, be used in bathing cats.

The symptoms of carbolic acid poisoning are similar to those in lead poisoning. There may be the characteristic odor of phenol, abdominal pain with symptoms of colic, vomiting, excessive salivation, diarrhea, difficult breathing, contraction of the pupils, and muscular trembling, followed by coma and death. Treatment consists in the administration of chalk and water or large doses of milk of magnesia; as an antidote whites of eggs and milk are also of value. Aromatic spirits of ammonia or black coffee may be given as stimulants. A stomach pump may be employed to wash out the stomach.

Gas poisoning occasionally occurs through the inhalation of coal gas, carbon monoxide, or illuminating gas. The symptoms are difficult respiration, feeble pulse, bluish discoloration of the visible mucous membranes, convulsions, subnormal temperature, and coma, followed by death. Treatment includes placing the animal in fresh air, giving it aromatic spirits of ammonia to inhale, artificial respiration, and the administration of oxygen if it is available.

Food poisoning is observed mostly in dogs that run loose and obtain part or all of their food by foraging from garbage cans and refuse. The poisoning is produced by the consumption of rotten meat, garbage, or decayed carcasses. The symptoms may be similar to those of acute gastroenteritis, including vomiting, bloody diarrhea, abdominal pain, and general weakness.

Treatment consists in removing irritant material from the stomach and intestines by the use of purgatives, the stomach pump, and enemas, and the administration of stimulants.

The danger of food poisoning as well as the risk of their acquiring infectious and parasitic diseases from contact with affected animals can be materially reduced by confining dogs and cats to their own premises.

Poison by snake bites—bites of rattlesnakes, copperheads, moccasins, and coral snakes—is not uncommon in farm and hunting dogs. The bite usually occurs on the face or legs and is shown by two tiny puncture wounds where the fangs have entered the tissues. A painful swelling quickly develops and spreads to adjacent tissues. There may be vomiting, convulsions, a weak pulse, and difficult breathing, followed by collapse and death.

Because of the rapid action of this type of poisoning, prompt attention is essential for successful treatment. If the bite is on a leg, a strong ligature should be applied to the leg between the bite and the heart to localize the poison. Small, deep incisions should be made into the wound and as much poisoned blood as possible expelled either by squeezing or by drawing it off with a small suction cup. The wound may be further treated by being washed out with a strong solution of potassium permanganate or pure hydrogen peroxide or by the application of silver nitrate.

Intravenous injection of polyvalent antivenin, a biological agent that has a specific action against several types of snake bite, is the most satisfactory treatment if given soon after the bite is received. When possible, dogs bitten by snakes should receive prompt veterinary attention.

CAR SICKNESS

Car sickness is not uncommon in dogs, especially those with a nervous disposition. It is characterized by nausea when traveling in moving vehicles, the symptoms being drooling of saliva and vomiting.

This trouble can be prevented to some extent by withholding both food and water for an hour or more before starting the journey and also by giving the dog an opportunity to empty the bowels and bladder. The administration of 3 to 5 grains of sodium bromide before starting the journey and at intervals during a prolonged trip may assist in controlling vomiting.

FIRST AID

It is of the utmost importance that pet owners be informed as to what to do in the event of injuries, accidents, poisoning, and other emergencies. With such knowledge the owner can often take care of minor injuries and conserve the strength of the patient until veterinary assistance can be obtained.

Abrasions of the skin, cuts, and particularly bites are more or less common in dogs and cats. Such injuries should be washed with soap and warm water to remove all dirt and hair. It is important in bites or deep punctures to remove all contaminating material to prevent infection. The hair should be clipped from around the injured area and antiseptics such as tincture of iodine, tincture of metaphen, or mild antiseptic dusting powders applied. In areas where tetanus is known to exist, it is advisable to have a veterinarian administer tetanus antitoxin to animals receiving deep puncture wounds.

When excessive bleeding occurs as a result of severe injury, the hemorrhage may be controlled by the use of a pressure bandage (a wad of absorbent cotton applied to the wound and tightly wrapped with gauze bandage) or by a tourniquet applied above the wound.

In case of severe wounds, sprains, dislocations, or fractures, every effort should be made to limit movements of the injured animal to prevent further injuries to surrounding tissues, and professional help should be summoned immediately. The animal, which may be suffering excruciating pain, should be handled with extreme care so that it will not scratch or bite persons attempting to administer aid. When animals are transported for treatment to a veterinary hospital they should preferably be placed in a large well-padded box or basket.

Mild burns or scalds may be relieved by treatment with a 1-percent picric acid solution, by spraying with a freshly prepared 2½- to 5-percent tannic acid solution, or by applications of saturated sodium bicarbonate (baking soda). Later, mild ointments such as boric acid ointment may be applied. Severe burns over large areas of the body require professional treatment.

When pet animals are struck by automobiles or fall from a great height, serious internal injuries not apparent to the owner may occur. It is therefore advisable to have such animals examined by a veterinarian.

Since cats and dogs occasionally contract infectious diseases transmissible to man, such as rabies and ringworm, precautions should be observed in handling sick animals, or those showing abnormal symptoms. It is a good sanitary practice always to cleanse the hands thoroughly with soap and water after handling pets, especially those that show symptoms of being affected with some diseased condition. Scratches and bites inflicted by pets should also receive prompt and appropriate attention.

SPAYING AND CASTRATION OF DOGS AND CATS

Spaying is a major surgical operation in which the ovaries are removed from female dogs and cats. The removal of the ovaries prevents sexual development and the occurrence of pregnancy. The periods of heat, or estrus, which are usually a source of great annoyance to the owners of female dogs and cats, are thus avoided.

The best time to spay the female dog is after the permanent teeth are cut and before the first period of heat, that is, between the ages of 6 and 8 months. In female kittens spaying should take place between the ages of 3 and 6 months. Spaying of old bitches and female cats is sometimes followed by apathy, laziness, and obesity.

Castration is a surgical operation for removal of the testicles in the male dog or cat. It is performed for the removal of diseased testicles, to curb extreme viciousness, to correct perverted sex habits, and to prevent wanderlust and interest in females. Castration is seldom performed on dogs but is a common operation in cats; castrated cats are sometimes referred to as altered or gelded cats. Cats of any age may be successfully castrated, but the best time to perform the operation is between the ages of 3 and 8 months. In some instances, castration has a tendency to increase the size of the matured animal, especially if it is performed while the animal is young.

At the time this book went to press, the drugs and other materials mentioned in various articles—chiefly as disinfectants, insecticides, and anthelmintics—were still available for veterinary and medical use. Under war conditions, however, it is possible that some of these materials may become scarce or unavailable. In that case, the reader should obtain professional advice from the Department of Agriculture, the State experiment station, a local veterinarian, or the county agent as to available substitutes.

Internal Parasites
of Dogs and Cats

BY EMMETT W. PRICE
AND PAUL D. HARWOOD [1]

THE LIFE HISTORIES of the more important internal parasites of dogs and cats are here described, together with an account of the injuries they produce and the symptoms of infestation. The article closes with a rather detailed discussion of methods of prevention and medicinal treatment.

DURING the course of their evolution, dogs and cats have acquired an imposing number of different kinds of parasites—a total of more than 500. They include the Protozoa, helminths (worms), and arthropods. The arthropods, including fleas, lice, ticks, and mites, usually live on the exterior of the body; they are discussed in other articles. The Protozoa and helminths are all internal parasites, that is, they occur within the body of their hosts. Many of the internal parasites are of little importance, occurring so rarely as to be little more than zoological curiosities. A few, however, cause marked injury and even death to their hosts. Only the more important of the injurious species are discussed here. Measures for their control are given at the end of the article.

The damage inflicted by parasites on their hosts and the losses they occasion cannot be stated accurately, as no reliable statistics on these subjects are available. In the case of dogs, however, some idea of the losses that may result from parasitism can be obtained from recent estimates given by Judy (*16*).[2] According to these estimates about 900,000 puppies are whelped annually in the United States. About 30 percent of this number fail to reach maturity. It may be assumed

[1] Emmett W. Price is Assistant Chief and Paul D. Harwood was formerly Associate Parasitologist, Zoological Division, Bureau of Animal Industry.
[2] Italic numbers in parentheses refer to Literature Cited, p. 1172.

that about one-third of this loss—a conservative estimate—is due to parasites.

Parasites infecting adult animals do not cause spectacular losses as a rule, and often parasitism is not suspected until after the death of the animal. This is especially true of parasites occurring in the lungs and the circulatory and urinary systems. In fact, it is only during recent years that veterinarians have come to realize the injuries that can be caused by parasites other than the most common of those occurring in the intestinal tract.

The most widely distributed of the parasites of pet animals are those that have a direct life history, such as hookworms, large intestinal roundworms, and whipworms. Those that require intermediate hosts for their perpetuation, and hence have an indirect life history, are usually restricted to certain areas. The restriction is not absolute, however, since the heart worm, which until recent years was unknown except in the Southern States or in dogs that had at some time been in the South, has now become established in a number of sections of the country where suitable intermediate hosts are present. Other parasites, such as the dog eye worm, esophageal worm (infecting the esophagus, or gullet), and salmon-poisoning fluke, are definitely restricted in their distribution, even though the increasing traffic in dogs has offered many opportunities for them to become established elsewhere.

PROTOZOA

Only a few diseases of dogs and cats are caused by the minute primitive animals classed as Protozoa. Two such diseases are of importance in this country. One of these, canine piroplasmosis, has been known to exist in the United States during recent years only; it occurs in Florida and possibly in other Southern States. The other protozoan disease is coccidiosis. Coccidial infection is widespread, especially in dogs, but acute infections are either rare or are not generally recognized.

CANINE PIROPLASMOSIS

The organism causing this disease is known as *Piroplasma canis*. It lives in the red blood cells and is somewhat similar in appearance to the organism causing tick fever (also a piroplasmosis) of cattle. As in the case of cattle, this parasite is transmitted from one dog to another by ticks. Several ticks have been shown to be capable of transmitting piroplasmosis, but in this country the most probable vector, or carrier, appears to be the brown dog tick, *Rhipicephalus sanguineus*, which is widely distributed throughout the South.

Canine piroplasmosis may assume either the acute or the chronic form. In the acute form of the disease the affected dog may show a rise in temperature, increased pulse and respiration rates, reddening of the visible mucous membranes, loss of appetite, and increased thirst. Jaundice is present in about half the animals affected. Acute cases are frequently fatal.

In the chronic form, fever may be noted during the first days of the infection, and in rare instances there may be an intermittent fever. The affected dog becomes listless, the mucous membranes are pale, the appetite diminishes, and the animal loses weight. Jaundice is usually absent, although it sometimes appears in the later stages of the disease.

In some respects the symptoms of canine piroplasmosis resemble those of distemper, and a positive diagnosis is therefore extremely important. Diagnosis is based on microscopic examination of the blood and the finding in the red blood cells of the causative organism of the disease. In chronic cases the organism may not be demonstrable, and it may be necessary to inoculate susceptible puppies with the blood from the sick animal in order to be certain that the disease in question is actually piroplasmosis. In inoculated puppies the piroplasms can be easily demonstrated in the blood in about 4 to 7 days.

COCCIDIOSIS

Coccidiosis in dogs and cats is an intestinal disease caused by protozoan parasites of the genus *Isospora.* Several species occurring in dogs and cats have been described. Some infect the cells lining the small intestine, while others live in the tissue beneath this lining. The parasites multiply in these locations and ultimately give rise to resistant egglike forms, known as oöcysts, which pass out in the animal's feces. These oöcysts become infective in the course of a few days and serve to infect other dogs and cats. Dogs appear to be more susceptible to coccidiosis than cats, although coccidia are frequently detected in the feces of cats.

In light infections, no symptoms may be detected in either dogs or cats, but in heavy infections a diarrhea, which may be severe and accompanied by the passage of blood and gas, appears at the time the oöcysts are passing in the feces. Sometimes a slight rise in temperature may be noted. Under unfavorable conditions, as in heavy infections in very weak or young animals, death may result. Since coccidiosis may be confused with other intestinal disorders, a diagnosis must be based on the demonstration in the feces, by microscopic examination, of the oöcyst stage of the parasite.

FLUKES

Most trematodes, or flukes, of carnivores require two intermediate hosts in order to complete their life cycle. The first of these is invariably a snail, and the second is usually a fish, although in a few instances other animals may serve as second intermediate hosts. The most important trematode parasite of the dog is the so-called salmon-poisoning fluke, which is associated with a serious disease of dogs in the Pacific Northwest.

THE SALMON-POISONING FLUKE

The fluke known scientifically as *Troglotrema salmincola* occurs in California, Oregon, Washington, and southwestern Canada, where it is associated with a disease of dogs, foxes, and coyotes known as salmon poisoning. The parasites are very small, hardly visible to the unaided eye, and live deeply imbedded in the mucous membrane of the small intestine.

The life cycle of this fluke is complex. The eggs produced by the mature fluke pass out in the feces of the host animal and on getting into water develop embryos within $2\frac{1}{2}$ to 3 months. The eggs then hatch and liberate ciliated, free-swimming larvae known as miracidia, which swim about and penetrate into a fresh-water snail (determined by investigators at the Oregon Agricultural Experiment Station to be *Goniobasis plicifera* var. *silicula*). After the miracidia penetrate into the snail they undergo certain changes and develop into small wormlike structures known as rediae. Within the body of the rediae are developed tadpolelike larvae known as cercariae. When the cercariae escape from the rediae they pass out of the snail into the water. On coming in contact with fish belonging to the salmon family, the cercariae penetrate into the fish and become encysted (enclosed in protective structures) in the flesh and various organs. When infected fish are eaten by dogs or other suitable hosts the encysted parasites, called metacercariae, are liberated in the small intestine, where they develop into mature flukes in 5 to 10 days.

Salmon poisoning in many respects resembles canine distemper. The first symptoms following the eating of infected fish occur in 7 to 10 days, or about the time the flukes reach maturity. The onset of the disease is sudden and is accompanied by a temperature of 105° to 107° F. The animal is depressed, refuses to eat, shows increased thirst, and frequently has a discharge from the eyes. In many cases the face is swollen, causing the eyes to appear sunken. After 24 to 48 hours the temperature drops, and diarrhea sets in, the feces at first being tinged with blood and later consisting almost entirely of blood. As the disease progresses, the animal becomes weak and emaciated; in about 6 to 8 days the temperature drops below normal, and death follows 1 to 2 days later. From 50 to 90 percent of untreated animals die. Those that recover are not susceptible to subsequent infection.

Salmon poisoning has been shown to be a disease associated with fluke infection but not actually caused by the parasite. The causative agent of the disease appears to be a virus associated with the cellular elements of the blood.

A fluke, *Nanophyetus schikhobalowi*, which appears to be indistinguishable from that associated with salmon poisoning in dogs, has been reported in man in southeastern Siberia. No symptoms attributable to the presence of the parasite were observed, however.

TAPEWORMS

The tapeworms infecting dogs and cats in the United States may be roughly divided into two general groups, the armed forms and the unarmed forms. Species of both groups resemble each other in having a head, neck, and chain of segments. In the armed forms the head is provided with four suckers and a rostellum, or prominence, bearing two or more rows of hooks. The segments have one or two sets of genital organs, and the genital openings or pores are located on the lateral margins of the segments. In the unarmed species the head is provided with a pair of sucking grooves instead of suckers, the segments have only a single set of genital organs, and the genital pores are located on the ventral, or under, surface of each segment. A further difference between the armed and the unarmed tapeworms is that the armed species require only a single intermediate host for the development of the larval stages, whereas the unarmed forms require two intermediate hosts.

THE ARMED TAPEWORMS

For convenience of discussion the armed tapeworms may be sub-divided into the double-pored species, belonging to the genus *Dipylidium*, and the single-pored forms, represented by the genera *Taenia, Multiceps,* and *Echinococcus.*

The double-pored tapeworm that is of common occurrence in dogs and cats in the United States is *Dipylidium caninum.* The adult tapeworm rarely exceeds 1 foot in length. The head is armed with 4 or 5 rows of tiny hooks, and the segments are shaped like cucumber seeds.

The single-pored tapeworms are, as a rule, much larger than the double-pored species. The head is armed with two rows of relatively large hooks, and the segments are more or less rectangular in shape (fig. 1). The size of these tapeworms varies considerably. The smallest species, *Echinococcus granulosus,* is about one-fourth inch or less in length and consists of a head and only three segments. The other species may vary from 6 inches to 16 feet in length and consist of a head and numerous segments. The single-pored tapeworms are not so frequently encountered as the double-pored form and are more common in rural areas than in cities.

The life histories of the armed tapeworms are all similar in that, as already noted, only one intermediate host is required for the development of the infective larval stages.

The intermediate hosts of the double-pored tapeworm are usually dog and cat fleas, and occasionally the biting dog louse. The infective larva of this tapeworm develops in the body cavity of the flea or louse and consists of little more than a head.

The infective larvae of the single-pored tapeworms develop in mammals, not in fleas or lice, and are usually referred to as bladder worms. The bladder worm consists of one or more tapeworm heads invaginated into a bladder, or vesicle, filled with fluid. Different names are given to the bladder worms, depending on their appearance and the number of heads they contain, as follows: A larva consisting of a bladder containing a single head is called *Cysticercus;* when the bladder contains several heads it is *Coenurus* or *Multiceps* (fig. 2); and when the larva consists of one or more bladders containing brood capsules composed of numerous heads it is *Echinococcus,* or a hydatid. When any of these larvae are eaten by the final host, the entire larva except the head is digested in the small intestine. The tapeworm head becomes attached to the gut wall, and in time, usually in about 2 months, a chain of segments is developed.

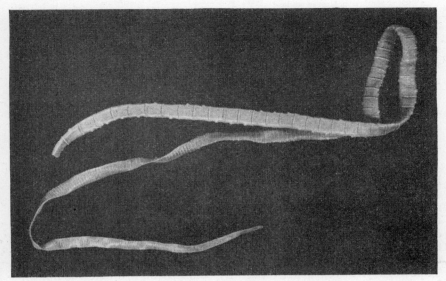

FIGURE 1.—*Taenia ovis*, one of the armed tapeworms of dogs. Natural size.

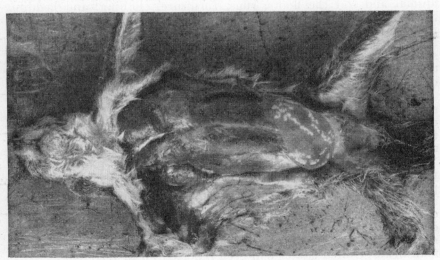

FIGURE 2.—Body of a squirrel, showing the bladder worm stage of *Multiceps serialis*.

The names of the common single-pored tapeworms of dogs and cats, their intermediate hosts, and the locations of their larvae are given in table 1.

77434°—51——74

TABLE 1.—*The common single-pored tapeworms of dogs and cats, their hosts, larval name, and location in the intermediate host*

Name of adult tapeworm	Host of adult	Name of larval tapeworm	Usual intermediate host	Usual location of larva in intermediate host
Taenia taeniaeformis...	Cat............	Cysticercus fasciolaris..	Rats, mice, and other rodents.	Liver.
Taenia pisiformis......	Dog, and, rarely, cat.	Cysticercus pisiformis..	Rabbits and hares.	Omentum, mesentery, and liver.
Taenia hydatigena.....	Dog............	Cysticercus tenuicollis..	Sheep, goats, cattle, and swine.	Omentum, mesentery, and lungs.
Taenia ovis...........	Dog............	Cysticercus ovis........	Sheep and goats...	Heart, diaphragm, and muscles.
Multiceps multiceps...	Dog............	Coenurus cerebralis or Multiceps multiceps	Sheep............	Brain.
Multiceps serialis......	Dog............	Coenurus or Multiceps serialis.	Rabbits and squirrels.	Beneath skin and between muscles
Echinococcus granulosus.	Dog............	Echinococcus granulosus.	Cattle, sheep, swine, and man.	Liver and lungs.

The injury produced by the armed tapeworms in their respective hosts is not well understood. When only a few tapeworms are present, and even in some cases of heavy infection, no injury or symptoms may be detected. In some instances, however, there may be digestive disturbances, a disposition to vomit, general restlessness, and cramps. Nervous symptoms and skin eruptions have been attributed to tapeworm infections, but the connection between the presence of the parasites and such symptoms has not been well demonstrated. Tapeworm-infected dogs, especially house pets, are often a nuisance because the segments are frequently passed involuntarily by the animal and soil the floors, rugs, furniture, clothing, and bedding. Such detached segments are frequently referred to as pinworms; this is not a correct designation because dogs and cats do not harbor the true pinworms, which are a special kind of roundworms. The passage by dogs of a segment or a chain of segments through the anus often causes irritation, which is manifested by the animal's sitting down and dragging itself forward on its haunches.

Cats infected with the cat tapeworm, *Taenia taeniaeformis*, may show loss of appetite, transient diarrhea followed by constipation, excessive salivation, and, occasionally, persistent vomiting. In kittens the abdomen may be distended, and the animals may exhibit evidence of acute abdominal pain.

Some of the armed tapeworms of dogs are of considerable importance as a cause of loss to the livestock industry, because of the presence of the larval stages in the muscles and other organs of food animals. Some are also of importance as parasites of man. The double-pored tapeworm is sometimes encountered in human beings, especially children, and the hydatid stage of *Echinococcus granulosus* may also occur in man; a total of 391 cases of hydatid infection in man in the United States had been reported up to 1938.

The unarmed tapeworms of dogs and cats belong to the genus *Diphyllobothrium*, the best known species being the broad or fish tapeworm, *D. latum*. This species occurs in dogs and other carnivores in the Great Lakes region, where the parasite is endemic (that is, always present in the region) in man. A related species, *D.*

mansoni, is of frequent occurrence in the West Indies and other tropical parts of the world. In some parts of Puerto Rico practically all cats and a high percentage of dogs are infected with this tapeworm. So far as is known, *D. mansoni* has not become established in continental United States. A third species of unarmed tapeworm, *D. mansonoides*, occurs in cats in New York and Louisiana, and has been found in dogs.

The life histories of these species are essentially the same. They require two intermediate hosts, the first of which are small crustaceans, or crayfishlike animals (*Cyclops* or *Diaptomus*); the second intermediate hosts may be fish, as in the case of *Diphyllobothrium latum*, or amphibians, reptiles, and mammals, as in the case of *D. mansoni* and *D. mansonoides*. In Puerto Rico the usual second intermediate host of *D. mansoni* is the common water frog, *Leptodactylus albilabris*, about 25 percent of which in some areas are infected. Dogs and cats acquire these tapeworms by eating the second intermediate hosts containing the infective larvae.

Little is known of the effects on dogs and cats of infections with these tapeworms. Usually no symptoms of importance are noted, but symptoms similar to those caused by the armed tapeworms have been reported. Mueller (*18*) reports that infections with *Diphyllobothrium mansonoides* produce a marked effect on cats, stating that "Infected animals become emaciated, and the belly hangs down in a flabby condition. The coat is rough, with much shedding, and pronounced hunger and nervousness appear in hitherto gentle animals." This author writes further that "If the cat is promptly wormed on appearance of symptoms it makes a marked recovery. Animals which have been kept infected over long periods of time, however, are definitely stunted, and even after worming fail to regain weight."

ROUNDWORMS

The nematodes, or roundworms, are the most injurious of all the parasites of dogs and cats. Those species, such as hookworms and large roundworms, which do not require intermediate hosts, are the most injurious to young animals. They infect animals at an early age before any resistance to infection is acquired and may be responsible for the loss of entire litters. Such roundworms as heart worms and esophageal worms are usually found in mature dogs; these parasites require intermediate hosts for their development, and the time necessary for the larvae to become infective and for the worms to reach maturity is usually greater than in the species with direct life histories. Death seldom results from infection with worms requiring intermediate hosts, but the usefulness of the animals may be partly or entirely destroyed.

HOOKWORMS

The hookworms are the most destructive of all the parasites of dogs and cats. Three species, *Ancylostoma caninum*, *A. braziliense*, and *Uncinaria stenocephala*, may be encountered. The first is the most widespread in its distribution and is accordingly the most important. *A. braziliense* occurs in the warmer parts of the world and is occasionally found in the South and Southwest. *U. stenocephala* is more northerly in its distribution; it occurs occasionally in dogs in the colder parts of the United States and in Canada, where it is a common parasite of foxes.

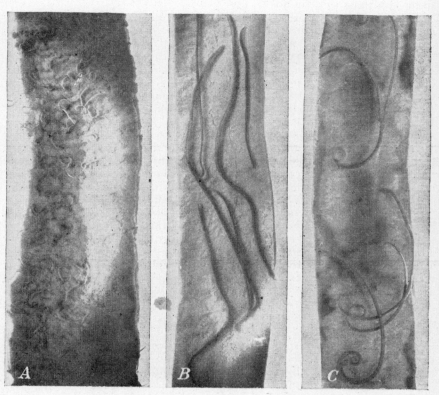

FIGURE 3.—Portions of the small intestines of dogs, showing infections with three of the common roundworms: *A*, The common hookworm, *Ancylostoma caninum; B* and *C*, the large roundworms, *Toxascaris leonina* and *Toxocara canis.*

The hookworms (fig. 3, *A*) are relatively small worms; the males rarely exceed half an inch in length, while the females are somewhat larger. The head end is curved upward and the mouth is provided with teeth or some other armature. The only certain way to distinguish between the different species is by miscroscopic examination of the head end. The mouth of the common dog and cat hookworm, *Ancylostoma caninum*, is provided with three pairs of large curved teeth; *Ancylostoma braziliense* has one pair of large and one pair of small teeth; and *Uncinaria stenocephala* has a cutting plate on each side of the mouth opening.

The life histories of the hookworms are relatively simple. The females produce numerous eggs, which pass out in the feces. In about 36 hours under favorable conditions a wormlike, active embryo has formed in the egg. In the course of 3 to 6 days the egg hatches and liberates the first-stage larva. In about 3 more days this larva molts, or sheds its skin, and becomes what is known as a second-stage larva, which again molts in about 8 days to become the third-stage, or infective, larva. Infection of the host animal may take place either through the mouth or through the skin. When the larvae enter the host animal through the skin they get into the circulation and ultimately reach the lungs, are coughed up, swallowed, and finally reach the intestine, where they develop to maturity. When the larvae are swallowed with contaminated food and water they pass directly to the intestine. After reaching the intestine the larvae undergo two more molts and become mature, eggs appearing in the animal's feces in 3 to 6 weeks.

Eggs of the dog hookworm sometimes appear in the feces of puppies as soon as 13 days after birth, this early maturity being accounted for by the fact that infection took place before birth. This has been demonstrated to be possible in experiments conducted by Foster (5).

Hookworm infection in puppies and young dogs gives rise to a condition sometimes spoken of as kennel anemia. In the early stages of infection there may be digestive disturbances and diarrhea in which the feces are streaked with blood. In severe infections the diarrhea may be severe, and the feces may consist almost entirely of pure blood. A marked anemia, evidenced by the pale appearance of the mucous membranes of the mouth and eyelids, also occurs. Infected puppies rapidly lose weight, the eyes are sunken, and there may be marked symptoms of depression. Often no marked symptoms appear until 2 or 3 days before death.

The symptoms of hookworm infection are largely due to the irritation of the small intestine caused by the bites of the worms, to the removal of blood, and to the bleeding that follows the bites. Wells (21) has shown that a single hookworm may take as much as 360 cubic millimeters of blood a day and that 1,000 hookworms in the course of 24 hours could withdraw 360 cubic centimeters—an amount equivalent to about 12 fluid ounces, or three-fourths of a pint. The amount may actually be much greater, since in this calculation no allowance was made for blood lost by direct hemorrhage at the points of attachment of the worms. That the anemia from hookworm infection is due to loss of blood rather than to some toxin, or poison, secreted by the parasites is supported by the findings of Foster and Landsberg (8), which show that hookworm anemia is of the type associated with chronic hemorrhage.

The hookworm most commonly found in cats is of the same species as the common dog hookworm, *Ancylostoma caninum*, but it has been shown to be a strain especially adapted to live in cats and not readily transmissible to dogs. The symptoms produced by heavy hookworm infection in cats are similar to those in dogs. Because cats are usually house pets and have cleanlier habits than dogs, opportunities for acquiring heavy infections are not so great, and clinical hookworm disease in cats is rarely observed.

The larvae of *Ancylostoma braziliense* in the superficial layers of the skin have been shown to cause a type of dermatitis in man known as creeping eruption. The disease is characterized by a linear or tortuous eruption accompanied by intense itching.

LARGE INTESTINAL ROUNDWORMS

The ascarids, or large intestinal roundworms, are the largest of the worm parasites occurring in the digestive tract of pet animals. These worms vary from about 1½ to 8½ inches in length, the males being considerable smaller than the females. On being passed by the host animal, the worms tend to coil in a springlike spiral, and apparently this is responsible for the name "spool worms" sometimes applied to them.

Two species of large roundworms, *Toxocara canis* and *Toxascaris leonina*, frequently parasitize dogs (fig. 3, *B* and *C*). The former is more commonly encountered in pups and young dogs and the latter in mature animals. Cats, especially kittens, are frequently infected with *Toxocara cati*, but they may also harbor *Toxascaris leonina*.

The life histories of the dog and cat ascarids are very similar to that of *Ascaris lumbricoides*, the large roundworm of man. Numerous eggs are deposited by the female worms in the intestinal tract of the host animals, and these are passed out in the feces. Under favorable conditions these eggs develop embryos in 2 to 6 days. The larvae undergo the first molt in the egg and the eggs then are infective. The infective eggs are swallowed by the host animal, and hatching takes place in the first part of the small intestine. The larvae of *Toxocara canis* and *T. cati* penetrate into the intestinal wall, enter the blood stream, by which they are carried to the liver and thence to the lungs, and finally are coughed up and swallowed. The larvae of *Toxascaris leonina*, according to Wright (*23*), penetrate deeply into the intestinal mucous membrane, where they undergo considerable growth. After about 10 days they emerge and escape into the intestinal cavity, where they grow to fertile maturity.

Infection of pups before birth has been shown to be possible by Fülleborn (*9*) and by Shillinger and Cram (*19*). This accounts for the appearance of mature or nearly mature worms in very young animals.

The large roundworms are particularly injurious to pups and kittens. The commonest symptoms of roundworm infection are unthriftiness, digestive disturbances, and bloating. The hair coat is dead and lusterless, and the breath may have a peculiar sweetish odor. Large numbers of roundworms may cause obstruction of the intestine and even penetration of the intestinal wall. In heavy infections the worms may wander into the bile ducts, stomach, and even the lungs and upper respiratory passages. The occurrence of large numbers of larvae of *Toxocara canis* and *T. cati* in the lungs may cause pneumonia, especially in very young animals.

WHIPWORMS

The dog whipworm, *Trichuris vulpis*, gets its name from its resemblance to a tiny whip. The front part of the worm is slender and hairlike, while the hind part is relatively thick. The total length of the worms rarely exceeds 3 inches. Whipworms are common parasites of dogs all over the world. They occur in the cecum, or blind gut, and sometimes, in extremely heavy infections, in the colon or large intestine.

The life history of the whipworm is direct, that is, no intermediate host is required for its development. The complete details of the life cycle are not well established. The eggs develop in much the same way as those of the large intestinal roundworms, except that the development of embryos requires from 2 weeks to several months, depending on temperature and moisture. When the infective eggs are swallowed by the dog, they hatch in the small intestine, and the larvae thus liberated ultimately reach the cecum, where they develop into mature worms. The time required for the worms to reach fertile maturity may be as long as 3 months.

The injury produced in dogs by the whipworm is not well understood. The worm attaches itself to the cecum by "sewing" its front end into the mucous membrane. In many instances these parasites appear to cause little damage, even in heavy infections. Occasionally the mucous membrane of the cecum may be considerably reddened and thickened, and this may cause considerable pain. A great variety of symptoms of an indefinite sort have been ascribed to infections with this parasite, including digestive disturbances, diarrhea, loss of weight, and general unthriftiness, as well as nervousness and convulsions. Though such symptoms may result from a number of conditions, the fact that marked improvement in an animal's health has in many cases followed surgical removal of the infected cecum lends support to the belief that whipworms are definitely injurious.

HEART WORMS

The heart worm, *Dirofilaria immitis*, occurs most commonly in the dog but has been reported occasionally from cats and other hosts. The worms are slender and whitish in color. The males are 5 to 7 inches in length and the females about twice this size. They usually occur in the right ventricle (fig. 4) and in the pulmonary artery; in rare instances the adult worms may occur in other locations. This parasite is world-wide in distribution but occurs most frequently in warm climates. In the United States it is most abundant in the Southern States and those along the Atlantic seaboard as far north as New York. In most instances infection with this worm in dogs in the Northern States is traceable to the animals' having at some time been in the South, but in some northern localities the parasites have become definitely established.

The life history of the heart worm is complex. Instead of the females depositing eggs, as in the case of the hookworms, roundworms, and whipworms, active larvae are discharged directly into the blood stream. These larvae correspond to first-stage larvae of other nematodes and are, therefore, not infective for other dogs. The larvae are most abundant in the blood during the hours of darkness, but they may also be found during daylight. They continue to circulate in the blood stream until they are removed by some bloodsucking insect, such as a mosquito. Numerous mosquitoes be-

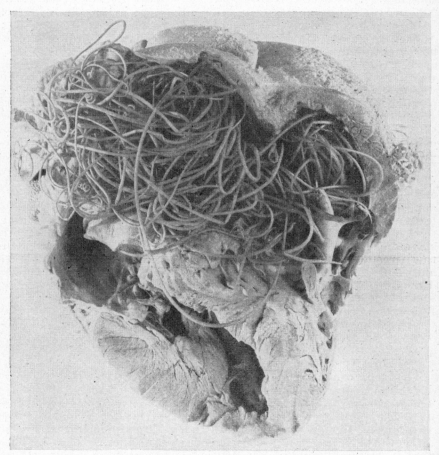

FIGURE 4.—Heart of a dog, showing heavy heart worm infection.

longing to the genera *Aedes*, *Culex*, and *Anopheles* have been shown to serve as satisfactory hosts for the development of heart worm larvae. These mosquitoes may not all be able to transmit heart worms, but the fact that the larvae can reach the infective stage in the insects, together with the fact that related worms are transmitted by mosquitoes, makes them the most likely vectors. Fleas have also been regarded as possible intermediate hosts and this possibility has recently been strengthened by Brown and Sheldon (*2*), who found the infective stage of the heart worm in naturally infected fleas. While this observation is not conclusive, since experimental transmission of heart worms through the bites of fleas has not been demonstrated, it is extremely interesting and supports the contention of many dog owners and veterinarians that these insects may be important intermediate hosts. The time required for the development of the heart worm to maturity following the bite of an infected insect is not definitely known. Brown (*1*) has reported the finding of numerous larvae in the blood of an 8-month-old dog, which indicates that the worms reach maturity in less than 8 months.

The symptoms of heart worm disease in dogs may vary considerably, and in some instances no indication of infection may be detected until the blood has been examined. Usually, however, the first symptoms appear following vigorous exercise. The infected animal may tire easily, lie down, gasp for breath, and collapse. After a short rest the dog may recover and for a time appear normal. Coughing is also a common symptom. In cases of long standing, ascites, or abdominal dropsy, may develop and, because of poor circulation, the legs and other parts of the body may swell. Nervous symptoms, such as fixity of vision, fear of light, and convulsions have also been noted in infected animals.

The only way of making a definite diagnosis is by microscopic examination of the blood and the finding of active larvae. Finding larvae in the blood does not always indicate, however, that the adult parasites are present in the heart, since in many cases it has not been possible on post mortem examination to locate the worms in their customary habitat. This may mean that the worms responsible for the larvae are in some unusual location in the body or that they had died and become absorbed. The fact that larvae may persist in the blood after the parent worms have died is shown by the finding of Underwood and Harwood (*20*) that heart worm larvae could be detected in blood transfused from an infected dog into a noninfected animal for as long as 2½ years.

ESOPHAGEAL WORMS

The esophageal worm of dogs, *Spirocerca lupi*, is blood red in color and about half the size of the large intestinal roundworms. Esophageal worms usually occur in tumors of the esophagus and stomach; as many as 30 individuals may be found in a single tumor. The species is distributed throughout the world; in the United States it occurs commonly in dogs in the Southern States.

Like the heart worm, this parasite requires an intermediate host for its larval development. When the eggs pass out of the host in the feces they already contain wormlike larvae. These eggs are eaten by dung beetles, in which they hatch, and the larvae penetrate into the body cavity of the beetles, where they become encysted. In about 2 months the larvae are infective for the final host. Should infected beetles be eaten by some animal other than the dog or a related host, the larvae reencyst and remain infective. Such an animal is known as a transfer host. When the infective larvae are swallowed by a dog with either the beetle or the transfer host, the young worms are liberated in the dog's stomach and migrate to their final location. Many, if not all, of the larvae reach their final location after taking a circuitous route through the walls of the larger blood vessels, including the aorta. In the walls of these vessels, particularly in the aorta, the injuries produced by the wandering larvae result in degeneration of the tissues, with resulting scarring and thinning of the vessel walls. In some instances the injured aorta may become dilated, and deposits of lime salts may occur in the vessel wall.

The symptoms of esophageal worm infection depend on the location and size of the tumors. Tumors in the esophagus may cause constriction of that organ, resulting in difficult swallowing, vomiting, and loss of weight. Perforation of the tumors may occur, with the discharge of pus and eggs into the thoracic or abdominal cavities, and the infected animal may die from either pleurisy or peritonitis. If the tumors are located where they can press upon the windpipe or lung, coughing, difficult breathing, and suffocation may result. Sudden death may occasionally occur from rupture of the weakened aorta.

LUNGWORMS

Lungworms are relatively rare in dogs and cats. Three kinds of lungworms are known to occur in this country, and in some districts the parasites may be of considerable importance. That little is known about them may be because they infect dogs and cats in rural areas, where the infections are not diagnosed.

One of the lungworms that infects dogs is known as *Filaroides osleri*. This parasite was first observed in Canada and has since been found in the United States. The worm is small and transparent and causes in the bronchial tubes wartlike tumors which may be sufficiently large and numerous to cause suffocation. Nothing is known of its life history or mode of transmission.

The cat lungworm, *Aelurostrongylus abstrusus*, is related to the dog lungworm and is common in some parts of the world. A few cases have been discovered in the United States, and the parasite is probably common in cats in rural districts. The worm is hairlike and occurs in the lung tissue. The females deposit their eggs in the air sacs, where they hatch, and the larvae thus liberated give rise to a pneumonia that may involve an entire lobe. According to Hobmaier and Hobmaier (*15*), the parasites require a snail intermediate host.

The capillarid lungworm, *Capillaria aerophila*, is related to the dog whipworm. It is primarily a parasite of foxes but also infects dogs and cats in fox-farming areas. The parasite is hairlike and whitish in color and lives in the large and small bronchial tubes. So far as is known, the life history is direct, and infection occurs through swallowing infective eggs with the feed and water.

The presence of lungworms in dogs and cats gives rise to a more or less persistent cough. The animals also wheeze owing to the accumu-

. lation of mucus in the trachea and bronchi. Emaciation and general unthriftiness, together with wheezing and coughing, should be regarded as symptoms suggesting lungworm infection. Diagnosis can be made by microscopic examination of the feces and the finding of active larvae of *Filarioides* or *Aelurostrongylus* or of eggs of *Capillaria*.

THE KIDNEY WORM

The so-called kidney worm, *Dioctophyma renale*, of dogs is the largest of the roundworms. It occurs in dogs and a number of other carnivores, especially mink, and has been reported in man on at least nine occasions. The fully mature parasite is blood red in color. The females may attain a length of 3 feet and the thickness of the little finger; the males are rarely half as large as the females. The kidney worm is not a common parasite of dogs in the United States.

The life history and the mode of infection of dogs are not known.

The presence of this worm in the kidney causes pressure and destruction of the functional tissue. Only one kidney is affected, the other increasing in size to compensate for the additional work demanded of it. When the worms occur in the abdominal cavity, the commonest location, the eggs given off by the females cause a chronic peritonitis. The symptoms of kidney worm infection are not well known; dullness, incoordination of movement, and nervous symptoms have been reported in animals subsequently found to be infected. The infected dog may sometimes show evidence of abdominal pain and die suddenly following exertion. Diagnosis is impossible on the basis of symptoms alone, as symptoms similar to those reported may be associated with other conditions. If the parasite is in the kidney, a diagnosis is possible by finding the eggs of the worm in the urine on microscopic examination.

THE EYE WORM

Only one species of eye worm, *Thelazia californiensis*, is known to occur in this country. This parasite has been described as occurring in dogs and has recently been reported in the cat, sheep, deer, and man. So far as is known, it occurs only in California. The worms are whitish and about half an inch long, and they live underneath the eyelids and in the tear ducts.

Nothing is known of the life history or mode of transmission. The parasite is related to Manson's eye worm of poultry, which is known to require an insect intermediate host.

The worms move about actively over the surface of the eyeball, causing considerable inflammation and a profuse flow of tears. Scarification (scratching) and ulceration of the eyeball may result from the activity of the worms, and opacity of the cornea and blindness may be the final outcome. In heavy infections the worms may easily be found under the eyelids or crawling over the surface of the eye, but when the infection is light a careful search is necessary before a diagnosis is warranted.

CONTROL OF PARASITISM IN DOGS AND CATS

GENERAL MEASURES

The control of parasites must obviously be based upon a knowledge of the organisms, their life cycles, and their resistance to physical and other factors inimical to their survival. Points that must be taken into consideration are the source of infection, whether the parasite requires one or more intermediate hosts, whether the route of infection is through the mouth or skin or by the bites of bloodsucking insects, the ability of the parasite in its infective stages to survive the action of sunlight and other natural physical agents, and the effect of chemicals and disinfectants on it during these stages.

The source of infection with parasites is for the most part contamination of the soil with feces or other excrements containing the eggs or infective stages of the organisms. Hence the most effective control measure is strict sanitation. In the case of such parasites as blood protozoans and filariids that are transmitted by insects, control consists in destroying the insects, protecting the host animals against their bites, or sterilizing the animal's blood by the use of medicinal agents. Where intermediate hosts become infected through eating infectious material passed by the definitive, or final, host, as in the case of tapeworms and some nematodes, control consists in strict sanitation and in preventing the final host from eating the infective stages of the parasite occurring in the intermediate host.

The general control measures discussed here are applicable to kennels and catteries where the animals are confined and where sanitation and other measures can be carried out. Under farm conditions and in suburban districts where dogs and cats are allowed to roam at large, such measures are difficult to apply, and the control of most parasites is largely a matter of treatment of the infected animals with anthelmintic drugs as discussed later.

Protozoan diseases.—Piroplasmosis and coccidiosis require different control measures. Piroplasmosis is transmitted from one animal to another by ticks, and measures for the control of this disease must be directed toward eradicating the ticks in kennels and controlling them on the dog host; this problem is discussed elsewhere. The control of coccidiosis involves the same procedures as are recommended later for the control of certain of the roundworms, such as large roundworms and whipworms.

Flukes.—Prevention of infection with trematodes, or flukes, involves keeping raw fish away from dogs and cats, as the infective stages of the majority of the fluke parasites of these animals occur in fish.

Tapeworms.—The prevention of tapeworm infection may be summed up by saying: Do not permit dogs and cats to feed on infected intermediate host animals. Unfortunately, this recommendation is difficult to enforce when animals are allowed to roam at large and to have access to the carcasses of dead animals and to offal on the farm. House pets have little opportunity to become infected with tapeworms except the doubled-pored species, which is acquired through eating infected fleas and lice. Preventing infection with this tapeworm means controlling fleas and lice by destroying the breeding places of these insects and by the frequent use of insect powders and washes on flea- and louse-infested animals.

The armed tapeworms, such as *Taenia hydatigena, T. ovis, Multiceps multiceps, and Echinococcus granulosus*, are controlled to some extent through the enforcement of Federal and municipal meat-inspection regulations, which require condemnation and proper disposal of carcasses and offal of sheep, goats, cattle, and swine infected with larval tapeworms. The disposal by burning or burial of similar infected material on the farm should be practiced as a means of keeping dogs from becoming infected and later contaminating the fields and pastures with tapeworm eggs that may be picked up by livestock and develop into bladder worms.

Roundworms.—The control of roundworms, with the exception of the heart worm, depends primarily on the prompt disposal of feces, keeping the animals in clean quarters and on clean ground, and using only clean utensils for feed and water. The runs or pens should be on clay and be free from sod. Clay soil is preferable to other types since it is more impervious than sand or loam, and parasite eggs and larvae remain on or near the surface where they are exposed to the destructive effects of sunlight and drying. Shady runways and pens should be avoided; such places are damp, and moisture favors the development and survival of worm eggs and larvae. Pens provided with wire-mesh floors that prevent the accumulation of manure are being used by some dog raisers with good results. The floors of such pens should be sufficiently high to permit the ground underneath to be cleaned readily.

There is no chemical treatment of value for destroying the eggs of such parasites as the large roundworms, whipworms, capillarid lung worms, and esophageal worms in contaminated soil. The eggs of these worms are provided with such impervious shells that disinfectants or other chemicals cannot penetrate them.

Hookworm-infected soil may be sterilized by the use of strong salt brine, a treatment that was first used in Canada for the control of hookworms in fox pens. This treatment was subsequently found to be effective for the destruction of the larvae of the dog hookworm in soil. The brine is prepared by stirring common salt into boiling water at the rate of 1½ pounds of salt to a gallon of water. The brine is sprinkled over the surface of the soil in an amount sufficient to saturate the earth to a depth of ½ to 1½ inches; about 1 pint of brine for each square foot of soil surface is necessary to accomplish this. The interval between treatments with the brine depends on the amount and frequency of the rainfall.

The prevention of heart worm infection is largely a matter of keeping dogs from being bitten by mosquitoes by confining them in mosquitoproof kennels during the late afternoon, night, and early morning. The possibility of transmission by fleas, which has already been mentioned, cannot be ignored, and kennels and dogs should be kept free from these insects. Destruction of stray dogs that may serve as reservoirs of infection and mosquito-destruction campaigns are measures that will tend to reduce the frequency of heart worm disease.

No control measures other than sanitation can be recommended for such parasites as the kidney worm, eye worm, and other worm parasites, the life histories of which are unknown.

Proper nutrition is an important factor in the prevention of losses from parasites. Foster and Cort (*6, 7*) have shown that hookworm-infected dogs kept on an adequate diet showed increased resistance and in some instances lost the greater part of their hookworm burden. When the same animals were put on an inadequate diet they again become susceptible to infection. Somewhat similar results were obtained by Wright (*23*), who showed that old dogs may be more easily parasitized by one of the large roundworms, *Toxocara canis*, if maintained on a diet deficient in vitamin A.

THE USE OF MEDICINAL AGENTS

In most instances the control measures already discussed, based as they are on a knowledge of the life cycles and other facts regarding the various parasites, serve to keep the parasites in check. They cannot be relied upon entirely to prevent losses from parasites, however, but must be supplemented, as occasion demands, by treatment of the individual animals with vermifuges and other agents.

Drugs and chemicals with specific action against disease-producing organisms, including parasites, have been developed largely during the present century. In the development of such agents the dog has played an important role by serving as a test animal, and as a result there are more specific treatments for the removal and control of the parasites of dogs than for those of any of the other domestic animals. Some of these treatments, notably those for the removal of the dog hookworms, are now commonly used for the removal of hookworms from man.

In spite of the many drugs of value for removing parasites from dogs and cats, there remain a number for which no satisfactory treatment has been discovered, such as those occurring in the respiratory and urinary organs, in the body cavities, and in tissues, such as the intestinal mucous membrane.

The advance of knowledge concerning the use of drugs in the control of parasites has led to considerable publicity regarding the value of such treatments. As a result, dog and cat owners have become "parasite conscious" and too often have felt that their pets should be dosed or wormed at regular intervals regardless of whether such treatments are necessary. Promiscuous dosing is a practice fraught with danger to the well-being of the animal. It should be remembered that all drugs for the destruction of parasites are poisonous to a certain degree and should be administered only when it is definitely known that the animal is suffering from parasitism. Diagnosis of parasitism is not always a simple matter. Many of the symptoms associated with parasitic infections also occur in connection with other diseases, and a laboratory examination may be necessary before a diagnosis of parasitism can be made. Consequently professional advice should be sought, and treatment for parasitism should be administered by or under the direction of a veterinarian. This is especially true in the case of cats, which require essentially the same treatment for a given parasite as do dogs but are much more sensitive to the toxic effects of drugs.

Protozoan diseases.—Of the two protozoan diseases, piroplasmosis and coccidiosis, affecting dogs in this country, medicinal treatment is available in the case of the former only. Several drugs are known that are effective in varying degrees against the causative organisms in the blood. These treatments are administered as injections beneath the skin (subcutaneously) or into the blood stream (intravenously). The most recently developed and apparently the most effective of the treatments for piroplasmosis is acaprin, a synthetic drug known chemically by the rather formidable name of "N–N'–(bismethylchinolylium-methylsulfate–6–)urea." Like most drugs administered intravenously, it is toxic, and the dose must be calculated accurately on the basis of body weight. Clarvoe (*3*) recommends that appropriate doses be injected every day for 2 or 3 days, depending on the response. He states that if the animal has not suffered serious tissue changes as a result of the disease, recovery is usually prompt.

No specific drug is available for use in the treatment of coccidiosis. The indicated treatment for this disease is good care and nursing.

Flukes.—The only disease of dogs in this country associated with fluke infestation that warrants medicinal treatment is salmon poisoning. This disease was formerly fatal to a large percentage of the animals affected. In 1938 sulfanilamide was found by Oregon investigators (*4*) to be a highly effective treatment. The drug was administered orally (by mouth) one to three times a day in doses of about 11 milligrams (0.7 gram) per pound of body weight.

Tapeworms.—The several species of tapeworms occurring in dogs and cats are not all removable by the same treatment. The most effective drug for the removal of the armed species is arecoline hydrobromide, the use of which was first advocated by Lentz (*17*) in 1921. This drug is a drastic purgative and acts within a few minutes to a half hour or so after administration. · The treatment should be given in the morning after the animal has fasted overnight, and food should be withheld for about 3 hours after dosing. The drug is not so effective against the double-pored tapeworm as against the other armed species, and it may be necessary to repeat the dose, since some of the heads may not be removed by the first treatment and regeneration of the tapeworm may occur in a few weeks.

Arecoline is not entirely satisfactory for the removal of the unarmed tapeworms, oleoresin of male fern being the most effective drug for use against these species. The drug should be given in appropriate doses after a fast of about 18 hours and should be followed by a purgative.

Both arecoline and oleoresin of male fern are toxic, and professional advice regarding the dosage, which must be computed carefully according to the kind of animal and its weight, should be sought before treatment with these drugs is attempted.

Large roundworms and hookworms.—Since the most injurious parasites of dogs and cats are the roundworms that occur in the intestinal tract, investigations to develop satisfactory remedies for their removal have been extensive. Following preliminary investigations by Hall and Foster (*12*), during which critical tests were carried out to determine the efficacy of drugs previously reported to have anthelmintic value, oil of chenopodium and mixtures of oil of chenopodium and chloroform were found to have considerable value for the removal of large roundworms and hookworms from dogs. Owing to the moderate efficacy of these drugs for the removal of hookworms, further experiments were carried out with compounds closely related to chloroform. These experiments resulted in the discovery that carbon tetrachloride (*11*), a chemical widely used as a noncombustible cleaning agent, in doses of 0.3 cubic centimeter per kilogram (2.2 pounds) of body weight was highly effective for the removal of both dog hookworms and roundworms. This chemical was soon adopted by veterinarians as the standard treatment for the removal of these parasites. After making tests on himself, Hall suggested that carbon tetrachloride be given a trial as a remedy for the removal of hookworms from man. This suggestion ultimately led to successful experiments, and the drug was adopted by many public-health officials as the best treatment for the removal of human hookworms.

Further tests carried out with other compounds resulted in the discovery by Hall and Shillinger (*13*) that tetrachlorethylene at the same dose rate was just as effective as the closely related carbon tetrachloride. Tetrachlorethylene soon supplanted carbon tetrachloride, as the latter drug was found under certain conditions to cause extensive and severe liver injury, and even death in some cases. Although tetrachlorethylene is much safer than carbon tetrachloride, it is less stable and, unless kept in a cool, dark place, may undergo a chemical change and become extremely toxic. Furthermore, in some animals it causes dizziness and even loss of consciousness. These effects, while quite alarming, are transitory, and the animal soon recovers if left undisturbed.

Later Wright and Schaffer (*24*) carried out extensive investigations of the halogenated hydrocarbons, the chemical group to which carbon tetrachloride and tetrachlorethylene belong, and showed that a number of compounds in this series possessed anthelmintic properties. Some were as effective for the removal of large roundworms and hookworms as tetrachlorethylene but were either too toxic or too expensive for general use. One of these compounds, normal butyl chloride, seemed to offer promise. Additional studies on this substance were undertaken (*14*) which showed that normal butyl chloride was as safe and effective as tetrachlorethylene. In addition to its effectiveness and safety, it did not appear to cause the alarming, though harmless, dizziness that often follows the administration of tetrachlorethylene. Normal butyl chloride is being tested extensively under practical conditions by veterinarians, and thus far encouraging results have been reported.

The amount of normal butyl chloride for dogs varies with the weight of the animal, and a schedule of suggested dosages is as follows:

Amount of drug	Weight of dog (pounds)
0.5 cc. (8 minims)	Less than 3
1 cc. (15 minims)	3 to 5
2 cc. (½ fluid dram)	5 to 10
3 cc. (¾ fluid dram)	10 to 20
4 cc. (1 fluid dram)	20 to 40
5 cc. (1¼ fluid drams)	More than 40

Whipworms.—Until recently there has been no satisfactory treatment for the removal of whipworms. These parasites live in the cecum, or blind gut, which is situated at the junction of the small and large intestines. To be effective in removing whipworms, a drug must enter the cecum and come in direct contact with the worms; but the entry of a drug into this location is largely accidental, and in order to increase the chances of its happening, large doses of a drug essentially harmless to the animal must be used. Normal butyl chloride, which had been ascertained to meet this requirement, was administered in large doses to whipworm-infested dogs, with the result that an average of about 60 percent of the whipworms present were removed (*14*). While this percentage of removal was not entirely satisfactory, it was greater than that attained by any other drug. The doses used were about four times greater than those effective for the removal of large roundworms and hookworms. The treatment may be repeated within a week if the results of the initial treatment prove unsatisfactory. Before treatment is undertaken the animal should be fasted for at least 18 hours; food may be allowed about an hour after dosing. Under ordinary conditions it is not necessary to administer a purge following treatment. If a heavy infestation of large roundworms is also present, a purgative dose of castor oil 1-hour after the administration of normal butyl chloride is recommended.

Another treatment for whipworms that appears to be promising was reported recently by Guthrie (*10*). It consisted of diphenylamine, in doses of 10 grams per animal, administered by mouth. This treatment removed 84 percent of 537 whipworms from 5 dogs. Additional experiments to standardize the dose and to determine its safety must be carried out before the drug can be recommended for general use.

Intestinal worms in general.—Whitney (*22*) has recently reported that hydrogen peroxide administered as an enema is very effective for the removal of all species of worm parasites commonly occurring in the intestinal tract of dogs. Since there is at present no single drug that will remove tapeworms, hookworms, large roundworms, and whipworms, this report is of interest. According to Whitney, a 1.5-percent solution of the drug is used. For dogs weighing 2 pounds a dose of 1½ ounces of the hydrogen peroxide solution was recommended, the amount being increased up to 24 ounces for dogs weighing 60 pounds. For successful treatment it is necessary that the animal vomit, and to facilitate this reaction a few ounces of the solution are administered by stomach tube just prior to the enema. This treatment should be used with caution, however, especially in animals suffering from diseases of the heart or other vital organs.

Heart worms.—Treatment of heart worm disease is still somewhat of a problem. More or less satisfactory results have been obtained by the use of antimony compounds, but these treatments are toxic and expensive. Of the several antimony preparations reported to be of value against heart worms, the most generally used is fuadin, a compound known chemically as sodium-antimony-III-bis-pyrocate-chin-disulfonate. Some dogs are peculiarly susceptible to antimony poisoning, and the treatment should not be attempted by the dog owner. Wright and Underwood (*25*) have shown, however, that the majority of animals can be treated successfully if the drug is administered carefully by a veterinarian. In appropriate doses it is administered either intramuscularly or intravenously daily over a period of 12 to 25 days, depending on the method used. There are a number of factors, such as the presence or absence of organic diseases of the heart, liver, and kidneys, the weight of the animal, and its tolerance for the drug, which must be considered before treatment is undertaken. If proper precautions are observed, about 90 percent of heart worm cases can be cured after one or two courses of treatment with fuadin. It should be remembered, however, that a mortality of about 5 percent may be expected even when the treatment is handled by competently trained individuals.

LITERATURE CITED

(1) BROWN, HAROLD W.
       1939. OBSERVATIONS ON THE DOG HEARTWORM, DIROFILARIA IMMITIS. North
             Amer. Vet. 20 (1) : 49–54.
(2) ——— and SHELDON, A. J.
       1940. NATURAL INFECTION OF FLEAS WITH THE DOG HEARTWORM (DIROFILARIA
             IMMITIS). North Amer. Vet. 21: 230–231.
(3) CLARVOE, H. M.
       1939. CANINE PIROPLASMOSIS. North Amer. Vet. 20 (7) : 50–52. 53.
(4) COON, E. W., MYERS, F. C., PHELPS, T. R., and others.
       1938. SULFANILAMIDE AS A TREATMENT FOR SALMON POISONING IN DOGS.
             North Amer. Vet. 19 (9) : 57–59, illus.
(5) FOSTER, A. O.
       1932. PRENATAL INFECTION WITH THE DOG HOOKWORM, ANCYLOSTOMA
             CANINUM. Jour. Parasitol. 19: 112–118.
(6) ——— and CORT, W. W.
       1931. THE EFFECT OF DIET ON HOOKWORM INFESTATION IN DOGS. Science
             73: 681–683.
(7) ——— and CORT, W. W.
       1932. THE RELATION OF DIET TO THE SUSCEPTIBILITY OF DOGS TO ANCY-
             LOSTOMA CANINUM. Amer. Jour. Hyg. 16: 241–265, illus.
(8) ——— and LANSBERG, J. W.
       1934. THE NATURE AND CAUSE OF HOOKWORM ANEMIA. Amer. Jour. Hyg.
             20: 259–290, illus.
(9) FÜLLEBORN, F.
       1921. ASKARISINFEKTION DURCH VERZEHREN EINGEKAPSELTER LARVEN UND
             ÜBER GELUNGENE INTRAUTERINE ASKARISINFEKTION. Arch. f.
             Schiffs u. Tropen Hyg. 25: 367–375, illus.
(10) GUTHRIE, JAMES E.
       1940. PRELIMINARY OBSERVATIONS ON THE EFFICACY OF DIPHENYLAMINE
             FOR THE REMOVAL OF INTESTINAL NEMATODES FROM DOGS. Hel-
             minthol. Soc. Wash. Proc. 7: 84–85.

(11) HALL, MAURICE C.
 1921. CARBON TETRACHLORIDE FOR THE REMOVAL OF PARASITIC WORMS, ESPECIALLY HOOKWORMS. Jour. Agr. Res. 21: 157–175.
(12) ———— and FOSTER, WINTHROP D.
 1918. EFFICACY OF SOME ANTHELMINTICS. Jour. Agr. Res. 12: 397–447.
(13) ———— and SHILLINGER, JACOB E.
 1925. TETRACHLORETHYLENE, A NEW ANTHELMINTIC FOR WORMS IN DOGS. North Amer. Vet. 6 (9): 41–52.
(14) HARWOOD, PAUL D., JERSTAD, A. C., UNDERWOOD, PAUL C., and SCHAFFER, JACOB M.
 1940. THE EFFICACY OF N-BUTYL CHLORIDE FOR THE REMOVAL OF INTESTINAL NEMATODES, ESPECIALLY WHIPWORMS, FROM DOGS. North Amer. Vet. 21: 35–41.
(15) HOBMAIER, M., and HOBMAIER, A.
 1935. INTERMEDIATE HOSTS OF ALEUROSTRONGYLUS ABSTRUSUS OF THE CAT. Soc. Expt. Biol. & Med. Proc. 32: 1641–1647, illus.
(16) [JUDY, W.]
 1940. DOG STATISTICS, SUMMARIES AND DIRECTORIES. Dog World 25(12): 6.
(17) LENTZ, WILLIAM J.
 1921. TREATMENT FOR TAPEWORMS IN DOGS. Pa. Univ. School Vet. Med., Vet. Ext. Quart. 21 (34): 2–3.
(18) MUELLER, JUSTUS F.
 1938. THE LIFE HISTORY OF DIPHYLLOBOTHRIUM MANSONOIDES MUELLER, 1935, AND SOME CONSIDERATIONS WITH REGARD TO SPARGANOSIS IN THE UNITED STATES. Amer. Jour. Trop. Med. 18: 41–66, illus.
(19) SHILLINGER, J. E., and CRAM, E. B.
 1923. PARASITIC INFESTATION OF DOGS BEFORE BIRTH. Amer. Vet. Med. Assoc. Jour. 63: 200–203.
(20) UNDERWOOD, PAUL C., and HARWOOD, PAUL D.
 1939. SURVIVAL AND LOCATION OF THE MICROFILARIAE OF DIROFILARIA IMMITIS IN THE DOG. Jour. Parasitol. 25: 23–33.
(21) WELLS, HERBERT S.
 1931. AN OBSERVATION WHICH SUGGESTS AN EXPLANATION OF THE ANEMIA IN HOOKWORM DISEASE. Science 73: 16–17.
(22) WHITNEY, LEON F.
 1939. HYDROGEN PEROXIDE AS A GENERAL ANTHELMINTIC FOR DOGS. Vet. Med. 34: 560–566, illus.
(23) WRIGHT, WILLARD HULL.
 1936. OBSERVATIONS ON THE LIFE HISTORY OF TOXOCARA CANIS AND TOX-ASCARIS LEONINA, AND THE INFLUENCE OF ENVIRONMENTAL FACTORS ON THEIR DEVELOPMENT. Geo. Wash. Univ. Bul., Sum. Doctoral Theses 1934–36: 14–16.
(24) ———— and SCHAFFER, JACOB M.
 1932. CRITICAL ANTHELMINTIC TESTS OF CHLORINATED ALKYL HYDROCARBONS AND A CORRELATION BETWEEN THE ANTHELMINTIC EFFICACY, CHEMICAL STRUCTURE AND PHYSICAL PROPERTIES. Amer. Jour. Hyg. 16: 325–428, illus.
(25) ———— and UNDERWOOD, PAUL C.
 1934. FOUADIN IN THE TREATMENT OF INFESTATIONS WITH THE DOG HEART-WORM DIROFILARIA IMMITIS. Vet. Med. 29: 234–246, illus.

Mange of Dogs

BY EMMETT W. PRICE AND F. C. BISHOPP [1]

A DOG suffering from a bad case of mange is a sorry sight, and the disease can easily have a fatal end. Three kinds of mites cause three kinds of mange; diagnosis is a job for experts, and cures are often difficult and may require long treatment. Here are the facts.

MANGE is a contagious skin disease caused by microscopic organisms, known as mites, that are distant relatives of spiders and ticks. This disease, of which there are several types, affects a large variety of animals as well as human beings. It was probably known at least as long ago as the time of Moses, who stated that cattle and sheep that are "Blind, or broken, or maimed, or have a wen, or scurvy, or scabbed, ye shall not offer these unto the Lord, nor make an offering by fire of them upon the altar unto the Lord" (Leviticus 22: 22). It seems reasonably certain that mange was one of the diseases referred to in this passage by the words "scurvy" and "scabbed."

The organisms that cause mange of dogs were not seen or described until the early part of the nineteenth century. The principal forms of the disease in dogs are sarcoptic mange, or scabies, ear mange, and demodectic, or red, mange. All three are relatively common and cause great suffering. If the sarcoptic or demodectic forms are allowed to go unchecked, they may soon reduce the most valuble dog to the level of a worthless mongrel. Early diagnosis and treatment of mange is important, and the dog owner should give prompt attention to any animal showing symptoms of the malady.

SARCOPTIC MANGE

Sarcoptic mange of the dog is caused by the mite *Sarcoptes scabiei canis.* The mites are very small, the largest specimens being little

---

[1] Emmett W. Price is Assistant Chief, Zoological Division, Bureau of Animal Industry, and F. C. Bishopp is Assistant Chief, Bureau of Entomology and Plant Quarantine.

more than a hundredth of an inch long. They are approximately oval in outline, and the four pairs of legs are very short, the hindermost pairs not projecting beyond the margin of the body. The female mites burrow into the upper layers of the skin, where each lays 20 to 40 eggs. The egg hatch in 3 to 7 days, liberating larvae that have three pairs of legs. The larvae grow by molting, or casting the skin, and after passing through a second, or nymph, stage become adult males and females, the entire life cycle requiring 2 to 3 weeks for completion. The larvae, nymphs, and males do not burrow into the skin, but live under crusts, or scabs, on the surface. The sarcoptic mite is not so prolific as some of its relatives, such as the ticks, but as the life cycle is very short, it has been estimated that a male and female may produce as many as 1,500,000 descendants in the course of 3 months.

Sarcoptic mange affects dogs of all ages and breeds. The disease usually makes its appearance on the head—on the bridge of the nose, around the eyes, or at the base of the ears. Sometimes, however, it is first noted on the front of the chest, on the lower abdomen, under the front legs, or on the inner surface of the thighs, and if it is not treated the entire body becomes involved.

Red points which soon develop into small blisters that are most easily seen on the unpigmented parts of the skin, such as the abdomen, are the first signs of the disease. As the female mites burrow into the skin, there is an exudation, or discharge, of serum, which dries and forms a scab. The affected parts of the skin soon become covered with branlike scales and later with grayish crusts. Itching is intense, especially in warm weather, or after exercise. As a result of the animal's scratching and of the irritation caused by the mites, the skin becomes thickened and wrinkled. The frequent rubbing and scratching favor secondary bacterial infections and the formation of sores. The hair may also become matted and fall out, leaving bare spots. Decomposition of the exuded serum gives rise to a peculiar mousy odor, which becomes more pronounced as the disease progresses. If the affection is allowed to go unchecked, the animal's digestion and other body functions become impaired, and death may follow in a few months. This form of mange is transmissible to human beings, and unnecessary handling of affected animals, especially by children, should be avoided.

Sarcoptic mange may be confused with other skin affections, such as demodectic (red) mange, ringworm, and eczemas of various sorts, and it is usually necessary to resort to a microscopic examination of scrapings from the diseased parts before a definite diagnosis can be made.

EAR MANGE

Ear mange is caused by mites (*Otodectes cynotis*) which live in the external auditory canal. These mites are somewhat similar in appearance to those causing sarcoptic mange, but they are much larger and have longer legs. They may be seen with the unaided eye, either in the ear or in material removal from it, as minute, slow-moving, white objects. The life cycle of the ear mite is not completely known, but it is probably similar to that of the sarcoptic mite.

These mites do not burrow in the skin; they are found deep in the ear canal near the eardrum, where they puncture the delicate skin and feed on the tissue juices. Considerable irritation results from their presence, and the normal production of the ear secretions is interfered with. The ear canal becomes filled with inflammatory products and modified ear wax as well as mites, causing the dog to scratch and rub its ears and to shake its head to relieve the itching. Frequently the dog will hold its head to one side, and in severe infections it will run in a circle or show other evidences of nervous disturbance. The presence of the mites and the injuries they cause may favor bacterial infections resulting in inflammation of the middle ear and even of the brain.

Ear mange may be confused with inflammations of the ear due to other causes, and it is necessary that the diagnosis be confirmed by microscopic examination of material removed from the ear canal before treatment is instituted.

DEMODECTIC (RED) MANGE

Demodectic or red mange is the most common of the parasitic skin diseases of dogs and also the most difficult to cure. It is caused by a wormlike mite, known as *Demodex canis*, which lives in the hair follicles and the sebaceous glands of the skin. The life cycle of this parasite is not well understood. The females lay eggs which hatch into young similar in appearance to the adults except that they are smaller and have only three pairs of legs. These larvae undergo molts as do other mites, acquire a fourth pair of legs, and become adult males and females. The time required for the completion of the cycle is unknown.

This type of mange may affect dogs of all ages but is most common in young animals, especially those of the short-haired breeds. The first evidence of demodectic mange is the appearance of areas from which the hair has fallen out. These spots are usually slightly reddened and commonly occur around the eyes, on the elbows, hocks, and toes, and elsewhere on the body. There is practically no itching at this time; itching may become pronounced as the disease progresses but is never so intense as in sarcoptic mange. In the course of time the hairless areas become larger and the skin has a copper color, which accounts for the name "red mange" (fig. 1); in severe cases the skin may appear lead gray or bluish. During this period the mites are multiplying in the hair follicles, and inflammatory changes become evident, with the appearance of small pustules.

The hairless, or depilatory, type of demodectic mange, due to uncomplicated mite infestation, becomes complicated in the course of time through lowered resistance and the invasion of pus-producing bacteria which lead to the formation of small pimples, or pustules, in the hairless areas. As the pustular stage progresses the skin becomes thickened and is susceptible to injury by scratching, rubbing, or contact with various objects. There is very little itching in this stage of the disease. Poisons are formed by the bacteria in the pustules, and the absorption of this toxic material deranges the body functions and affects the general health of the animal, leading to emaciation, weakness, and the development of an unpleasant odor. The disease runs a slow course, often extending over a period of 2 years or longer. Unless it is treated, it usually terminates in death, although occasionally spontaneous recovery occurs, especially if the animal has been kept on a good, nourishing diet.

Demodectic mange may be confused with a number of other skin diseases, including sarcoptic mange, fungus infections, acne, and eczema. A definite diagnosis can be made only by microscopic examination of scrapings of the skin or of material from the pus-

FIGURE 1.—A moderately severe case of demodectic, or red, mange. The hair has fallen out over the extensive light-colored areas on the dog's body.

tules. Failure to find the mites, particularly in the early stages of the disease, does not exclude the possibility that the condition is demodectic mange, and it may be necessary to make several examinations at different times before arriving at a diagnosis.

TREATMENT OF MANGE

Medicinal treatment of mange, regardless of the type, should be undertaken only by or under the supervision of a veterinarian who is able to diagnose the condition accurately and to prescribe the proper treatment.

Ear mange is the type most amenable to treatment, since the mites are on the surface of the skin and are easily destroyed by the use of suitable insecticides. The affected animal should be restrained so that the ear canals can be cleaned and the wax and other material removed by forceps or a swab without injuring the eardrum. After

being cleansed, the canal should be swabbed with one of the following
mixtures: (1) 1 percent phenol in glycerin, (2) 5 percent phenol in
castor oil or olive oil, or (3) a mixture of 1 part carbon tetrachloride
and 3 parts of castor oil. An oil solution of rotenone is also reported
to be effective. The treatment should be repeated daily until all
traces of the infestation have disappeared.

An ointment consisting of 1 part by measure of derris powder
containing 5 percent rotenone in 10 parts of petrolatum or olive oil
has also been found effective against the ear mange mites. The material is applied to the ears with a cotton swab. Usually two such
treatments, 1 week apart, are sufficient to clear up an infestation.

Sarcoptic and demodectic mange are more difficult to treat since
the mites in the skin are not easily reached with medication. Dogs
affected with either of these types of mange should be clipped before
treatment is attempted. The animal should be bathed and all crusts
and scabs removed with the aid of a moderately stiff brush. In
most instances it is advisable to apply the indicated remedy to one-
fourth of the body each day, so that in the course of 4 days the entire
body has been covered. After a complete course of treatment the
animal should be bathed and the same routine repeated until a cure
has been effected.

In most of the effective treatments for sarcoptic mange the active
ingredient is sulfur. One of the simple mixtures that frequently
gives good results is an ointment prepared by thoroughly mixing 1
part of flowers of sulfur with 8 parts of lard. Another ointment
that has given good results consists of 2 parts of sublimed sulfur,
1 part oil of tar, 1 part potassium carbonate, and 8 parts lard. Lime-
sulfur dip as prepared for the treatment of scab in sheep is likewise
an effective remedy.

Derris ointment similar to that recommended for the treatment of
ear mange and a wash consisting of 4 ounces of derris powder (containing 5 percent rotenone), 1 ounce of neutral soap, and 1 gallon
of warm water have been found highly effective in curing sarcoptic
mange. The wash should be well rubbed in with a brush. The surplus wash is taken up with a towel and the remainder of the material
is permitted to dry on the animal. Two or three treatments are
usually necessary to effect a cure. Exposure to sulfur dioxide gas has
also been reported to give good results. The affected animal is placed
in a gas-tight box from which his head protrudes, and the body is
then exposed to the gas. Afterwards the head is treated with sulfur
ointment. Cases have been cured after two or three such treatments.

The treatment of demodectic mange is often very discouraging
because of the care, time, and expense involved. Many remedies
have been used, but in spite of some cures there have been many failures. The most promising remedy appears to be a 1-percent solution
of rotenone in alcohol or oil. The solution is prepared by dissolving
the rotenone in a small amount of acetone and then adding the
proper amount of either alcohol or a bland oil, depending on the
kind of application desired; an oil solution is generally preferred
because it tends to keep the skin soft and pliable. The remedy is
applied daily, with a moderately rough massage, to the affected parts

or the entire body, depending on the extent of the lesions. Constant treatment for several weeks is frequently necessary to effect a cure. The derris wash recommended for sarcoptic mange, applied every other day for 2 weeks then once a week for 4 weeks, has effected cures in a number of instances. Another remedy that has been recommended widely and has given good results in some cases consists in the use, once a week, of a preparation composed of 8 ounces of kerosene, 8 ounces of raw linseed oil, 1 ounce of carbolic acid, 1 ounce of oil of tar, and ¼ pound of sulfur. This mixture is applied with mild rubbing, but in using it not more than one-fourth of the dog's body should be treated at a time, as there is some danger of carbolic acid poisoning. Two or three complete treatments are usually necessary to effect a cure. With all these treatments, care should be taken to keep the material out of the animal's eyes, as severe inflammation and even blindness may result.

In connection with medicinal treatment for either sarcoptic or demodectic mange, supplementary measures in the form of good, nourishing food containing adequate vitamins and minerals, laxatives, and warm comfortable quarters will enhance the animal's chances of recovery.

It should be remembered that the premises frequented by mangy dogs are infected, and disinfection is therefore necessary to prevent reinfection of the treated animals or the spread of the disease to healthy dogs. So far as possible all litter and bedding should be burned and the kennels disinfected with a hot, strong coal-tar-creosote solution. Where effective disinfection is impossible or impractical, as in the case of yards and large runways, dogs should be kept off such premises for at least 3 weeks to allow sufficient time for any mange mites that might be present to die.

At the time this book went to press, the drugs and other materials mentioned in various articles—chiefly as disinfectants, insecticides, and anthelmintics—were still available for veterinary and medical use. Under war conditions, however, it is possible that some of these materials may become scarce or unavailable. In that case, the reader should obtain professional advice from the Department of Agriculture, the State experiment station, a local veterinarian, or the county agent as to available substitutes.

Ticks Affecting Dogs

BY F. C. BISHOPP
AND CARROLL N. SMITH [1]

NOT EVERYONE realizes that the so-called wood tick is also a dog tick and that there are eight species of these creatures, several of which carry such diseases as Rocky Mountain spotted fever and tularemia. Few dog owners have not at one time or another had to deal with the tick problem. The most effective methods are described in this article.

AS THE TERMS "dog ticks" and "wood ticks" are commonly used, they refer to eight different species of ticks so similar in appearance and habits that few persons not entomologists are able to differentiate between them. All are of importance as parasites of dogs, and many will also feed on other domestic animals and human beings. Some of them serve as carriers of diseases of animals or man, in addition to inflicting irritating bites.

All ticks have somewhat similar habits in that they must feed on blood in order to reproduce. The eggs are always deposited on the ground or elsewhere after the female has become engorged with blood and dropped from the dog or other animal upon which she has fed. Among the different kinds of ticks, however, there are minor differences in life history, the hosts attacked, and egg laying and other habits, and also in the role the ticks play in disease transmission (*1, 5, 6, 9*).

The American dog tick (*Dermacentor variabilis*), the most widely distributed and abundant species, is most numerous along the Atlantic and Gulf coasts, in the Mississippi Valley, and along the Pacific coast as far north as Oregon. Scattered infestations may be found in nearly all the other parts of the United States except the Rocky Mountain region and the Pacific Northwest. A closely related species, called the Rocky Mountain spotted fever tick (*Dermacentor*

---

[1] F. C. Bishopp is Assistant Chief and Carroll N. Smith is Assistant Entomologist, Bureau of Entomology and Plant Quarantine.
[2] Italic numbers in parentheses refer to Literature cited, p. 1187.

andersoni), occurs in the Rocky Mountain region, and a second closely related species, the Pacific coast tick (*Dermacentor occidentalis*) occurs in California and southern Oregon. The brown dog tick (*Rhipicephalus sanguinius*), a species having somewhat different habits, causes permanent outdoor infestations only in Florida and Texas but infests houses and other heated buildings in many localities over the entire United States. The black-legged tick (*Ixodes ricinus scapularis*) occurs throughout the eastern part of the United States, and a closely related species, the California black-legged tick (*Ixodes ricinus californicus*), is found in the West. The Gulf coast tick (*Amblyomma maculatum*) is found in the States bordering the Gulf of Mexico and the Atlantic Ocean as far north as South Carolina. The lone star tick (*Amblyomma americanum*) occurs in the eastern part of the United States and as far west as Texas.

THE AMERICAN DOG TICK

In many localities the American dog tick (*3, p. 422*)[3] is the most important pest of dogs. In heavily infested areas dogs that are allowed to run freely frequently pick up several hundred ticks each day, and this causes severe irritation, a bad disposition, and loss of condition. Although the authors have observed no cases of dogs having been killed by these severe infestations, animals are known to have been destroyed because of their weakened condition, ill temper, and suffering, and canine paralysis has been attributed to the attacks of these ticks. In resort areas considerable economic losses are sustained when visitors avoid certain localities because of the injury to their pets caused by these parasites and the fear of being bitten themselves.

A strong incentive to keep dogs free of the American dog tick is the fact that the bite of this species transmits the dreaded human diseases, Rocky Mountain spotted fever and rabbit fever (tularemia). These diseases do not occur in every locality where ticks are found, and in localities where they do occur only one in several hundred ticks is infected, so that most persons bitten suffer no ill effects; but when the tick happens to be infected, a bite has serious results.

The American dog tick and related species pass through four stages—the egg; the seed tick, or larva; the nymph; and the adult. The eggs are laid in a mass in protected places on the ground, particularly in thick clumps of grass. Each female lays only one such mass, which contains 3,000 to 6,000 eggs. The eggs hatch into tiny six-legged seed ticks, which attach themselves to meadow mice or other small rodents. In 2 to 12 days they fill themselves with blood, drop to the ground, and shed their skins, or molt. The tick that emerges from the old skin has eight legs and is called a nymph. The nymphs attach themselves to small rodents and become engorged with blood in 3 to 10 days (fig. 1), after which they drop to the ground and molt, becoming adults. The adult males and females, shown in figure 2, also have eight legs but are distinguished from the younger stages by the white markings on a hardened part of the back called the shield.

[3] See also BISHOPP, F. C., and SMITH, CARROLL N. COMBATING THE AMERICAN DOG TICK, CARRIER OF ROCKY MOUNTAIN SPOTTED FEVER IN THE CENTRAL AND EASTERN STATES. U. S. Bur. Ent. and Plant Quar. Cir. E–454, 5 pp., illus. 1938. [Processed.]

Adults of both sexes attach themselves to dogs or other large animals and feed on blood, but the females become tremendously enlarged, as shown in figure 3, while the males never increase in size. Mating

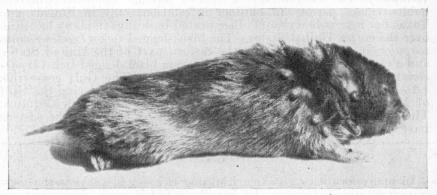

FIGURE 1.—Nymphs of the American dog tick attached to a meadow mouse.

occurs while the females are feeding, and when they have mated and become fully engorged, which requires from 5 to 13 days, they drop to the ground, lay their eggs (fig. 4), and die. At no time do the

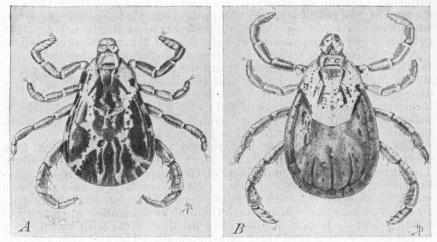

FIGURE 2.—The American dog tick: *A*, Unfed male; *B*, unfed female. Much enlarged.

ticks feed on anything but the blood of mammals. The larvae and nymphs may live for a year without feeding, and the adults for over 2 years. In the Northern States the adult ticks are most active in the spring and early summer, few being encountered after August 1, but in the South their activity is less sharply restricted by seasons.

The most effective way to prevent injury to dogs by ticks is to wash or immerse the dogs twice a week in derris dip. The dip is prepared by dissolving an ounce of mild soap in a gallon of warm water and stirring 2 ounces of fine derris or cube powder into the solution. These powders should contain at least 3 percent of rotenone, the active insecticidal principle. If a suitable dipping vat is available, a large quantity may be prepared and used repeatedly, as the mixture will retain its strength for about 3 weeks if kept in the dark. If only a small quantity is prepared, it is best to place the dog in a tub and pour the dip slowly over it, working the liquid well into the hair with the fingers. The liquid may then be dipped up from the tub and poured over the dog repeatedly until the hair and skin over the entire body are thoroughly soaked. Care should be taken to prevent the dip from getting into the dog's eyes. If possible, the dip should be allowed to dry on the dog. The dip will kill the ticks that are attached, and for 2 or 3 days after a treatment the powder remaining in the hair will reduce the number of ticks that become attached and kill most of those that do. These materials act slowly, sometimes requiring as long as 24 hours to complete the kill. Occasional treatments will benefit the animals to some extent, but for good control the treatments should be given regularly twice a week.

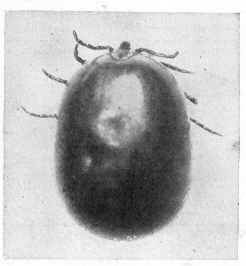

FIGURE 3.—Fully engorged female. American dog tick. Much enlarged.

If a dip cannot be used conveniently, derris or cube powder may be applied as a dust, care being taken that it penetrates the hair and reaches the skin. If the dogs breathe or swallow the derris they may vomit but will not be harmed, but it should not be permitted to get into the eyes. This treatment is also highly effective in controlling fleas.

Since the dog is the principal host on which the adult tick feeds and since each female lays several thousand eggs after feeding, treating the dogs regularly will not only bring them immediate relief but will definitely limit the reproduction of ticks.

When only a few ticks are present, they may be removed by hand. For this it is best to use tweezers or forceps, since human beings handling infected ticks may become infected with Rocky Mountain spotted fever. The ticks should be killed by being dropped into turpentine or kerosene as soon as they are picked off; if they are crushed, the blood should not be allowed to touch the skin. The hands should be thoroughly washed as soon as the job is done.

Methods of eradication applicable to all the different conditions under which the American dog tick exists have not been discovered but several things can be done to reduce their abundance, particularly around houses, in addition to the systematic care of dogs.

The destruction of rodents, particularly meadow mice, by trapping or poisoning, reduces the number of ticks in the following year by depriving the immature ticks of the hosts they require for larval and nymphal feeding (*10*). Almost complete eradication of the mice is necessary, however, if the reduction in the tick population is to be appreciable. Poisoning is more effective than trapping, but owing to the danger to other animals it should be carried on only under the direction of competent authorities.

Keeping underbrush, grass, and weeds closely cut tends to drive out rodents and removes protection favorable to the ticks themselves. Burning vegetation accomplishes the same results.

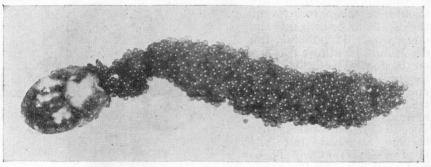

FIGURE 4.—Engorged female depositing eggs. Much enlarged.

Close grazing of brushy and weedy areas by sheep will do much to reduce the tick population. If fine-wooled sheep are used, relatively few ticks become engorged on them, and many are killed by the wool grease.

Many of the ticks on an infested area may be killed by thoroughly applying a spray consisting of 1 part of nicotine sulfate (40 percent nicotine), 1 part of soap, and 288 parts of water (this is about 8 teaspoonfuls of nicotine sulfate to 3 gallons of water). As ticks often concentrate on the sides of roads and paths, such places are most in need of treatment. Sprayed vegetation remains relatively free of ticks for about 3 days. More permanent results may be obtained by adding 4 ounces of sodium fluoride to the 3 gallons of spray, but this will cause some injury to the vegetation. Additional information on control is given by Bishopp and Smith in the circular cited in footnote 3 (p. 1181).

THE ROCKY MOUNTAIN SPOTTED FEVER TICK AND THE PACIFIC COAST TICK

The Rocky Mountain spotted fever tick and the Pacific coast tick are so similar to the American dog tick in appearance that they can be distinguished only by microscopic examination. They cause the same injury to dogs, but the Rocky Mountain spotted fever tick is particularly dangerous as a vector of the fever which gives it its name, as well as of tularemia and Colorado tick fever, and also as a cause of tick paralysis in dogs and human beings.

The life history and habits of these species are much like those described for the American dog tick, except that the larvae and nymphs feed on a much greater variety of mammals. Further information on the biology of the Pacific coast tick is given elsewhere by Hooker, Bishopp, and Wood (*6*), and the biology and control of the Rocky Mountain spotted fever tick have been discussed by several writers (*4, 6, 7, 9*).

The derris dip recommended for killing the American dog tick should be effective in destroying the Rocky Mountain spotted fever tick and others—except the ear tick—on dogs. Reducing the number of ticks on cattle and horses and destroying ground squirrels and other rodent hosts of the ticks have been advocated from time to time. These measures have not always been found to be practicable, but undoubtedly they do reduce the number of ticks. It is also worth while to clear away underbrush and keep dogs and livestock out of heavily infested areas.

DOG-INFESTING TICKS FOUND IN THE OPEN

Other species of ticks that are found in the open and commonly infest dogs are the black-legged tick, the California black-legged tick, the lone star tick, the Gulf coast tick, and the ear tick. Their range has already been given (p. 1181). The Gulf coast tick resembles the American dog tick in appearance but can be distinguished from the latter with a magnifying glass. The lone star tick differs from others in having the shield marked with a single white spot at the back in the female and with two white semicircles at the back in the male. Neither variety of the black-legged tick has white markings on the shield, which is dark brown or nearly black.

The life histories of these species are similar to that of the American dog tick except that the larvae and nymphs feed on a greater variety of animals, including mammals, birds, and, in the case of the black-legged tick, even reptiles. Also the larvae and nymphs as well as the adults of all but the Gulf coast tick feed readily on dogs. The Gulf coast tick in its immature stages feeds mainly on ground-inhabiting birds (*2*).

The treatment with derris dip recommended for the control of the American dog tick will also control the other species on dogs. Systematic treatment of the ears of livestock, especially on the inside, with commercial pine-tar oil will largely protect these animals and ultimately reduce the infestation on pastures. Clearing, burning, and grazing, as recommended, will assist in reducing the tick population.

Dogs are frequently infested by the spinose ear tick. This pest attaches itself deep in the convolutions of the ears and often causes irritation and pain, evidenced by the dog's scratching its ears, shaking its head, and holding the head to one side. Derris or cube powder (5 percent rotenone) mixed with medicinal mineral oil (1 part of the former to 10 parts of the latter by measure) and dropped into the ears will kill these ticks. Only a few drops are required, but it is best to squeeze the base of the ear to work the material in among the ticks. A few drops of pine-tar oil (1 part) and cottonseed oil (3 parts) may also be used in the ears. Further information regarding this tick is given in Farmers' Bulletin 980, The Spinose Ear Tick (8).

THE BROWN DOG TICK

The brown dog tick is a particularly troublesome pest of dogs because of its habits. Whereas the other ticks of dogs require a vegetative cover and wild animal hosts to complete their development, the brown dog tick is adapted to life in the drier environment of kennels, houses, etc., with the dog as the only necessary host. It is also of some importance as a vector of canine piroplasmosis, although this disease is not widespread in the United States. Additional information on this pest has been published by Bishopp.[4]

The brown dog tick often infests houses in considerable numbers, both immature and adult ticks hiding around baseboards, window casings, and furniture, and in the folds of curtains. Dogs kept in houses are thus constantly exposed to attack and frequently become infested with hundreds of larvae, nymphs, and adults. As noted in the paragraph on distribution, this species has become established in many northern localities because of its ability to live in heated buildings.

Aside from the difference in environment and the fact that the ticks in all stages feed on dogs, the life history of the brown dog tick is like that of the American dog tick. The adults, however, do not bite human beings. This tick differs from the American dog tick in appearance in that the adult has no white markings on the shield, which is plain brown.

In combating the brown dog tick it is necessary to treat not only the infested animals but also their sleeping places.

Clipping long-haired dogs aids in keeping them free of ticks but is not really necessary. Use of the derris dip according to the procedure recommended for controlling the American dog tick will kill the brown dog tick in all stages. As the dogs are constantly exposed to reinfestation, treatment should be given at 3-day intervals.

Infested dogs should be kept in one place, especially during their sleeping hours, to confine the ticks more or less and make the treatment easier. The kennels in which infested animals sleep should be thoroughly sprayed with undiluted creosote oil. This is the same material that is used for the prevention of decay in posts and timbers. Since it stains and is very caustic, it should not be used in houses or be allowed to come in contact with animals or plants. It penetrates wood and cracks and can be relied upon to destroy in a single treatment practically all the ticks in a building. If corrugated or other metal kennels or cages are being used, it is probably best not to use the creosote oil but to spray with creosote dip. The strength should be triple that usually recommended for disinfecting purposes.

The face and hands of spray operators, or persons applying creosote in any manner, should be protected, as creosote in this form is highly irritating.

[4] BISHOPP, F. C. THE BROWN DOG TICK, WITH SUGGESTIONS FOR ITS CONTROL. U. S. Bur. Ent. and Plant Quar. Cir. E-292, 3 pp., illus. 1939. (Revised.) [Processed.]

The use of a gasoline torch or "prickly pear burner" in concrete or other fireproof buildings destroys the ticks in the cracks and floors, but it is not approved. The use of a torch in a wooden building should be prohibited.

In dog and cat hospitals special attention should be given to having the cages and building constructed so as to reduce the number of hiding places for ticks to a minimum. Smooth concrete floors and walls are desirable, and cages made of metal give much less opportunity for ticks to hide than those made of wood.

When residences become infested, it is best to keep the dogs out of doors except when they are allowed to enter the house to serve as traps for free ticks. The baseboards, window casings, and other infested places should be sprayed frequently with one of the standard fly sprays, which are essentially kerosene extracts of pyrethrum. The ticks are quite resistant to sprays of this kind and must be wetted thoroughly if they are to be killed. In addition to the spray, the use of fresh pyrethrum or derris powder scattered behind baseboards and other hiding places is advised. If the dog is kept indoors it should be treated regularly as described. The treatment of the dog and the premises must be persisted in for several months to eradicate the pests completely.

Fumigation of infested houses is seldom advisable because the ticks are usually present in entryways, around porches, and in outbuildings where they cannot be reached with a fumigant, and they are also very resistant to fumigants.

LITERATURE CITED

(1) BISHOPP, F. C.
 1935. TICKS AND THE ROLE THEY PLAY IN THE TRANSMISSION OF DISEASES. Smithsn. Inst. Ann. Rpt. 1933, pp. 389–406, illus.
(2) ——— and HIXSON. HOMER.
 1936. BIOLOGY AND ECONOMIC IMPORTANCE OF THE GULF COAST TICK. Jour. Econ. Ent. 29: 1068–1076, illus.
(3) ——— and SMITH, CARROLL N.
 1938. THE AMERICAN DOG TICK, EASTERN CARRIER OF ROCKY MOUNTAIN SPOTTED FEVER. U. S. Dept. Agr. Cir. 478, 26 pp., illus.
(4) COOLEY, R. A.
 1932. THE ROCKY MOUNTAIN WOOD TICK. Mont. Agr. Expt. Sta. Bul. 268, 58 pp., illus.
(5) HERMS, WILLIAM B.
 1939. MEDICAL ENTOMOLOGY WITH SPECIAL REFERENCE TO THE HEALTH AND WELL-BEING OF MAN AND ANIMALS. Ed. 3, 582 pp., illus. New York.
(6) HOOKER, W. A., BISHOPP, F. C., and WOOD, H. P.
 1912. THE LIFE HISTORY AND BIONOMICS OF SOME NORTH AMERICAN TICKS. U. S. Bur. Ent. Bul. 106, 239 pp., illus.
(7) HUNTER, W. D., and BISHOPP, F. C.
 1911. THE ROCKY MOUNTAIN SPOTTED FEVER TICK. U. S. Bur. Ent. Bul. 105, 47 pp., illus.
(8) IMES, MARION.
 1918. THE SPINOSE EAR TICK. U. S. Dept. Agr. Farmers' Bul. 980, 8 pp., illus.
(9) PARKER, R. R., PHILIP, CORNELIUS B., DAVIS, GORDON E., and COOLEY, R. A.
 1937. TICKS OF THE UNITED STATES IN RELATION TO DISEASE IN MAN. Jour. Econ. Ent. 30: 51–69.
(10) SILVER, JAMES.
 1930. MOUSE CONTROL IN FIELD AND ORCHARD. U. S. Dept. Agr. Farmers' Bul. 1397, 14 pp., illus. (Revised.)

Fleas

BY F. C. BISHOPP [1]

FLEAS do so much harm and they are so great an annoyance to animals and human beings that it is worth while to maintain a perpetual campaign against them. The control measures outlined here are not difficult but require persistence.

DOGS AND CATS are all too often beset by hundreds of bloodthirsty fleas. Frequently these pests do not confine their attacks to pet animals but overrun homes, barns, and poultry houses, sorely annoying human beings, livestock, and poultry.

There are many kinds of fleas, but those most important so far as the health and comfort of pet animals are concerned are the species commonly known as the human flea (*Pulex irritans*), the dog flea (*Ctenocephalides canis*), and the cat flea (*Ctenocephalides felis*) (fig. 1). When the latter two species appear as troublesome pests in farm or city houses, they are always associated with dogs or cats. The human flea may breed on these animals and also on hogs as well as on man.

The sticktight flea (*Echidnophaga gallinacea*) is another species that attacks dogs and cats. The edges of the ears of these animals often become rimmed with hundreds of the pests, and they attach themselves in considerable numbers to other parts of the body.

Needless to say, fleas are extremely annoying to dogs and cats, causing them to almost continuously scratch and bite in an effort to get rid of the pests. The coats of pet animals are soiled and roughened by the fleas and the scratching they induced. Fleas also appear to be connected in some way with summer eczema of dogs; at least, this diseased condition of the skin usually clears up when the fleas are eliminated.

The cat flea, dog flea, and human flea all serve as hosts for young stages of the dog tapeworm. The fleas swallow the tapeworm eggs that get into the dog's hair from segments of tapeworms passed by dogs. The eggs hatch and go through certain developmental stages

---

[1] F. C. Bishopp is Assistant Chief, Bureau of Entomology and Plant Quarantine.

in the fleas, and if one of the insects is then swallowed by the dog in biting itself—or accidentally by a child, as occasionally happens—the young tapeworm, in what is called the cysticercoid stage, passes to the intestine of the new host, where the worm attaches itself and develops.

All three of the species of fleas mentioned are also capable of carrying the deadly disease of human beings and rats, bubonic plague. At present, however, this disease occurs only in restricted areas in the West, and it is ordinarily transmitted by rodent fleas.

From the standpoint of human comfort and welfare, the most important aspect of the problem is the frequency with which homes become overrun by fleas that breed on pet animals and in their sleeping places, so that life in the infested house is well-nigh impossible.

The human flea is most often found in troublesome numbers in the Mississippi Valley and in California, where it frequently infests houses, stores, warehouses, and barns. Barns in which hogs are permitted to sleep very often become heavily infested. Horses, mules, and cattle are much annoyed in such cases, and of course human beings suffer greatly from the flea bites.

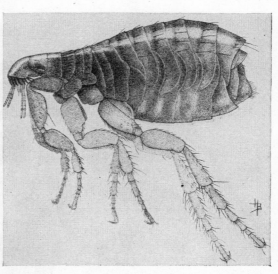

FIGURE 1.—A female cat flea. Greatly enlarged.

The sticktight flea (fig. 2) is a common pest in the Southern States. It is not only troublesome to dogs and cats but is a serious pest of poultry and a source of considerable annoyance to persons who tend the fowls. Young chickens and turkeys are sometimes killed by heavy infestations, grown fowls become weakened, and egg production is greatly reduced.

The ability of fleas to jump, bite, and elude one's best efforts to capture them is well known. Few people realize, however, that these pests must have warm-blooded animals on which to feed and that the young fleas, which resemble maggots, live and develop in the dust and debris in the sleeping places of animals. The oval white eggs are deposited while the fleas are on their hosts. The eggs then drop to the floor or ground and in a few days hatch into minute maggotlike larvae which complete their growth in 2 weeks or more, depending on the temperature. The larva spins a cocoon about the size of a wheat kernel around itself, and in from 1 week to 2 or 3 months the adult flea emerges. Most of the life of the adult fleas is spent on animals. The attacks on human beings are mainly by newly emerged fleas that have not yet found an animal on which to live. The attack on fleas must be directed against the adults on dogs, cats, and hogs, and against the immature stages of the fleas on the floor or ground.

Fleas on dogs and cats are easily destroyed by the application of a small amount of derris or cube powder scattered through the hair next to the skin along the neck and back of the animal (fig. 3).

FIGURE 2.—Sticktight fleas on the head of a chicken.

Fresh, finely ground pyrethrum powder dusted into the hair is also effective. Washing the animal in water containing derris or cube powder and soap is an excellent method of control. Two ounces of the powder and an ounce of neutral soap—preferably in flaked form—are mixed with a gallon of water. This is applied to the animal either by dipping or washing. The surplus water is removed with a towel and the remaining solution left on the animal.

Since fleas are continually picked up by dogs and cats that are allowed to run free, the treatment usually has to be repeated every 10 days or 2 weeks.

Fleas on hogs may be killed by sprinkling the backs of the animals lightly with crude petroleum or strained crankcase oil. Poultry need not be treated, because infestations of the sticktight flea can be wiped out by treating the breeding places as described in the following paragraph.

The destruction of the immature fleas on infested premises is accomplished by cleaning out and burning straw and other debris from the sleeping places of the animals and spraying the ground thoroughly with creosote oil. This treatment also kills any adult fleas present. Creosote oil, commonly used as a wood preserver, is destructive to plants, stains paint, and is caustic to animals. Its use, therefore, is limited to outbuildings and basements where nothing subject to injury is stored. It should be applied with a good force pump, such as a bucket pump with a strong hose and secure connections. Creosote oil is reasonable in price so that it may be used

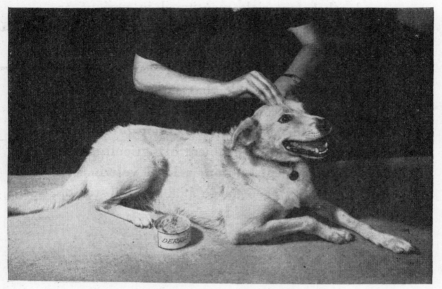

FIGURE 3.—A dog being dusted with derris powder for flea control.

freely on the ground and in and around barns where heavy infestations occur.

Fleas sometimes spread to lawns from heavily infested sheltered places, such as a garage and the ground beneath a porch. Keeping the grass closely cut will usually cause the fleas to die out in a short time. If they persist, spraying with nicotine sulfate at the rate of 6 teaspoonfuls to 1 gallon of warm soapy water will be effective.

In stores and in the living quarters in houses, creosote oil cannot be used. Flaked naphthalene is recommended for such situations, and it may also be used in basements. It should be scattered thickly over floors and infested furniture, after which the rooms should be vacated and left closed for 48 hours or longer. This kills both the adult and the young fleas. The naphthalene remaining after treatment may be swept up and saved in a tight container for future use.

If only an occasional flea is present in a house, fly spray may be used, but only the insects actually struck by the spray are killed.

There is little reason for pet animals to suffer from fleas and for people to be practically driven from their homes by these pests when simple, inexpensive, and effective weapons are at hand to use against them.

At the time this book went to press, the drugs and other materials mentioned in various articles—chiefly as disinfectants, insecticides, and anthelmintics—were still available for veterinary and medical use. Under war conditions, however, it is possible that some of these materials may become scarce or unavailable. In that case, the reader should obtain professional advice from the Department of Agriculture, the State experiment station, a local veterinarian, or the county agent as to available substitutes.

Running Fits (Fright Disease)

BY C. D. STEIN [1]

FRIGHT DISEASE is seldom fatal, but it can be very alarming to the dog owner who suddenly encounters it and confuses the condition with rabies. Here is a summary of the little that is known about this mysterious malady.

RUNNING FITS is a nervous affection of dogs commonly known also as fright disease, barking fits, furious fits, or canine hysteria. The condition occurs in dogs of all breeds, of all ages, of both sexes, and at all times of the year. Although more or less prevalent throughout the United States, it seems to be more common in the Southern States than elsewhere.

SYMPTOMS

The condition is characterized by periodic attacks of running and barking, together with manifestations of excitement and great fear. Between the attacks the animal usually appears normal, though sometimes becoming dull and listless. Usually the first symptoms noticed are restlessness, a staring expression of the eyes, and fright. In most instances the affected animal suddenly starts to run and bark as if pursued. The attacks, lasting from a few minutes to a half hour or longer, may occur at intervals of days, weeks, or months and may continue over a period of years. The mortality rate is usually low.

In mild attacks, after a short period of running, the dog will hide in a dark place, coming out later seemingly normal. Severe attacks may terminate in spasms or convulsions and may be accompanied by champing of the jaws, with a copious flow of saliva or involuntary passage of feces and urine. Less frequently the animal will remain

---

[1] C. D. Stein is Veterinarian, Pathological Division, Bureau of Animal Industry.

timid or in a state of fear, will bark or snap at the slightest provocation, and will fail to recognize or obey commands given by its master. Occasionally the animal will suddenly commence to yelp and run until it falls exhausted. This type of attack occurs most frequently in hunting dogs.

The fits or convulsions that sometimes occur in young puppies heavily infested with intestinal parasites or cutting the permanent teeth should not be confused with this condition.

The symptoms of running fits are sometimes thought to be those of rabies because of the common but mistaken belief that a mad dog rushes wildly through the streets. Those who know the symptoms of rabies, however, seldom confound the two diseases. A veterinarian should be consulted when there is doubt as to the true nature of the trouble.

THEORIES AS TO CAUSE

The basic cause of running fits is still unknown. Several theories have been advanced, suggesting as the cause specific infection, hereditary predisposition, inbreeding, circulatory disturbances, faulty or deficient diet, indigestion, alimentary toxemias, foreign bodies in the digestive tract, parasitic infestation, estrum (heat), and sundry irritations and excitements. None of these theories, however, have been substantiated by sound experimental evidence.

Practicing veterinarians and investigators in the Bureau of Animal Industry and elsewhere have frequently observed that improper feeding, especially a long-continued diet composed largely of meal, cereals, breadstuffs, or dog biscuits, may produce a condition much like running fits, particularly in dogs that are kept confined. On the other hand, dogs that have liberty to run about and are on a diet in which meat plays a major part seldom develop the disease.

In recent years considerable attention has been given by investigators to dietary deficiency as a cause of running fits.[2] Walston[3] reported experimental evidence to indicate that the affection may be due to vitamin A deficiency. Dogs affected with this condition and fed largely on cereals recovered when the diet was changed so as to contain more vitamin A. Patton,[4] working with prepared dog foods processed by heat, reported experimental evidence to indicate that running fits may be a vitamin B_1 deficiency and advocated the administration of thiamin in treatment.

Arnold and Elvehjem[5] reported experiments in which symptoms of running fits in dogs were produced by foods that had been subjected to high temperatures. They suggest that the deficiency in heat-processed dog foods is in the protein rather than the vitamin content. Morgan[6] reported that heated proteins show a decrease in biological value, that vitamin B_1 withstands heat poorly and is likely to be low

---

[2] For a further brief discussion of nutritional aspects of the disease, see p. 1211.
[3] WALSTON, H. D. HYSTERIA IN DOGS. Nature [London] 132 (3328) : 243. 1933.
[4] PATTON, JOHN W. FRIGHT DISEASE AN AVITAMINOSIS. Vet. Med. 34 : 372–381, illus. 1939.
[5] ARNOLD, AARON, and ELVEHJEM, C. A. IS RUNNING FITS A DEFICIENCY DISEASE? Amer. Vet. Med. Assoc. Jour. 95 : 303–308, illus. 1939.
[6] MORGAN, AGNES FAY. DEFICIENCIES AND FALLACIES IN CANINE DIET. North Amer. Vet. 21 : 476–483. 1940.

in all heat-treated dog foods, and that the foodstuffs in all diets on which symptoms of running fits have been produced experimentally were baked or autoclaved (cooked by steam under pressure).

Schlotthauer,[7] on the other hand, reported that he was unable to produce symptoms of running fits in normal dogs by feeding heat-treated dog food or by various diets deficient in vitamin B_1. He suggests that running fits are produced in normal dogs by some toxic substance in the diet, but that they may be produced in dogs with hereditary epileptic tendencies or in dogs infected with neurotropic organisms (those affecting the nerves) by feeding irritating substances or by deficient diets.

TREATMENT AND PREVENTION

In the treatment of this affection and in the prevention of further attacks, careful regulation of the diet of affected dogs is of first importance. Fresh meat, milk, and eggs should constitute a large part of the diet. The importance of fresh meat in the diet of a dog is stressed. The bowels must be well regulated at all times. Faulty sanitary conditions should be corrected, and care should be taken to prevent overexertion or undue excitement. At the present time no specific medicinal treatment is known.

Since infestation with parasites, constipation, indigestible material in the digestive tract, occlusion, or stoppage, of the anal pouches, or ear mites may aggravate mild affections of running fits and intensify the symptoms, measures for detecting and correcting any of these difficulties must also be included in the treatment.

In animals that do not have liberty to run about, the occasional use of small amounts of cod-liver oil, calcium lactate, and yeast as supplements in the regular diet is sometimes advisable.

During an attack, if affected animals are placed in a dark room, kept free from annoyance, and not molested, they will often recover in a short time. Following recovery, the animal should be kept as quiet as possible to avoid a recurrence of symptoms. Dogs that remain in a state of nervousness or show signs of increased nervous irritability should be given nerve sedatives. In some cases the removal of irritating, indigestible material from the digestive tract by intestinal irrigation is followed by immediate improvement. It is suggested that actual treatment be undertaken by a qualified veterinarian only.

[7] SCHLOTTHAUER, CARL F. FRIGHT DISEASE (RUNNING FITS) NOT A DIETARY DEFICIENCY. North Amer. Vet. 21: 355–356. 1940.

Nonparasitic Skin Diseases of Dogs and Cats

BY C. D. STEIN [1]

THIS ARTICLE deals with 11 skin diseases of dogs and cats, describing the symptoms, discussing the known or possible causes, and outlining any treatments that have been found useful.

THE SMALL DOMESTICATED ANIMALS, particularly the dog and the cat, are subject to a number of different skin affections of a nonparasitic nature. These troublesome and sometimes perplexing afflictions, which are more or less common in dogs and to a lesser extent in cats, include such noncontagious diseases as alopecia, dermatitis, acne, seborrhea, impetigo, urticaria, and eczema, as well as affections due to specific causes such as dermatomycosis, or fungus infection of the skin.

Skin diseases of all types, especially in the dog, are often erroneously referred to by laymen as either mange or eczema. Since each type of skin affection in both dogs and cats usually requires a separate and special treatment, it is highly essential that the nature of the trouble and its cause be definitely determined if possible. Although a tentative diagnosis can be made from the characteristic features in some types of skin disease, it is necessary in most cases to resort to a microscopic examination to determine definitely whether the disease is of a parasitic or nonparasitic nature or whether it is due to fungi. Culture tests are also necessary at times, especially in cats, to determine the presence of ringworm.

When skin affections in dogs and cats become well established or chronic, they are sometimes difficult to cure, requiring persistent and painstaking attention for a long period. Even then results are occasionally unsatisfactory. The best results can be expected when the treatment is under the supervision of a qualified veterinarian with experience in treating small animals.

[1] C. D. Stein is Veterinarian, Pathological Division, Bureau of Animal Industry.

In the treatment of nonparasitic skin disorders, too much stress should not be placed on external medication. The nonirritating medicinal preparations, such as oils, dusting powders, lotions, and ointments, commonly used on skin affections are merely relief measures to allay itching and promote healing and in most instances do not remove the primary cause of the trouble, which must be done in order to effect a cure.

The causative factors in nonparasitic skin diseases, except ringworm and favus (a specific skin affection due to fungi), are numerous and sometimes obscure.

The appearance and condition of the coat of dogs and cats are influenced to a great extent by the general health of the animal. Disturbances in the general metabolism brought about by infectious conditions, diseases of the digestive, nervous, circulatory, or excretory systems, faulty feeding, and the administration of certain drugs are usually reflected in the skin and hair. Although the skin and hair normally show a marked resistance to ordinary external conditions, certain mechanical, chemical, or temperature influences have an extremely irritating effect, and, together with invasion by infective organisms, play a part in the production of skin affections.

ALOPECIA (LOSS OF HAIR)

Loss of hair, or alopecia, may be general or localized. A general loss of hair may occur in the normal process of molting. A dog normally sheds its coat once or twice yearly, the old hair being replaced with a new growth in about 6 weeks. Heavy-coated dogs and long-haired breeds that are kept indoors in the winter may shed more or less continuously. The annoyance caused by shedding can be lessened to some extent by daily grooming and keeping the dog outdoors. General shedding may also occur in debilitating diseases, such as distemper, diabetes, and jaundice, and as a result of senility. A localized loss of hair may occur in such skin diseases as mange, ringworm, and eczema, and in infestation by lice or fleas. It is also seen as a result of burns, scalds, chemical irritants, and thyroid deficiency.

DANDRUFF, OR SCURFINESS

Dandruff is characterized by the presence of grayish-white scales on the skin or in the hair due to excessive exfoliation (falling off) of the upper layer of the skin. A dry, scaly skin may be caused by the use of strong bath soap, irritating chemical preparations, decreased sebaceous secretion, parasitic infestation, digestive disorder, and deranged secretion of the thyroid gland. Daily grooming to stimulate local circulation and the application of coconut or olive oil to relieve dryness are sometimes beneficial. When loss of hair accompanied by scurfiness is due to thyroid deficiency, the condition may be improved by a course of treatments with thyroid extract.

DERMATITIS

Inflammation of the skin (dermatitis) in dogs and cats is usually accompanied by redness (erythema), itching (pruritis), and sometimes loss of hair (alopecia) and the formation of dandruff (scurf). Skin ruptures consisting of papules (pimples), vesicles (blisters), and pustules (purulent papules) may also occur in some forms of dermatitis.

Dermatitis may be local or general and may occur as an acute or subacute inflammation. It may also occur as a symptom during the course of distemper in dogs, or as a secondary symptom in parasitic infestation with tapeworms, hookworms, or heart worms. It is most commonly caused by extremely irritating external influences, such as pressure and rubbing from collars and harness, close clipping, the use of stiff grooming brushes, running through bushes, insect bites (by flies, fleas, bees, or wasps), and lying on hard rough floors. Prolonged exposure to the direct rays of the sun, burning, scalding, and freezing may also produce a form of dermatitis, and the condition may appear after a bath with strong caustic soaps or the application of irritating chemicals to the skin.

Dermatitis is usually characterized by redness of the skin and extreme itching. Repeated scratching, rubbing, and licking of the affected part tend to aggravate the condition. The lesions, or injuries, produced by the scratching and rubbing are frequently invaded by dirt and infective micro-organisms (*Staphylococcus* or *Streptococcus*), which often set up a septic dermatitis.

Mild forms of the disease usually clear up in a short time after the cause is determined and eliminated. The application of soothing lotions such as witch hazel or ichthyol ointment to relieve the itching, and dusting with mild antiseptic powders such as boric acid are usually beneficial.

During the fly season a dermatitis of the ears causes much concern to dog owners in many localities. Flies attack the tips of the ears and sometimes the eyelids and corners of the mouth, producing a dermatitis which, if untreated, may become very serious. When it is impractical to confine dogs in screened kennels, this condition can be relieved to some extent by the application of an ointment comprised of 5 percent of oil of tar in a lanolin base. This serves both as a healing agent and as a fly repellent.

Chronic cases of dermatitis accompanied by a thickening and hardening of the skin with a discharge of serum, formation of crusts, and loss of hair require long and persistent treatment to effect a cure and often terminate in chronic eczema. In persistent cases in which the condition can be ascribed to no external irritant, the animal should be examined for the presence of intestinal parasites. The diet should be checked and altered if necessary to provide a balanced ration.

ECZEMA

Eczema, which is frequently mistaken for mange or ringworm, is often referred to by laymen as red mange. It is one of the most common skin diseases in dogs but is less prevalent in cats.

The disease is characterized by erythema, the development of papules, vesicles, and pustules, a serous discharge, formation of crusts, intense itching, appearance of scurf, loss of hair, and a marked tendency to become chronic.

Eczema occurs in two forms—as an acute moist condition referred to as weeping eczema, or, more commonly, as a dry chronic condition. In the acute form the development of the disease is rapid. It is characterized principally by an intense erythema, marked itching, the formation of vesicles, a serous exudate, loss of hair, and a glistening moist appearance of the skin. This type frequently affects long-haired dogs.

The chronic type usually starts as a simple dermatitis and slowly develops into chronic eczema. It is characterized by inflammation and eruptions of the skin, intense itching, loss of hair, and formation of scurf, crusts, and scabs. It appears to be more common in coarse- and wire-haired breeds of dogs.

The most common site for the development of eczema is the region around the base of the tail and extending along the back line to the shoulders and neck. The skin around the scrotum or the vulva is also often affected. A moist form of eczema with a brownish discharge often affects the ear canal and the skin between the toes.

The disease is most prevalent during the summer, especially during hot, humid weather. In some dogs it has a tendency to clear up during the winter months, only to reappear during the early spring and summer. On account of its seasonal occurrence it is frequently referred to as summer eczema or periodic eczema.

The different forms of external irritation mentioned as possible causes of dermatitis may also be the primary causative agents in eczema.

A number of other factors, a few of which appear to have some connection with the fact that the disease occurs in summer, have been advanced as possible causative agents: (1) Allergy—certain foodstuffs, principally those with a high protein content, are believed to produce a reaction in the skin known as allergic eczema; (2) hypersensitivity, manifested in some dogs by extreme sensitivity to certain drugs and chemicals; (3) photosensitization, a condition that occurs in animals with light skin due to certain sensitizing agents as well as to lack of protective skin pigmentation and producing a mild inflammation or extensive blistering of the skin; (4) fungus infections, prevalent principally during the summer; (5) flea or chigger infestation, common during the summer; (6) environment—for example, confinement in small, hot, poorly ventilated quarters, with little or no exercise; (7) faulty feeding, including overfeeding, feeding excessive amounts of proteins or carbohydrates, and vitamin or mineral deficiencies.

General measures for the control of this trouble include reducing the protein or carbohydrate content of the diet, decreasing the food intake of overfed dogs, bathing less frequently, regular brushing and combing to keep the hair and skin clean, keeping affected animals in cool, dry, well-ventilated quarters free from flies and other insects, regular exercise in the cool part of the day, regular evacuation of the bowels and bladder, and keeping the animal free from internal parasites and particularly from such external parasites as fleas, lice, ticks, and harvest mites.

The use of mild lotions, ointments, and dusting powders to allay itching and promote healing is of some value in most cases.

IMPETIGO

Impetigo is rare in adult dogs but occasionally occurs in puppies. It is characterized by an eruption of small yellow vesicles or pustules which spread rapidly and tend to rupture, discharge a yellow pus, and later form scabs. The abdominal surface and the region inside the thighs are most commonly affected. It may occur as a secondary symptom in intestinal parasitic infestation, distemper, and other infectious diseases. In treating this condition applying a mild antiseptic to affected areas is helpful.

SEBORRHEA

Seborrhea, commonly known as greasy skin, is due to an excessive secretion of the oil glands of the skin. The condition occurs most frequently in fat, overfed house pets deprived of regular exercise. The lesions first appear in the region of the ears, neck, and root of the tail and gradually extend to other areas. The hair has an oily appearance and may gradually fall out, and there is usually an unpleasant characteristic odor associated with the malady.

ACNE

Acne in dogs and cats, also known as furunculosis or folliculitis, is an inflammation of the hair follicles or the skin glands, with a bacterial invasion resulting in suppuration (discharge of pus). It is characterized by the appearance of pimples or pustules which rupture, discharge pus, and form dry scabs. The condition most frequently affects the skin of the face, particularly the nose and cheeks, but may occur on other parts of the body. As the disease progresses, boils or carbuncles may develop at the site of the original lesions. In the treatment of the condition, good results have been reported following the administration of autogenous bacterins (those made from bacteria isolated from the skin lesions of the affected animal). Local treatment consists in opening the nodules and applying mild antiseptics to the affected parts. The administration of arsenicals internally has also been reported of value in some cases.

Furunculosis in cats frequently follows bites, bruises, and other injuries to the skin. The root of the tail and the back are the regions most commonly affected. The condition has a tendency to spread and become chronic, and surgical treatment is often required to effect a cure.

LIP ULCERATION IN CATS

Ulceration of the skin of the upper lip is a condition peculiar to cats. It usually becomes chronic and does not respond readily to treatment. Good results are sometimes obtained by treating with iodine preparations. Application of silver nitrate (5 percent) has also been reported to be of some value.

In treating skin affections in cats under no circumstances should soaps or disinfectants containing phenol, creosote, tar, creolin, or naphthol be used, as cats are extremely sensitive to these materials.

URTICARIA

Urticaria, also known as nettle rash and hives, is rather uncommon in the dog. It is characterized by the sudden appearance of large blotches or swellings. The eruptions may be found on all parts of the body surface, but sometimes they are confined principally to the head, causing a diffuse swelling of the skin of the face. The exact cause of the disease is not known. Sometimes it is apparently due to external irritation, but in most instances it appears to be the result of an intestinal toxemia, or poisoning brought about by faulty feeding. Allergy has also been advanced as a cause. The course of the disease is usually short. Affected animals recover, and lesions disappear in many instances within a few hours without treatment. Recovery can be hastened by the administration of purgatives.

RINGWORM

Ringworm is a communicable disease of the skin occurring in both dogs and cats and readily transmissible to man and some other animals. The disease is caused by specific fungi (chiefly *Microsporon* and *Trichophyton* species), which are somewhat similar to certain ordinary molds. The lesions of ringworm usually appear on the face, head, or legs, but they may occur on any part of the body.

The disease in dogs is characterized by small circular areas of dirty gray or brownish-yellow crusts or scabs partially devoid of hair. As the disease progresses, the lesions increase in size and number and merge to form larger patches covered with crusts containing broken-off hairs. A raw, bleeding surface appears when crusts are removed by scratching or rubbing to relieve itching. In some cases, however, there is little or no itching.

In cats the lesions appear as small, raised, scaly or scabby areas covered by hair, but detectable by running the finger tips over the skin. Microscopic examination and culture tests are necessary for an accurate diagnosis.

If treatment of affected dogs is started early, when only a few lesions are present, the disease can be cured in 5 or 6 weeks. Treatment consists in clipping the hair from around the lesions, removing scabs, and applying tincture of iodine or 5-percent salicylic acid solution two or three times weekly until recovery takes place. Scabs and hair removed during treatment should be burned to destroy the infection. Due precautions should be observed in handling animals affected with ringworm, as this disease is readily transmissible to man and other animals. Isolation of affected animals is essential to prevent the spread of the disease.

FAVUS

Favus is caused by a fungus known as *Achorion schonleinii*. It occurs principally in young cats and rarely in dogs. The sites most frequently affected are the paws, especially the skin of the toes near the claws, and the head and face. Lesions may occur in other parts of the body.

The disease is characterized by circular yellowish or grayish patches that develop into thick layers of crust of a sticky consistency.

Applications of tincture of iodine, a 5-percent solution of chlorine, or a 5-percent solution of salicylic acid are of value in treatment. This condition, like ringworm, is contagious to human beings, and affected animals·should therefore be isolated and handled with due precautions.

At the time this book went to press, the drugs and other materials mentioned in various articles—chiefly as disinfectants, insecticides, and anthelmintics—were still available for veterinary and medical use. Under war conditions, however, it is possible that some of these materials may become scarce or unavailable. In that case, the reader should obtain professional advice from the Department of Agriculture, the State experiment station, a local veterinarian, or the county agent as to available substitutes.

Nutritional Diseases
of Dogs and Cats

BY I. P. EARLE [1]

AS THEY OCCUR under practical conditions, nutritional diseases are more likely to be the result of several dietary deficiencies than of any single one. It is well to know the characteristics of single vitamin and mineral deficiencies, however, as a guide to the proper feeding of dogs and cats and an aid to the diagnosis of nutritional diseases.

THE ANCESTORS of the dog and cat hunted food for themselves and their young from the plains and the woods. Since they ate the vitamin-rich organs and viscera of their prey and the mineral-rich bones as well as the muscles, they probably suffered from no nutritional deficiencies as long as game was plentiful and they were skillful and lucky as hunters. Their meat diet was probably supplemented occasionally with a few green leaves, and they had free access to sunshine. The descendants of these hardy ancestors for the most part no longer hunt their own food but remain in the kennel, around the house, or in the house and accept the food provided for them by man. The food may be the scraps from the table, or it may be a mixture of various products of the slaughterhouse and the mill. In either case the adequacy of the diet largely depends on the care and judgment of the human master.

Some metabolic disturbances in dogs and cats are produced by hereditary defects, but many other conditions of this nature are brought about by a deficiency or unbalance of the nutritional factors required by the animal for maintenance, growth, reproduction, and physical activity. Sometimes nutritional deficiencies are secondary to other conditions which interfere with the proper assimilation and

---

[1] I. P. Earle is Associate Biochemist, Animal Nutrition Division, Bureau of Animal Industry.

utilization of nutritive factors, but more often they are the direct result of an inadequate supply of the required factors in the diet.

Although many studies have been made of the nutritive requirements of dogs and of the effects of specific deficiencies, little is known concerning the nutritional requirements or nutritional diseases of cats. However, since the dietary habits of the wild members of the cat and dog families are somewhat similar, it is assumed that the two species are probably subject to similar deficiency diseases. This assumption is supported by what scant knowledge is available concerning the nutritional diseases of cats.

The most commonly occurring errors in the diet of domestic pet animals are deficiencies in vitamins, minerals, and proteins of good quality. Except in the case of rickets, a positive diagnosis of which can be made by means of the X-ray, some information concerning the previous diet of the animal is often essential in diagnosing a disease of nutritional origin. The careful investigations of the laboratory have been concerned chiefly with the effects of deficiencies of single factors, whereas the disease conditions resulting in actual practice from dietary deficiencies are more often the result of multiple deficiencies. Also the characteristic effects of specific deficiencies usually occur in combination with nonspecific symptoms which may be induced by one or more of several causes. The most common of these nonspecific symptoms is the retardation of growth, which may result from simple starvation, inadequate proteins of good quality, deficient or unbalanced calcium or phosphorus, or a deficiency of one or more of several vitamins. Likewise a degeneration of the central and peripheral (outer) nervous system, with resulting incoordination of movements, may occur as a result of vitamin A deficiency or of some type of vitamin B deficiency.

Some of the more common diseases which are fairly easily recognized as of nutritional origin when they occur in dogs are discussed here. Although the discussion shows that the use of pure vitamins, either by injection or by addition to the feed, may be of value in the treatment of a disease condition for the immediate relief of symptoms, the use of a well-balanced diet of natural feedstuffs which contain adequate amounts of the essential factors constitutes the most important treatment for deficiency diseases, as well as the best preventive measure.

RICKETS

Any disturbance in the mineral metabolism that results in defective or abnormal calcification, or hardening, of growing bones is usually termed rickets. The clinical indications of rickets include lethargy and listlessness, arched neck, crouched stance, knobby and deformed joints, bowed legs, and flabby muscles. The changes characteristic of defective calcification in the young animal are most marked in the zones of growth of the long bones of the legs—at the junction of the end (epiphysis) and shaft—and at the cartilaginous junction of the ribs. At such points there is a cessation of calcification with an excessive production of cartilage and a deposition of fat. In the more advanced stages the entire bone becomes soft and easily deformed or broken. The development of the teeth is also retarded.

The X-ray is a reliable and practical means of diagnosing early rickets and of determining the severity of the disease and the progress of healing. In the dog the characteristic changes are easily recognized, especially in the lower end of the ulna—the large bone of the foreleg—at the joint which corresponds to the wrist joint in man. In the young animal the calcified shaft of the long bone is separated from its more lightly calcified head by a band of uncalcified cartilage. Normally this cartilage grows and is rapidly calcified at the end of the shaft; as the animal matures the cartilage decreases in width and eventually becomes calcified. In the rachitic animal, however, the cartilage continues to grow but is not calcified, thus increasing the width of the uncalcified band. Changes in the normal calcification of bone may be detected by means of the X-ray at a much earlier stage than that at which clinical evidence of rickets appear.

It is now known that rickets may result from a deficiency of calcium, phosphorus, or vitamin D and that it may be prevented and cured, if it is not too advanced, by the inclusion in the diet of adequate amounts of calcium and phosphorus and enough vitamin D to regulate the absorption and assimilation of the minerals.

The dog's requirements for the three factors calcium, phosphorus, and vitamin D have been studied extensively by Morgan and associates (*17, 18, 19, 21, 22*).[2] She has demonstrated that in puppies fed on diets deficient in either calcium or phosphorus severe bone deformities result. The conditions produced by the mineral deficiency can be ameliorated but neither prevented nor cured by vitamin D. She has noted, however, that rickets in dogs is usually of the low-phosphorus type, and has ascribed the condition to a faulty utilization of phosphorus rather than to a deficiency of phosphorus in the diet, since low-phosphorus diets are less likely to be encountered than low-calcium diets. The phosphorus in the cereals which frequently form a large part of the dog's ration is not well utilized by the dog.

There is a wide divergence in the estimates made in different laboratories of the requirements of the dog for vitamin D. The requirements vary with the age of the animal, and apparently with the breed, the amount of sunlight the animal receives, and the ratio of calcium to phosphorus, as well as with the content of calcium and phosphorus, and apparently also a number of other factors in the diet.[3]

It is evident that puppies of the small breeds require far less vitamin D for normal bone development than the large, rapidly growing types with heavy bones. It is also recognized that the requirements of puppies raised indoors are far greater than those of puppies with even limited outdoor life and moderate exposure to sunlight. How-

---

[2] Italic numbers in parentheses refer to Literature Cited, p. 1214.

[3] Arnold and Elvehjem (*1*) found that 5.5 International units of vitamin D per pound of body weight was sufficient to prevent rickets in large-boned puppies on rations containing calcium and phosphorus in a ration of 1.2 : 1, whereas when the calcium-phosphorus ratio was increased to 2 : 1 this amount of vitamin D was insufficient. It has been reported from Morgan's laboratory (*19*) that with the usual purified ration used there, which has a calcium-phosphorus ratio of 1.7 : 1, 33 units of vitamin D per pound per day is sufficient for Cocker Spaniels, but severe rickets can develop in German Shepherds on this same level. The Fleischmann laboratories (*27*) have reported that although 13 units of vitamin D per pound of body weight per day is sufficient for terrier puppies, growing dogs of large breeds may require more than 123 units of vitamin D per pound of body weight per day. The diet that was used in these studies supplied calcium and phosphorus in a ratio of 2.2 : 1.

ever, the minimum requirements obviously vary widely with other factors in the ration.

Experiments (*19*) with very large doses of irradiated ergosterol equivalent to 4,545 or more International units of vitamin D per pound of body weight per day for several weeks have shown that a condition of hypervitaminosis D—too much vitamin D—can be induced in the dog. This condition is characterized by vomiting, greasy hair, bloody diarrhea, and deposition of calcium in the arteries and organs. The range between the body requirements and the toxic dose is wide, but the possibility of overdosage should not be overlooked.

The specific treatment of rickets consists in the administration of vitamin D in addition to an adequate supply of calcium and phosphorus. The best sources of vitamin D are fish-liver oils, irradiated ergosterol, irradiated foods, and the action of sunlight on the skin, which enables the animal to manufacture its own vitamin D..

Bonemeal at a level of 1 or 2 percent of the ration will usually provide sufficient supplementary calcium and phosphorus for puppies of small breeds. Puppies of the larger breeds should have bones and milk in addition. About 0.5 percent each of calcium and phosphorus (in the mineral form, not as bonemeal) in the diet is probably sufficient, however. Arnold and Elvehjem (*1*) have given as an optimum figure 0.27 percent for calcium and 0.22 percent for phosphorus.

Although the requirements of older dogs for calcium and phosphorus and vitamin D are much less than those of young dogs, a condition called osteomalacia, or late rickets, is sometimes observed in grown dogs as a result of the same kinds of deficiencies that cause infantile rickets. In such cases a softening of the bones leads to lameness and deformity.

TETANY OF PARTURITION, OR ECLAMPSIA

Eclampsia occurs sometimes in female dogs and cats shortly before, during, or after the delivery of young. It is apparently the result of a calcium deficiency, possibly associated with a vitamin D deficiency. It is most common in females nursing large litters, in which case the demands of the mother for calcium for milk production are heavy. The symptoms vary in severity from nervousness and mild convulsions to severe attacks which may terminate in coma and death. It has been found that the seizures can be controlled by the administration of calcium, and recurrence is prevented by additions of readily utilized calcium and vitamin D to the diet.

SCURVY

Efforts to produce experimental scurvy in the dog with vitamin C-deficient rations have been unsuccessful, and the evidence is that dogs normally synthesize their own vitamin C. Nevertheless, there are occasional reports of a spontaneously occurring condition resembling scurvy which is relieved by the administration of ascorbic acid (vitamin C) or some vitamin C-rich substance such as lemon juice. Collet (*4*) has described such a condition in young dogs that had been maintained on a diet low in vitamin C. The symptoms observed were a slight anemia, a swelling of the jaw, and signs of pseudoparalysis (a condition resembling paralysis) of the legs. The condition was completely relieved by the administration of lemon or orange juice. Flohil (9) also described symptoms resembling those of scurvy which occurred in dogs fed entirely on cooked feeds and which cleared upon the administration of lemon juice. A similar report has been made by Jordan (15). Gregoire (11) has ascribed a condition in young dogs which he calls Barlow's disease to a vitamin C deficiency in the ration. The animals became anemic, signs of rickets were present, and there was considerable pain on pressure of certain bones near the joints. Although in good condition, the affected animals remained lying down much of the time. He found a lower than normal excretion of vitamin C in the urine of these animals. Some individuals responded to massive doses of ascorbic acid, and others did not. The condition seems to occur only in young animals and appears to result from a failure in vitamin C metabolism, suggesting a failure in the normal functioning of the animal organism in the synthesis of ascorbic acid, the causes of which are not known.

NUTRITIONAL ANEMIAS

Anemia is a deficiency in hemoglobin, the oxygen-carrying pigment in the blood. The physiological effects of anemia result from the diminished power of the blood to absorb oxygen and remove carbon dioxide and include an increase in pulse and respiration rates, rapid onset of fatigue with exercise, and general weakness. Even a mild degree of anemia is recognizable by the pale color of the visable mucous membranes and by blood examination. Anemias may result from such causes as hemorrhage, internal parasites, chronic infectious diseases, and poisoning, or from a faulty diet. Nutritional anemias occur as a result of diets inadequate in the quantity of the constituents that function in the production of hemoglobin. They are most commonly associated with a deficiency of iron or copper or of the B vitamins, or with long-continued underfeeding of proteins essential for the formation of red blood cells.

Copper itself is not a constituent of the hemoglobin molecule, but it is required by the canine as well as by some other species for the utilization of iron, which is essential in hemoglobin formation. Only minute amounts appear to be needed, however. Potter, Elvehjem, and Hart (24) found that growing dogs made anemic by bleeding responded unfavorably when kept on a diet poor in iron and copper supplemented with 30 milligrams of iron a day, but a rapid regeneration of hemoglobin occurred when the ration was supplemented with 30 milligrams of iron and 4 milligrams of copper. Since copper is required in such small amounts it seems unlikely that the ordinary ration of the dog will ever be deficient in the mineral unless the animal is kept on a diet of milk, which is low in both iron and copper. However, the addition of minute amounts of copper seems advisable when an inorganic iron supplement is used in the treatment of anemia.

An iron deficiency in the dog's ration is not rare, but the iron requirements of the normal dog are amply met by a ration containing as much as 10 percent of meat scraps or a reasonable amount of fresh meat. The requirements of the bitch are increased during pregnancy, when she may need a more liberal allowance of iron-containing feeds. The normal pup, in common with other sucklings, has at birth a store of iron which is considerably depleted during the suckling period when the principal food is milk. This loss of iron is repaired as soon as iron-containing feeds are added to the diet to supplement the milk. If the pup's diet fails to include feeds that are good sources of iron, an anemia may result which can be cured by correcting the iron deficiency. Feeds of particular value as sources of iron are liver, kidney, red meat, egg yolk, apricots, peaches, and prunes. Small amounts of inorganic iron (iron oxide or iron citrate) may also be used effectively as sources of available iron.

Another type of anemia results from a deficiency of one of the vitamins of the B complex. The production of anemia in dogs maintained on a blacktongue-producing diet (one lacking in part of the B vitamins) was observed by Spies and Dowling (*26*). They effected an immediate correction of the anemic condition by the administration of yeast. They suggested as a possible explanation of the multiplicity of symptoms seen in dogs on this diet that several essential dietary factors are present in that part of the B complex which was lacking in the diet. The more recent work of Fouts, Helmer, and Lepkovsky (*10*), in which an anemia characterized by small, pale red blood cells was produced in dogs maintained on a synthetic diet amply supplemented with other known B factors, has identified the antianemic factor as apparently identical with vitamin B_6 (pyridoxine), the rat antidermatitis factor. Fresh liver, liver concentrates, liver extract, and yeast are most effective in providing the factor B_6, which is required by both pups and older dogs for the maintenance of a normal hemoglobin level.

The treatment of the primary cause of an anemia depends on the factor responsible for the condition, but the treatment of the anemia itself is much the same in all cases. It consists, aside from emergency measures, in the administration in readily available form of ample supplies of the blood-building materials, including proteins of good quality, iron, copper, and certain of the B vitamins. Liver, either fresh or dried, is a good source of all these factors. Medicinal supplements of inorganic iron and copper or of liver extract or liver concentrates can sometimes be used to good advantage, together with feeds rich in good proteins and in the B vitamins. Meat diets have been found to be strikingly more efficient in regenerating the blood of dogs after repeated blood depletion than diets rich in carbohydrates or in which the proteins were largely supplied by milk and cereals (*29*).

VITAMIN A DEFICIENCY

A diagnosis of vitamin A deficiency in dogs is usually based on symptoms that appear in the advanced stages of the disease, when some animals may fail to recover even when the deficiency is corrected. Probably the most easily recognized symptom is a characteristic disease of the eye called xerophthalmia. Many other conditions less specific and often not so easily recognized as of dietary origin are associated with a deficiency of vitamin A. These include loss of weight, rough coat and scaling skin, incoordination of movements, probably lowered resistance to infections, and, in growing puppies, a stunting of growth.

Frequently the diet supplies almost but not quite enough vitamin A to meet the dog's requirements, and a subacute deficiency extremely difficult to diagnose results. Crimm and Short (5) found that the disease in its subacute stages, before the appearance of obvious clinical symptoms, was characterized by a shift in the percentage of immature cells among the white blood cells of a certain type. This they interpreted as indicating a disturbance in the normal formation of white blood cells. Dogs kept for a year on rations in which the vitamin A deficiency was not severe enough to produce loss of weight or xerophthalmia showed changes in the epithelial (surface) cells lining the small bronchial tubes of the lungs as well as changes in the white blood cells.

Experimental work with some other animal species has indicated that one of the earliest symptoms of a vitamin A deficiency is night blindness, or a failure in the adaptability of the eyes to dim light. Although apparently little attention has been given to the effects of vitamin A on the night vision of dogs, it seems likely that the vitamin plays the same role in this species as in the others studied.

While xerophthalmia may develop relatively early in young dogs deprived of sufficient vitamin A, it is indicative of an acute deficiency that develops gradually. First the eyes appear watery and glassy, and the conjunctiva becomes congested. Later the tear ducts become blocked, infection appears, and there is inflammation and edema (watery swelling) of the cornea and finally ulceration. Permanent blindness usually results from xerophthalmia after it has reached the advanced stages of severe degeneration of the cornea. Eye symptoms are usually accompanied by other symptoms of disturbances in the body, such as loss of appetite, unhealthy skin and coat, and a muscular incoordination and weakness that eventually end in paralysis. This condition is the result of the nerve degeneration induced by lack of the vitamin.

Deafness appears to be another manifestation of a deficiency of vitamin A which occurs in young dogs. Mellanby (16) reported in 1938 that puppies fed for some months on diets of natural feedstuffs deficient in vitamin A evidenced incoordination in movements, inattentiveness, and deafness. He found in such animals an overgrowth of bone near the brain in such a position as to stretch the auditory nerve, thereby causing it to degenerate. Poor growth and faulty tooth development are also associated with a deficiency of vitamin A in the pup.

Higgins (14) has reported the experimental production of urinary stones in dogs deprived of vitamin A. There are occasional reports of the finding of kidney or bladder stones in vitamin-deficient dogs on post mortem examination. It has been shown in some other species that a relationship exists between the formation of urinary stones and vitamin A deficiency, but apparently other factors are also involved. The use of vitamin A therapy in the treatment of urinary stones is a subject for further experimentation.

Fish-liver oil is commonly used as a concentrated source of vitamin A for supplementing the diet as well as for medicinal treatment. Bradfield and Smith (*3*), however, have reported that puppies utilize vitamin A in cod-liver oil, pure carotene in oil, and carotene as it occurs naturally in carrots and other foods equally well as a source of vitamin A in repairing a deficiency. Carotene, however, is probably utilized less economically than true vitamin A for storage in the body. Feeds that are particularly valuable as sources of vitamin A in the dog's diet are liver, green leaves of vegetables, and alfalfa leaf meal of good quality.

Various estimates of the amount of vitamin A needed by the dog range from 10 International units to more than 360 per pound of body weight. According to suggestions made by Guilbert, Howell, and Hart (*12*), 80 units (16 micrograms) of vitamin A per pound of body weight per day is a good allowance for dogs. Morgan (*19*), however, has recommended an amount in excess of 360 International units per pound of body weight per day. In treating a deficiency very large doses can apparently be given with safety.

DEFICIENCIES OF THE B VITAMINS

THIAMIN, OR VITAMIN B₁, DEFICIENCY

Spontaneous outbreaks of a disease in dogs which closely parallels beriberi in humans have been reported. Symptoms are a loss of appetite, vomiting, either a diarrhea or constipation, cutaneous edema (watery swelling of the skin), muscular tenderness, and a periodic inability to stand. The symptoms yield rather promptly to injections of thiamin and to the addition to the diet of dried brewers' yeast or some other good source of vitamin B_1.

The antiberiberi factor (vitamin B_1, or thiamin) is required preformed in the ration for the normal growth of young dogs and the maintenance of health in both young and adults. The earliest and most conspicuous effect of a deficiency is a marked loss of appetite, which occurs in dogs more promptly as a result of thiamin deficiency than of any other vitamin deficiency. In general, the symptoms associated in the dog with a deficiency of vitamin B_1 may be grouped as arising either from the failure of normal functioning of the gastrointestinal tract, with a marked loss of tone, or from disorders of the nervous system. The appearance of symptoms varies with the severity of the deficiency and undoubtedly with the extent of complications arising from other deficiencies that may result from decreased food consumption or impaired adsorption and assimilation. The early stages of the deficiency are marked by loss of appetite, fatigue, nervousness, restlessness, and irritability, whereas the advanced stages are characterized by manifestations of polyneuritis (inflammation of many nerves at once) such as muscular tenderness, incoordination of movements, and paralysis of the hindquarters.

Although degenerative changes in the nerves have often been demonstrated in association with thiamin deficiency, more recent evidence (8) shows that the nervous symptoms of uncomplicated thiamin deficiency are not due to any actual break-down of tissues in the nervous system. When degeneration of nerve tissues occurs, it may probably be attributed to deficiencies of vitamin A or of other factors of the B complex. The profound nervous disturbances which occur in an uncomplicated deficiency of thiamin and which respond within a few hours to the administration of thiamin are probably produced by disturbances of nerve metabolism rather than by degenerative changes in the nerve tissues themselves.

Thiamin is believed to have a specific role in the carbohydrate metabolism of nerve tissue. The thiamin requirements of the animal are related directly to the nonfat calories of the diet rather than to body weight; hence diets low in fat and high in carbohydrates require a higher level of thiamin than diets high in fat. Arnold and Elvehjem (1) have shown that both growing and mature dogs can be protected from the loss of appetite associated with thiamin deficiency by 360 micrograms, or 120 International units, of thiamin to each pound of a ration low in fat. This supplies 3 to 4.5 units of thiamin per pound of body weight per day for an average-sized mature dog. Therapeutic (medicinal) doses of 10 times this amount or more have been used to give prompt relief from nervous symptoms of thiamin deficiency.

Of the group of B vitamins, thiamin is the most easily destroyed by heat. It has been shown that as much as 80 percent of the thiamin content may be lost during the canning of dog food. Likewise the processing of meat scrap at high temperatures reduces the thiamin content. Grain byproducts from which the germ and outer covering have been removed, as well as all processed foods, are likely to be low in this vitamin.

Thiamin occurs, along with other members of the B complex, in organ and muscle meats (pork muscle is 7 to 8 times as rich in thiamin as beef muscle), yeast, the germ and outer portions of grains, milk, egg yolk, and most fruits.

Fright Disease

Fright disease is adequately discussed in the article by C. D. Stein, page 1193. However, since there have been many reports of a response of the condition to a change of ration and other reports of the immediate relief of symptoms with thiamin treatment in cases characterized by the nervous-running-howling-convulsions complex, the possible relation of the condition to a thiamin deficiency should be mentioned here. Patton (23) has recently observed the production of fright disease in dogs fed a certain commercial feed low in vitamin B_1. The nervous condition was relieved within a few hours by thiamin injection. Many attempts have been made to produce the condition on experimental diets low in thiamin, diets low in protein, and

diets containing protein denatured by heat. Arnold and Elvehjem
(*2*) succeeded in producing the symptoms with a diet of meat scrap
and wheat which had been heated to 392° F.; the animals failed to
respond to thiamin administration.

RIBOFLAVIN DEFICIENCY

Since a deficiency of riboflavin, or vitamin B_2, probably never
occurs spontaneously in the diet of the dog except in the presence of
deficiencies of other B vitamins, the specific effects of a ribroflavin
deficiency alone may never be observed uncomplicated by other factors except in the laboratory. These effects consist, in the early stages,
of a variable dermatitis, or skin inflammation, partial loss of appetite,
and loss of weight and, in the acute stages, of sudden collapse followed by death unless treatment with riboflavin intervenes. The dermatitis appears first as a reddening of the skin, followed by a dry
scaliness. It occurs usually on the chest and abdomen and the inner
surfaces of the legs near the body. In the male it involves the scrotum. In the acute stage of the deficiency the animal becomes apa-
thetic, walks with a staggering gait if it walks at all, and evidences
a marked weakness. If no treatment is given the animal soon passes
into a coma and dies within several hours, apparently from respiratory failure. Sebrell and Onstott (*25*) have described a characteristic
yellow mottling of the liver and degenerative changes in the central
nervous system in such animals.

The injection of 0.34 milligram of riboflavin per pound of body
weight into animals in this collapsed state results in prompt recovery
if given in time. Street and Cowgill (*28*) have found that 11.4
micrograms of riboflavin per pound of body weight per day in the
ration is sufficient to satisfy the dog's requirements for an extended
period.

Riboflavin is widely distributed in plant and animal tissues. It is
present in milk, meat, yeast, eggs, and many fruits and vegetables.
It occurs in higher concentration in the liver and kidney than in
muscle meat. Yeast is an especially rich source. Although it is less
sensitive to heat than thiamin, riboflavin is destroyed by high temperatures somewhat above boiling. The content of riboflavin in meat
is decreased by frying or roasting.

BLACKTONGUE AND NICOTINIC ACID

Elvehjem, Madden, Strong, and Woolley (*6*) were the first to report that nicotinic acid will prevent and cure the condition in dogs
known as blacktongue. It has recently been shown by Heath, Mac-
Queen, and Spies (*13*) that cats are subject to a similar condition
which responds to the same treatment. However, as this disease
occurs spontaneously, it is probably the result of a multiple deficiency,
since ordinary rations deficient in nicotinic acid are likely to be
deficient in other vitamins of the B complex also. The occurrence
of blacktongue has been observed most often in those areas of the
South where the dog's ration is somewhat similar in character to the

diets producing pellagra in man, that is, where the ration consists largely of such products as corn meal, salt pork, cowpeas, and sweetpotatoes.

The onset of typical blacktongue is characterized by lassitude, loss of appetite, and sometimes vomiting. The mouth gives off a characteristic foul odor. The mucous membranes of the cheeks, gums, and tongue are reddened and inflamed, sometimes showing more or less extensive purplish-red areas where the congestion is most marked. The front end of the tongue is most likely to be affected in this way. The inner surfaces of cheeks and lips may even be covered with pustules and ulcers. Constipation is often noted at the onset of the disease, and a diarrhea develops in the later stages.

If the disease has not progressed too far, recovery may be effected by proper treatment; otherwise, death results. Nicotinic acid or liver extract may be given by injection as an emergency measure. Attention should be given to cleansing the mouth, if this is needed. Aside from these measures, treatment consists in adjustment of the diet to include foods such as fresh liver, dried yeast, beef muscle, wheat germ, eggs, and milk, which are good sources of nicotinic acid and other vitamins of the B complex.

It has been shown that 0.23 milligram of nicotinic acid per pound of body weight per day will cure the symptoms of blacktongue in the dog (7). Half this amount is probably sufficient to give protection against blacktongue, although it will not promote normal growth in young dogs.

Morgan (20) has called attention to the possible dangers of administering large amounts of nicotinic acid in the presence of a deficiency of other factors of the B complex. She has observed that dogs receiving purified rations deficient in both nicotinic acid and the so-called filtrate fraction of the B complex suffer a more rapid decline if nicotinic acid alone is administered than if neither factor is given. In the treatment of blacktongue, care should be exercised to avoid bringing about a condition of unbalance among the various B factors by using nicotinic acid alone without including other factors of the B complex.

Deficiencies of Other Factors of the B Complex

The anemia produced by a deficiency of pyridoxin, or vitamin B_6, has already been mentioned.

In addition to thiamin, riboflavin, nicotinic acid, and pyridoxin, dogs require two or more of the remaining factors of the B complex. It has been shown that pantothenic acid is necessary for normal growth and health of the dog, and that filtrate factor W, referred to as the anti-gray-hair factor, is necessary for the maintenance of a healthy condition of the fur and for neuromuscular control. Morgan (20) has demonstrated an interrelation between nicotinic acid, pantothenic acid, and the filtrate factor W and has indicated that there may be other factors of the B complex which have a function in canine nutrition. The requirements for pantothenic acid and the factor W are not yet determined.

LITERATURE CITED

(1) ARNOLD, AARON, and ELVEHJEM, C. A.
   1939. NUTRITIONAL REQUIREMENTS OF DOGS. Amer. Vet. Med. Assoc. Jour. 95: 187–194, illus.
(2) ———— and ELVEHJEM, C. A.
   1939. IS RUNNING FITS A DEFICIENCY DISEASE? Amer. Vet. Med. Assoc. Jour. 95: 303–308, illus.
(3) BRADFIELD, DOROTHY, and SMITH, MARGARET CAMMACH.
   1938. THE ABILITY OF THE DOG TO UTILIZE VITAMIN A FROM PLANT AND ANIMAL SOURCES. Amer. Jour. Physiol. 124: 168–173.
(4) COLLET, P.
   1935. LA MALADIE DE BARLOW SPONTANÉE CHEZ LE CHIEN (SCORBUT INFANTILE). Rev. Vét. [Toulouse] 87: [497]–537, illus.
(5) CRIMM, PAUL D., and SHORT, DARWIN M.
   1937. VITAMIN A DEFICIENCY IN THE DOG. Amer. Jour. Physiol. 118: 477–482, illus.
(6) ELVEHJEM, C. A., MADDEN, R. J., STRONG, F. M., and WOOLLEY, D. W.
   1937. RELATION OF NICOTINIC ACID AND NICOTINIC ACID AMIDE TO CANINE BLACK TONGUE. Amer Chem. Soc. Jour. 59: 1767–1768.
(7) ———— MADDEN, ROBERT J., STRONG, F. M., and WOOLLEY, D. W.
   1938. THE ISOLATION AND IDENTIFICATION OF THE ANTI-BLACK TONGUE FACTOR. Jour. Biol. Chem. 123: 137–149, illus.
(8) ENGEL, R. W., and PHILLIPS, P. H.
   1938. THE LACK OF NERVE DEGENERATION IN UNCOMPLICATED VITAMIN B_1 DEFICIENCY IN THE CHICK AND THE RAT. Jour. Nutr. 16: 585–596.
(9) FLOHIL, J.
   1933. SCORBUT BIJ HONDEN [SCURVY IN DOGS]. Tijdschr. v. Diergeneesk. 60: 633. [In Dutch. English summary, p. 634.]
(10) FOUTS, PAUL J., HELMER, OSCAR M., and LEPKOVSKY, SAMUEL.
   1940. NUTRITIONAL MICROCYTIC HYPOCHROMIC ANEMIA IN DOGS CURED WITH CRYSTALLINE FACTOR I. Amer. Jour. Med. Sci. 199: 163–166.
(11) GREGOIRE, C.
   1938. [VITAMIN C AND BARLOW'S DISEASE IN THE DOG.] Ann. Med. Vét. 83: 366–371. [Abstract in North Amer. Vet. 21: 164. 1940.]
(12) GUILBERT, H. R., HOWELL, C. E., and HART, G. H.
   1940. MINIMUM VITAMIN A AND CAROTENE REQUIREMENTS OF MAMMALIAN SPECIES. Jour. Nutr. 19: 91–103, illus.
(13) HEATH, M. K., MACQUEEN, J. W., and SPIES, T. D.
   1940. FELINE PELLAGRA. Science 92: 514.
(14) HIGGINS, C. C.
   1936. URINARY LITHIASIS. EXPERIMENTAL PRODUCTION AND SOLUTION WITH CLINICAL APPLICATION AND END-RESULTS. Jour. Urol. 36: 168–177.
(15) JORDAN, MARJORIE G.
   1940. A CASE OF VITAMIN C DEFICIENCY. Vet. Jour. 96: 214–215.
(16) MELLANBY, EDWARD.
   1938. THE EXPERIMENTAL PRODUCTION OF DEAFNESS IN YOUNG ANIMALS BY DIET. Jour. Physiol. 94: 380–398, illus.
(17) MORGAN, AGNES FAY.
   1933. EFFECT OF DIET ON RESPONSE TO PARATHYROID EXTRACT AND VITAMIN D. IV. THE EFFECT OF DIETS OF NORMAL CALCIUM AND PHOSPHORUS CONTENT IN DOGS. Amer. Jour. Physiol. 105: 621–634, illus.
(18) ————
   1934. THE EFFECT OF ACID, NEUTRAL, AND BASIC DIETS ON THE CALCIUM AND PHOSPHORUS METABOLISM OF DOGS. Calif. Univ. Publs., Physiol. 8: 61–106, illus.
(19) ————
   1940. DEFICIENCIES AND FALLACIES IN CANINE DIET. North Amer. Vet. 21: 476–483.
(20) ————
   1941. THE EFFECT OF IMBALANCE IN THE "FILTRATE FRACTION" OF THE VITAMIN B COMPLEX IN DOGS. Science 93: 261–262.

(21) MORGAN, AGNES FAY, and GARRISON, E. ALTA.
1933. THE EFFECT OF DIET ON RESPONSE TO PARATHYROID EXTRACT AND VITA-
MIN D. II. THE EFFECT OF HIGH CALCIUM-LOW PHOSPHORUS DIETS IN
DOGS. Amer. Jour. Physiol. 105: 596–607, illus.
(22) ——— GARRISON, E. ALTA, and HILLS, MARGUERITE J.
1933. THE EFFECT OF DIET ON RESPONSE TO PARATHYROID EXTRACT AND VITA-
MIN D. III. THE EFFECT OF LOW CALCIUM-HIGH PHOSPHORUS DIETS
IN DOGS. Amer. Jour. Physiol. 105: 608–620, illus.
(23) PATTON, JOHN W.
1939. FRIGHT DISEASE AN AVITAMINOSIS. Vet. Med. 34: 372–381, illus.
(24) POTTER, V. R., ELVEHJEM, C. A., and HART, E. B.
1938. ANEMIA STUDIES WITH DOGS. Jour. Biol. Chem. 126: 155–173.
(25) SEBRELL, W. H., and ONSTOTT, R. H.
1938. RIBOFLAVIN DEFICIENCY IN DOGS. U. S. Pub. Health Serv., Pub. Health
Rpts. 53: 83–94.
(26) SPIES, TOM D., and DOWLING, ALEXANDER S.
1935. THE EXPERIMENTAL PRODUCTION OF ANEMIA IN DOGS BY MEANS OF A
BLACKTONGUE-PRODUCING DIET. Amer. Jour. Physiol. 114: 25–29,
illus.
(27) STANDARD BRANDS INCORPORATED.
1939. A SYLLABUS ON VITAMIN D AND METHODS OF SUPPLYING IT TO FARM
ANIMALS. Vitamin D Digest 1: 37–40.
(28) STREET, HAROLD R., and COWGILL, GEORGE R.
1939. ACUTE RIBOFLAVIN DEFICIENCY IN THE DOG. Amer Jour. Physiol.
125: 323–334.
(29) WHIPPLE, G. H., ROBSCHEIT, F. S., and HOOPER, C. W.
1920. BLOOD REGENERATION FOLLOWING SIMPLE ANEMIA. IV. INFLUENCE OF
MEAT, LIVER AND VARIOUS EXTRACTIVES, ALONE OR COMBINED WITH
STANDARD DIETS. Amer. Jour. Psysiol. 53: 236–262.

At the time this book went to press, the drugs
and other materials mentioned in various articles—chiefly as disinfectants, insecticides, and
anthelmintics—were still available for veterinary and medical use. Under war conditions,
however, it is possible that some of these materials may become scarce or unavailable. In
that case, the reader should obtain professional
advice from the Department of Agriculture, the
State experiment station, a local veterinarian,
or the county agent as to available substitutes.

Diseases of Wildlife and Their Relationship to Domestic Livestock

BY J. E. SHILLINGER [1]

CONSERVATIONISTS have discovered that wild animals are more subject to diseases and parasites than most people realize. Some of the problems raised by this situation are important to livestock producers and the general public as well as to those interested in our wildlife resources.

MOST OF THE STUDIES of diseases of wildlife have been carried on primarily in relation to human welfare and the transmissibility of these diseases to domestic livestock rather than for the benefit of wildlife itself. Today the emphasis is changing somewhat, and wildlife diseases are being studied as a necessary part of conservation.

Despite the views of many older writers, losses among wild species from disease are very considerable. The isolation of many wild animals in places remote from human habitations and their general tendency to scatter rather than to concentrate make it difficult to obtain information on the mortality from disease among them. It is also a characteristic of wild animals, when they are sick, to secrete themselves in dense cover or in burrows, thus making their discovery unlikely; and scavenger insects, birds, and animals rapidly dispose of carcasses in exposed places, so that shortly after their death little trace of them remains. Nevertheless, from time to time epizootics, or severe outbreaks of disease, of varying degrees of de-

[1] J. E. Shillinger is in Charge, Section of Disease Investigations, Division of Wildlife Research, Fish and Wildlife Service, Department of the Interior.

1217

structiveness have been found to occur in practically all species of wildlife thus far studied.

In this article, cross references will be made to other articles in the Yearbook in which specific diseases are discussed at greater length in relation to domestic animals.

BACTERIAL DISEASES

The disease in cattle known as brucellosis (p. 501), or Bang's disease, and also commonly referred to as contagious abortion (*11*)[2] is a rather common infection among certain big-game ruminants. There has been little opportunity to examine many specimens from the wild, but studies made of those under semicontrolled conditions on large fenced ranges and in parks have revealed a fairly high degree of incidence. The course of the disease in buffaloes is similar to that in domestic cattle. After infection has been established in a herd for some time the rate of loss of calves is not high, but reactors can be detected by agglutinins in the blood serum.

Isolated infecting agents and the agglutinins found indicate that the organisms present in infected buffaloes and elk are identical with *Brucella abortus* of cattle, but because of the vicious nature of the wild animals and the danger to the attendants, as well as to the beasts themselves, occasioned by repeated handling, no organized effort has been made to eradicate brucellosis from these big-game groups by the removal of reactors. Immunization of herds by calf vaccination, however, is being put in practice where feasible. Thus it is planned eventually to be able to maintain herds of buffaloes and elk free of infection to be used for restocking.

On various occasions hemorrhagic septicemia (see p. 526) has been responsible for extensive losses among deer and buffaloes. Deer of the eastern white-tailed species, as well as the mule deer of the West, are not infrequently victims and large concentrated herds may suffer very great losses. The infection attacks adults as well as fawns. On autopsy the same pathological picture as that in domestic stock is evident. An especially effective protective bacterin has been produced from a highly virulent organism that has been isolated from buffaloes (*5*).

Tuberculosis (see p. 237) has been frequently diagnosed in deer, foxes, wild ducks, and wild pheasants, but it is not considered likely that it is spread extensively among wild species. There is ample opportunity, however, for such animals as deer and foxes to be infected by domestic cattle and for wild birds to acquire the disease from domestic poultry.

Where large wild ruminants are fed by attendants, as they have often been in Jackson Hole, Wyo., for example, losses are frequently caused by organisms associated with pollution of the soil. One of the most destructive of these is *Actinomyces necrophorus*, which infects through abrasions of the mucous lining of the mouth, causing necrobacillosis, or necrotic stomatitis. This organism is a common

---

[2] Italic numbers in parentheses refer to Literature Cited, p. 1225.

inhabitant of moist, loamy soils, especially where there are accumulations of animal droppings or decaying vegetation.

The growth of the organism in the wound produces a general swelling of the part affected, followed by a rather rapid degeneration and destruction of adjacent tissues.   In young animals death usually takes place soon, but adults may survive a more chronic type of the disease for a considerable period.   Fawns raised in enclosed pens have shown as high incidence of this disease as have domestic calves kept in an insanitary environment.

To control losses in elk it is recommended that the animals be discouraged from congregating in concentrated herds and that if it is necessary to feed them they be fed at new places each day.   Hay containing sharp awns or beards that may penetrate the animals' gums should not be given them.   Small pens in which fawns are confined should be kept as sanitary as possible.

On several occasions malignant edema has been diagnosed in deer (*8, 9*).   The outbreaks were limited to comparatively small areas and short periods of time, but during their progress losses were marked.   The disease usually makes its appearance on ranges where animals have been abundant for some time.

The length of the incubation period is not known, but in severe cases infected animals survive only a few days after the first symptoms are recognized.   The causative organism is *Clostridium septique*, and the symptoms produced are somewhat like those of blackleg (see p. 523).   Swellings of the large muscles of the quarters occur, with gaseous cavities and a bloody exudate, or discharge, in the tissues just beneath the skin.   The internal organs do not always show pronounced changes, though sometimes the lungs and spleen are grossly affected and there are bloody effusions into the abdominal cavity.

The organism is widely distributed in the soil, and pollution with animal wastes furnishes an ideal environment for its multiplication. Dispersal of concentrations of deer and removal of the animals, if possible, from the areas where losses are prevalent are therefore recommended.

Among the diseases of wildlife transmissible to man, tularemia, caused by the organism *Pasteurella tularense*, has attracted Nationwide attention (fig. 1).   Because the infection in a large proportion of the cases in human beings has been traced to wild rabbits, the disease is frequently called rabbit fever.   Investigations have shown, however, that a great variety of animals, including some species of birds, are susceptible to the infection (see p. 295).   Rodents and related groups of mammals are especially susceptible.[3]   The carnivorous mammals are somewhat less likely to become infected, but they do not entirely escape.

The causative organisms, which are transmitted from animal to animal and from animal to man either by direct contact or by the bites of insects and ticks, are widespread in nature.   Severe epizootics of tularemia occur among cottontail rabbits and cause extensive losses over large areas; and although the disease may or may not be the

---

[3] BELL, W. B., and SHILLINGER, J. E.   TULAREMIA, AN ANIMAL-BORNE DISEASE.   U. S. Bur. Biol. Survey Wildlife Res. and Mangt. Leaflet BS–5, 3 pp. 1935. [Processed.]

cause of the periodic decline of certain game species, its ravages among dense populations of certain groups are marked.   At present, control measures in the wild are not practicable.

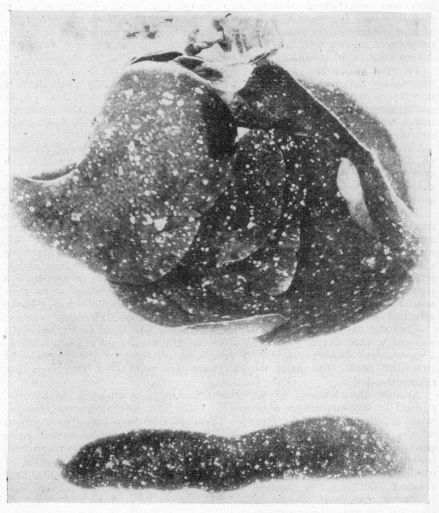

FIGURE 1.—Characteristic appearance of the liver and spleen of a rabbit affected with tularemia.   Multiple white spots on these organs are an indication of the disease.

Human beings may reduce the likelihood of contracting the disease by avoiding contact with sick rabbits or other animals and by protecting themselves against the bites of ticks and deer flies.

FILTRABLE VIRUS DISEASES

Foot-and-mouth disease, or aphthous fever (p. 263), is probably the most important of the diseases shared by domestic stock and wildlife. The great infectivity of the virus of this disease for wild cloven-footed animals has long been recognized in European countries, and extensive losses of deer (7) from foot-and-mouth disease occurred in this country several years ago.

Lameness and soreness, with the formation of small swellings filled with fluid above the hoof and between its halves, as well as around the muzzle and within the mouth, are the symptoms of foot-and-mouth disease in deer, as in cattle and swine. Since the disease is not now present in the United States, it is not an immediate menace to deer. The highly infectious nature of the virus, however, demands that special consideration be given to the big-game ruminants as well as to the domestic species in the event that it is again introduced into this country.

Experimentation thus far indicates that treatment is of little avail in stamping out an epizootic of this disease, and hence slaughter and deep burial are prescribed for its eradication. In the single known American outbreak affecting deer, this plan was used, and despite the wide ranging habits of the affected animals it was completely effective.

The devastating disease of horses known as encephalomyelitis (see p. 375) is caused by a filtrable virus that investigations have shown is sometimes present also in wild pheasants (12) and semiwild pigeons (4) as well as in various other wild birds and mammals. The occurrence of such a pathogenic, or disease-producing virus, in wild, free-flying species is a serious obstacle to adequate control or eradication of the disease, and the readiness with which the virus is carried from one animal to another by mosquitoes adds to the menace of infection from wild reservoirs of the disease.

In several sections of the United States cottontail rabbits with long, horny, tumerous growths have been observed. Most often seen about the head, these hard outgrowths are usually referred to by hunters as "horns." They are caused by a filtrable virus and can be produced on test animals with invariably fatal results.

A less dangerous fleshy type of tumor caused by a filtrable virus is found on the feet and legs of cottontails and is mildly infectious among domestic rabbits also. It is not fatal to either group and in domestic rabbits produces an immunity or protection against the fatal virus disease myxomatosis, which is very destructive to commercially raised rabbits.

PROTOZOAN DISEASES

In various parts of the country a protozoan, *Leucocytozoon anatis*, which lives in the blood, has been observed to cause extensive losses among young wild ducks. This organism appears to infest adult birds without causing serious injury, but when it is transferred to the young the mortality may be high. It is transmitted by bites of the blackfly (*Simulium venustrum*), an insect that has a wide distribution and breeds in rippling streams. The mortality rate is said (*10*) to be 10 to 100 percent for young ducklings and less than 1 percent among adults.

According to investigations conducted at the University of Michigan leucocytozoa (p. 1018) are equally infectious for domestic and wild ducks, and numerous cases are recorded in which the infection was traced from penned birds of domestic as well as wild species to free-flying waterfowl.

Control measures consist in eliminating the habitats of the vector flies or, in the case of penned birds, the avoidance of hatching out ducklings during the period in midsummer when the flies are abundant. Screening the pens to prevent the flies from infecting the young ducklings is recommended for places where such a practice is feasible.

Examination of sharp-tailed grouse from the North Central States, where losses were occurring, showed a malarial organism (*Plasmodium pedioecetae*) in the red blood cells (*13*). Of 130 birds from one area in North Dakota, 53 showed the infection. Studies of this malaria are in progress to ascertain its importance and its relationship to losses in other wild and domestic birds. It is transmissible to the bobwhite quail but apparently not to chickens. While naturally affected grouse were observed to live for several weeks with chronic infections, artificially infected grouse developing acute cases died in a much shorter time.

It has been demonstrated (*1*) that the blood parasite *Anaplasma marginale*, recognized in recent years as the cause of a widespread disease in cattle (see p. 579), is infectious also for the Columbian black-tailed deer. It has not been shown that anaplasmosis is seriously pathogenic to the deer, and it may be that these animals serve as reservoirs from which the infection can be transmitted to livestock. The studies made have been too limited to demonstrate the distribution of the disease, but it appears possible that other kinds of big game also may carry the infection.

PARASITIC DISEASES

The possibility of the transmission of external parasites from domestic stock to wild animals and vice versa has aroused much conjecture. As to mange, no differences in the causative mites occurring on animals of the respective groups have been detected. Individual strains of these parasites appear to have a preference for certain species of animals, although under the microscope the strains show similar characters. It has not been determined whether host preference itself may be relied upon for differentiation or whether in suitable situations the mites may be cross-transmitted.

In the Southern States, where stockmen have been plagued by summer losses of farm animals due to screwworms, or larvae of the fly *Cochliomyia americana* (see p. 313), conservationists have also observed losses among deer and other wildlife. Infestation usually follows skin wounds, many of which are caused by ticks. The losses among deer are widely distributed throughout the South and in some localities are quite heavy. Where domestic and wild animals are permitted to remain unattended, several broods of the flies may be produced each season, thus building up a very heavy degree of parasitism. Whenever these flesh fly larvae become numerous in a wound the damage is extensive, resulting in rapid destruction of the flesh and even of bone tissue (fig. 2). When vital parts are reached, death may follow within a few days.

Several kinds of roundworms of domestic stock are parasitic in important wildlife species, causing injury to organs and damage to health comparable to that seen in livestock (see p. 113).

The lungworm of domestic cattle (*Dictyocaulus hadweni*) is also common in wild ruminants (*2*), having been recorded in this country from the buffalo, moose, elk, reindeer, and three species of deer. Likewise the lungworm common to sheep (*D. filaria*) is parasitic in the eastern white-tailed deer and the western black-tailed deer.

The stomach worm of sheep and cattle (*Haemonchus contortus*) (*3*), which causes anemia and unthriftiness is a common parasite of deer, becoming very numerous under conditions of overpopulation

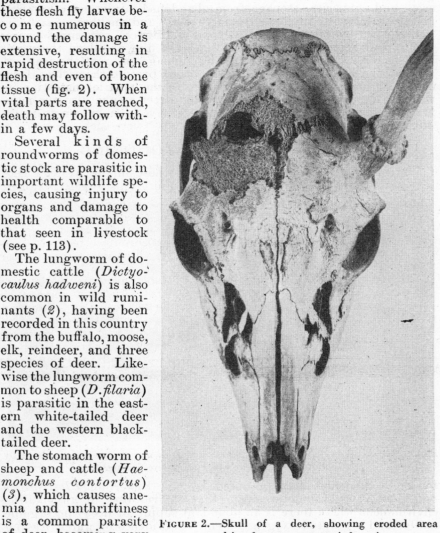

FIGURE 2.—Skull of a deer, showing eroded area resulting from screwworm infestation.

and contributing to the heavy winter losses that occur when feed is scarce and living conditions difficult.

POLLUTION

Extensive waste of wildlife has been observed as a result of water pollution, which in many instances has rendered the aquatic environment uninhabitable. Much damage is done to fishes, although aquatic mammals and birds suffer also (fig. 3). Chief among the sources of pollution are city sewage; wastes from sawmills, paper mills, creameries, and canneries; seepage from abandoned mines and oil works; and chemical waste products from dye works and smelters.

Pollution by oil and certain toxic substances sometimes causes widespread destruction. Even a very thin film of oil on the water used by waterfowl will adhere to the plumage and mat the feathers, so that the birds are unable to fly or to protect themselves from cold. Poisonous chemicals may adhere to the aquatic vegetation on which waterfowl feed, causing death by direct action. In this manner lead deposits released from smelters have been known to result in considerable losses.

BOTULISM, OR FOOD POISONING

Waterfowl and shore birds, especially those in the western lake regions (6), are frequent victims of botulism. This disease is caused

FIGURE 3.—A group of whistling swans affected with metallic poisoning caused by pollution of the lake where they were feeding.

by the toxic substances produced by the bacterium *Clostridium botulinum*, type C, an organism that thrives best in an alkaline environment where there is an abundant supply of decaying organic matter and a reduced oxygen content. Subsidence of water, leaving pools little affected by flowage or wind action, is frequently followed by extensive outbreaks of this disease. Birds feeding in these pools ingest sufficient toxin with their food to cause progressive weakness, paralysis, and death. Losses have sometimes been enormous.

The best-known control measure is to manipulate the water level so as to prevent stagnation in shallow places. Areas in the danger regions where an ample supply of fresh water is not available during late summer and fall should be drained completely dry if possible.

LITERATURE CITED

(1) BOYNTON, WILLIAM HUTCHINS, and WOODS, GLADYS M.
 1940. ANAPLASMOSIS AMONG DEER IN THE NATURAL STATE. Science 91: 168.

(2) DIKMANS, G.
 1936. A NOTE ON DICTYOCAULUS FROM DOMESTIC AND WILD RUMINANTS. Wash. Acad. Sci. Jour. 26: 298–303, illus.

(3) ———
 1939. HELMINTH PARASITES OF NORTH AMERICAN SEMIDOMESTICATED AND WILD RUMINANTS. Helminthol. Soc. Wash. Proc. 6: 97–101.

(4) FOTHERGILL, LEROY D., and DINGLE, JOHN H.
 1938. A FATAL DISEASE OF PIGEONS CAUSED BY THE VIRUS OF THE EASTERN VARIETY OF EQUINE ENCEPHALOMYELITIS. Science 88: 549–550.

(5) GOCHENOUR, WM. S.
 1924. HEMORRHAGIC SEPTICEMIA STUDIES: THE DEVELOPMENT OF A POTENT IMMUNIZING AGENT (NATURAL AGGRESSIN) BY THE USE OF HIGHLY VIRULENT STRAINS OF HEMORRHAGIC SEPTICEMIA ORGANISMS. Amer. Vet. Med. Assoc. Jour. 65: 433–441.

(6) KALMBACH, E. R., and GUNDERSON, MILLARD F.
 1934. WESTERN DUCK SICKNESS: A FORM OF BOTULISM. U. S. Dept. Agr. Tech. Bul. 411, 82 pp., illus.

(7) KEANE, CHARLES.
 1926. THE EPIZOOTIC OF FOOT AND MOUTH DISEASE IN CALIFORNIA. Calif. Dept. Agr. Spec. Pub. 65, 54 pp., illus.

(8) LE DUNE, E. K., and VOLKMAR, FRITZ.
 1934. MALIGNANT EDEMA IN DEER. Vet. Med. 29: 276–279.

(9) MCKENNEY, F. D.
 1938. MALIGNANT EDEMA IN DEER. North Amer. Wildlife Conf. Trans. 3: 886–889.

(10) O'ROKE, EARL C.
 1934. A MALARIA-LIKE DISEASE OF DUCKS CAUSED BY LEUCOCYTOZOON ANATIS WICKWARE. Mich. Univ. School Forestry and Conserv. Bul. 4, 44 pp., illus.

(11) TUNNICLIFF, E. A., and MARSH, H.
 1935. BANG'S DISEASE IN BISON AND ELK IN THE YELLOWSTONE NATIONAL PARK AND ON THE NATIONAL BISON RANGE. Amer. Vet. Med. Assoc. Jour. 86: 745–752, illus.

(12) TYZZER, ERNEST EDWARD, SELLARDS, ANDREW WATSON, and BENNETT, BYRON L.
 1938. THE OCCURRENCE IN NATURE OF "EQUINE ENCEPHALOMYELITIS" IN THE RING-NECKED PHEASANT. Science 88: 505–506.

(13) WETMORE, PSYCHE W.
 1939. A SPECIES OF PLASMODIUM FROM THE SHARP-TAILED GROUSE INFECTIVE TO OTHER BIRDS. Jour. Wildlife Mangt. 3: 361–365, illus.

Diseases of Farm-Raised Game Birds

BY J. E. SHILLINGER [1]

ON A GOOD MANY FARMS today domestic game birds are raised for restocking. Diseases and parasites, of course, are among the major hazards of this business. Here is a brief discussion of some of the more common and destructive maladies the producer encounters.

DESTRUCTION of the natural environment of upland game birds and ever-increasing pressure for more birds for hunting have led to attempts by conservationists to utilize artificially propagated birds for restocking. Sportsmen and others concerned with the artificial or controlled production of these birds have learned through costly experience that losses from pathological factors are often tremendous. Corrections in the rations and in the methods of incubation, breeding, and sanitation have had beneficial effects, but various infectious and parasitic diseases continue to cause extensive mortality and to make game farming unduly hazardous.

Some of the maladies observed among artificially propagated stocks are apparently new to veterinary science, but others are familiar diseases acquired from poultry. Permitting domesticated birds to utilize the same range as the game birds and using domesticated hens to incubate game-bird eggs and brood the young are practices that favor the transfer of infections. In Stoddard's book (7)[2] on the bobwhite quail, this situation is referred to as follows:

The danger of infecting bobwhites that range near human habitations with poultry diseases and parasites * * * is of importance, as these birds are known to be susceptible to several poultry diseases, and some of their worst intestinal parasites are shared with poultry.

[1] J. E. Shillinger is in Charge, Section of Disease Investigations, Division of Wildlife Research, Fish and Wildlife Service, Department of the Interior.
[2] Italic numbers in parentheses refer to Literature Cited, p. 1231.

To avoid repetition, diseases and parasites affecting poultry are not described in detail in this article. Instead, cross references are made to other articles in the Yearbook.

BACTERIAL DISEASES

Although pullorum disease (see p. 931) apparently does not cause serious losses among game birds, it has been observed occasionally in pheasants (*6*) and in quail (*3*); but it is evident that the latter birds are more resistant to it than are domestic chickens.

One of the most striking examples of a disease transmitted from domestic chickens to game birds is tuberculosis (*6*; see also p. 237 of this Yearbook). It has been a common practice on the older game farms to use domestic hens for incubating pheasant eggs and for hovering the young, and numerous instances are known in which pheasants raised under tuberculous hens have been grossly affected with the disease. Since treatment is useless the remedy lies in preventing association of possibly infected birds with the young stock.

Ulcerative enteritis is the most destructive disease of quail and grouse known on game farms (*6*). Although there is still some question concerning the exact nature of the causative agent, it is known to be one that does not pass through even the most porous of porcelain filters. The disease is quite readily reproduced by feeding particles of the liver or intestinal tract of an affected bird or of the ingesta it contains. In nature the infection is spread by direct contamination through droppings or through the medium of flies.

The characteristic lesions of ulcerative enteritis are numerous crater-like ulcerations in the lining of the small intenstine, in the center of each of which is frequently found a yellowish, caseous (cheeselike) mass. It is not uncommon for the ulcers to perforate the wall of the intestine, in which case the affected bird promptly dies. The organism responsible is evidently an active toxin producer, as subserous lesions (that is, lesions under a lining membrane) give evidence of toxic action.

Thus far, in stamping out an epizootic, or extensive outbreak, of this disease, only strict hygienic practices have been found of value. Dividing a flock into small, isolated groups in order to avoid possible spread to all the birds is recommended, and screening against flies and daily scrubbing of equipment to remove fecal contamination are necessary to reduce dissemination of infective material. Outbreaks allowed to proceed unchecked will frequently cause a mortality of 70 to 100 percent in affected groups.

Outbreaks on quail farms of a disease of obscure origin and character have repeatedly been studied. The most frequently found organisms identified as the causative agents have belonged to the *Salmonella* group. Such an organism of the *S. oranienburg* type has been described (*2, 4*) as pathogenic, or disease producing, and another similar to, if not identical with, *S. aertrycke* has also been identified. Intermediate coliform organisms (*1*)—that is, similar in form to colon bacilli—likewise have been found to be pathogenic in some outbreaks on game farms among quail and other upland game birds.

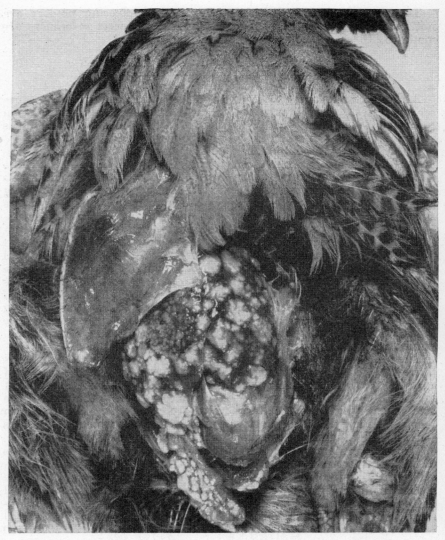

FIGURE 1.—Tuberculous lesions in the liver of a pheasant. This bird, which might have been raised on a game farm, was picked up dead in the wild. (Courtesy of E. K. LeDune.)

PROTOZOAN DISEASES

A familiar disease of turkeys, known as blackhead or enterohepatitis (see p. 1017), appear to attack birds from wild sources as well as strains that have been domesticated for centuries. On game farms where wild turkeys are propagated for restocking, destructive epizootics have killed a high percentage of the poults when effective methods of protection have not been practiced.

Among quail and ruffed grouse, blackhead does not ordinarily assume the proportions of an epizootic infection (6) if reasonably hygienic precautions are observed. Under the unusual physical demand of continued egg production, however, many quail hens die from this disease; and during the midsummer period, when laying is at its height, losses are especially high. Death apparently comes suddenly, and egg production may be continued until the day of death.

Coccidiosis, well known as a plague of young chickens (see p. 1041), is equally destructive to young game birds. In general it may be said that the organisms of this group are host specific—that is, each affects only one kind of host—and are rarely cross-transmitted among different kinds of hosts. Most of the severe losses in quail are believed to be due to species of coccidia peculiar to this bird; but at least two species of coccidia parasitic in chickens have also been found in quail, and the two species common to domestic turkeys are pathogenic to wild turkeys (5).

Although severe losses among quail and wild turkeys raised on game farms are attributable to infestations with intestinal trichomonads (see p. 1019), knowledge of the occurrence of the causative parasites in game birds is very incomplete. The organisms found in these outbreaks appear to be identical with those observed in similar infestations among domestic poultry, although preliminary studies indicate that they require slightly different media for artificial cultivation. The symptoms and the rate and percentage of losses parallel those observed in domestic birds.

CONTROL OF PROTOZOAN DISEASES

The possibility of preventing the diseases caused by protozoans (see p. 1008) depends upon the efficacy of hygienic procedures, such as maintaining the stock on wire-mesh floors and providing range so extensive that opportunity for infection is reduced until it is negligible. Flies have been implicated in the spread of some of these organisms and should be screened out wherever practicable. Diligent scrubbing of pens and coops and drying them in direct sunlight are recommended for eliminating infections. Spraying the pens, coops, and other equipment with light oils, preferably fortified with 2 to 4 percent of compound solution of cresol is suggested.

FUNGUS DISEASES

In an effort to provide suitable yet cheap litter for young quail, the mistake has frequently been made of using substances that carry the spores of *Aspergillus fumigatus*, a fungus that produces fatal infections of wild waterfowl as well as of quail on game farms and that appears to be more highly pathogenic for these birds than for domestic chickens. Involvement of the lungs, heart, and anterior, or frontal, body cavity, including the air sacs, is very noticeable and in young quail causes losses often as high as 90 percent in the broods affected.

Control measures recommended are prompt removal of all possibly infected litter, such as straw, leaves, and pine needles, and the substitution of planing-mill shavings, sawdust, or even dry sand.

The fungus organism *Saccharomyces albicans*, which causes a disease called thrush (see p. 995), also has been observed as destructive to young quail and wild turkeys. In advanced cases, whitish ulcers in the mouth and crop, mucoid, or mucuslike, deposits in the proventriculus, or true stomach, and ulcers in the gizzard are notable characteristics of the disease, although the organism is sometimes so virulent as to kill before extensive lesions are formed. As control measures, the sick birds should be isolated, any visible fragments of pseudomembranes or of other deposits in the mouth should be removed, and the affected parts within reach should be treated with a mild antiseptic solution such as a one-fourth strength of tincture of iodine in glycerin or painting with a one-half percent solution of crystal violet.

WORM PARASITES

The well-known gapeworm (*Syngamus trachea*) infests many species of wild birds as well as domestic poultry (see p. 1035) and interferes with health in varying degrees. Among young bobwhites in ground-floored pens the losses due to gapeworms may be considerable. The loss of the blood withdrawn by the parasite and, more important, the occlusion, or stopping-up, of the trachea (windpipe), producing partial or complete suffocation, may cause a mortality of 40 to 60 percent of the exposed birds.

Practically all parts of the digestive system in game birds may be the habitat of worm parasites, as the feeding habits of the birds expose them to infestation by a great variety of worms. If the birds are allowed to pick their feed from the ground where insects and annelids, serving as intermediate hosts, are abundant or where the ground has been polluted by infested birds, massive parasitic invasions usually follow.

Imbedded in the mucous membranes of the esophagus, or gullet, are often found slender, threadlike worms (*Capillaria annulata*) that cause an inflammation in quail.

The common nematode (*Dispharynx spiralis*) burrows into the wall of the proventriculus in grouse, quail, pheasants, and other game birds. Thickening of the wall and ulceration cause an interference with the functioning of the secretory glands in these infestations.

The gizzard worm (*Cheilospirura spinosa*) produces an inflammation of the gizzard muscles which is followed by degenerative changes and loosening of the corneous, or hard, lining. Infested birds suffer from an interference with proper grinding of their food.

Several species of *Ascaridia*, including *A. lineata* and *A. compar* (7), have been recognized as parasitic in quail and other game-farm species. They frequent the small intestine of upland game birds. This organ is also the habitat of various species of tapeworms of the genera *Hymenolepis* and *Raillietina* (7), which do considerable damage to quail by preventing proper digestion and assimilation of food.

The ceca of practically all upland game birds are infested with the *Heterakis gallinae* and related species of nematodes. Although these parasites do not appear to cause much actual damage, they do interfere with the passage of food.

Many of the parasites of game birds require an intermediate host for completing their life cycle, and those having a direct life cycle are spread mechanically by insects and annelids. The preferred method of control, therefore, is to maintain the stock on wire-mesh floors, where the opportunity for infestation is reduced to a minimum.

NUTRITIONAL DISEASES

Nutritional roup (*6;* see also p. 973 of this volume) is common on game farms where there is insufficiency of vitamin A in the ration, and it may bring about rather extensive losses before it is suspected and corrective measures can be applied. It is manifested by thick discharges from the nostrils and eyes, the eyes often becoming inflamed. On autopsy the mouth, esophagus, and visceral organs usually show whitish-gray accumulations. A deficiency of vitamin D likewise may prevail on game farms where game birds are on a restricted diet, and although the rachitic conditions it causes are not ordinarily responsible for extensive loss, they damage young growing stock considerably. Both these diseases are readily controlled by the use of adequate rations. Liberal quantities of fresh fruits and green leafy vegetables, with the addition of cod-liver oil when possible, are recommended. (See the article on Nutritional Diseases of Poultry, p. 1075.)

The tendency of quail, particularly young birds, to injure others by picking the feet as well as the flesh around the base of the beak and the vent has long been considered evidence of some nutritional irregularity. Only recently it has been shown [3] that this form of cannibalism is due to an insufficiency of salt; the addition of salt in the proportion of 2 or 3 percent of the ration stopped the vice within 24 hours.

LITERATURE CITED

(1) DURFEE, THOMAS, and LERNER, M. WOLFE.
   1940. A COLIFORM INTERMEDIATE FROM DISEASED QUAIL. Amer. Vet. Med. Assoc. Jour. 96: 245–246.
(2) EDWARDS, PHILIP R.
   1936. THE OCCURRENCE OF SALMONELLA, ORANIENBERG TYPE, IN AN INFECTION OF QUAIL. Jour. Bact. 32: 259–263.
(3) EMMEL, M. W.
   1936. PULLORUM DISEASE IN CAPTIVE QUAIL. Amer. Vet. Med. Assoc. Jour. 89: 716–717.
(4) GRAHAM, ROBERT.
   1936. SALMONELLA ISOLATED FROM BABY QUAIL. Amer. Vet. Med. Assoc. Jour. 88: 763–764.
(5) SHILLINGER, J. E.
   1939. RELATIONSHIP OF DISEASES COMMON TO GAME BIRDS AND DOMESTIC POULTRY. 7th World's Poultry Cong. and Expo. Proc., pp. 241–243
(6) ――― and MORLEY, L. C.
   1937. DISEASES OF UPLAND GAME BIRDS. U. S. Dept. Agr. Farmers' Bul. 1781, 34 pp., illus.
(7) STODDARD, HERBERT L.
   1931. THE BOBWHITE QUAIL: ITS HABITS, PRESERVATION AND INCREASE. 559 pp., illus. New York.

---

[3] NESTLER, RALPH B. COMMON SALT AS A CURATIVE FOR CANNIBALISM AMONG GAME BIRDS IN CAPTIVITY. U. S. Bur. Biol. Survey Wildlife Leaflet BS–163, 2 pp. 1940. [Processed.]

Diseases of Fur Animals

BY J. E. SHILLINGER [1]

HERE is a concise discussion of some of the principal diseases and parasites that affect silver foxes and minks as raised on fur farms, with suggestions for prevention and treatment.

THE BUSINESS of raising animals for their fur has passed rapidly through progressive stages to a degree of efficiency comparable with that of other branches of animal husbandry. With this development has come fairly efficient control of the diseases of these animals. Since silver foxes and minks are the species most frequently propagated on fur farms, research on the diseases of these animals has been given the most consideration. Some of the ailments of these groups are very similar to those of other animals under domestication, while others appear to be peculiar to the fox and mink.

Since construction of the pens and kennels necessary for keeping fur animals is expensive, most fur farmers concentrate many animals in small pens or on limited areas (fig. 1). This crowding permits easy and rapid transmission of infections from animal to animal (fig. 2). Feed of the kind supplied to fur animals—composed largely of a mixture of meats, fish, and cereals—attracts rats, birds, and flies, which add to the danger of spreading infections through their movement from pen to pen.

Cross references are given in this article to other articles in the Yearbook.

INFECTIOUS DISEASES

PARATYPHOID

While organisms belonging to the paratyphoid group are infectious to a variety of animals and to man, many of them appear to be rather specific to certain hosts. Epizootics, or severe outbreaks, of para-

[1] J. E. Shillinger is in Charge, Section of Disease Investigations, Division of Wildlife Research, Fish and Wildlife Service, Department of the Interior.

typhoid are rather frequent among silver foxes raised on fur farms. Affected animals are ordinarily sick for 2 or 3 weeks. The first evidence of the infection is a decline in appetite, followed by a gradual

FIGURE 1.—Arrangement of pens on a typical fur farm. Such crowding of the animals permits ready spread of disease germs. (Courtesy of Herbert A. Nieman and Co., Thiensville, Wis.)

FIGURE 2.—A pair of silver foxes on a fur range, showing the possibility for disease spread if one animal is infected. (Courtesy of Herbert A. Nieman and Co., Thiensville, Wis.)

loss of flesh and of the luster of the fur. There is usually diarrhea, and the passages may be streaked with blood.

When paratyphoid is chronic, entailing continuous lack of appetite, emaciation is extreme, and the eyes are sunken. In some cases the disease terminates in pneumonia. Usually a purulent discharge from the eyes and nose aids in giving the animal an unthrifty appearance.

On autopsy the spleen is generally found enlarged and dark. It is frequently possible to isolate pure cultures of the paratyphoid bacillus from this organ. Jaundice is sometimes found in the organs on post mortem examination, and it may be so pronounced as to be evident before death.

Treatment with vaccine made from the strain of the organism present on the fur farm is recommended; properly made and administered, it may be very effective in checking outbreaks. Commercial vaccines containing several of the more common strains of paratyphoid organisms also have been used on a number of fur farms with excellent results. While the use of stock vaccines for this disease among foxes is not recommended when vaccine can be made from the particular strain causing an outbreak, they may be resorted to in emergencies.

INFECTIOUS ENTERITIS

Bacteria belonging to the *Salmonella* group, which produce extensive intestinal injury, frequently become established on fur farms. Contaminated feed or water and the bringing in of animals from infected herds are the usual channels by which the disease is introduced. *Salmonella* organisms thrive in the intestinal tract, where they cause extensive inflammation of the mucous membrane. As this inflammation progresses, considerable destruction of tissue occurs, entailing constant oozing of blood. Autopsies of animals dying from this disease usually reveal sloughing of the mucous membrane throughout the small intestine.

No biological product, such as vaccine, bacterin, or serum, seems to be of much value in checking outbreaks of enteritis on fur farms, and poor results have followed the use of astringents, such as tannic acid, alum, and limewater. Astringents may temporarily relieve symptoms, but they are ineffective against the organisms themselves. A number of ranchers have reported very beneficial results from the use of buttermilk, preferably that made by the action of *Lactobacillus acidophilus*. The fermented milk may be given alone if the animals can be induced to take it, or it may be combined with the regular ration. In combating enteritis on fur farms, it is highly important to prevent the spread of infectious material from pen to pen. Disinfection of utensils and equipment with coal-tar or chlorine products is recommended. (See Disinfection and Disinfectants, p. 179.)

DISTEMPER

The term "distemper" was formerly loosely applied to various epizootic diseases of animals—that is, diseases occurring in severe outbreaks—but the condition recognized as canine distemper (see p. 1124) is now known to be a definite ailment due to a specific filtrable virus, to which foxes and minks as well as dogs are susceptible. It also appears that certain other viruses that are closely related and cause somewhat similar symptoms are common infections on fur farms.

Distemper is a highly contagious disease of dogs, ferrets, foxes, and minks. While it may also attack other animals, it is best known in the species named, in which the most complete studies of the disease have been made.

Silver foxes usually show symptoms of distemper—listlessness, loss of appetite, and fever—within a few days after exposure. A bloody diarrhea is often evident, and the fur has an unkept appearance. Closer examination shows a dry muzzle, although there may sometimes be a watery discharge from the nose. The conjunctiva (mucous membrane covering the eyeball and the inner side of the eyelid) is almost invariably much reddened. Only during the early stages of the disease is a sick animal likely to infect others. The virus is readily transmitted from pen to pen by attendants, and hence it is not unusual for the infection to appear almost simultaneously in various parts of the ranch.

Autopsy of distempered animals may fail to disclose any pronounced changes in the organs. The spleen and liver are often slightly enlarged and somewhat darker than usual. The muscles may appear paler than normal, with occasional small hemorrhagic spots. An absence of food materials in the digestive tract because of the lack of appetite preceding death is often noted, although it is not unusual to find an excess of mucus tinged with blood and an inflamed mucous membrane lining the stomach and intestine.

In minks a discharge from the eyes as well as from the nose frequently becomes purulent and tends to seal the eyelids and clog the nostrils. The feet of minks are frequently swollen, especially on the under side, which makes the pads appear unusually large.

In the control of distemper on a fur farm it is essential that the caretaker exercise extreme precautions to prevent spread of the virus from infected to healthy animals. Since so many agents can carry the infection, it is recommended that affected animals be isolated so that birds, rodents, and flies will not have access to them, or at least are not likely to visit them and then go among the healthy stock. Likewise the attendant should take care not to carry the infection on his clothing or on equipment and feeding utensils. The practice of liberating large numbers of silver foxes on furring ranges or in furring sheds where they may come in intimate contact with each other affords an ideal opportunity for the spread of the disease. Considerable evidence is now available indicating that distemper, as well as other infections, is probably spread through nasal secretions.

Medicinal treatments are of little if any value as curative measures. The use of anti-canine-distemper serum,[2] if it is administered in adequate quantities before symptoms appear, provides effective protection for a temporary period. Experiments are in progress to develop a vaccine that will produce a more lasting immunity.

[2] OTT, GEORGE L. TREATMENT OF FOX DISTEMPER. Amer. Vet. Med. Assoc. Jour. 94 : 522–524, 525, illus. 1939.
SHILLINGER, J. E. DISEASES OF FUR ANIMALS. U. S. Dept. Agr. Farmers' Bul. 1777, 22 pp., illus. 1937.

ANTHRAX

On various occasions during recent years, anthrax, a disease well known in domestic stock (see p. 250), has been diagnosed on mink farms.[3] In all these instances the infection was directly traceable to feeding minks parts of the carcass of an animal that proved to have had this disease. Since it is the common practice to grind the meat portion of the ration fine and mix it with cereals and other food products, most of the animals on a mink farm have usually been given the anthrax-infected meat and consequently are infected before the condition is recognized. Because of the great loss anthrax entails and because of the danger to human beings, it is highly important that every precaution be taken to prevent the use of diseased beef or other meat in feeding fur animals.

INTERNAL PARASITES

In the earlier stages of fur-animal husbandry severe losses often resulted from gross infestation of the animals by internal parasites. (See p. 124.) Hookworms of the species *Uncinaria stenocephala* may become very numerous in animals kept in pens on the ground, without floors. These worms, attached to the mucous lining of the intestinal tract, make wounds from which they extract blood. Heavy hookworm infestation results in pronounced anemia and may be recognized by unthriftiness of the animals and by their pasty, grayish droppings.

The use of tetrachlorethylene in doses of about 0.1 cubic centimeter per pound of body weight has proved effective in expelling these parasites. The treated animals should be removed to uncontaminated enclosures or placed in clean pens with wire-mesh floors.

Ascarids, or roundworms, of the species *Toxacara canis* are frequently parasitic in silver foxes, especially among the young animals. These worms, when mature, may measure 4 inches in length, and if they are numerous they may cause extensive injury and even death. So generally present are they on fur farms that it is the regular practice to treat all fox pups raised in ground-floored pens at about 3 to 5 weeks of age with a suitable anthelmintic. Oil of chenopodium, in doses of 0.025 to 0.05 cubic centimeter per pound of body weight, is satisfactory. Because of the irritating effects of this medicine in the digestive tract some fur farmers prefer tetrachlorethylene in the same dose recommended for hookworms, even though it is somewhat less efficient.

Feed and the animals' fur become contaminated with ascarid eggs passed out in the droppings, and the infestation is acquired in the feed or when the animals lick their fur. Many fur farmers are now raising their silver foxes in pens with elevated wire-mesh floors, and this sanitary precaution usually prevents any harmful degree of parasitism.

Lungworms also are a serious menace on some farms where foxes are maintained on the ground. Two species, *Eucoleus aerophila* and

[3] PINKERTON, HENRY. AN OUTBREAK OF ANTHRAX INFECTION IN MINKS WITH INFECTION OF RANCH OWNER. Amer. Med. Assoc. Jour. 112: 1148–1149. 1939.

Crenosoma decoratum, are parasitic in these animals. They lodge in the minute air passages of the lungs and in the lung tissue and cause a profuse secretion of mucus that hinders breathing. Frequent coughing and wheezing are symptoms of lungworm infestation. The excessive mucus·and the tissue damage caused by the worms are likely to induce verminous pneumonia. These parasites produce great numbers of eggs that are highly resistant to chemical disinfection or to the action of the weather.

No form of medication appears to be practicable for the removal of lungworms, but the use of pens with wire-mesh floors that permit the contaminating material to fall through and out of reach of the animals will prevent serious infestations.

EXTERNAL PARASITES

Though external parasites alone may not be responsible for extensive losses on fur farms, infestation by fleas and mange mites (see p. 1188 and p. 1174) may render the pelts unsightly and of low value. Fleas become numerous on some fur farms. Control is effected most successfully by repeated use of dry powders rather than by the more severe treatment with fluid dips and oily ointments. Pyrethrum powder, flowers of sulfur, or derris powder may be used. The last, if of good quality, is preferable.

Body mange seldom affects fur animals. When it does become established, it is often advisable to destroy a few affected animals rather than to attempt to treat them and run the risk of the infestation spreading. Ear mange, however, is a common disease of silver foxes. It results from infestation by the mite *Otodectes cynotes,* which causes sufficient irritation of the skin on the inner surface of the ear to produce scabs and an increase of waxy secretion. These accumulate as large crusts. The affected animals are inclined to hold the head to one side, turn in circles, shake the head, and attempt to scratch the part involved. Because of the ease with which this parasite is spread, a large proportion of the animals on a ranch are usually affected before the trouble is recognized. It is advisable, therefore, to treat all the animals on a ranch when attempting to get rid of the infestation.

After removal of the incrustations with blunt forceps, treatment with one of the following remedies is recommended:

(1) Iodoform, 1 part; ether, 10 parts; cottonseed oil, 25 parts.

(2) Oil of cade, 1 part; cottonseed oil, 8 parts.

(3) Carbolic acid crystals (phenol), 2 parts; cottonseed oil or liquid petrolatum, 98 parts.

These substances can be applied with a brush or a cotton swab. It may be necessary to repeat the treatment in 10 to 14 days to insure killing all the mites.

NUTRITIONAL DISEASES

Some years ago the well-known disease, rickets, was rather common on fur farms. More complete knowledge of the nutritional requirements of fur animals, however, has since made this condition a rarity. A sufficient quantity of vitamin D in the ration is effective in preventing rickets. This is usually supplied in the form of feeds high in this element, such as eggs and cod-liver oil.

When attendants are careless about the care and storage of feed, botulism or other types of food poisoning sometimes occur, especially in minks. Poor refrigeration of stored meats permits spoilage, and the unused portions of such feed allowed to remain in the pens undergo decomposition rapidly. Such material may cause severe losses from various types of food poisoning, of which botulism is the most common. Adequate refrigeration of feed and the removal of uneaten remains will prevent losses from this cause.

A form of nutritional irregularity that has been observed among silver foxes to which liberal quantities of fresh fish have been fed has been described under the name "Chastek paralysis." [4] This condition results from a deficiency of vitamin B_1 in the ration. Recent work has indicated that there is a factor in certain fish that is destructive to vitamin B_1,[5] but that this factor can be eliminated by adequate cooking of the fish.

In this malady the animals suffer a spastic paralysis, which usually terminates in death. Sick animals respond rapidly to the administration of vitamin B_1, however, and an outbreak ceases rather promptly when fresh fish is excluded from the ration or when the fish is well cooked before it is fed.

---

[4] GREEN, R. G. CHASTEK PARALYSIS IN NURSING FOX PUPS. Natl. Fur News 10 (9): 11, 24. 1941.

[5] COOMBES, A. IRVING. FEEDING FISH TO FUR BEARING ANIMALS. Amer. Natl. Fur and Market Jour. 19 (3): 5–6, 24–25, illus. 1940.

INDEX